Physical Chemistry

Physical Chemistry

D. F. Eggers, Jr.

N. W. Gregory

G. D. Halsey, Jr.

B. S. Rabinovitch

University of Washington

JOHN WILEY AND SONS, INC. • NEW YORK • LONDON • SYDNEY

Library of Congress Catalog Card Number: 63-18624
Printed in the United States of America

Preface

This book is intended as an undergraduate text in physical chemistry. It is used at the University of Washington in a one-year course offered to science and engineering majors, most of whom are in their junior year. The presentation assumes a knowledge of calculus and a good background in general physics for science majors.

The course given here proceeds in the order of the chapters as presented so as to take advantage of a foundation of quantum and statistical mechanics. However, the textual material has been developed so that the book will also serve those who prefer a thermodynamic approach to physical chemistry. In that case, Chapter 2, Section 1, may be followed directly by Chapters 7–10, after which a return to Chapter 2 is suggested.

Chapters 1–11 and, to a lesser extent, Chapters 12 and 13 present the fundamentals of the subject. Especially toward the ends of many chapters there is material of a more advanced or specialized nature that can be left out or summarized without extensive proof. In our course, more than half of the year is used to reach the end of Chapter 11. More material is presented in the last five chapters than can possibly be covered in the time available. However, much of this material is in the nature of applications and extensions of basic principles. It is intended that the instructor shall select topics according to his interests and inclinations. We have considered it appropriate to raise the level of this last portion somewhat.

Answers have been provided to most of the numerical problems. A few of the more difficult exercises have been marked with an asterisk.

We are particularly indebted to Professor E. C. Lingafelter, who participated actively in the early planning of the book. We are grateful also for the various criticisms, suggestions, and corrections offered by our colleagues, Professors Davidson, Simpson, Slutsky, and Vincow. Professor W. W. Newschwander of

Central Washington State College has generously assisted by teaching from page proof and has made many helpful suggestions. We also thank Professor James M. Stewart of the University of Maryland. Our graduate students, especially Mr. R. E. Miller, and students in our classes have been most helpful.

In the inevitable way, we have no doubt that readers will discover errors and omissions. Remaining faults are solely our responsibility. We would appreciate any comments or corrections that readers may care to offer.

D. F. Eggers, Jr.
N. W. Gregory
G. D. Halsey, Jr.
B. S. Rabinovitch

Seattle, Washington
March, 1964

Contents

Chapter One

Some Aspects of Electromagnetic
Radiation and Matter

In this chapter we anticipate the presentation of some of the methods and results from quantum mechanics which follow in succeeding chapters. We present a brief summary of the nature of electromagnetic radiation, and the quantum theory resolution by Planck and Einstein of the centuries-old wave-corpuscle dilemma regarding the nature of light. The extension of these ideas to matter by de Broglie and the development by Heisenberg of the principle of indeterminacy provide a further foundation for the understanding of the quantized nature of the allowed energy levels of matter, as well as of the statistical nature of some aspects of the quantum mechanical description of matter.

In the study of chemistry we are interested in certain properties of matter. A model of the structure of matter has now been developed, of which some general features, as in the Rutherford and Bohr theories of the atom, are already familiar to the student from his previous courses in chemistry and physics. We state that matter is composed of atoms; each atom is made up of electrons and a small massive central nucleus; the nucleus is a complex structure involving protons and neutrons. In addition to these three particles, electrons, protons, and neutrons, a number of other subatomic particles such as neutrinos and mesons have been postulated and discovered since the early thirties. Although the latter particles are of fundamental importance in nuclear physics and are of incipient importance in chemistry, as manifested by the transient existence of new "elements" such as positronium (positron-electron) and muonium (μ meson-electron), nevertheless the behavior of electrons, which move in the field of positive nuclei and interact with each other, is the principal concern of chemistry.

For example, the four particles which constitute the H_2 molecule are two electrons and two protons. The electron and the proton have the same magnitude of electric charge, 4.8030×10^{-10} esu, but opposite signs, minus and plus, respectively; their masses are 9.109×10^{-28} gram and 1.6725×10^{-24} gram, respectively. We treat the electron and proton as mathematical points which have only electric charge and mass. The forces between these elementary particles are assumed to be due only to their electric charges and to be given by the usual Coulomb inverse-square law. Gravitational forces are very much smaller, and hence negligible, in comparison to electrical forces. Our problem is to understand and explain the behavior of hydrogen in terms of these four particles. The set of assumptions about the properties and nature of the electrons and protons (nuclei) is the model. Thus far the description sounds very much like the problems treated in physical mechanics (Newton's equations) except for the magnitudes of the masses and charges. This difference is a very important one; treatment of the motions of pendulums or planetary orbits and the oscillations of a watch spring, for example, by Newton's equations gives results in good agreement with experiment. This is not true for atoms and molecules; the laws which they obey are embodied in the principles of quantum mechanics.

We shall return to this matter again in Chapter 2.

1. Wave Nature of Electromagnetic Radiation

Considerable information concerning the nature of atoms and molecules has been obtained by the study of their interaction with light. By the latter half of the nineteenth century much experimental evidence suggested that light should be described as a wave motion. This evidence included the fact that light displays interference and diffraction phenomena. At this time, the electromagnetic wave theory was developed in a very powerful and satisfactory way by J. C. Maxwell (1864). His famous differential equations involving the electric and magnetic fields describe the light wave and its properties, similar to the way in which the equations of motion are applicable to the analysis of sound waves.

By use of the electromagnetic wave theory of light we can correlate the entire range of wavelength λ, from very short gamma rays ($\lambda \sim 10^{-10}$ cm), through X-rays ($\lambda \sim 10^{-8}$ cm or 1 angstrom), ultraviolet light ($\lambda \sim 10^{-5}$ cm), visible light ($\lambda \sim 4\text{--}7 \times 10^{-5}$ cm), infrared light ($\lambda > 10^{-4}$ cm), and microwaves ($\lambda \sim 0.1\text{--}1$ cm), to ordinary radio waves ($\lambda \gtrsim 10^2$ cm). All these superficially different forms of radiation travel in a vacuum at the same velocity, $c = 2.998 \times 10^{10}$ cm sec^{-1}.

A light wave may be characterized by either frequency or wavelength. The frequency ν is the reciprocal of the wavelength, λ, multiplied by the magnitude of the velocity of light, c.

$$\nu = \frac{c}{\lambda} \tag{1.101}$$

Radiation Laws.   Consider some relations between light, energy, and matter. When gases are exposed to an electric discharge or heated to high temperatures, a characteristic emission of light is observed. This may consist of a series of distinct lines, or of bands of radiation distributed at various frequencies, with little or no radiation at intermediate frequencies. A plot of the intensity of radiation as a function of wavelength represents the emission spectrum of the gas. The spectrum is a characteristic of the particular gas under observation. The aurora borealis or northern lights are spectacular examples of emission. Sodium- and mercury-arc street lights are familiar examples.

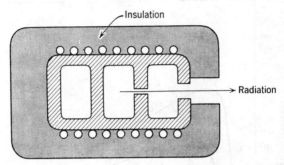

Fig. 1.101   Longitudinal cross section of a wire-wound electric furnace constructed to behave as a black body. The core may be of any material, preferably with blackened interior. The dummy chamber on the left helps to provide a uniform temperature in the emitting chamber.

A heated solid, on the other hand, produces a spectrum that appears to be a continuous function of wavelength. Such a spectrum is called an ideal *black-body* or normal spectrum if the solid has the property of absorbing all radiation incident upon its surface. An evacuated hollow inside any solid may be maintained at equi- librium with respect to both emission and absorption; if the only radiation that escapes from the hollow comes out of a tiny hole (Fig. 1.101), the spectrum obtained is that of an ideal black body and does not depend on the nature, size, or shape of the solid, but only on the temperature. Thus an evacuated space inside solid walls at the temperature T is not empty but is filled with radiation energy at a certain density (ergs per cubic centimeter). By the examination of black-body radi- ation, it has been established experimentally that the total energy (all wavelengths) has the density ρ, given by the Stefan-Boltzmann law,

$$\rho = \sigma T^4 \qquad\qquad (1.102)$$

where σ is a constant, 7.56×10^{-15} erg cm^{-3} deg^{-4}, and T is absolute temperature. Equation 1.102 is converted to a plane flux with units of ergs per square centimeter second by multiplying the right side by $c/4$. If a radiation detector and spectroscope are used to find the distribution of energy over various wavelengths, a smooth plot of energy vs. wavelength emerges (Fig. 1.102). These curves form a family; the shape of each curve depends on the temperature. The various maxima of the curves can be related to each other through the Wien displacement law,

$$\lambda_{max} = \frac{\text{const}}{T} \tag{1.103}$$

where λ_{max} is the wavelength at the maximum of the curve.

The development of an equation to reproduce the experimental form of the dependence of the radiation energy on the wavelength of the light was one of the

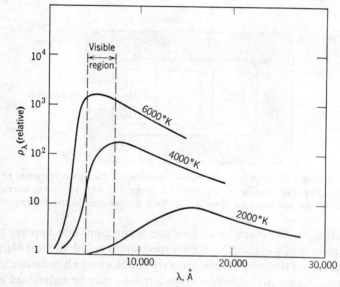

Fig. 1.102   Density of black-body radiation as a function of wavelength. The ordinate gives the relative energy in a wavelength interval of 1 Å.

central problems of the physics of the last century. A detailed discussion of its history and solution will not be given here. However, a brief examination of some of the equations developed serves to contrast the black-body spectrum with the line and band spectra we shall find of chemical interest. In addition, an examination and manipulation of these equations is of value in giving some idea of the origin of the Planck and Boltzmann constants and of approximate and limiting forms of physical laws that are valid only in certain regions.

Two equations for the density of energy, ρ_λ, in equilibrium with matter, successful in different spectral regions, were derived shortly before Planck eventually gave the solution to this problem. The Rayleigh-Jeans equation, which is "classical" (pre-quantum theory) in its derivation, agreed with experiment only at long wavelengths,

$$\rho_\lambda = \frac{8\pi kT}{\lambda^4} \tag{1.104}$$

where k is the Boltzmann constant, 1.380×10^{-16} erg deg^{-1}, and ρ_λ is energy of radiation per unit volume per unit wavelength range. At short wavelengths, suitable agreement with experiment could be obtained with the Wien equation,

$$\rho_\lambda = \frac{C_1 e^{-C_2/\lambda T}}{\lambda^5} \tag{1.105}$$

where C_1 and C_2 are constants independent of temperature.

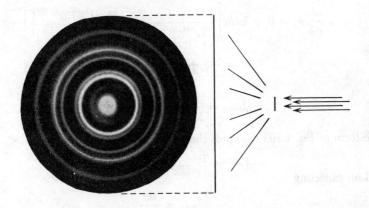

Fig. 1.103   Comparison of the Planck radiation law (P) with the predicted behavior of the Wien (W) and Rayleigh-Jeans equations (R-J) and with the experimental data of Coblentz for 1600°K [*NBS Bull.*, **13**, 476 (1916)]. The ordinate for the curves on the right has been multiplied by 10.

The derivation by Planck in 1901 of a radiation law which covers the entire frequency range (Fig. 1.103) is regarded as the beginning of modern physics,

$$\rho_\lambda = \frac{8\pi hc}{\lambda^5 (e^{hc/\lambda k T} - 1)} \tag{1.106}$$

Later on, in Chapter 5, we will have developed enough theoretical background to be able to derive this equation. A new feature is the introduction of Planck's constant, $h = 6.6256 \times 10^{-27}$ erg sec. In older theories, the vacuum was represented as an incompressible elastic medium (the ether), with elastic constants so set that it was capable of transmitting waves which traveled with the observed velocity of light. Radiation into or out of a given piece of this medium corresponded to taking or giving up vibrational energy, and classically there was no limiting size to the increments or decrements of energy possible. Planck's theory asserts, however, that only definite discrete increments or decrements are possible, and no others. The size of this quantum is fixed, at a given frequency, and its magnitude as a function of frequency is given by a simple linear relation that serves to define Planck's constant,

$$|\Delta\epsilon| = h\nu = \frac{hc}{\lambda} \tag{1.107}$$

where $\Delta\epsilon$ can be considered either positive or negative, depending on whether energy is received or given up by the vacuum.

ILLUSTRATION. Obtain Eq. 1.103 by the use of Planck's radiation law.

A necessary condition that λ becomes λ_{max} is that the derivative $d\rho_\lambda/d\lambda = 0$. From Eq. 1.106

$$\rho_\lambda = \frac{8\pi hc}{\lambda^5} \cdot \frac{1}{(e^{hc/\lambda kT} - 1)}$$

so

$$\frac{d}{d\lambda}\rho_\lambda = 0 = 8\pi hc \left[\frac{-5}{\lambda^6(e^{hc/\lambda kT} - 1)} + \frac{(hc/\lambda^2 kT)e^{hc/\lambda kT}}{\lambda^5(e^{hc/\lambda kT} - 1)^2} \right]$$

or

$$0 = -5 + \frac{hce^{hc/\lambda kT}}{\lambda kT(e^{hc/\lambda kT} - 1)}$$

or

$$\lambda_{max} = \frac{hce^{hc/\lambda_{max}kT}}{5kT(e^{hc/\lambda_{max}kT} - 1)}$$

The form of Eq. 1.103 demands that

$$(e^{hc/\lambda_{max}kT} - 1) \simeq e^{hc/\lambda_{max}kT}$$

and on canceling

$$\lambda_{max} = \frac{hc}{5kT}$$

to good approximation.

The student may now show that the constant in Eq. 1.103 is 0.29 cm deg and that the approximate equality above is valid to better than 99 per cent.

---

2. Distribution Functions

Expressions of the type of Eq. 1.106, when looked at more closely, are seen to be density expressions or distributions. A little thought shows that, if the distribution is continuous, the amount of radiation at a given exact frequency must be zero, i.e., if $d\lambda \to 0$. This follows because the number of points on a line (the range of λ) is limitless, and if at each λ there were a finite amount of radiation the total radiation would be infinite. Actually, the function ρ_λ is the density of energy radiated per unit wavelength, and it must be multiplied by the interval $d\lambda$ to give the quantity radiated over the interval. Strictly speaking, this is a differential quantity and should be integrated over a finite range of frequency to get the total radiation over this range; however, over a short range $\Delta\lambda$ we can assume that ρ_λ is constant. To obtain the total radiation (i.e., the Stefan-Boltzmann law, Eq. 1.102), we integrate Eq. 1.106 over the whole range of λ from 0 to infinity

$$\rho = \int_0^\infty \rho_\lambda \, d\lambda = \sigma T^4 \tag{1.201}$$

This is the first example of the use of a distribution function which we have encountered; we shall meet others. In each case, the distribution function is associated with some differential such as $d\lambda$, and the function must be integrated over a given range to obtain the total value in that range.

ILLUSTRATION. Show the relationship between distribution functions for the density of radiation expressed in terms of wavelength and of frequency.

In Chapter 5, we shall see that the number of frequencies possible for a photon confined in a volume V is given by a distribution function. The total number of frequencies below a certain frequency v is given by the expression

$$N_v = \text{const } (Vv^3)$$

The number of frequencies within a range dv, or in other words the density distribution function in frequency, is found by differentiating this expression:

$$dN_v = \text{const}' \, (Vv^2) \, dv$$

We can express this result in terms of wavelength instead of frequency. From Eq. 1.101 we find that

$$dv = -\frac{c}{\lambda^2} \, d\lambda$$

On substitution for v and dv in terms of λ and $d\lambda$ into the right-hand side of the expression for dN_v, the distribution function in wavelength becomes

$$dN_\lambda = \frac{\text{const}''}{\lambda^4} \, d\lambda$$

If we assume that each vibration frequency or wavelength gives rise to radiation of the same amount of energy (which is equivalent to the classical principle of equipartition of energy in Chapter 6), the form of the Rayleigh-Jeans radiation law, Eq. 1.104, follows immediately.

The student may now obtain the terms in the constant in the expression for N_v above.

---

3. Wave-Particle Dualism of Light and Matter

The Particulate Nature of Light.   As was pointed out by Einstein (1905), the quantum of energy hv by which the light field changes is like a particle in that it is indivisible. Superficially, the quantum appears different from other subatomic particles because there is an indefinite variety of them, of all frequencies, which are constantly being created and destroyed by collision with the walls containing the vacuum. These particles are called photons and are identified by the amount of energy of which they consist. Einstein was able to explain the *photoelectric effect* in terms of these ideas as follows.

When light of suitable frequency falls on a cold alkali metal surface, maintained as the cathode in a diode electronic tube, a current is observed (Fig. 1.301). This photocurrent is proportional to the intensity of the illumination. For light of wavelength greater than a certain value, called the threshold wavelength, no effect is produced. As long as the light is of a wavelength less than the threshold (or of a frequency greater than the corresponding threshold), the current is proportional to the number of quanta impinging, as calculated from the radiant energy by Planck's

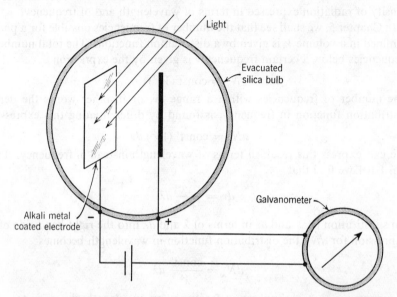

Fig. 1.301   Simple experimental arrangement for study of the photoelectric effect.

relationship $\epsilon_{total} = nh\nu$, where n is the number of quanta; the photocurrent is not simply determined by the total energy of the incident light.

It appears that for each change of $h\nu$ in the energy of the light field a photon knocks loose a valence electron from the alkali metal. The threshold energy, $W_0 = h\nu_0$, called the *work function* of the metal, is the minimum amount of energy needed to knock out an electron.

What happens to the excess energy if the light frequency is above the threshold value? If the kinetic energy $\frac{1}{2}m_e v^2$ of the released electron is determined, the relationship

$$\frac{1}{2}m_e v^2 = h\nu - W_0 \tag{1.301}$$

is found. R. A. Millikan used a retarding potential to measure the electron energy. A plot of some typical data is given in Fig. 1.302. Doubling the light intensity doubles the photocurrent but does not alter ν_0.

ILLUSTRATION.   Evaluate h accurately from the photoelectric effect.

R. A. Millikan [*Phys. Rev.*, **7**, 355 (1916)] in a precision measurement of h determined the slope of the line in Fig. 1.302 as 4.124×10^{-15} "volt-frequency." He found the value of h in erg seconds as follows.

From Eq. 1.301,

$$h = d(\tfrac{1}{2}m_e v^2/dv) \text{ in units of energy seconds}$$
$$= 4.124 \times 10^{-15} \text{ ev sec}$$

where the energy is expressed in electron volts.

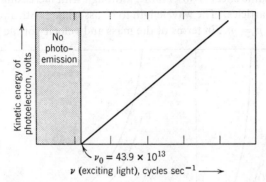

Fig. 1.302   Kinetic energy of photoelectrons from sodium as a function of frequency of the exciting light [after the experiment of R. A. Millikan, *Phys. Rev.*, **7**, 355 (1916)].

With the charge on the electron set at 4.774×10^{-10} esu of charge as determined by himself in another famous experiment, and using the definition 1 volt $= 1/299.8$ esu of potential, Millikan had

$$1 \text{ ev} = (4.77 \times 10^{-10})(1/299.8) = 1.59 \times 10^{-12} \text{ erg per particle}$$
or $$h = (4.124 \times 10^{-15})(1.59 \times 10^{-12}) = 6.56 \times 10^{-27} \text{ erg sec}$$

The accepted value of e is now 4.803×10^{-10} esu. The student may correct Millikan's value of h and compare it with the presently accepted value [*NBS Tech. News Bull.*, **47**, 175 (1963)].

The recognition of the particulate nature of radiation, supported by later discoveries such as the Compton effect (1923) dealing with the transfer of momentum from a photon to an electron on collision, showed that the wave and particle formulations represent different ways of describing the same thing. This aspect of nature has been called wave-particle dualism or the *principle of complementarity*.

The de Broglie Wavelength.   Einstein's equation for the energy of a photon

$$\epsilon = h\nu$$

is sufficient to introduce quantization to radiation in the electromagnetic field of a vacuum. A complementary problem is to consider whether the wave character extends to particles other than photons.

Waves of light in the visible region undergo diffraction when incident on a grating ruled on a plate if this plate has lines separated by a distance of roughly the same magnitude as the wavelength of the light. Since X-rays are short-wavelength electromagnetic radiation, they should also undergo diffraction with objects of the correct scale. This prediction by M. Von Laue (1912) was verified when crystals were used as an atomic-scale diffracting target for an X-ray beam.

In addition to this, beams of electrons were shown by Davisson and Germer and by G. P. Thomson (1927) to give interference effects with atomic-scale gratings (Fig. 1.303). The same effect is observable, although with increasing difficulty, with beams of heavier particles. The wavelength to be associated with a particle depends on the momentum $p = mv$, in terms of the mass and velocity of the particle, rather

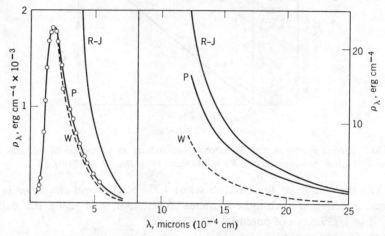

Fig. 1.303   Schematic representation of electron diffraction pattern obtained by G. P. Thomson when a beam of high-speed electrons was incident on a thin film of gold and a photographic plate was placed 30 cm behind [cf. *Introduction to Physical Optics*, Third Edition, by J. R. Robertson, D. Van Nostrand Co., Princeton, N.J., 1941, Plate VII, Figure 2 (photograph)].

than on any more specific property. The momentum has a simple reciprocal relationship to the wavelength involving only Planck's constant,

$$p = \frac{h}{\lambda} \tag{1.302}$$

This equation can be used as a postulate to develop the quantum theory of matter, as was shown by de Broglie (1924). We shall not follow this route, however. Instead, in the following chapters we shall use Schrödinger's treatment, which is based on the formulation of classical mechanics put forward by Hamilton but modified according to a set of postulates which can be interpreted as working rules. The method is called wave mechanics, a particular formulation of quantum mechanics. We shall use this treatment to calculate the energy levels allowed for molecular systems, just as the Planck theory permits a calculation of the allowed energy levels of the vacuum.

The Heisenberg Uncertainty Principle.   We may facilitate the introduction of the working rules for quantum mechanics in Chapter 2 if we consider one of the philosophical foundations of the quantum theory of matter: it is impossible to observe anything without in some way interacting with it and thus affecting it. This idea was given expression in the Heisenberg *indeterminacy* or *uncertainty* *principle* which states, in one form, that it is impossible to know simultaneously the exact values of the position and the momentum of a particle. Simultaneous knowledge of both these quantities is subject to some uncertainty, and the limiting product of the uncertainties is of the order of magnitude of the Planck constant, h. Thus

$$\Delta x \, \Delta p_x \gtrsim h; \quad \text{at best, } (\Delta x \, \Delta p_x)_{\min} \approx h \tag{1.303}$$

where Δx is the uncertainty in the x coordinate of the position of some particle, and Δp_x is the simultaneous uncertainty in the x component of the momentum of that particle. We note that Eq. 1.303 provides a warning that any equation that contains x and p_x simultaneously must be subjected to careful scrutiny. This equation can be used to indicate, at least approximately, some simple useful results.

For example, if we have a cannon ball which starts at position x_0 and moves with a constant momentum p in the x direction, we can write its position at time t as

$$x_t = \frac{p}{m} t + x_0$$

Strictly speaking, this equation is not in harmony with Heisenberg's principle. But if we put in reasonable numerical values, an uncertainty of 1 micron, i.e., 10^{-4} cm, in the position of the ball corresponds to an unmeasurably small uncertainty in the momentum, i.e.,

$$10^{-4}\Delta p \approx 6.625 \times 10^{-27} \text{ erg sec}; \quad \Delta p \approx 6.6 \times 10^{-23} \text{ g cm sec}^{-1}$$

On the other hand, if an electron is substituted for the cannon ball, and we require that the position of the electron be given to a precision comparable to atomic dimensions, the uncertainty in its momentum is large and is comparable to the total momentum of the electron in typical situations.

ILLUSTRATION.   We verify the previous statement and show its relation to an important practical matter in microscopy.

Consider an electron beam which has been accelerated through 70 volts. Now 70 ev $= 70(4.803 \times 10^{-10})$ (1/300) erg, from the previous Illustration. Thus, $\frac{1}{2}m_e v^2 = 1.121 \times 10^{-10}$ erg, and since $m_e = 9.108 \times 10^{-28}$ gram, then

$$v = [2(1.12 \times 10^{-10})/9.108 \times 10^{-28}]^{\frac{1}{2}} \text{ cm sec}^{-1}$$

and $\qquad p = mv = [2(1.12 \times 10^{-10})(9.108 \times 10^{-28})]^{\frac{1}{2}} \text{ g cm sec}^{-1}$

$$= 4.5 \times 10^{-19} \text{ g cm sec}^{-1}$$

If the electron position were desired to be specified within 1 Å, i.e., atomic dimensions, then

$$\Delta p \approx 6.62 \times 10^{-27}/1 \times 10^{-8} = 6.62 \times 10^{-19} \text{ g cm sec}^{-1}$$

that is, the uncertainty in the momentum exceeds its calculated magnitude.

The wavelength to be associated with the 70-ev beam of electrons can also be calculated; it is

$$\lambda = h/p = 6.62 \times 10^{-27}/4.5 \times 10^{-19} = 1.47 \times 10^{-8} \text{ cm}$$

a much smaller value than the wavelength of visible light. The electron microscope puts to use this great difference in wavelength. The maximum useful magnification of any kind of microscope is fundamentally limited by diffraction of the radiation used to illuminate and form an enlarged image of the object. If, in the object, we attempt to observe detail having dimensions comparable to the wavelength of the radiation, diffraction causes blurring and loss of most of the detail. The electron microscope employs a beam of electrons instead of a beam of light. Since λ for the electron beam is much smaller than λ of visible light, the electron microscope can resolve detail much smaller than is possible with the conventional optical microscope. For an accelerating potential of 7000 volts (which is closer to the operating conditions of an electron microscope), $p = 4.5 \times 10^{-18}$ g cm sec^{-1}, and $\lambda = 1.47 \times 10^{-9}$ cm. Since beams of electrons are much less penetrating than light, the technology is quite different: the electron microscope must operate with the electron beam in a high vacuum, and the "lenses" consist of special magnetic fields.

Even the electron microscope, which has important limitations, falls somewhat short of ability to distinguish atoms; this has been done by Müller with the field *ion* microscope, which employs ionic particles of several thousand-fold greater mass than the electron. This microscope has been used to display atoms and molecules adsorbed on the tip of a sharply pointed piece of metal [E. W. Müller, *Am. Scientist*, **49**, 88 (1961)].

If a particle is confined to a certain range of x (i.e., is in a one-dimensional box of length x), it is apparent that the uncertainty in x cannot be larger than this total range. Similarly, the total momentum of a particle so confined must equal or be larger than its corresponding uncertainty. This serves to put a rough lower limit on the energy of a particle. By such qualitative arguments, it can be shown, for example, that the nucleus is not composed of protons and electrons. The nucleus is too small to confine a particle with a mass as small as that of an electron, at a reasonable energy. This is the simplest argument for the proton-neutron model of the nucleus.

The student will note the similarity in form between de Broglie's relation and the uncertainty principle. By a comparison we see that a particle with a given momentum can at most be confined to a region as small as the value of a single wavelength of the particle.

If we consider a particle with momentum p_x traveling for a time Δt, a measure of the distance it will travel is

$$\Delta x = \frac{p_x}{m} \Delta t$$

If its kinetic energy is given by $\epsilon = \frac{1}{2}mv^2 = p_x^2/2m$, the variation of this quantity becomes $\Delta\epsilon = p_x \cdot \Delta p_x/m$, and $\Delta p_x = \Delta\epsilon \cdot m/p_x$. If we substitute these results in Eq. 1.303, we find an alternate form of the uncertainty principle

$$\Delta\epsilon \cdot \Delta t \geqslant h \qquad\qquad (1.304)$$

If the particle stays at the same energy level and is undisturbed for a long time, then Δt can be very large and $\Delta\epsilon$ very small; or in other words the energy could be specified very closely. There is nothing in the uncertainty principle to keep us from specifying the exact energy of a particle that stays forever in an undisturbed condition or stationary state. On the other hand, if the system were to remain undisturbed forever, we would not be able to check the theoretical calculations.

Equation 1.304 applies also to complex molecules, and to internal molecular energy levels as well. A valid theory of atoms and molecules must contain the fact that simultaneous precise knowledge of position and momentum is not possible. It must also recognize that material particles have wave characteristics. In Chapter 2 we proceed to the wave mechanical treatment of atomic and molecular systems.

Note: A table of integrals is given in the appendix (Table 1.401(A)).

4. Review Problems

1.401   Show that the Planck law gives the Stefan-Boltzmann law when integrated. HINT: Hold T constant, let $x = hc/\lambda kT$, and change variables from λ to x. See Table 1.401(A) for integral.

1.402   The sun exhibits its most intense radiation at 4750 Å in the blue-green of the visible spectrum. Calculate the corresponding surface temperature.

1.403   Explain why a piece of metal when heated to incandescence appears dull red when its temperature is $\sim$800°C.

1.404   What volume of a vacuum must be taken to contain an amount of radiant energy kT at (a) 8°K? (b) 800°K?

1.405   (a) Show that the Planck radiation law when expressed in terms of frequency, v, takes the form

$$\rho_v = \frac{8\pi h v^3}{c^3(e^{hv/kT} - 1)}$$

(b) Write down an explicit mathematical condition that must hold for the Wien equation to agree with the Planck law within 15 per cent.

1.406   The Planck law assumes the Rayleigh-Jeans and the Wien form for $\lambda \to \infty$ and 0, respectively. Find the respective values of λ for which both the Rayleigh-Jeans and Wien radiation density expressions differ in magnitude by 10 per cent from the Planck law at (a) 500°K, (b) 5000°K. Can you explain the shift between (a) and (b)?

1.407   By use of the information in Problem 1.401 demonstrate that σ has the value 7.56×10^{-15} erg cm^{-3} deg^{-4}.

1.408   Determine expressions for the Wien law constants C_1 and C_2 by use of the limiting form of the Planck law at short wavelengths.

1.409   Using the surface temperature of the sun as determined in Problem 1.402 and for a solar diameter of 865,000 miles, calculate the rate of energy loss by radiation per second. How much of this energy is intercepted by Earth, which is 93,000,000 miles from the sun?

1.410   A space capsule presents to view about 10 ft^3 in surface area which is heated to a temperature of about 2000°K on re-entry. How much radiant energy falls on a 20-ft-diameter detector mirror which is 50 miles away?

1.411   (a) Calculate roughly the momentum and kinetic energy of an electron in a nucleus of radius 10^{-12} cm if the value of p must be at least as large as the uncertainty Δp. Does this value correspond to a reasonable energy relative to binding energies found for nucleons of the order of several million electron volts (mev)?

(b) Repeat this calculation for a neutron (mass $= 1.6748 \times 10^{-24}$ g).

1.412   Light of wavelength 1000 Å caused photoelectric emission of electrons of wavelength 4.2 Å. What is the value of the threshold energy W_0?

1.413   Calculate the kinetic energy of an electron with a wavelength of 1.0 Å. If the electron acquired this kinetic energy by acceleration in an electrostatic field, what voltage would be required? If all the kinetic energy were converted into a single photon of light what would be the associated wavelength?

1.414   Calculate the wavelength of a proton with a velocity of 3×10^9 cm sec^{-1}. If this proton was suddenly stopped and emitted all its kinetic energy as a single photon, calculate the wavelength associated.

*1.415   As the velocity of a particle approaches the velocity of light, a "relativity" correction must be applied. The total energy may be expressed in the form $W = m_0c^2(1 - v^2/c^2)^{-\frac{1}{2}}$. Use the binomial theorem to expand the radical; evaluate the first three terms in the series.

How large may v become before an error of 1 per cent appears in the kinetic energy term when evaluated as $\frac{1}{2}m_0v^2$? (Let $W = m_0c^2 + \mathcal{T}$, where $\mathcal{T}$ is the kinetic energy.)

General References

Eisberg, R. M., *Fundamentals of Modern Physics*, John Wiley and Sons, New York, 1961.

Gray, D. E., Editor, *American Institute of Physics Handbook*, McGraw-Hill Book Co., New York, 1957, Section 6, Optics.

Handbook of Chemistry and Physics, Chemical Rubber Co., Cleveland.

Herzberg, G., *Atomic Spectra and Atomic Structure*, Prentice-Hall, Englewood Cliffs, N.J., 1937.

Kaye, G. W. C., and T. H. Laby, *Tables of Physical and Chemical Constants*, Twelfth Edition, Longmans, Green and Co., New York, 1958.

Lange's Handbook of Chemistry, Ninth Edition, Handbook Publishers, Sandusky, Ohio, 1956.

Resnick, R., and D. Halliday, *Physics for Students of Science and Engineering*, Part I, 1960, and Part II, Second Edition, 1962, John Wiley and Sons, New York.

Richards, J. A., F. W. Sears, M. R. Wehr, and M. W. Zemansky, *Modern University Physics*, Addison-Wesley Publishing Co., Reading, Mass., 1960.

Richtmyer, F. K., E. H. Kennard, and T. Lauritsen, *Introduction to Modern Physics*, Fifth Edition, McGraw-Hill Book Co., New York, 1955.

* An asterisk indicates a problem of greater difficulty.

Chapter Two

Quantum Mechanical Energy Levels

for Some Simple Systems

In this chapter, we present the Schrödinger wave mechanical method for obtaining theoretical time-independent energy levels for some model systems. For this purpose we need the classical expressions for the total energy of the model, in terms of coordinates and momenta, called the *Hamiltonian function*. We review first a few definitions and concepts of classical mechanics.

1. Some Definitions in Classical Mechanics

Force, Energy, and Degrees of Freedom.   In the application of Newton's equations of motion to classical systems, one deals with forces explicitly, e.g., the force of gravity, the force of a stretched spring, the force of friction. When friction is absent, we may equally well deal with potential energy, $V(x)$, which is related to force, f, by the equation

$$f = - \frac{d}{dx} V(x)$$

or

$$f_x = - \frac{\partial}{\partial x} V(x,y,z) \tag{2.101}$$

In the first expression we consider only motion along a straight line, so that potential energy is a function of the position (x coordinate) on the line, and the

force is of necessity directed along the line. The derivative is the total one. In the
second expression we have the more general possibility of motion in three directions,
so that the potential energy is a function of three coordinates, and we use partial
differentiation with respect to the variable x. The force has a subscript to show that
it is the component parallel to the x axis.

In the cgs system of units, energy is expressed in ergs, and force in dynes; the
differentiation in Eq. 2.101 employs centimeters as the units of x. A more familiar
version of this equation, and a more general one, is

$$W = -\int_{x_1}^{x_2} f_x \, dx \qquad (2.102)$$

where W is the work done by a force acting from the point x_1 to the point x_2.
Work is expressed in terms of the energy unit, the erg, given by the product of the
force unit, the dyne, and the distance unit, the centimeter. This equation is more
general than Eq. 2.101 since the forces may involve friction and may not be deriv-
able from a potential function.

As a simple example, consider the expansion of a gas which pushes against a
piston and moves it against a constant external pressure. The force on the piston is
the product of the pressure and area, $P \cdot A$, so that

$$W = -\int_{x_1}^{x_2} P \cdot A \, dx \qquad (2.103)$$

or, since $A \, dx$ is the volume change, dV,

$$W = -\int_{V_1}^{V_2} P \, dV \qquad (2.104)$$

The symbol V, commonly used for volume, is not to be confused with the potential
energy function, $V(x)$. Since the pressure is constant during this process, we have
work equals (force × distance),

$$W = -P(V_2 - V_1) \qquad (2.105)$$

Another example is the force of gravity. It may be derived from the potential
energy expression

$$V(x) = mgx \qquad (2.106)$$

where m is the mass of an object, g the gravitational acceleration constant, and x
the vertical distance above a reference point, say on Earth. By Eq. 2.101, the force
is then $-mg$. Actually, g is not constant and varies with x, but this dependence is
usually neglected when the variation of x is small relative to the radius of the earth.

An example of a force which varies with the position is an ideal spring (Fig.
2.101). The potential energy is

$$V(x) = \tfrac{1}{2}k(x - x_e)^2 \qquad (2.107)$$

where k is a spring constant, or *force constant*, and $x - x_e$ is the displacement from
the equilibrium position, x_e. By Eq. 2.101, the force is $-k(x - x_e)$.

In atoms and molecules, forces arise chiefly from electrostatic attraction and repulsion. For a single proton and a single electron, for example,

$$V(r) = \frac{-e^2}{r} \tag{2.108}$$

where e is the magnitude of the electronic charge, r is the distance between the charges, and the negative sign means an attractive interaction. The force, by Eq. 2.101, is now $-e^2/r^2$, the familiar inverse-square law of Coulomb. If both

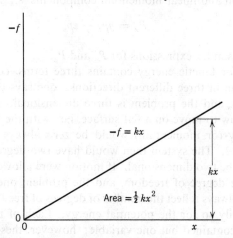

Fig. 2.101   The force opposing the stretching of a spring is $-f = k(x - x_e) = kx$, if x_e is set at zero. The area under the force curve is the work done. (By permission, after R. Resnick and D. Halliday, *Physics for Students of Science and Engineering*, John Wiley and Sons, Part I, 1960.)

particles have the same charge, such as two protons, the potential energy is positive and the particles repel each other, corresponding to a positive sign of the force.

We are also accustomed to writing the kinetic energy (frequently denoted as $\mathscr{T}$) of a mass m in terms of its velocity, v, as

$$\mathscr{T} = \tfrac{1}{2}mv^2 \tag{2.109}$$

Since the velocity may have components v_x, v_y, and v_z along the x, y, and z axes, respectively, the kinetic energy may also be written

$$\mathscr{T} = \tfrac{1}{2}m(v_x^2 + v_y^2 + v_z^2) \tag{2.110}$$

For purposes of quantum mechanics, it is more convenient to write the kinetic energies in terms of momenta. Momentum is related to velocity in a complex way for an arbitrary choice of coordinate system; however, in Cartesian coordinates the x component of momentum is

$$p_x = \left(\frac{\partial \mathscr{T}}{\partial v_x}\right) = mv_x \tag{2.111}$$

and similarly for the y and z components. This is, of course, the usual Newtonian definition of momentum. The kinetic energy may then also be written

$$\mathscr{T} = \frac{p_x^2 + p_y^2 + p_z^2}{2m} \tag{2.112}$$

Another kind of momentum, the angular momentum, P, is important for rotational motion. The x component of angular momentum for a particle is given in terms of the position and linear momentum components

$$P_x = yp_z - zp_y \tag{2.113}$$

with symmetrically similar expressions for P_y and P_z.

Equation 2.112 for kinetic energy contains three terms, corresponding to the possibility of motion in three different directions; one says the system has three degrees of freedom, and the problem is three dimensional. If the particle were constrained somehow to move on a flat surface, i.e., with the z coordinate always zero, the z velocity (or momentum) would be zero always and dropped from Eqs. 2.110 and 2.112. The system then would have two degrees of freedom, and the problem would be two dimensional. If motion were allowed only along a line, there would be one degree of freedom, and the problem one dimensional. The kinetic energy will always reflect the number of degrees of freedom for the problem; this is not necessarily so for the potential energy. Each of the potential energy expressions above contained but one variable; however, these expressions might appear in equations involving kinetic energy in one, two, or three dimensions.

The total energy, the sum of kinetic energy and potential energy, is an important property of many systems. It may be written in a variety of equivalent ways. When it is written in terms of coordinates and momenta (rather than, for instance, in terms of coordinates and velocities), it is called the (classical) Hamiltonian function, or the Hamiltonian.

The One-Dimensional Classical Harmonic Oscillator.   A Simple Hamiltonian.
One of the simpler Hamiltonian functions is that for a mass m on a spring, moving on the x axis only. This model is called the one-dimensional harmonic oscillator. The potential energy is given by Eq. 2.107, and the kinetic energy is also a quadratic function.

$$\mathscr{T} = \frac{p_x^2}{2m} \tag{2.114}$$

The Hamiltonian is then defined as the sum of these two:

$$\mathscr{H}(p_x, x) = \mathscr{T} + V(x) = \frac{p_x^2}{2m} + \frac{k}{2}(x - x_e)^2 \tag{2.115}$$

If we let $x_e = 0$, Newton's equation for this system,

$$f = ma$$

where a is the acceleration, becomes with the use of Eq. 2.101,

$$-kx = m\frac{d^2x}{dt^2} \qquad (2.116)$$

We may try certain functions to see if they satisfy this differential equation; both sines and cosines will. Let

$$x = x_0 \cos bt \qquad (2.117)$$

where x_0 is a constant, the amplitude of oscillation. On substituting in Eq. 2.116 we find

$$-kx_0 = -mx_0 b^2 \qquad (2.118)$$

or, solving for b and substituting in Eq. 2.117,

$$x = x_0 \cos \left(\frac{k}{m}\right)^{1/2} t \qquad (2.119)$$

The mass, then, oscillates between the limits $+x_0$ and $-x_0$ with a time for one complete cycle given by the time in which the argument of the cosine changes by 2π, or $t = 2\pi(m/k)^{1/2}$. The reciprocal of this number is the frequency of oscillation, ν, the number of complete cycles of oscillation in a time of 1 second,

$$\nu = \frac{1}{2\pi}\left(\frac{k}{m}\right)^{1/2} \qquad (2.120)$$

Note also that we have not determined the amplitude of oscillation, x_0; it can be any number, including zero, depending on how much energy the system has received.

The total energy of the oscillator may be found by substituting Eq. 2.117 into the Hamiltonian, Eq. 2.115, along with the momentum,

$$p_x = m\frac{dx}{dt} \qquad (2.121)$$

$$= -mx_0 b \sin bt$$

$$\mathscr{H} = \frac{m^2 x_0^2 b^2 \sin^2 bt}{2m} + \frac{kx_0^2 \cos^2 bt}{2} \qquad (2.122)$$

and by Eq. 2.118,

$$\mathscr{H} = \frac{kx_0^2}{2}\sin^2 bt + \frac{kx_0^2}{2}\cos^2 bt$$

$$= \frac{kx_0^2}{2} \qquad (2.123)$$

The total energy is then independent of x and of t and depends only on the force constant and the maximum displacement.

Even if the total energy is a constant, kinetic and potential energies, and also displacements and velocities, are not constant. A way of representing this is shown in Fig. 2.102, in which the instantaneous values of p_x and x are plotted for constant energy; the curve is an ellipse. The displacement may have values anywhere between $-x_0$ and $+x_0$, and the momentum likewise varies between a maximum and a minimum value. When the displacement has its extreme value, the momentum is zero, and vice versa. Although the total energy is constant, there is a continual transformation between kinetic and potential energy as the mass oscillates. The system may have infinitely many values of total energy, including zero and any

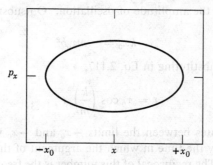

Fig. 2.102 p_x as a function of x for a certain constant value of total energy.

positive quantity; there are, thus, infinitely many ellipses lying within and beyond the one drawn in the figure.

ILLUSTRATION. The Bohr theory of the hydrogen atom as an application of classical mechanics in which imposition of an arbitrary quantum condition gives results in agreement with atomic spectra.

The model has a fixed central positive charge e, the nucleus, and a single electron of mass m and charge $-e$ moving around the nucleus in a circular "orbit" of radius r. The latter condition reduces the number of pertinent coordinate parameters to one, r. Then

$$\text{centrifugal force} = \frac{mv^2}{r} \tag{2.124}$$

where v is the linear velocity of the electron, and

$$\text{electrostatic force} = -\frac{e^2}{r^2} \tag{2.125}$$

For a stable orbit, these two forces must be equal in magnitude, so

$$\frac{mv^2}{r} = \frac{e^2}{r^2}$$

or

$$mv^2 = \frac{e^2}{r} \tag{2.126}$$

This gives a relation between r and v; in a strictly classical system we may have a stable orbit with any arbitrary value of r, which would lead to total energies of any arbitrary value. At this point, however, Bohr assumed that r may have only certain values; that is, those for which the circumference of the orbit is a whole-number multiple of the de Broglie wavelength,

$$2\pi r = n\lambda = n\,\frac{h}{mv} \tag{2.127}$$

where h is Planck's constant and n is an integer, $1, 2, 3, \ldots$. Rearrangement of Eq. 2.127 gives

$$mvr = \frac{nh}{2\pi} \tag{2.128}$$

or orbital angular momentum, mvr, is an integral multiple of $h/2\pi$. Bohr's work actually preceded that of de Broglie, and Bohr invented Eq. 2.128 by making the revolutionary postulate of quantization of orbital angular momentum of the electron. Solving either of these equations for v or r, and substituting in Eq. 2.126, we find

$$r = \frac{n^2 h^2}{4\pi^2 m e^2}, \qquad v = \frac{2\pi e^2}{nh} \tag{2.129}$$

as the only allowed values of orbit radius and velocity. Since the total energy, ϵ, is the sum of the kinetic energy, $\mathscr{T} = \tfrac{1}{2}mv^2$, and the potential energy, $V(r) = -e^2/r$, we have

$$\epsilon = \tfrac{1}{2}m\left(\frac{4\pi^2 e^4}{n^2 h^2}\right) - e^2\left(\frac{4\pi^2 m e^2}{n^2 h^2}\right)$$

$$= -\frac{2\pi^2 m e^4}{n^2 h^2} \tag{2.130}$$

This expression does indeed give the energy levels of the hydrogen atom. It will also be noticed that the kinetic and potential energies, $\mathscr{T}$ and V, are related by the expression

$$\mathscr{T} = -\tfrac{1}{2}V; \quad \epsilon = \mathscr{T} + V = +\tfrac{1}{2}V \tag{2.131}$$

The student may now calculate
(a) The value of the orbital radius, r_0, for $n = 1$.
(b) The energy required to excite the atom from $n = 1$ to 2.
(c) The ionization potential, I (energy required to excite the electron from $n = 1$ to ∞, i.e., remove it from the atom).

Problems

2.101 The lowest energy level of the hydrogen atom is about -10^{-11} erg. Estimate the value of r. Using this value of r, apply the uncertainty principle to calculate the kinetic energy of the electron and compare the result with the starting value.

2.102 Reconcile the opposite signs used in Eqs. 2.106 and 2.108.

2. The Schrödinger Method;   the Harmonic Oscillator

We present here a brief account of the Schrödinger method for treating the time-independent behavior of certain systems, using a postulatory approach. Much of this treatment may appear different from and unrelated to classical mechanics as expressed in Newton's equations. There are at least two reasons for this. First, Newton's equations contain explicit dependence on time. A more general and thorough-going treatment of time-dependent quantum mechanics shows much better the similarities between classical and quantum mechanics. Second, there are more elaborate versions of classical mechanics which also show the similarities of classical and quantum mechanics. In fact, the quantum approach and the classical approach must give identical results when applied to the same appropriate large-scale systems. This requirement is called the *correspondence principle*; we shall point out its application in some of the examples to follow. For atomic systems, and especially for small quantum numbers, there may be, and usually are, large differences between the results of classical and quantum mechanics. When such a discrepancy is found, it is invariably true that the classical results disagree with experiment, whereas the results calculated by means of quantum mechanics agree well with experiment.

There are many approaches to quantum mechanics, of which the Schrödinger method is but one. Some of these have great apparent differences, both in the mathematics used, and in the initial assumptions or postulates. In spite of these differences, all these quantum approaches give identical results for identical systems. Our choice of one method, that due to Schrödinger, is based upon its more familiar mathematics and the relative ease of deriving useful results.

Postulates;   Models of Real Systems. Any theory must have some starting-point or set of basic assumptions; in classical mechanics these are implicit in Newton's equations. For systems of suitable size, they can be verified in the laboratory by direct measurement of masses, forces, and accelerations. Another good test is to calculate the motions of some system, such as the rotation of the moon around the earth, and to compare the behavior observed with that calculated. On the atomic scale, however, we must be very careful that a proposed test does not violate the uncertainty principle. The calculation of precise paths or orbits in which the electron rotates about the nucleus of the hydrogen atom is then not a suitable test. However, Eq. 1.304 shows that the uncertainty in total energy of the hydrogen atom can be extremely small; a test made by measurement of the energy, such as by observations of the spectrum, is consistent with the uncertainty principle. Tests of the quantum theory involving a variety of measurable properties have agreed well with the results of the calculations. On this basis it is believed that the postulates and methods of procedure are correct. However, it is also possible that another method and set of postulates would also agree; such a set would then also qualify as correct.

As remarked in Chapter 1, we begin with a description of the system we wish to treat; this leads to the concept of a model system or a model. The model here will mean the properties of the particles being treated, such as charge and mass, and also the potential energy (i.e., law of force) by which they would be governed, classically. A model may or may not closely describe a real system; frequently one idealizes or simplifies certain parts, especially the potential energy, in order to render the equations more readily solved. Quite often, if the simplifications are wise, the model systems still give results very close to the behavior of the real systems of interest which are observed in the laboratory. The four steps of the Schrödinger procedure for finding quantum energy levels follow.

The Classical Hamiltonian. After the model is chosen, the classical Hamiltonian is written in terms of the coordinates and Cartesian momenta (see discussion in Sec. 2.1). For the harmonic oscillator, if we choose the origin of the extension coordinate so that $x_e = 0$, Eq. 2.115 becomes

$$\mathcal{H}(p_x, x) = \frac{p_x^2}{2m} + \frac{k}{2} x^2 \tag{2.201}$$

This is already a simplification; there is no "spring," either in the large-scale world or in the atomic world, which has such a simple potential energy. However, this model is a useful simplification for many purposes.

The Hamiltonian Operator. There are several alternative formulations for obtaining quantum mechanical operators corresponding to the classical quantities in Eq. 2.201. They all lead to the same results; our choice is convenient for systems with discrete energy levels, such as atoms and molecules. The Hamiltonian operator is obtained by substitution of $(h/2\pi i)(d/dx)$ for p_x wherever it occurs in the classical Hamiltonian energy function; parts of the Hamiltonian which contain only coordinates x, y, z are included without change; h is Planck's constant, and i is the square root of -1. If p_x is squared, cubed, etc., this is understood to mean repeated application of the differential operator, giving $-(h^2/4\pi^2)(d^2/dx^2)$, $-(h^3/8\pi^3i)(d^3/dx^3)$, etc. The operator is not defined for fractional or negative powers of p_x. If there should be several coordinates, such as x, y, z, etc., one uses partial derivatives in place of total derivatives, $(h/2\pi i)(\partial/\partial x)$, $(h/2\pi i)(\partial/\partial y)$, etc. The harmonic oscillator example then gives

$$\boldsymbol{H} = -\left(\frac{h^2}{8\pi^2 m} \frac{d^2}{dx^2}\right) + \left(\frac{k}{2} x^2\right) \tag{2.202}$$

where the boldface reminds us that $\boldsymbol{H}$ is an operator and is without significance by itself. That is, we do not think of Eq. 2.202 as meaning that we substitute certain numbers in the right-hand side and calculate a numerical value for the left-hand side. Rather, some function of x must be written to the right of the terms on both sides of Eq. 2.202 and expanded in such a way that

$$\left(\frac{d^2}{dx^2}\right) A(x) = \frac{d^2 A(x)}{dx^2} \tag{2.203}$$

that is, d^2/dx^2 "operates" on $A(x)$. Writing the function to the left of H would mean something entirely different, so that the order is important, i.e., the quantities may not be permuted. Those parts of H containing only coordinates will, of course, also multiply A in the usual fashion; $(x^2)A(x) = x^2A(x)$.

The Schrödinger Equation. This is obtained by placing the operator expression for H in the equation

$$H\psi(x) = \epsilon\psi(x) \tag{2.204}$$

Here ϵ is a number, which is an energy of the system, called an *eigenvalue*, and ψ is some characteristic function of the coordinates of the problem, called an *eigen-function* or *wave function*. The Schrödinger equation for the harmonic oscillator is finally

$$-\frac{h^2}{8\pi^2 m}\frac{d^2\psi(x)}{dx^2} + \frac{k}{2}x^2\psi(x) = \epsilon\psi(x) \tag{2.205}$$

The wave function is required to be well behaved, i.e., single-valued, continuous, and finite, and is required to possess first and second derivatives for all values of the coordinates. For other problems some of these restrictions may be relaxed.

Solution of the Schrödinger Equation. The Schrödinger equation, such as Eq. 2.205, contains given quantities h, m, and k; however, both the function $\psi(x)$ and the number ϵ are unknowns. Solving the Schrödinger equation consists in finding a function, or perhaps a number of different functions, and a number, or numbers, ϵ, which will satisfy the equation. And further, if a certain function is a solution, the equation must be satisfied for all values of x with the same numerical constant for ϵ.

ILLUSTRATION.   Attempt the solution of Eq. 2.205 by trial and error.

One method of solving the equation might be to substitute various simple functions and see how they work. Simple powers of x will not work; for example, if x^5 is tried, Eq. 2.205 becomes

$$-\frac{20h^2}{8\pi^2 m}x^3 + \frac{k}{2}x^7 \overset{?}{=} \epsilon x^5$$

This equation could be true for a few certain values of x; but if ϵ is to be some fixed constant, it cannot be true for all x.

The student may show similarly that sines, cosines, and logarithmic functions fail.

As a systematic approach to the solution of the Schrödinger equation, consider the properties of $\psi(x)$. What happens if x becomes very large? Since ϵ is finite, this means Eq. 2.205 reduces to

$$-\frac{h^2}{8\pi^2 m}\frac{d^2\psi(x)}{dx^2} + \frac{k}{2}x^2\psi(x) = 0 \tag{2.206}$$

as the limiting form, for $\epsilon\psi(x)$ is a lower order of infinity than $x^2\psi(x)$, as $x \to \infty$. The task reduces to finding a function which, when differentiated twice, gives back the same function multiplied by x^2 and a constant into which are lumped the constants h, m, k, π, etc. This suggests that the function when differentiated should give the same function multiplied by x and some constant. This is a property of the function e^{x^2}, whose derivative is just $2xe^{x^2}$. We try a more general function e^{ax^2}, where a is a constant. Equation 2.205 becomes

$$-\frac{h^2}{8\pi^2 m}\frac{d^2(e^{ax^2})}{dx^2} + \frac{k}{2}x^2 e^{ax^2} \stackrel{?}{=} \epsilon e^{ax^2}$$

$$-\frac{h^2}{8\pi^2 m}(2ae^{ax^2} + 4a^2 x^2 e^{ax^2}) + \frac{k}{2}x^2 e^{ax^2} \stackrel{?}{=} \epsilon e^{ax^2}$$

or

$$\left(-\frac{h^2 a}{4\pi^2 m} - \frac{h^2 a^2 x^2}{2\pi^2 m} + \frac{k}{2}x^2\right)e^{ax^2} \stackrel{?}{=} \epsilon e^{ax^2}$$

We see that, although the first derivative had the right form, the function can satisfy the Schrödinger equation only if the quantity a has such a value that the last two terms in parentheses, which are still functions of x, cancel exactly. This requires that

$$\frac{h^2 a^2}{2\pi^2 m} = \frac{k}{2}$$

or

$$a = \pm\frac{\pi}{h}(km)^{\frac{1}{2}} \tag{2.207}$$

With this value of a, the tentative equation becomes

$$-\frac{h^2 a}{4\pi^2 m}e^{ax^2} = \epsilon e^{ax^2}$$

or

$$\epsilon = -\frac{h^2}{4\pi^2 m}\left[\pm\frac{\pi}{h}(km)^{\frac{1}{2}}\right] \tag{2.208}$$

This expression contains the usual sign ambiguity of the square root. Can both signs give satisfactory functions and energies? The answer is no, since one of the functions violates the well-behaved requirement. The range of the variable x extends from minus infinity to plus infinity; at either of these extremes the function e^{+ax^2} becomes infinite. The function e^{-ax^2} approaches zero as x becomes infinite and is also well behaved for other values of x. We are left with the wave function

$$\psi(x) = e^{-ax^2} \tag{2.209}$$

and its associated energy level or eigenvalue

$$\epsilon = \frac{h}{4\pi}\left(\frac{k}{m}\right)^{\frac{1}{2}} \tag{2.210}$$

Other Solutions of the Schrödinger Equation for the Harmonic Oscillator.   There are also other functions which are eigenfunctions of the Schrödinger equation, Eq. 2.205, each with its associated eigenvalue. For instance, it can be shown by substitution that xe^{-ax^2} is an eigenfunction with associated eigenvalue

$$\epsilon = \frac{3h}{4\pi}\left(\frac{k}{m}\right)^{\frac{1}{2}} \tag{2.211}$$

In fact, there are infinitely many such eigenfunctions and eigenvalues; the next few higher eigenvalues are found to be

$$\epsilon = \frac{5h}{4\pi}\left(\frac{k}{m}\right)^{\frac{1}{2}}, \quad \frac{7h}{4\pi}\left(\frac{k}{m}\right)^{\frac{1}{2}}, \quad \text{etc.} \tag{2.212}$$

All the eigenfunctions contain the same exponential term; their differences lie in the polynomial coefficients.

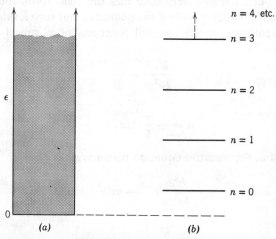

Fig. 2.201   Comparison of allowed energies for the harmonic oscillator; (a) continuous levels of classical mechanics and (b) discrete levels of quantum mechanics.

The expression $(1/2\pi)(k/m)^{\frac{1}{2}}$ is, in classical mechanics, simply the vibration frequency, ν, of the system; see Eq. 2.120. The quantum energy levels may then be written in terms of this classical vibration frequency, and be expressed in one equation by

$$\epsilon_n = (n + \tfrac{1}{2})h\nu \tag{2.213}$$

where $n = 0, 1, 2, 3, \ldots$. The quantity n is a quantum number and also serves as an index of the various eigenfunctions $\psi_n(x)$ and their eigenvalues, ϵ_n. Further investigation proves that these are the only eigenvalues of the harmonic oscillator.

This energy expression is different from the classical result, Sec. 2.1, in several important respects. First, only certain special values of energy are possible; in the classical approach all values of energy are allowed (Fig. 2.201). Second, an energy of zero is impossible; in the classical system, we may have a zero amplitude of vibration which leads to an energy of zero. This smallest possible energy, in the quantum approach, is called *zero-point energy* because it will still be present at the absolute zero of temperature. Zero-point energy may also be regarded as a result of the Heisenberg uncertainty principle; if the energy were zero, the coordinate would always be exactly zero and the kinetic energy, and hence momentum, would also be exactly zero.

Comparison with Experiment.   Chemical interest in the spectra of gases was indicated in Sec. 1.1. Spectra of gases may be studied in two general ways: by emission and by absorption. In an emission spectrum, the gas is excited by an electric discharge, high temperature, or other means and emits radiation whose frequency distribution is measured. Except for monatomic and certain diatomic gases, this method can lead to complexities because of chemical reactions and the large amount of excitation given to the gas. In contrast, the use of absorption spectra permits the sample to be kept at fixed temperature and thus simplifies certain aspects of interpretation. The general arrangement consists of some continuous light source, such as a tungsten lamp or heated rod, whose emitted radiation is allowed to pass through the sample enclosure, or cell, and then to the spectrometer. The radiation passing through the sample is compared to that passing through an identical evacuated enclosure, the "blank" cell. In general, the transmitted radiation energy is the same for the sample and for the blank cell. However, there may be narrow regions of the spectrum for which the transmitted energy of the sample is less than that of the blank; the name absorption spectrum derives from the fact that some of the radiation energy is being absorbed by the sample.

The absorption spectrum of a sample of carbon monoxide gas is shown in Fig. 2.202. The sample cell was arranged so that light could pass through a total length of 10 cm containing the gas at 1 atm pressure. A weak absorption is found at 2.33×10^{-4} cm, and a stronger one centered about the value 4.67×10^{-4} cm. The sample is quite transparent in other spectral regions at both longer and shorter wavelengths, until very long wavelengths, a few millimeters, and very short wavelengths, about 0.15×10^{-4} cm, are reached. The large separation of the latter regions suggests that they are due to different processes from those shown in the figure.

Transparency of the sample over a wide range of the spectrum is a very important experimental fact. Equation 1.107 relates the frequency of the photon absorbed, v, to the difference in energy $\Delta\epsilon$, between the initial and final states of the atom or molecule:

$$|\Delta\epsilon| = hv \qquad\qquad (1.107)$$

If the sample molecules or atoms could have any value of energy over a continuous range, then it would be possible to satisfy Eq. 1.107 for values of v over a continuous range. If the sample molecules or atoms have only certain allowed values of energy, then Eq. 1.107 can be satisfied only for certain special frequencies. Photons of

other frequencies will pass through the sample without any absorption, and this is
observed. The discrete character of the absorption spectrum is then an experimental indication of the existence of energy levels.

Association of the absorptions in Fig. 2.202 with molecular vibration is completely consistent with all information on carbon monoxide from other spectral
regions, and from thermal and equilibrium data. But if there are a great many
discrete energy levels, why is the spectrum so simple? The answer is related to

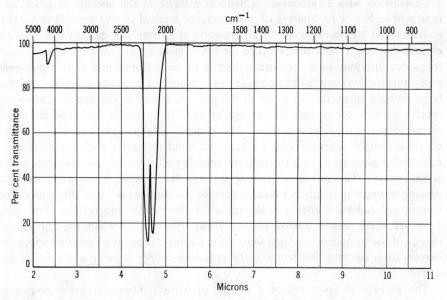

Fig. 2.202 Absorption spectrum of carbon monoxide at 1 atm pressure and 10 cm path. A
background ripple due to instrumental "noise" is evident. [By permission from Pierson, Fletcher,
and Ganz, *Anal. Chem.*, **28**, 1218 (1956).]

selection rules (Chapters 4 and 16), derived from theory, which govern the allowed
transitions. These rules show that absorption of radiation requires the presence of
an asymmetric charge distribution in the molecule. Hence in a diatomic molecule
composed of identical atoms, such as O_2, H_2, and N_2, vibrational transitions cannot
be observed in the spectrum. And even in a molecule with different atoms, such as
CO, HCl, and NO, only transitions in which the vibrational quantum number
changes by one unit are (strongly) allowed. Transitions with changes of two,
three, etc., are progressively weaker and may escape detection in a limited optical
path.

The vibrational levels are quite widely spaced, and the sample at room temperature will have essentially all its molecules in the $n = 0$ state (see Chapter 5). The
absorption at 4.67×10^{-4} cm is then due to the $n = 0 \rightarrow 1$ transition, and that at
2.33×10^{-4} cm is due to the $n = 0 \rightarrow 2$ transition. With more accurate values we
can test the validity of the harmonic oscillator model for carbon monoxide. It is

convenient to work in some kind of frequency units for this purpose; cycles per second gives rather large magnitudes, so one divides cycles per second by the velocity of light, c, and obtains a unit called wave numbers, with dimensions cm^{-1}, which is simply the reciprocal of the wavelength.

For stable diatomic molecules, vibration frequencies lie in the range about 200 to 4000 cm^{-1}. Molecules which contain several heavy atoms, such as I_2 and IBr, or molecules with very small force constants tend to have low frequencies; molecules which contain at least one light atom, such as hydrogen, or molecules with large force constants tend to have higher frequencies. Isotopic substitution does not alter the force constant, calculated from Eq. 2.120, in which m is an effective mass.

ILLUSTRATION. Show that the carbon monoxide molecule is not exactly a harmonic oscillator by calculating the difference between the observed and predicted values for $n = 0 \rightarrow n = 2$, assuming the value for $n = 0 \rightarrow n = 1$ is correct for the harmonic model. The accurate values for the absorption centers are, for $n = 0 \rightarrow 1$, 2143.27 cm^{-1}, and, for $n = 0 \rightarrow 2$, 4260.06 cm^{-1} [Plyler, Blaine, and Connor, J. Opt. Soc. Am., **45**, 102 (1955); Rank, Guenther, Saksena, Shearer, and Wiggins, ibid., **47**, 686 (1957)].

If the molecule were strictly harmonic, then the $n = 0 \rightarrow 2$ wave number should be exactly twice the $n = 0 \rightarrow 1$ wave number. But 4260.06 is not the same as 2×2143.27, or 4286.54. The percentage difference, however, is only about 0.62; this is remarkably small.

Assume that the levels above may be fitted to a power series in n, i.e., of the form $an + bn^2$, and evaluate the constants a and b. For $n = 1$, we have

$$2143.27 = a(1) + b(1)^2$$

and for $n = 2$, we have

$$4260.06 = a(2) + b(2)^2$$

These two equations may be solved simultaneously by multiplying the first by 2 and subtracting.

$$-26.48 = 2b, \, b = -13.24 \text{ cm}^{-1}$$

and

$$a = 2156.51 \text{ cm}^{-1}$$

This is the required expression. The student may calculate the expected wave numbers for the $n = 0 \rightarrow 3$ and $n = 0 \rightarrow 4$ transitions. Compare with the observed values, 6350.43 cm^{-1} and 8414.45 cm^{-1}.*

Problems

2.201   Calculate the energy, in ergs per mole, corresponding to the vibrational transition $0 \rightarrow 1$ for CO.

* In order to measure the $0 \rightarrow 4$ transition, a sample equivalent to about 500 meters path at 1 atm was used; a search for the $0 \rightarrow 5$ band, with path equivalent of 3000 meters at 1 atm, was not successful [G. Herzberg and K. N. Rao, J. Chem. Phys., **17**, 1099 (1949)].

2.202   The HCl^{35} molecule has transitions observed at 2885.98 cm^{-1}* $(0 \rightarrow 1)$ and 5667.98 cm^{-1}† $(0 \rightarrow 2)$. Determine the constants a and b in the simple quadratic formula; see the preceding Illustration.

2.203   From the constants in Problem 2.202 calculate the positions of the transitions $0 \rightarrow 3$, $0 \rightarrow 4$, and $0 \rightarrow 5$ for HCl^{35}. They are observed at 8346.78, 10,922.80, and 13,396.19 cm^{-1}, respectively.‡

2.204   The HCl^{35} molecule has an effective mass for vibration of 0.9799, and the DCl^{35} molecule has an effective mass of 1.905. Estimate the energy in wave numbers of the $0 \rightarrow 1$ transition for DCl^{35}. (It is found at 2091.0 cm^{-1}, experimentally.§)

2.205   The effective (reduced) mass of the CO molecule for vibrations is given as 6.858 on the atomic weight scale; if 2143.27 wave numbers represents a harmonic oscillator frequency, calculate the force constant for classical vibration. Avogadro's number may be taken as 6.025×10^{23}.

2.206   Calculate, from the data of the preceding problems, the difference between the zero-point energies of HCl^{35} and DCl^{35}.

3. Wave Functions and Probabilities

We now turn to a discussion of wave functions and probability distribution functions. Another of the basic postulates of quantum mechanics is that the probability function, $P_n(x)$, is given by the square of the wave function, $P_n(x) = |\psi_n(x)|^2$. A discussion of the meaning of probability distribution function is given, followed by consideration of a few actual wave functions and probabilities.

Statistical Interpretations.   In Chapter 1 we saw that it is not possible to determine with unlimited accuracy both the position and the momentum of a particle (Heisenberg uncertainty principle). In this section we consider the probability of finding the particle at a certain place or, alternatively, of finding a certain coordinate of the system with a given value. This value might be specified within very narrow limits so that the quantity Δx is very small. This is still consistent with the uncertainty principle. The measurement might, at least in principle, be made in the following way. Light illuminates the region of interest, and if the particle is there at a certain instant a photon is scattered from it and detected. If the particle was not there no photon is scattered or detected. After such scattering the particle has been disturbed and may not even be in its original state. The fact of interest, however, is whether or not the particle was there originally, i.e., just before the measurement. It should be clear that such a measurement says nothing about the behavior of the system with time.

One visualizes having a large number of identical systems, all of which are in the same energy state, i.e., have the same wave function. Identical measurements, such as described above, are carried out on all of them at corresponding positions (range of values of the certain coordinate), and the number of times the particle is found is divided by the total number of systems examined, which gives the probability. One also imagines repeating this experiment for different locations,

* E. K. Plyler and D. Tidwell, *Z. Electrochem.*, **64**, 717 (1960).
† Rank, Birtley, Eastman, Rao, and Wiggins, *J. Opt. Soc. Am.*, **50**, 1275 (1960).
‡ *Ibid.*
§ J. Pickworth and H. W. Thompson, *Proc. Roy. Soc.*, **A218**, 37 (1953).

again with all systems having the same wave function as before, which generally will result in different probabilities. Of course, if the range of values of coordinates is larger, the probability must be a larger value. The $P(x)$ curves plotted in Fig. 2.301 are really probability per unit length, and the probability from x to $x + dx$ is $P(x)\,dx$, a dimensionless quantity (pure number). For the lowest state of the

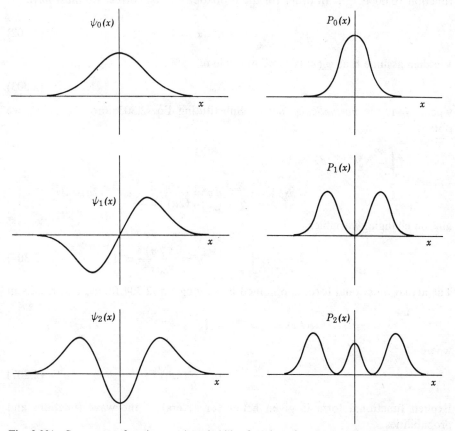

Fig. 2.301   Some wave functions and probability functions for the one-dimensional harmonic oscillator.

harmonic oscillator, the coordinate value with greatest probability is at the center, i.e., $x = 0$. For the next state, the probability of finding the x coordinate of the particle with the value zero is very low but is higher on either side of the center.

   Instead of considering the probability in a length dx, we may consider the total probability from $x = a$ to $x = b$. This is obtained by adding the probabilities in each of the infinitesimal lengths comprising the total range, or integrating.

$$\left.\begin{array}{l}\text{total probability of finding}\\ \text{the particle with } x \text{ coordinate}\\ \text{between } x = a \text{ and } x = b\end{array}\right\} = \int_a^b P(x)\,dx \qquad (2.301)$$

If we choose the values of a and b to encompass the entire range of possible x values, $x = -\infty$ to $x = +\infty$, then the integrated probability must be one, since the particle must have some x coordinate. This is a *normalizing* condition and gives us the means to complete the mathematical description of the wave function. The function e^{-ax^2}, for example, satisfies the Schrödinger equation, but so does the function $10,000e^{-ax^2}$. In order for the probability to be correct we must have

$$\int_{-\infty}^{+\infty} [\psi_0(x)]^2 \, dx = 1 \tag{2.302}$$

We then assume that $\psi_0(x)$ is some multiple of e^{-ax^2},

$$\psi_0(x) = N_0 e^{-ax^2} \tag{2.303}$$

where N_0 is the *normalizing factor*. Substituting Eq. 2.303 into Eq. 2.302, we obtain

$$\int_{-\infty}^{+\infty} N_0^2 e^{-2ax^2} \, dx = 1$$

$$= N_0^2 \int_{-\infty}^{+\infty} e^{-2ax^2} \, dx = \frac{N_0^2}{(2a)^{1/2}} \int_{-\infty}^{+\infty} e^{-2ax^2} (2a)^{1/2} \, dx$$

and on changing variables

$$= \frac{N_0^2}{(2a)^{1/2}} \int_{-\infty}^{+\infty} e^{-v^2} \, dy = \frac{N_0^2 (\pi)^{1/2}}{(2a)^{1/2}} = 1 \tag{2.304}$$

The actual functional form is obtained by solving Eq. 2.304 for N_0 and results in

$$\psi_0(x) = N_0 e^{-ax^2} = \left(\frac{2a}{\pi}\right)^{1/4} e^{-ax^2}$$

where

$$a = \frac{2\pi^2 vm}{h} \quad \text{or} \quad \frac{\pi}{h}(km)^{1/2} \tag{2.207}$$

Explicit functional form is given below for several of the wave functions and probabilities.

$$\psi_0(x) = \left(\frac{2a}{\pi}\right)^{1/4} e^{-ax^2}; \qquad P_0(x) = \left(\frac{2a}{\pi}\right)^{1/2} e^{-2ax^2} \tag{2.305}$$

$$\psi_1(x) = \left(\frac{2a}{\pi}\right)^{1/4} 2a^{1/2} xe^{-ax^2}; \qquad P_1(x) = \left(\frac{2a}{\pi}\right)^{1/2} 4a x^2 e^{-2ax^2} \tag{2.306}$$

$$\psi_2(x) = \left(\frac{a}{2\pi}\right)^{1/4} (4ax^2 - 1)e^{-ax^2}; \quad P_2(x) = \left(\frac{a}{2\pi}\right)^{1/2} (4ax^2 - 1)^2 e^{-2ax^2} \tag{2.307}$$

General Remarks about Wave Functions.   All the wave functions given in Fig. 2.301 show that the probability goes rapidly to zero as x goes to infinity. This is unlike the classical oscillator, which has only a finite maximum amplitude. But the values of the wave functions may be positive or negative and even cross the axis numerous times. In fact, the number of crossings of the axis (called nodes by analogy with a vibrating string) is equal to the quantum number n. And the larger n is, the wider is the region in which the wave function has moderately large amplitude maxima. This is also in line with our expectations; the more energy a vibrating system has, the larger the amplitude of oscillation. For quantum numbers somewhat larger than those used in Fig. 2.301, we find that the outermost loops in the probability function are considerably higher than the others. This corresponds, in the classical motion, to the fact that the velocity is slowest near the extremes of the oscillation; the probability is then largest there.

Such connections between the quantum mechanical system and the classical description of the system are not accidental; the correspondence principle of Bohr states that the system must approach classical behavior in the limit of very large quantum numbers.

ILLUSTRATION. Evaluate the constant a in Eq. 2.305 and then determine the distance at which the wave function $\psi_0(x)$ is 0.5, 0.1, and 0.01 of its maximum value. Assume a frequency of 3000 cm^{-1} and an effective mass of 3×10^{-24} gram.

The constant a is $(2\pi^2/h)\omega cm$, where ω is in wave numbers. On substitution, we find

$$a = \frac{2 \times (3.14)^2 \times 3000 \times 3 \times 10^{10}}{6.62 \times 10^{-27}} \times 3 \times 10^{-24}$$

$$= 80.5 \times 10^{16} \text{ cm}^{-2}, \text{ or } 80.5 \text{ Å}^{-2}$$

So the wave function $\psi_0(x)$ is $N_0 e^{-80.5x^2}$, if x is in angstrom units. Since N_0 is constant and we wish to compute only ratios of ψ's, we need not evaluate it.

In tables of exponentials, we find $y = 0.69$ for $e^{-y} = 0.5$. Therefore

$$0.69 = 80.5x^2; \quad x^2 = 0.0086, \quad \text{and} \quad x = 0.093 \text{ Å}$$

Similarly, for $e^{-y} = 0.1$ and $e^{-y} = 0.01$, we find

$$x = 0.17 \text{ Å} \quad \text{and} \quad x = 0.24 \text{ Å, respectively.}$$

The student may determine the x values corresponding to the same relative values of $P_0(x)$.

A very important property of wave functions is that given by

$$\int_{\text{all } x} \psi_i(x)\, \psi_j(x)\, dx = 0 \tag{2.308}$$

for all pairs of values i and j, where $i \neq j$. This property is called the *orthogonality* of wave functions. The functions $\psi_i(x)$ and $\psi_j(x)$ are any two wave functions of a certain quantum mechanical system; this relation is true for all quantum mechanical systems. A set of normalized wave functions which are orthogonal is called an *orthonormal set*. In the treatment of some systems it may be convenient to use wave functions whose values are not always real numbers. In such cases, the orthogonality integral, Eq. 2.308, and the normalization integral, Eq. 2.302, will indicate the complex conjugate of one of the wave functions comprising the integrand. This extension ensures that the value of the integral will be a real number.

Problems

2.301   Use the same constants as in the Illustration and calculate the x values in angstrom units for maximum amplitude of $\psi_1(x)$, the wave function of the one-dimensional harmonic oscillator in its first excited state.

2.302   Calculate the x values for which the wave function $\psi_2(x)$ of the oscillator crosses the axis, i.e., where $\psi_2(x) = 0$.

*2.303   Find a value of $x = \xi$ for the ground state of the oscillator such that

$$\int_{-\xi}^{+\xi} |\psi_0(x)|^2 \, dx = \tfrac{1}{2}$$

4. The Schrödinger Method;   the Particle in a Box

In Secs. 2.2 and 2.3, the only model treated was the one-dimensional harmonic oscillator; this issued from a classical Hamiltonian containing the potential energy $\tfrac{1}{2}kx^2$. Another useful model is that of a mass point moving in one dimension with no restoring force, i.e., $V(x) = 0$. In order to obtain a result of more physical interest, we shall also suppose the particle is confined and cannot go beyond certain limits on the x axis. To put this in mathematical terms, we shall require that $V(x)$ be infinite outside the allowed limits of x (Fig. 2.401). Again, this is a useful idealization which makes the mathematics somewhat simpler.

Schrödinger Equation and Energy Levels.   The necessary equation is obtained just as before, with the classical Hamiltonian $\mathscr{H} = p^2/2m + V(x)$. For the two regions, where $V(x) = 0$ and $V(x) = \infty$, we have

$$-\frac{h^2}{8\pi^2 m} \frac{d^2\psi(x)}{dx^2} = \epsilon\psi(x) \qquad [V(x) = 0]$$

and

$$-\frac{h^2}{8\pi^2 m} \frac{d^2\psi(x)}{dx^2} + \infty\,\psi(x) = \epsilon\psi(x) \qquad [V(x) = \infty] \qquad (2.401)$$

These equations do not represent separate problems to be solved but must be satisfied in the different regions with the same value of ϵ.

The second part is more readily solved. On rearranging, for ϵ finite we obtain

$$\frac{d^2\psi(x)}{dx^2} = \infty\,\psi(x) \qquad\qquad (2.402)$$

Equation 2.402 states that a function, when differentiated twice, gives that same function, multiplied by a large positive (infinite) number. This is a property of exponentials, such as e^{ax} or e^{-ax}. Of these two, the first function becomes infinite and is not well behaved as $x \to +\infty$, so we should not use it. The function e^{-ax} will approach zero as $x \to +\infty$; however, to satisfy the Schrödinger equation, the constant a must be ∞. Thus, the function $e^{-\infty x}$, for x positive, turns out to be just $\psi(x) = 0$. For negative x the function e^{ax} is the proper solution and we also find $\psi(x) = 0$. Thus the probability is also zero in regions where $V = \infty$; our mass point is confined, just as we wanted.

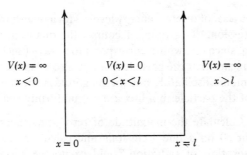

Fig. 2.401   Potential function for a particle in a one-dimensional box.

To solve the first part of Eq. 2.401, we wish to find a function which when differentiated twice gives the same function, multiplied by some negative constant. This is a property of the functions sine and cosine, i.e.,

$$\frac{d^2}{dx^2}(\sin ax) = -a^2 \sin ax; \qquad \frac{d^2}{dx^2}(\cos ax) = -a^2 \cos ax \qquad (2.403)$$

Thus we find different properties from those of the harmonic oscillator; different regions of the variable x correspond to different functional forms.

The requirement that the wave function be continuous is important in establishing the proper values for a in Eq. 2.403. In the region outside the box (where the potential function is infinite) the wave function is everywhere zero. The wave function inside the box is not everywhere zero; however, the continuity requirement demands that the inside wave function must become zero at the place where inside and outside join, or at the "boundary"; this type of requirement is called a *boundary condition*.

To be specific, let the region where $V(x)$ is zero extend from $x = 0$ to $x = l$. The only allowable wave functions which satisfy the Schrödinger equation and the boundary conditions are the sine functions, since, for $x = 0$, $\cos x = 1$ and not 0. Furthermore, only certain special sine functions will equal zero at $x = l$, namely, those for which

$$al = n\pi, \quad n = 1, 2, 3 \ldots \qquad (2.404)$$

where angular measure is expressed in radians. On solving for a and substituting in Eq. 2.401, this gives

$$-\frac{h^2}{8\pi^2 m}\frac{d^2}{dx^2}\left(\sin\frac{n\pi}{l}x\right) = \epsilon\sin\frac{n\pi}{l}x \tag{2.405}$$

$$-\frac{h^2}{8\pi^2 m}\left(-\frac{n^2\pi^2}{l^2}\right)\sin\frac{n\pi}{l}x = \epsilon\sin\frac{n\pi}{l}x$$

or

$$\frac{n^2h^2}{8ml^2} = \epsilon \tag{2.406}$$

Once again we have a set of discrete energy levels with a quantum number contained in the energy expression. This time, of course, the quantum number n may not have the value zero, since this would correspond to a wave function identically zero everywhere. This means that the particle in a box also possesses zero-point energy, similar to the harmonic oscillator, but the magnitudes are quite different. Also, the energy levels of the particle in a box are not uniformly spaced.

ILLUSTRATION.   Calculate the magnitude of zero-point energy for a particle of molecular weight 60 on a line 1 cm long and calculate also the frequency of radiation *if* absorption of radiation could excite the system from $n = 1$ to $n = 2$.

Now $m = 10^{-22}$ gram and $l = 1$ cm. Substituting in Eq. 2.406,

$$\epsilon = \frac{1^2(6.6\times 10^{-27})^2}{8\times 10^{-22}\times 1^2} = 5.45\times 10^{-32} \text{ erg molecule}^{-1}$$

or

$$3.3\times 10^{-8} \text{ erg mole}^{-1}$$

For the $1\to 2$ transition, the energy would be $2^2 - 1^2 = 3$ times as large, or 16×10^{-32} erg molecule^{-1}. Equating this to $h\nu$, we find

$$\nu = \frac{16\times 10^{-32}}{6.6\times 10^{-27}} = 2.5\times 10^{-5} \text{ cycle sec}^{-1}$$

The energy and frequency calculated here, assuming typical molecular values, are extremely small quantities. For neutral molecules spectral transitions cannot arise because they are forbidden by the selection rules to absorb radiation; even if they were allowed, such very low frequencies have not been studied experimentally. The student may show that the frequency of the $1\to 2$ transition for an electron confined to a one-dimensional box of molecular size may lie in the visible or ultraviolet region. A more sophisticated version of a "free electron" model has been used to explain the color of dyes.

_____

The translational energy spacing is extremely small for molecules in macroscopic containers. The model of a particle in a box is widely used in treating the thermal behavior of gas molecules. At ordinary temperatures, gas molecules are distributed

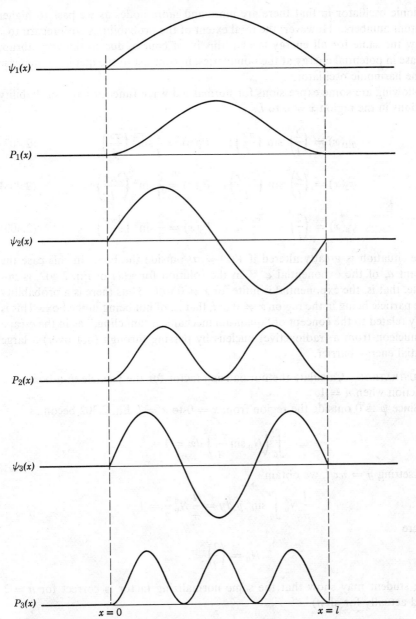

Fig. 2.402   Some wave functions and probability functions for the particle in a box.

among a large number of different quantum states, and a further useful approximation considered in Chapter 6 is to treat the energy as though it were continuous.

Wave Functions and Probabilities.   A few of the wave functions and probabilities are sketched in Fig. 2.402.   There is a strong qualitative resemblance to those of the harmonic oscillator in that there are more and more nodes as we pass to higher quantum numbers. However, the total extent of the probabilities with regard to x is now the same for all energy levels; this is, of course, due to the very abrupt increase in potential energy at the boundaries, in contrast to the quadratic increase for the harmonic oscillator.

Following are some expressions for normalized wave functions and probability functions in the region $x = 0$ to l.

$$\psi_1(x) = \left(\frac{2}{l}\right)^{\!1/2} \sin\left(\frac{\pi x}{l}\right); \quad P_1(x) = \frac{2}{l}\sin^2\left(\frac{\pi x}{l}\right) \tag{2.407}$$

$$\psi_2(x) = \left(\frac{2}{l}\right)^{\!1/2} \sin\left(\frac{2\pi x}{l}\right); \quad P_2(x) = \frac{2}{l}\sin^2\left(\frac{2\pi x}{l}\right) \tag{2.408}$$

$$\psi_3(x) = \left(\frac{2}{l}\right)^{\!1/2} \sin\frac{3\pi x}{l}; \quad P_3(x) = \frac{2}{l}\sin^2\left(\frac{3\pi x}{l}\right) \tag{2.409}$$

The situation is greatly altered if $V(x) \neq \infty$ outside the box. In this case the constant a, of the exponential e^{-ax} in the solution for $\psi(x)$ of Eq. 2.402, is not infinite, that is, the exponential is finite for $x \neq 0$ to l. Thus there is a probability of the particle being in the region $x \neq 0$ to l, that is, of not being in the box. This is closely related to the concept of "quantum mechanical tunneling," as in the escape of a nucleon from a (radioactive) nucleus by passing through (not over) a large potential energy barrier.

ILLUSTRATION. Calculate the normalizing factor for the particle-in-a-box wave function when $n = 1$.

Since $\psi \equiv 0$ outside the region from $x = 0$ to $x = l$, Eq. 2.302 becomes

$$\int_0^l \left(N_0 \sin\frac{\pi x}{l}\right)^2 dx = 1$$

On setting $y = \pi x/l$, we obtain

$$\frac{l}{\pi} N_0^2 \int_0^\pi \sin^2 y \, dy = \frac{l}{\pi} N_0^2 \frac{\pi}{2} = 1$$

where

$$N_0 = \left(\frac{2}{l}\right)^{\!1/2}$$

The student may show that the same normalizing factor is correct for $n = 2$ (and actually for all n).

Problems

2.401   If the simple free electron model were applied to the energy of conjugated double-bond systems such as butadiene, C_4H_6, and the polyene carotene, which has a conjugated chain 22 carbons in length, what ratio would be predicted for the energy difference between the $n = 1$ and $n = 2$ states? Take an average carbon-carbon distance of 1.4 Å.

2.402   Calculate what would be the classical limits for the amplitude of vibration of the oscillator in Problem 2.301 when it has a total energy equal to the zero-point energy. Use the distance between these limits as the length of a box, and calculate the zero-point energy of a particle of mass 3×10^{-24} gram, confined in a box of length you have just determined. Compare this zero-point energy with that of the oscillator.

2.403   Calculate the probability of finding the x coordinate between the values $0.49l$ and $0.51l$ for the ground state of the particle in a box. The property of a maximum in $P_1(x)$ (Fig. 2.402) may be used with Eq. 2.407 as an adequate approximation. Calculate the probability of finding the x coordinate in the same range for $n = 2$, with use of integration.

5. Several Degrees of Freedom; the Particle in a Two-Dimensional Box

All previous examples contained only one coordinate, and hence we could use total derivatives. We shall now look at examples involving several coordinates. This will require the use of partial derivatives.

Separation of the Schrödinger Equation.   The model system is a particle of mass m which is free to move so that its x coordinate may vary from 0 to l, and its y coordinate may also be from 0 to l. The potential energy is again zero in this range and infinite everywhere else. The classical Hamiltonian is then

$$\mathscr{H} = \frac{p_x^2}{2m} + \frac{p_y^2}{2m}, \text{ for } 0 < x < l \text{ and } 0 < y < l$$

$$\mathscr{H} = \frac{p_x^2}{2m} + \frac{p_y^2}{2m} + \infty, \text{ elsewhere} \tag{2.501}$$

The Schrödinger equation becomes, for $0 < x < l$ and $0 < y < l$,

$$-\frac{h^2}{8\pi^2 m}\left[\frac{\partial^2 \psi(x,y)}{\partial x^2} + \frac{\partial^2 \psi(x,y)}{\partial y^2}\right] = \epsilon\psi(x,y) \tag{2.502}$$

and elsewhere

$$-\frac{h^2}{8\pi^2 m}\left[\frac{\partial^2 \psi(x,y)}{\partial x^2} + \frac{\partial^2 \psi(x,y)}{\partial y^2}\right] + \infty\,\psi(x,y) = \epsilon\psi(x,y)$$

Simplification of this equation could be achieved if it were possible to separate it into two equations, each containing but one independent variable. Since the x and y coordinates are independent of each other, this suggests that the complete wave function may be written

$$\psi(x,y) = \psi(x)\psi(y) \tag{2.503}$$

We shall see whether this function can be used to satisfy the equations. We shall also make use of the fact that $\psi(y)$ is independent of x, i.e.,

$$\frac{\partial \psi(x)\psi(y)}{\partial x} = \psi(y)\frac{\partial \psi(x)}{\partial x} = \psi(y)\frac{d\psi(x)}{dx} \tag{2.504}$$

and the same for $\partial/\partial y$. When x and y lie between 0 and l, Eq. 2.502 becomes

$$-\frac{h^2}{8\pi^2 m}\left[\psi(y)\frac{d^2\psi(x)}{dx^2} + \psi(x)\frac{d^2\psi(y)}{dy^2}\right] = \epsilon\psi(x)\psi(y) \qquad (2.505)$$

Dividing both sides by $\psi(x)\psi(y)$, we obtain

$$-\frac{h^2}{8\pi^2 m}\left[\frac{1}{\psi(x)}\frac{d^2\psi(x)}{dx^2} + \frac{1}{\psi(y)}\frac{d^2\psi(y)}{dy^2}\right] = \epsilon \qquad (2.506)$$

This equation states that a function of x plus a function of y is always equal to a constant ϵ, no matter what the values of x and y. This can be true only if each of the terms is also a constant since x and y are independent variables,

$$-\frac{h^2}{8\pi^2 m}\left[\frac{1}{\psi(x)}\frac{d^2\psi(x)}{dx^2}\right] = \epsilon_a \qquad (2.507)$$

$$-\frac{h^2}{8\pi^2 m}\left[\frac{1}{\psi(y)}\frac{d^2\psi(y)}{dy^2}\right] = \epsilon_b \qquad (2.508)$$

where

$$\epsilon_a + \epsilon_b = \epsilon$$

We find, after multiplying Eq. 2.507 by $\psi(x)$ and Eq. 2.508 by $\psi(y)$, that each of these is identical with Eq. 2.401. It is, indeed, possible then to simplify Eq. 2.502 by the assumption that the total wave function can be written as the product of a function of x only and a function of y only. This is a particularly simple case, since the potential energy term was zero. In other examples, where $V(x,y)$ is not zero, it may be necessary to change from Cartesian to some other coordinates in order to simplify and separate the equations.

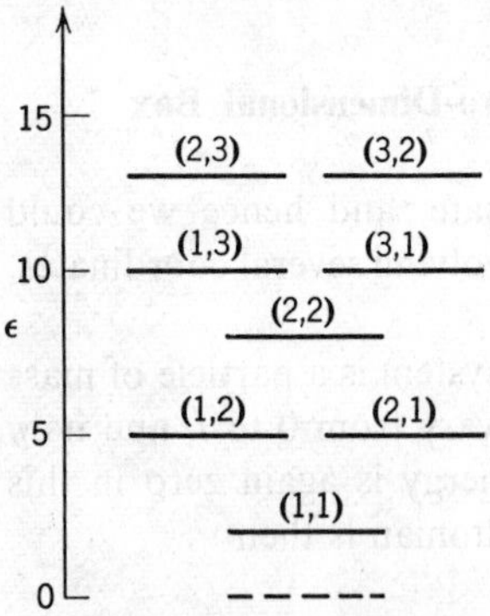

Solutions of the Equations and Degeneracy.   The previous results of Sec. 2.4 may now be utilized to describe the two-dimensional problem. The energies are given by the expression.

$$\epsilon = \frac{h^2}{8ml^2}(n_a^2 + n_b^2) \qquad (2.509)$$

and the wave functions (unnormalized) by

$$\psi(x,y) = \sin\frac{n_a\pi x}{l}\sin\frac{n_b\pi y}{l} \qquad (2.510)$$

The quantum numbers n_a and n_b now independently range over the integers 1, 2, 3, . . . ; Fig. 2.501 shows some of the pairs of values n_a, n_b and the corresponding energy values. Here something new is evident: distinct sets of quantum numbers, corresponding to different wave functions, sometimes give the same

Fig. 2.501   Energy levels and degeneracies of the particle in a two-dimensional box. The quantum numbers n_a and n_b are given in parentheses (n_a, n_b). Energy is in units of $h^2/8ml^2$.

energies. For instance, the functions

$$\psi = \sin\frac{\pi x}{l}\sin\frac{2\pi y}{l} \quad \text{and} \quad \psi = \sin\frac{2\pi x}{l}\sin\frac{\pi y}{l}$$

both correspond to the eigenvalue

$$\epsilon = \frac{5h^2}{8ml^2} \tag{2.511}$$

This is an example of degeneracy, more specifically double degeneracy, since two different functions satisfy the Schrödinger equation and give the same energy. There may also be triple, quadruple, etc., degeneracy in other problems; the energies of electrons in atoms often show considerable degeneracy (Chapter 4).

Problems

2.501   Suppose that the x limits for the particle in a two-dimensional box had been 0 to l, and the y limits 0 to $2l$. Is there still any degeneracy? Sketch the first eight energy levels.

2.502   For the particle in a three-dimensional box, write down an expression for the eigenvalues deduced from Eq. 2.509 and make a figure similar to Fig. 2.501 for a maximum value of 3 for each of n_a, n_b, or n_c. All edges of the box have length l.

6. Separation of Translation and Internal Motions

Suppose now that our model is one of two interacting particles, each of different mass, free to move only along the x axis; furthermore, the potential energy of the particles depends only on their relative distance, $x_1 - x_2$, not on their location on the axis.

Schrödinger Equation.   The classical Hamiltonian is now

$$\mathcal{H} = \frac{p_1^2}{2m_1} + \frac{p_2^2}{2m_2} + V(x_1 - x_2)$$

and the Schrödinger equation becomes

$$-\frac{h^2}{8\pi^2}\left[\frac{1}{m_1}\frac{\partial^2\psi(x_1,x_2)}{\partial x_1^2} + \frac{1}{m_2}\frac{\partial^2\psi(x_1,x_2)}{\partial x_2^2}\right] + V(x_1 - x_2)\psi(x_1,x_2)$$
$$= \epsilon\psi(x_1,x_2) \tag{2.601}$$

Separation of the Schrödinger Equation.   A simple product substitution for $\psi(x_1,x_2)$ is now not useful because of the presence of $V(x_1 - x_2)$. Suppose, instead, that we choose some new coordinates related to the old ones. A useful new coordinate might be

$$x = x_1 - x_2$$

since this substitution would completely take care of the potential energy term. Let the other coordinate be X. We have two new coordinates, x and X, such that x_1 is some function of x and X, and also x_2 is another function of x and X. We must now transform the partial derivatives in Eq. 2.601. The fundamental mathematical relation using partial derivatives is

$$\frac{\partial \psi}{\partial x_1} = \frac{\partial \psi}{\partial x}\frac{\partial x}{\partial x_1} + \frac{\partial \psi}{\partial X}\frac{\partial X}{\partial x_1} \tag{2.602}$$

where, in differentiating partially with respect to x, X is kept constant, and vice versa; in differentiating partially with respect to x_1, x_2 is kept constant, and vice versa. Repeated application of this relation then gives

$$\frac{\partial^2 \psi}{\partial x_1^2} = \frac{\partial(\partial \psi/\partial x_1)}{\partial x}\frac{\partial x}{\partial x_1} + \frac{\partial(\partial \psi/\partial x_1)}{\partial X}\frac{\partial X}{\partial x_1}$$

$$= \frac{\partial^2 \psi}{\partial x^2}\left(\frac{\partial x}{\partial x_1}\right)^2 + 2\frac{\partial^2 \psi}{\partial x\,\partial X}\left(\frac{\partial X}{\partial x_1}\right)\left(\frac{\partial x}{\partial x_1}\right) + \frac{\partial^2 \psi}{\partial X^2}\left(\frac{\partial X}{\partial x_1}\right)^2 \tag{2.603}$$

$$\frac{\partial^2 \psi}{\partial x_2^2} = \frac{\partial^2 \psi}{\partial x^2}\left(\frac{\partial x}{\partial x_2}\right)^2 + 2\frac{\partial^2 \psi}{\partial x\,\partial X}\left(\frac{\partial X}{\partial x_2}\right)\left(\frac{\partial x}{\partial x_2}\right) + \frac{\partial^2 \psi}{\partial X^2}\left(\frac{\partial X}{\partial x_2}\right)^2 \tag{2.604}$$

Now the derivative-containing expressions on the left-hand side of Eq. 2.601 can be obtained by multiplying Eq. 2.603 by $1/m_1$, Eq. 2.604 by $1/m_2$, and adding. At the same time, the expressions can be simplified by employing the fact that

$$\frac{\partial x}{\partial x_1} = +1, \quad \frac{\partial x}{\partial x_2} = -1 \tag{2.605}$$

The result of the addition is then

$$\frac{1}{m_1}\frac{\partial^2 \psi}{\partial x_1^2} + \frac{1}{m_2}\frac{\partial^2 \psi}{\partial x_2^2} = \left(\frac{1}{m_1} + \frac{1}{m_2}\right)\frac{\partial^2 \psi}{\partial x^2} + 2\frac{\partial^2 \psi}{\partial x\,\partial X}\left(\frac{1}{m_1}\frac{\partial X}{\partial x_1} - \frac{1}{m_2}\frac{\partial X}{\partial x_2}\right)$$

$$+ \frac{\partial^2 \psi}{\partial X^2}\left[\frac{1}{m_1}\left(\frac{\partial X}{\partial x_1}\right)^2 + \frac{1}{m_2}\left(\frac{\partial X}{\partial x_2}\right)^2\right] \tag{2.606}$$

This expression would be greatly simplified if the term containing the mixed partial derivative dropped out, that is, if its coefficient were zero. We can do this by specifying the coordinate X as

$$X = \frac{m_1 x_1 + m_2 x_2}{m_1 + m_2} \tag{2.607}$$

and substitution of Eq. 2.606 into the left-hand side of Eq. 2.601 gives

$$-\frac{h^2}{8\pi^2}\left(\frac{1}{m_1} + \frac{1}{m_2}\right)\frac{\partial^2 \psi}{\partial x^2} - \frac{h^2}{8\pi^2}\left(\frac{1}{m_1 + m_2}\right)\frac{\partial^2 \psi}{\partial X^2} + V(x)\psi = \epsilon\psi \tag{2.608}$$

This equation is now ready to be separated by the assumption of a product for the wave function

$$\psi = \psi_i(x)\psi_t(X) \tag{2.609}$$

and, proceeding just as before, we find two equations

$$-\frac{h^2}{8\pi^2}\left(\frac{1}{m_1}+\frac{1}{m_2}\right)\frac{\partial^2 \psi_i}{\partial x^2} + V(x)\psi_i = \epsilon_i \psi_i \qquad (2.610)$$

and

$$-\frac{h^2}{8\pi^2}\left(\frac{1}{m_1+m_2}\right)\frac{\partial^2 \psi_t}{\partial X^2} = \epsilon_t \psi_t \qquad (2.611)$$

These expressions are more frequently written with the total mass, $M = m_1 + m_2$ and μ, the reduced mass, defined by

$$\frac{1}{\mu} = \frac{1}{m_1} + \frac{1}{m_2} \quad \text{or} \quad \mu = \frac{m_1 m_2}{m_1 + m_2} \qquad (2.612)$$

Interpretation of the Equations.   The second of these equations, Eq. 2.611, is just the same as Eq. 2.401 for the particle in a box. Furthermore, the coordinate X (Eq. 2.607) has the classical interpretation of representing the position of the center of gravity of the two particles. This means that in Eq. 2.611 the system of two particles acts as if it were one particle of mass equal to the sum of the two masses and located at the center of gravity of the system. This was also done without mathematical approximation so that the result is exact as long as $V(x)$ depends only on $x_1 - x_2$. We have used subscripts t here to indicate the usual name translation for this type of motion and its associated energy levels. The energy levels and wave functions are just the same as those given earlier with M here replacing m in Eq. 2.406.

This result was derived only for motion along the x axis. A similar result could be obtained by considering two- (or three-) dimensional motion for each of the two particles; the only difference is that two (or three) different translational equations would be found to separate out.

The other part of this separation gave us Eq. 2.610, in which the coordinate x is the independent variable. An identical equation would have been obtained if we had started with a different model, that is, a particle of mass μ moving under the influence of a potential energy $V(x)$. This is tantamount to imagining that one of the two particles, say m_2, is fixed at $x = 0$ and the particle of mass m_1 is replaced by a particle of mass μ. We note also that nothing has been said about the nature of the potential function; it is perfectly general. The "effective mass for vibration," used in Sec. 2.2, is actually the reduced mass of the two atoms in the molecule.

Problem

2.601   Verify the reduced mass magnitudes of Problems 2.204 and 2.205.

7. Expectation Values

A very important part of the Schrödinger method concerns the calculation of the average value of a physical quantity if the wave function describing the state of the system is known. This is very general and requires only that one writes a certain mathematical expression, an operator, corresponding to the physical quantity. We shall apply this method to obtain equations for some simple systems which are similar to the uncertainty principle.

Operators and Expectation Values. The Hamiltonian operator is a special case, although a very important one, of the general class of operators. The same methods can be used to obtain operators corresponding to physical quantities other than the total energy. Some examples are the following:

Physical Quantity	Operator
x	$x \equiv x$
x^2	$x^2 \equiv x^2$
p_x	$(h/2\pi i)\partial/\partial x$
p_x^2	$-(h^2/4\pi^2)\partial^2/\partial x^2$

Now, if we just call the operator α, then the expectation formula, for the state described by the normalized Schrödinger eigenfunction ψ, is for real wave functions

$$\bar{\alpha} = \int \psi \alpha \psi \, d\tau \tag{2.701}$$

For wave functions whose values are not always real numbers, a more general form is

$$\bar{\alpha} = \int \psi^* \alpha \psi \, d\tau$$

The quantity $\bar{\alpha}$ is defined as the *expectation value*, or quantum mechanical average value, of the physical quantity α, and $d\tau$ denotes the volume element of integration. This relationship is most evident in the case where α is a function of coordinates only. Then Eq. 2.701 may be written as

$$\bar{\alpha} = \int \alpha \psi^2 \, d\tau = \int \alpha P \, d\tau$$

The integral is then the average of the quantity α weighted by the distribution function P. However, when α is also a function of momenta, the formal rearrangement cannot be made. Physically, we might imagine that the quantity is measured many times in the system and the results averaged to obtain $\bar{\alpha}$. The integral is to be evaluated over all possible values of the coordinate(s). We shall be most interested in evaluating and comparing the expectation values of x, p, and their squares.

As was pointed out at the beginning of Sec. 2.2, we are considering only systems whose behavior is independent of time. This means that in each eigenstate the probability function P and hence the various expectation values are also independent of time; such states are called *stationary states*.

Consider the lowest quantum state of the harmonic oscillator, described by the eigenfunction $(2a/\pi)^{1/4} e^{-ax^2}$. The expectation value of x is

$$\bar{x} = \left(\frac{2a}{\pi}\right)^{1/2} \int_{-\infty}^{+\infty} xe^{-2ax^2} \, dx \equiv 0 \tag{2.702}$$

This is to be expected since the probability function is symmetrical about $x = 0$; there will be just as many negative values of x as positive values. But what about the expectation value of x^2, which is always positive?

$$\overline{x^2} = \left(\frac{2a}{\pi}\right)^{\frac{1}{2}} \int_{-\infty}^{+\infty} x^2 e^{-2ax^2} \, dx = \frac{1}{4a}$$

$$= (4a)^{-1} \tag{2.703}$$

Proceeding similarly for p and p^2, we find

$$\bar{p} = 0, \qquad \overline{p^2} = \frac{ah^2}{4\pi^2} \tag{2.704}$$

Let x stand for the result of a single measurement. Then $x - \bar{x} = \Delta x$ is the deviation of this measurement from the average, and $(x - \bar{x})^2$ is its square. The square can also be averaged:

$$\overline{(\Delta x)^2} = \overline{(x - \bar{x})^2} = \overline{x^2 - 2x\bar{x} + \bar{x}^2}$$

$$= \overline{x^2} - 2\bar{x}^2 + \bar{x}^2$$

$$= \overline{x^2} - \bar{x}^2 \tag{2.705}$$

Taking the square root, we find the root-mean-square or standard deviation

$$\Delta x = (\overline{x^2} - \bar{x}^2)^{\frac{1}{2}} \tag{2.706}$$

which, for the harmonic oscillator with $n = 0$, is from Eqs. 2.702 and 2.703

$$(\Delta x)_{\text{rms}} = \tfrac{1}{2} a^{-\frac{1}{2}}$$

Similarly

$$(\Delta p_x)_{\text{rms}} = \frac{h}{2\pi} a^{\frac{1}{2}}$$

and

$$(\Delta x)_{\text{rms}}(\Delta p_x)_{\text{rms}} = \frac{h}{4\pi} \tag{2.707}$$

For the general state of the harmonic oscillator with quantum number n, the corresponding result is:

$$(\Delta x)_{\text{rms}}(\Delta p_x)_{\text{rms}} = (2n + 1)\frac{h}{4\pi} \tag{2.708}$$

For the particle in a box, the various states give products of coordinate and momentum uncertainties with still different values, but all somewhat larger than $h/4\pi$ (see Problem 2.805). It can be shown on general grounds that the smallest possible uncertainty product in any quantum mechanical system is that found above for the lowest state of the harmonic oscillator. Therefore, the uncertainty principle may be written in general terms,

$$\Delta x \, \Delta p_x \geq \frac{h}{4\pi} \tag{2.709}$$

Furthermore, the minimum uncertainty product might have a value different from $h/4\pi$ if another method of computing the averages were used. For these several reasons, the uncertainty relation given in Chapter 1 was written in an approximate fashion.

ILLUSTRATION. Calculate the expectation values for the total energy and its square, using the Hamiltonian operator and its square.

Rather than carrying through the integrations, which could be quite tedious, we shall use the Schrödinger equation, with a ground state wave function ψ_0

$$H\psi_0 = \epsilon_0\psi_0$$

in the expectation formula, Eq. 2.701

$$\bar{\epsilon} = \int \psi_0 H\psi_0 \, d\tau = \int \psi_0 \epsilon_0 \psi_0 \, d\tau = \epsilon_0 \int \psi_0 \psi_0 \, d\tau = \epsilon_0$$

$$\bar{\epsilon^2} = \int \psi_0 H^2 \psi_0 \, d\tau = \int \psi_0 H(H\psi_0) \, d\tau = \int \psi_0 H(\epsilon_0\psi_0) \, d\tau$$

$$= \epsilon_0 \int \psi_0 H\psi_0 \, d\tau = \epsilon_0^2$$

But, since $\Delta\epsilon = (\overline{\epsilon^2} - \bar{\epsilon}^2)^{1/2}$,

$$\Delta\epsilon \equiv 0$$

or we can determine the total energy exactly (apart from limitations imposed by Δt). Note that we should obtain an entirely false result by using the classical energy expression and adding the uncertainties in x^2 and in p_x^2, that is, in the potential and kinetic energies.

----

8. Review Problems

2.801   A half-dollar, with mass of 12 grams, is suspended on a rubber band. It has a vibration frequency of 3 cycles sec^{-1}. Calculate (a) the force constant of the rubber band; (b) the zero-point energy if we treat the system by quantum mechanics; (c) the total vibrational energy if the vibrational displacement has maximum and minimum values of $+0.5$ cm and -0.5 cm; (d) the vibrational quantum number corresponding to the energy in part c.

2.802   Show that for an idealized molecule which has an effective vibrational mass of exactly one atomic weight unit and a force constant of exactly 1×10^5 dynes cm^{-1} the vibration frequency is 1303 cm^{-1}. This quantity is very useful, since it eliminates the need for repeated use of Avogadro's number, π, c, etc.

2.803   Calculate the force constant k for the HCl molecule and compare with that of the CO molecule. The vibration frequency for the Cl_2^{35} molecule is 557 cm^{-1}. Calculate the force constant; the atomic weight of Cl^{35} is 34.98.

2.804   A handball has a mass of 59 grams, and the longest dimension of the court is about 12 meters. Work out the expression for the energy levels of the system, treating it as a one-dimensional particle in a box. What quantum number would correspond to a velocity of the ball of 50 miles hr^{-1}?

*2.805 Work out the necessary expectation values and obtain an expression for $\Delta x \, \Delta p_x$ for the particle in a box corresponding to that obtained for the oscillator in Sec. 2.7. (NOTE: this result is correct; for powers of p higher than the second, the discontinuity in the derivative of ψ necessitates a more advanced mathematical treatment.)

2.806 Show by integration that the orthogonality integrals

$$\int_0^l \psi_1 \psi_2 \, dx = 0 \quad \text{and} \quad \int_{-\infty}^{+\infty} \psi_0 \psi_1 \, dx = 0$$

(particle in a box)   (harmonic oscillator)

2.807 A two-dimensional oscillator, quite similar to the two-dimensional particle in a box, can be set up and solved completely. Use the same kinetic energy, Eq. 2.501, and $kx^2/2 + ky^2/2$ for the potential energy. The limits on x and y are, of course, $+\infty$ and $-\infty$. Carry through, using the results of the one-dimensional oscillator wherever helpful, and plot a diagram showing the first four energy levels, their quantum numbers, and their degeneracies.

2.808 Calculate the reduced masses of an electron-positron pair and of an electron-proton pair in units of the electron mass.

2.809 Find the average energy $\bar{\epsilon}$ for the second excited level of a one dimensional harmonic oscillator.

2.810 Write out the Hamiltonian operator for the free motion of a particle on a plane.

General References

Eyring, H., J. Walter, and G. E. Kimball, *Quantum Chemistry*, John Wiley and Sons, New York, 1944.

Kauzmann, W., *Quantum Chemistry*, Academic Press, New York, 1957.

Pauling, L., and E. B. Wilson, Jr., *Introduction to Quantum Mechanics*, McGraw-Hill Book Co., New York, 1935.

Pitzer, K. S., *Quantum Chemistry*, Prentice-Hall, Englewood Cliffs, N.J., 1953.

Resnick, R., and D. Halliday, *Physics for Students of Science and Engineering*, Part I, 1960, and Part II, Second Edition, 1962, John Wiley and Sons, New York.

Rojansky, V., *Introductory Quantum Mechanics*, Prentice-Hall, Englewood Cliffs, N.J., 1946.

Chapter Three

Hydrogen and Other Atoms

In this chapter we consider the energy levels of atoms and their quantitative description. These levels divide into the translational levels, which are so closely spaced that they are almost continuous, and the electronic levels, which are widely spaced and must be considered individually.

1. Separation of the Schrödinger Equation

The quantum mechanical treatment of atoms and molecules is, in principle, the same as that of the simpler systems described in Chapter 2. A classical Hamiltonian is written for the system and includes the kinetic energy of each particle (electron, nucleus), as well as the potential energy; the potential energy arises only from the Coulombic term, e^2/r, for *each* pair of charged particles. The Hamiltonian is then substituted into the Schrödinger equation by the usual transformation, and a partial differential equation is obtained containing $3\mathcal{N}$ variables, where $\mathcal{N}$ is the total number of electrons and nuclei in the system, i.e., $\mathcal{N} = 2$ for the hydrogen atom, 3 for the helium atom, etc.

Most of the important results in this chapter arise on separating the complete Schrödinger equation for a system of several particles into simpler equations as in Sec. 2.6. We saw that this can always be done if the Hamiltonian can be expressed as the sum of two or more parts, H_a, H_b, etc., each independent of the others. Then, if we write the total wave function as the product of an *a*-dependent part and a b-dependent part, for a two-part Hamiltonian

$$\psi = \psi_a \psi_b \tag{3.101}$$

we may proceed as in Sec. 2.5,

$$H\psi = \epsilon\psi; \quad (H_a + H_b)\psi_a\psi_b = \epsilon\psi_a\psi_b \tag{3.102}$$

and

$$H_a\psi_a = \epsilon_a\psi_a, \quad H_b\psi_b = \epsilon_b\psi_b \tag{3.103}$$

A similar result would hold for three, four, etc., different coordinates or groups of coordinates. The general procedure is thus to find a set of coordinates in terms of which the Hamiltonian operator is separable. In atoms there are two such groups of coordinates, which are called translation and electronic; in molecules, there are additional rotational and vibrational groups.

2. The Hydrogen Atom

The model for the hydrogen atom is one of a single electron and a single proton, each with three degrees of freedom, i.e., an x, a y, and a z coordinate. One part of the potential energy is Coulombic and depends on the distance between the proton and the electron. In addition, if the atom is confined in a rectangular container of volume abc, the potential function has a second part which becomes infinite outside the limits from 0 to a in the x coordinate, 0 to b in the y coordinate, and 0 to c in the z coordinate. Within these limits, this part of the potential function is zero. Proceeding as before, we find a Schrödinger equation in terms of m_e, the mass of the electron, and x_e, y_e, and z_e, its coordinates, and m_p, the mass of the proton, and x_p, y_p, and z_p, its coordinates. Inside the container we have

$$-\frac{h^2}{8\pi^2 m_e}\left(\frac{\partial^2\psi}{\partial x_e^2} + \frac{\partial^2\psi}{\partial y_e^2} + \frac{\partial^2\psi}{\partial z_e^2}\right) - \frac{h^2}{8\pi^2 m_p}\left(\frac{\partial^2\psi}{\partial x_p^2} + \frac{\partial^2\psi}{\partial y_p^2} + \frac{\partial^2\psi}{\partial z_p^2}\right)$$
$$-\frac{e^2\psi}{[(x_e - x_p)^2 + (y_e - y_p)^2 + (z_e - z_p)^2]^{1/2}} = \epsilon\psi \tag{3.201}$$

This ψ is, of course, a function of all six coordinates, although for reasons of brevity this fact is not explicitly indicated.

Separation of Translation. By introducing coordinates of the center of gravity, X, Y, and Z, we can begin the simplification of this equation. The other three coordinates, x, y, and z, are those of the electron relative to the proton. Thus:

$$x = x_e - x_p \qquad\qquad y = y_e - y_p \qquad\qquad z = z_e - z_p$$

$$X = \frac{m_e x_e + m_p x_p}{M} \qquad Y = \frac{m_e y_e + m_p y_p}{M} \qquad Z = \frac{m_e z_e + m_p z_p}{M} \tag{3.202}$$

where $M = m_e + m_p$. In similar fashion to Sec. 2.6, we find that the Hamiltonian can be separated into the sum of four parts. The wave function may be written as the product of four functions,

$$\psi = \psi(X)\,\psi(Y)\,\psi(Z)\,\psi(x,y,z) \tag{3.203}$$

The Schrödinger equation is separated into four simpler equations. Three are associated with the motion of the center of gravity of the atom, and one with the separation of the subatomic particles.

$$-\frac{h^2}{8\pi^2 M}\frac{d^2\psi(X)}{dX^2} = \epsilon_X \psi(X) \tag{3.204}$$

$$-\frac{h^2}{8\pi^2 M}\frac{d^2\psi(Y)}{dY^2} = \epsilon_Y \psi(Y) \tag{3.205}$$

$$-\frac{h^2}{8\pi^2 M}\frac{d^2\psi(Z)}{dZ^2} = \epsilon_Z \psi(Z) \tag{3.206}$$

$$-\frac{h^2}{8\pi^2 \mu}\left[\frac{\partial^2\psi(x,y,z)}{\partial x^2} + \frac{\partial^2\psi(x,y,z)}{\partial y^2} + \frac{\partial^2\psi(x,y,z)}{\partial z^2}\right]$$

$$-\frac{e^2\psi(x,y,z)}{(x^2+y^2+z^2)^{1/2}} = \epsilon_e\psi(x,y,z) \tag{3.207}$$

Now μ is the reduced mass (Eq. 2.612), $m_e m_p/(m_e + m_p)$, and of course the total energy, ϵ, is the sum

$$\epsilon = \epsilon_X + \epsilon_Y + \epsilon_Z + \epsilon_e = \epsilon_t + \epsilon_e \tag{3.208}$$

where ϵ_t is the total translational energy. Solutions of expressions such as Eqs. 3.204, 3.205, and 3.206 have been given previously for the problem of a particle in a box; the result for translational energy is simply

$$\epsilon_t = \frac{h^2}{8M}\left(\frac{n_X^2}{a^2} + \frac{n_Y^2}{b^2} + \frac{n_Z^2}{c^2}\right) \tag{3.209}$$

The translational quantum numbers, n_X, n_Y, n_Z, may have the values 1, 2, 3, ... independent of each other. For any ordinary size of container, the translational energy levels are exceedingly close together; they are almost always treated as a continuous distribution.

It is important to note that translation has been eliminated from the remainder of the problem which is electronic in character. This problem is quite complicated, so we shall not solve the electronic Schrödinger equation in detail but shall outline the treatment.

Electronic Energies. Progress in solution of Eq. 3.207, the Schrödinger equation for electronic energy, ϵ_e, is aided by the introduction of spherical coordinates, r, θ, and ϕ; see Fig. 3.201. Here r is the proton-electron distance, $(x^2 + y^2 + z^2)^{1/2}$, and the angles give the orientation of a line drawn from the proton to the electron, with respect to the x, y, and z axes. The angle θ is the angle between the line and the z axis. The line is also projected into the xy plane, and the angle ϕ is the positive rotation from the x axis to this projection. The angle θ thus has a range of 0 to 180°, and the angle ϕ has a range of 0 to 360°. The function $\psi(x,y,z)$ is replaced by $\psi(\phi)\psi(\theta)\psi(r)$.

These new coordinates are useful, since the potential energy depends only on the distance r and is independent of the angles. Even so, the Schrödinger equation is not separable in the sense of Sec. 3.1; the Hamiltonian is not a sum of terms, with

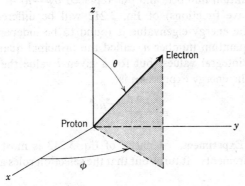

Fig. 3.201   Definition of angles θ and ϕ; only the positive directions of the x, y, and z axes are shown.

each term depending on only one variable, since there are terms containing several of the variables together. However, it is possible to obtain three separate equations.

$$\frac{d^2\psi(\phi)}{d\phi^2} = \alpha\psi(\phi) \tag{3.210}$$

$$\frac{d^2\psi(\theta)}{d\theta^2} + \frac{\cos\theta}{\sin\theta}\frac{d\psi(\theta)}{d\theta} + \frac{\alpha}{\sin^2\theta}\psi(t) = \beta\psi(\theta) \tag{3.211}$$

$$-\frac{h^2}{8\pi^2\mu}\left[\frac{d^2\psi(r)}{dr^2} + \frac{2}{r}\frac{d\psi(r)}{dr} + \frac{\beta}{r^2}\psi(r)\right] - \frac{e^2}{r}\psi(r) = \epsilon_e\psi(r) \tag{3.212}$$

The solutions of the angular equations do *not* give energy eigenvalues. The energy eigenvalues are found from the equation in r, alone.

The quantities α, β, and ϵ_e are constants to be determined in the course of solving these equations; α and β are dimensionless, while ϵ_e is the energy eigenvalue and has, of course, dimensions of energy. The general requirements on wave functions (Sec. 2.2) are important in determining the allowed values of these quantities. The equations are conveniently solved in the order written, with the quantities α, β, and ϵ_e determined in that order. It is found first that the parameter α must be zero or negative, and in magnitude must be the square of an integer. Again, then, a quantum number arises very naturally; it is given the symbol m and the name magnetic quantum number because it is important in determining the energy of the hydrogen atom in a magnetic field. In place of α in the equations we may write $-m^2$.

But now notice that Eq. 3.211 in the angle θ will have a term containing m^2, as well as the quantity β. The solutions of this equation, and the allowed values for the quantity β, will depend on which m value is being considered. It is found that β can have only the values given by $-l(l + 1)$, where l is an integer equal to or larger than the magnitude (absolute value) of m. This quantity, l, is given the name azimuthal quantum number, and β is replaced by $-l(l + 1)$.

The solutions (wave functions) of Eq. 3.212 will be different for different l values; however, the energy eigenvalue is found to be independent of l and to depend only on a quantum number n, called the principal quantum number. It must have positive integral values, but for a given l value the smallest n value allowed is $l + 1$. The energy expression is

$$\epsilon_e = -\frac{2\pi^2\mu e^4}{n^2 h^2} \tag{3.213}$$

Comparison with Experiment. A check of Eq. 3.213 is most readily made by spectroscopic measurements. It turns out that the selection rules are easily satisfied,

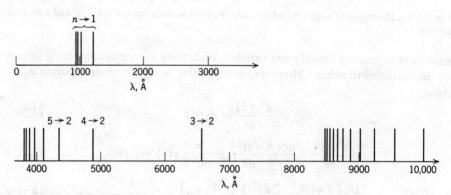

Fig. 3.202   Part of the atomic spectrum of hydrogen. Some of the transitions are labeled.

and we should (and do) find transitions between energy levels corresponding to any pair of n values. Emission spectroscopy is more convenient than absorption spectroscopy, and a simple "neon sign" tube, containing hydrogen gas at a few millimeters pressure, serves as the source. The electric discharge dissociates some of the hydrogen molecules into atoms and also gives them sufficient energy to populate the levels $n = 2$, 3, 4, etc., as well as $n = 1$. Atoms with higher energy spontaneously emit light and drop to lower levels, so that the frequency of light emitted is given by the expression

$$\epsilon_i - \epsilon_f = h\nu = \frac{2\pi^2\mu e^4}{h^2}\left(\frac{1}{n_f^2} - \frac{1}{n_i^2}\right) \tag{3.214}$$

where n_i is the quantum number of the initial level, and n_f that of the final level. The actual spectrum is found to consist of groups of lines, each group corresponding to a certain n_f value, and the lines within the group to various n_i values; see Fig. 3.202.

Since Eq. 3.213 contains only fundamental physical constants and no unknown parameters, such as force constants or bond distances, it might be possible to compare it with experiment by using the known values of μ, e, and h, and comparing these calculated frequencies with those observed. However, this is unsatisfactory because of the limited accuracy with which these constants, especially e and h, are known. These uncertainties mean that calculated frequencies are probably no better than about one part in ten thousand, whereas the spectrum lines can be measured to better than one part in a million. To make use of this great precision, we regard Eq. 3.213 as giving a functional form for the energy levels, and use the experimental data to see how closely this form is obeyed. The agreement is better than one part in ten thousand. The remaining discrepancies can be calculated on the basis of relativistic quantum mechanics, and by including effects of nuclear and electron spin. With these modifications, the agreement of theory and experiment is even better than one part in a million. In fact, the experimental data were once used to aid in evaluation of the fundamental constants e and h.

ILLUSTRATION.   Determine how closely Eq. 3.214 holds, given that, among other lines, the hydrogen atom emits light of wavelengths 6564.658 Å and 4862.713 Å in the transitions $n = 3 \rightarrow 2$ and $n = 4 \rightarrow 2$, respectively. [These wavelengths are from the measurements of W. V. Houston, *Phys. Rev.*, **30**, 608 (1927); his values were measured in air and are corrected here to vacuum conditions.]

If the formula were obeyed exactly, the frequencies should be in the ratio

$$\frac{\nu_{3,2}}{\nu_{4,2}} = \left(\frac{\dfrac{1}{2^2} - \dfrac{1}{3^2}}{\dfrac{1}{2^2} - \dfrac{1}{4^2}} \right) = \frac{20}{27}$$

and the wavelengths would then be in the ratio 27/20. The product $4862.713 \times (27/20)$ is 6564.466; this differs from the measured value by 0.192 Å, or about one part in thirty thousand.

The student may calculate the expected wavelengths of the $n = 5 \rightarrow 2$ and the $n = 4 \rightarrow 3$ transitions.

Angular Wave Functions and Probabilities.   It is convenient to discuss the angular functions first and the radial functions later. The ϕ functions are particularly simple and may be represented by sines and cosines. For a given magnitude of m greater than zero the functions are

$$\psi_{m\,\cos}(\phi) = (\pi)^{-\frac{1}{2}} \cos m\phi$$

$$\psi_{m\,\sin}(\phi) = (\pi)^{-\frac{1}{2}} \sin m\phi \qquad (3.215)$$

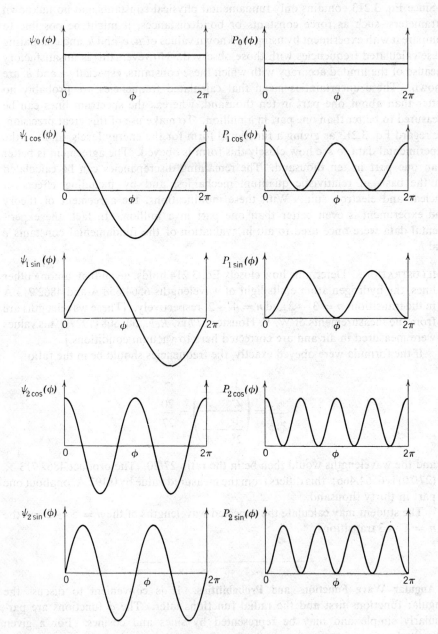

Fig. 3.203   Wave functions and probabilities in ϕ.

If $m = 0$, however, the function is the constant

$$\psi_0(\phi) = (2\pi)^{-\frac{1}{2}} \tag{3.216}$$

For the atom placed in an external magnetic field (Zeeman effect), it is more convenient to use wave functions with a complex variable such as

$$\psi_m(\phi) = (2\pi)^{-\frac{1}{2}} e^{im\phi} \tag{3.217}$$

where $e^{im\phi}$ may be expanded as $\cos m\phi + i \sin m\phi$. We shall treat only the real functions, since they are more convenient for chemical bonds. Figure 3.203 shows the functions and probabilities for m having magnitudes of 0, 1, and 2. As the normalization suggests, the probability is given per unit angle, instead of per unit

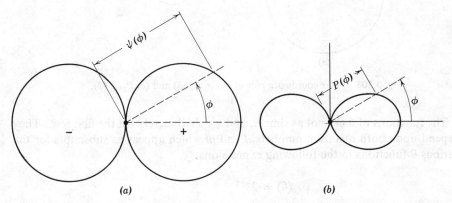

Fig. 3.204   Polar coordinate plot of (a) $\psi_{1\,cos}$ (ϕ) and (b) $P_{1\,cos}$ (ϕ).

length as in previous examples. For $m = 0$, all ϕ angles occur with equal probability, and no direction is more probable than any other. For the $\psi_{1\,cos}$ function, however, the angles 0 and 180° have the highest probability, while the angles 90 and 270° have very low probability.

Another diagrammatic representation of these probability curves may be made in which $\psi(\phi)$ and $P(\phi)$ are plotted as distance from the center, using polar coordinates. For the $\psi_{1\,cos}$ function this plot gives two circles which are tangent at the origin, as shown in Fig. 3.204. The probability value can be found for any angle, as shown in the figure; however, we must remember that this distance has nothing whatever to do with the radial probability function. For the $m = 0$ function, the figure is a circle centered at the origin, and for the $\psi_{1\,sin}$ function, the earlier figure is simply rotated by 90°; see Fig. 3.205. Functions for larger m values resemble clover leaves with four, six, eight, etc., branches. These wave functions are already normalized, e.g.,

$$\int_0^{2\pi} (\pi^{-\frac{1}{2}} \cos \phi)^2 \, d\phi = \frac{1}{\pi} \int_0^{2\pi} \cos^2 \phi \, d\phi = \frac{1}{\pi} \pi = 1 \tag{3.218}$$

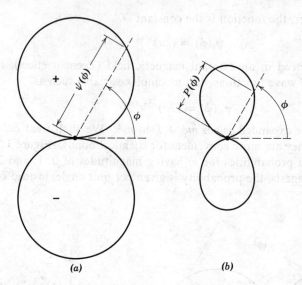

Fig. 3.205   Polar coordinate plot of (a) $\psi_{1\ \sin}(\phi)$ and (b) $P_{1\ \sin}(\phi)$.

The functions of θ are not as simple, and we shall merely list the first few. They depend upon both quantum numbers, l and m which appear as subscripts for the various θ functions in the following expressions:

$$\psi_{0,0}(\theta) = 2^{-\frac{1}{2}}$$

$$\psi_{1,0}(\theta) = \frac{6^{\frac{1}{2}}}{2}\cos\theta$$

$$\psi_{1,1}(\theta) = \frac{3^{\frac{1}{2}}}{2}\sin\theta$$

$$\psi_{2,0}(\theta) = \frac{10^{\frac{1}{2}}}{4}(3\cos^2\theta - 1) \qquad (3.219)$$

$$\psi_{2,1}(\theta) = \frac{15^{\frac{1}{2}}}{2}\sin\theta\cos\theta$$

$$\psi_{2,2}(\theta) = \frac{15^{\frac{1}{2}}}{4}\sin^2\theta$$

The probability functions $P_{l,m}(\theta)$ are normalized in the following way:

$$\int_0^\pi P_{l,m}(\theta)\sin\theta\,d\theta = 1$$

The allowed range of the angle is from 0 to π; in addition, the squared wave function $P_{l,m}(\theta)$ must be multiplied by $\sin\theta$ before integration. The reason for the inclusion of $\sin\theta$ is found in the form that the volume element $dx\,dy\,dz$ takes for spherical coordinates, $r^2\sin\theta\,d\theta\,d\phi\,dr$. Curves are shown for these functions in Fig. 3.206.

The total angular wave function is given by the product of the $\psi(\theta)$ function and $\psi(\phi)$; however, only the pairs that have the same m values may be combined. Thus $\psi_{0,0}(\theta)$ is multiplied only by $\psi_0(\phi)$, giving a function which is a constant. Similarly, the function $\psi_{1,0}(\theta)$ is multiplied by $\psi_0(\phi)$, and the result is a function with large values along the z axis but small values near the xy plane. The various possible combinations are listed in Eq. 3.220. The commonly used notation s, p, and d indicates l quantum numbers of 0, 1, and 2, respectively.

$$\psi_{0,0}(\theta)\psi_0(\phi) = \frac{1}{2\pi^{\frac{1}{2}}} \qquad\qquad s$$

$$\psi_{1,0}(\theta)\psi_0(\phi) = \frac{1}{2}\left(\frac{3}{\pi}\right)^{\frac{1}{2}}\cos\theta \qquad\qquad p_z$$

$$\psi_{1,1}(\theta)\psi_{1\cos}(\phi) = \frac{1}{2}\left(\frac{3}{\pi}\right)^{\frac{1}{2}}\sin\theta\cos\phi \qquad\qquad p_x$$

$$\psi_{1,1}(\theta)\psi_{1\sin}(\phi) = \frac{1}{2}\left(\frac{3}{\pi}\right)^{\frac{1}{2}}\sin\theta\sin\phi \qquad\qquad p_y$$

$$\psi_{2,0}(\theta)\psi_0(\phi) = \frac{1}{4}\left(\frac{5}{\pi}\right)^{\frac{1}{2}}(3\cos^2\theta - 1) \qquad\qquad d_{z^2} \qquad\qquad (3.220)$$

$$\psi_{2,1}(\theta)\psi_{1\cos}(\phi) = \frac{1}{2}\left(\frac{15}{\pi}\right)^{\frac{1}{2}}\sin\theta\cos\theta\cos\phi \qquad\qquad d_{xz}$$

$$\psi_{2,1}(\theta)\psi_{1\sin}(\phi) = \frac{1}{2}\left(\frac{15}{\pi}\right)^{\frac{1}{2}}\sin\theta\cos\theta\sin\phi \qquad\qquad d_{yz}$$

$$\psi_{2,2}(\theta)\psi_{2\cos}(\phi) = \frac{1}{4}\left(\frac{15}{\pi}\right)^{\frac{1}{2}}\sin^2\theta\cos 2\phi \qquad\qquad d_{x^2-y^2}$$

$$\psi_{2,2}(\theta)\psi_{2\sin}(\phi) = \frac{1}{4}\left(\frac{15}{\pi}\right)^{\frac{1}{2}}\sin^2\theta\sin 2\phi \qquad\qquad d_{xy}$$

The previous polar coordinate diagram can now be extended to include these functions by use of space polar coordinates. The s function is represented by a sphere centered at the origin; all directions are equally probable. The three various p functions are identical in shape, different only in orientation. The first is represented by two spheres tangent at the origin, and lying centered along the positive

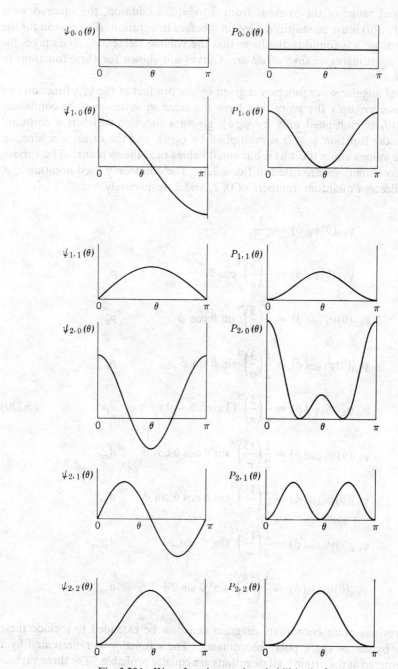

Fig. 3.206   Wave functions and probabilities in θ.

and negative z-axis directions. The last four d functions are also alike in shape and size but different in their orientation; they resemble three-dimensional four-leaf clovers. The first d function is different; see the sketches in Fig. 3.207.

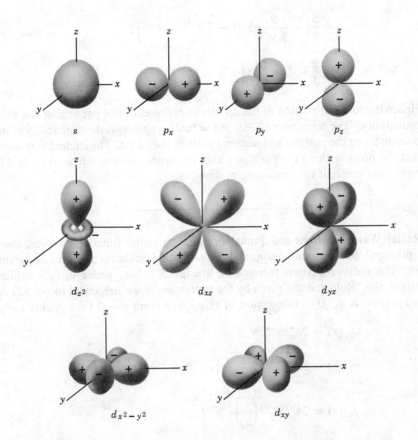

s p_x p_y p_z

d_{z^2} d_{xz} d_{yz}

$d_{x^2-y^2}$ d_{xy}

Fig. 3.207   Spatial visualization in polar coordinates of some complete angular wave functions for the hydrogen atom (taken by permission from R. G. Pearson, *Chem. Eng. News*, June 29, 1959).

ILLUSTRATION.   Determine the total probability P for the d_{z^2} function in all of the region where the corresponding wave function is negative, the toroidal region.

The factor $(3 \cos^2 \theta - 1)$ will be negative for all angles such that $\cos \theta < 3^{-\frac{1}{2}}$, i.e., between $54°44'$ and $125°16'$. Then

$$P = \int_{\phi=0}^{\phi=2\pi} \int_{\theta=54°44'}^{\theta=125°16'} \frac{5}{16\pi} (3 \cos^2 \theta - 1)^2 \sin \theta \ d\theta \ d\phi$$

Integration over the range of ϕ gives the quantity 2π. Hence

$$P = \frac{5}{8} \int_{\theta=54^{\circ}44'}^{\theta=125^{\circ}16'} (9 \cos^4 \theta - 6 \cos^2 \theta + 1) \sin \theta \, d\theta$$

$$= \frac{5}{8}\left(+ \frac{9}{5 \times 9} 3^{-\frac{1}{2}} - \frac{2}{3} 3^{-\frac{1}{2}} + 3^{-\frac{1}{2}} \right) 2$$

$$= \frac{2}{3} 3^{-\frac{1}{2}} = 0.384$$

Hence the toroidal portion of the d_{z^2} orbital represents 38.4 per cent of the total probability. The remainder, $1 - 0.384 = 0.616$, represents the probability of the portion along the positive and negative parts of the z axis. The student may show that the portion along the positive z axis, i.e., with values of θ from 0 to $54^{\circ}44'$, represents one half the remaining probability.

Radial Wave Functions and Probabilities. The radial functions depend upon the principal quantum number n, and the azimuthal quantum number l as parameters. The radial functions through $3d$ are listed below, where a_0 is a defined constant, the "Bohr radius" given by the expression $h^2/4\pi^2\mu e^2$, equal to ~ 0.529 Å. The notation is $\psi_{n,l}(r)$. Integration of $r^2[\psi_{n,l}(r)]^2$ from $r = 0$ to ∞ yields unity.

$$\psi_{1,0}(r) = 2a_0^{-\frac{3}{2}} e^{-r/a_0}$$

$$\psi_{2,0}(r) = 8^{-\frac{1}{2}} a_0^{-\frac{3}{2}} \left(2 - \frac{r}{a_0} \right) e^{-r/2a_0}$$

$$\psi_{2,1}(r) = 24^{-\frac{1}{2}} a_0^{-\frac{3}{2}} \left(\frac{r}{a_0} \right) e^{-r/2a_0}$$

$$\psi_{3,0}(r) = 2(81)^{-1} 3^{-\frac{1}{2}} a_0^{-\frac{3}{2}} \left[27 - 18 \frac{r}{a_0} + 2\left(\frac{r}{a_0} \right)^2 \right] e^{-r/3a_0} \qquad (3.221)$$

$$\psi_{3,1}(r) = 4(81)^{-1} 6^{-\frac{1}{2}} a_0^{-\frac{3}{2}} \left[6 \frac{r}{a_0} - \left(\frac{r}{a_0} \right)^2 \right] e^{-r/3a_0}$$

$$\psi_{3,2}(r) = 4(81)^{-1} (30)^{-\frac{1}{2}} a_0^{-\frac{3}{2}} \left(\frac{r}{a_0} \right)^2 e^{-r/3a_0}$$

The squares of these expressions are the various probability functions. However, as suggested by the normalizing factor, they are the probability per unit volume. This must be so since the two angular functions represent probability per unit angle, which is dimensionless, while the total probability function, the product of the r, θ, and ϕ parts, refers to unit volume. Examination of the 1,0 function shows that the greatest probability is for an r value of zero; thus the most likely place to find the electron, *per unit volume*, is at the nucleus.

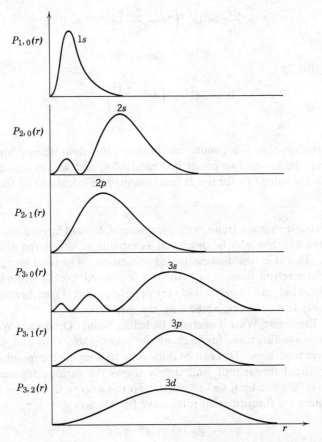

Fig. 3.208 $P(r)$ for some hydrogen atom functions; scales for r are the same for all graphs. The 1s function ordinate is compressed relative to the others about threefold. (Taken by permission from K. S. Pitzer, *Quantum Chemistry*, Prentice-Hall, Englewood Cliffs, N.J., 1953.)

If, instead, we wish the radial electron probability per unit distance from the nucleus, the functions are different. The volume element, after integration over the angles of the spherical element $r^2 \sin \theta \, d\theta \, d\phi \, dr$, becomes $4\pi r^2 \, dr$. The 4π factor has been absorbed into the angular functions, Eq. 3.220. The squares of the various radial functions in Eq. 3.221 are multiplied by r^2, and the result is $P(r)$; these are plotted in Fig. 3.208. It is seen that $P_{1,0}(r)$ is not a maximum at the nucleus since r^2 is zero there.

ILLUSTRATION. Calculate the most probable r value for the $1s$ and for the $2p$ functions, where the integer in this notation represents the quantum number n, and the letters $s, p, d, \ldots$ represent values of the quantum number $l = 0, 1, 2, \ldots$.

$$P_{1,0}(r) = 4a_0^{-3}r^2e^{-2r/a_0}$$

$$\frac{dP}{dr} = 4a_0^{-3}\left(2r - \frac{2r^2}{a_0}\right)e^{-2r/a_0} = 0$$

$$\therefore \quad r = a_0$$

Similarly, for $2p$

$$0 = 24^{-1}a_0^{-5}\left(4r^3 - \frac{r^4}{a_0}\right)e^{-r/a_0}$$

$$\therefore \quad r = 4a_0$$

This illustration shows a connection between the Bohr theory and quantum mechanics; the lowest two orbits had radii of a_0 and $4a_0$, as found here. The most probable value of r for the $2s$ function may be calculated by the student.

––––––––––––

These $P(r)$ curves show a trend, with increasing n, toward larger size. In the limit of $n \to \infty$, the electron may be described as moving to very large distances from the nucleus. This is called dissociation or ionization. The total energy necessary to change the electron from $n = 1$ to $n = \infty$, called the ionization energy or ionization potential, can be calculated very precisely; direct measurements, though of considerably less accuracy, agree with the calculations.

Complete Electronic Wave Functions Including Spin; Orbitals. We may now combine the wave functions for each of the coordinates r, θ, and ϕ into more complete wave functions. This can be done only by keeping the quantum numbers l and m consistent throughout, and clearly shows the various degeneracies. For $n = 1$, there is just one total wave function, so this energy level is not degenerate; for $n = 2$, there are four different total wave functions:

$$\psi_{2s} = \psi_{2,0}(r)\,\psi_{0,0}(\theta)\,\psi_0(\phi)$$
$$\psi_{2p_z} = \psi_{2,1}(r)\,\psi_{1,0}(\theta)\,\psi_0(\phi)$$
$$\psi_{2p_x} = \psi_{2,1}(r)\,\psi_{1,1}(\theta)\,\psi_{1\,\cos}(\phi) \qquad (3.222)$$
$$\psi_{2p_y} = \psi_{2,1}(r)\,\psi_{1,1}(\theta)\,\psi_{1\,\sin}(\phi)$$

Since each of these gives the same energy eigenvalue, the $n = 2$ energy level is four-fold degenerate; similarly, for the nth level of the hydrogen atom, the degeneracy is n^2. Wave functions, such as those in Eq. 3.222, are frequently called *orbitals*; the name is designedly similar to, but different from, the term orbit, as in Bohr theory. Note also the designation of orbitals as $1s$, $2s$, $2p_z$, etc. We also speak of orbitals in other atoms and even orbitals in molecules; the meaning conveyed is a total (space-dependent) wave function for a single electron.

The specification of the complete wave function requires the introduction of a spin wave function, which depends on the spin orientation but is independent of the location of the electron.

A number of different observations cannot be completely understood solely in terms of charge, mass, and positional coordinates ascribed to the electron. Goudsmit and Uhlenbeck (1925) assumed an intrinsic spin angular momentum and a magnetic moment which are characteristic of the electron itself, in addition to angular momentum and magnetic moment associated with the spatial distribution of the electron, and characterized by the quantum numbers l and m. The student will recall from physics that a short bar magnet is characterized by a value of magnetic moment, which governs the torque exerted on the magnet by a steady magnetic field. A small coil of wire, carrying a steady electric current, also is characterized by a magnetic moment. Since a finite-sized charge distribution spinning around an axis passing through its center would have, classically, both an angular momentum and a magnetic moment, the additional property of the electron is called spin. A convenient unit of magnetic moment for atoms and molecules is the Bohr magneton, μ_B, defined to be $eh/4\pi mc = 0.9273 \times 10^{-20}$ erg gauss^{-1}. The intrinsic magnetic moment of the electron is found to be slightly larger, about $2.0022\, m_s \mu_B = 1.0011\, \mu_B$.

These spin wave functions and their behavior are quite different from those of previous functions. There are only two spin wave functions, whereas most systems we have studied had very many different wave functions. These wave functions correspond to the two possible orientations of the spin angular momentum (and the spin magnetic moment) of the electron with respect to an applied magnetic field. The energy levels or eigenvalues of the spin wave function depend on an external parameter, the magnetic field; previous systems had energies depending on internal parameters only. Finally, we are not concerned with the analytical form of the spin wave function.

There is a spin quantum number, denoted as m_s, for which there are only two possible values, $+\frac{1}{2}$ and $-\frac{1}{2}$. The value $m_s = +\frac{1}{2}$ is associated arbitrarily with the spin function denoted α, and $m_s = -\frac{1}{2}$ is associated with the function denoted β. The spin quantum number gives the component of spin angular momentum in a certain direction in units of $h/2\pi$.

Since the spin coordinates and positional coordinates are independent, this suggests that the spin wave function simply multiplies the orbital wave function of an electron to give the complete wave function. The hydrogen atom in its lowest (ground) electronic state is represented as having the wave function

$$(1s)(\alpha) \quad \text{or} \quad (1s)(\beta)$$

Except in powerful magnetic fields, the energies of these states are so close that they may be considered identical.

Removal of Orbital and Spin Degeneracy in a Magnetic Field. In the treatment of the hydrogen atom earlier in this section, the magnetic quantum number was denoted by m. This will hereafter be denoted as m_l to distinguish it from the spin quantum number m_s.

A magnetic field of strength $\mathcal{H}$ gauss has an effect on the energy of an electron which in general depends in a complex way on the atomic environment of the electron, but is relatively simple for several limiting cases. Consider a moment which arises entirely from electron spin; the two spin functions have the same eigenvalues in the absence of a magnetic field. In a steady magnetic field of $\mathcal{H}$ gauss, the α function is increased in energy by $1.0011\mu_B\mathcal{H} = 0.9283 \times 10^{-20}\,\mathcal{H}$ erg, and the β function is decreased in energy by $0.9283 \times 10^{-20}\,\mathcal{H}$ erg. Examples approaching this limiting behavior are some free radicals in solution, and the hydrogen atom in s states.

Consider next only the orbital magnetic moment. In the absence of a magnetic field, a set of p orbitals, for example, is degenerate. In the presence of a steady magnetic field the degeneracy would be removed; the change in energy is given by $\mu_B\mathcal{H}m_l = 0.9273 \times 10^{-20}\mathcal{H}m_l$, so that three equally spaced levels result. The same expression applies to the splitting of degeneracy for d and f orbitals. Since m_l can only be zero for s orbitals, the magnetic field does not change their energy. Examples of effects due *only* to orbital angular momentum cannot be found in atoms having only one electron, because of spin. In atoms with several electrons, there are excited electronic states for which all electron spins are paired, and which possess orbital angular momentum only.

For the hydrogen atom in states other than s, or in general for atoms with several electrons, the magnetic behavior is quite complex. The energy change on application of a magnetic field is described in terms of the interaction of the external magnetic field with a net atomic magnetic moment arising from the coupling of spin and orbital angular momentum.

For the majority of chemical applications, the energy associated with electron spin is insignificant; the important effect arises through the symmetry of the total wave functions. Further discussion of electron spin is presented in Sec. 3.4 and in Chapter 16.

Problems

3.201   Plot the potential energy as a function of distance between a proton and an electron. Indicate on this drawing the first fifteen levels of the hydrogen atom permitted by quantum mechanics. What level of the atom is closest to one half of the ionization energy, I?

3.202   Calculate the wavelength of the Lyman α line of hydrogen, $n = 2 \rightarrow 1$, with quanta of energy 1.63×10^{-11} erg. Compare this energy with that predicted by Eq. 3.213, applied to the two lowest electronic levels of the hydrogen atom.

3.203   Calculate the quantum number for translation in the x direction of a hydrogen atom, moving in a 10-cm box, with a velocity in the x direction, corresponding to the energy of dissociation of the hydrogen atom.

3.204   Show that the total probability represented by one of the four lobes of the d_{xz} function is 0.25.

*3.205   Show that the last four d functions, Eq. 3.220, are identical in contour. (SUGGESTION: make those angle changes which will transform one of the functions into another one of the set.)

3.206   The d_{xy} function has all its maxima in the xy plane, and one of them is found at the angle $\phi = 45°$. Determine the numerical value of the probability function (a) at the maximum; (b) at the angle $\phi = 40°$ and in the xy plane; (c) at the angle $\phi = 45°$ and the angle $\theta = 85°$. Do these results suggest that this lobe of the d_{xy} function is symmetrical around the 45° line, elongated in the xy plane, or elongated perpendicular to the xy plane?

3.207   Show that the $\psi(\phi)$ functions, Eqs. 3.215, are solutions of the appropriate part of the Schrödinger equation. Substitute a typical function into the proper one of Eqs. 3.210 to 3.212; you will have to determine the possible value(s) of one or more of the parameters α and β.

3.208   Show that the $\psi(\theta)$ functions, Eq. 3.219, are solutions of the appropriate part of the Schrödinger equation. Substitute, in turn, the various functions into the proper one of Eqs. 3.210 to 3.212. Determine the values of the parameters α and β necessary for each function.

3.209   Verify the normalization constants for the $1s$ and the $2p$ radial wave functions. Use tables of definite integrals.

3.210   Calculate the probability that the r value of the electron in a $1s$ function will have a value between 0 and a_0.

3.211   Calculate the probability that the r value of the electron in a $1s$ function will be found between $0.99a_0$ and $1.01a_0$. Do not integrate; use Δr. Repeat for r values between $1.50a_0$ and $1.52a_0$.

3.212   Calculate the expectation values of r and also of $1/r$ for the $1s$ function. The expectation value of $1/r$, multiplied by $-e^2$, is the quantum mechanical average value of the potential energy. Show that this is, in magnitude, just twice the total energy of the atom in the $1s$ state.

3.213   Verify that the $\psi_{1,0}(r)$ and $\psi_{2,1}(r)$ functions, Eq. 3.221, are solutions of the appropriate Schrödinger equation, Eqs. 3.210 to 3.212, and give the correct energy eigenvalues.

*3.214   The lithium ion Li^{++} is similar to the hydrogen atom except that it has a nuclear charge of $+3e$. The angular equations, Eqs. 3.210 and 3.211, and their solutions are the same as for hydrogen; the radial equation and its solutions are different. How is the radial equation for Li^{++} different from Eq. 3.212? The $1s$ orbital in Li^{++} is described by a radial function $\psi = 2(27)^{1/2}a_0^{-3/2}e^{-3r/a_0}$. Show that this satisfies the radial equation, and determine the energy eigenvalue. Compare with the hydrogen energy eigenvalue.

3.   Atomic Orbitals and Energies of Many-Electron Atoms

The spectra of many-electron atoms, in contrast to the spectrum of the hydrogen atom, are exceedingly complex. The former have many more possible energy levels than hydrogen, corresponding to many possible modes of excitation of the different electrons; the levels are not given, in general, by an algebraic formula, simple or otherwise. In fact, atoms are frequently excited by a spark or electric discharge and may be present as ions in which one or more electrons have been removed. The resulting spectrum may extend from the infrared to the X-ray region and possess none of the simple regularity of the hydrogen spectrum. For most elements, the known experimental spectra are but a small fraction of the complete spectrum; the spectra of virtually all highly ionized atoms are just not known.

These facts suggest that the theoretical treatment of many-electron atoms is much more complex than that of the hydrogen atom. The wave equation cannot be exactly separated into smaller parts and solved, though this is done as an approximation; each electron exerts a repulsive potential on other electrons. Since experimental energies are not correlated by analytical expressions, it is frequently uncertain which energy levels of the experiment are to be compared with theory.

With such difficulties, we will not attempt as complete a treatment for many-electron atoms as we did for the hydrogen atom. Major emphasis will be placed on understanding the general constitution of the atom, especially the symmetry properties of wave functions involving several identical particles (here electrons). We shall assume that the student has a general familiarity with the building-up principle of the periodic table, by successive filling of electron shells.

The Schrödinger Equation for Electrons in an Atom.   After the three translations of the center of gravity are removed, the Schrödinger equation is

$$- \frac{h^2}{8\pi^2 m_e} \sum_{i=1}^{n} \left(\frac{\partial^2 \psi}{\partial x_i^2} + \frac{\partial^2 \psi}{\partial y_i^2} + \frac{\partial^2 \psi}{\partial z_i^2} \right) - Ze^2 \psi \sum_{i=1}^{n} \frac{1}{r_i} + e^2 \psi \sum_{i,j>i}^{n} \frac{1}{r_{ij}} = \epsilon \psi \quad (3.301)$$

where m_e is the mass of the electron and is used in place of a complicated reduced mass term of similar magnitude. The first sum arises from the kinetic energy of each of the n electrons, the second sum from the potential energy of each electron due to attraction by the charge of $+Ze$ on the nucleus; the third term is due to the repulsion of each electron by all the others, where $j > i$ ensures that each term is counted once only. The terms r_i and r_{ij} are the distance of electron i from the nucleus, and the distance between electrons i and j, respectively. If an atom has five electrons, for instance, the nuclear attraction sum has five terms, and the electron repulsion sum has ten terms. Also, ψ is a function of all the coordinates of each electron, i.e., a total of fifteen coordinates.

An exact solution of Eq. 3.301, even in terms of complex functions, has not been found. The failure is due to the presence of the repulsion terms. If these terms were completely neglected, the Hamiltonian would separate into the sum of several parts, one for each of the electrons, and the resulting equations could easily be solved. This is such a bad approximation that it is of no value. A much better method will now be described.

The Central Field Approximation.   All the parts of the third sum in Eq. 3.301 that involve a certain number for i represent the instantaneous contribution to the potential energy due to the repulsions between electron i and all the other electrons. Instead of an instantaneous contribution, consider an average contribution: imagine the i electron fixed, but allow all other electrons to move, and compute the average repulsion potential energy. The result will depend on the coordinates of the ith electron but cannot depend upon the coordinates of any other electron; they disappear in the averaging process. Furthermore, even though the potential may depend on the direction of i from the nucleus, we simply take an average over all directions. The only remaining variable in the repulsion potential is r_i. Since we do not know *a priori* the functional form of this potential, we denote it here as $V(r_i)$.

By this approximation, it is possible to separate Eq. 3.301 into n separate equations of the general form

$$-\frac{h^2}{8\pi^2 m}\left[\frac{\partial^2 \psi(x_i,y_i,z_i)}{\partial x_i^2} + \frac{\partial^2 \psi(x_i,y_i,z_i)}{\partial y_i^2} + \frac{\partial^2 \psi(x_i,y_i,z_i)}{\partial z_i^2}\right]$$

$$-\frac{Ze^2 \psi(x_i,y_i,z_i)}{r_i} + V(r_i)\psi(x_i,y_i,z_i) = \epsilon_i \psi(x_i,y_i,z_i) \quad (3.302)$$

In this equation $V(r_i)$ may be a different function for each of the n electrons, hence the need for a subscript; the wave functions $\psi(x_i,y_i,z_i)$ may also be different for each of the n electrons. The great advantage is that we now have n one-electron equations as opposed to one n-electron equation, Eq. 3.301. There are various methods for obtaining rather good estimates of the functions $V(r_i)$ and also for checking their self-consistency; their discussion is beyond the present scope.

ILLUSTRATION.   Write the Schrödinger equation for the electronic energy of the lithium atom, and the three equations obtained from this by the central-field approximation.

$$-\frac{h^2}{8\pi^2 m_e}\left(\frac{\partial^2 \psi}{\partial x_1^2} + \frac{\partial^2 \psi}{\partial y_1^2} + \frac{\partial^2 \psi}{\partial z_1^2} + \frac{\partial^2 \psi}{\partial x_2^2} + \frac{\partial^2 \psi}{\partial y_2^2} + \frac{\partial^2 \psi}{\partial z_2^2} + \frac{\partial^2 \psi}{\partial x_3^2} + \frac{\partial^2 \psi}{\partial y_3^2} + \frac{\partial^2 \psi}{\partial z_3^2}\right)$$

$$-3e^2\left(\frac{1}{r_1} + \frac{1}{r_2} + \frac{1}{r_3}\right)\psi + e^2\left(\frac{1}{r_{12}} + \frac{1}{r_{13}} + \frac{1}{r_{23}}\right)\psi = \epsilon\psi$$

where ψ is a function of the nine coordinates $x_1, y_1, \ldots, z_3$. By the central field approximation, we obtain:

$$-\frac{h^2}{8\pi^2 m_e}\left[\frac{\partial^2 \psi(x_1,y_1,z_1)}{\partial x_1^2} + \frac{\partial^2 \psi(x_1,y_1,z_1)}{\partial y_1^2} + \frac{\partial^2 \psi(x_1,y_1,z_1)}{\partial z_1^2}\right]$$

$$-\frac{3e^2 \psi(x_1,y_1,z_1)}{r_1} + V(r_1)\psi(x_1,y_1,z_1) = \epsilon_1 \psi(x_1,y_1,z_1)$$

$$-\frac{h^2}{8\pi^2 m_e}\left[\frac{\partial^2 \psi(x_2,y_2,z_2)}{\partial x_2^2} + \frac{\partial^2 \psi(x_2,y_2,z_2)}{\partial y_2^2} + \frac{\partial^2 \psi(x_2,y_2,z_2)}{\partial z_2^2}\right]$$

$$-\frac{3e^2 \psi(x_2,y_2,z_2)}{r_2} + V(r_2)\psi(x_2,y_2,z_2) = \epsilon_2 \psi(x_2,y_2,z_2)$$

and

$$-\frac{h^2}{8\pi^2 m_e}\left[\frac{\partial^2 \psi(x_3,y_3,z_3)}{\partial x_3^2} + \frac{\partial^2 \psi(x_3,y_3,z_3)}{\partial y_3^2} + \frac{\partial^2 \psi(x_3,y_3,z_3)}{\partial z_3^2}\right]$$

$$-\frac{3e^2 \psi(x_3,y_3,z_3)}{r_3} + V(r_3)\psi(x_3,y_3,z_3) = \epsilon_3 \psi(x_3,y_3,z_3)$$

Wave Functions and Energies of One-Electron Orbitals. Equation 3.302 may be further simplified by the introduction of polar coordinates, as was done for hydrogen. The function $\psi(x_i, y_i, z_i)$ is replaced by its equivalent, $\psi(r_i)\psi(\theta_i)\psi(\phi_i)$, and for each electron there are a radial equation and two angular equations. The

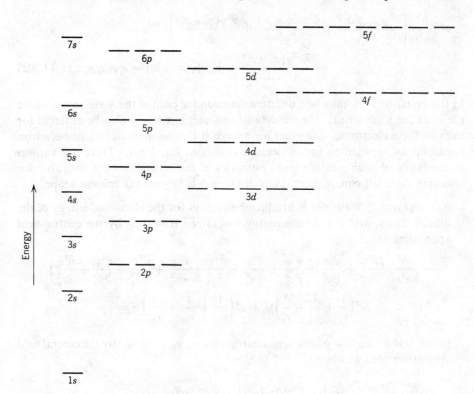

Fig. 3.301   Energy levels and degeneracies of atomic orbitals.

angular equations, containing θ_i and ϕ_i, are the same as Eqs. 3.210 and 3.211 for the hydrogen atom, and have exactly the same functional solutions. We may describe them as s functions, p functions, d functions, etc.

The radial equations, however, are different from Eq. 3.212 for the hydrogen atom, and the radial wave functions and energies are different from those of hydrogen. Indeed, we find that these are different for each of the different atoms in the periodic table, so that we cannot discuss them with completeness or in any real detail. An energy level diagram frequently used to discuss the periodic table of elements is shown in Fig. 3.301. This diagram is also consistent with the results of central field calculations of one-electron energies. The diagram implies that there are, in any atom, various radial functions. One class of radial functions combines only with s angular functions; different ones of this restricted set give different one-electron energies, ϵ_i; the one-electron functions are denoted $1s$, $2s$, $3s$, etc., in order of increasing energy. Another class of radial functions combines only with p angular functions; again they have different one-electron energies, and the total one-electron functions are denoted $2p$, $3p$, $4p$, etc., in increasing energy. The general ordering of energies is shown in Fig. 3.301. The horizontal separation is used only to avoid overcrowding on the ordinate. Observe, though, that the $2p$ (or $3p$, etc.) set contains three levels, because of the fact that there are three different angular functions which combine with the same radial function; this energy is triply degenerate. The d and f levels have degeneracy of five and seven, indicated by the number of lines at the same vertical height. The existence of electron spin doubles these degeneracies.

There are several ways in which a set of degenerate orbitals, such as a p or d or f set, may be partially filled with electrons. In the nitrogen atom, for example, there are three electrons to be placed in the three $2p$ orbitals. Two of the electrons might be placed in one of the p orbitals and the other electron in one of the remaining p orbitals, or each p orbital might contain a single electron. The latter arrangement corresponds to the lower energy, and the former arrangement corresponds to an excited electronic state quite close to the lower state.

A word of caution is pertinent at this point about too-literal interpretation of diagrams such as Fig. 3.301. The very basis for the diagram is the separation of the n-electron Schrödinger equation, which was an approximation. Furthermore, the detailed ordering of close-lying energy levels depends on the atomic number being considered; this is especially true of the $4s$ and $3d$ levels, as for the transition elements. Finally, the energies depend strongly on atomic number; for this reason no scale is shown. The $1s$ orbital in lithium is relatively less stable than the $1s$ orbital in a heavy element, such as bromine.

The Pauli Exclusion Principle. Figure 3.301 is useful in understanding the periodic table; electrons successively fill the various orbitals, starting with the lowest energy one, with a maximum of two electrons in any orbital in accordance with the Pauli exclusion principle. This well-known principle states that two electrons in an atom may not have identical values of the four quantum numbers n, l, m_l, and m_s; thus two electrons, in an orbital described by particular values of the quantum numbers n, l, and m_l, exhaust the possible different values of m_s. Use of the principle and the above-described degeneracies of p, d, and f orbitals explain many features of the periodic table.

The electron configuration of an atom is simply the arrangement of the electrons in the various orbitals of the atom. The common system of notation (e.g., H, $1s$; He, $1s^2$; Li, $1s^2 2s$; N, $1s^2\,2s^2\,2p^3$) is assumed to be known to the student.

In the next section, we shall look in more detail at the basis for limiting an orbital to a maximum of two electrons.

Reference

G. Herzberg, *Atomic Spectra and Atomic Structure*, Prentice-Hall, Englewood Cliffs, N.J., 1937, Ch. 1, p. 148.

Problems

3.301   Give the complete electronic configuration of the atoms chlorine, titanium, dysprosium, and radon.

3.302   List all possible sets of the four quantum numbers, n, l, m_l, and m_s, for an electron with $n = 4$. Indicate which groups comprise $4s$, $4p$, etc.

3.303   Calculate the separation between the two electron spin energy levels in the earth's magnetic field of about 0.19 gauss.

3.304   Slater [*Phys. Rev.*, **36**, 57 (1930)] has given some simple analytical functions which are useful, approximate, one-electron atomic orbitals for some light atoms. The radial parts of a few of these are:

For the helium atom $1s$ orbitals:

$$\psi_{1s}(r) = 2\left(\frac{1.70}{a_0}\right)^{3/2} e^{-1.70r/a_0}$$

For the carbon atom $1s$, $2s$, and $2p$ orbitals:

$$\psi_{1s}(r) = 2\left(\frac{5.70}{a_0}\right)^{3/2} e^{-5.70r/a_0}$$

$$\psi_{2s}(r) = \psi_{2p}(r) = 24^{-1/2}\left(\frac{3.25}{a_0}\right)^{5/2} re^{-3.25r/2a_0}$$

Show that each of these functions is normalized. Compare and contrast these functions with the hydrogen radial wave functions.

4. Identical Particles and Symmetry of the Total Wave Function

In all of Sec. 3.3, we have labeled coordinates and energy levels with numerical subscripts to denote electron number 1, 2, etc. In actual fact, all electrons are identical and indistinguishable; the labeling is merely for our convenience in treating the problem. This is true not only of electrons but also of protons, neutrons, nuclei of the same isotope of the same element, and of atoms. This indistinguishability of identical particles has important consequences for the way we may write wave functions, and a simple model system will now be described to show some of these consequences.

Two Identical Particles in a One-Dimensional Box. We shall examine first a model of simple composition. Consider a one-dimensional box, as in Sec. 2.4, which contains two particles, identical in every way. The system is idealized in that there is no interaction between the particles; each of them has energy levels and wave functions just as if the other one were absent. We can separate and solve the Schrödinger equation by assuming that the total wave function is just the product of two particle-in-a-box wave functions, one for each particle. Suppose that the first particle has quantum number $n = 1$, and the second has $n = 2$. With use of the coordinates x_1 and x_2, the total wave function may be written

$$\psi = N_{12} \sin\frac{\pi x_1}{l} \sin\frac{2\pi x_2}{l} \tag{3.401}$$

where N_{12} is a normalizing constant. The square of this wave function gives the probability function. For example, the probability of finding particle 1 between $l/2 - \Delta_1$ and $l/2 + \Delta_1$ (i.e., near the center) and, at the same time, particle 2 between $l/4 - \Delta_2$ and $l/4 + \Delta_2$ (near $l/4$) is $\psi^2 2\Delta_1 2\Delta_2 = (N_{12})^2 2\Delta_1 2\Delta_2$ or $4P(l/2,l/4)\Delta_1\Delta_2$. However, the probability of finding particle 2 near the center and particle 1 near $l/4$ is zero. Since, however, the particles were assumed indistinguishable we would not know which of them, 1 or 2, was found near the center. Clearly the wave function is not a good one for indistinguishable particles; we need a function which predicts experimental results treating all identical particles alike.

The related wave function

$$\psi_{\text{sym}} = N_{\text{sym}}\left(\sin\frac{\pi x_1}{l}\sin\frac{2\pi x_2}{l} + \sin\frac{2\pi x_1}{l}\sin\frac{\pi x_2}{l}\right) \qquad (3.402)$$

and probability function

$$P = \psi_{\text{sym}}^2 \qquad (3.403)$$

have the property of treating particles 1 and 2 as indistinguishable; both probability statements in the example now have the same answer. This property is frequently described by saying that the probability function is symmetric to interchange of these identical particles; if the numerical subscripts 1 and 2 are interchanged, the probability function will give the same numerical values for all possible pairs of x_1, x_2 values. This must be true not only of the probability function but also of any imaginable or possible physical measurement not in conflict with the basic principles of quantum mechanics.

Note, however, that this requirement applies to the probability function, not necessarily to the wave function. The wave function might retain algebraic sign (be *symmetrical*), or change sign (be *antisymmetrical*), under an exchange of identical particles, and the probability function would be symmetrical in both cases. We could write an antisymmetrical wave function for this system.

$$\psi_a = N_a\left(\sin\frac{\pi x_1}{l}\sin\frac{2\pi x_2}{l} - \sin\frac{2\pi x_1}{l}\sin\frac{\pi x_2}{l}\right) \qquad (3.404)$$

$$P = \psi_a^2 \qquad (3.405)$$

Although this probability function is symmetrical in the identical particles, its detailed distribution is quite different from that given in Eq. 3.403. Equations 3.402 and 3.404 cannot both represent the total wave function; only one of them is possible. The nature of the identical particles determines whether the symmetrical or antisymmetrical wave function occurs; for electrons the total wave function is antisymmetrical (though it must also contain a spin part; see below); for helium atoms the total wave function is symmetrical.

The wave functions 3.402 and 3.404 were formed from 3.401 by a simple permutation process. For the symmetrical one, the permuted function was added to the original; for the antisymmetrical, it was subtracted. The antisymmetrical function may be written as a determinant, a useful form

$$\psi_a = N_a \begin{vmatrix} \sin\dfrac{\pi x_1}{l} & \sin\dfrac{\pi x_2}{l} \\[2mm] \sin\dfrac{2\pi x_1}{l} & \sin\dfrac{2\pi x_2}{l} \end{vmatrix} \tag{3.404}$$

Electron Spin and Determinantal Wave Functions. Before the methods of the preceding section can be applied to wave functions written for electrons in atoms, the spin functions for the electrons must be included. When an atom has two or more electrons, we must pay attention to the symmetry. A general requirement, which is a rephrasing of the Pauli exclusion principle, is that the total electronic wave function must be antisymmetric in interchange of a pair of electrons. This may be made evident by the following example.

The ground state of the helium atom has (Sec. 3.3) two $1s$ electrons. The orbital part must be written as $\psi_{\text{orb}} = 1s(1)1s(2)$. This much gives a symmetrical orbital wave function. The use of the spin wave function $\alpha(1)\alpha(2)$ to give the total wave function

$$\psi = 1s(1)1s(2)\alpha(1)\alpha(2) \tag{3.406}$$

is not correct, since this would correspond to the two electrons having the same set of four quantum numbers. Moreover, this unacceptable wave function is symmetrical in exchange of electrons and violates the Pauli principle as restated. No single combination of α and β proves satisfactory; however, the permutation

$$\alpha(1)\beta(2) - \beta(1)\alpha(2) \tag{3.407}$$

is antisymmetrical and gives the total wave function

$$\psi = 1s(1)\alpha(1)1s(2)\beta(2) - 1s(1)\beta(1)1s(2)\alpha(2) \tag{3.408}$$

Equation 3.408 is written out in a particular way in order to clarify its relationship to the determinantal form

$$\psi = \begin{vmatrix} 1s(1)\alpha(1) & 1s(2)\alpha(2) \\ 1s(1)\beta(1) & 1s(2)\beta(2) \end{vmatrix} \tag{3.409}$$

We can also see again why the electrons must be of different spin: the determinantal form obtained by permutation of Eq. 3.406

$$\psi = \begin{vmatrix} 1s(1)\alpha(1) & 1s(2)\alpha(2) \\ 1s(1)\alpha(1) & 1s(2)\alpha(2) \end{vmatrix}$$

is zero since two rows (or columns) are identical; such states do not exist.

These determinants, called *Slater determinants*, are very useful. They always give the correct property of antisymmetry of the total wave function. In general, more complete wave functions for an atom will involve a sum of Slater determinants. In atoms having three or more electrons, the total wave function is required to be antisymmetrical in the exchange of *any* pair of electrons; this leads to a considerable number of terms in the wave functions when each determinant is expanded. In the lithium atom, for instance, we have three electrons. If two of these are $1s$ and one is $2s$, as suggested by Fig. 3.301, one such Slater determinant becomes (assuming the spin function for the $2s$ electron is α)

$$\begin{vmatrix} 1s(1)\alpha(1) & 1s(2)\alpha(2) & 1s(3)\alpha(3) \\ 1s(1)\beta(1) & 1s(2)\beta(2) & 1s(3)\beta(3) \\ 2s(1)\alpha(1) & 2s(2)\alpha(2) & 2s(3)\alpha(3) \end{vmatrix}$$

Upon expansion six terms are obtained.

ILLUSTRATION. Show by use of the determinantal form that a maximum of two electrons can be placed in the $1s$ orbital of lithium.

If all three electrons of the lithium atom are placed in $1s$ orbitals, the determinantal form would be either

$$\begin{vmatrix} 1s(1)\alpha(1) & 1s(2)\alpha(2) & 1s(3)\alpha(3) \\ 1s(1)\beta(1) & 1s(2)\beta(2) & 1s(3)\beta(3) \\ 1s(1)\beta(1) & 1s(2)\beta(2) & 1s(3)\beta(3) \end{vmatrix}$$

or

$$\begin{vmatrix} 1s(1)\alpha(1) & 1s(2)\alpha(2) & 1s(3)\alpha(3) \\ 1s(1)\beta(1) & 1s(2)\beta(2) & 1s(3)\beta(3) \\ 1s(1)\alpha(1) & 1s(2)\alpha(2) & 1s(3)\alpha(3) \end{vmatrix}$$

But these are both identically zero (since two rows, 2 and 3, or 1 and 3, respectively, of the determinants would be identical); hence such states cannot exist. The student may write out determinantal forms for beryllium.

Multiplicity of States. It is also possible to write approximations for some of the higher-energy (excited) electronic states. For the helium atom, suppose that one of the electrons is in a $1s$ orbital, and the other in a $2s$ orbital. We may write total wave functions which are antisymmetric in the exchange of the two electrons as follows:

$$[1s(1)2s(2) + 2s(1)1s(2)][\alpha(1)\beta(2) - \beta(1)\alpha(2)] \qquad (3.410)$$

and

$$[1s(1)2s(2) - 2s(1)1s(2)][\alpha(1)\alpha(2)]$$

$$[1s(1)2s(2) - 2s(1)1s(2)][\alpha(1)\beta(2) + \beta(1)\alpha(2)] \qquad (3.411)$$

$$[1s(1)2s(2) - 2s(1)1s(2)][\beta(1)\beta(2)]$$

Notice that the last three functions have exactly the same orbital function and hence have identical probability functions. The first function has a different orbital function and a different probability function. Except in powerful magnetic fields, the three eigenfunctions of Eq. 3.411 correspond to the same eigenvalue, and accordingly the level is degenerate; the functions are said to constitute a *triplet* state. The single function, Eq. 3.410, corresponds to a different energy level and is said to be a *singlet* state. The ground state of the helium atom, with electron configuration $1s^2$, corresponds also to a singlet state, since the only acceptable spin function which can combine with the symmetric orbital part (to give an antisymmetric total wave function) is the single antisymmetric function $\alpha(1)\beta(2) - \beta(1)\alpha(2)$. The ground state of the hydrogen atom, described by the two total wave functions

$$1s(1)\alpha(1) \quad \text{and} \quad 1s(1)\beta(1)$$

is said to constitute a *doublet* state. No question of symmetry of the electronic wave function on interchange of electrons can occur for only one electron. The terms singlet, doublet, triplet, quartet, etc., describe the *multiplicity* of an atom (or molecule) in a particular state.

The multiplicity may frequently be determined without the need to write detailed expressions like Eqs. 3.410 and 3.411. For all possible total wave functions, we may form the sum of spin quantum numbers ($\frac{1}{2}$ for α functions and $-\frac{1}{2}$ for β functions) for all electrons, Σm_s. The various total wave functions which comprise a certain multiplet will yield different sums; there will always be a member which gives the largest sum, $(\Sigma m_s)_{max}$. Twice this value plus one gives the multiplicity of the state to which this total wave function belongs,

$$\text{multiplicity} = 2(\Sigma m_s)_{max} + 1$$

For the hydrogen atom, $m_s = \frac{1}{2}$, corresponding to $\alpha(1)$, and $-\frac{1}{2}$ for $\beta(1)$; so $(\Sigma m_s)_{max} = \frac{1}{2}$, and the multiplicity $= 2$. For the triplet functions of helium with configuration $1s2s$, $(\Sigma m_s)_{max} = 1$ and the multiplicity $= 3$. This maximum corresponds to 1 for the spin function $\alpha(1)\alpha(2)$, i.e., $\frac{1}{2} + \frac{1}{2}$; the sum is 0 for $\alpha(1)\beta(2) + \alpha(2)\beta(1)$, for which $\Sigma m_s = \frac{1}{2} - \frac{1}{2} = 0$, and the sum is -1 for $\beta(1)\beta(2)$. Since helium has only two electrons, the only possible multiplicities are singlet, as for the unique spin wave function of the ground state electron configuration, and triplet as for three of the four possible functions for the excited state, as described previously.

In the spectrum of helium, lines corresponding to transitions from one singlet state to another singlet state are easily observed, as are also those corresponding to transitions from a triplet state to another triplet state. Lines corresponding to transitions between a singlet and a triplet state are so extremely weak that only one has been observed. (Transitions between singlet and triplet states can be accomplished by electron bombardment, as in an electric discharge.) Before the discovery of electron spin, the spectrum was explained by assuming that there were two different kinds of helium atoms, which could not be separated from each other.

In atoms of larger atomic number, spectrum transitions involving such changes in multiplicity are frequently observed because the spin selection rules become less rigorous.

Term Symbols. In addition to spin multiplicity, each state of an atom has another important characteristic which is expressed in the term symbol. The angular momentum was defined in Sec. 2.1; each state of an atom may be characterized by a certain definite total (or net) orbital angular momentum, which must be an integral multiple (including zero) of $h/2\pi$. The term symbols S, P, D, and F correspond to total orbital angular momenta of 0, $h/2\pi$, $2h/2\pi$, and $3h/2\pi$, respectively. The spin multiplicity is then added as a superscript, giving the *term symbol* for the state, such as ^2S, ^3D, etc. For the hydrogen atom, the term symbol denotes the type of orbital which is occupied by the electron: the $1s, 2s, 3s, \ldots$ configurations give ^2S terms; the $2p, 3p, 4p, \ldots$ configurations give ^2P terms, etc. For an atom such as nitrogen with several electrons, several different terms (states) may arise from a given configuration by various possible combinations of the angular momentum contribution of each electron. For example, the configuration $1s^2 2s^2 2p^3$ gives rise to ^2P, ^2D, and ^4S terms (each with a different energy). Term symbols are important in the study of atomic spectra, and are also used to designate a certain energy state in an atom.

The preceding discussion has shown how a set of one-electron wave functions may be combined to form a total wave function for the atom. Much work is being done to determine good one-electron wave functions for atoms and to calculate various properties of these atoms for comparison with experiment. The one-electron energies, ϵ_i of Eq. 3.302, are not strictly comparable with any experimental quantity. The total energy of the atom, that is, the minimum energy necessary to remove all electrons to infinite distances from the nucleus and from each other, may be calculated. (It is not simply the sum of the ϵ_i since this includes the repulsion terms twice; corrections can be made, however.) In the lighter atoms, this total energy is known experimentally with excellent precision; the best calculations using optimized one-electron functions and complete determinants usually come within 1 or 2 per cent of the experimental value. The remaining discrepancy is due to correlation effects; the electrons, so to speak, move in such a way as to avoid coming very close to each other, thus causing the total energy to be even lower than that calculated. The calculations can be refined to include the correlation effect, although they then become quite laborious. In this way the calculated and experimental energies become essentially identical. Good atomic wave functions can form the starting point for molecular electronic calculations; in addition, the computational methods used for atoms may also be applicable in the more complicated calculations on molecules.

Reference

E. T. Stewart, *Annual Reports on the Progress of Chemistry*, 1961, Vol. 58, pp. 7–28, "Wave Mechanical Calculations on Atoms and Small Molecules."

Problems

3.401   Write the electronic configuration for the ground states of boron and of carbon. Write some Slater determinants for these configurations. Classify the various total wave functions obtained from these configurations as singlet, doublet, triplet, etc. Note that three different p orbitals are available.

3.402   Write an electronic configuration for the lowest energy state of the lithium atom which could give rise to a quartet state. Write the four spin wave functions and also the (one) orbital wave function.

3.403   Approximate values for one-electron energies are given by Slater [*Phys. Rev.*, **98**, 1039 (1955)]. Some of these are:

$$\text{Lithium:} \quad 1s = -4.77,\ 2s = -0.40$$
$$\text{Boron:} \quad 1s = -14.5,\ 2s = -1.03,\ 2p = -0.42$$
$$\text{Nitrogen:} \quad 1s = -30.0,\ 2s = -1.88,\ 2p = -0.95$$

These energies are given in Rydberg units, which are the natural units for atomic structure. This unit is the energy required to remove the $1s$ electron of a hydrogen atom to an infinite distance from the nucleus. Plot an energy level diagram for each atom, similar to Fig. 3.301, for the levels given. Use the same energy scale for all three graphs. The experimental total energies are, for the ground state atoms, in the same units, lithium $= -14.957$, boron $= -49.319$, and nitrogen $= -109.227$, according to Slater (General References). Compare these total energies with those obtained by adding the appropriate one-electron energies given above. Using fairly simple analytical forms for radial parts of one-electron wave functions, but ignoring correlation, Slater, and E. A. Burke and J. F. Mulligan [*J. Chem. Phys.*, **28**, 995 (1958)] obtained the following calculated values: lithium $= -14.836$, boron $= -49.005$, nitrogen $= -108.553$. Suggest reasons for the difference.

*3.404   Try to write a single Slater determinant for each of the excited state helium atom functions, Eqs. 3.410 and 3.411. Can this be done? If not, can each function be represented by a sum or difference of two Slater determinants? Write out the necessary determinants.

5. Review Problems

3.501   Show that the $1s$ and $2s$ hydrogen atomic orbitals are orthogonal.

3.502   Show that the $2s$ and $2p$ hydrogen atomic orbitals are orthogonal. Is a radial integration necessary? Explain.

3.503   Are the Slater functions for carbon $1s$ and $2s$ atomic orbitals orthogonal? By what magnitude do they depart from orthogonality? See Problem 3.304.

*3.504   What is the appropriate function to determine the probability governing the electron distribution for a volume element dx by dy by dz in the hydrogen atom?. Calculate a few values and plot for the $2p_x$ orbital, choosing points along the x axis. Compare with the $P(r)$ curves.

3.505   Write the radial equation obtained by introducing the coordinates r, θ, and ϕ in the one-electron central field equation, Eq. 3.302.

3.506   For an atom of positronium, in which the proton is replaced by a positron, calculate:

(a) The appropriate reduced mass μ in units of the electron mass, m_e.

(b) The most probable value of the interparticle distance r for $1s$ and $2p$ radial functions.

(c) The value of $\epsilon_2 - \epsilon_1$, the "Lyman α energy."

(d) The ionization potential, I, and compare the quantities in (b), (c), and (d) with those for hydrogen in terms of a_0.

(e) Are the angular functions changed in form? In magnitude?

3.507 By inspection of the form of the trigonometric functions of θ and ϕ in Eq. 3.220, show which of the p and d functions have probability "lobes" that possess cylindrical symmetry.

3.508 The external electronic configuration of manganese is $3d^5 4s^2$. What are the possible multiplicities of the atom? Given that the state of highest multiplicity is the most stable arrangement, how do the ground state multiplicities of manganese and iron differ? The configuration of iron is $3d^6 4s^2$.

3.509 Show that the angular parts of p and d orbitals (Eqs. 3.220) are orthogonal.

General References

In addition to the references of Chapter 2 the student may consult the following:

Slater, J. C., *Quantum Theory of Atomic Structure*, Vols. I and II, McGraw-Hill Book Co., New York, 1960.

White, H. E., *Introduction to Atomic Spectra*, McGraw-Hill Book Co., New York, 1934.

Chapter Four

Hydrogen and Other Molecules

The treatment of molecules is, in principle, no different from that of atoms as discussed in Chapter 3. Molecules, like atoms, are found to have translational and electronic energy levels; in addition, unlike atoms, molecules also have energy levels corresponding to rotation and to vibration. We shall describe some aspects of the treatment for hydrogen and other diatomic molecules, with applications to rotational and vibrational spectra. Some simple extensions to polyatomic molecules are also given.

1. The Hydrogen Molecule

As in the case of many-electron atoms, an exact solution of the Schrödinger equation for the hydrogen molecule has not been found. Nevertheless, it is possible to find some approximate solutions which agree very well with experiment and which lead to many further useful results. Some separation of the Schrödinger equation is still possible. One of our chief interests will be to obtain information about molecular energies from molecular spectra.

Model for the Hydrogen Molecule. We shall not follow through all the steps, but it is important to point out some basic assumptions of the treatment. The hydrogen molecule is assumed to consist of four point masses: two electrons and two protons. The potential energy arises from Coulombic forces between the various (six) pairs of charged particles; there is, of course, a total of twelve degrees of freedom.

Separation of Translation. In a complete treatment, including all steps, we would begin by writing the Schrödinger equation in terms of the twelve Cartesian coordinates, three for each particle. The next step would be to introduce the three coordinates of the center of gravity of these four particles, plus nine coordinates of the four particles relative to the center of gravity. The result would be essentially as before (Sec. 3.2); the same translational wave functions are obtained. The energy eigenvalues are changed only by the substitution of the molecular mass for M in Eq. 3.209. This much of the treatment is exact; three degrees of freedom are removed and the remaining problem has nine degrees of freedom.

Separation of Rotation. In all subsequent parts of the treatment approximations are involved. For some parts the approximations are very good; for others they are crude. The separation of rotation involves the introduction of angle coordinates which describe the orientation in space of a line connecting the two nuclei. Two equations in these angle coordinates, of the same form as Eqs. 3.210 and 3.211, can be separated, and these have exact solutions which are the same as the hydrogen atom functions $\psi(\theta)$ and $\psi(\phi)$. To avoid confusion, the quantum numbers for rotation are called J and M, the latter associated with the ϕ functions only, and both of them with the θ functions. J is the total angular momentum quantum number, and M is the magnetic (angular momentum) quantum number. As before, J may have values $0, 1, 2, \ldots,$ and M for a given J has values $-J, -J + 1, \ldots, +J$. Figure 4.101 illustrates these relationships.

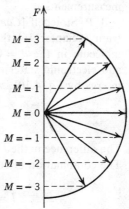

Fig. 4.101   An example of the relationship between the quantum numbers J and M, for $J = 3$. In any of these seven states, the magnitude of J is constant, but the direction of J in space varies. F denotes the direction of an external magnetic field. (Adapted by permission from R. P. Bauman, *Absorption Spectroscopy*, John Wiley and Sons, 1962).

The expression for rotational energy eigenvalues is found to be

$$\epsilon_{rot} = \frac{h^2}{8\pi^2 I} J(J + 1) = J(J + 1)Bhc \qquad (4.101)$$

where I is the moment of inertia of the molecule about an axis through the center of gravity. The constant $B = h/8\pi^2 Ic$; it is called the *rotational constant* and has units of reciprocal centimeters (cm^{-1}). For a given value of J, the quantum number M may have the different values from $-J$ to $+J$; hence the degeneracy of a rotational energy level is $2J + 1$. The moment of inertia depends on the masses of the atoms, m_1 and m_2, and on the distance between them, r; i.e.,

$$I = \frac{m_1 m_2 r^2}{m_1 + m_2} \qquad (4.102)$$

The mass-containing terms are of the same form as the reduced mass, Eq. 2.612; the right-hand side may thus be written μr^2.

In contrast to the hydrogen atom, the energy expression now involves the quantity r in addition to the fundamental constants. A value for r must be supplied, or, as we shall see (Illustration), a value may be calculated from experimental data on rotational energy. In an experimental measurement, the value of r is obtained from the effective moment of inertia, which is a characteristic average even though the molecule is vibrating and the distance is not fixed. This average value can be measured with great precision; in a favorable example, as for H_2, the accuracy is better than one part in several thousand.

ILLUSTRATION.   Determine the internuclear distance of H_2 from spectroscopic measurements.

B. P. Stoicheff [*Can. J. Phys.*, **35**, 730 (1957)] has found in the Raman spectrum (Chapter 16) that the difference in rotational energy of the hydrogen molecule in the $J = 0$ and the $J = 2$ states (both in the lowest vibrational and electronic states), divided by hc, is 345.9 cm^{-1}. Since the energy is given in ergs by Eq. 4.101, we convert to wave-number units by the factor I/hc,

$$\frac{\epsilon_{\text{rot}}}{hc} = G_{\text{rot}} = \frac{h}{8\pi^2 Ic} J(J+1)$$

The difference in the $J = 0$ and 2 states is $6h/8\pi^2 Ic$, so that $h/8\pi^2 Ic = 57.65$ cm^{-1}. The combination of constants $h/8\pi^2 c$ is 27.98×10^{-40} g cm.

$$\therefore \quad I = \frac{27.98 \times 10^{-40}}{57.65} = 0.4853 \times 10^{-40} \text{ g cm}^2$$

Furthermore,

$$I = \mu r^2 = \frac{m_H}{2} r^2$$

$$r^2 = \frac{2I}{m_H} = \frac{2 \times 0.4853 \times 10^{-40}}{\left(\dfrac{1.008}{6.025 \times 10^{23}}\right)} = 0.5848 \times 10^{-16} \text{cm}^2$$

$$r = 0.765\text{Å}$$

Each of the effective interatomic distances at the higher vibrational levels is about 1 per cent more than the preceding level; there is also a dependence of r on the value of J. These differences are due to incomplete separation of rotation and vibration; note that the value of r_e in Table 4.101 is different.

The spacing of rotational energy levels in the hydrogen molecule, and also in its various isotopic derivatives, is quite large. In most other molecules, especially those containing two heavy atoms, the spacing is much smaller. For such, the distribution of molecules among rotational levels can often be treated as a continuous distribution (Chapter 5). For molecules containing hydrogen, it is usually necessary to examine the problem carefully before making such an approximation.

Electronic Problem; Born-Oppenheimer Approximation.   After the separation of translation and rotation for the hydrogen molecule problem, a Schrödinger equation in seven variables is left which describes the relative positions of the two nuclei and the two electrons. We can think of a line joining the two nuclei as fixed in space; that is, the line does not rotate, and neither does the center of gravity translate. Each electron has x, y, and z coordinates with respect to this system; the seventh coordinate is the distance between the nuclei.

Born and Oppenheimer have shown that a further simplification is possible. Because of the great difference in mass between the proton and the electron, derivatives with respect to the internuclear distance can be omitted from the electronic part of the problem, but the internuclear potential must be included.

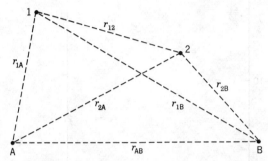

Fig. 4.102   Model for the hydrogen molecule; 1 and 2 are electrons, and A and B are protons.

The derivative with respect to internuclear distance appears in the vibrational problem, which will be discussed later. Figure 4.102 shows the numbering with respect to the model; electrons are numbered 1 and 2, and protons are indicated by A and B. The Schrödinger equation for the two electrons is then

$$-\frac{h^2}{8\pi^2 m_e}\left(\frac{\partial^2\psi}{\partial x_1^2}+\frac{\partial^2\psi}{\partial y_1^2}+\frac{\partial^2\psi}{\partial z_1^2}+\frac{\partial^2\psi}{\partial x_2^2}+\frac{\partial^2\psi}{\partial y_2^2}+\frac{\partial^2\psi}{\partial z_2^2}\right)$$

$$+e^2\left(-\frac{1}{r_{1A}}-\frac{1}{r_{1B}}-\frac{1}{r_{2A}}-\frac{1}{r_{2B}}+\frac{1}{r_{12}}+\frac{1}{r_{AB}}\right)\psi=\epsilon\psi \quad (4.103)$$

We may inquire why there is no reduced mass factor here, such as appeared in the hydrogen atom. In this case, where there are four particles, the correct reduced mass is by no means as simple as for the atom and in addition depends also on the nature of the electronic wave function in a complicated way. Hence we will not attempt to include this refinement. Until quite recently, theoretical calculations gave energies differing from experimental values by much more than the magnitude of the reduced mass effect. Fortunately, on the experimental side it is possible to evaluate this effect by use of isotopic atoms.

The procedure is then to choose some fixed value of r_{AB} and to obtain the corresponding electronic energy eigenvalue by solution (in practice, approximate solution) of Eq. 4.103. Physically, this is equivalent to saying that the masses of the nuclei are relatively so large that the electrons make hundreds of oscillations in the time the nuclei make one; as far as the electrons are concerned, the nuclei are standing still. Other values of r_{AB} are chosen, and the electronic energy is again calculated. The electronic energies so found are different for different r_{AB} values; there is one value for which the energy is lower than any other and this gives the expected bond distance of the molecule.

The energies directly calculated in this way are found to be extremely large negative quantities when the zero of energy is chosen for all four particles at

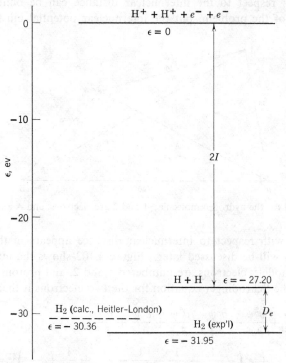

Fig. 4.103   Energy level diagram showing energies (electron volts) of two hydrogen atoms, and of the hydrogen molecule (calculated and observed) relative to two protons and two electrons. D is the bond dissociation energy of the molecule, and I is the ionization potential of the atom.

infinite distances from each other. The classical bond dissociation energy, D_e, is the difference between the minimum electronic energy and the energy of two hydrogen atoms, each in its ground electronic state (Fig. 4.103).

The Variation Method.   We have, in this discussion, presumed that the electronic energy levels of the molecule can be calculated; since this cannot be done by direct solution of the Schrödinger equation, approximation methods must be used. The details of various methods are beyond the scope of the present treatment, but the basis of an important example, the variation method, can be indicated easily. For any energy level, say ϵ_a, the Schrödinger equation is, in very general terms,

$$H\psi_a = \epsilon_a\psi_a \tag{4.104}$$

Multiplying both sides by ψ_a and integrating, we obtain

$$\int \psi_a H \psi_a \, d\tau = \epsilon_a \int \psi_a \psi_a \, d\tau$$

or

$$\epsilon_a = \frac{\int \psi_a H \psi_a \, d\tau}{\int \psi_a^2 \, d\tau} \tag{4.105}$$

By retaining the denominator, we do not even need to have the function ψ_a normalized. But now, suppose that in place of ψ_a we insert the expression $\psi = \psi_a + c\psi_b$ under the integral signs, where ψ_b is another eigenfunction with the different eigenvalue ϵ_b, and c is any constant. Equation 4.105 takes the form,

$$\begin{aligned}
\epsilon &= \frac{\int (\psi_a + c\psi_b) H (\psi_a + c\psi_b) \, d\tau}{\int (\psi_a + c\psi_b)^2 \, d\tau} \\[2mm]
&= \frac{\int (\psi_a + c\psi_b)(\epsilon_a \psi_a + c\epsilon_b \psi_b) \, d\tau}{\int (\psi_a^2 + 2c\psi_a \psi_b + c^2 \psi_b^2) \, d\tau} \\[2mm]
&= \frac{\epsilon_a \int \psi_a^2 \, d\tau + \epsilon_b c^2 \int \psi_b^2 \, d\tau}{\int \psi_a^2 \, d\tau + c^2 \int \psi_b^2 \, d\tau} \\[2mm]
&= \frac{\epsilon_a + c^2 \epsilon_b}{1 + c^2} = \epsilon_a + \frac{c^2}{1 + c^2} (\epsilon_b - \epsilon_a)
\end{aligned} \tag{4.106}$$

by use of the fact that the two functions ψ_a and ψ_b are orthogonal (see Eq. 2.308). If ϵ_a and ϵ_b were identical, the quantity ϵ would be just ϵ_a. But if ϵ_a is chosen to be the lowest eigenvalue, ϵ_b must be larger, and ϵ must therefore be larger than ϵ_a. This conclusion is true also if more functions ψ_c, ψ_d, etc., are included, since their eigenvalues too are larger than ϵ_a.

In the usual application of this discussion, the eigenfunctions of H are not known. Many trial functions may be chosen and substituted in the integral

$$\epsilon = \frac{\int \psi H \psi \, d\tau}{\int \psi^2 \, d\tau} \tag{4.107}$$

This is done for various trial functions; all the ϵ's so calculated will be larger than the true lowest eigenvalue. The lowest calculated ϵ will be the closest to the true eigenvalue. By trying a large number of functions and possible combinations and weights of these, we obtain calculated ϵ values which are still lower; but none of these can be lower than the true ϵ_a. Instead of solving a differential equation to determine energy eigenvalues (which cannot always be done), we may instead calculate integrals over known functions and operators. It is always possible to evaluate integrals; this can be done very efficiently by high-speed digital computers. For some purposes, functions may even be employed which are not given by algebraic expressions but are obtained from numerical tables. In principle, at least, approximations to energy eigenvalues may be calculated for any system for which the Hamiltonian operator can be written. However, the choice of trial wave functions is still an important step. This type of calculation, applied even to molecules containing ten and more electrons, is an important area of present-day research in physical chemistry.

ILLUSTRATION.   Obtain an approximate value of the lowest energy for the particle in a one-dimensional box, using $\psi = xl - x^2$ as a variation function.
From Eq. 4.107

$$\epsilon = \frac{\displaystyle\int_0^l (xl - x^2)\left(-\frac{h^2}{8\pi^2 m}\frac{d^2}{dx^2}\right)(xl - x^2)\,dx}{\displaystyle\int_0^l (xl - x^2)^2\,dx}$$

$$= \frac{\displaystyle\int_0^l (xl - x^2)\left(-\frac{h^2}{8\pi^2 m}\right)(-2)\,dx}{\displaystyle\int_0^l (x^2 l^2 - 2x^3 l + x^4)\,dx}$$

$$= \frac{\dfrac{h^2 l^3}{24\pi^2 m}}{\tfrac{1}{30} l^5} = \frac{10}{\pi^2}\frac{h^2}{8ml^2}$$

which is only $10/\pi^2 = 1.0132$ times larger than the true value, or an error of 1.3 per cent. The student may plot the functions $xl - x^2$ from $x = 0$ to l, and $\sin(\pi x/l)$ (the true eigenfunction) for comparison.

The Heitler-London Treatment of H_2.   Although elaborate approximation functions are more accurate, a rather simple trial wave function can often give important results. Since the hydrogen molecule is composed of hydrogen atoms, and the atomic functions are known, one of these might be used to make a useful trial function. Consider the model (Fig. 4.102) when r_{AB} is very large. One of the electrons goes with one proton, the other electron with the other proton. The Schrödinger equation then reduces to the sum of two identical parts, one for each hydrogen atom. As in Sec. 2.5, the appropriate wave function is then the product of two hydrogen atom wave functions. This suggests that a possible trial wave function for the molecule, with r_{AB} around normal bonding distances, might be a product of hydrogen atom functions (Eq. 3.221)

$$\psi = e^{-r_{1A}/a_0}\, e^{-r_{2B}/a_0} \tag{4.108}$$

This function is an exact solution at large r_{AB}, providing of course that it is electron 1 which goes with proton A and electron 2 with B.

We then have only to substitute this expression in Eq. 4.105, using the Hamiltonian operator as in Eq. 4.103, and calculate the energy. The integration is not particularly difficult but will not be worked out here; the resulting energy is disappointingly far from the true energy determined by experiment. The observed bond dissociation energy is 4.75 ev, but the calculated value is 0.58 ev.

This large discrepancy simply means that the trial wave function was a poor approximation to reality. A much better wave function, first used by Heitler and London, is closely related to the question of which electron goes with proton A upon dissociation. Their function is the linear combination

$$\psi_{\text{H-L}} = e^{-r_{1A}/a_0}\, e^{-r_{2B}/a_0} + e^{-r_{2A}/a_0}\, e^{-r_{1B}/a_0}$$

or

$$= 1s_A(1)1s_B(2) + 1s_A(2)1s_B(1) \qquad (4.109)$$

The more compact notation says that the $1s$ atomic functions are used, and the subscripts and parentheses denote which nucleus and electron are involved. The

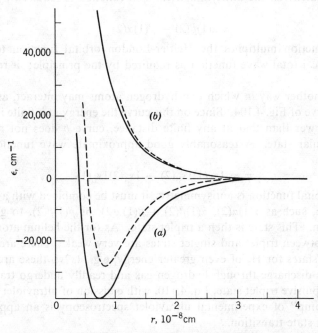

Fig. 4.104   Calculated and observed energy for the hydrogen molecule. The dotted line represents the Heitler-London calculation; the solid line, a more refined calculation which agrees with experiment. (a) The singlet state, (b) the triplet state. (Adapted by permission from G. Herzberg, *Spectra of Diatomic Molecules*, Second Edition, D. Van Nostrand Co., Princeton, N.J., 1950.)

calculated energy, 3.16 ev, is now in much better agreement with the experimental value. Comparison of this calculation with the experimental curve is shown in Fig. 4.104.

This is a very important and remarkable result. No experimental information on the hydrogen molecule was used in the calculation, and yet the result accounts for the major part of the molecular binding energy. The Bohr theory could account for the energy of the hydrogen atom; however, it failed badly when applied to the hydrogen molecule. The Heitler-London result suggests that the

methods of quantum mechanics are conceptually correct. The use of more elegant
trial wave functions results in much better agreement; the calculation of Kolos
and Roothan [*Revs. Mod. Phys.*, **32**, 205 (1960)] agrees within about one part in
thirty thousand with the experimental value of Herzberg and Monfils [*J. Mol.
Spec.*, **5**, 482 (1960)] for the molecular dissociation energy. Other measurable
physical quantities are also correctly calculated by quantum mechanical methods.
This very excellent agreement suggests that the assumptions and procedures of
quantum mechanics are essentially correct.

The total electronic wave function for the hydrogen molecule must also contain
a spin wave function. Since the Heitler-London (orbital) wave function, Eq.
4.109, is symmetrical, the antisymmetrical spin function is required by the Pauli
principle

$$\alpha(1)\beta(2) - \beta(1)\alpha(2)$$

This spin function multiplies the Heitler-London orbital function to give the
antisymmetrical total wave function as required by the principle; it represents a
singlet state.

There is another way in which two hydrogen atoms may interact, as shown in
the upper curve of Fig. 4.104. Since on this curve the energy at infinite interatomic
distance is lower than that at any finite distance, curve b does not represent a
stable molecular state. A reasonably good approximate wave function for this
state is

$$\psi = 1s_A(1)1s_B(2) - 1s_A(2)1s_B(1) \qquad (4.110)$$

Since this orbital function is antisymmetric, it must be combined with a symmetric
spin function, such as $\alpha(1)\alpha(2)$, $\alpha(1)\beta(2) + \beta(1)\alpha(2)$, or $\beta(1)\beta(2)$, to give a total
wave function. This state is then a triplet state. As for the helium atom, spectral
transitions between triplet and singlet states are very weak. There are, however,
other triplet states for H_2 of even greater energy, e.g., $1s2s$; these are produced
in an electric discharge through hydrogen gas and readily undergo transitions to
the lowest repulsive triplet state, Eq. 4.110, with emission of ultraviolet light. The
"hydrogen lamp" of experimental ultraviolet spectroscopy is an application of
such a triplet state transition.

Separation of Vibration. The final stage of the Born-Oppenheimer approximation gives an equation for vibration, which uses the distance r_{AB} as its coordinate.
Since the other r's need not be considered in the vibration problem, we shall drop
the subscripts

$$-\frac{h^2}{8\pi^2\mu}\frac{d^2\psi(r)}{dr^2} + V(r)\psi(r) = \epsilon_v\psi(r) \qquad (4.111)$$

The $\psi(r)$ is the vibrational wave function, ϵ_v the vibrational energy, and μ the
molecular reduced mass. The potential function, $V(r)$, is just the function obtained
as the energy eigenvalue in the electronic problem, which is a function of r. Since
this is by no means a simple function, the solution of Eq. 4.111 is not an easy task.

In the region near the minimum of $V(r)$, however, the curve is quite closely
approximated by a parabola; this approximation leads to the simple harmonic

oscillator equation, which was solved in Chapter 2. As was also seen in Chapter 2 by comparison with experimental data, the harmonic oscillator model does not agree completely with experiment. In general, we find that real, anharmonic molecules have only a finite number of discrete vibrational energy levels, all of which lie below the horizontal asymptotic level of the $V(r)$ curve (Fig. 4.105). In addition to these discrete levels, Eq. 4.111 also has solutions which correspond to energies above the horizontal asymptote of $V(r)$. These latter energies are so

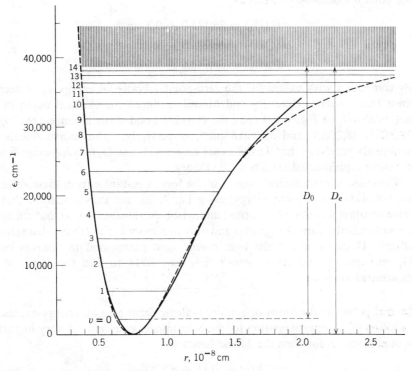

Fig. 4.105   Potential curve of the H_2 ground state with discrete vibrational levels below and continuous energy levels above the dissociation limit. The full curve is experimental. The broken curve is a Morse curve. (By permission from G. Herzberg, *Spectra of Diatomic Molecules*, D. Van Nostrand Co., Princeton, N.J., 1950.)

close together that they may be treated as a continuous distribution; they correspond physically to the fact that a "molecule" with so great a vibrational energy must dissociate into two atoms, each with closely spaced translational energy levels. The "vibrational" levels with continuous distribution are important in certain spectra discussed in Chapter 16. For the hydrogen molecule, experiment shows that a total of only fifteen vibrational energy levels exists below the dissociation limit. Figure 4.105 reveals that the potential function does not closely approximate the parabolic form except near the bottom. The difference in energy between the $n = 0$ level and the bottom of the parabolic well is the vibrational zero-point energy, ϵ_0. The bond dissociation energy D_0 equals $(D_e - \epsilon_0)$.

ILLUSTRATION.   The accurate measurement of the bond dissociation energy of hydrogen and the zero-point vibrational energy of the molecule.

G. Herzberg and A. Monfils [*J. Mol. Spec.*, **5**, 482 (1960)] studied the far-ultraviolet (845 to 864 Å) absorption of H_2, HD, and D_2 which results in dissociation into two atoms. By detailed analysis of their data, they calculated the bond dissociation energies as

$$D_0(H_2) = 36,113.0 \pm 0.3 \text{ cm}^{-1}$$
$$D_0(HD) = 36,399.9 \pm 1.0 \text{ cm}^{-1}$$
$$D_0(D_2) = 36,743.6 \pm 0.5 \text{ cm}^{-1}$$

By combining with values for the zero-point vibrational energy ϵ_0 of each of these three species, Herzberg and Monfils deduced the classical depth of the potential well of Fig. 4.104 (i.e., the classical bond dissociation energy D_e) as 38,292.3, 38,290.3, and 38,290.8 cm^{-1}, respectively. The measurements are sufficiently precise so that the difference between H_2 and D_2 may have significance for more sophisticated aspects of the theory.

The student may calculate values of the force constant k from these values of the vibrational zero-point energy, using Eq. 2.120, and thus determine that the force constant k is almost invariant under isotope substitution, so that change of v results mainly from change of μ and only to a lesser extent from anharmonicity effects. Does the ultraviolet light energy used correspond to dissociation of H_2 into two ground state atoms? Use Eq. 3.214 to find the states of the dissociated atoms.

Several potential functions of a more realistic form give an energy expression by solution of, or approximation to, the Schrödinger equation. A very important potential function has been the Morse function,

$$V(r) = D_e(1 - e^{-\beta \, \Delta r})^2 \tag{4.112}$$

where D_e is the classical bond dissociation energy, Δr is the displacement $(r - r_e)$ of the bond length from its equilibrium value, r_e, and β is a constant related to the bond, $\beta = 1.218\omega(\mu/D_e)^{1/2}$, where the frequency ω and D_e are in wave numbers. The vibrational Schrödinger equation can be solved exactly, for this potential function, with energy levels given by Eq. 4.113. In this equation and hereafter we will use v as the symbol for vibrational quantum number instead of the n used previously.

$$\epsilon_v = (v + \tfrac{1}{2})h\nu_e - (v + \tfrac{1}{2})^2 h\nu_e x_e \tag{4.113}$$

where v is limited for real molecules; it has the maximum value 14 for H_2. This expression gives a much better overall fit of experimental vibrational data; the ν_e is the classical vibration frequency for infinitesimal amplitude of vibration and does not correspond to any spacing of energy levels. The quantity x is the anharmonicity constant and is typically several per cent [Table 4.101(A)*]. For isotopically related molecules, force constants calculated from v_e agree very well.

As can be seen by a rough calculation, the spacing of vibrational levels is quite large. A continuous distribution approximation is valid for vibrations only in the

Table 4.101 Some Related Properties of Ground State Diatomic Molecules*

Molecule	r_e, Å	μ	ω_e, cm^{-1}	$x_e\omega_e$	D, ev
H_2	0.741	0.5040	4395.2	118.0	4.476
HD	0.741	0.6719	3817.1	94.96	4.511
HT	. . .	0.7556	3608.3	87.6	4.524

The complete Table 4.101(A) will be found in the Appendix.

* Selected values by permission from G. Herzberg, *Spectra of Diatomic Molecules*, D. Van Nostrand Co., Princeton, N.J., 1950.

special case of molecules with heavy atoms in which the bonds have very small force constants.

As an alternative to the Morse equation, the Lippincott function

$$V(r) = D_e(1 - e^{-n(\Delta r)^2/2r})$$ (4.114)

where $n = k_e r_e/D_e$ (k_e is the force constant), is frequently used. This function seems to be more accurate for correlation of experimental data. However, it does not permit an exact solution for the vibrational Schrödinger equation.

Since the hydrogen molecule contains identical atoms, it is forbidden to absorb or emit light by means of a vibrational transition. However, the vibrational levels have been determined as in the preceding Illustration by a study of spectra involving electronic as well as vibrational transitions. Upon isotopic substitution the vibrating molecule possesses a small oscillating dipole moment and is allowed to make vibrational transitions with absorption or emission of light. G. Herzberg and coworkers have observed this type of weak vibrational absorption band for HD in the infrared region.

ILLUSTRATION.   Show the decrease in level spacings of an anharmonic oscillator by considering the molecule HBr. Find the vibrational interval, according to Eq. 4.113, which is nearest to one half the energy of the $v = 0 \rightarrow v = 1$ interval.

According to G. Herzberg (see *General References*), the molecule HBr has values of $\omega_e = 2649.7$ cm^{-1} and $\omega_e x_e = 45.2$ cm^{-1}. The separation of adjacent

* Tables designated (A) will be found in the Appendix at the back of the book.

vibrational levels can be written in general terms as follows:

$$\frac{1}{hc}\left(\epsilon_{v+1} - \epsilon_v\right) = \omega_e(v + 1 + \tfrac{1}{2}) - \omega_e x_e(v + 1 + \tfrac{1}{2})^2$$
$$- \omega_e(v + \tfrac{1}{2}) + \omega_e x_e(v + \tfrac{1}{2})^2$$

Then,

$$\frac{\Delta\epsilon}{hc} = \omega_e - 2\omega_e x_e(v + 1)$$

But for $v = 0$,

$$\frac{\Delta\epsilon}{hc} = \omega_e - 2\omega_e x_e$$

$$\frac{\Delta\epsilon}{2hc} = \frac{\omega_e}{2} - \omega_e x_e = \omega_e - 2\omega_e x_e(v + 1)$$

and

$$v + 1 = \frac{(\omega_e/2) + \omega_e x_e}{2\omega_e x_e}$$

Using these values,

$$v + 1 = \frac{1370}{90.4} = 15.1, \quad \therefore\ v = 14$$

The student may verify this by computing the energy spacings for $v = 13 \rightarrow 14$, $14 \rightarrow 15$, and $15 \rightarrow 16$ and comparing with the energy corresponding to $\frac{1}{2}(v = 0 \rightarrow 1)$.

References

Herzberg, G., *Nature*, **166**, 563 (1950).
Kauzmann, W., *Quantum Chemistry*, Academic Press, New York, 1957, Ch. 12, Tables 12.1 and
    12.2: summary of results of various approximations for the hydrogen molecule.
Lippincott, E. R., and R. Schroeder, *J. Chem. Phys.*, **23**, 1131 (1955).
Morse, P. M., *Phys. Rev.*, **34**, 57 (1929).

Problems

4.101   The $v = 0 \rightarrow 1$ transition frequency of I_2 is 214 cm^{-1}. The moment of inertia is 743×10^{-40} g cm^2. (At. wt. $= 127$.)
(a) What is the internuclear distance?
(b) What is the vibration frequency in cycles per second?
(c) What is the zero-point energy in calories per mole?
(d) What is the classical maximum amplitude associated with the $v = 2$ state?
4.102   (a) Find the energy level spacings between the first five rotational states of I_2.
(b) At what value of J is the spacing $\approx kT$ at 300°K?
4.103   Find the relative magnitude of the energy separation of the ground and first excited state of the H_2 molecule for each of translational, rotational, and vibrational excitation. The container is a cube 1 cm on edge.
4.104   Estimate separation in wave numbers of the $J = 1$ and $J = 3$ rotational levels in the molecule HD. Assume that the bond distance is the same as H_2, p. 80, and the atomic weight of D $= 2.015$.

2. Spectra of Diatomic Molecules

The model for any diatomic molecule, or for that matter for a polyatomic molecule, is simply an extension of that which we have already used. In a manner similar to that described in Sec. 4.1, we write the Hamiltonian and the Schrödinger equation. The same general procedure is followed to obtain the solution; that is, the translations, the rotations, the electronic motions, and the vibrations are separated in that order.

There are, as always, three degrees of translational freedom, and the standard expression for the translational energy levels, Eq. 3.209 holds.

The separation of rotation for diatomic molecules, identical in procedure to that for the hydrogen molecule, results in rotational energy levels given by Eq. 4.101. Since the atomic masses and bond distances in other molecules are different from those in hydrogen, the moments of inertia are also different. The pattern of energy levels provides information about bond distances.

For the moment we shall omit discussion of the electronic degrees of freedom. The separation and solution of the vibrational Schrödinger equation is formally the same as for the hydrogen molecule, Eq. 4.110, but in practice an important complication enters. The potential function $V(r)$ which appears in Eq. 4.111 was obtained quite accurately by an approximate solution of the electronic problem. For molecules composed of polyelectronic atoms the electronic problem has been solved only by rough approximation, if at all; thus in general the function $V(r)$ is not available in this way. Consequently eigenvalues (i.e., vibration frequencies and force constants) are found principally by experimental spectroscopic measurements. Force constants provide information about bond strengths.

Two points should be noted by way of introduction to the subject of spectroscopic measurements. First, actual energy levels are not directly measurable; the spectrum shows only transitions, or energy differences, between various pairs of levels. And, second, the conventional spectroscopic measurement provides no direct means for assigning quantum numbers to the two states involved. It becomes necessary to estimate the general spectral pattern expected and the frequency region and then to compare these with the observations.

Selection Rules. Although spectral absorption or emission corresponds to transitions between pairs of levels, it is found that not all possible pairs may combine. It is possible by a theoretical study of molecular wave functions, and especially their symmetry properties, to derive certain selection rules. The rules will tell whether or not certain quantum jumps are allowed, caused by absorption or emission of radiation; however, the rules will not tell whether an allowed quantum jump is strongly or weakly allowed, that is, whether the spectral feature is strong or weak.

Translational Selection Rules. For a quantum jump accompanied by absorption or emission of light, there can be no change in translational quantum numbers. This rule is rigorous for neutral molecules. Of course, there may be such processes as collisions with other molecules, or with the walls of the container, which frequently cause changes in translational quantum numbers. We are considering only the spectral selection rules, and within this limitation the translational selection rules are:

$$\Delta n_x = 0, \quad \Delta n_y = 0, \quad \Delta n_z = 0 \tag{4.201}$$

where Δn denotes the change in a translational quantum number.

Rotational Selection Rules. The rotational selection rule is, in one respect, the opposite of the translational: the rotational quantum number *must* change during a spectral transition, and it may change only by plus or minus one; i.e.,

$$\Delta J = +1 \quad \text{or} \quad \Delta J = -1 \tag{4.202}$$

where $\Delta J = +1$ if the final value of J is larger than the original value and corresponds to absorption of energy by the molecule from a radiation source (light beam). The selection rule for J is rigorous for all diatomic molecules in which the electron spins are completely paired (singlet states). If the molecule has an odd electron or if some of the spins are not paired, it is also possible to have optical transitions with $\Delta J = 0$ in addition to $\Delta J = \pm 1$. Some other quantum number, usually associated with vibration, must change if $\Delta J = 0$ or nothing will have happened! The molecule NO, having one unpaired electron, is a common example to which the selection rule $\Delta J = 0$ applies. These are rigorous selection rules for real molecules, and $\Delta J = \pm 2, \pm 3$, etc., is strictly forbidden.

Vibrational Selection Rules. The selection rule for the harmonic oscillator is that the vibrational quantum number must change by plus or minus one,

$$\Delta v = +1 \quad \text{or} \quad \Delta v = -1 \tag{4.203}$$

The selection rule for vibration is approximate rather than exact in its application to real molecules. We have seen in Chapter 2 that actual molecules deviate from the simple harmonic model. For actual molecules we also observe transitions having Δv of $\pm 2, \pm 3$, etc. although these become progressively weaker for larger changes in v; thus experimental difficulties such as a requirement for an impractically great path length may prevent observations of transitions when changes in v are large.

Further Requirements; Dipole Moment. The selection rules given above are necessary conditions but of themselves are not sufficient to assure that spectral transitions will occur; in order to assure that a spectrum will be observed certain conditions must be met by the property called dipole moment. The dipole moment is conveniently defined in terms of charges and coordinates. For neutral molecules the choice of coordinate origin is immaterial; for ions this is not so. The contribution of electrons to the dipole moment must be included, but for these purposes it is sufficient to take average positions of the electrons. An x axis is chosen to pass through both nuclei, and the dipole moment M is defined as

$$M = \sum_i e_i x_i \tag{4.204}$$

where e_i and x_i are the charge and the x coordinate of the ith particle, and the sum is to be taken over all the charged particles, electrons, and nuclei in the system; the electron coordinates in this equation are the average coordinates.

In homonuclear diatomic molecules, the molecular dipole is zero since there are electronic charges and nuclear charges symmetrically located. In heteronuclear molecules the distribution of electrons is usually not such as to completely cancel the distribution of nuclear charge, and M is not zero; the molecule is said to have a dipole moment. A convenient unit for dipole moments is the debye, which is 10^{-18} cgs unit. To give some idea of the magnitude of this unit, a proton and an electron 1 Å apart have a dipole moment of about 4.8 debye units. Dipole moments are of some interest in themselves, as they are a property, although an average property, of electronic wave functions (and nuclei). Note that the only quantities averaged in the definition though were electron coordinates. If the nuclei were at some distance other than the equilibrium distance, the dipole moment might be different. If so, the dipole moment is a function of distance, or the derivative dM/dr is not zero.

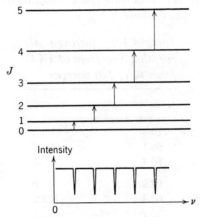

Fig. 4.201   Rotational energy levels, allowed transitions, and rotational spectrum.

In addition to satisfying selection rules, a further requirement must be met in order for a molecular transition to be observable in the spectrum. For a rotational transition, with no change in vibrational quantum number, the further requirement is that the molecule have a dipole moment, i.e., $M \neq 0$. For a vibrational transition, with or without accompanying rotational transition, the further requirement is that the dipole moment must change with interatomic distance, i.e., $dM/dr \neq 0$. Chapter 16 contains a more complete discussion of selection rules and dipole moments.

Rotational Spectra.   Experience has shown that pure rotational transitions are found at wavelengths from about 25 microns all the way to the centimeter region. Since rotational energy spacings are usually quite small compared to thermal energies, molecules may be raised from the $J = 0$ state to higher states at ordinary temperatures by nonradiative transitions due to collisions. Figure 4.201 shows a set of rotational energy levels, and the vertical arrows transitions (absorption) allowed by the selection rule. Below this is shown the corresponding spectrum, which will appear as a series of absorption lines.

By use of the energy level expression, Eq. 4.101, we may derive an expression for the spectral frequencies; for $J \rightarrow J + 1$, the absorption is found at

$$v = \frac{\Delta\epsilon}{h} = \frac{(J+1)(J+2)h^2}{8\pi^2 I} - \frac{J(J+1)h^2}{8\pi^2 I} = \frac{(J+1)2h}{8\pi^2 I} \text{ cycles sec}^{-1}$$

or

$$\omega = \frac{v}{c} = \frac{(J+1)2h}{8\pi^2 I c} \text{ wave numbers} \tag{4.205}$$

Since the initial J may have values 0, 1, 2, 3 ..., transitions between adjacent energy levels give rise to a spectrum showing absorption lines spaced at equal intervals. Measurement of this (average) spacing then eliminates the need to determine J values for a certain absorption line.

ILLUSTRATION. From the following pure rotational absorptions of HCl, determine the interatomic distance.

Table 4.201   Infrared Absorption Spectrum of HCl*
from 44 to 120 microns

λ, microns	ω, cm^{-1}
120.4	83.0
96.1	104.1
80.4	124.3
68.9	145.0
60.4	165.5
53.8	185.9
48.5	206.4
44.1	226.5

* According to M. Czerny, Z. Physik, **34**, 227 (1927).

The spacing between adjacent lines varies between 20.1 and 21.1 cm^{-1}. The average of alternate spacings is 20.5 cm^{-1}. This must equal $2B$, which gives

$$I = 2.72 \times 10^{-40} \text{ g cm}^2$$

The moment of inertia is also equal to μr^2 (see Eq. 4.102), so

$$\frac{1 \times 35.5}{\frac{1 + 35.5}{6.023 \times 10^{23}}} r^2 = 2.72 \times 10^{-40}$$

$$r^2 = 1.68 \times 10^{-16}$$

$$r = 1.30 \times 10^{-8} \text{ cm}$$

In similar fashion, bond distances can be found for all diatomic molecules which give a measurable absorption spectrum. Unfortunately, this region of the spectrum presents considerable experimental difficulties, which are due in part to the small amount of energy available from black-body sources (see Chapter 1). Fortunately we can obtain moments of inertia and bond distances equally well from experimental information on rotational transitions which accompany other transitions, such as vibrational transitions.

Vibrational Selection Rule and Spectra. As noted earlier for anharmonic oscillators, transitions in addition to $\Delta v = \pm 1$ may occur; however, these are considerably weaker. Since the energy levels of anharmonic oscillators are not equally spaced (Sec. 2.2), this can lead to extensive overlapping and confusion of spectra. Fortunately, since vibrational energy level spacings are quite large compared to thermal energies, most molecules in a given sample are in the lowest vibrational state. The vibrational transitions $v = 1 \rightarrow 2$, $2 \rightarrow 3$, etc., are thus very weak and do not confuse the basic simplicity of the *fundamental* transition, $v = 0 \rightarrow 1$. The anharmonic transitions, called *overtones*, $v = 0 \rightarrow 2$, $0 \rightarrow 3$, which occur at large frequency separations from $v = 0 \rightarrow 1$, can be analyzed by the same methods we shall discuss for the fundamental transition.

For vibrational transitions of a diatomic molecule, one of the selection rules requires that the rotational quantum number simultaneously change by $\Delta J = \pm 1$. To understand better the consequences of this, consider the vibrational transition $v = 0 \rightarrow 1$, for which the rotational selection rule must also be satisfied. This is indicated on Fig. 4.202, which shows the two vibrational levels and, on an exaggerated scale, also some rotational levels for these vibrational states. A molecule which starts with $v = 0$, $J = 0$ must go to $v = 1$, $J = 1$. The frequency of light for this transition is given by the expression

$$\nu = \frac{1}{h}(h\nu_0 + 2hcB) = \nu_0 + 2Bc \qquad (4.206)$$

where we have denoted the frequency of the forbidden transition $(v = 0, J = 0) \rightarrow (v = 1, J = 0)$ as ν_0. But suppose that a molecule starts at $v = 0$, $J = 1$; it may go to either of two rotational levels in the upper vibrational state. For each of these the frequency is given by

$$\nu = \frac{1}{h}(h\nu_0 + 6hcB - 2hcB)$$

$$= \nu_0 + 4Bc \qquad (4.207)$$

$$\nu = \frac{1}{h}(h\nu_0 + 0 - 2hcB)$$

$$= \nu_0 - 2Bc \qquad (4.208)$$

Notice that one of these is a higher frequency than that given by Eq. 4.206, whereas the other is lower. We can derive a general expression for the frequencies

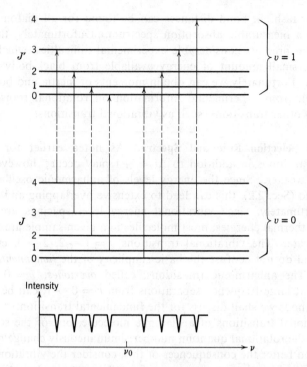

Fig. 4.202 Rotational energy levels in two different vibrational states, showing allowed transitions and resulting spectrum.

of all the permitted transitions by letting the J value of the vibrational state $v = 1$ be J', and the J of the lower state be simply J. The frequency of a transition from a level J to a level J' is then given by the expression

$$v = v_0 + J'(J' + 1)Bc - J(J + 1)Bc \qquad (4.209)$$

Take first the selection rule $\Delta J = +1$. This means that $J' = J + 1$, which results in an expression

$$v = v_0 + (2J + 2)Bc \qquad (4.210)$$

If we let $J' = J - 1$, we find

$$v = v_0 - 2JBc \qquad (4.211)$$

For Eq. 4.210 J may assume values 0, 1, 2, etc.; for Eq. 4.211, values 1, 2, 3, etc. These two equations may be combined into one by letting the symbol m equal $J + 1$ in the first expression, and $-J$ in the second; then also dividing by c, to put everything in terms of wave numbers,

$$\frac{v}{c} = \omega = \omega_0 + 2mB \qquad (4.212)$$

where $m = \pm 1, \pm 2, \pm 3$, etc., but *not* zero. This implies that a vibrational spectrum should appear as a series of lines with spacing, in wave numbers, equal to

$2B$; at the center, corresponding to the forbidden value $m = 0$, there is no absorption and thus a spacing $4B$.

A sketch of the observed spectrum for HCl gas is shown in Fig. 4.203. It does indeed exhibit the predicted behavior, with the additional feature of a decrease in intensity at the higher values of J, where the index m assumes somewhat larger magnitudes. Rather accurate values of the moment of inertia may be obtained from precise measurements of the absorption frequencies. A few of the absorption frequencies are listed in Table 4.202; an average value of the spacing is 20.55 cm^{-1}, from which again the bond distance can be computed in the same way as for the pure rotational spectrum. The spacing between successive lines is found to be smaller at higher frequencies, and this has its origin in slightly different values of B for the states with $v = 0$ and with $v = 1$. The explanation of this effect lies in the slight increase in the moment of inertia caused by an increased effective atomic separation at higher values of v.

Table 4.202   Some Absorption Frequencies of HCl for the Cl^{35} Isotope Only*

m	ω, cm^{-1}
-3	2821.58
-2	2843.63
-1	2865.10
$+1$	2906.25
$+2$	2925.91
$+3$	2944.92

* According to E. K. Plyler and E. Tidwell, *Z. Elektrochem.*, **64**, 717 (1960).

The precision of the data is much better than in the pure rotational region; a hundredth of a wave number is a significant digit. A much better fit of the data can be obtained by adding a quadratic term in m; that is, the expression

$$\omega = 2885.98 + 2m(10.28) - m^2(0.305) \qquad (4.213)$$

fits the data exceedingly well. The justification for the quadratic term is found in the variation in B as v changes from 0 to 1. The remaining discrepancies are real and require the use of a cubic term in m, especially at higher values of m.

The constant term in this equation can be treated as the (hypothetical) purely vibrational transition. If it were possible for the transition $(v = 0, J = 0) \rightarrow (v = 1, J = 0)$ to occur, it would appear at 2885.98 cm^{-1} for the HCl^{35} molecule. The values quoted in Sec. 2.2 and called vibrational frequencies were obtained in just this way by analysis of the rotational structure.

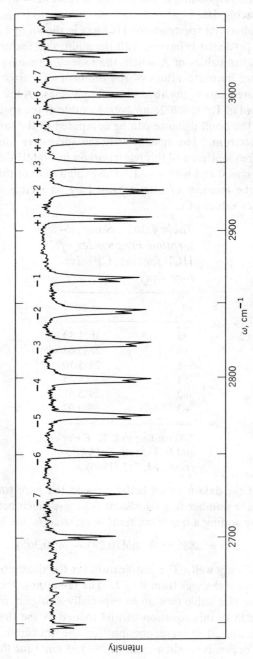

Fig. 4.203   Spectrum of HCl (the *m* values appear above some absorption lines). Splitting of each peak is due to Cl³⁵ and Cl³⁷ isotopes. [By permission from *Pure and Appl. Chem.*, **1**, 572 (1960).]

Problems

4.201   The molecule ICl^{35} has a bond distance of 2.32 Å. Calculate the frequencies of the first three pure rotational transitions in cycles per second and also in reciprocal centimeters (cm^{-1}). Iodine is monoisotopic; the atomic weight of Cl^{35} is 34.979.

4.202   Derive an equation, similar to Eq. 4.209, which gives the positions of the rotational lines in a vibrational band of a diatomic molecule, but assuming that the B values may be different in the upper and the lower vibrational states. Compare with Eq. 4.213.

4.203   Estimate the ω_0 values for HCl^{37} and for DCl^{35}, assuming the force constant k is the same for all isotopic species. Use data for HCl^{35}.

4.204   Label the m values (Table 4.202) on the diagram, Fig. 4.202. Find pairs of lines which terminate on the same rotational energy level in the state with $v = 1$; subtract their frequencies and obtain an energy difference between two rotational levels in the ground vibrational state. Compare the B values obtained from several such computations.

4.205   Show that the difference in frequency between two adjacent lines in a pure rotational spectrum is a constant.

4.206   Assign J transitions to the values in Table 4.201.

3. Energy Levels of Polyatomic Molecules

The discussion of polyatomic molecules is similar in many respects to that of diatomic molecules and will be considered only briefly at this time. An account of resonance phenomena, including spectra, of polyatomic molecules will be given in Chapter 16.

Nothing need be added to the previous discussions of translational energy levels.

Rotation.   The rotational problem for linear polyatomic molecules (that is, those for which all the nuclei are on a straight line for the configuration of minimum potential energy) is identical with the diatomic molecule problem. The rotational coordinates are again limited to two, and the energy levels are also given by Eq. 4.101.

For nonlinear molecules, three angular coordinates are always needed to describe all possible orientations of the molecule; to the angles θ and ϕ, the angle coordinate χ must be added (see Fig. 4.301). Calculation of the energy levels is relatively simple, or more complex, depending upon whether the molecule is symmetrical in structure or is not. No matter how irregularly shaped the molecule, however, only three parameters are important for the energy calculation. These are the three moments of inertia, I_x, I_y, and I_z, which are taken about the x, y, and z axes of a coordinate system which is fixed in the molecule, and which has its origin at the center of gravity of the molecule. The moments of inertia are defined as

$$I_x = \sum_i m_i(y_i^2 + z_i^2) \tag{4.301}$$

where m_i is the mass of the ith atom, and y_i and z_i are the values of the y and z coordinates. As may be seen in Fig. 4.302, $(y_i^2 + z_i^2)$ is the square of the perpendicular distance of the ith atom to the x axis. Similar expressions may be written

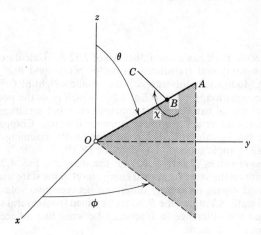

Fig. 4.301 The definition of angles θ, ϕ, and χ. The axis OA and line BC are fixed in the molecule (see also Fig. 3.201).

for I_y and I_z. So far the orientation in the molecule of the axis system has not been specified. Certain choices of orientation materially simplify the problem (Chapter 16); for example, in benzene an axis may be perpendicular to the plane of the molecule. For such an optimum choice of orientation, the axes are designated as *principal axes*. The moments of inertia calculated with respect to these special axes are called the *principal moments of inertia* with the symbols I_A, I_B, and I_C. A, B, and C denote the three principal axes. The student should note that, by contrast, a linear molecule has two independent axes, which are perpendicular to each other and to the axis of the molecule. There are thus two degrees of freedom for rotation for a linear molecule, and three for a nonlinear molecule.

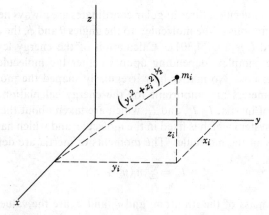

Fig. 4.302 Coordinates of a particle and distances involved in the moment of inertia about the x axis.

Vibration. We shall, for the present, omit a discussion of the electronic functions and energies and turn to the vibrations. With two or more different bonds in the molecule, there are several different vibrations, but how many? Each electron and each nucleus in the molecule has three degrees of freedom. When electronic coordinates are separated out, we have left, then, only the nuclear coordinates for the other degrees of freedom: translation, rotation and vibration. For $\mathcal{N}$ nuclei there is a total of $3\mathcal{N}$ such degrees of freedom. Translation of the center of mass always requires three coordinates; rotation of a linear molecule requires two coordinates, and of a nonlinear molecule three coordinates. All that are left are vibrational degrees of freedom: $3\mathcal{N} - 6$ for a nonlinear molecule, and $3\mathcal{N} - 5$ for a linear molecule. If the potential functions governing vibrational displacements from equilibrium are harmonic, the total vibrational motion may be described in terms of $3\mathcal{N} - 6$ (or, for a linear molecule, $3\mathcal{N} - 5$) different characteristic modes of vibration, called *normal modes*. A simple example is the description of the three modes for the water molecule shown in Fig. 4.303.

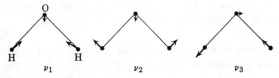

Fig. 4.303 Normal modes of vibration for H_2O (by permission from Wilson, Decius, and Cross, *Molecular Vibrations*, McGraw-Hill Book Co., New York, 1955).

The analysis that leads to an exact algebraic description of these motions, in terms of the coordinates of the atoms, is a lengthy process even for a simple molecule like H_2O. In general, however, the normal modes are complicated functions of the single atomic motions and depend on the exact geometry of the molecule and the force constants of the bonds. We shall return to this problem in Chapter 16. In general, corresponding to each normal mode there is a set of vibrational energy levels. For instance, for each vibrational degree of freedom of the water molecule there is a quantum number v_i. Each of these quantum numbers may have the values 0, 1, 2, . . . quite independent of the other two, and the vibrational energy expression is

$$\epsilon_v = (v_1 + \tfrac{1}{2})h\nu_1 + (v_2 + \tfrac{1}{2})h\nu_2 + (v_3 + \tfrac{1}{2})h\nu_3 \qquad (4.302)$$

where ν_1, ν_2, and ν_3 are the classical vibration frequencies corresponding to the three normal modes. This expression turns out to be surprisingly accurate in practice; it can be made to fit experimental data even more precisely by adding some anharmonic terms, quadratic in the quantum numbers.

Internal Rotation. The essential difference between rotation and vibration, physically, is that the former has a potential energy zero for all angles and hence independent of displacement, whereas the latter has a potential function, usually taken as quadratic, which depends on the displacement. For many of the larger molecules, frequently there is one (or even more) internal motion which could be either rotation or vibration, depending on the potential energy. For instance, consider the internal rotation about the carbon-carbon bond in ethane and its derivatives. This might have a potential function which changes by a large amount as one group twists with respect to the other; or in the alternative extreme the function may not change at all with the internal rotation, that is, free rotation. In the latter case, theory shows that one of the eighteen vibrational degrees of freedom becomes more like a rotation, with approximately quadratic dependence of energy levels on quantum number, rather than like a vibration, with linear dependence of energy levels on quantum number. For intermediate potentials, the energy level pattern is quite complex. Such a degree of freedom is called a torsional motion for both intermediate and high potential barriers.

Problem

4.301   The frequencies of vibration in the H_2O molecule are $\omega_1 = 3652$ cm^{-1}, $\omega_2 = 1595$ cm^{-1}, and $\omega_3 = 3756$ cm^{-1}. Plot a graph showing the zero-point energy and including all energy levels up to and including the level $v_1 = 2$, $v_2 = 2$, $v_3 = 2$.

We have, in the preceding sections, derived or stated some algebraic expressions for the allowed energy levels of translation, rotation, and vibration in molecules. Application of some of these expressions to rotational and vibrational spectra illustrated the determination of bond distances and vibration frequencies. The succeeding chapters will apply the energy level expressions to aid in the calculation of macroscopic properties for substances.

Our treatment of electronic levels has been limited to a few states of the hydrogen molecule, and we shall not extend the discussion of molecular electronic levels at this time. The applications of the succeeding chapters will not require such detail, since under most conditions the lowest electronic state is the only one appreciably populated. Furthermore, its energy relative to the lowest electronic states of related atoms and molecules is usually obtained with sufficient accuracy only by experiment. A more appropriate place for an extended discussion is in a treatment of molecular structure and molecular spectra, especially in the visible and ultraviolet region as in Chapter 16.

4. Review Problems

4.401   A few lines near the center of the fundamental band of HBr are found at 2606.03, 2590.76, 2575.00, 2542.06, 2524.91, and 2507.30 cm^{-1}. Determine from this information the ω_0 value, the force constant, and the HBr bond distance, using 79.92 as the (average) bromine atomic weight. Compare with values in Table 4.101.

4.402   Estimate the corresponding line positions in the fundamental band of DBr (see Problem 4.401).

4.403   Calculate the wavelengths of the pure rotational lines of HBr which fall in the range from 50 microns to 125 microns.

4.404   Use the distances in the hydrogen molecule and in the HBr molecule to estimate a bonding radius for the bromine atom. The Br_2 molecule has $h/8\pi^2 Ic = 0.0809$ cm^{-1}; how closely does its bond distance agree with twice the bonding radius above? Compare with Table 4.101.

4.405   Derive the expression $I = \mu r^2$ for the moment of inertia about the center of mass of a diatomic molecule.

4.406   Write the number of vibrational degrees of freedom for each of these molecules: NH_3, C_4H_2 (diacetylene, linear), $C_{10}H_{14}$.

*4.407   Use the expression $x^2 l^2 - 2x^3 l + x^4$ as a variation function for the lowest state of the particle in a one-dimensional box of length l. Is this energy closer to the true value than that obtained on p. 84? Try a combination of these two variation functions to obtain an energy even closer to the true value.

General References

In addition to the General References of Chapter 2, the following are recommended:

Gaydon, A. G., *Dissociation Energies and Spectra of Diatomic Molecules*, Dover Publications, New York, 1950.

Herzberg, G., *Spectra of Diatomic Molecules*, D. Van Nostrand Co., Princeton, N.J., 1950.

Chapter Five

Statistical Mechanics

1. Introduction

Nature of the Problem. In the previous chapters we have been concerned with individual atoms and molecules. In some instances (for example, the spectroscopy of dilute gases) the energy levels derived for the single molecules can be applied to the interpretation of experiment. However, in many other experiments such as the measurement of the molar heat capacity of a gas, the result, although related to the same energy levels, reflects the average behavior of Avogadro's number of molecules. In such a case we neither need nor want to have complete information on the energy levels of all N molecules, but we shall wish to develop a treatment that will give the required average.

Two analogies may make this point clearer. First, in attempting to verify the assertion that heads and tails have equal probability when a "perfect" coin is tossed, we want to know not the order in which heads and tails appeared, but only the total number of tosses, N, and the difference in numbers of heads and tails. This is the statistical approach. Similarly, in the synthesis from inactive materials of a total of N dextro- and levorotary molecules (optical isomers), we need a theory that will predict the formation, when N is very large, of a racemic mixture, that is, equal numbers of levo and dextro product molecules. We do not need a theory that predicts the outcome of each individual molecular synthesis. In the one case, $N_{head} + N_{tail} = N$, and in the other, $N_{dextro} + N_{levo} = N$. It will be shown that, if N is large (that is, for a statistical number of experiments), the magnitude of one result over the other does not on the average tend to zero, but increases as $N^{1/2}$. The relative size of this deviation, to the size of the whole sample, *decreases* as $N^{1/2}/N$, i.e., $1/N^{1/2}$. Thus when N is very big, the product of the synthesis is a racemic mixture.

The application of statistical method to the mechanics of molecules gives rise to the term statistical mechanics.

Equilibrium and Statistical Degeneracy. A basic assertion of statistical mechanics *is that at equilibrium any particular arrangement of the total energy among a group of molecules is as probable as any other.* If, for some reason, we choose to consider several of these distinguishable arrangements as members of a single group, then the probability of that group being found increases as the definition of the group is widened. A similar phenomenon occurs in card games. In playing bridge, any exactly specified deal, that is, any specified distribution of 52 cards, is as probable as any other. But bad hands, are, with minor differences, essentially the same in value and a wide variety of these are grouped together as "poor." There are progressively fewer ways to get hands that are called "good." Therefore, a good hand is less probable.

These ideas apply to the behavior of molecules in equilibrium at a certain temperature. The total energy of a system of molecules is important in determining the average behavior of the system. A random type of shuffling of the energy among the molecules occurs.

There are many different ways of selecting a group of molecules for consideration. For example, we may focus attention on a sealed flask of various interacting atoms immersed in an ice bath at $0°C$. Rather than defining now what we mean by $0°C$ we shall instead simply imagine that the flask is completely isolated from its surroundings in such a manner that its total energy is fixed. This is called an *isolated* system. The shuffling process involves all the different identifiable ways (quantum states of the system) of distributing this energy among the energy levels that are available in the system. These quantum states correspond to the energy eigenvalues, and for each one there is a corresponding eigenfunction which can in principle be written down and distinguished from all the others. It will be very convenient, however, to put these levels in large groups. For example, we usually wish to lump all the vast number of eigenfunctions, corresponding to a particular molecular arrangement of the atoms present, into a single group for that compound. Thus the shuffling process in this example can be considered to correspond to formation of various molecular configurations in various allowed total energy states. An additional effect of this lumping of equivalent but different eigenfunctions is that it will allow us to use mathematical techniques that are applicable only to very large numbers.

We may illustrate some of these ideas by a simple example as follows. If two groupings of the same atoms, corresponding to the isomeric molecules A and B, have the same energy levels as each other, then by symmetry we expect that these two molecules will be equally probable, that is, appear in equal numbers, $N_A = N_B$, when the molecules exist in large numbers in equilibrium with each other. If there are three such isomers, A, B, and C, then $N_A = N_B = N_C$. If C and B, which are distinguishable, are so nearly the same that we want to group them and call them the same species, say B' (the case of two optical isomers), then $N_{B'} = 2N_A$. The same result would have arisen if B had exactly the same energy levels as A, but twice as many states at each level. The situation is illustrated by Fig. 5.101. If an additional isomer of B, i.e., D, exists with like properties, then $N_B + N_C + N_D = 3N_A$.

The number of eigenfunctions or states at a given energy level i is denoted by the degeneracy or statistical weight g_i, which is greater than or equal to unity. If

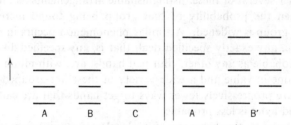

Fig. 5.101   A schematic energy level diagram.

$g_i = 1$, the level is called nondegenerate. If, in the above example, the levels of B were triply degenerate, i.e., $g_i = 3$, whereas the A levels were nondegenerate, then $N_B = 3N_A$.

We have been able to obtain these limited results by a symmetry argument; we shall now go on to develop a more general method for finding the most probable and also the average properties of a molecular system. We shall show that the most probable value and the average value are the same. We take as the fundamental principle of equilibrium statistical mechanics the idea that an average property represents an *average over all individual quantum states*, subject to the limitations of the problem. This average is identified with the experimental value of the quantity.

These ideas are closely related to some discussions concerning weighting factors and expectation values already encountered in Chapters 1 and 2. It is worth restating these in the following way, used in mathematical statistics. For a set of values of some quantity x_i, each having weight w_i (as allowed by the problem), the weighted average is

$$\bar{x}_{wa} = \frac{\sum_{i=1}^{n} w_i x_i}{\sum_{i=1}^{n} w_i} \tag{5.101}$$

This equation may be considered as a mathematical statement of the basic principle of statistical mechanics. The w_i give the relative occurrence or importance of each x_i, and, together, the set of w_i values constitutes a distribution function. If the normalizing factor $\sum_{i=1}^{n} w_i$ is 1, then the weighting factors are already normalized.

If the values of x are closely spaced between the limiting values x_i and x_n, we may write

$$\bar{x}_{wa} = \frac{\displaystyle\int_{x_i}^{x_n} w(x)\, x\, dx}{\displaystyle\int_{x_i}^{x_n} w(x)\, dx} \tag{5.102}$$

where w_i is now written explicitly as a density function $w(x)$.

For example, in the equilibrium

$$H_2 + I_2 = 2HI$$

let x_i correspond to the degree of completion of the reaction. Then every eigen-function ψ_i corresponds to a certain value x_i. The experimental value of the extent of reaction is the average value of x_i, that is, the sum of all possible x_i divided by the total number of possible eigenstates. The number and nature of these is determined by the specified limitations of the problem; that is, the total energy, the total number of hydrogen and iodine atoms, and the volume of the vessel containing the mixture.

Problems

5.101   Suppose that the probability of finding a particle at a certain point along the x axis is $P(x) = e^{-x^2}$. Calculate the most probable and the average value of x. Normalize the probability.

5.102   Repeat Problem 5.101 for the function $P(x) = xe^{-x^2}$, where the probability is defined as zero for negative values of x.

5.103   A coin is tossed 10 times. What is the probability of getting 5 heads and 5 tails? 4 heads and 6 tails? 5 straight heads and then 5 tails? 4 straight heads and then 6 tails? 10 heads?

5.104   A partially deuterated methane sample is analyzed and found to contain equal molar quantities of hydrogen and deuterium. On a random basis calculate the percentage of species CH_4, CH_3D, CH_2D_2, CHD_3, and CD_4.

5.105   Enumerate the species that are present in a partially deuterated ethylene sample, and then calculate the relative abundance of each at equilibrium and 25 per cent overall deuterium content.

5.106   For a pair of perfect dice find the relative probability of the possible casts from 2 to 12.

5.107   If a perfect coin is tossed N times, find the relative chance that heads should exceed tails by at least 10 as N increases from 10 to 10^2 to 10^4. Does your answer contradict the discussion in the text?

2. The Boltzmann Distribution Law

Localized Systems.   We shall now develop a somewhat more general approach to statistical equilibrium as determined by available energy levels and parameters such as total energy. In order to simplify description of the eigenstates, we take as our model a group of distinguishable molecules, each with a set of nondegenerate energy levels which may differ. As a physical picture of this model, we may imagine a rigid framework to which these molecules are bound. It is sufficient to imagine them bound in a line with an identifying letter for each position. We may think of each one as an oscillator, not necessarily harmonic, with a set of numbered

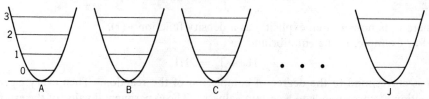

Fig. 5.201   A set of localized oscillators.

energy levels. Such a model is shown in Fig. 5.201. Because the system composed of oscillators is bound down and the oscillators are identified by letter, the system is said to be *localized*.

First consider some very small systems of oscillators. We start with only two oscillators, labeled A and B, with identical equally spaced levels (harmonic oscillators). For a total of three quanta of energy, there are only two possible distributions

		I		II		Relative Population
3	B		A			2
2				B	A	2
1				A	B	2
0	A		B			2

ϵ_i (on the left, labeling rows 3, 2, 1, 0)

Fig. 5.202   Possible distributions of three quanta among two oscillators.

as shown in Fig. 5.202. In terms of the population (number of oscillators N_i) in each energy level these distributions are:

Case I: $N_0 = N_3 = 1$; $N_1 = N_2 = 0$

Case II: $N_0 = N_3 = 0$; $N_1 = N_2 = 1$

The N_i are obviously subject to the condition that

$$\sum_i N_i \equiv 2 \equiv N$$

The relative population of each energy level is found by summing horizontally. Each distribution may be realized in two ways, corresponding to the fact that we may place either of the two oscillators at a particular energy, but then there is no further choice in the placement of the second oscillator because the total number of quanta is fixed. This system is too simple to be of much interest, and it does not follow the form of the distribution law to be obtained later in this chapter, namely, $N_0 > N_1 > N_2$, etc. However, the example illustrates that statistical laws valid for many particles must not be applied to only a few.

A larger system of three quanta distributed among three identical oscillators, A, B, and C, is more revealing. Three possible distributions, I, II, III, are shown in Fig. 5.203. They may be summarized as

$$I: \; N_0 = 2, \; N_1 = N_2 = 0, \; N_3 = 1$$
$$II: \; N_0 = N_1 = N_2 = 1, \; N_3 = 0$$
$$III: \; N_0 = N_2 = N_3 = 0, \; N_1 = 3$$

There are three, six, and one ways, respectively, of realizing each of the energy distributions, and these ways or weights give the relative probability of each distribution arising. Distribution II has weight 6, corresponding to the fact that

	I			II						III	Relative Population
3	C	B	A								3
2				C	B	C	A	B	A		6
1				B	C	A	C	A	B	ABC	9
0	AB	AC	BC	A	A	B	B	C	C		12

Fig. 5.203   Possible distributions of three quanta among three oscillators.

there are three choices, A, B, and C, for the first oscillator to be placed at level 2 and two choices for the second oscillator to be placed at level 1 since, of the three, A, B, and C, one has been used in filling level 2. These independent possibilities combine as $3 \times 2 = 6$. Distribution I has only weight 3 because the two choices for the zero level, after selection of the occupant of level 3, are indistinguishable. The weighting W of each distribution corresponds to the general formula for such permutations and combinations,

$$W = \frac{N!}{N_0! \, N_1! \, N_2! \, N_3!} \tag{5.201}$$

so, if W_1 is the number of ways of achieving distribution I,

$$W_I = \frac{3!}{2! \, 0! \, 0! \, 1!} = 3$$

and

$$W_{II} = \frac{3!}{1! \, 1! \, 1! \, 0!} = 6$$

$$W_{III} = \frac{3!}{0! \, 3! \, 0! \, 0!} = 1$$

No one of the distributions corresponds qualitatively to the expected energy distribution law requirement of $N_0 > N_1 > N_2 > N_3$. In this example, the size of the assembly is again so small that the law is masked in its detailed fulfillment. However, we can begin to see some of the statistical features. The most probable distribution is obviously W_{II}, which has $N_0 = N_1 = N_2 > N_3$. If we examine the average distribution given in the relative population column of Fig. 5.203 we find that $N_0 > N_1 > N_2 > N_3$, which now obeys the anticipated general rule for distributions of large numbers of quanta among large numbers of oscillators.

Consider a larger system of thirty quanta distributed among thirty oscillators. The working of random probability, so that the large majority of distributions correspond more closely with the distribution law, is then more clearly revealed. One possible distribution is $N_0 = 0$, $N_1 = 30$, $N_{2-30} = 0$. Then

$$W_{0,30,0,\ldots,0} = \frac{30!}{0!\,30!\cdots 0!} = 1$$

Now, if a quantum is transferred from one of the oscillators to another, the result is one oscillator in the ground state, twenty-eight with one quantum, and one with two quanta; then the weight becomes

$$W_{1,28,1,\ldots,0} = \frac{30!}{1!\,28!\,1!\,0!\cdots 0!} = 870$$

while further repetition of this process would eventually give rise to the distribution for which

$$W_{10,10,10,0,\ldots,0} = \frac{30!}{10!\,10!\,10!\,0!\cdots 0!} = 5.5 \times 10^{12}$$

Thus, as a distribution tends more in the direction of conformity with the distribution law, the probability of its occurrence increases enormously. We can improve on this even further by using a trial distribution with the qualification $N_0 > N_1 > N_2$, etc., e.g.,

$$W_{13,9,4,3,1,0,\ldots,0} = \frac{30!}{13!\,9!\,4!\,3!\,1!\,0!\cdots 0!} = 8.2 \times 10^{14}$$

It is clear, however, that this is not a reasonable way to find either the most probable or the average distribution, because even for the very small sample of thirty quanta and thirty oscillators we would have to examine about 10^{16} distributions. We therefore seek a mathematical method for dealing with this problem, or rather the limit of this problem, as the number of quanta and oscillators increases indefinitely.

The Most Probable Distribution.   We wish to obtain a general expression for the most probable energy distribution in statistically large systems of the kind we have been considering. By statistically large we mean large enough so that the behavior of the system is close to that of a system with an indefinitely large number of particles. We assert that the most probable distribution in such a system will be a good representation of the average distribution in a collection of the order of Avogadro's number of oscillators.

The characteristic of the *most probable* or *maximum* value of a function is that small variations of the independent variables cause a negligible variation in the function. If we use the symbolism $f(x_i)$ for a function of a number of independent variables x_i, this variation process can be indicated by the variation symbol δ. We thus can write

$$\delta f(x_i) = 0 \qquad (5.202)$$

for the condition at the maximum. This symbolism implies that the function is differentiated, in turn, with respect to every x_i; if the x_i are independent then each partial derivative is set equal to zero. Enough equations result so that we can find the maximum by solving them simultaneously.

ILLUSTRATION.   For a system of quanta and harmonic oscillators, find the relative populations of the energy levels when W is a maximum, that is, find the condition for a most probable distribution.

For a very large number of quanta in a system consisting of N harmonic oscillators, where N is very large also, we have

$$W_{\max} = \frac{N!}{N_1! \, N_2! \cdots N_i! \cdots}$$

where N_1, N_2, N_i are assumed to be just those values that make W a maximum. Then $\delta W_{\max} = 0$, where the variation refers to small changes of the N_i from their optimum values. Call $W'_{\max}$ the new probability given by

$$W'_{\max} = \frac{N!}{N_1! \, N_2! \cdots (N_{i-1}+1)! \, (N_i - 2)! \, (N_{i+1}+1)! \cdots}$$

where $W_{\max}$ has been subjected to the variation that two members of the ith level have moved to the adjacent $i - 1$th and $i + 1$th levels; this causes no change in total energy. It follows then, since $\delta W_{\max} = 0$, that

$$\frac{W_{\max}}{W'_{\max}} = 1 = \frac{(N_{i-1}+1)! \, (N_i - 2)! \, (N_{i+1}+1)!}{N_{i-1}! \, N_i! \, N_{i+1}!}$$

where all other N quantities have canceled. Then

$$1 = \frac{(N_{i-1}+1)(N_{i+1}+1)}{N_i(N_i - 1)}$$

But for N_{i-1}, N_i, and N_{i+1} very large, $N_{i-1} + 1 \simeq N_{i-1}$, etc., so that the ratio becomes

$$1 = \frac{(N_{i-1})(N_{i+1})}{N_i^2}$$

or

$$\frac{N_{i-1}}{N_i} = \frac{N_i}{N_{i+1}} = \text{constant for all values of } i$$

That is, for $W_{\max}$ the level populations are in geometric progression.

The student may satisfy himself by considering a small system, say six quanta and six oscillators, that the constant is equal to or less than unity.

This result suggests that the distribution is of the form of an exponential function

$$N_i \propto e^{-bi}$$

where b is a constant. The ratio of populations in adjacent levels is e^{-b}.

The general problem is somewhat complicated, because the treatment must include the fact that the variables (number of oscillators in each level, N_i) are not all independent, and are large integers and not continuous variables. We wish to maximize the expression for the number of ways of assigning N oscillators among q energy levels,

$$W = \frac{N!}{N_0! \, N_1! \, N_2! \cdots N_{q-1}!} \tag{5.203}$$

where the N_i are the populations of each of the levels. The distribution is subject to the initial limitation on the total energy E to be distributed among the N oscillators. We may express these specifications or constraints as

$$\sum_{i=0}^{q-1} N_i = N \tag{5.204}$$

the condition for a constant number of particles, and

$$\sum_{i=0}^{q-1} N_i \epsilon_i = E \tag{5.205}$$

the condition for a constant energy. Also, for $W = W_{\max}$

$$\delta W = 0 \tag{5.206}$$

If we take the logarithm of Eq. 5.203

$$\ln W = \ln N! - \sum_{i=0}^{q-1} \ln N_i! \tag{5.207}$$

Near a maximum, $\delta \ln W = 0$. This statement is equivalent to Eq. 5.206 because the log of a function is an extremum if the function itself is at a maximum. Therefore

$$\delta \ln W = -\sum_i \delta \ln N_i! = 0 \tag{5.208}$$

There are two points to be noted in this step. First, the summation is over the same range as in the preceding equations, but the notation has been abbreviated. Second, the term in $\delta \ln N!$ vanishes because N is constant.

Some mathematical difficulties will now be considered. We have implied that the numbers N_i are large enough for us to vary them over short ranges in the region of the maximum, so that the logarithm of the probability does not change much. We shall also need the condition that the N_i are large to approximate the factorial in terms of standard functions that can be differentiated.

Stirling's Approximation. We consider the approximation for $N!$ in terms of standard functions. The factorial can be written

$$\ln N! = \sum_{x=1}^{x=N} \ln x \tag{5.209}$$

If we replace this summation by an integration, then

$$\ln N! \approx \int_{x=1}^{x=N} \ln x \, dx = N \ln N - N + 1 \approx N \ln N - N \tag{5.210}$$

which is the crude form of Stirling's approximation. The $+1$ has been omitted in the final expression because we are interested in the variation only, and any constant term drops out; thus

$$\delta \ln N! \approx \ln N \, \delta N + N \, \delta \ln N - \delta N = \ln N \, \delta N \tag{5.211}$$

which is the expression we require.

Lagrange's Method of Undetermined Multipliers.   If we insert Stirling's approximation in Eq. 5.207 we obtain the expression

$$\ln W = -\sum_i N_i \ln N_i + N \ln N \tag{5.212}$$

and (note that $\delta \sum_i N_i = \delta N = 0$)

$$\delta \ln W = -\sum_i \ln N_i \, \delta N_i = 0 \tag{5.213}$$

instead of Eq. 5.208. Note again that δN is identically zero since N is fixed. We may also express the constraints, Eqs. 5.204 and 5.205, equivalently as

$$\sum_i \delta N_i = \delta N = 0 \tag{5.214}$$

$$\sum_i \epsilon_i \, \delta N_i = \delta E = 0 \tag{5.215}$$

These equations assert that not all N_i in Eq. 5.213 are independent; that is, two of the N_i, say N_0 and N_1, are fixed if $N_2 \cdots N_{q-1}$ are fixed. We may eliminate the superfluous N_0 and N_1 from Eq. 5.213 by multiplying Eqs. 5.214 and 5.215 by suitable constants α and β, such that when these are added to Eq. 5.213 the coefficients of δN_0 and δN_1 will be zero. For example, the coefficient of δN_1 becomes $\alpha + \beta \epsilon_1 + \ln N_1 \equiv 0$ when the identity is ensured by suitable choice of α and β. We are left with the sum

$$\sum_{i=2}^{q-1} (\ln N_i + \alpha + \beta \epsilon_i) \, \delta N_i = 0 \tag{5.216}$$

Now all remaining N_i are independent variables. Since all δN_i could be zero except, say, δN_2 if we so chose, it follows that Eq. 5.216 would require

$$\ln N_2 + \alpha + \beta \epsilon_2 = 0$$

and in general

$$\ln N_i + \alpha + \beta \epsilon_i = 0$$

for $i = 2$ up to $q - 1$. Thus

$$N_i = e^{-\alpha} e^{-\beta \epsilon_i} \tag{5.217}$$

The undetermined multipliers α and β are so fixed as to make this true for $i = 0$ and 1 also.

ILLUSTRATION. A simple example will help in the understanding of the use of undetermined multipliers.

If x and y are right-angle directions along the ground, and z is elevation, a simple equation for a mountain-shaped area is

$$z = \exp\left[-(x^2 + y^2)\right] \tag{5.218}$$

If we wish to maximize z, or find the highest point on the mountain, we can do this by finding an extreme value of $\ln z$ by simple partial differentiation.

$$\frac{\partial \ln z}{\partial x} = 2x = 0$$

and

$$\frac{\partial \ln z}{\partial y} = 2y = 0$$

Hence we obtain the obvious answer that the top of the mountain is at the point $x = 0$, $y = 0$.

Suppose we had a restriction

$$x + y = 1 \tag{5.219}$$

which represents a path across the mountain that does not go through the summit. What is the highest point reached? One way to solve this problem is by substitution of $y = 1 - x$ in Eq. 5.218

$$-\ln z_{\text{path}} = 2x^2 - 2x + 1 \tag{5.220}$$

Then by differentiation

$$\frac{-d \ln z_{\text{path}}}{dx} = 4x - 2 = 0$$

hence $x_{\text{max}} = \frac{1}{2}$. Substitution in the path equation gives the result that the maximum elevation, subject to the condition of the path, is at the point $x = \frac{1}{2}$, $y = \frac{1}{2}$.

We may now obtain the same result by the method of undetermined multipliers. We find for the variation in the equation of the mountain at a maximum

$$-\delta \ln z = 2x\, \delta x + 2y\, \delta y = 0 \tag{5.221}$$

For the variation in the path condition we have

$$\delta x + \delta y = 0$$

We then multiply this expression by the undetermined multiplier α and add to Eq. 5.221 to obtain

$$2x\, \delta x + 2y\, \delta y + \alpha\, \delta x + \alpha\, \delta y = 0$$

or

$$(2x + \alpha)\, \delta x + (2y + \alpha)\, \delta y = 0 \tag{5.222}$$

These are now independent variations, so both coefficients must be equal to zero. Thus

$$x = -\frac{\alpha}{2}; \qquad y = -\frac{\alpha}{2}$$

This result in combination with the original restraint $x + y = 1$ gives the previous answer, that the highest point, subject to the path restriction, is at $x = \frac{1}{2}$ and $y = \frac{1}{2}$.

This method is rather cumbersome and unnecessary for just two variables, but when there are many, it is the more elegant procedure.

Evaluation of α and β. The condition Eq. 5.204 is now used to eliminate the undetermined multiplier α. Since (Eq. 5.217)

$$\sum N_i = N = e^{-\alpha} \sum_i e^{-\beta \epsilon_i} \tag{5.223}$$

then

$$e^{-\alpha} = \frac{N}{\sum_i e^{-\beta \epsilon_i}} \tag{5.224}$$

$$\frac{N_i}{N} = \frac{e^{-\beta \epsilon_i}}{\sum_i e^{-\beta \epsilon_i}} \tag{5.225}$$

We now have a choice of procedure with regard to the multiplier β. We may use the condition for the conservation of energy to eliminate β, or we may leave it in, with due regard to the fact that it is a parameter set by the total energy. We may anticipate by stating that β is the temperature parameter in the distribution law, with the value

$$\beta = \frac{1}{kT} \tag{5.226}$$

where k is Boltzmann's constant. The first procedure involves setting up the equation for the total energy from the condition Eq. 5.205 and the distribution law, Eq. 5.225,

$$E = \sum_i N_i \epsilon_i = \frac{N \sum_i \epsilon_i e^{-\beta \epsilon_i}}{\sum_i e^{-\beta \epsilon_i}} \tag{5.227}$$

This is an equation which can in principle be solved for β, but only when the values of the energy levels have been specified.

Boltzmann Distribution Law. If we regard Eq. 5.226 as the definition of temperature or, alternatively, anticipate that such an equation will be shown to be in harmony with the absolute temperature scale, we can write Eq. 5.225 as

$$\frac{N_i}{N} = \frac{e^{-\epsilon_i/kT}}{\sum_i e^{-\epsilon_i/kT}} \tag{5.228}$$

which is the Boltzmann distribution law. Now from Eq. 5.228, if we set $\epsilon_0 = 0$

as the zero of energy

$$\frac{N_0}{N} = \frac{e^{-\epsilon_0/kT}}{\sum_i e^{-\epsilon_i/kT}} = \frac{1}{\sum_i e^{-\epsilon_i/kT}} \tag{5.229}$$

We may express the Boltzmann distribution law in another form by dividing Eq. 5.228 by Eq. 5.229,

$$\frac{N_i}{N_0} = e^{-\epsilon_i/kT} \tag{5.230}$$

If some of the levels are degenerate, each level must be included with its proper weighting, g_i. We write

$$\frac{N_i}{N} = \frac{g_i e^{-\epsilon_i/kT}}{\sum_i g_i e^{-\epsilon_i/kT}} \tag{5.231}$$

The student will note that, if this expression is summed over all values of i, the result is unity. The ratio in Eq. 5.231 represents the probability that an oscillator will be found in a particular state i.

ILLUSTRATION.   Show an explicit connection between the Boltzmann distribution law and the earlier results for simpler localized systems.

Equation 5.230 shows that the populations of excited levels i increase relative to the ground state population N_0 if the temperature rises. This latter condition is understood to mean the same thing as "if the average energy, or number of quanta, in the system increases." For a localized system of three quanta and three molecules (Fig. 5.203) we earlier had the relative populations, $N_0:N_1:N_2:N_3:N_4 = 12:9:6:3:0$, i.e., $4:3:2:1:0$. The populations $N_5 = N_6 = N_7$, etc., were also zero, as for N_4.

For four quanta in three oscillators the possible random statistical distributions are as follows:

	I			II					III			IV			Relative Population
5															
4	A	B	C												3
3				A	A	B	B	C	C						6
2									AB	AC	BC	A	B	C	9
1				B	C	A	C	A	B			BC	AC	AB	12
0	BC	AC	AB	C	B	C	A	B	A	C	B	A			15

The relative populations are now $N_0:N_1:N_2:N_3:N_4 = 5:4:3:2:1$, which has indeed increased every value of N_i/N_0 ($i = 1$ to 4), relative to the earlier case for three quanta. The fifth level is still unpopulated.

The student may find the populations for a further rise to five quanta of energy.

Average Values; Alternative Derivation of Boltzmann's Law.   In Sec. 5.1 we asserted that the fundamental operation of statistical mechanics was the averaging of a property over all quantum states accessible to the system. In terms of the problem of finding a distribution law for quanta among oscillators, the property that we have been concerned with is the number N_i of oscillators with exactly i quanta. We have already calculated the most probable value of this quantity, which is given by Boltzmann's distribution law. If we now use this distribution to calculate the average energy, we are averaging, not over all distributions, but only over the most probable one. We are leaving out of consideration even the slightly less probable distributions available to the quanta. Instead, we are taking one special distribution that is representative and averaging over it alone. We are familiar with this sort of sampling in every-day life. Let us say that the most probable result of a million tosses of a coin is $N_{\text{head}} = N_{\text{tail}} = 500,000$. If we always bet on heads, an average of the property "winnings" over just this one most probable distribution comes out zero. This is the correct answer, and it is the same as if we were to average over all possible distributions, starting with $N_{\text{head}} = 1$, etc.

It turns out that the same is true with more complicated averages over the various distributions of energy among a group of oscillators. We will show this for a simple model, consisting of s harmonic oscillators and an extra or special oscillator, which represents any system capable of accepting energy in a nondegenerate way. We will later wish to take this system to be just an extra harmonic oscillator of the same frequency, but it will still be convenient to regard it as a separate system.

The fundamental assertion of statistical mechanics is that every distinguishable eigenstate (corresponding to each wave function) is equally probable. Thus the statistical weight or probability of any arrangement of energy between the two systems in equilibrium is proportional to the number of ways it can be realized. We consider two such systems. The first is any system whatsoever in a definite state having weight unity and energy ϵ. The other is assumed to be a collection of equal and low-frequency harmonic oscillators, s in number and of total energy $E - \epsilon$. The total energy for both systems is thus E. For convenience, we shall use the characteristic quantum $h\nu$ of the oscillators as the unit of energy; thus there will be E such quanta altogether, $E - \epsilon$ of which will be distributed among the s oscillators conveniently arranged in a row. The weight of all the states taken together that put an energy of exactly ϵ in the first system is equal to the number of ways to arrange $E - \epsilon$ quanta in the s oscillators. Any particular arrangement can be indicated by an arrangement of $E - \epsilon$ balls that represent quanta, and $s - 1$ partitions that distinguish the oscillators:

$$\text{OO/OOO//O/}\cdots\text{OO/O}$$

In this diagram, there are two quanta in the first oscillator, three in the next, none in the third, etc. If all quanta and partitions were different, there would be $(E - \epsilon + s - 1)!$ such arrangements, but when we take account of the fact that the quanta and partitions are indistinguishable, then

$$W = \frac{(E - \epsilon + s - 1)!}{(E - \epsilon)!(s - 1)!} \tag{5.232}$$

Now all that is necessary is a mathematical evaluation of this expression in its limiting form for large values of s and E. The result is that the weight is an exponential function of the energy ϵ,

$$W = \text{const } e^{-\epsilon/t} \tag{5.233}$$

where t is a constant. Now, if we make the special oscillator the same as each of the s oscillators, we can look upon each of the $s + 1$ oscillators in turn as the special one. We are not now looking at the most probable distribution but at all possible ones compatible with the selected oscillator having an energy of ϵ quanta. We have found (Eq. 5.233) that the total distribution has the same exponential form as the most probable distribution, Eq. 5.230. For this reason we get the same result by averaging over the most probable distribution as over the whole distribution.

ILLUSTRATION.   We shall now prove Eq. 5.233.

This can be done most conveniently if we assume that the quanta are small (low-frequency oscillator) so that $E - \epsilon$ is much greater than s. We now apply Stirling's approximation to evaluate the factorials; Eq. 5.210 can be written $N! \approx N^N e^{-N}$ so

$$W = \frac{(E - \epsilon + s - 1)^{E-\epsilon+s-1}}{(E - \epsilon)^{E-\epsilon}(s - 1)^{s-1}} \tag{5.234}$$

It will now be convenient to use the fact that $(1 + x/N)^N$ approaches e^x if N is very large compared to 1 and also to x. Thus by rearrangement

$$W = \left[1 + \frac{s - 1}{E - \epsilon}\right]^{E-\epsilon+s-1} \frac{(E - \epsilon)^{s-1}}{(s - 1)^{s-1}} \tag{5.235}$$

$$= e^{s-1}\left[\frac{E}{s - 1} + \frac{E}{E - \epsilon}\right]^{s-1}\left[1 - \frac{\epsilon(s - 1)}{E(s - 1)}\right]^{s-1} \tag{5.236}$$

Now, if we define an average energy per oscillator, E/s, equal to $E/(s - 1)$ if s is large, and give it the symbol t, we find

$$W = \text{const } e^{-\epsilon/t} \tag{5.233}$$

if we approximate $E/(E - \epsilon)$ by unity. The quantity t is really the quantity kT, and so this derivation implies that kT is the average energy per oscillator at temperature T. This fact will help to identify the β of the previous treatment of Boltzmann's law with the temperature.

Physical Justification of the Boltzmann Law.   This second derivation of the Boltzmann distribution law provides some insight into its origin that is lacking in the derivation based on Lagrange's method of undetermined multipliers. If we assign an energy of ϵ quanta to a selected oscillator, $E - \epsilon$ quanta are left to distribute among a fixed number of other oscillators. Obviously, the more quanta we take for the selected oscillator, the fewer are left to distribute and the lower the value of W. On the other hand, if we take a single quantum from the ones in the selected oscillator, we may put it in any of the $s - 1$ other oscillators. This increases the total weight by a multiplicative factor of $s - 1$. The physical basis for the exponential decline of W as the energy is increased in a specified oscillator is thus made apparent.

Problems

5.201   Make a table showing the possible distributions of three quanta among four localized oscillators.

5.202   For a system of thirty quanta and thirty oscillators calculate the weight of the distribution $N_0 = 11$, $N_1 = 8$, $N_2 = 11$. Compare it with the result in the text for $N_0 = 10 = N_1 = N_2$.

5.203   Calculate the percentage error in ln N caused by using Stirling's approximation in the form of Eq. 5.210 when N is 5, 10, and 15.

5.204   A more exact form of the Stirling formula is

$$N! > \sqrt{2\pi}\, N^{N+\frac{1}{2}} e^{-N}$$

Also $N!$ is less than this same expression multiplied by $\left(1 + \dfrac{1}{4N}\right)$. Use these limiting forms in place of Eq. 5.210 to show what effect the approximation has on the final form of Boltzmann's law, Eq. 5.230, if all N's are very large.

5.205   Use the very crude approximation

$$N! = N^N$$

in the derivation of Boltzmann's equation and see what effect this substitution has.

5.206   Suppose that an array of harmonic oscillators had a common frequency of 10^{13} per second. Calculate the ratio of oscillators in the 10th quantum state ($n = 9$) to those in the ground state at 0, 300, and 1000°K.

3. The Partition Function

Definition.   The denominator of the Boltzmann expression, Eq. 5.231, consists of the sum

$$Z = \sum_i g_i e^{-\varepsilon_i/kT} \tag{5.301}$$

which when written out is

$$Z = g_0 e^{-\epsilon_0/kT} + g_1 e^{-\epsilon_1/kT} + g_2 e^{-\epsilon_2/kT} + \cdots$$

This summation is called the partition function. All its terms are positive. Formally, the sum terminates at the term for the qth level. In actual practice, the levels usually continue to an indefinite high energy. However, since the succeeding terms decay exponentially in magnitude, the contributions of the higher terms in the sum ultimately become negligible when q is large enough. If the energy zero is taken as the lowest state, i.e., $\epsilon_0 = 0$, the first term is ≥ 1, and in this case the partition function is always greater than unity. Z is the normalizing factor for the Boltzmann law. Each of the separate terms of the partition function is proportional to the relative number of oscillators in the level of that energy.

Equilibrium Constant from the Partition Function. Consider again two isomeric molecules A and B, which need not be nearly identical. We shall take as our formal representation of these molecules a series of nondegenerate energy levels, some of which are those of A, and the others those of B. There is an equilibrium constant

$$K_{eq} = \frac{N_B}{N_A} \tag{5.302}$$

which indicates the relative stability of the two. If we separate the energy levels of A and B, we can write two partition functions Z_A and Z_B,

$$Z_A = \sum_i e^{-\epsilon(A)_i/kT} \tag{5.303}$$

and

$$Z_B = \sum_i e^{-\epsilon(B)_i/kT} \tag{5.304}$$

In these equations $\epsilon(A)_i$ and $\epsilon(B)_i$ are the energy levels of the A and B molecules, respectively.

From a different standpoint, the two species of molecules A and B may be viewed as different configurations of the same molecule, since they are both made of the same atoms. This general molecule has all the energy levels of both A and B and has a partition function that is bigger than either; in fact we sum over *all* levels to find a total partition function

$$Z = Z_A + Z_B \tag{5.305}$$

which is simply the sum of the two individual partition functions. The probability that a molecule would be in any particular state, or the fraction of the total in that state, say an A state, is

$$\frac{N_i^{(A)}}{N_T} = \frac{e^{-\epsilon(A)_i/kT}}{Z_A + Z_B} \tag{5.306}$$

where N_T is the sum of N_A and N_B, the total number of molecules. The total fraction of A molecules is found by summing over all the A states,

$$\frac{N_A}{N_T} = \frac{Z_A}{Z_A + Z_B} \tag{5.307}$$

A similar expression holds for B molecules:

$$\frac{N_B}{N_T} = \frac{Z_B}{Z_A + Z_B} \tag{5.308}$$

If the ratio of these two expressions is written and compared with Eq. 5.302, we find

$$K_{eq} = \frac{Z_B}{Z_A} \tag{5.309}$$

This equation provides a link between equilibrium theory and the basic theory of the energy levels of a molecule, via the partition function of statistical mechanics. Equation 5.309 contains an implicit assumption about the zero of energy which is now considered.

Zero of Energy in the Partition Function. It is important to understand that Eq. 5.309 is based on Eq. 5.305, in which, by the addition, it is implied that Z_A and Z_B are based on the same zero of energy. It is natural, however, in writing the partition function for a molecule to select either the lowest energy level or the bottom of the potential well as the zero of energy. The selected reference level is not the same for A and B (except by accident); hence the partition functions will not be based on the same energy zero. The situation is schematically represented in Fig. 5.301. The broken lines represent a choice of energy zero for Z_A and Z_B based

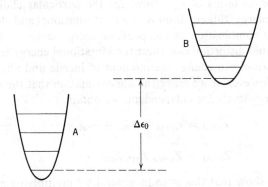

Fig. 5.301 Two oscillators with different zero energy levels.

on the lowest level for each molecule. They are separated by an energy $\Delta\epsilon_0$. If, however, the partition function Z_B is multiplied by the factor $e^{-\Delta\epsilon_0/kT}$, this corrects the zero energy level of Z_B to the zero energy level of Z_A. Thus, if each partition function is based on its individual zero of energy, Eq. 5.309 should be written

$$K = \frac{Z_B}{Z_A} e^{-\Delta\epsilon_0/kT} \tag{5.310}$$

where $\Delta\epsilon_0 = \epsilon(B)_0 - \epsilon(A)_0$. This quantity can be either positive or negative, depending on which molecule has the higher energy.

It is pertinent to note that Eq. 5.310 applies to gas-phase equilibria when the energy levels used in the partition function have been obtained from measurements or theories of single molecules in the gas. But if we know, can calculate, or can neglect the effect of a solvent, this equation can be applied to homogeneous reactions in solution as well.

Further development of the statistical mechanical theory of equilibrium constants is deferred to Chapter 11, after the development of the thermodynamic theory of equilibrium constants.

Separation of Partition Functions into Products.   We recall from Chapters 3 and 4 that the total energy of a molecule with several modes of motion that do not affect one another, such as vibration and translation, can be expressed as a sum of separate energies. Suppose, for example, that a molecule has a translational energy ϵ_i and a vibrational energy ϵ_j. The sum of these is

$$\epsilon_{ij} = \epsilon_i + \epsilon_j \tag{5.311}$$

There will be two partition functions, one for translation and one for vibration, with a term $e^{-\epsilon_i/kT}$ in the first and $e^{-\epsilon_j/kT}$ in the second.   Since

$$e^a e^b = e^{a+b} \tag{5.312}$$

there will be a term $e^{-(\epsilon_i + \epsilon_j)/kT}$ in the product of the two partition functions. If Eq. 5.311 holds, this is exactly the term we would get if we wrote the combined partition function in terms of ϵ_{ij}. Now, for the particular choice, translational and vibrational energy, this equation is exact; if rotational and electronic energies are included, the combination of independent energy levels by addition is often inexact. Rotational distortion can affect the vibrational energy levels, and in turn vibrational excitation can change the moment of inertia and affect the rotational energy levels. However, if we make the approximation that the molecule is rigid and that the energy levels are independent, we obtain

$$\epsilon_{\text{total}} = \epsilon_{\text{trans}} + \epsilon_{\text{vib}} + \epsilon_{\text{rot}} + \cdots$$
and

$$Z_{\text{total}} = Z_{\text{trans}} Z_{\text{vib}} Z_{\text{rot}} \cdots \tag{5.313}$$

The student can show that this is so in general by multiplying algebraically two partition functions with different sets of energy levels, and noting that a term is produced which corresponds to combination of every one of the first set of levels with each one of the second; that is, if there are n_1 levels in the first set and n_2 in the second, there are $n_1 n_2$ levels in the combined set, and also that many terms in the partition function.

We can now develop the various partition function expressions for different kinds of motion before we combine them by multiplication to obtain the total partition function for a molecule. We now derive one kind of partition function; others will be given in Chapter 6.

Partition Function for the Harmonic Oscillator.   The harmonic oscillator is the simplest system for which to write a partition function because the energy levels are equally spaced; $\epsilon_v = (v + \frac{1}{2})h\nu$, where ν is the frequency of the oscillator. We must evaluate

$$Z = \sum_{v=0}^{\infty} e^{-(v+\frac{1}{2})h\nu/kT} = e^{-\frac{1}{2}h\nu/kT} \left(\sum_{v=0}^{\infty} e^{-vh\nu/kT} \right) \tag{5.314}$$

In this form of the partition function, the zero of energy is taken at the bottom of the parabolic energy well, rather than at the lowest energy level, where $v = 0$. The latter is $\frac{1}{2}h\nu$ above the bottom of the well.

If we write $e^{-h\nu/kT} = x$, the expression within the parentheses in Eq. 5.314 is clearly $1 + x + x^2 + x^3 + \ldots$. Now by algebraic division

$$\frac{1}{1-x} = 1 + x + x^2 + x^3 + \cdots \tag{5.315}$$

Because of this fact, Eq. 5.314 can be written in closed form

$$Z = \frac{e^{-\frac{1}{2}h\nu/kT}}{1 - e^{-h\nu/kT}} \tag{5.316}$$

To write the partition function with the zero of energy at the lowest energy level, rather than at the bottom of the potential well, we leave out the zero-point energy $\frac{1}{2}h\nu$. In this case the partition function of the harmonic oscillator becomes

$$Z = \frac{1}{1 - e^{-h\nu/kT}} \tag{5.317}$$

The student will note that Eq. 5.316 is similar in form to the Planck radiation law; indeed it is by treating the ether as a collection of harmonic oscillators that the law will be derived. For small values of $h\nu/kT$, both Eqs. 5.316 and 5.317 reduce to the "classical" limit, when $e^x \approx 1 + x$,

$$Z = \frac{kT}{h\nu} \tag{5.318}$$

This simplification is analogous to the reduction of the Planck law to the Rayleigh-Jeans law. It is appropriate to use this simple form at high temperatures or with low-frequency oscillators. The test of validity is that the Z so calculated should be considerably larger than unity.

At the opposite limit, where $h\nu/kT$ is very large, Eq. 5.316 for Z approaches zero; Eq. 5.317 approaches unity.

Average Energy from the Partition Function.   The average energy of the system is clearly equal to the energy of a given level ϵ_i, multiplied by its probability N_i/N, and summed over all such terms. Or to put it in another, exactly equivalent way, if we have N systems, with N_i in each level, we multiply ϵ_i by N_i, sum for all levels, and then divide by N. Thus, denoting an average by a bar,

$$\bar{\epsilon} = \frac{\sum_i \epsilon_i N_i}{N} = \frac{\sum_i (\epsilon_i e^{-\epsilon_i/kT})}{\sum_i e^{-\epsilon_i/kT}} \tag{5.319}$$

Now this is exactly equal to the compact expression

$$\frac{-\partial \ln Z}{\partial(1/kT)} = \bar{\epsilon} \tag{5.320}$$

which relates the average energy to the partition function.

Fluctuations; Deviation from the Average Energy.   We can obtain an important equation if we differentiate Eq. 5.319 with respect to $-(1/kT)$.

$$\frac{-\partial\bar{\epsilon}}{\partial(1/kT)} = \frac{+Z\sum_i \epsilon_i^2 e^{-\epsilon_i/kT} - \left(\sum_i \epsilon_i e^{-\epsilon_i/kT}\right)^2}{Z^2}$$

$$= \overline{\epsilon^2} - \bar{\epsilon}^2 \tag{5.321}$$

This is equivalent to

$$\sigma_\epsilon^2 \equiv \overline{(\epsilon - \bar{\epsilon})^2} = \overline{\epsilon^2 - 2\epsilon\bar{\epsilon} + \bar{\epsilon}^2} = \overline{\epsilon^2} - 2\bar{\epsilon}\bar{\epsilon} + \bar{\epsilon}^2 = \overline{\epsilon^2} - \bar{\epsilon}^2$$

We thus have a way to obtain the standard deviation σ_ϵ of the energy of each oscillator from the average energy. Note carefully the position of the bar on the top of a quantity to indicate a particular kind of average. We have indicated the average energy, the square of the average energy, and the average of the square of the energy. We also have the average of the square of the deviation from the average, $\overline{(\epsilon - \bar{\epsilon})^2}$.

ILLUSTRATION.   Take the numbers 1, 2, and 3 and find all these averages.
The average is of course 2. The square of the average is 4. The average of the squares is $\frac{14}{3}$. The average deviation from the average is, as always, zero because two deviations have opposite signs and cancel, and the third is zero. The average of the square of the deviations is $\frac{2}{3}$, and the standard deviation is $\sqrt{\frac{2}{3}}$. Thus all these quantities have different and definite meanings.

Equation 5.321 is a formula for what is called the mean-square fluctuation, or in other words the deviations from the average energy, expressed in terms of the partition function. If we replace the average energy in Eq. 5.321 by its formula in terms of the partition function Eq. 5.320, we find

$$\frac{\partial^2 \ln Z}{\partial(1/kT)^2} = \overline{(\epsilon - \bar{\epsilon})^2} \tag{5.322}$$

which is always a positive quantity because the square of any deviation, positive or negative, is always positive.

ILLUSTRATION.   Calculate the average energy and fluctuation for the harmonic oscillator in the classical region where $h\nu \ll kT$.
From Eq. 5.318 we have

$$Z = \frac{kT}{h\nu}$$

We differentiate this once to find the average energy (Eq. 5.320)

$$\bar{\epsilon} = \frac{-\partial \ln(kT/h\nu)}{\partial(1/kT)} = kT \tag{5.323}$$

If we differentiate this once more we find the mean-square fluctuation

$$\overline{(\epsilon - \bar{\epsilon})^2} = (kT)^2 \tag{5.324}$$

The square root of this quantity, the standard deviation, is

$$\sigma_\epsilon = \left[\overline{(\epsilon - \bar{\epsilon})^2}\right]^{\frac{1}{2}} = kT \qquad (5.325)$$

Thus, roughly speaking, we may say that the average deviation from the average energy of a harmonic oscillator in the classical region is as large as the average energy. This corresponds to the fact that if we look at a very small sample (one oscillator) the fluctuations are relatively large.

Application of the Energy Equation to the Harmonic Oscillator.   The use of Eq. 5.320 can be demonstrated by the substitution of the partition function for the harmonic oscillator (Eq. 5.316). This yields an expression for the average energy of the harmonic oscillator as a function of temperature.

$$\bar{\epsilon} = \tfrac{1}{2}h\nu + \frac{h\nu}{e^{h\nu/kT} - 1} \qquad (5.326)$$

This expression is plotted in Fig. 5.302. The first term in this expression, $\tfrac{1}{2}h\nu$, is the zero-point energy of the oscillator, and its presence reflects the fact that the partition function has been written with the bottom of the potential as the zero of energy.

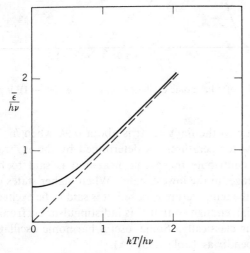

Fig. 5.302   Average energy of a harmonic oscillator as a function of temperature. Note the asymptotic approach to the dashed line at higher T.

If the lowest state is taken as the zero of energy, this quantity disappears. Since it is impossible to remove this last half-quantum of energy from the oscillator, it is perhaps more logical to base the energy on the lowest state. The corresponding partition function is given by Eq. 5.317. This yields, by the use of Eq. 5.320, the expression for the energy

$$\bar{\epsilon} = \frac{h\nu}{e^{h\nu/kT} - 1} \qquad (5.327)$$

This result differs from Eq. 5.326 only by the omission of the zero-point energy. This is exactly what we would expect, because the energy zeros of the two versions of the partition function differ by the same quantity.

Heat Capacity.   Energy is often not reported as such but rather as its derivative, the heat capacity, defined for our purposes here (see Chapter 7) as

$$C = \frac{d\bar{\epsilon}}{dT} \tag{5.328}$$

If this further differentiation of Eq. 5.326 is made, we obtain a function (Fig. 5.303) that has two very simple limits: at low T the heat capacity tends to zero; it rises

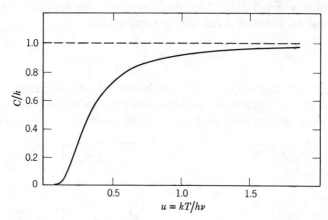

Fig. 5.303   Heat capacity of a harmonic oscillator. $C/k = u^2 e^u/(e^u - 1)^2$ is plotted as a function of $u = kT/h\nu$.

to become asymptotic to the limit k. It is about $0.9k$ when $h\nu/kT$ is unity (Fig. 5.303). Thus, at low temperatures, as determined by the ν/T ratio, a harmonic oscillator does not contribute to specific heat and is said to be unexcited; it remains, on the average, in the lowest state. When higher states contribute to the average behavior as the temperature is raised, it is said to be excited. Finally, when the temperature is high enough so that C is indistinguishable from k, the oscillator is said to be behaving classically. Some useful harmonic oscillator functions are tabulated in the Appendix as Table 5.301 (A).

Problems

5.301   Show that the limiting values of the heat capacity of a harmonic oscillator are zero and k at low and high temperatures, respectively.

5.302   Calculate the average value of the energy at the various temperatures for the same oscillators. What happens to the value as the temperature is raised?

5.303   Calculate the fluctuation in energy and standard deviation for these oscillators. What happens to the fluctuation in energy as the temperature is raised?

5.304   Calculate the heat capacity for these oscillators. What happens as the temperature is raised? (HINT: use Fig. 5.303.)

5.305   What is the effect on the calculations in the preceding problems of using the partition function Eq. 5.317 instead of 5.316? Could you tell by an experiment which form of the partition function is correct or is to be preferred?

5.306   The value of the N_i given by the Boltzmann distribution, Eq. 5.228, can now be substituted into Eq. 5.212 to obtain an expression for ln W_{max}. This expression can now be numerically evaluated for the oscillators of Problem 5.206. Set the total number of oscillators equal to 10^{23} and calculate W_{max} at the various temperatures. What happens as T is raised?

5.307   Draw a figure like Fig. 5.301 with the energy zeros taken at the bottom of the wells. What is the change in $\Delta \epsilon_0$ if the two oscillators are assumed to be harmonic?

5.308   Why is Eq. 5.305 a sum and Eq. 5.313 a product of individual partition functions?

4. Many Harmonic Oscillators;   Model for Solids

Law of Dulong and Petit; the Einstein Model.   Each of the atoms in a solid element has three degrees of freedom and moves against what is roughly a harmonic restoring force. If we indicate Avogadro's number by a boldface **N**, there are then 3**N** harmonic degrees of freedom per mole. If each degree of freedom had a heat capacity that approached k, the heat capacity of the solid would be $3\mathbf{N}k = 3R \approx$ 6 cal mole^{-1} deg^{-1}. This is substantially the law of Dulong and Petit. At lower temperature, the heat capacity is observed to fall off toward zero, as predicted by Fig. 5.303. This harmonic oscillator model for the solid is called the Einstein model when all the frequencies are taken to be equal. When the curve of Fig. 5.303, which applies directly to this model, is compared to experimental data, the fit is very poor at low temperature because the frequencies are not all the same, as was assumed. However, at reasonably high temperature, the heat capacity for an element levels out to the limiting value of $3R$ corresponding to classical behavior of all 3**N** degrees of freedom; hence there must be an effective upper limit to the frequency.

Identification of β.   As crude and unsatisfactory as the Einstein model is, it may be used to clarify one very important point. If we write the partition function for the harmonic oscillator as it would be if we had never identified β^{-1} with kT, the high-temperature or classical limit would be

$$Z = (\beta h \nu)^{-1} \tag{5.401}$$

The average energy in terms of this partition function would then be

$$\bar{\epsilon} = \frac{1}{\beta} \tag{5.402}$$

The average energy of a collection of 3**N** of these oscillators is then

$$\bar{E} = \frac{3\mathbf{N}}{\beta} \tag{5.403}$$

The heat capacity is then

$$\frac{d\bar{E}}{dT} = \frac{d(3\mathbf{N}/\beta)}{dT} \tag{5.404}$$

which can be set equal to the heat capacity of a real solid in the temperature range where it conforms to the law of Dulong and Petit:

$$\frac{d(3N/\beta)}{dT} = 3Nk \tag{5.405}$$

This equation is satisfied by the identification of β with $1/kT$. In Chapter 6, we shall see that the same identification reproduces the experimental fact of the perfect gas law, and finally, in Chapter 7, we shall identify the perfect gas temperature with the absolute thermodynamic temperature. This will complete the chain of proof.

Partition Function for the Einstein Model. In Sec. 5.3 we observed (Eq. 5.313) that the partition function for a collection of independent systems, each with a set of energy levels, was the product of the individual partition functions. If the partition function for each harmonic oscillator is Z, then the partition function for $3N$ independent oscillators of equal frequency is

$$Z_{\text{total}} = Z \times Z \times \cdots = Z^{3N} \tag{5.406}$$

From this expression and the equation for the average energy, Eq. 5.320, we can formally show that

$$\bar{E} = -\frac{d \ln Z_{\text{total}}}{d(1/kT)} = \frac{-3N \, d \ln Z}{d(1/kT)}$$

$$= 3N\bar{\epsilon} \tag{5.407}$$

We therefore establish the obvious fact that the total energy is proportional to N, or in other words to the amount of material present. In thermodynamics this is called an extensive property (Chapter 7).

Fluctuations in Solid Energy. We now focus attention on a group of N_C atoms in a large crystal that can be represented by $3N_C$ oscillators. The partition function for this group of atoms is the sum over a series of exponential terms, each containing an energy level E_C given by the sum of the individual energy levels of each oscillator,

$$E_C = \epsilon_1 + \epsilon_2 + \epsilon_3 + \cdots + \epsilon_{3N_C} \tag{5.408}$$

As before, the average energy of this part of the crystal can be obtained from the partition function

$$Z_C = Z^{3N_C} \tag{5.409}$$

where Z is the partition function for a single oscillator. This average energy is of course $3N_C\bar{\epsilon}$. When we calculate the mean-square fluctuation for this group of atoms, we get an important result. From Eq. 5.322 we find

$$\overline{(E_C - \bar{E}_C)^2} = \frac{d^2 \ln Z_C}{d(1/kT)^2}$$

$$= \frac{3N_C \, d^2 \ln Z}{d(1/kT)^2} \tag{5.410}$$

or for the standard deviation

$$\sigma_E = \text{const } N_C^{\frac{1}{2}} \tag{5.411}$$

Thus the average fluctuation increases with the number of atoms, but only with the square root of this number. The average energy, on the other hand, increases in a manner directly proportional to N_C. Thus the percentage error made by asserting that the average energy is always the *exact* energy of the crystal declines by a factor $1/N_C^{1/2}$ as the size of the sample is increased. This result justifies the assertion in Sec. 5.1 that the fluctuations become negligible with samples of large size.

Change in Variable from E to T.   When we began the derivation of Boltzmann's law, there were two fixed quantities: N, the number of oscillators, and E, the total energy (Eqs. 5.204 and 5.205). These may be regarded as external variables, subject to laboratory control. They were replaced by the undetermined multipliers α and β. The multiplier α was later eliminated in favor of N, and thus N was retained as an external variable. The quantity β which replaced E was identified with $1/kT$. Physically, this corresponds to change from an isolated system of constant energy, with no fluctuations possible, to a system at temperature T, in which fluctuations in energy are possible.

The preceeding discussion shows that such a change is without important effect if the system is large enough. Thus, for a macroscopic system we may identify $\bar{E}$ with E with no significant error. For large systems, we will use the expressions energy and average energy interchangeably. In Chapter 11, we will see that if we retain the multiplier α it can be related to another external variable, the chemical potential.

Distribution of Frequencies in an Elastic Solid.   Consider the motion of an atom in a crystal of an element. It can move against its neighbors while they stay fixed or move against it. Such a motion has a large restoring force acting on a small mass and thus is one of the higher frequencies possible in the crystal. At lower frequencies larger numbers of molecules can move together in cooperation with each other. At lowest frequency, relatively large portions of the sample twist and pulsate macroscopically under thermal agitation. These last modes are clearly small in number and very low in frequency. There is, therefore, a distribution of frequencies over a spectrum ranging from zero to a maximum. At the very lowest temperature, when only the macroscopic motions are excited, the model of a crystal composed of discrete atoms can be replaced by a continuous structureless solid with specified elastic constants. If we consider that we have a cube of this solid, clamped at its edges, we can calculate just what frequencies are allowed, very much as we calculated what eigenfunctions were allowed for a particle in a box. The wavelength of any standing wave must be such that it fits into the box with no motion at the boundary. Some allowed and unallowed wavelengths are pictured in Fig. 5.401 for one dimension only. The condition of fitting-in is that

$$a = n\frac{\lambda}{2}, \quad \text{or} \quad \frac{2}{\lambda} = \frac{n}{a} \qquad (5.412)$$

where λ is the wavelength, and a the length of the cube edge. The number n, which is the index number of the wave, must be integral and is like a quantum number.

If both sides of Eq. 5.412 are squared the analogy becomes clearer

$$\left(\frac{2}{\lambda}\right)^2 = \frac{n^2}{a^2} \tag{5.413}$$

This expression is similar to Eq. 2.406 for the energy levels of a particle in a one-dimensional box. The more difficult problem of fitting a three-dimensional wave into a box has as its condition of fitting-in

$$\left(\frac{2}{\lambda}\right)^2 = \left(\frac{1}{a}\right)^2 (n_x^2 + n_y^2 + n_z^2) \tag{5.414}$$

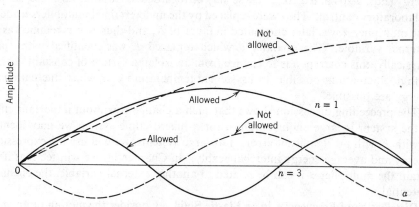

Fig. 5.401   Standing waves in a one-dimensional box.

This equation has a form similar to Eq. 3.209 for the energy levels of a particle in a three-dimensional box. It can be rearranged to read

$$\left(\frac{2a}{\lambda}\right)^2 = n_x^2 + n_y^2 + n_z^2 \tag{5.415}$$

This equation resembles that for the surface of a sphere centered at the origin,

$$X^2 + Y^2 + Z^2 = R^2 \tag{5.416}$$

where R is the radius of the sphere. If we identify the geometrical X, Y, and Z with n_x, n_y, and n_z, we see by comparison that

$$R = \frac{2a}{\lambda} \tag{5.417}$$

Now X, Y, and Z are continuous variables, but the indices n_x, n_y, and n_z are defined only at integral positive values. For a given value of λ these integral values can be thought of as a set of lattice points lying in the positive octant of the sphere defined by Eq. 5.415. The number of possible solutions is proportional to the area of this octant in the limit of large values of the indices. This area is of course one eighth of the area of the whole sphere. Thus the number of possible waves with wavelength

λ is proportional to the area of the sphere. If we increase the wavelength we decrease the radius of the sphere. The volume of one eighth of the sphere corresponds to the number of solutions of the eigenvalue problem with wavelengths larger than those defined by Eq. 5.415. Therefore the total number of waves with wavelength greater than or equal to λ is proportional to the volume of the sphere:

$$N_\lambda = \text{const} \left(\frac{a}{\lambda}\right)^3 = \text{const} \cdot \frac{V}{\lambda^3} \qquad (5.418)$$

Here we have introduced the physical volume of the cubical sample

$$V = a^3$$

which is not to be confused with the volume of the sphere in lattice space. The number of wavelengths within a small range $d\lambda$ can be obtained by taking the differential of N_λ to obtain a density function n_λ multiplied by $d\lambda$. It is

$$dN_\lambda = n_\lambda \, d\lambda = \text{const} \frac{V}{\lambda^4} d\lambda \qquad (5.419)$$

This is the differential distribution function for wavelengths in an elastic solid. The constant has been left unspecified but is a function of the elastic constants of the medium only. If we put this expression in terms of frequencies (cf. Chapter 1), we find

$$n_\nu \, d\nu = \text{const} \, V\nu^2 \, d\nu \qquad (5.420)$$

Thus, as the frequency rises, the available energy levels become much more numerous as the density increases with the second power of the frequency.

Derivation of Planck's Radiation Law. If we assume that electromagnetic radiation is propagated in a hypothetical elastic solid, that is, consists of waves sustained by the ether, the distribution function, Eq. 5.420, gives the density of frequencies available in a given frequency range. If we treat these frequencies as those of harmonic oscillators, the energy density is obtained by multiplication of this distribution function by the energy of each oscillator at that frequency. The latter is given by Eq. 5.327. Thus we combine these two expressions to obtain Planck's law, aside from a constant term,

$$\rho_\nu \, d\nu = \text{const} \frac{\nu^3 \, d\nu}{e^{h\nu/kT} - 1} \qquad (5.421)$$

The student will observe that we have left out the zero-point energy. A discussion of this omission, which is essential to the derivation, is beyond the scope of this treatment. The problem is that, since there are an infinite number of frequencies, the sum of all the zero-point energies of the oscillators would be infinite.

Debye's Low-Temperature Approximation to the Specific Heat of an Element. In the preceding paragraphs, we made a short digression to show how the Planck radiation law is derived. Debye assumed that a similar law for the distribution of frequencies held for an atomic solid, but only up to the point where $3N$ frequencies had been distributed. At this frequency he assumed that there was a sharp cut-off ν_D where n became zero. This is illustrated in Fig. 5.402. The true distribution is certainly not exactly like this, but two points are correct: it starts out at low frequencies as a parabolic function of ν; in addition, the total number of frequencies must be $3N$

$$\int_0^\infty n_\nu \, d\nu = 3N \tag{5.422}$$

These two conditions will hold for any solid; the first is true because at low frequencies, that is, long wavelengths, the assumption of a continuous solid on which the ν^2 law is based is valid. The waves are very large scale compared to the atomic spacing. The second condition is always true because, however the fre-

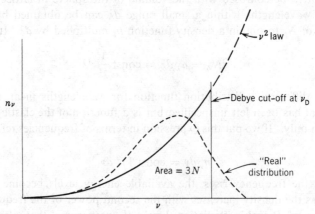

Fig. 5.402   Distribution of frequencies in a solid.

quencies are distributed, there must be exactly $3N$ degrees of freedom for N atoms. Note that there is no reason not to include the zero-point energy here, because the number of frequencies is finite.

Now the actual form of the heat capacity that can be derived from Debye's distribution is a rather complex function. However, because of the arbitrary nature of the Debye cut-off, its exact form is not of much importance. At very low temperatures, the asymptotic form of the law is very simple, the so-called Debye cube law

$$C = \text{const } T^3 \tag{5.423}$$

This law is obeyed quite accurately at low temperature, and perhaps fortuitously at somehat higher temperatures, by many substances. A strict analysis indicates that its range of validity is perhaps only up to a few degrees Kelvin; this is still a matter of controversy.

We can derive this law very simply if we observe that at low enough temperatures the oscillators near the cut-off will not be excited, and therefore the total energy content of a crystal should have the same form as that for the ether of the radiation field. This has a total energy that depends on the fourth power of T, as given by the Stefan-Boltzmann law.

$$E = \text{const } T^4 \tag{5.424}$$

The constant is not the same as that in the Stefan-Boltzmann law (Eq. 1.102) but the temperature dependence will be the same. We then have merely to differentiate Eq. 5.424 once with respect to temperature to obtain a law of the form of Eq. 5.423. All that remains is to find the numerical value of the constant in terms of ν_D, the cut-off frequency. We will simply state this result without deriving it. It is convenient to define a characteristic temperature

$$\theta = \frac{h\nu_D}{k} \tag{5.425}$$

The constant in Eq. 5.424 is $\frac{3}{5}\pi^4 Nk/\theta^3$. In terms of this parameter, the molar heat capacity is

$$C = \frac{\frac{12}{5}\pi^4 NkT^3}{\theta^3} \tag{5.426}$$

Heat capacity and the exact definition of the conditions under which it is measured will be discussed again in Chapter 7. We should remark that the C discussed here is to be measured at constant volume, C_V. Most of the experiments reported for solids involve heat capacity at constant pressure, C_P, or at the saturated vapor pressure of the material, C_S. We will develop equations in Chapter 7 that show the differences between these three quantities are negligible for the usual solid.

Heat Capacity of Compounds. In the case of covalent compounds, the whole molecule often behaves as a unit and acts like an elemental substance in that it should be handled by the Debye theory. The various internal motions behave very much as they do isolated in the gas phase and so should be treated as a set of Einstein oscillators, a certain number of one frequency, some of another, and so on. The Debye modes are often called acoustical modes because they are the motions that transmit sound; the rest are called optical modes because they are the same motions that give rise to the spectrum of the gaseous form of the same compound.

Simple ionic crystals behave much like atomic crystals if the ions are of similar mass, or more like a compound if the ions vary greatly in mass.

ILLUSTRATION. Ionic salts such as KCl and KBr behave in a manner similar to the elements. W. T. Berg and J. A. Morrison [*Proc. Roy. Soc.* (*London*), **A242**, 467 (1957)] give the following data:

Ionic Salt	C, cal mole^{-1} deg^{-1}					
	2.5°K	5.0°K	10.0°K	20.0°K	40.0°K	80.0°K
KCl	0.00112	0.00904	0.0804	0.713	3.558	8.157
KBr	0.00278	0.0237	0.2319	1.604	5.300	9.325

In order to see whether the Debye limiting law, Eq. 5.426, is obeyed we may examine the C ratios for KCl at temperatures which differ by a factor of 2:

$$\frac{C\,(5.0°)}{C\,(2.5°)} = \frac{0.00904}{0.00112} = 8.07; \quad \frac{C\,(10°)}{C\,(5°)} = \frac{0.0804}{0.00904} = 8.89$$

$$\frac{C\,(20°)}{C\,(10°)} = \frac{0.713}{0.0804} = 8.87; \quad \frac{C\,(40°)}{C\,(20°)} = \frac{3.558}{0.713} = 4.99$$

$$\frac{C\,(80°)}{C\,(40°)} = \frac{8.157}{3.558} = 2.293$$

Hence, since $(T_1/T_2)^3 = 8.0$, we see that the law is roughly obeyed at low T but not at higher T. If we solve Eq. 5.426 for θ, from the data at 2.5°,

$$\theta = \left(\frac{\frac{12}{5}\pi^4 NkT^3}{C}\right)^{\frac{1}{3}} = 235°$$

where N = twice Avogadro's number for a mole of salt, where there are two moles of ions. Now, since $\theta = h\nu_D/k$, a variation in θ at low T signifies a fluctuation in effective ν_D, that is, a departure of the actual frequency spectrum of the solid from the assumed simple dependence on ν^2.

The student may determine the situation for KBr and plot C vs. T.

Theoretical Prediction of Debye's θ.   Since the low-temperature frequencies of a solid are essentially mechanical vibrations on a large scale, it should be possible by a measurement of the elastic constants and density of a solid to calculate the

Table 5.401   Debye θ at 0°K*

Substance	θ_{calc}, °K	$\theta_{expt'l}$, °K
Cubic materials		
Copper	344	345
Silver	226	226
Gold	162	165
LiF	734	740
Hexagonal materials		
Magnesium	386	405
Zinc	328	305

* Simplified from table of G. A. Alers and J. R. Neighbours, *Revs. Mod. Phys.*, **31**, 675 (1959).

frequency spectrum in this region. In order to do this properly, however, the elastic constants must be known or extrapolated down to the region of a few degrees K, because this is where the heat capacity reflects the low frequencies alone. This comparison has been made by G. A. Alers and J. R. Neighbours; some of their results are shown in Table 5.401. They have collected values of θ based on elastic constants and compare them with values of θ obtained from low-temperature heat capacity.   Elastic constants were extrapolated from 4.2°K.

The type of plots that were used to estimate the value of θ are shown in Fig. 5.403.   Instead of plotting C against T^3, C/T is plotted against T^2.   Note that the theory holds well only below $\theta/50$, that is, only up to about 5°K.   This has led to the conclusion that the Debye theory of specific heats should be used only in the T^3 region, and then only with extreme caution.

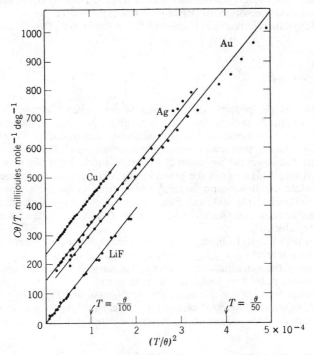

Fig. 5.403   Comparison of calculated specific heat (lines) with experimental points [by permission from G. A. Alers and J. R. Neighbours, *Revs. Mod. Phys.*, **31**, 675 (1959)].

Also note that the lines for the metals do not extrapolate to zero at $T = 0$.   This is due to a contribution to C that is linear in T caused by the metallic electrons. We shall return to this effect in Chapter 11.   It is for this reason, however, that C/T is plotted.   If the heat capacity is of the form

$$C = aT + bT^3 \qquad (5.427)$$

it is clear that C/T plotted vs. T^2 will be a straight line.

Problems

5.401   Explain why the law of Dulong and Petit was historically useful for heavy elements, while at the same time it failed for common light elements such as carbon.

5.402   Assume that the Einstein model applies to an element such as gold. Furthermore, assume that at room temperature the classical form of the partition function applies. Then calculate the total vibrational energy in a cube of gold 1 mm on an edge. Also calculate the average fluctuation in this energy if the small cube is in thermal contact with a large crystal of gold (density = 20).

*5.403   Use the data of Berg and Morrison (see the Illustration on p. 133) to calculate graphically the energy content of KCl at the temperatures given. Plot a smooth curve, as a function of T, of both the real energy and that predicted by the T^3 law for heat capacity. What is the percentage difference between these curves at $T = \theta$? Up to what fraction of θ is the theoretical curve within 10 per cent of the experimental curve?.

5.404   Plot the data referred to in Problem 5.403 in the form C/T vs. T^2 and estimate the values of θ.

5. Review Problems

5.501   Work out the possible distributions of four quanta among four harmonic oscillators. Calculate from these the average oscillator populations of each energy level.

5.502   Toss five coins twenty times and determine the deviation from the expected statistical result. Repeat this several times to get other samples of 100 tosses, and then combine all results and get the deviation of the grand total. From the time taken, calculate how long it would take to run the grand total up to Avogadro's number.

5.503   Calculate the Boltzmann factor, $e^{-\epsilon/kT}$, at 27°C for the following energies: (a) 10^{-12} erg molecule^{-1} (b) 1000 cal mole^{-1}, (c) 1.5 ev. Repeat the calculations for 1000°K. Note that these energies are given in various units, and the student should use the appropriate value of k.

5.504   Show that Eq. 5.313 holds. Take as an example the case where there are only three translational levels (ϵ_{t1}, ϵ_{t2}, ϵ_{t3}) and four vibrational levels (ϵ_{v1}, ϵ_{v2}, ϵ_{v3}, ϵ_{v4}).

5.505   Calculate the magnitude of the energy fluctuations for a harmonic oscillator if $h\nu/kT$ is (a) very large, (b) very small, (c) equal to unity.

*5.506   Obtain a formula for the mean-square fluctuations (Eq. 5.410) of energy for a small crystal, in terms of the heat capacity of the crystal. Apply the result to a 1 mm cube of diamond, at room temperature. Assume a density of 3.5 and a specific heat of 0.15 cal g^{-1}.

References

Davidson, N., *Statistical Mechanics*, McGraw-Hill Book Co., New York, 1962.

Guggenheim E. A., *Boltzmann's Distribution Law*, North Holland Publishing Co., Amsterdam, The Netherlands, 1959.

Gurney, R. W., *Introduction to Statistical Mechanics*, McGraw-Hill Book Co., New York, 1949.

Hill, T. L., *An Introduction to Statistical Thermodynamics*, Addison-Wesley Publishing Co., Reading, Mass., 1960.

Resnick, R., and D. Halliday, *Physics for Students of Science and Engineering*, Part I, 1960, and Part II, Second Edition, 1962, John Wiley and Sons, New York.

Rushbrooke, G. S., *Introduction to Statistical Mechanics*, Oxford University Press, Oxford, England, 1949.

Schrödinger, E., *Statistical Thermodynamics*, Cambridge University Press, Cambridge, England, 1948.

Chapter Six

The Theory of Gases

In this chapter we derive a number of macroscopic and microscopic properties of gases. We use some results from statistical mechanics and take the opportunity to demonstrate the power and usefulness of statistical methods. We first treat the case of an *ideal* or *perfect* gas and then take up real gases.

Model for the Perfect Gas. In thermodynamics, the perfect gas will be defined in terms of its macroscopic behavior. Here we shall assume the molecular picture and show that this leads to the familiar ideal behavior. In classical terms, the model is one of N vanishingly small spheres, with appropriate molecular masses, moving in a volume V. The molecules possess neither rotational nor vibrational energy, but only translational energy in three independent coordinate directions. At no time are these spheres subject to any intermolecular force or to an external force, except when they strike the wall and are reflected back into the volume V. Because they have infinitesimal volume and exhibit neither repulsive nor attractive forces, intermolecular collisions do not occur.

In terms of quantum mechanics, the picture is one of N particles in a box of volume V, each with energy levels characteristic of a single particle in the same volume. There is no term in the Hamiltonian function for interaction energy between the particles, but only terms in linear momentum. Inside the volume there is only kinetic energy; outside the volume the potential energy is infinite everywhere and keeps the particles within V.

1. Maxwell Distribution Laws for Velocity and Speed

Some important expressions relating to the properties of gases are those given by Maxwell (1860) and Boltzmann, which summarize the translational behavior of the gas molecules. It will be instructive to obtain these expressions in several alternative ways.

Distribution Functions. We shall now investigate the distribution law for velocity components u, v, and w in three coordinate directions among N molecules in a gas. The components u, v, and w may be thought of as constituting a vector. There is a density function or probability distribution in u, v, and w called $f(u,v,w)$, which, when multiplied by a differential velocity interval $du\, dv\, dw$, gives the fraction of molecules within this velocity interval,

$$\frac{dN_{uvw}}{N} = f(u,v,w)\, du\, dv\, dw \tag{6.101}$$

That is, dN_{uvw}/N is the fraction of molecules which have simultaneously a velocity component in the x direction between u and $u + du$, in the y direction between v and $v + dv$, and in the z direction between w and $w + dw$. Obviously, if the differential interval $du\, dv\, dw$ were made larger, the fraction of molecules with the specified velocity properties would increase. The function f must be normalized; that is, the total number of molecules with *any* velocity must be N, and the sum of the relative probability must be unity

$$\int\!\!\!\int\!\!\!\int_{-\infty}^{\infty} f(u,v,w)\, du\, dv\, dw = 1 \tag{6.102}$$

Notice that the distribution function $f(u,v,w)$ is analogous to the square of the wave function; it is always positive and represents the probability of finding a particle in a given velocity range. Equation 6.102 is the analog of Eq. 2.302. Note particularly that $f(u,v,w)$ does not have to be squared in the normalization equation; it already represents probability, whereas the wave function, which itself is often negative in sign, must be squared.

Maxwell's Argument. It is of interest to describe Maxwell's own derivation which, although very sophisticated, requires little more than the concept of the function of velocity f. Maxwell asserted that the probability function for each molecule depends on u, v, and w only through its total kinetic energy. This is a function of the sum $u^2 + v^2 + w^2$, with no other u, v, or w terms (Eq. 2.110). He also asserted that the probability of velocity in one direction is independent of the velocity in a perpendicular direction; this requires that f be equal to a product of three independent functions, $f(u)f(v)f(w)$. The most general function that has these properties is an exponential one. Thus, if we insert the kinetic energy into an exponential function,

$$f(u,v,w) = \text{const} \cdot e^{bm(u^2 + v^2 + w^2)/2} = \text{const} \cdot e^{bmu^2/2} \cdot e^{bmv^2/2} \cdot e^{bmw^2/2} \tag{6.103}$$

The pre-exponential constant is evaluated from Eq. 6.102; the constant b is shown later to be equal to $-1/kT$, when the distribution is used to derive the perfect gas law.

ILLUSTRATION.   Prove that, if $f(x + y) = f(x)f(y)$ and if $f(x)$ is finite, continuous, and not identically zero, the exponential function is a general representation of $f(x)$.

We have first

$$f(a + 0) = f(a)f(0)$$

which proves $f(0) = 1$.   Then

$$1 = f(0) = f(x - x) = f(x)f(-x)$$

Hence $f(x)$ is never zero, and

$$f(-x) = 1/f(x)$$

Then

$$f(x) = f\left(\frac{x}{2} + \frac{x}{2}\right) = \left[f\left(\frac{x}{2}\right)\right]^2$$

which, being a square, is always positive.   Thus

$$f(x) > 0$$

If m is an integer, just as $f(1 + 1) = [f(1)][f(1)] = f(2)$, in general

$$f(m) = f(1)f(1)f(1)\cdots = [f(1)]^m$$

Also, if n is an integer, just as $f(\frac{1}{2} + \frac{1}{2}) = [f(\frac{1}{2})][f(\frac{1}{2})] = f(1)$,

$$\left[f\left(\frac{1}{n}\right)\right]^n = f(1)$$

From these two results,

$$f\left(\frac{m}{n}\right) = [f(1)]^{m/n}$$

Now m/n is a rational number that can be made arbitrarily close to any x in value.   Thus

$$f(x) = [f(1)]^x$$

The number $f(1)$ can be given any positive value A that is not unity, and since

$$A \equiv e^{\ln A}$$

we can write

$$f(x) = [e^{\ln A}]^x = e^{x \ln A}$$

which is of the form e^{bx}, the exponential function.   The student can easily generalize this proof to $x + y + z$.   The proof is due to A. Cauchy.

Quantum Statistical Derivation of the Maxwell Distribution Law of Velocities in One Dimension.   A more explicit derivation of Maxwell's law is now appropriate.

We shall consider first the quantum picture for motion in one dimension. There are three steps in the derivation. First, we find the specific form which the Boltzmann distribution law takes when the energy levels for a particle in a box are inserted. Second, this energy distribution function is converted to a momentum function. The final step is the simplest—the momentum function is converted to a velocity distribution function.

The translational energy levels of a particle free to move in the x direction only and confined to a length a are nondegenerate and are given by Eq. 2.406

$$\epsilon_x = \frac{n^2 h^2}{8ma^2} \tag{6.104}$$

On substitution in the Boltzmann law (Eq. 5.231), the fraction of molecules in the quantum level having the quantum number n is given by

$$\frac{N_n}{N} = \frac{e^{-n^2 h^2 / 8ma^2 kT}}{\displaystyle\sum_{n=1}^{\infty} e^{-n^2 h^2 / 8ma^2 kT}} \tag{6.105}$$

The expression in the denominator is just the partition function per molecule for translation in one dimension. If we take advantage of the close spacing of the levels, we can treat the quantum number n as a continuous variable. We can take the total number of molecules N and the length a both large enough so that the differential change dN_n is a large number, when the range of quantum number dn that corresponds to dN_n is taken. This is simply a matter of mathematical convenience. We can thus replace the summation in the denominator of Eq. 6.105 by an integration

$$Z_{\text{trans}(1)} = \int_0^\infty e^{-n^2 h^2 / 8ma^2 kT} \, dn = \frac{(2\pi mkT)^{\frac{1}{2}} a}{h} \tag{6.106}$$

Therefore Eq. 6.105 can be written

$$\frac{N_n}{N} = \frac{e^{-n^2 h^2 / 8ma^2 kT}}{(2\pi mkT)^{\frac{1}{2}} a / h} \tag{6.107}$$

Equation 6.107 is an *energy* distribution function which gives the fractional population of one level. We now perform step 2 and transform this equation into a *momentum* distribution function. Since the energy can be written in terms of the classical momentum as $\epsilon = p^2/2m$, we can use Eq. 6.104 to find

$$\frac{n^2 h^2}{8ma^2} = \frac{p^2}{2m} \tag{6.108}$$

or

$$\frac{nh}{2a} = |p|$$

and thus

$$dn = \frac{2a}{h} \, d|p| \tag{6.109}$$

where dn represents a range of values of the quantum number n and $d|p|$ is the associated range of momentum. The bars around p mean absolute value, because the quantum number n is associated with both positive and negative momenta of equal absolute magnitude. There are thus twice as many states in $d|p|$ as in a similar dp with given sign. Now if dn is small enough so that the energy does not change appreciably, Eq. 6.107 predicts that the populations in each level within dn are virtually equal. To get the total population in the interval dn, Eq. 6.107 is multiplied by dn

$$\frac{dN_n}{N} = \frac{N_n}{N} \, dn \tag{6.110}$$

If we now combine Eqs. 6.107 to 6.110, we obtain the distribution function in terms of $d|p|$

$$\frac{dN_{|p|}}{N} = \frac{(2a/h)e^{-p^2/2mkT}}{(2\pi mkT)^{\frac{1}{2}}(a/h)} \, d|p|$$

Now we wish to express the distribution in terms of ordinary momentum p rather than $|p|$. We therefore simplify and divide by 2 to obtain

$$\frac{dN_p}{N} = f(p) \, dp = \frac{e^{-p^2/2mkT} \, dp}{(2\pi mkT)^{\frac{1}{2}}} \tag{6.111}$$

This factor of 2 arises because, if $d|p|$ is set equal to dp, then in that interval $dN_{|p|} = 2dN_p$.

Finally, we perform step 3 in terms of the velocity in the x direction, $p = mu$, and $dp = m \, du$. On making the substitution

$$\frac{dN_u}{N} = f(u) \, du$$

$$= \frac{e^{-mu^2/2kT} \, du}{(2\pi kT/m)^{\frac{1}{2}}} \tag{6.112}$$

The student can demonstrate that each of these expressions is normalized; note that the integration range of u and p is $-\infty$ to $+\infty$, while for $|p|$ and the quantum number n it is 0 to $+\infty$.

Equation 6.112 is the Maxwell distribution law of velocities for one degree of translational freedom. $f(u)$ has the symmetrical form shown in Fig. 6.101. The most probable value of the velocity u is zero. We shall return shortly to further consideration of this curve and some of its properties.

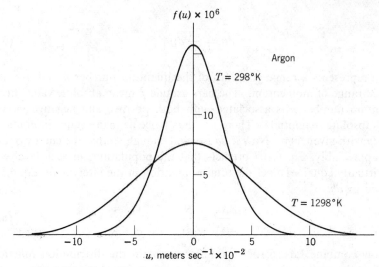

$f(u) \times 10^6$

Argon

$T = 298°K$

10

5

$T = 1298°K$

-10 -5 0   5   10

u, meters sec$^{-1} \times 10^{-2}$

Fig. 6.101   Maxwell's distribution of velocity in one degree of freedom.

ILLUSTRATION.   Compute the magnitude of $Z_{\text{trans}(1)}$ for chlorine gas at 25°C for $a = 1$ cm. Compare the result with Z_{vib} calculated from Eq. 5.316 if $\omega_{\text{Cl}_2} = 565$ cm^{-1}.

$$Z_{\text{trans}(1)} = \frac{(2\pi m k T)^{1/2} a}{h}$$

$$= \frac{(2 \times 3.14 \times 71.0 \times 1.38 \times 10^{-16} \times 298.2)^{1/2} \times 1}{6.62 \times 10^{-27} \times (6.02 \times 10^{23})^{1/2}}$$

$$= 8.36 \times 10^8$$

$$Z_{\text{vib}} = \frac{e^{-h\nu/2kT}}{1 - e^{-h\nu/kT}}$$

$$= \frac{e^{-hc\omega/2kT}}{1 - e^{-hc\omega/kT}}$$

where

$$e^{-hc\omega/2kT} = \frac{\exp(-6.624 \times 10^{-27} \times 2.998 \times 10^{10} \times 565)}{(2 \times 1.380 \times 10^{-16} \times 298.2)} = e^{-1.36}$$

$$Z_{\text{vib}} = \frac{e^{-1.36}}{1 - e^{-2.72}} = \frac{0.257}{1 - 0.066}$$

$$= 0.257 \times 1.071$$

$$= 0.275 \text{ for the classical zero of energy}$$

or 1.071 for the zero-point energy level taken as the zero of energy.

In connection with later applications, the student should note that for ordinary molecular or atomic masses $Z_{\text{trans}(1)} \sim 10^8 - 10^9$, while $Z_{\text{vib}} \sim 1$ at low temperatures, where "low" means that $hc\omega \geqslant kT$. It is important to note also that, since the spacings of the levels of translational energy ϵ_x depend on the length of the line (size of the box) in which the particle is confined, $Z_{\text{trans}(1)}$ also depends on this quantity.

How small would the box have to be in order that Eq. 6.106 for $Z_{\text{trans}(1)} \approx Z_{\text{vib}}$? The student should try to advance a qualitative argument as to why the value of $Z_{\text{trans}(1)}$ would in fact actually fall below the nominal value given by Eq. 6.106 before a shrank to the required value.

Maxwell Distribution Law of Velocities in Three Dimensions.   In the same way as for motion in the x direction, we have for the velocity along the y axis

$$\frac{dN_v}{N} = f(v)\,dv = \left(\frac{m}{2\pi kT}\right)^{\!\frac{1}{2}} e^{-mv^2/2kT}\,dv \tag{6.113}$$

with a similar expression for $f(w)$.

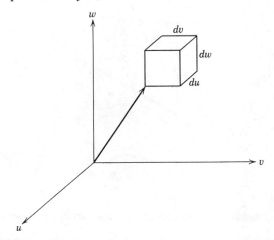

Fig. 6.102   Differential element of velocity space, *du dv dw*.

With the use of the postulate that motions in the three coordinate directions are independent, the probability that any molecule simultaneously has velocity in the range u to $u + du$ in the x direction, v to $v + dv$ in the y direction, and w to $w + dw$ in the z direction is found by compounding the individual probabilities of type Eqs. 6.112 and 6.113, so

$$\frac{dN_{uvw}}{N} = f(u,v,w)\,du\,dv\,dw = \frac{e^{-m(u^2+v^2+w^2)/2kT}\,du\,dv\,dw}{(2\pi kT/m)^{\frac{3}{2}}} \tag{6.114}$$

This is the complete Maxwell distribution law of velocities. It represents the fraction of molecules with the specified velocity properties, that is, those whose velocity vector terminates within the infinitesimal box of Fig. 6.102. It is evident that in correspondence to the range u to $u + du$ the quantum number for translational energy assumes values in the range n_x to $n_x + dn_x$; similarly for n_y and n_z. We might construct a figure similar to Fig. 6.102 in which n_x, dn_x, etc., were used.

Partition Function for Translation in Volume V.   By analogy with Eq. 6.106 the partition function for three-dimensional translation is

$$Z_{\text{trans}(3)} = \frac{(2\pi mkT)^{3/2} abc}{h^3} = \frac{(2\pi mkT)^{3/2} V}{h^3} \tag{6.115}$$

where V, the volume of the rectangular enclosure, equals the product of the lengths of the sides, abc. Evidently $Z_{\text{trans}(3)}$ is the product of three one-dimensional partition functions. This reflects the fact that the energies in each of the three dimensions are independent (Eq. 3.208).

The exponential terms in Eqs. 6.112 and 6.114 involve only the translation energy, and the exponent contains no contribution from energy in either rotational or

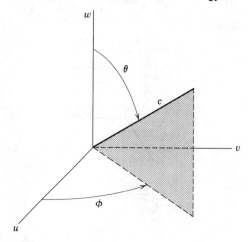

Fig. 6.103   The relation between the speed c and the velocity components u, v, and w.

internal degrees of freedom. Although a real gas molecule, as opposed to an ideal gas particle, may possess such degrees of freedom, the translational energy problem may be separated from that of the other degrees of freedom, as was pointed out earlier in Sec. 2.6 and in the derivation of Eq. 5.313.

The Maxwell Distribution in Terms of the Speed.   We have heretofore been concerned with $f(u,v,w)$ which gives the probability density of velocity within a volume element $du\, dv\, dw$. We now develop a new distribution function, based on the speed of the molecules, which is defined as the positive square root

$$c = + (u^2 + v^2 + w^2)^{1/2} \tag{6.116}$$

This is a radial coordinate, with the same geometric construction as the radial coordinate r for the hydrogen atom (Fig. 3.201); c is the magnitude of a vector at an angle θ to the vertical axis, and at an angle ϕ around this axis (see Fig. 6.103). What we are now interested in is the magnitude c without regard to the value of these angles. That is, we are concerned with the speed of the molecule and not the direction in which it is traveling. Thus the volume element $du\,dv\,dw$ has a particular orientation in terms of θ and ϕ; the interval dc covers all values of these angles and defines a spherical shell of radius c and thickness dc.

We must therefore transform Eq. 6.114 in the variables u, v, and w into the new variables c and the angles θ and ϕ. The transformation in the exponent is simple, since it is already a function of $u^2 + v^2 + w^2 = c^2$. The volume element $du\,dv\,dw$ must be replaced by the volume element in polar coordinates:

$$c^2 \sin\theta\,dc\,d\theta\,d\phi$$

If we do this we obtain

$$\frac{dN_{c,\theta,\phi}}{N} = \frac{e^{-mc^2/2kT}}{(2\pi kT/m)^{3/2}} c^2 \sin\theta\,dc\,d\theta\,d\phi \tag{6.117}$$

as the distribution function in these three variables. However, if we are concerned not with the direction of motion, but only the speed c, we can integrate over all values of θ from 0 to π, and all values of ϕ from 0 to 2π. We thus find for the distribution in speed alone

$$\frac{dN_c}{N} = \frac{e^{-mc^2/2kT}}{(2\pi kT/m)^{3/2}} \int_0^{2\pi} \int_0^{\pi} c^2 \sin\theta\,dc\,d\theta\,d\phi$$

$$= f(c)\,dc = \left(\frac{2}{\pi}\right)^{1/2} \left(\frac{m}{kT}\right)^{3/2} c^2 e^{-mc^2/2kT}\,dc \tag{6.118}$$

This expression is called the Maxwell distribution of speed in three dimensions. It is normalized; by a single integration over c from 0 to ∞, we find

$$\int_0^{\infty} f(c)\,dc = 1 \tag{6.119}$$

Equation 6.118 differs importantly in form from Eq. 6.114 by the factor c^2, which causes $f(c)$ to be skewed toward higher speeds. The most probable speed is not zero (Fig. 6.104). The student will recall a similar situation in Chapter 3 for the 1s state of the hydrogen atom. The electron probability per unit volume is highest at the origin, but the most probable distance is not zero but the Bohr radius, because of an r^2 factor in the total volume element at a given distance, r. The analogy is not complete, however, because the exponential part of the 1s function (Eq. 3.221) leads to a probability function that falls off as e^{-2r/a_0}; the corresponding function here is $e^{-mc^2/2kT}$.

A direct and accurate experimental verification of the Maxwell law has been made in a molecular beam study by Miller and Kusch (1955), although indirect experimental verification of the consequences of the law has been long and abundantly obtained. In this experiment, a beam of atoms of potassium or thallium, heated to a particular temperature in the oven O (Fig. 6.105), was formed by allowing molecules to effuse randomly out of the oven and by collimating them with the slits S and S'. A rotating cylinder, C, carrying helical grooves G, turned

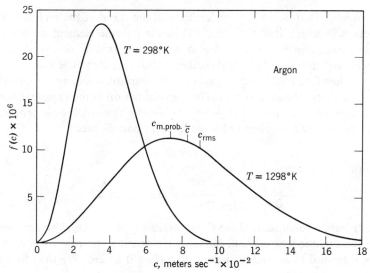

Fig. 6.104   Maxwell distribution in speed. Some special averages discussed in the next section are indicated. The most probable speed is also indicated.

with an angular velocity such that a molecule entering the grooves at 1 passed along the length of the groove without striking the wall. By varying the angular speed of the velocity selector C, the number of atoms in different narrow ranges of velocity was measured with the detector D and the law verified within experimental error.

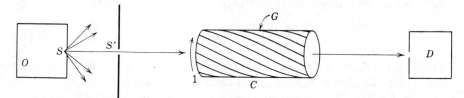

Fig. 6.105   Schematic diagram of molecular beam apparatus.

ILLUSTRATION.   R. C. Miller and P. Kusch [*Phys. Rev.*, **99**, 1314 (1955)] give the dimensions of their velocity selector (Fig. 6.106) as $\phi_0 = 2\pi/74.7$ radians, $L = 20.40$ cm, $r_0 = 10.00$ cm, and $l = 0.0424$ cm. Find the angular velocity ω of the cylinder which will pass potassium atoms having a speed $c = 1.0 \times 10^4$ cm sec^{-1}.

Now the time required for the atoms to travel the distance L is L/c. If ω is the required angular velocity in radians per second, then the time required for the cylinder to spin ϕ_0 radians so that the molecule moves down the groove without striking the groove wall is $L/c = \phi_0/\omega$, or

$$\omega = \frac{c\phi_0}{L} = \frac{1.0 \times 10^4 \times 2\pi}{20.40 \times 74.7} \text{ radians sec}^{-1}$$

If the groove has finite width l, the student may show, with the use of the above equation and the well-known relation between arc, angle, and radius of a circle ($a = r_0\phi_0$), that in the apparatus of Miller and Kusch the actual speeds admitted at this value of ω would range over c_{max} to c_{min} of 1.05×10^4 to 0.95×10^4 cm sec^{-1}.

The speed at the maximum of the distribution function was found to be 3.92×10^4 cm sec^{-1} for thallium atoms and 6.28×10^4 cm sec^{-1} for potassium

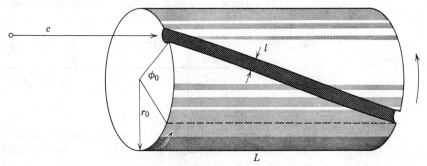

Fig. 6.106   Detail of velocity selector.

atoms at the temperatures used. The student may calculate the angular velocity in revolutions per second which was used by the investigators to pass these atoms through the selector.

Semiclassical Derivation of $f(u)$.   It is instructive to restate the derivation of $f(u)$ in a somewhat different way.

Previously, we started with the Boltzmann distribution law and then used Eq. 6.109 to give a relation between dn and dp, that is, between the size of an element of "volume" in "energy space" and in "momentum space." Starting again from the Boltzmann law, we may in effect perform steps 1 and 2 of the derivation together as follows.

Consider the motion of gas molecules having velocity u, the molecules being in a one-dimensional volume (line) of size (length) a. We may appeal to the uncertainty principle for information on the meaning of g_i in Eq. 5.231. If we treat the translational energy as continuous, we recall that $\Delta x\, \Delta p \geqslant h$, and Planck's constant thus gives the volume of the smallest element or cell in a combined two-dimensional space, of which one coordinate describes the momentum ($p = mu$) of a molecule in the x direction, and another coordinate describes the position of the particle in the box of length a (Fig. 6.107). Then two molecules whose x and p coordinates lie within a range x to $x + dx$ and p to $p + dp$, such that $dx\, dp \leqslant h$, exist in indistinguishable states; and the number of states, g, within the arbitrary ranges dx and dp of the variables x and p, treated as continuous, is

$$g = \frac{dx\, dp}{h} \qquad (6.120)$$

It will be noted that g is independent of the magnitude of p (i.e., of n) and is the same for all p. Then

$$\frac{dN_{xp}}{N} = \frac{e^{-p^2/2mkT}\, dx\, dp/h}{\displaystyle\int_{-\infty}^{\infty}\int_0^a e^{-p^2/2mkT}\, dx\, dp/h} \tag{6.121}$$

Now as far as the velocity distribution is concerned, it is of no consequence where the particle is located, so that on integration over the allowed values of x we have

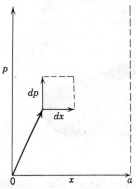

$$\frac{dN_p}{N} = \frac{\dfrac{1}{h}\displaystyle\int_0^a e^{-p^2/2mkT}\, dx\, dp}{\dfrac{1}{h}\displaystyle\int_{-\infty}^{\infty}\int_0^a e^{-p^2/2mkT}\, dx\, dp} = \frac{\dfrac{a}{h}\, e^{-p^2/2mkT}\, dp}{\dfrac{(2\pi mkT)^{1/2}a}{h}}$$

Simplification yields Eq. 6.111.

It should be noted that the semiclassical analog of the quantum summation given for $Z_{\text{trans}(1)}$ in Eq. 6.106 is

$$Z_{\text{trans}(1)} = \frac{1}{h}\int_{-\infty}^{+\infty}\int_0^a e^{-p^2/2mkT}\, dx\, dp \tag{6.122}$$

$$= \frac{(2\pi mkT)^{1/2}a}{h} \tag{6.106}$$

Fig. 6.107 Two-dimensional position-momentum space.

where h has been identified as the element of volume in the two-dimensional x, p space.

The Maxwell Distribution in Speed; Statistical Weights. We shall now consider the problem of replacing u, v, and w by the speed, c, in terms of statistical weights. We begin by briefly considering the one-dimensional case. Here the velocities u to $u + du$ and $-u$ to $-(u + du)$ both correspond to the same speed c to $c + dc$ (Fig. 6.108). Thus dc includes both of the infinitesimal elements of the line du and $-du$. In terms of our earlier discussion of velocity, where g was $dx\, dp/h$, now $g_c = 2dx\, dp/h = 2m\, dx\, dc/h$. It should be noted that g_c is still a constant independent of the magnitude of c and involves only the interval dc. Hence

$$\frac{dN_c}{N} = 2\left(\frac{m}{2\pi kT}\right)^{1/2} e^{-mc^2/2kT}\, dc \tag{6.123}$$

The range of integration for normalization is 0 to ∞.

In three dimensions, c is defined by Eq. 6.116. All speeds in a range from c to $c + dc$ lie in every direction within a shell of radius c and thickness dc. The volume of this shell is a function of c equal to $4\pi c^2\, dc$. The ratio $4\pi c^2\, dc/du\, dv\, dw$ is also the ratio of g_{3c}/g_3, where g_3, the degeneracy factor for the three-dimensional semiclassical velocity formulation, is $dx\, dy\, dz\, dp_x\, dp_y\, dp_z/h^3$ in analogy with Eq. 6.120 and is a constant independent of velocity, and g_{3c} is $4\pi m^3 c^2\, dc\, dx\, dy\, dz/h^3$.

The dependence of g_{3c} on c, as well as the constancy of the degeneracy g of velocity space whether in one, two, or three dimensions, may also be readily understood in quantum statistical terminology: in one dimension, a given energy level, quantum number n_x, corresponds to motion on the line in both x directions, that is, c is two-fold degenerate. In three dimensions, a given energy, characterized by specified values of n_x, n_y, and n_z, is unaffected by the choices of two possible signs of the velocities; it corresponds to eight possible velocity vectors, as given

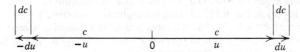

Fig. 6.108   The relationship between dc and du in one dimension.

by compounding the possibilities $2 \times 2 \times 2$ for each of three choices of sign. Figure 6.103 represents one of these. In addition to this eight-fold contribution to the degeneracy of the speed quantity, there are many more contributions. If for simplicity we choose a cubic volume, $a = b = c$, the translational energy levels are (Eq. 3.209)

$$\epsilon_{trans} = \frac{(n_x^2 + n_y^2 + n_z^2)h^2}{8ma^2}$$

and if we fix the energy level, then any combination of $n_x^2 + n_y^2 + n_z^2$ whose sum is invariant is acceptable and corresponds to another eight-fold degeneracy in c. Thus, if $n_x = 2$, $n_y = 3$, $n_z = 5$, $n^2 = n_x^2 + n_y^2 + n_z^2 = 4 + 9 + 25 = 38$. Other

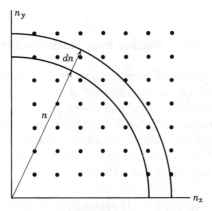

Fig. 6.109   Two-dimensional representation in the $n_x n_y$ plane, showing how the possible combinations of n_x and n_y, corresponding to the total n, increase with n.

acceptable combinations are 3, 2, 5; 5, 3, 2; 5, 2, 3; 2, 5, 3; 3, 5, 2; 6, 1, 1,; 1, 6, 1; etc. In fact, for $n_x^2 + n_y^2 + n_z^2$ large, the possible combinations of n_x, n_y, and n_z corresponding to n^2 increase as the number of lattice points in a given shell of n space (Fig. 6.109).

When a change to a single variable c is made in Eq. 6.114, and g_3 is replaced by g_{3c}, Eq. 6.118 results.

Problems

6.101 Normalize the energy function $f(\epsilon)\, d\epsilon = e^{-\epsilon/kT}\, d\epsilon$, where $0 \leq \epsilon \leq \infty$.

6.102 At what value of n would the one-dimensional translational energy level spacings of chlorine gas be $\sim hc\omega$ $(a = 1\ \mathrm{cm})$? See Illustration for value of ω.

6.103 Why is $f(u)$ in Eq. 6.112 already normalized, as derived?

6.104 Show mathematically that the most probable value of u is zero, i.e., $u_{\mathrm{mp}} = 0$.

6.105 Write the limiting forms of $f(u)$ for $T \to \infty$ and $T \to 0$. In the latter case write down the value of the following expressions:

(a) $f(u)$, for $u \neq 0$.

(b) $\displaystyle\int_{-\infty}^{\infty} f(u)\, du$.

6.106 For motion in two directions, what is the number of states encompassed by the range of the variables $dx\, dy\, dp_x\, dp_y$? What is the number of states if dp_x and dp_y are replaced by $d\,|p_x|$ and $d\,|p_y|$?

6.107 If a He^+ ion is accelerated in a mass spectrograph by a potential drop of 2000 volts, calculate the momentum and velocity of the ion.

6.108 To what value of n_x would the energy of the He^+ correspond most closely in Problem 6.107 if the ion was in a box of the length of the spectrograph, $\sim 1\ \mathrm{m}$?

6.109 Find all the possible degeneracies associated with each sum of translational quantum numbers for the range $n_x^2 + n_y^2 + n_z^2 = 96$ to 104.

6.110 Find graphically, by plotting $f(u)$, the fraction of N_2 molecules in the atmosphere that have velocities in the vertical direction in excess of a mile per minute. Take the temperature as $0°C$.

2. Some Average Quantities Obtained from Maxwell's Distribution Functions

Now that we have obtained some density or distribution functions, we can define exactly a surprisingly large number of speed and velocity averages. Aside from their intrinsic usefulness, these definitions are a good example of the need for precision in the statement of what would appear to be intuitively clear notions. In order to find the average value of a quantity q we must first note whether q is a function of u, v, and w, or whether it is a function of c. In the first case we might have (compare Eqs. 2.701 and 6.102)

$$\overline{q(u,v,w)} = \iiint_{-\infty}^{+\infty} q\, f(u,v,w)\, du\, dv\, dw \tag{6.201}$$

In the second case,

$$\overline{q(c)} = \int_{0}^{+\infty} q\, f(c)\, dc \tag{6.202}$$

Note the difference in the limits; also Eq. 6.201 is a triple integral whereas Eq. 6.202 is single. In both types of average, the averaged quantity is no longer a function of the variables over which it was averaged. The variables u, v, and w, or c, respectively, have been integrated over their entire range. The averaged quantity is a function only of the parameters in the distribution functions such as the temperature T or the mass of the particles m.

These expressions are quite similar to Eq. 2.701 for the expectation values in quantum mechanics. In the special case where the operator α commutes with the ψ functions, the quantity ψ^2 plays exactly the same role as $f(u,v,w)$ or $f(c)$. These latter functions invariably commute with the quantities being averaged.

Average Velocities and Speeds.   The *average velocity in one dimension*, say along the y axis, is, from Eq. 6.114,

$$\bar{v} = \int\!\!\!\int\!\!\!\int_{-\infty}^{+\infty} vf(u,v,w)\, du\, dv\, dw$$

$$= \left(\frac{m}{2\pi kT}\right)^{3/2} \int\!\!\!\int\!\!\!\int_{-\infty}^{+\infty} v\, e^{-m(u^2+v^2+w^2)/2kT}\, du\, dv\, dw \qquad (6.203)$$

$$= 0$$

It should be noted that Eq. 6.203 may be written in simpler form as a consequence of the *physical* postulate that motions in the x, y, and z directions are independent. This postulate ensures that integration over the variables not of interest here (i.e., over u and w) merely reduces to unity,

$$\frac{m}{2\pi kT} \int\!\!\!\int_{-\infty}^{+\infty} e^{-m(u^2+w^2)/2kT}\, du\, dw = 1 \qquad (6.204)$$

which leaves the net expression

$$\bar{v} = \left(\frac{m}{2\pi kT}\right)^{1/2} \int_{-\infty}^{+\infty} ve^{-mv^2/2kT}\, dv = 0 \qquad (6.205)$$

Thus, all molecules contribute to $\bar{v}$ in a manner independent of their u and w velocities. It may be noted further that, although $\bar{v} = 0$, the quantity $|\bar{v}| \neq 0$; also, the average value $\bar{v}$ is the same as the most probable value, $v_{mp} = 0$.

The *average three-dimensional speed* is from Eq. 6.118

$$\bar{c} = \int_0^{\infty} cf(c)\, dc$$

$$= \left(\frac{2}{\pi}\right)^{1/2}\left(\frac{m}{kT}\right)^{3/2} \int_0^{\infty} c^3 e^{-mc^2/2kT}\, dc \qquad (6.206)$$

$$= \left(\frac{8kT}{\pi m}\right)^{1/2}$$

so that two quantities, $\bar{c}$ and $\bar{v}$, that might superficially be thought to be the same are quite different.

A variety of other averages can be calculated; *the mean-square three-dimensional speed* is

$$\overline{c^2} = \left(\frac{2}{\pi}\right)^{1/2}\left(\frac{m}{kT}\right)^{3/2}\int_0^{+\infty} c^4 e^{-mc^2/2kT}\, dc = \frac{3kT}{m} \tag{6.207}$$

Note that $\overline{c}^2$, obtained by squaring Eq. 6.206, is distinct from this average. Also, the mean-square one-dimensional velocity is

$$\overline{u^2} = \overline{v^2} = \overline{w^2} = \left(\frac{m}{2\pi kT}\right)^{1/2}\int_{-\infty}^{\infty} u^2 e^{-mu^2/2kT}\, du = \frac{kT}{m} \tag{6.208}$$

The squared quantities are often expressed in square root form; for example, the root-mean-square one-dimensional velocity is

$$u_{\text{rms}} = \left(\overline{u^2}\right)^{1/2} = \left(\frac{kT}{m}\right)^{1/2} \tag{6.209}$$

The relative positions of some of these averages are indicated in Fig. 6.104.

Most Probable Speed.   The speed for which $f(c)$ is a maximum is found simply by differentiation of $f(c)$ from the condition $df(c)/dc = 0$. The result is

$$c_{\text{mp}} = \left(\frac{2kT}{m}\right)^{1/2} \tag{6.210}$$

The most probable velocity is of course zero, as seen earlier.

Fluctuations in Velocity.   Now that we have evaluated a number of velocity averages, we can take up the problem of the mean-square fluctuation in the velocity in one direction, $\overline{(u - \bar{u})^2}$. We find

$$\overline{(u - \bar{u})^2} = \overline{u^2} = \frac{kT}{m} \tag{6.211}$$

The steps in this derivation are simple; first we note that $\bar{u}$ is zero; then we use Eq. 6.208 for $\overline{u^2}$ (compare with Eq. 2.705). The fluctuations are thus directly given by the mean-square velocity, which is proportional to T. If is of importance to note that the mean-square fluctuations are also directly proportional to T, and that the mechanical chaos that these fluctuations measure is the microscopic aspect of the temperature.

Gauss Distribution Law.   The particularly simple behavior of the velocity fluctuations in a gas is an instance of a more general statistical phenomenon formulated by Gauss. The Maxwell distribution of velocities in one dimension is a special case of the Gauss normal distribution, or error law. This law has a wide range of applicability to measurements that deviate in a random way from a central or average value. For example, an individual measurement of the velocity of a single molecule in a gas will in general yield a nonzero value. A number of such measurements would cluster around the value zero, with larger deviations less probable than small ones. If δ is the deviation of any such measurement from the average value, the probability density $P(\delta)$ is, according to the Gauss normal distribution curve,

$$P(\delta) = \frac{1}{(2\pi)^{\frac{1}{2}}\sigma} \cdot e^{-\delta^2/2\sigma^2} \tag{6.212}$$

$P(\delta)$ is the same as Maxwell's $f(u)$, if we associate u with δ and set

$$\sigma^2 = \frac{kT}{m} \tag{6.213}$$

The shape of the curve is exactly the bell shape of Fig. 6.101. The parameter σ^2 is called the *variance*, and σ itself is known as the *standard deviation*.

The student may show that the inflection points on the curve, defined by $d^2P(\delta)/d\delta^2 = 0$, come at $\delta = \pm\sigma$. Also, the curve is normalized

$$\int_{-\infty}^{\infty} P(\delta) \, d\delta = 1$$

In the particular case of the Gauss distribution, only the quantity δ^2 enters, and so no distinction between positive and negative errors is necessary. In this case, $\sigma^2 = \overline{\delta^2}$. However, for any distribution function whatsoever, as in Sec. 2.7 and Sec. 5.3, we have defined a variance and a standard deviation given by the formula

$$\sigma_x^2 = \overline{(x - \bar{x})^2} \tag{6.214}$$

and its square root. The distribution need not be Gaussian or even symmetrical. The quantity x can be any measurement; $\bar{x}$ does not have to be zero.

Averages over Only Part of the Integration Range. If we ask what fraction of molecules has a velocity or speed in excess of, or less than, a certain limit, then it becomes necessary to integrate the normalized distribution function over only part of its range. One very simple problem can be worked by symmetry. What fraction of the molecules are moving in the positive direction of x? The answer is clearly one half. But for the more difficult problem, to determine the fraction of molecules which has a velocity in excess of 1 meter sec^{-1} (positive) in the x direction, the integral that results is not tabulated in the indefinite form. However, numerical values of the integral, Eq. 6.215, as a function of t'

$$A = \left(\frac{1}{2\pi}\right)^{\frac{1}{2}} \int_0^{t'} e^{-t^2/2} \, dt \tag{6.215}$$

are tabulated as the area of the normal curve of error. (See, for example, the mathematical tables in the *Handbook of Chemistry and Physics*, Chemical Rubber Co., Cleveland, under *Error*.) Note that, for t very large, this integral approaches the value one half. With appropriate care as to units and substitutions, the numerical answer for such a problem can be found.

Average Translational Kinetic Energy.   Equipartition Principle. The average kinetic energy in one dimension is the average of $mu^2/2$; $m/2$ is a constant, so the result desired can be obtained from Eq. 6.208 for the average value of u^2:

$$\bar{\epsilon}_x = \tfrac{1}{2}m\overline{u^2} = \tfrac{1}{2}kT \tag{6.216}$$

The average kinetic energy in three degrees of freedom of translational motion can be obtained similarly by averaging the expression $mc^2/2$ (Eq. 6.207),

$$\bar{\epsilon}_c = \tfrac{1}{2}m\overline{c^2} = \tfrac{3}{2}kT \tag{6.217}$$

Thus, the total kinetic energy of a gas molecule is divided equally between x, y, and z directions; of course, since individual molecules may vary greatly in behavior, according to the postulates of the gas model, it is understood that this statement refers to the average behavior of a large group of molecules. This result is an example of the principle of the equipartition of kinetic energy among degrees of freedom, one of the general results of classical statistical mechanics. In general, if the energy depends on the square of a variable, whether a coordinate or momentum quantity, the principle states that the average magnitude of the energy is $\tfrac{1}{2}kT$ for each quadratic or square term. The principle of equipartition of energy holds in the absence of quantum effects, that is, at temperatures such that kT is much larger than the energy level spacings concerned. If the energy in a particular degree of freedom contains other than square terms, the principle does not hold.

ILLUSTRATION. Calculate some typical values of u_{rms} for helium gas.

The value for u_{rms} is given in Eq. 6.209. By comparison with Eq. 6.213 we see that this is also the value for σ. For helium at 9° and 900°K

$$u_{\mathrm{rms}} = \left(\frac{kT}{m}\right)^{1/2} = \frac{(1.38 \times 10^{-16} \times T)^{1/2}}{(4/6.02 \times 10^{23})^{1/2}} = 4.557 \times 10^3 T^{1/2} \text{ cm sec}^{-1}$$

$$= 1.37 \times 10^4 \text{ cm sec}^{-1} \text{ at } 9°$$

$$= 1.37 \times 10^5 \text{ cm sec}^{-1} \text{ at } 900°$$

Collisions with the Wall.   Maxwell's distribution laws can be used to calculate the average number of collisions made by molecules with the wall of a vessel containing N' gas molecules per cubic centimeter. If 1 cm² area of wall $ABCD$ (Fig. 6.201) in the y, z plane is the target, only the components of velocity in the $+x$ direction enter the problem, i.e., u. Of a group of molecules having velocity u, all the molecules within a linear distance u of the surface will reach the surface in unit time. They are in a volume of u cc. The number of molecules in 1 cc with velocity between u and $u + du$ is simply $N'f(u)\,du$ for the same reason discussed after Eq. 6.203. This number, multiplied by the volume u which contains the ones that will strike, i.e., $N'uf(u)\,du$, is the number in the velocity range u to $u + du$ that strike in unit time. To get the total number striking, integrate over the range $u = 0$ to ∞, if the positive direction is chosen as the one that leads to collision.

Thus, the collision number per unit area of the wall is

$$\mathscr{Z}_w = N' \int_0^\infty uf(u)\, du$$

$$= N' \left(\frac{kT}{2\pi m}\right)^{1/2} \text{molecules cm}^{-2} \text{sec}^{-1} \qquad (6.218)$$

By use of Eq. 6.206, we can write

$$\mathscr{Z}_w = \tfrac{1}{4} N' \bar{c} \text{ molecules cm}^{-2} \text{sec}^{-1} \qquad (6.219)$$

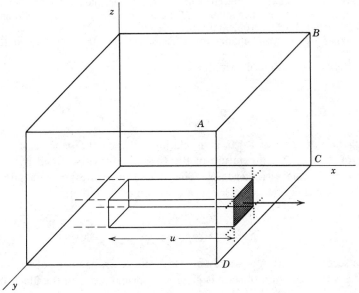

Fig. 6.201   Illustration of geometrical relationships in collisions of gas molecules with a wall.

$\mathscr{Z}_w$ has nothing to do with the symbol for the partition function. This equation is useful in finding the number of molecules in a molecular beam, and in the study of rates of absorption on surfaces or of rates of reaction at interfaces.

Problems

6.201   What fraction of helium atoms has velocities in excess of 1.0 mile sec^{-1} in the vertical direction at (a) 25°C; (b) 6000°C?

6.202   What is the magnitude of $|u|$ which half the atoms of helium gas will not exceed at 9° and 900°K? This quantity may be called the "probable magnitude" of u. Compare its magnitude with σ.

6.203   If the potassium atom pressure inside the oven in the experiment of Miller and Kusch (p. 146) was 0.12 mm at 544°K, what would be the surface area of the oven slit (Fig. 6.105) if 3×10^{16} molecules sec^{-1} leave the oven?

*6.204   Calculate the value of $\bar{u}$ for the molecules which leave the oven in Problem 6.203. [HINT: the number leaving at any value of u is proportional to $f(u)$ and *also* to the magnitude of u.]

6.205   Find the total average kinetic energy of a helium atom at 25°C, and express the answer in electron volts (ev) and calories per mole.

6.206   What temperature would be required so that He^{++} ions might have an average kinetic energy $\bar{\epsilon}$ of 2000 ev?

6.207   One of the lowest pressures ever measured is $\sim 10^{-13}$ mm; this corresponds to approximately 10^3 molecules cc^{-1} at 1027°C. How long would it take for aluminum atoms at this pressure to cover a mirror with a close-packed film one atom thick if the area of an atom is effectively ~ 5 Å^2, and the atoms stick on every collision and migrate to an empty site?

6.208   What fraction of N_2 molecules in the atmosphere have velocities in the vertical direction in excess of a mile per minute? Take the temperature as 0°C. Compare your answer with the result from Problem 6.110.

6.209   What fraction of helium atoms has speeds greater than c_{rms} at (a) 30°K? (b) 300°K?

6.210   Repeat Problem 6.209 with the limit $\bar{c}$.

3. The Ideal Gas Law

An *equation of state* of a gas is a relation between the dependent quantities, pressure of the gas P, temperature of the gas T, volume occupied by the gas V, and number of molecules of gas N. Since these quantities are not independent, any one of them may be expressed as a function of the others. So

$$P = f(V,T,N)$$
$$V = f'(P,T,N)$$

etc. The second equation is simply an algebraic rearrangement of the first. For a perfect gas the equation of state is given the special name of the ideal or perfect gas law.

Derivation of Ideal Gas Law from Statistical Mechanics.   Consider a gas from the quantum standpoint, with each molecule of the gas in one of the translational energy levels characteristic of the volume V. What happens if the volume is changed slightly, say by moving a piston of area A, which closes one end of the container, a distance dx? If we consider only one level, ϵ_i, with one molecule in it, the contribution of this level to the pressure, P_i, is obtained as follows. The total force on the piston due to the molecule in level ϵ_i is

$$f_i = \frac{-\partial \epsilon_i}{\partial x} \qquad (6.301)$$

This equation is a consequence of the conservation of energy. If by a small change in coordinate, Δx, the energy changes by an amount $\Delta \epsilon_i$, this change in energy must be reflected in the work done, which is the force multiplied by the displacement. The total change in energy must be zero, i.e., $f_i \Delta x + \Delta \epsilon_i = 0$. In the limit of small displacement, this leads to Eq. 6.301. If we divide Eq. 6.301 by the area A, we obtain the force per unit area, which is a pressure. We also can replace $A \, \partial x$ by ∂V. Therefore, the contribution to the pressure from a molecule in the level ϵ_i is

$$P_i = \frac{-\partial \epsilon_i}{\partial V} \tag{6.302}$$

The total pressure is obtained from Eq. 6.302 by multiplication of the pressure per molecule in each level by the population in that level, Eq. 5.231, followed by summation over all levels:

$$P = -\sum N_i \frac{\partial \epsilon_i}{\partial V} = -N \sum_i \frac{N_i}{N} \frac{\partial \epsilon_i}{\partial V}$$

$$= -N \sum_i \frac{1}{Z} g_i e^{-\epsilon_i / kT} \frac{\partial \epsilon_i}{\partial V}$$

This is exactly what results, however, from a differentiation of the partition function in the following manner:

$$P = NkT \left(\frac{\partial \ln Z}{\partial V} \right)_T \tag{6.303}$$

This is a very compact equation which is reminiscent of Eq. 5.320. It is a general result, not restricted to a gas.

If we now use Eq. 6.115 for Z, we can derive the equation of state for a perfect gas. Everything is held constant except the term in V, so $\partial \ln Z / \partial V = 1/V$ and

$$P = \frac{NkT}{V} \tag{6.304}$$

For a mole of gas, when N is Avogadro's number $\mathbf{N}$, we obtain the ideal gas law

$$PV = \mathbf{N}kT = RT \tag{6.305}$$

and

$$PV = nRT$$

for n moles of gas. R is called the gas constant. Since $k = 1.380 \times 10^{-16}$ erg molecule^{-1} deg^{-1} and $\mathbf{N} = 6.023 \times 10^{23}$ molecule mole^{-1}, $\mathbf{N}k = R = 8.315 \times 10^7$ ergs mole^{-1} deg^{-1}. PV has the dimensions of energy.

ILLUSTRATION.   Calculate the magnitude of R in various units by application of the ideal gas law to some experimental P, V, T results.

For 1 mole of the nearly ideal gas helium, White, Rubin, Camky, and Johnston [J. Phys. Chem., **64**, 1607 (1960)] found at a pressure $P = 4.515$ atm and temperature $T = 300.0°K$ that the experimental value of V was 5.464 liters.

Therefore

$$R = \frac{PV}{T} = \frac{4.515 \times 5.464}{300.0} = 0.08223 \text{ l-atm mole}^{-1} \text{ deg}^{-1}$$

$$= \frac{4.515 \times 5.464 \times 76}{300.0} = 6.249 \text{ l-cm (Hg) mole}^{-1} \text{ deg}^{-1}$$

$$= \frac{4.515 \times 5.464 \times 76 \times 1000}{300.0}$$

$$= 6.249 \times 10^3 \text{ cm}^3\text{-cm (Hg) mole}^{-1} \text{ deg}^{-1}$$

$$= \frac{4.515 \times 5.464 \times 76 \times 1000 \times 13.60}{300.0}$$

$$= 8.498 \times 10^4 \text{ g cm mole}^{-1} \text{ deg}^{-1}$$

$$= \frac{4.515 \times 5.464 \times 76 \times 1000 \times 13.60 \times 980.7}{300.0}$$

$$= 8.334 \times 10^7 \text{ ergs mole}^{-1} \text{ deg}^{-1}$$

Comparison with the correct value of R first given will indicate the magnitude of deviation from ideal behavior.

Derivation of the Ideal Gas Law from Impacts on the Wall. In Sec. 6.2 we considered the problem of calculating the number of collisions per unit time and per unit area with the wall. We will now consider the total force per unit area produced by these collisions; this is the pressure exerted by the gas molecules on the wall. An equal and opposite force per unit area must be exerted to keep the wall in place; this is the pressure on the molecules. If we refer to Fig. 6.201, all the molecules within a distance u of the surface of the wall will strike in a unit of time. As before, the number of molecules striking unit area in unit time within a given range du is $N'uf(u)\,du$. We must now calculate the contribution of one such collision per unit time to the force per unit area. When the elastic molecule hits a reflecting surface in the y, z plane its velocity changes from u to $-u$. This is a change of $-2u$ per unit time, so the acceleration $a = -2u$. If the acceleration is multiplied by the mass of the molecules and the number in the range du, we obtain the contribution to the impulsive force in this range of u

$$-(2mu)(N'uf(u)\,du)$$

This must be integrated over all positive u to obtain the total force per unit area

$$f = -2mN' \int_0^\infty u^2 f(u)\,du \qquad (6.306)$$

The integral is just the same as that for $\overline{u^2}$, Eq. 6.208, except that the limits are over the positive range only; since the integral is an even function of u, the value of the integral is just one half the result of Eq. 6.208, i.e., $F = -2mN'\,\overline{u^2}/2$. The force on the wall is the same magnitude as on the molecules but acting against it, so

$$P = -f = mN'\overline{u^2} = N'kT \qquad (6.307)$$

Now, since the number per unit volume $N' = N/V$, we have proved in a second way that

$$PV = NkT$$

ILLUSTRATION.   Compare the speed of sound and the root-mean-square velocity in a perfect gas.

The speed of sound in a perfect gas can be shown to be

$$v = \left(\frac{\gamma P}{\rho}\right)^{\!\frac12}$$

where P is the pressure and ρ is the density of the gas; for a monatomic gas the constant γ has the value 1.67. The density can be calculated from the perfect gas law, $PV = NkT$, as follows:

$$\rho = \frac{Nm}{V} = \frac{mP}{kT}$$

If this result is substituted in the expression for v, we find

$$v = \left(\frac{1.67kT}{m}\right)^{\!\frac12}$$

When we compare this with the expression for u_{rms} (Eq. 6.209),

$$u_{\mathrm{rms}} = \left(\frac{kT}{m}\right)^{\!\frac12}$$

we find that, aside from a numerical factor close to unity, the rate of propagation of sound is the same as the rms velocity of the molecules in the direction of propagation.

Problems

6.301   Calculate the helium pressure in the first Illustration in this section in terms of dynes per square centimeter.

6.302   What is the relationship between PV and the average kinetic energy of perfect gas molecules?

4. Heat Capacity of a Perfect Gas

We shall consider here the heat capacity measured at constant volume. We show later in Chapter 7 what the thermodynamic meaning of this quantity is. Here we will anticipate that discussion by the use of the symbol C_V, defined as the derivative of the average energy with respect to T at constant volume and, of course, constant amount of gas. We can divide C_V into the contributing parts. Heat capacity per mole will be indicated by a bar, $\bar{C}_V$. Real molecules may show limiting ideal translational behavior; however, they are not point masses and *may* also rotate and vibrate as well.

Heat Capacity for Translation. It was seen earlier from our kinetic treatment that the energy per molecule (we need not specify "average energy," but this is to be understood by the context) for translation in three degrees of freedom is $\frac{3}{2}kT$ (Eq. 6.217). We can also show the same result by the use of the general Eq. 5.320 together with the partition function for translation

$$Z_{\text{trans}(3)} = Z_{\text{trans}(1)}^3 = \frac{(2\pi mkT)^{3/2}V}{h^3} \tag{6.115}$$

Then

$$\bar{\epsilon} = \frac{-\partial \ln Z_{\text{trans}(3)}}{\partial(1/kT)} = \tfrac{3}{2}kT \tag{6.401}$$

The heat capacity for translation per molecule is thus

$$C_V = \left(\frac{\partial \bar{\epsilon}}{\partial T}\right)_V = \frac{3k}{2}; \quad \text{and} \quad \bar{C}_V = \frac{3R}{2}, \text{ per mole} \tag{6.402}$$

Partition Function for Rotation. Polyatomic gas molecules possess rotational and vibrational degrees of freedom in addition to the three translational ones. We have seen in Chapter 4 that rotational energy is quantized, with wider-spaced levels than those for translational energy. Therefore, for rotational energy, E_{rot}, the situation is somewhat like that for vibration. At very low temperature there will be very little excitation and therefore no rotational energy or heat capacity contribution. As the temperature rises, the energy curve approaches a classical limit, just as for vibration (Chapter 5). This happens for rotation at much lower temperatures since, aside from a few molecules such as H_2, D_2, and CH_4 which have very small moments of inertia, rotational energy spacings become $<kT$ at temperatures above $10°K$.

The details are much more complicated for the rotation of polyatomic molecules in general, because of both physical and mathematical complexities. We shall therefore consider only the two-dimensional partition function for rotation of a diatomic or linear molecule, obtained by summing over the rotational energy levels given in Chapter 4, i.e.,

$$\epsilon_{\text{rot}} = \frac{J(J+1)h^2}{8\pi^2 I}, \quad \text{and} \quad g_J = 2J + 1 \tag{4.101}$$

Then

$$Z_{\text{rot}(2)} = \sum_{J=0}^{\infty} (2J + 1)e^{-J(J+1)h^2/8\pi^2 IkT} \tag{6.403}$$

This is easily evaluated in the classical limit as

$$Z_{\text{rot}(2)} = \int_0^\infty (2J + 1)e^{-J(J+1)h^2/8\pi^2 IkT}\, dJ$$

by substituting $\xi = J(J + 1)$, and $d\xi = (J + 1)\, dJ + J\, dJ = (2J + 1)\, dJ$. We have

$$Z_{\text{rot}(2)} = \int_0^\infty e^{-\xi h^2/8\pi^2 IkT}\, d\xi = \frac{8\pi^2 IkT}{h^2} \qquad (6.404)$$

This formula is valid as it stands for heteronuclear molecules such as HCl and (linear) NNO. For homonuclear molecules such as N_2 and H_2 (linear), symmetry rules for the eigenfunctions introduce restrictions that at higher temperatures merely cause the partition function to be divided by 2.

Since in the derivation of Eq. 6.404 we have replaced a sum by an integral, the approximation is valid only when the rotational quantum number is on the average large; it is a good approximation to the rotational partition function when the resulting value, which is calculated by using it, is much greater than unity. The gas molecules to which it is not applicable are H_2 and D_2 below 200°K. Other molecules which have small moments of inertia are readily condensable, in general, and so the deviations that would be noticed at much lower temperatures are not important in practice.

To the same approximation, the partition function of a nonlinear polyatomic molecule is

$$Z_{\text{rot}(3)} = \frac{8\pi^2 (2\pi kT)^{3/2} (I_A I_B I_C)^{1/2}}{h^3} \qquad (6.405)$$

where I_A, I_B, and I_C are the principal moments of inertia. This partition function is valid only for polyatomic molecules that have no symmetry; otherwise it must be divided by a symmetry number σ that increases with the degree of symmetry of the molecule. As examples, σ is 3 for methyl chloride and 12 for methane. However, the value of the symmetry number does not affect the average energy of the molecule because when $\ln Z$ is differentiated with respect to $1/kT$ the constant term $\ln \sigma$ drops out.

Rotational Heat Capacity. We may now employ Eq. 5.320 to obtain the rotational energy and heat capacity in the high-temperature or classical limit. For the two rotational degrees of freedom of a linear molecule

$$\bar{\epsilon}_{\text{rot}}(\text{linear}) = kT; \quad C_V = k; \quad \bar{C}_V = R \qquad (6.406)$$

For the three degrees of freedom of a nonlinear molecule

$$\bar{\epsilon}_{\text{rot}(3)} = \tfrac{3}{2}kT; \quad C_V(\text{nonlinear}) = \frac{3k}{2}; \quad \bar{C}_V = \frac{3R}{2} \qquad (6.407)$$

These results support the equipartition of kinetic energy in the classical limit. The energy in each degree of freedom is proportional to a square term (Eq. 6.408) and contributes $\frac{1}{2}k$ to the heat capacity. For a linear molecule the classical Hamiltonian has two square terms in p_θ and p_ϕ,

$$\mathscr{H}(p,q) = \frac{[p_\theta^2 + p_\phi^2/\sin^2 \theta]}{2I} \qquad (6.408)$$

Vibrational Heat Capacity. Insofar as the vibration can be treated as a harmonic oscillator, the treatment has already been given in Chapter 5. At low temperature, the vibrations are not excited and there is no contribution from levels above the ground state. At high temperatures, each harmonic oscillator (representing one vibrational degree of freedom) would contribute kT to the energy (RT per mole), half-kinetic and half-potential energy, from the generalized law of equipartition of energy. A real oscillator tends to behave anharmonically at high energies (high T), and equipartition of energy would not apply to any potential energy terms other than quadratic.

Electronic Heat Capacity. Occasionally, a low-lying electronic level or levels can be excited at temperatures where the molecule is still stable; the situation is rare, and each case is treated individually.

Table 6.401   Classification of Degrees of Freedom in an $\mathscr{N}$-Atomic Molecule; Contribution to the Heat Capacity in the Classical Limit

	Number of Degrees of Freedom		Contribution to C_V per Degree of Freedom
Type of Motion	Linear Molecule	Nonlinear Molecule	
Translation	3	3	$\frac{1}{2}k$
Rotation (pure)	2	3	$\frac{1}{2}k$
Vibration	$3\mathscr{N} - 5$	$3\mathscr{N} - 6 - x$	k
Internal rotation*	0	x	$\frac{1}{2}k$ to k
Total	$3\mathscr{N}$	$3\mathscr{N}$	

* The presence and exact kind of motion classified as internal rotation depend on the individual molecular structure.

Combination of Heat Capacity Terms. The heat capacity of a gas composed of $\mathscr{N}$-atomic molecules can be divided between the total of $3\mathscr{N}$ degrees of freedom. There are always three degrees of translational freedom. If the molecule is linear, it has two degrees of rotational freedom; if it is nonlinear, it has three degrees of rotational freedom. There remain the $3\mathscr{N} - 5$ other degrees of freedom for a linear molecule, and $3\mathscr{N} - 6$ degrees of freedom for a nonlinear molecule. For simple molecules, these remaining degrees of freedom are most often vibrational in character. For complex molecules, the possibility was described in Chapter 4 of an internal motion that is close in character to a rotation. These relations are summarized in Table 6.401. The total experimental heat capacity of a molecule can be shown to be a sum of the individual heat capacities due to the various degrees of freedom.

Comparison with Experiment.   For a diatomic molecule there is a single degree of vibrational freedom.   Most diatomic gases give plots for C_V against T that have the same shape.   In Fig. 6.401, a curve that applies to O_2, N_2, CO, Cl_2, etc., is presented.   The behavior of the observed heat capacity per molecule as a function of the magnitudes of the ratio of kT to the rotational (*a*) and vibrational (*b*) energy constants, respectively, is portrayed in the figure.   It is evident that the heat capacity rises with increase of temperature and approaches the classical value.

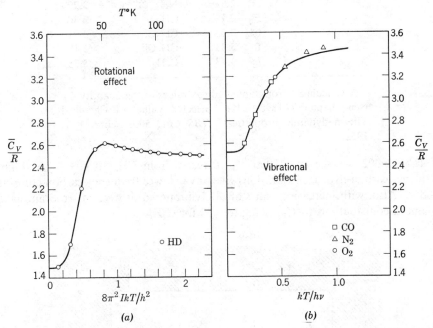

Fig. 6.401   Temperature dependence of the heat capacity of diatomic molecules.

Table 6.402 presents some values of C_V for actual gases.   Some interesting features emerge on consideration of the tabulated values.   It is evident that He and Ne correspond closely to the ideal gas value, while N_2 and O_2 have the added contribution k for two rotational degrees of freedom.   The "stiff" vibrations, i.e., high vibrational frequencies of H_2, N_2, and O_2, are scarcely excited.   On going from F_2 to I_2, as expected from the decreasing bond energies (i.e., decreasing force constants) and increasing reduced masses, the vibration frequencies in the halogens decrease [Table 4.101(A)].   It is evident that the vibrational degree of freedom of I_2 is most actively excited, and $\bar{C}_V(I_2)$ is close to the classical limit of the equipartition law, $3.5R$.   In effect, as we go down the halogen series we proceed across from left to right on the vibration half of Fig. 6.401.   In this instance we have raised the ratio $kT/h\nu$ by changing from one molecule to another having decreasing ν

values; if we had stayed with F_2 and raised T, we would find the same type of behavior for this molecule at different values of T. Finally, from the last column

Table 6.402   Sample Values of C_V at 298.16°K in Units of R per Mole or k per Molecule*

Monatomic		Diatomic		Tri- and Polyatomic	
He	1.50	H_2	2.47	CO_2 (linear)	3.47
Ne	1.50	N_2	2.50	SO_2 (nonlinear)	3.79
		O_2	2.53	NH_3	3.29
		F_2	2.78	CH_4	3.30
		Cl_2	3.08	CH_3Cl	3.91
		Br_2	3.33	CH_2Cl_2	5.18
		I_2	3.43	C_2H_6	5.33

* Calculated from tabulated gas values of the quantity $\bar{C}_P^\circ$ (see Chapter 7) (298.16°K), "Selected Values of Chemical Thermodynamic Properties," *NBS Circ.* 500, February 1, 1952.

of Table 6.402, we see again that C_V increases from CH_4 to CH_2Cl_2 as high-frequency carbon-hydrogen vibrations give way to lower-frequency carbon-chlorine modes. Also, with increasing value of $\mathcal{N}$, vibrational degrees of freedom make enhanced contributions to C_V, rising to 5.33 for C_2H_6.

Bath

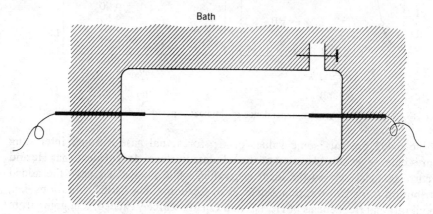

Fig. 6.402   Hot-wire apparatus for the measurement of the heat capacity of gases.

A variety of techniques has been used for the measurement of the heat capacities of gases. In the hot-wire method, the amount of heat conducted by a gas at known pressure away from a long wire, maintained at a higher temperature than the wall, is measured electrically (Fig. 6.402). Obviously, heat conduction by the gas depends, among other known factors, on C_V of the gas. Since one factor involved is the number of collisions of the gas with the wire, the method may be inverted and used for the measurement of pressure, the so-called Pirani gauge. At 300°K, Vanderkooi and De Vries find by this method that $\bar{C}_V$ for CHF_3, $CClF_3$, and CH_3CF_3 is, respectively, 10.23 ± 0.13, 14.10 ± 0.38, and 16.83 ± 0.18 cal mole^{-1} deg^{-1}. The increase is again in line with the changes in $kT/h\nu$ involved ($\nu_{CH} > \nu_{CF} > \nu_{CCl}$), and the increase in number of vibrational degrees of freedom with molecular complexity. As we have indicated (see also Problem 6.401), not only may information about frequencies of vibration be obtained from such thermal measurements, but in this case the potential barrier to internal rotation in CH_3CF_3 was also calculated by these workers, by comparison with spectroscopic data, to be 3370 cal mole^{-1}. [See Table 5.301(A).]

ILLUSTRATION. W. N. Vanderkooi and T. De Vries [*J. Phys. Chem.*, **60**, 636 (1956)] used a variant of the hot-wire method at pressures of only a few microns of mercury [1 micron $= 10^{-3}$ mm], where real gases behave ideally. The dimensions of the wire were 7×10^{-3} cm diameter and 15 cm length. Find the number of collisions made by the reference gas argon at $p = 5.0$ microns at $T = 25°C$.

Now $\mathscr{Z}_w = \frac{1}{4}N'\bar{c}a$, where a is the area of the wire. Using $PV = NkT$ in proper units, from the Illustration of R given in Sec. 6.3,

$$\mathscr{Z}_w = \frac{1}{4}\frac{P}{kT}\left(\frac{8kT}{\pi m}\right)^{\frac{1}{2}} 2\pi rl$$

where k is in units of cubic centimeters millimeter (Hg) per molecule per degree and ergs per molecule per degree, respectively. So

$$\mathscr{Z}_w = \frac{1}{4}\frac{5.0 \times 10^{-3} \times 1.36 \times 981}{1.38 \times 10^{-16} \times 298.2}$$

$$\times \frac{(8 \times 1.38 \times 10^{-16} \times 298.2 \times 6.02 \times 10^{23})^{\frac{1}{2}}}{(3.142 \times 39.9)^{\frac{1}{2}}}$$

$$\times 2 \times 3.14 \times 3.5 \times 10^{-3} \times 15$$

$$= 5.31 \times 10^{17} \text{ molecules sec}^{-1}$$

If the vessel is a cylinder 4 cm in diameter, the student may calculate the relative probability of the molecule hitting the wire or the wall, and see whether molecules in the vessel do remain effectively at bath temperature.

Problems

6.401 Starting with the $\bar{C}_V$ values of Table 6.402, obtain approximate values of the vibration frequencies of F_2, Cl_2, Br_2, and I_2 by use of Fig. 6.401. Compare with values from Table 4.101.

6.402 Explain why $\bar{C}_V(CO_2)$ is lower than $\bar{C}_V(SO_2)$ at 298°K. What value would the ratio $\bar{C}_V(CO_2)/\bar{C}_V(SO_2)$ approach at high temperature if electronic excitation or other complications were ignored?

6.403   Why does the tetratomic molecule NH_3 have a lower value of $\bar{C}_V$ than triatomic SO_2 at 298°K?

6.404   Given that $r_{H-H} = 0.742$ Å and $r_{Br-Br} = 2.28$ Å [Table 4.101(A)], find the values of Z_{rot} at 300° and 1000°K.

6.405   Find the temperatures at which $2h^2/8\pi^2 IkT = 1$ for H_2 and Br_2. Use the information of Problem 6.404; consider your answers also in the light of the answers there.

6.406   Use the information of Problem 6.401 to find the temperature at which $h\nu/kT = 1$ for Br_2.

5. Real Gases; Intermolecular Forces

Although under the usual conditions of low pressure most gases obey the perfect gas law within a few per cent, all real gases must at times be treated by a more realistic equation of state. In addition, there are certain phenomena that cannot be explained at all according to the perfect gas model. These include condensation,

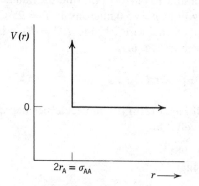

Fig. 6.501   Hard-sphere potential function.

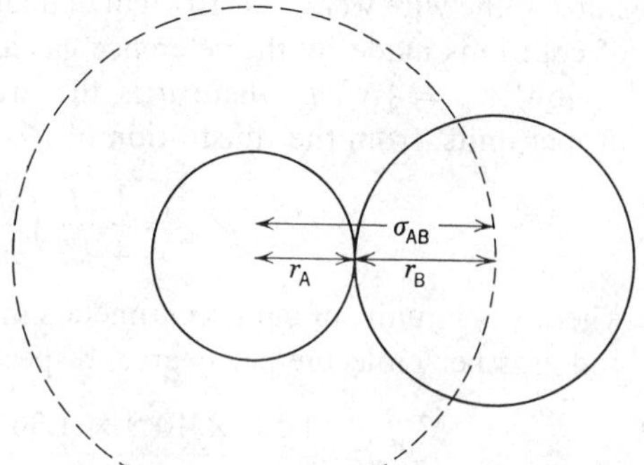

Fig. 6.502   Excluded volume for the collision of hard spheres.

intermolecular collisions, and a variety of transport properties, such as diffusion and viscosity. The modification of the perfect gas model that is required is the inclusion of attractive and repulsive intermolecular forces.

Hard-Sphere Model.   The simplest improvement on the perfect gas model is to consider each gas molecule to be a rigid sphere of radius r_A. Then a gas molecule A is under no force until it is within the force field of another molecule, at which time the potential energy becomes infinitely positive and thus repulsive (Fig. 6.501). Since we keep as coordinates the centers of the molecules, the distance σ_{AA} between centers when repulsion occurs is $\sigma_{AA} = 2r_A$. In the case of two dissimilar molecules, A and B, with radii r_A and r_B the distance of closest approach is (Fig. 6.502)

$$\sigma_{AB} = r_A + r_B \tag{6.501}$$

This "diameter" σ_{AB} is really the radius of an excluded volume that is bigger than either molecule. In fact, in the case of molecules of the same size, it is equal to eight times the volume of a molecule, $4\pi(2r_A)^3/3 = 8 \times 4\pi r^3/3$.

The hard-sphere model is useful for a gas at high pressure, if the temperature is high enough so that the effective attractive force is negligible. It is also the simplest model that predicts collisions, other than with the wall.

Hard-Sphere Collision Number. It is possible to use Maxwell's distribution function to calculate the number of collisions between two molecules of type A and B. The method is the same in principle as the calculation of the number of collisions with a stationary wall, but is much more complicated in practice because both molecules are moving, and follow a Maxwellian distribution of velocities. The result, however, is simple (Eq. 6.502); for dissimilar molecules the collision number $\mathscr{Z}_{AB}$ is directly proportional to the number density of molecules (number per cubic centimeter), to their cross-sectional area, and to a relative speed quantity,

$$\mathscr{Z}_{AB} = 2[N'_A N'_B][\sigma^2_{AB}]\left[\left(\frac{2\pi kT}{\mu}\right)^{\frac{1}{2}}\right] cc^{-1} \, sec^{-1} \qquad (6.502)$$

where σ^2_{AB} is defined in Eq. 6.501 and is sometimes called the collision cross-section; N'_A and N'_B are the number of molecules per cubic centimeter; and μ is the reduced mass, $m_A m_B/(m_A + m_B)$. For identical molecules A, the same formula holds with B replaced by A, but it is divided by two, the symmetry number, as will be discussed further in Chapter 13. The collision number and the related idea of free path of a molecule between collisions are extensively applied to problems dealing with transport properties and rates of reaction (Chapters 13 and 14).

Representation of Gas Nonideality; PV Isotherms. The isothermal plot of the pressure against volume for a perfect gas is given by the locus of a rectangular hyperbola, corresponding to the equation $PV = $ const. A clearer test of ideality is to plot the ratio PV/RT against pressure at constant temperature, which gives a horizontal straight line for an ideal gas. Real gases deviate either "positively" (above the line) or "negatively" (below the line), as is shown in Fig. 6.503. Roughly speaking, positive deviations correspond to the steric interference between the cores of the molecules, and negative deviations correspond to intermolecular attraction. The latter become relatively more important at lower temperatures. The two effects can sometimes balance and produce pseudo-ideality, when $PV/RT = 1$ at a single high pressure. It is thus necessary to know the PV/RT ratio over some range of pressure to decide how nonideal a gas really is. The student will appreciate this factor fully when we calculate fugacities in Chapter 7.

The fact that these two types of interaction exist for all materials is responsible for such a phenomenon as the condensation of a gas into a liquid, and for the very fact that matter in all its forms occupies a finite volume set by the repulsive forces of the cores of the molecule. We will not deal with condensation here; we shall discuss it in terms of thermodynamics and statistical mechanics in Chapters 7 and 11. But in connection with this problem, van der Waals developed an equation of state, which we will now discuss, as an early development that later led to more rigorous treatment of nonideality.

The Equation of van der Waals. The most celebrated equation of state, aside from the ideal gas law, is the van der Waals equation. It is semiempirical in origin and takes into account the force of molecular attraction, as well as repulsion. The equation is

$$\left(P + \frac{a'N^2}{V^2}\right)(V - b'N) = NkT \tag{6.503}$$

or, for n moles,

$$\left(P + \frac{an^2}{V^2}\right)(V - bn) = nRT$$

The constants a' and b' are positive and account for attraction and repulsion, respectively. The dimensions of $(a'N)/V$ are energy per molecule, and a' therefore may be thought to have some relation to attractive energy between two molecules.

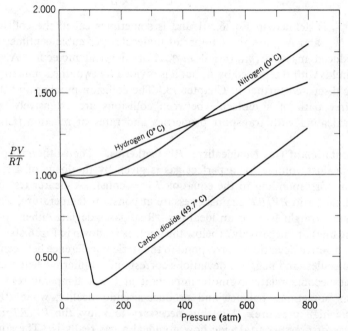

Fig. 6.503   Behavior of gases near room temperature (by permission from J. G. Aston and J. J. Fritz, *Thermodynamics and Statistical Thermodynamics*, John Wiley and Sons, New York, 1959).

The a' correction allows for the net attractive force inward, exerted by neighbors on each other, which gives rise to an *internal pressure* in the opposite sense to the dynamic pressure of the gas molecules; the cohesive force in a liquid or solid is due to this effect. Van der Waals assumed that the attractive forces had a very short range and that only near neighbors interact; he reasoned that the magnitude of the effect on a given molecule depends on the concentration of neighbors, while the number of molecules on which these act also increases with N. Thus the correction depends on N^2.

The constant b' has the dimension of volume per molecule and is often called the volume of the molecules. A careful analysis of the equation with $a' = 0$, called the co-volume equation,

$$P(V - b'N) = NkT \tag{6.504}$$

where $b'N$ is called the co-volume, shows that at low concentration

$$b' = \tfrac{16}{3}\pi r_A^3 = 4v_m \tag{6.505}$$

four times the actual volume of the molecule. The plausibility of this quadrupling is seen from Fig. 6.502. We had that the excluded volume per collision, i.e., for two molecules, was $8v_m$ or $8v_m/2$ per molecule; the total excluded volume is $N \times 8v_m/2 = 4Nv_m$. If we place this value of b' in Eq. 6.504 we should find that,

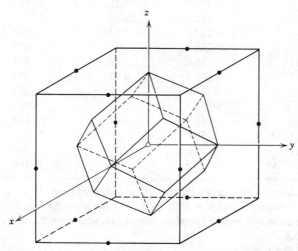

Fig. 6.504 The dodecahedron formed by planes bisecting the distances between a molecule located at the origin and its twelve close-packed neighbors. The dodecahedron represents the volume per molecule, $v = V/N$. [From Buehler, Wentorf, Hirschfelder, Curtiss, *J. Chem. Phys.*, **19**, 61 (1951).]

at infinite pressure, $V = 4Nv_m$. This is clearly inconsistent with the requirement that the smallest volume possible per molecule is the volume of the dodecahedron with a spherical volume v_m within it, a volume which may be seen by inspection to be quite close to v_m (Fig. 6.504). We therefore conclude that the van der Waals equation is not really suitable for use at high density. However, because it is relatively easy to handle in thermodynamic calculation, and because it can be fairly closely fitted to many data, it has a wide application in illustrating nonideal thermodynamics (Chapter 7) and in practical calculation. The co-volume equation is often used empirically at very high density and temperature, as in a detonation of a solid explosive.

In Table 6.501 some a' and b' values taken from the literature are presented for a variety of gases. It is seen that the higher molecular weight, i.e., higher boiling, molecules (and the more polar molecules) have larger attractive constants a' and, of course, larger volume constants b' corresponding to the increasing number of atoms per molecule. These are only rough correlations, it will be noted, but are intuitively useful. In Fig. 6.503 it may be seen that the depth of the PV/RT minimum increases in the same direction that the a' values also increase.

Table 6.501   van der Waals Constants (25°C)*

Gas	T_{bp}, °C	$a = a'N^2$, l^2-atm mole^{-2}	$b = b'N$, l mole^{-1}
He	−268.9	0.034	0.024
Ne	−245.9	0.21	.017
Ar	−185.9	1.34	.032
H_2	−252.8	0.24	.027
N_2	−195.8	1.4	.039
HCl†	− 85.0	3.67	.041
HBr†	− 66.4	4.45	.044
NH_3†	− 33.4	4.17	.037
CH_4	−164	2.25	.043
C_3H_8	− 36	8.67	.084
CH_3CN†	81.6	17.6	.117
n-C_5H_{12}	36.1	19.1	.146
C_3H_7CN†	117.9	25.7	.160

* Selected by permission from Landolt-Bornstein, *Physikalisch-Chemische Tabellen*, Fifth Edition, J. Springer, Berlin, 1923. The constants are temperature dependent, and rounded values suffice.
    † Polar molecule.

van der Waals Force.   It is clear from a study of the equation of state for even an inert gas, such as argon, that some sort of attractive energy of the order of kT operates at low temperature to produce negative deviation from ideality. London showed by a quantum mechanical treatment of these molecules that an attractive pair-wise force field with the potential energy

$$\epsilon_a = \frac{-K_a}{r^6} \qquad (6.506)$$

exists. K_a is a constant that may be evaluated theoretically, and r is the distance between the molecules. This energy exists between all atoms and molecules and between parts of molecules. Other forces exist also, such as those caused by specion chemical factors or by electrical imbalance, but the London attraction or dispersific force is a general molecular property.

As the molecules get closer to each other, there must eventually be a repulsion energy ϵ_r simply due to electron overlap. However, the theoretical form that this must take has never been too well approximated. Lennard-Jones suggested the empirical form

$$\epsilon_r = \frac{+K_r}{r^{12}} \tag{6.507}$$

as being more realistic than the hard-sphere approximation. These are combined in the Lennard-Jones "6–12 potential" for nonpolar molecules:

$$\epsilon(r) = \epsilon_a + \epsilon_r = \frac{-K_a}{r^6} + \frac{K_r}{r^{12}} \tag{6.508}$$

The shape of this potential is shown in Fig. 6.505. It is more instructive when put in terms of the natural parameters ϵ^*, the depth of the minimum, and r^*, the distance at this point.

$$\epsilon(r) = \left[-2\left(\frac{r^*}{r}\right)^6 + \left(\frac{r^*}{r}\right)^{12} \right] \epsilon^* \tag{6.509}$$

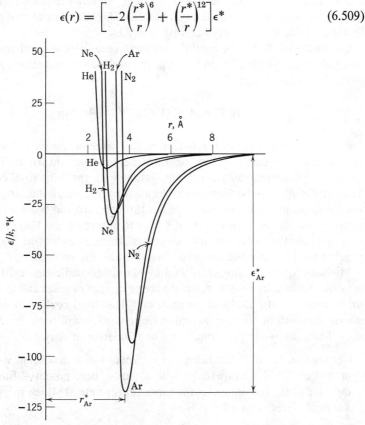

Fig. 6.505   Lennard-Jones potentials for several gases. The values of ϵ^* and r^* are indicated on the curve for argon. (By permission from R. H. Fowler and E. A. Guggenheim, *Statistical Thermodynamics*, Cambridge University Press, 1939.)

When r is r^*, $\epsilon(r)$ becomes $-\epsilon^*$. This quantity can be evaluated theoretically or experimentally, and r^* is estimated from some measurement, such as the density of the solidified gas. A rough correlation may be seen between ϵ^* values, estimated from the figure, and van der Waals a values from Table 6.501. We shall return to these matters in Chapter 11.

The Virial Equation of State. Equation 6.509 cannot be used to evaluate the van der Waals constant, a, because a precise theoretical interpretation of a does not exist. For that reason, equation-of-state data are fitted to a power series in V^{-1} suggested by Kammerlingh-Onnes in 1901

$$PV = NkT\left[1 + \frac{NB(T)}{V} + \frac{N^2C(T)}{V^2} + \cdots\right] \qquad (6.510)$$

$B(T)$ is called the second virial coefficient and is a function of temperature only; $C(T)$ is called the third virial coefficient, etc. Enough terms are taken to accommodate the accuracy of the data available. The equation of van der Waals may be shown to be correct only in terms to $B(T)$.

Evaluation of $B(T)$. A careful argument in statistical mechanics leads to an equation which yields $B(T)$ in terms of the molecular interaction energy $\epsilon(r)$. It is in the form of an integral

$$B(T) = \tfrac{1}{2}\int_0^\infty (1 - e^{-\epsilon(r)/kT})4\pi r^2 \, dr \qquad (6.511)$$

For the particular case of the 6–12 law, the value of the second virial coefficient can be found exactly. Its temperature dependence, shown in Fig. 6.506, was determined experimentally for helium, along with the third virial coefficient $C(T)$. The units of $B(T)$ are volume per molecule (or per mole), but clearly $B(T)$ is not the volume *of* the molecule because it passes through zero and becomes negative at low temperature. It has a maximum at a high temperature and then declines with rise of T because the faster-moving molecules, more abundant at high temperature, penetrate further into the repulsive force field on the average.

Methods for calculating third and higher virial coefficients exist and, although tedious, are actually used to calculate the properties of gases and mixtures of gases, for example, in the study of combustion. The virial coefficient expansion is the modern method of treating gas imperfections. We will show in Chapter 11 how the calculations, once performed, can be tabulated for easy use.

ILLUSTRATION. $B(T)$ for helium (Fig. 6.506) has a maximum value of 12.24 cc mole^{-1} at 175°K. Evaluate r^* with a hard-sphere potential function by using the data at the maximum as the most appropriate at which to approximate the Lennard-Jones value of r^*. Now

$$\epsilon(r) = 0, \quad r^* \leqslant r \leqslant \infty$$

$$\epsilon(r) = \infty, \quad 0 \leqslant r \leqslant r^*$$

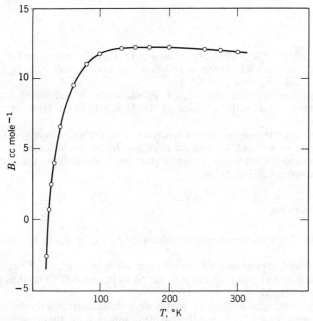

Fig. 6.506   The second virial coefficient $B(T)$ for helium [by permission, after White, Rubin, Camky, and Johnston, *J. Phys. Chem.*, **64**, 1607 (1960)].

So

$$B(T) = \tfrac{1}{2}\int_0^\infty (1 - e^{-\epsilon(r)/kT})4\pi r^2\, dr$$

$$= \tfrac{1}{2}\left[\int_0^{r^*} (1 - e^{-\epsilon(r)/kT})4\pi r^2\, dr + \int_{r^*}^\infty (1 - e^{-\epsilon(r)/kT})4\pi r^2\, dr\right]$$

$$= \tfrac{1}{2}\left[\int_0^{r^*} (1 - e^{-\infty/kT})4\pi r^2\, dr + \int_{r^*}^\infty (1 - e^{-0/kT})4\pi r^2\, dr\right]$$

$$= \tfrac{1}{2}\cdot\frac{4\pi r^{*3}}{3} = \frac{2\pi r^{*3}}{3}$$

So
$$r^* = \left(\frac{3 \times 12.24}{2 \times 3.142 \times 6.02 \times 10^{23}}\right)^{1/3}$$
$$= 2.13 \times 10^{-8}\ \text{cm}$$

This value corresponds to $2r_{\text{He}}$. Since $B(T)$ is a function of temperature, the hard-sphere collision diameter is not a constant but must vary with temperature; the model ignores the fact that atoms and molecules are really ill-defined "soft" spheres. In other words, the hard-sphere model does not apply very well to the problem, especially at extremes of temperature.

Problems

6.501   For arsine $\epsilon^*/k = 281°$ and $r^* = 4.5$ Å. Plot $\epsilon(r)$ against r for the 6-12 law.

6.502   Calculate the total number of collisions per second made by a single N_2 molecule in air at 25°C. Take $\sigma_{N_2} \cong \sigma_{O_2} = 3.5$ Å.

6.503   Compare molecular volumes of liquids found or calculated from data in a suitable reference book with b values in Table 6.501. Plot both of these against molecular weight.

6.504   Compare the van der Waals equation with the virial equation for helium by plotting $(PV)_{\text{calc}}$ vs. V^{-1} at 0°C; neglect third and higher coefficients.

*6.505   Compare the volume of a hard-sphere molecule with the volume of the close-packed dodecahedron in Fig. 6.504.

6. Review Problems

6.601   Show that the normalizing constant for $f(c)$ as given in Eq. 6.118 is correct. (Integrate.)

6.602   Work out expressions for the averages for u, v, w, u^2, v^2, w^2; c, c^2.

6.603   Calculate and plot $f(u)$ and $f(c)$ for N_2 at 0° and 500°C, each as a function of the independent variable.

6.604   A gaseous metal atom has a doubly degenerate electronic level ϵ_1 above the non-degenerate ground state. Write out the partition function for these levels; calculate the energy and the heat capacity. Assume $\epsilon_1 = 10$ kcal mole^{-1} and plot C_V against T from 300 to 3000°K.

6.605   Find the temperature at which the lowest translational energy *spacing* for H_2 is $\simeq kT$ in a 1-cm linear box. At what translational energy levels would this condition obtain if $T = 10$°K?

6.606   Obtain an expression for $f(c)$ for two degrees of translational freedom.

6.607   Find the number of neon atoms that issue from a slit, 1 mm × 0.01 mm, located in the wall of a vessel containing the gas at 298°K and 0.1 mm Hg in 1 sec.

*6.608   Do the issuing molecules in Problem 6.607 have the same velocity distribution as the molecules in the vessel? Calculate the average energy of beam molecules.

6.609   Show by a rough calculation that the rotational heat capacity behavior of a gas is almost classical even if the condition $8\pi^2 IkT/h^2 \simeq 1$, rather than $\gg 1$, holds.

6.610   Find the values of r at which $\epsilon(r) = \pm\frac{1}{2}\epsilon^*$ and $\epsilon(r) = 0$, according to the Lennard-Jones 6-12 potential.

General References

Hirschfelder, J. O., C. F. Curtiss, and R. B. Bird, *Molecular Theory of Gases and Liquids*, John Wiley and Sons, New York, 1954.

Kennard, E. H., *The Kinetic Theory of Gases* (or similar textbooks, such as those of Loeb, Jeans, or Present, on this subject), McGraw-Hill Book Co., New York, 1938.

Ramsey, N. F., *Molecular Beams*, Oxford University Press, Oxford, 1956.

Resnick, R., and D. Halliday, *Physics for Students of Science and Engineering*, Part I, 1960, and Part II, Second Edition, 1962, John Wiley and Sons, New York.

Taylor, H. S., Editor, *A Treatise on Physical Chemistry*, Third Edition, D. Van Nostrand and Co., Princeton, N.J., 1942.

Chapter Seven

Thermodynamics

1. Introduction

Thermodynamics is based on two fundamental laws, called the *first* and *second* laws of thermodynamics, which are concerned with the interrelation of various forms of energy and the transfer of energy from one system to another. In classical thermodynamics, the approach to the study of the energetic properties of matter is from the macroscopic experimental point of view. The two primary postulates are Newtonian type laws, deduced from experiment. The complicated substratum of molecules, described by the kinetic molecular theory, may be ignored. Classical thermodynamics is thus free of any uncertainties or approximations associated with such theories. The two laws of thermodynamics constitute one of the most powerful tools of physical chemistry. Thermodynamic properties of chemical substances may be determined unambiguously by experiment; from these properties the feasibility of reactions and the character of *equilibrium systems* in which these substances participate can be predicted.

Reference will frequently be made to descriptions of the energetic properties of substances in terms of well-established molecular theory. Thermodynamics provides important tests for theoretical chemistry. As discussed in Chapter 5, the properties of matter in bulk may be calculated from the properties of the molecules by the methods of statistical mechanics; the calculation of thermodynamic properties in this manner is called statistical thermodynamics. Statistical thermodynamics must predict results in accord with the findings of experimental thermodynamics if theories to which statistical methods are applied are valid.

At the outset, a brief review of the meaning of "energy" in the sense in which it is used in classical thermodynamics is in order. Energy is not easily defined in a simple statement. When an object or system receives or loses energy, at least one of its directly observable properties is changed. By observable properties, we refer to the physical attributes by which the system or object may be described: its temperature, pressure, density, volume, etc. Usually only two of the large number of such properties which may be conceived need be specified in order to completely establish all others in any homogeneous equilibrium system of fixed composition. (For unusual cases, such as the volume of liquid water in the vicinity of 4°C, multiple values may be possible in a very limited range.) Hence the energy of a *closed* (defined as containing a fixed amount of material) homogeneous system may be expressed as a function of any two observed properties, such as temperature and volume, taken as independent variables. It will be shown later that the energy of a perfect gas does not change with its volume; hence in this idealized case energy is a function of temperature alone. The two independent variables may change in such a way that the energy changes associated with each separately are of opposite sign and equal in magnitude. In our introductory discussions certain variables, e.g., the position of the system in a gravitational field, are assumed to be constant.

For properties to have meaning in the sense of the preceding paragraph, they must be equilibrium characteristics of the system. The temperature, for example, must be uniform throughout the sample. A system is in a *well-defined thermodynamic state* when all its properties have values which do not change with time.

Extensive and Intensive Properties. Energy and volume are examples of extensive properties; their magnitude for a given system at a specified temperature and pressure depends on the quantity of material in the system. On the other hand, temperature, pressure, density, etc., are intensive properties; their magnitude is not dependent on the quantity of material in the system. Extensive properties are generally tabulated as quantities per mole, e.g., molar volume, and thereby become intensive. This will be indicated by a bar over the symbol: $\bar{V}$, $\bar{F}$, etc.

Kinds of Energy. Energy may be added to or removed from a given system by interaction with its surroundings. It is customary to refer to the energy transferred by a name indicative of the type of interaction, such as mechanical work, heat, or electrical energy.

Work. The principal type of work W of interest in chemical systems is that associated with PV changes and, as discussed in Chapter 2, it is evaluated if possible by an expression of the form of Eq. 2.102. It has been noted (Chapter 6) that PV has the dimensions of energy. Expansion of the system against its surroundings removes an amount of energy from the system equal in magnitude to the work done; compression of the system by its surroundings increases the energy content of the system by the work done on the system.

Heat. If a system at temperature T_1 is placed in surroundings at T_2, it is found that after a sufficient length of time the two will come to the same temperature (that of the surroundings if the latter is infinitely large compared with the system). The relationship of temperature to molecular motion has been considered in Chapter

6. Energy transferred solely as a result of a temperature gradient is described as heat. According to molecular theory, such an energy transfer may be achieved through molecular collisions at the interface of the two systems. It cannot be easily analyzed in terms of forces and displacements as in the case of mechanical work; hence it is convenient to describe such an energy transfer in a different way. In classical thermodynamics, consideration of the mechanism of transfer of heat is not necessary. We may simply say that objects initially at different temperatures, when contacted, will come to the same temperature as a result of transfer of heat from the object at the higher temperature to that at the lower. When thermal equilibrium (equal temperatures) has been established, no further net transfer of heat energy occurs.

Energy may be exchanged between objects at different temperatures via radiation as well as by conduction. Radiant energy is included as part of heat, since a net transfer of energy between equilibrium systems at different temperatures results from a temperature difference. Classical thermodynamics is not concerned with the mechanism of energy transfer, whether conduction or radiation.

Electrical and Other Forms of Energy. Energy may be transferred through the action of electrical forces. The student will recall that the product of electromotive force and quantity of electricity gives the energy involved ($\mathscr{E}_v It$ or $\mathscr{E}_v Q_e$ or $RI^2 t$). If international electrical units are used, the energy has units of international joules. Other forms of energy, such as magnetic and surface, will not be considered in detail at this time. In ordinary applications of thermodynamics, no attempt is made to calculate an "absolute energy" of a system; the mass-energy equivalence according to the $E = mc^2$ relationship is usually not involved, since "small" energy changes have a negligible effect on mass.

Temperature. In the most abstract development of thermodynamics it is not necessary to specify any particular scale of temperature. All that is required is that temperature indicate the direction of the flow of heat, by declining in one body and increasing in a second when they are placed in thermal contact. This requires that the temperature be a number that arranges a group of bodies or heat reservoirs in a unique order of their ability to raise or lower the energy of the others.

However, in much of what follows, it is convenient to regard temperature as the absolute temperature associated with the perfect gas of Chapter 6. When we make a true thermodynamic definition of a temperature scale (Sec. 7.3), it will be purposely arranged to agree with this absolute temperature, although the definition of the thermodynamic temperature will be logically independent of the perfect gas law.

Heat Capacity. The heat capacity of an object may be defined as the heat-temperature coefficient, $dQ/dT = C$. Under specified conditions, usually constant volume or constant pressure, this coefficient is a characteristic property of the object or system and may be used to calculate the total heat change associated with a temperature change of the object:

$$Q = \int C \, dT$$

C and its dependence on temperature may be determined experimentally. A more detailed discussion of heat and heat capacity will be presented later (see also Chapters 5 and 6).

2. The First Law of Thermodynamics

The first law of thermodynamics asserts that the energy change associated with the change of an equilibrium system from one state to another is independent of the path followed. Furthermore, energy is neither created nor destroyed in any process. This is a law of experience. No attempt will be made to justify it on theoretical grounds or to explain the basic nature of energy other than the observational basis described. The law cannot be proved generally valid; however, no experiment has yet been discovered which has been shown to contradict the law, and hence it is generally accepted.

Equivalence of Heat and Work.   The relationship between the various forms of mechanical energy can easily be derived by the simple relationship of units, dyne-centimeter, liter-atmospheres, etc. For example, the number of ergs equivalent to one pound-inch is determined by the relationships

$$14.7 \text{ lb in.}^{-2} = 1 \text{ atm} = 1.013 \times 10^6 \text{ dynes cm}^{-2}$$
$$1 \text{ in.}^3 = (2.54)^3 \text{ cm}^3$$

and

$$1 \text{ lb in.} = \frac{1.013 \times 10^6 (2.54)^3}{14.7} \text{ ergs}$$

On the other hand, the mechanical equivalent of heat was first established by experiment. This was done in many experiments in which a measured amount of work is transformed into a heat effect. With the validity of the first law accepted, the calorie (originally defined roughly as the energy necessary to raise the temperature of one gram of liquid water one degree centigrade) is now given a precise definition:

$$\text{one calorie (defined)} = 4.1833 \text{ international joules (obsolete)}$$
$$= 4.1840 \text{ absolute joules}$$

The absolute joule (1×10^7 ergs) is the recommended basic unit of energy; however, the calorie continues to receive common use in chemistry.

In thermodynamics it is customary to summarize the various forms of energy into one of two categories; heat, the energy transferred as the result of a temperature gradient; and work, the energy transferred through the action of some directed force. The first law may then be expressed

$$\Delta E = E_2 - E_1 = Q + W \tag{7.201}$$

ΔE represents the total change in energy of a defined system, that is, the difference between its energy content at the end of the process, E_2, and at its initial state, E_1.

Q is the heat change and W the work done in the process. Such an expression establishes certain sign conventions. Positive values of Q and W mean that E_2 is larger than E_1 (conversely for negative values of Q and W). This sign convention for work is not universal; engineers primarily concerned with heat engines frequently give the work available from the system a positive sign (in this case, the first law would be written $\Delta E = Q - W$). We will usually be concerned only with energy in the form of heat or PV work, but other forms may be attached to Eq. 7.201 if necessary. It is obvious that Q and W must be expressed in the same units before they may be summed.

It is important to recognize that the energy of a well-defined thermodynamic state has a definite value, independent of the history of the system. Energy is said to be a function of state only. Such behavior is required by the first law. If the energy change accompanying a transformation from one equilibrium state to another were to depend on the path (the "path" refers to the manner in which the change is carried out), we could devise cycles in which a net gain or loss of energy occurred, that is, energy could be created or destroyed. Perpetual-motion machines (devices which yield an unlimited amount of energy) violate the first law and fail on this basis.

Unlike the total energy, Q and W are not thermodynamic properties of the system, that is, are not "functions of state," but depend on the manner in which the change is made. The only limitation imposed by the first law is that the *sum* of Q and W gives the total change in energy. Heat and work simply represent modes of transfer of energy from one system to another. If, however, a process is carried out by any well-defined path which permits measurement of Q and W for the change, these quantities may be summed to evaluate the change in energy of the system. For example, a sample of gas at fixed initial conditions may be heated and allowed to expand against a piston, doing work, or it can be brought to the same final temperature and volume by expansion into a vacuum, followed by constant-volume heating to the desired temperature. The heat and work terms for these two processes are different, but ΔE is the same for both paths.

Adiabatic and Isothermal Processes.   Processes carried out in such a manner that heat is not exchanged between the system and its surroundings are called adiabatic. In thermodynamics, when a process is said to occur adiabatically Q is set equal to zero.

An isothermal process is one carried out at constant temperature.

Determination of ΔE by Measurement of Q and W.   Calorimetry.   The experimental measurement of heat is based on operation of a calorimeter. One calorimetric method measures the temperature rise of the finite surroundings of a system produced by the heat liberated by the process under consideration. For example, the process may be carried out with the system in contact with a water bath, insulated so that all heat released is used to change the temperature of a known quantity of water. The effect may then be reproduced by electrical heating, in which the quantity of energy transferred (which must then be the same as in the original experiment) can be accurately determined.

ILLUSTRATION.   An adiabatic calorimeter (one in which no heat is exchanged
with the surroundings) is calibrated by passing a measured electrical current
(0.1745 ampere) through a known resistance (20.46 ohms) for 25.32 minutes.
If the temperature of the calorimeter and its contents changes by the same
amount as is produced during the combustion in excess oxygen of 26.02 ml
of methane, measured at 25°C and 1 atm pressure, calculate the molar heat
of combustion of CH_4. Assume that CH_4 is a perfect gas.

$$RI^2t = 946.5 \text{ joules}$$
$$= 226.3 \text{ cal}$$

This must be the same as the heat of combustion of the CH_4. Since 26.02 ml at
1 atm, 25°C, is 0.001063 mole, combustion of 1 mole will release $-(226.3/0.001063) = -213$ kcal. The sign should be negative (reaction releases heat).

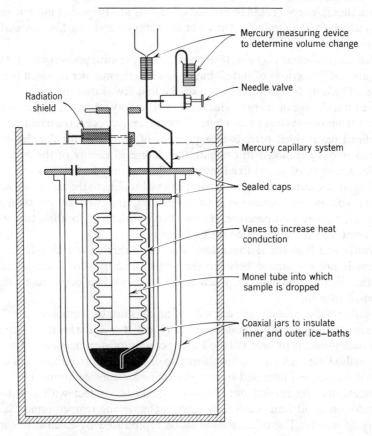

Fig. 7.201   A schematic representation of Bunsen ice-calorimeter used by M. Hoch and H. L.
Johnston, *J. Phys. Chem.*, **65**, 856 (1961), reproduced by permission.

Another method, sometimes used in high-temperature heat capacity measurements, employs an ice calorimeter. The object or sample to be studied is heated to a measured temperature and then dropped into an insulated container surrounded by an equilibrium mixture of liquid water and ice. The heat liberated by the object as it comes to 0°C causes some of the ice to melt. The quantity of ice melted can be measured by the volume change of the liquid-solid mixture. Hence, from the known heat of fusion of water, the heat change can be calculated. Figure 7.201 illustrates an ice calorimeter used to measure the heat capacity of wolfram and of tantalum between 1000 and 3000°K.

Calorimetric measurements constitute an important source of basic thermodynamic data; a variety of devices has been used, all involving a measurement of the temperature change caused in some standard substance, or the change in state caused by the heat transfer, as in the ice calorimeter. We can give only this brief indication of the principles of calorimetry at this time, but the interested reader will find many excellent references in which this important subject is discussed in proper detail (e.g., see *Experimental Thermochemistry*, Vol. I, edited by F. D. Rossini, Interscience Publishers, New York, 1956).

ILLUSTRATION.   The following sample of results illustrates the type of data and precision claimed in a study of the heat of combustion of carbon disulfide by Good, Lacina, and McCullough, *J. Phys. Chem.*, **65**, 2229 (1961).

The authors determined the energy equivalent of their calorimeter $\mathscr{E}_{(calor)}$ by combustion of benzoic acid (a National Bureau of Standards standard sample with certified heat of combustion of 26.434 ± 0.003 abs kj g^{-1}). Seven calibration experiments gave the value $\mathscr{E}_{(calor)}$ = 4025.54 ± 0.19 cal deg^{-1} (mean value and standard deviation).

Mass of sample (CS_2)	0.50056 gram
Mass of hydrocarbon oil (std.) (used to initiate combustion)	0.47061 gram
Mass of polyester bag used to contain CS_2	0.04455 gram
Temperature change (ΔT) of calorimeter on combustion	1.99709°
$\mathscr{E}_{(calor)} \times (-\Delta T)$	−8039.37 cal
Total contribution from oil, polyester bag, and other factors (enumerated in paper)	−5403.63 cal
Net energy due to combustion of CS_2	−2635.74 cal

The student may show that the heat of combustion is −5265.58 cal g.$^{-1}$ What is the molar heat of combustion?

Evaluation of Work.   Work may be directly evaluated for a process only when the force acting between the system and its surroundings is known. The following are four situations for which the PV work can be evaluated. (1) Expansion against zero opposing pressure, called a *free expansion* since the system expends no energy to overcome restraining forces of the surroundings and the work done is zero. (2) A constant-volume process. The PV work is also zero for any process carried out at constant volume, since the displacement term dV in the work expression is zero. (3) A volume change against constant pressure. W is simply $-P_{ex}(V_2 - V_1)$, where P_{ex} is the constant external pressure against which the expansion occurs. (4) A reversible expansion or compression. The concept of reversibility is an important one in thermodynamics and will now be considered.

Reversible Process. In a reversible process the system is assumed to remain in virtual equilibrium at all stages of the change; i.e., the changes in pressure, volume, temperature, and other associated properties must occur infinitesimally slowly so that within the system the normal equilibrium relationship between these properties may be assumed valid. A reversible process is a hypothetical one, not attainable in a practical sense because an infinite time would be required to effect a finite change. For an ideal gas undergoing a reversible expansion or compression, the equation of state $PV = nRT$ may be assumed valid continuously throughout the process. Hence with reference to the work

$$W = -\int_{V_1}^{V_2} P\, dV = -\int_{V_1}^{V_2} nRT\, \frac{dV}{V} \tag{2.104}$$

Eq. 2.104 is integrable if the temperature and n are held constant. This substitution for P_{ex} is permissible under reversible conditions because the internal gas pressure may be assumed only infinitesimally different from the external force on the system at all times.

Even though a reversible process is not physically realizable, the concept is of great value as a means of evaluating a change in thermodynamic properties such as ΔE. Since the change ΔE is fixed by the nature of the initial and final states and is independent of path, it is permissible to evaluate this change by a hypothetical reversible path. The value so determined is then characteristic of any path. Again we emphasize that Q and W are not thermodynamic properties of a given system but characterize a mode of energy transfer. Hence the preceding statement does not apply to heat and work separately.

ILLUSTRATION. Evaluate the work done on *isothermal reversible* expansion of 1 mole of an ideal gas from a volume of 2 liters to a volume of 6 liters.

In general

$$W = -\int_{V_1}^{V_2} P_{ex}\, dV$$

In the present case, P, the internal pressure of the gas at each infinitesimal stage of the expansion, may be assumed equal to RT/V and for a reversible expansion the external pressure P_{ex} is only infinitesimally less than P. Since the process is isothermal, the temperature of the system never deviates more than an infinitesimal amount from T (heat flows in to replace energy extracted as work). Hence

$$W = -\int_{V_1}^{V_2} (P - dP)\, dV$$

If we neglect the second-order infinitesimal $dP\,dV$, this becomes

$$W = -\int_{V_1}^{V_2} P\,dV$$

$$= -\int_{V_1}^{V_2} RT\,\frac{dV}{V}$$

$$= -RT\ln 3$$

The solution shown in the illustration is correct only for an isothermal reversible ideal gas expansion. If the expansion is not conducted reversibly, then the substitution of RT/V for P is not correct. It is seen that the work on expansion is negative (system loses energy); the work on compression will be positive, that is, energy is added to the system as the compression occurs. A graphical representation of isothermal reversible work is shown in Fig. 7.202.

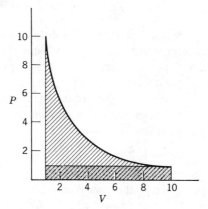

Fig. 7.202   Graphical representation of the work done (the area under the P vs. V curve) for the isothermal expansion of an ideal gas from $P = 10$ atm, $V = 1$ liter, to $P = 1$ atm, $V = 10$ liters, under reversible conditions ▧ and against a constant external pressure of 1 atm ▨.

The reversible work of an isothermal expansion represents the maximum limiting value of $-W$ that can be obtained for a given volume change, since the pressure exerted always has its maximum possible value. Similarly the work needed for the isothermal compression of a gas has a minimum value when the compression is carried out reversibly. From the first law, it follows that Q_{rev} must also represent the maximum numerical value of Q for an expansion and a minimum for a compression.

ILLUSTRATION.   (a) Find the maximum work that can be done when 2 moles of an ideal gas expand isothermally at 300°K from 1 liter to 10 liters. What is the minimum work? Evaluate Q for these two values of W. (b) Suppose that the expansion occurred against a constant external pressure of 1 atm; find the values of Q and W.

(a) Maximum work = reversible work = $-(2)(R)(300) \ln \dfrac{10}{1}$

$$= -113 \text{ l-atm}$$

ΔE for an ideal gas is zero for an isothermal process,

$$\Delta E = 0 = Q + W; \quad Q = 113 \text{ l-atm}$$

Minimum work = 0, i.e., expansion against zero pressure does no work
Minimum $Q = 0$

(b) For isothermal expansion against constant pressure,

$$W = -\int P \, dV = -1(10 - 1) = -9 \text{ l-atm}$$

Since $\Delta E = 0$, $Q = -W = 9$ l-atm

PV work is usually of an important magnitude only for gas processes. The small amount by which the volume of solids (or liquids) changes, with change of pressure or temperature, generates only small work terms unless ΔP (or ΔV) is unusually large.

Relationship of Energy to the Properties of Substances. As stated earlier, the energy of a system containing a fixed amount of a homogeneous phase of constant composition is generally fixed by specifying any two properties of the phase. For energy, T and V prove to be the most convenient variables; thus we let $E = f(T,V)$. A change in either of these variables (properties) reflects a possible energy change. The change in energy accompanying an infinitesimal change in T and V may be written as the total differential

$$dE = \left(\frac{\partial E}{\partial T}\right)_V dT + \left(\frac{\partial E}{\partial V}\right)_T dV \tag{7.202}$$

where the coefficient $\left(\dfrac{\partial E}{\partial T}\right)_V$ gives the energy change with temperature alone, V held constant, and the coefficient $\left(\dfrac{\partial E}{\partial V}\right)_T$ gives the energy change with volume, temperature held constant. From a classical thermodynamic point of view these coefficients (partial derivatives) are properties of the system and must be determined by experiment. The partial derivatives $\left(\dfrac{\partial E}{\partial T}\right)_V$ and $\left(\dfrac{\partial E}{\partial V}\right)_T$ may both be functions of T and V and have particular numerical values only for given values of T and V. The partial derivatives must be expressed as functions of the independent variable before integration can be performed.

Exact Differentials. A differential, such as dE above, of the general form $dZ = M \, dX + N \, dY$, where M and N are both functions of X and Y, cannot be integrated unless either X or Y can be eliminated, e.g., $X = f(Y)$, where f is an equation for a path on the XY plane. Such an integration is a function of path and is called inexact unless it passes the test for exactness. This test requires that

$$\left(\frac{\partial M}{\partial Y}\right)_X = \left(\frac{\partial N}{\partial X}\right)_Y \tag{7.203}$$

called the *reciprocity relationship.* When Eq. 7.203 is found to apply, integration from point $X_1 Y_1$ to point $X_2 Y_2$ will give a change of the dependent variable which is independent of the path followed; that is, the overall change in Z is dependent not on the relationship between X and Y at intermediate stages of the change, but only on the initial and final values of X and Y.

ILLUSTRATION. Given $dz = (51x^2y + 47y^4)\, dx + (17x^3 + 188xy^3)\, dy$, see if dz is an exact differential.

In this case

$$M = 51x^2y + 47y^4 \quad \text{and} \quad N = 17x^3 + 188xy^3$$

hence

$$\left(\frac{\partial M}{\partial y}\right)_x = 51x^2 + 188y^3 = \left(\frac{\partial N}{\partial x}\right)_y = 51x^2 + 188y^3$$

Thus dz is an exact differential.

The statement concerning integration of exact differentials, when applied to energy as the dependent variable, is the equivalent of the first law. The energy change dE expressed in the form of Eq. 7.202 is an exact differential, and ΔE for any finite change may be evaluated by integrating over any convenient path. The reciprocity equation is a powerful tool in thermodynamics and provides many useful relationships. Note that dQ and dW are not exact differentials.

ILLUSTRATION. Exact and inexact differentials in the reversible expansion of a perfect gas.

Consider a perfect gas that undergoes a change from V_1, P_1, T_1 to V_2, P_2, T_2 by two possible paths as shown in Fig. 7.203. The path AC is directly

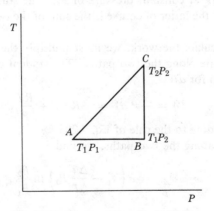

Fig. 7.203 Two paths on the P, T plane.

along the diagonal in the P, T plane. The second path, ABC, consists of two parts, a compression at constant T to point B, followed by a temperature increase at constant pressure to point C. The volume change can be written as a total differential (compare Eq. 7.202)

$$dV = \left(\frac{\partial V}{\partial T}\right)_P dT + \left(\frac{\partial V}{\partial P}\right)_T dP = \frac{R}{P} dT - \frac{RT}{P^2} dP$$

The student may immediately verify that this is an exact differential, both from the definition and by differentiation according to Eq. 7.203.

We will proceed to calculate the volume change by integration along the paths of change. The equation of the diagonal line in Fig. 7.203 is

$$T - T_1 = \frac{\Delta T}{\Delta P}(P - P_1)$$

where $\Delta T = T_2 - T_1$ and $\Delta P = P_2 - P_1$. Thus

$$dT = \frac{\Delta T}{\Delta P} dP$$

We then can find that

$$dV = R\left(\frac{\Delta T}{\Delta P} P_1 - T_1\right) \frac{dP}{P^2}$$

This expression can be integrated between the limits P_1 and P_2 to give

$$\Delta V_{AC} = \frac{R(T_2 P_1 - P_2 T_1)}{P_1 P_2}$$

The integration along the path ABC consists of two parts. First, the second term of the equation for dV is integrated along the constant temperature path to T_1, P_2 for one part of ΔV; then the second part is evaluated by integration of the first term of dV at constant pressure of P_2. The student should show that $\Delta V_{AC} = \Delta V_{ABC}$; the latter of course is the sum of the two parts of the volume change.

In order to calculate the work, we must multiply the expression for dV by P and then integrate along the two paths. The student can immediately verify that the expression for dW

$$dW = -P\, dV = -R\, dT + \frac{RT}{P} dP$$

is not exact, according to the rule of Eq. 7.203.

If we integrate along the two paths, we find

$$W_{AC} = R\left(T_1 - \frac{\Delta T}{\Delta P} P_1\right) \ln \frac{P_2}{P_1}$$

and

$$W_{ABC} = R\left(T_1 \ln \frac{P_2}{P_1} - \Delta T\right)$$

which indeed are not the same.

Integrating Factor   The foregoing Illustration can be described in the following manner: dW, as we have shown, is an inexact differential; dV is shown to be exact. Formally, multiplication by $-1/P$ makes the inexact differential dW exact. Such a multiplier is termed an *integrating factor*. Later on, we shall find such a factor for the other important inexact differential, dQ.

Heat Capacity at Constant Volume, C_V.   For constant volume, the energy change may be regarded solely as a function of temperature

$$\Delta E = Q_V = \int_{T_1}^{T_2} \left(\frac{\partial E}{\partial T}\right)_V dT \qquad (7.204)$$

$\left(\dfrac{\partial E}{\partial T}\right)_V$·is called the heat capacity of the system at constant volume and hereafter will be represented by the symbol C_V (see also Sec. 6.4).

$$C_V = \left(\frac{\partial E}{\partial T}\right)_V \qquad (7.205)$$

C_V may be determined experimentally by measuring the temperature change in the constant-volume system produced by absorption of or removal of measured amounts of energy; if ΔE or Q_V is plotted against temperature, the slope of the line at any point is the value C_V at that temperature. C_V is the limiting value

$$C_V = \operatorname*{limit}_{\Delta T \to 0} \left(\frac{\Delta Q}{\Delta T}\right)_V$$

Q_V may be described by an empirical equation written as a power series in temperature; this equation may then be differentiated with respect to temperature to determine the heat capacity.

Enthalpy.   In many cases, particularly with solids or liquids, it is more convenient to work at constant pressure. When a volume change occurs against a nonzero pressure, PV work will be exchanged with the surroundings. Assuming that no other mechanical forces are involved, the first law becomes $Q_P = \Delta E + P\,\Delta V$; the subscript P indicates a constant-pressure process. For processes in which T and P are the most convenient variables, it is found useful to define a thermodynamic property, closely related to energy, called enthalpy and represented by the symbol H. By definition

$$H = E + PV \qquad (7.206)$$

For any change, $\Delta H = \Delta E + \Delta(PV)$. Like ΔE, $\Delta(PV)$ is simply the difference between the PV product at the final state, P_2V_2, and that at the initial state, P_1V_1, i.e.,

$$\Delta(PV) = P_2V_2 - P_1V_1 \qquad (7.207)$$

Hence, if ΔE has been determined and P and V are known in the initial and final states, ΔH may be calculated. However, for a constant-pressure process it will usually be found more convenient to measure the change in enthalpy and then to determine ΔE from Eq. 7.206. For a constant-pressure process, $Q_P = \Delta E + P\Delta V = \Delta H$. This relationship between Q and ΔH must be recognized as a special case; only when the pressure is constant *throughout* the process does ΔH equal Q.

Since E, P, and V are all thermodynamic properties of any equilibrium system, H must also be a thermodynamic function of state. Like dE, dH is an exact differential; dQ is not, which emphasizes an important difference between H and Q.

Heat Capacity at Constant Pressure, C_P. From the temperature change produced by adding varying amounts of heat to an object maintained at constant pressure, a plot of Q_P against T may be constructed. The slope of such a line at any temperature gives the value of $\underset{\Delta T \to 0}{\text{limit}}\left(\dfrac{\Delta Q}{\Delta T}\right)_P$, defined as C_P, the heat capacity of the object at constant pressure. A corresponding definition is

$$C_P = \left(\frac{\partial H}{\partial T}\right)_P \tag{7.208}$$

the enthalpy-temperature coefficient at constant pressure.

Like energy, the enthalpy may (with rare exceptions) be regarded as a function of any two variables for a homogeneous system of fixed amount of material. T and P are the convenient variables,

$$H = f(T,P)$$

$$dH = \left(\frac{\partial H}{\partial T}\right)_P dT + \left(\frac{\partial H}{\partial P}\right)_T dP \tag{7.209}$$

For a constant-pressure process $dP = 0$, and the enthalpy is a function of temperature only and may be determined by integrating the expression

$$\Delta H_P = H_2 - H_1 = \int_{T_1}^{T_2} C_P \, dT \tag{7.210}$$

The variation of C_P with temperature has been determined for many substances and is usually reported as an empirical power series in $T°K$ of one of the following forms:

$$\begin{aligned}\bar{C}_P &= a + bT + cT^{-2}\\ \bar{C}_P &= a' + b'T + c'T^2 + \cdots\end{aligned} \tag{7.211}$$

As many terms as are needed to fit the experimental curve are included; a, b, c, etc., are constants characteristic of the given material [see Table 7.201(A)]. Heat capacities are extensive properties but are generally reported for 1 mole of substance, i.e., as intensive variables $\bar{C}_P$ (or $\bar{C}_V$). Values for simple gas molecules are calculated by methods to be described later.

Table 7.201   *Molar Heat Capacities, $\bar{C}_P^{\circ}$, cal mole^{-1} deg^{-1}, at 1 atm Pressure and at 298°K and Above*

$$\bar{C}_P^{\circ} = a + bT + cT^{-2}$$

Substance	a	$b \times 10^3$	$c \times 10^{-5}$	Upper Temp. Limit, °K
Al(c)	4.94	2.96	...	932
Al$_2$O$_3$(c)	27.49	2.82	−8.38	1800
AlN(c)	5.47	7.80	...	900

The complete Table 7.201(A) will be found in the Appendix.

Heat capacity data permit calculation of ΔH (from C_P) for a temperature change at constant pressure, and of ΔE (from C_V) for a temperature change at constant volume. The two kinds of heat capacity may be interrelated through the defining equation for H. Because of the great many processes of interest at constant pressure (of the atmosphere) C_P is used more often than C_V. The latter, however, is more directly related to the internal energy of the system.

ILLUSTRATION.   A particular block of metal has a heat capacity given by the equation $C_P = 15 + 0.002T$ cal deg^{-1} between 0 and 500°C. Its volume at 0° is 20 cc, and it expands to 20.4 cc at 500°C. Find ΔE and ΔH for the block if it is cooled from 500 to 0°C under constant pressure of 1 atm.
From Eq. 7.210

$$\Delta H = \int_{773}^{273} C_P \, dT = \int_{773}^{273} (15 + 0.002T) \, dT$$

$$= 15(273 - 773) + 0.001(273^2 - 773^2) \text{ cal}$$

Then

$$\Delta E = \Delta H - \Delta(PV)$$

$$= 15(273 - 773) + 0.001[(273)^2 - (773)^2] - 1(20 - 20.4)\left(\frac{1.987}{82}\right) \text{ cal}$$

$$= -8023 \text{ cal (the last term above is very small)}$$

Thermodynamic Equations of State.   It might appear that the coefficients $\left(\dfrac{\partial E}{\partial V}\right)_T$ and $\left(\dfrac{\partial H}{\partial P}\right)_T$ would have to be evaluated experimentally and presented as a series expansion in V or P, similar to the expansion needed for the heat capacity. However, it is simpler to evaluate them from PVT data; it will be shown in Sec. 7.3 that the relationships

$$\left(\frac{\partial E}{\partial V}\right)_T = T\left(\frac{\partial P}{\partial T}\right)_V - P \qquad\qquad (7.212)$$

and

$$\left(\frac{\partial H}{\partial P}\right)_T = -T\left(\frac{\partial V}{\partial T}\right)_P + V \tag{7.213}$$

may be derived by application of the second law of thermodynamics. Equation 7.212 and 7.213 are sometimes called thermodynamic equations of state. A general relationship between C_P and C_V.

$$C_P - C_V = T\left(\frac{\partial P}{\partial T}\right)_V \left(\frac{\partial V}{\partial T}\right)_P \tag{7.214}$$

will also be derived in Sec. 7.3.

Evaluation of First-Law Quantities for Physical Processes.   *Ideal Gases.*   An ideal gas obeys the equation of state $PV = nRT$. Values of the gas constant R have been given in Sec. 6.3.

First-law calculations are simplified for perfect gases because Eqs. 7.212 and 7.213 give, as a consequence of the form of the equation of state, $\left(\frac{\partial E}{\partial V}\right)_T$ and $\left(\frac{\partial H}{\partial P}\right)_T$ both zero. This behavior was suggested by experiments by Joule, who studied the adiabatic free expansion of real gases at low pressures where the behavior approximated that of a perfect gas. If both Q and W are zero at each infinitesimal step of the process,

$$dE = C_V \, dT + \left(\frac{\partial E}{\partial V}\right)_T dV = 0$$

Joule observed no temperature change; since neither C_V nor ΔV is zero, it is necessary that $\left(\frac{\partial E}{\partial V}\right)_T = 0$ if $\Delta T = 0$.

In this chapter ideal or perfect gas behavior will be taken only to imply that we may use the equation of state $PV = nRT$. Many gases approximate ideal behavior sufficiently well, at pressures in the vicinity of and below 1 atm and at moderate temperatures, that the perfect gas equation may be used. It may still be necessary to consider the heat capacity as a function of temperature, however.

For ideal gases E and H are functions of temperature only. When an ideal gas undergoes any isothermal change, both ΔE and ΔH must be zero. If the temperature of an ideal gas changes, $\Delta E = \int C_V \, dT$, regardless of what happens to the volume or pressure; similarly $\Delta H = \int C_P \, dT$. Of course ΔE and ΔH are directly related by the defining equation for H, i.e., $\Delta H = \Delta E + \Delta(PV)$. For an ideal gas $\Delta(PV) = \Delta(nRT)$. Thus a simple relationship between C_P and C_V may be shown for an ideal gas

$$H = E + PV$$
$$dH = dE + d(PV)$$
$$= dE + d(nRT)$$

Hence

$$n\bar{C}_P \, dT = n\bar{C}_V \, dT + nR \, dT$$

i.e., $$n\bar{C}_P = n\bar{C}_V + nR$$

or $$\bar{C}_P = \bar{C}_V + R \qquad (7.215)$$

where R corresponds to the work of expansion (per degree per mole) against the external constant pressure in the C_P case

$$d(PV) = P\,dV = nR\,dT = -dW \quad \text{when } P \text{ is constant}$$

The C_P, C_V relationship may also be confirmed by Eq. 7.214.

ILLUSTRATION.   Ten moles of an ideal gas, for which $\bar{C}_V = 5$ cal mole^{-1} deg^{-1}, initially at 20°C and 1 atm pressure, receives 200 cal of heat. If P remains constant at 1 atm, find ΔE for the gas. What is the value of W?
    From Eq. 7.215

$$\bar{C}_P = \bar{C}_V + R = 5 + 1.987 = 6.987 \text{ cal mole}^{-1}\text{ deg}^{-1}$$

From Eq. 7.210

$$Q_P = \Delta H_P = \int_{T_1}^{T_2} C_P\,dT = 69.87(T_2 - T_1) = 200 \text{ cal}$$

Hence

$$T_2 - T_1 = \frac{200}{69.87} = 2.86$$

Then

$$T_2 = 22.86°C$$

From Eq. 7.204

$$\Delta E = \int_{T_1}^{T_2} C_V\,dT = 50(2.86) = 143 \text{ cal}$$

Hence

$$W = \Delta E - Q = 143 - 200 = -57 \text{ cal}$$

From the properties of partial differentials in general, $\left(\dfrac{\partial E}{\partial P}\right)_T = \left(\dfrac{\partial E}{\partial V}\right)_T \left(\dfrac{\partial V}{\partial P}\right)_T$. Hence, $\left(\dfrac{\partial E}{\partial P}\right)_T$ must also be zero for an ideal gas, as is $\left(\dfrac{\partial H}{\partial V}\right)_T$. Since ΔE is zero for any isothermal change of volume of an ideal gas, it follows that $Q = -W$. The situations in which the work can be calculated have been discussed earlier.

In adiabatic processes, $Q = 0$ and $\Delta E = W$. If the change occurs reversibly, the work integral may be written

$$-\int P\,dV = -\int \frac{nRT\,dV}{V}$$

but cannot be evaluated directly since the temperature does not remain constant. However, since $dE = -P\,dV$ and since for an ideal gas $dE = n\bar{C}_V\,dT$, it is possible to separate the variables and obtain a relationship between the final temperature

T_2 and volume V_2 and the initial values T_1 and V_1 for an adiabatic reversible process

$$dE = -P\,dV$$

$$n\bar{C}_V\,dT = -\frac{nRT}{V}\,dV$$

$$\bar{C}_V\frac{dT}{T} = -R\frac{dV}{V} \tag{7.216}$$

If the heat capacity may be assumed independent of temperature, this expression integrates simply to $\bar{C}_V \ln T_2/T_1 = R \ln V_1/V_2$. Hence, if the final volume is given, the final temperature may be calculated, or vice versa. From the final temperature, ΔE and hence ΔH and W may be evaluated. If $\bar{C}_V$ is a known function of temperature, the integrated form is different, but the new result is reached in the same way. If the final pressure is specified instead of the volume, a substitution $V_2 = nRT_2/P_2$ may be made in the integrated equation.

ILLUSTRATION.   Show that PV^γ is constant for the reversible adiabatic expansion of an ideal gas of constant heat capacity, where γ is C_P/C_V.
    From Eq. 7.216

$$\bar{C}_V\frac{dT}{T} = -R\frac{dV}{V}$$

may be changed to the form

$$\bar{C}_V\left(\frac{dV}{V} + \frac{dP}{P}\right) = -R\frac{dV}{V}$$

since $dV/V + dP/P = dT/T$ from the perfect gas law.   Thus

$$\frac{dP}{P} = -\frac{(\bar{C}_V + R)}{\bar{C}_V}\frac{dV}{V} = -\frac{\bar{C}_P}{\bar{C}_V}\frac{dV}{V} = -\gamma\frac{dV}{V}$$

or, in integrated form,

$$\ln\frac{P_2}{P_1} = \ln\left(\frac{V_1}{V_2}\right)^\gamma$$

or

$$P_2V_2^\gamma = P_1V_1^\gamma = \text{const} \tag{7.217}$$

Figure 7.204 shows a comparison of PV behavior for isothermal and adiabatic reversible expansions.   The student may derive the following relationships for an adiabatic reversible-ideal gas change

$$\frac{T_2}{T_1} = \left(\frac{V_1}{V_2}\right)^{\gamma-1} \tag{7.218}$$

$$\frac{T_2}{T_1} = \left(\frac{P_2}{P_1}\right)^{(\gamma-1)/\gamma} \tag{7.219}$$

These equations are valid only for a *reversible* adiabatic process involving an *ideal gas*, for which C_V is constant over the temperature interval involved.

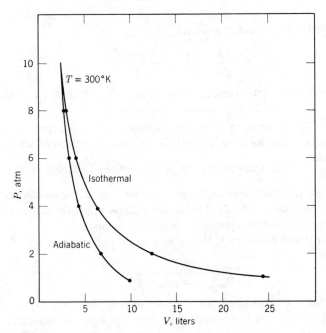

Fig. 7.204   Comparison of pressure-volume relationship for 1 mole of a perfect gas with $\gamma = 1.67$, starting at $P = 10$ atm, $V = 2.46$ liters, and $T = 300°$K, for an isothermal and adiabatic reversible expansion, respectively.

ILLUSTRATION.   Consider the prediction of the temperature of the atmosphere, based on a simple adiabatic expansion model.

The dependence of pressure on height is given by the barometric formula

$$dP = -\rho g \, dx$$

where ρ is the density of the atmosphere, x the height, and g the acceleration due to gravity.   For a perfect gas the density is

$$\rho = \frac{MP}{RT}$$

where M is the average molecular weight of air;   hence

$$dP = -\frac{gM}{R}\frac{P}{T}\,dx$$

We now assume that the masses of air are so large (no heat loss) and move so slowly up into the atmosphere that the relationship between P and T is given by that for an adiabatic, reversible expansion, which in logarithmic form is

$$\frac{dT}{T} = \frac{\gamma - 1}{\gamma} \frac{dP}{P}$$

This result yields the constant gradient

$$\frac{dT}{dx} = -\frac{\gamma - 1}{\gamma} \frac{gM}{R}$$

This is about $-10°C$ km^{-1} (actual mean value up to 10 km is *ca.* $-6°$ km^{-1}).

Real Gases. The evaluation of first-law quantities for changes involving real gases is somewhat more involved because of the nonzero values of the coefficients $\left(\frac{\partial E}{\partial V}\right)_T$ and $\left(\frac{\partial H}{\partial P}\right)_T$. The treatment may be generalized in terms of the equation of state which the gas is assumed to follow. A similar generalization is not possible for condensed phases since the PVT behavior of these phases cannot be described by a simple equation of state applicable to many substances.

If the van der Waals equation for n moles is employed (see Sec. 6.5)

$$P = \frac{nRT}{V - nb} - \frac{n^2 a}{V^2} \tag{6.503}$$

this value of P may be substituted, for example, into the isothermal reversible work expression, Eq. 2.102; the integrated result now includes the constants a and b. Use of the van der Waals equation in Eq. 7.212 shows that $\left(\frac{\partial E}{\partial V}\right)_T = n^2 a/V^2$. This result is in convenient form since it is explicit in V; hence the general expression for energy, $dE = C_V\, dT + \left(\frac{\partial E}{\partial V}\right)_T dV$, is integrable if the temperature change and volume change are specified, and if C_V is a known function of T; in this case ΔE may be evaluated directly.

The van der Waals equation is only partially successful and is only one of many empirical equations of state which may be used to represent the behavior of real gases over limited temperature intervals.

Berthelot's equation is widely used in the form

$$P\bar{V} = RT + \frac{9RPT_c}{128P_c}\left(1 - 6\frac{T_c^2}{T^2}\right) \tag{7.220}$$

where T_c is the critical temperature (see Chapter 11). This equation is similar to the limited virial form (compare Eq. 6.510)

$$P\bar{V} = RT + BP \tag{7.221}$$

where

$$B = \frac{9R}{128}\frac{T_c}{P_c}\left(1 - 6\frac{T_c^2}{T^2}\right) \tag{7.222}$$

With Eq. 7.221 it is easier to evaluate $\left(\dfrac{\partial H}{\partial P}\right)_T$ from Eq. 7.213 than to evaluate the energy-volume coefficient. ΔH may be evaluated first, when convenient, and then ΔE, through the defining equation $\Delta H = \Delta E + \Delta(PV)$.

Joule-Thomson Experiment.   An experiment called the Joule-Thomson (throttled) expansion can be used to show the variation of H, and hence of E, with pressure for real gases. This experiment effectively measures the same property as the Joule free adiabatic expansion described earlier, but provides a more sensitive method for detection of gas imperfection. A schematic representation of the apparatus is shown in Fig. 7.205. Two chambers A and B are separated by a nonconducting porous plug through which the gas may flow in such a way as

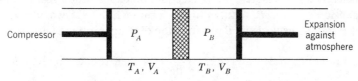

Fig. 7.205   Schematic representation of the Joule-Thomson expansion experiment.

to permit a constant pressure differential to be maintained between A and B, and to cause no frictional heat loss as the gas passes through. The pressure in A is maintained at P_A with a compressor, and in B at P_B through motion of a piston, e.g., expanding against the atmosphere. Adiabatic conditions prevail so $Q = 0$. Hence the change in energy as the gas passes from A to B will be the difference between the work done on the gas by the compressor and the work done by the gas against the atmosphere.

Consider the Joule-Thomson expansion of 1 mole of gas. The net change in energy will be
$$\Delta \bar{E} = -\Delta(P\bar{V})$$
hence
$$\bar{E}_B - \bar{E}_A = P_A \bar{V}_A - P_B \bar{V}_B$$

where $\bar{V}_A$ = molar volume at P_A, and $\bar{V}_B$ = molar volume at P_B. This relation shows that
$$\bar{H}_A = \bar{E}_A + P_A \bar{V}_A = \bar{E}_B + P_B \bar{V}_B = \bar{H}_B$$

that is, no change in enthalpy occurs. Hence the general expression for dH may be set equal to zero
$$dH = C_P\, dT + \left(\frac{\partial H}{\partial P}\right)_T dP = 0$$

Therefore
$$\left(\frac{\partial T}{\partial P}\right)_H = -\left(\frac{\partial H}{\partial P}\right)_T / C_P \tag{7.223}$$

The ratio $\left(\dfrac{\partial T}{\partial P}\right)_H$ is called the *Joule-Thomson coefficient* and is usually represented by the symbol μ_{JT}. Since $\left(\dfrac{\partial H}{\partial P}\right)_T$ is zero for perfect gases, the Joule-Thomson coefficient is also zero for perfect gases. A nonzero value of μ_{JT} indicates deviation from ideal behavior. Joule-Thomson coefficients are negative in certain temperature and pressure ranges (the temperature increases as the gas expands) and positive at other temperatures and pressures (temperature decreases as P decreases). The particular temperature at which μ_{JT} changes sign, that is, where μ_{JT} is zero, is called the *inversion temperature*. The inversion temperature depends on pressure. The behavior of imperfect gases is of considerable importance in the problem of gas liquefaction and in the theoretical study of interaction of gas molecules. The information provided by the Joule-Thomson throttled expansion experiment can also be calculated from PVT data, using Eq. 7.213, together with C_P.

At sufficiently low pressures, the virial equation of state for a real gas, expressed as an expansion series in P, reduces to the form of Eq. 7.221 when P^2 and higher powers of P may be neglected. B is a function of temperature but is independent of pressure. From Eqs. 7.213 and 7.221 $\left(\dfrac{\partial H}{\partial P}\right)_T$ is then found equal to $B - T\dfrac{dB}{dT}$.

Hence the Joule-Thomson coefficient (from Eq. 7.223) does not approach zero in general as P approaches zero for a real gas.

Condensed Phases. Experiments involving solids and liquids are usually carried out at constant pressure. Hence ΔH can be evaluated for temperature changes from C_P data alone, and ΔE calculated from Eq. 7.206. The application of the first law to phase changes and chemical reactions will be considered in a subsequent chapter.

Summary. It has been shown how the first law of thermodynamics provides an experimental basis for evaluating the difference in energy content of a system in two different states. For such a change, either a direct experimental measurement of the heat and work exchanged between the system and its surroundings may be made, or the energy change may be evaluated from heat capacity and the PVT behavior of the substance concerned. No reference to quantum theory and atomic or molecular structure is required. The relationship of energy, heat capacity, PVT behavior, etc., to molecular properties has been discussed in earlier chapters, and the reader will now see how the results of theory may be tested against thermodynamic measurements.

For gases composed of simple molecules at low pressure, statistical mechanics provides a means of calculating heat capacities at different temperatures from molecular structure information with greater accuracy than is attainable by thermochemical measurement. Equations (Chapters 5 and 6) have been given relating the energy and heat capacities to the partition function; simple equations of this form cannot be used for very complex molecules or developed accurately for condensed states, although the theoretical treatment of the heat capacity of simple solids has had limited success (Chapter 5). The evaluation of thermodynamic properties from partition functions will be considered further (Chapter 11) after discussion of the second law and the free energy concepts.

Problems

7.201   An object weighing 5 kg falls a distance of 100 meters. Assuming the gravitational constant $(g = 980.665$ cm sec$^{-2})$ not to vary with height, calculate the change in potential energy of the object. Give your answer in ergs, absolute joules, and calories.

7.202   The force necessary to elongate a certain spring is related to the displacement d from its zero position by $f = 2 \times 10^7 d + 1.6 \times 10^3 d^2$ dynes.

(a) Calculate the work in joules necessary to extend this spring 2 cm from its zero (equilibrium) position.

(b) What mass would be required to extend this spring 1 cm if g has the value given in Problem 7.201?

7.203   Calculate the work done (in ergs) against the atmosphere when 10 grams of water vaporizes at 373°K against a constant external pressure of 1 atm; assume that steam obeys the perfect gas law.

7.204   A current of 5 amperes flows through a resistance of 50 ohms for 20 minutes. How many calories of heat are generated in the resistance? Express this quantity of energy in international joules, watt-seconds, kilowatt-hours, electron-volts, volt-Faradays, and liter-atmospheres.

7.205   Fifty grams of O_2 expands reversibly under isothermal conditions from a volume of 1.5 liters to 45 liters at 300°K. Evaluate Q, W, ΔE, and ΔH; assume perfect gas behavior.

7.206   Twenty grams of CO_2 is heated at a constant pressure of 1 atm: $Q_P = 80$ cal. What is the final temperature if $\bar{C}_P$ is assumed constant at the value predicted in Table 7.201(A) at 300°K? What is ΔE if the gas is considered ideal? Assume $T_1 = 300$°K.

7.207   Two moles of a perfect gas for which $\bar{C}_V = 6$ cal deg^{-1} mole^{-1} undergoes expansion from a pressure of 5 atm at 27°C to a final pressure of 1 atm at 7°C. If 100 cal of heat was withdrawn from the gas during the process, calculate the work done in the expansion.

7.208   Four-tenths mole of a perfect gas, $\bar{C}_V = 8$ cal deg^{-1} mole^{-1} at an initial temperature of 25°C and pressure of 1 atm is heated by passing a current of 0.2 ampere through a resistance of 20 ohms for 2 minutes. If the pressure on the gas is kept constant throughout the process, what is the final temperature of the gas, assuming no loss of heat? (1 cal = 4.1833 international joules; $R = 1.987$ cal mole^{-1} deg^{-1}.)

7.209   One mole of an ideal gas, initially at 25°C, is heated at constant volume by a current flowing for 5 minutes through a resistance of 10 ohms across which the voltage drop is 5 volts. The gas is then expanded adiabatically against a constant external pressure of 1 atm until its temperature again reaches 25°C. What must be the volume change in this expansion? If the final pressure of the gas is 1 atm, what must have been its initial pressure (n constant)?

7.210   Calculate the heat liberated by 1 mole of an ideal gas compressed isothermally and reversibly at 300°K from an initial volume of 10 liters to a final volume of 1 liter. Repeat this calculation for a van der Waals gas if a is 18 liter^2-atm mole^{-2} and b is 11.5×10^{-2} liter mole^{-1}.

7.211   Two moles of an ideal gas is compressed from an initial pressure of 1 atm at 27°C by the application of 500 joules of work. Thirty calories of heat is removed during the compression. What is the final temperature of the gas if $\bar{C}_V = 7.0$ cal deg^{-1} mole^{-1}?

7.212   An ideal gas expands reversibly and adiabatically from $T = 400$°K and $P = 10$ atm to a final pressure of 1 atm. If $\bar{C}_V = 5$ cal deg^{-1} mole^{-1}, what is the final temperature?

7.213   Two moles of a perfect gas is compressed reversibly and adiabatically from $T_1 = 300$°K and $P_1 = 1$ atm by the expenditure of 300 joules of work. What are the final temperature and pressure of the gas? $\bar{C}_V = 5$ cal deg^{-1} mole^{-1}.

7.214 Thirty-five hundredths mole of an ideal gas, $\bar{C}_V = \frac{3}{2}R$, is expanded under adiabatic conditions from a volume of 1 liter at 400°K to a volume of 5 liters against a constant external pressure of 0.5 atm. What is the final temperature of the gas? What is the change in enthalpy of the gas in this process?

7.215 Ten grams of oxygen, initially at 25°C and 1 atm pressure, is compressed adiabatically until its temperature reaches 60°C. If $\bar{C}_V = \frac{5}{2}R$ and ideal gas behavior is assumed, calculate the amount of work done on the gas. What can you say about the final pressure and volume of the gas?

*7.216 Five moles of a van der Waals gas, initially at 400°K, undergoes a free adiabatic expansion from a volume of 10 liters to a volume of 50 liters. If $\bar{C}_V = 6.0 + 0.002T$ cal deg⁻¹ mole⁻¹, $a = 10$ liters²-atm mole⁻², and $b = 0.0015$ liter mole⁻¹, calculate the final temperature of the gas and the change in enthalpy for the process.

7.217 A particular gas may be assumed to follow the equation of state $P\bar{V} = RT + bP$. Calculate ΔH and ΔE for the isothermal expansion of 1 mole at 25°C from $P = 10$ atm to $P = 2$ atm; assume b is a given constant. What can you say about Q and W for this process? What is the maximum possible value of Q?

7.218 For HCl(g), $\bar{C}_P = 6.73 + 0.43 \times 10^{-3}T + 0.37 \times 10^{-6}T^2$ cal deg⁻¹ mole⁻¹ at 1 atm pressure. Calculate ΔH, ΔE, Q, and W for the process in which 100 grams of HCl gas is cooled from 50 to 25°C under a constant pressure of 1 atm. Assume that HCl follows the equation of state given in Problem 7.217, with $b = 0.04$ liter mole⁻¹.

7.219 From data in Problems 7.217 and 7.218 evaluate the Joule-Thomson coefficient for HCl gas at 1 atm pressure and 25°C.

7.220 The density of solid lead at 20°C is 11.34 g cm⁻³ and at 325°C is 11.00 g cm⁻³. The heat capacity of lead may be assumed given by the equation $\bar{C}_P = 5.77 + 2.02 \times 10^{-3}T$ cal deg⁻¹ mole⁻¹ over this temperature interval. Calculate ΔE for the process

$$\text{Pb (100 grams solid, 20°C, 1 atm)} \rightarrow \text{Pb (100 grams solid, 325°C, 1 atm)}$$

7.221 M. Hoch and H. L. Johnston [*J. Phys. Chem.*, **65**, 856 (1961)] give data leading to the following equation for the enthalpy of wolfram at temperature t°C relative to the enthalpy at 0°C (range of validity 1109° → 2620°C) at constant pressure: $H_t - H_0 = 0.850 + 3.176 \times 10^{-2}t + 2.184 \times 10^{-6}t^2$ cal g⁻¹. Calculate the value of $\bar{C}_P$ for wolfram at 2000°K.

3. The Second Law of Thermodynamics

One of the principal objectives in the application of thermodynamics to chemistry is the prediction of chemical behavior. When will reactions occur spontaneously and, if equilibrium mixtures result, what is the composition of the final system? We are not yet prepared to consider the thermodynamic analysis of a change as complicated as a chemical reaction. However, the predictability of spontaneous change follows a general thermodynamic principle which we may develop by considering simple physical changes of one-component systems.

Spontaneous Change. From the first law one might mistakenly propose a "minimum energy principle," that changes occur spontaneously if the energy of the final state is less than the energy of the initial state. Such behavior is analogous to experience in mechanics; objects tend to move to states of minimum potential energy. Although this principle has an important place in thermodynamic considerations (chemical reactions in which large amounts of energy are released do occur spontaneously, although they may be inhibited kinetically), it is not difficult to find examples of changes which occur spontaneously with no change in energy, and of others (e.g., the isothermal solution of NaCl in water) which actually have positive values of ΔE. Hence the first law does not provide a suitable criterion for predicting change. Furthermore, the mere existence of equilibrium mixtures is not consistent with a minimum energy principle; if the final state has a lower energy content than the initial one, such a principle would predict complete conversion of reactants to products.

We shall see that the second law embodies the sought-after criterion of spontaneous change and, together with the first law, forms a convenient basis for predicting the nature of equilibrium systems under various conditions of restraint.

Analysis of a simple spontaneous change in which ΔE is zero will serve as a suitable way to introduce the second-law principle. Consider the free adiabatic expansion of 1 mole of an ideal gas: since $W = 0$ and $Q = 0$, $\Delta E = 0$ and hence $\Delta T = 0$, that is, the process is also isothermal; furthermore $\Delta(PV)$ and thus ΔH equal zero. No change in first-law properties has occurred; yet it is common experience that expansion of a gas into an evacuated space occurs spontaneously until the entire available volume is uniformly occupied. Some new thermodynamic property is needed to indicate that such a change is expected to take place.

It is instructive to reverse this change, that is, to bring the gas back to its initial state and to consider the overall effect of the two processes on the system (the gas) and its surroundings. Suppose that the expanded gas in a volume V_2 were to be compressed reversibly and isothermally back to its original volume, V_1. This process would require an amount of work $-RT \ln V_1/V_2$, positive in sign, indicating that energy is added to the gas in the compression. Since the gas temperature is held constant, an equivalent amount of energy must leave the system in the form of heat. As a final result of the cycle, the gas is in its initial state and all its properties must then be the same as before the expansion occurred. The surroundings lost an amount of energy in the form of work but gained an equivalent amount of energy in the form of heat.

If the original expansion had been carried out reversibly, not spontaneously, the surroundings would have gained an amount of work during the expansion (assume this work energy to be stored in a spring) and lost an amount of heat. On reversing the process, the work gained during the expansion could be used to compress the gas and the heat lost by the surroundings during expansion would then be replaced during the compression. Thus, when the complete cycle is performed reversibly, everything, system and surroundings, reverts to its initial state. However, in the case of the spontaneous change, the final result of the completed cycle was a loss of work in the surroundings, although energy was conserved in that the work equivalent appeared as heat.

A similar result is found for any isothermal change. When all changes are carried out reversibly and a cycle is completed which brings the system back to the initial state, the surroundings will also be the same as before the change was initiated. If

any part of the cycle involves a spontaneous, i.e., irreversible step, then on completion of the cycle the surroundings will have lost some potential for doing work
(work energy removed) and have gained an equivalent amount of heat. As a law
of experience, the isothermal conversion of heat to work is impossible without
simultaneously effecting other changes, e.g., expansion of the system; this is one
way of stating the second law. In this sense, the second law is sometimes referred
to as a principle of degradation of energy; the net result of spontaneous change
is the loss of a directed force, that is, of potential for doing work.

Carnot Cycle for a Perfect Gas.   It is of interest to study processes in which
heat may be converted into work. Such an approach can lead us to the definition of

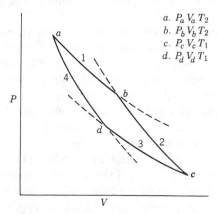

$a.\ P_a\ V_a\ T_2$
$b.\ P_b\ V_b\ T_2$
$c.\ P_c\ V_c\ T_1$
$d.\ P_d\ V_d\ T_1$

Fig. 7.301   Schematic representation of steps in the Carnot cycle.

a thermodynamic property called *entropy*, in terms of which mathematical expression can be given to the principles of the second law. The limitation which governs
the conversion of heat into work may be illustrated by a description of a cycle
(Fig. 7.301) named after Sadi Carnot. A system consisting of two heat reservoirs
and one mole of an ideal gas in a cylinder is chosen for simplicity (Fig. 7.302),
though the conclusions to be drawn are in no way restricted by use of an ideal gas.
The gas is carried through a cycle consisting of four steps: (1) an isothermal
expansion, (2) an adiabatic expansion in which the temperature of the gas drops,
(3) an isothermal compression at the lower temperature, followed by (4) an adiabatic
compression such that the gas is returned to its initial state. All these processes
are carried out reversibly so maximum efficiency is obtained. Although the
Carnot cycle may at first seem arbitrary, its form is dictated by the restriction to
only two heat reservoirs, at temperatures T_1 and T_2. The only reversible process
that can be conducted in contact with each reservoir is an isothermal expansion or
compression, and in the absence of any other heat reservoirs the only reversible
path between the two temperatures is an adiabatic expansion or compression.

The PV changes of the gas are illustrated in Fig. 7.301 for the various steps. In
the first isothermal expansion, work done by the gas may be considered stored as

mechanical energy in a spring system or some device; an equivalent amount of heat is withdrawn from the thermal reservoir, which is so large that its temperature T_2 may be considered constant. Thus for the first step, $a \rightarrow b$, for the gas

$$Q_2 = -W_{ab} = RT_2 \ln \frac{V_b}{V_a}$$

In the second step, $b \rightarrow c$, Q is 0 and

$$W_{bc} = \Delta \bar{E}(\text{gas}) = \int_{T_2}^{T_1} \bar{C}_V \, dT$$

The additional amount of work W_{bc} is stored in the spring system; the removal of this energy causes the temperature of the gas to fall from T_2 to T_1.

The gas is then compressed isothermally at T_1 from volume V_c at the end of the second step to a new volume V_d. To accomplish this compression, an amount of work W_{cd} must be taken from the spring system and used to compress the gas. Simultaneously, the gas liberates the equivalent amount of energy as heat to a large thermal reservoir, at constant temperature T_1; thus for the gas

$$Q_1 = -W_{cd} = RT_1 \ln \frac{V_d}{V_c}$$

which is negative since V_d is less than V_c.

The final step in the cycle is a reversible adiabatic compression which takes the gas back to its initial state $Q = 0$, $d \rightarrow a$,

$$\Delta \bar{E} = W_{da} = \int_{T_1}^{T_2} \bar{C}_V \, dT$$

The volume V_d at the end of the third step is chosen so that the final reversible adiabatic compression will produce the initial state. In this part of the cycle, the temperature of the gas is increased by the work removed from the spring system to effect the compression.

Since the cycle is now complete, the first law requires that the total energy change for the ideal gas be zero. However, a quantity of heat Q_2 was removed from a reservoir at T_2, and a quantity Q_1 added to a reservoir at T_1. Further analysis will show that these two quantities of heat are not equal; their difference represents the net amount of work made available in the cycle.

The two reversible adiabatic steps of the cycle connect the same temperatures. In step 2, from Eq. 7.216, we may write

$$\int_{T_2}^{T_1} \frac{\bar{C}_V \, dT}{T} = -\int_{V_b}^{V_c} \frac{R \, dV}{V}$$

and in step 4

$$\int_{T_1}^{T_2} \frac{\bar{C}_V \, dT}{T} = -\int_{V_d}^{V_a} \frac{R \, dV}{V}$$

Therefore $R \ln (V_c/V_b) = R \ln (V_d/V_a)$; thus $V_b/V_a = V_c/V_d$. It will be observed that the sum of W_{bc} and W_{da} is zero; the net work done in the cycle is

$$-W_{\text{net}} = RT_2 \ln \frac{V_b}{V_a} + RT_1 \ln \frac{V_d}{V_c} = R(T_2 - T_1) \ln \frac{V_b}{V_a}$$

Since $Q_2 = RT_2 \ln V_b/V_a$, the ratio of the net work available to the heat withdrawn from the hot reservoir is

$$\frac{-W_{\text{net}}}{Q_2} = \frac{T_2 - T_1}{T_2} \tag{7.301}$$

Equation 7.301 is the *efficiency* relation for an ideal heat engine. It shows that the maximum amount of work obtainable from a quantity of heat removed from a reservoir at T_2 (which must remain virtually constant) is determined by the constant temperature T_1 of the cold reservoir to which part of the heat must be transferred. Only the fraction $(T_2 - T_1)/T_2$ can be changed to work; the remainder must reach the cold reservoir. When the latter approaches absolute zero (unattainable), the efficiency approaches unity. If there is no temperature difference between the reservoirs (isothermal conditions) the efficiency is zero; it is impossible to have a conversion of heat into work at constant temperature and to return the engine (ideal gas in this case) and surroundings to their original state.

Any heat engine is subject to the same basic limitation in efficiency. Frictional and other losses in the apparatus will reduce the efficiency from the ideal value. These general statements, which must be regarded as a law based on experience, represent the essence of the second law as applied to heat engines.

It is useful to write the efficiency equation in a slightly different form. Since energy is conserved, the value of $-W_{\text{net}}$ must be equal to the sum $Q_2 + Q_1$. Hence we may write

$$\frac{Q_2 + Q_1}{Q_2} = \frac{T_2 - T_1}{T_2}$$

which may be rearranged to give

$$\frac{Q_2}{T_2} + \frac{Q_1}{T_1} = 0 \tag{7.302}$$

Any such transfer of heat may be accomplished by the operation of a Carnot cycle; such a device or its equivalent must be used if the heat is to be transferred reversibly (heat flowing only under an infinitesimal temperature gradient), and it is only under reversible conditions that

$$\sum_i \frac{Q_i}{T_i} = 0 \tag{7.303}$$

If the reservoirs are finite in size, the efficiency relation must be applied in infinitesimal steps, since T_2 and T_1 are not constant. It is then convenient to use Eq. 7.302 in the form

$$\frac{dQ_{\text{rev(2)}}}{T_2} + \frac{dQ_{\text{rev(1)}}}{T_1} = 0 \tag{7.304}$$

valid at each infinitesimal step of the process, since for the transfer of an infinitesimal amount of heat the temperatures may be considered constant. The dQ terms may now be expressed as functions of temperature to make this expression integrable.

ILLUSTRATION.   A heat engine operates for a limited time; it removes heat from 10 kg of water initially at 90°C until its temperature falls to 60°C, and transfers heat to a cold reservoir consisting of 5 kg of water initially at 5°C. Assume that the engine operates with maximum efficiency, that the heat capacity of water remains constant over the temperature interval at 1 cal g^{-1}, and that no energy losses occur. Calculate the amount of work which could be done by the engine.

Since the temperatures of the reservoirs change, the efficiency cannot be calculated by the simple form of Eq. 7.301. The work done, however, is equal to the negative of $Q_2 + Q_1$ (see Fig. 7.302). Then for the reservoirs

$$Q_2 = \int_{363}^{333} C_{P_2}\, dT_2$$

$$= 10,000 \int_{363}^{333} dT_2$$

$$= -(10,000)(30) \text{ cal}$$

To find Q_1, the final temperature of the cold reservoir must be evaluated from the second-law principle in the form of Eq. 7.304. Since $dQ_2 = C_{P_2}\, dT_2$ and $dQ_1 = C_{P_1}\, dT_1$,

$$10,000 \int_{363}^{333} \frac{dT_2}{T_2} + 5000 \int_{278}^{T_f} \frac{dT_1}{T_1} = 0$$

Thus $10,000 \ln 333/363 + 5000 \ln T_f/278 = 0$, from which the final temperature of the cold reservoir may be calculated. Then $Q_1 = 5000(T_f - 278)$, and $-W = 10,000(333 - 363) + 5000(T_f - 278) \text{ cal} = $ work reservoir energy change.

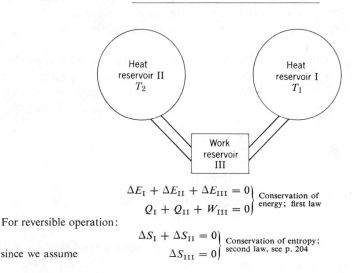

$$\begin{aligned} \Delta E_I + \Delta E_{II} + \Delta E_{III} &= 0 \\ Q_I + Q_{II} + W_{III} &= 0 \end{aligned}$$ Conservation of energy; first law

For reversible operation:

$$\begin{aligned} \Delta S_I + \Delta S_{II} &= 0 \\ \Delta S_{III} &= 0 \end{aligned}$$ Conservation of entropy; second law, see p. 204

since we assume

Fig. 7.302   Schematic representation of heat-work relationship in heat engine problems.

Entropy.   General Statement of the Second Law.   From a chemical point of view, the principal interest in the Carnot cycle and the operation of heat engines is that they illustrate the very useful nature of the function dQ_{rev}/T. The latter may be used to define a new thermodynamic property called entropy. The following statements may be made about entropy and together constitute a useful summary of the second law of thermodynamics.

1. Any system has a characteristic property called entropy, S. For an infinitesimal change, the change in entropy is given by the equation

$$dS = \frac{dQ_{rev}}{T} \qquad (7.305)$$

2. The entropy is a well-behaved thermodynamic property (its change for a system undergoing any given process is determined entirely by the nature of the final and initial equilibrium states).

3. In any reversible process, for the system and its surroundings

$$\Delta S_{sys} + \Delta S_{surr} = 0$$

4. In any spontaneous (irreversible) process, for the system and its surroundings

$$\Delta S_{sys} + \Delta S_{surr} > 0$$

The first three statements are obviously related to the results brought out by the Carnot cycle, although they are now to be regarded as postulates, not dependent on any particular experiment or model. The fourth summarizes the important behavior of entropy in spontaneous changes, which will be discussed further in some examples. These statements cannot be proved to have general applicability. However, they are accepted as a formulation of the second law because no experiment or machine has been devised which is found to contradict them. Like the first law, the second is a law of experience.

Entropy and Exact Differentials.   Statement 2 is equivalent to the assertion that dS, and hence dQ_{rev}/T, is an exact differential. Since dQ_{rev} itself is not an exact differential, $1/T$ serves as an *integrating factor*. This may be verified for a perfect-gas PVT change, in which only $P\,dV$ reversible work is involved, as follows

$$dS = \frac{dQ_{rev}}{T} = \frac{dE}{T} + \frac{P\,dV}{T}$$

For a perfect gas, $dE = C_V\,dT$, since $(\partial E/\partial V)_T = 0$;

hence
$$dS = \frac{C_V\,dT}{T} + \frac{P\,dV}{T}$$

The reciprocity test, Eq. 7.203, shows that dS is exact. In the general case, i.e., for any fluid, Eq. 7.202 must be used for dE; and, as will be shown on p. 209, Eq. 7.212 must be valid if dS is exact.

Entropy and Spontaneous Change. Statement 4 points out an important difference between entropy and energy and shows how entropy may be used as a criterion for spontaneous change. This difference may be emphasized by quoting the celebrated statement of Clausius: "Die Energie der Welt ist konstant; die Entropie der Welt strebt einem Maximum zu." Within an isolated system (constant energy and volume) spontaneous changes result in an increase in the entropy of the system; reversible changes do not change the entropy of the system. Hence, when all possibilities for spontaneous change have been exhausted, the entropy of the isolated system has its maximum possible value. This is a characteristic of an isolated equilibrium state. If the system is not isolated, changes in the surroundings must also be considered to see if there is an overall increase in entropy. The evaluation of entropy changes for various kinds of processes is very important. Let us illustrate the behavior of entropy, in accordance with statements 3 and 4, when heat is transferred between two objects initially at different temperatures (a) under reversible conditions and (b) by direct spontaneous flow. Consider the hot reservoir to be 1 kg of liquid water at 373.16°K and the cold reservoir 1 kg of liquid water at 273.16°K. For simplicity, it will be assumed that water has a constant heat capacity of 1 cal g^{-1} and that no other energy losses occur. Heat will be transferred until the two reservoirs come to the same final temperature.

. (a) The only way in which these two reservoirs can be brought to the same final temperature reversibly is through the operation of a heat engine. According to the second law, the sum of the entropy changes of the two reservoirs is *zero* for the reversible case. Hence, if T_f is the same for both reservoirs,

$$1000 \int_{373.16}^{T_f} \frac{dT_2}{T_2} + 1000 \int_{273.16}^{T_f} \frac{dT_1}{T_1} = 0$$

from which T_f equals 319.3°K. The amount of work made available by the engine can now be calculated by evaluating the Q's for the two reservoirs: $-W = Q_2 + Q_1$. W reflects the energy change in III (see Fig. 7.203).

(b) If the thermal equilibrium is established by direct transfer of heat (with no energy lost or transferred to other forms), the final temperature of each reservoir must, by the first law, be the mean 323.16°K, since both reservoirs have the same heat capacity. In the general case $Q_2 = C_{P_2}(T_f' - 373.16) = -Q_1 = -C_{P_1}(T_f' - 273)$. The entropy changes of the reservoirs are determined only by their temperature changes. Hence we may calculate ΔS for each by considering a reversible process which has the same temperature change, i.e.,

$$\Delta S_2 = 1000 \int_{373}^{323} \frac{dT_2}{T_2} = 1000 \ln \frac{323}{373} \quad \text{and} \quad \Delta S_1 = 1000 \int_{273}^{323} \frac{dT_1}{T_1} = 1000 \ln \frac{323}{273}$$

The sum of these changes will be found to be a positive quantity, in accordance with part 4 of the general statement of the second law. The total entropy of the two reservoirs has been increased by the spontaneous change.

Consider again the free adiabatic expansion of an ideal gas discussed at the beginning of this section. For the same volume change V_1 to V_2 at constant temperature,

$$Q_{rev} = -W_{rev} = RT \ln \frac{V_2}{V_1}$$

Hence

$$\Delta S = \frac{Q_{rev}}{T} = R \ln \frac{V_2}{V_1}$$

a positive quantity in accordance with the second law. The entropy of the gas has increased in this spontaneous change; no change occurred in the surroundings. If the same expansion is carried out reversibly, the entropy change of the gas is the same, i.e., ΔS is independent of path; however, in the reversible case, the surroundings also undergo a heat change, $-Q_{surr} = Q_{sys}$. For simplicity, we will assume that heat received or given up by the surroundings involves only reversible, isothermal changes in the surroundings; any irreversible process in the surroundings would have to be described in detail and dealt with as a separate problem. The entropy change in the surroundings is then taken as equal to Q_{surr}/T, equal but opposite in sign to that of the system. Hence the total entropy change in the reversible case is zero. Note that, to evaluate the entropy change of the gas for the spontaneous process, Q for this change is not of value; only Q_{rev} may be used to obtain the entropy change of the system, that is, the same initial and final states must be related by a reversible process. The fact that $Q = 0$ for the spontaneous change is useful, however; it tells us that no entropy change occurred in the surroundings.

For any given process, we may write $dS \geq dQ/T$, where the $=$ sign applies for a reversible process and the $>$ sign to an irreversible process. From arguments presented in Sec. 7.2, it is apparent that $Q_{irrev} < Q_{rev}$, that is, Q_{rev} is always a larger positive number (or smaller negative number) than Q_{irrev} for the same overall change.

A Thermodynamic Basis for Temperature. We wish to find a quantitative basis for temperature which is independent of the mode of measurement and of the properties of any particular substance. Temperature is a thermodynamic property, just as are energy and entropy, and, in spite of its familiarity, is equally difficult conceptually. Its value is assigned from the observed behavior of some thermometric property, such as length, volume, or resistance of some material. The second law of thermodynamics provides a basic definition of temperature as it relates to energy and entropy. For a constant-volume process $dQ_{rev} = dE$; hence $dE = T \, dS$ or, to show clearly the constant-volume restriction,

$$\left(\frac{\partial E}{\partial S}\right)_V = T \tag{7.306}$$

This relationship is of general validity, not associated with the properties of any specific material, and may be taken as a thermodynamic definition of T. That is to say, we may use the Carnot cycle to define temperature; we may assert that temperature is a thermodynamic property of a system, related to heat and work in the manner shown for T in Eq. 7.301 or 7.302. Either of these expressions may then be taken as a definition of temperature.

From Eq. 7.302 the problem encountered in attempting to reach absolute zero may be shown. Consider a heat engine operated as a refrigerator. It removes heat Q_1 from a cold reservoir at T_1 through application of work, and releases heat Q_2 at a higher temperature T_2. Then, in the limit as T_1 approaches zero, Q_2 must become infinitely large if Q_1 has a nonzero value; i.e., work required must become infinitely large. See Sec. 9.3.

Either Eq. 7.306 or Eq. 7.302 defines temperature but does not establish the magnitude of the degree. The latter has been done by international agreement so as to approximate closely the centigrade degree by fixing the triple point of water as $273.16°K$. Once this single point is specified, the entire temperature scale is established by Eq. 7.306 or its equivalent.

Although the thermodynamic basis for temperature provides an unambiguous foundation, it is not a practical means of measuring temperature. The limiting ideal behavior of all gases at low pressures provides a practical basis for establishing a temperature scale and corresponds to the thermodynamic scale, as shown

Table 7.301   Defining Fixed Points*

	Temperature, °C (Int. 1948)
Temperature of equilibrium between liquid oxygen and its vapor (oxygen point)	−182.97
Temperature of equilibrium between ice, liquid water, and water vapor (triple point of water)	0.01
Temperature of equilibrium between liquid water and its vapor (steam point)	100
Temperature of equilibrium between liquid sulfur and its vapor (sulfur point)	444.6†
Temperature of equilibrium between solid silver and liquid silver (silver point)	960.8
Temperature of equilibrium between solid gold and liquid gold (gold point)	1063

* H. F. Stimson, *NBS J. Research*, **65A,** 139 (1961). Exact values assigned. The pressure is 1 standard atmosphere, except for the triple point of water.
† In place of the sulfur point, it is recommended to use the temperature of equilibrium between solid zinc and liquid zinc (zinc point) with the value 419.505°C (Int. 1948). The zinc point is more reproducible than the sulfur point and the value which is assigned to it has been so chosen that its use leads to the same values of temperature on the International Practical Temperature Scale as does the use of the sulfur point.

by the Carnot cycle for a perfect gas. Reliable fixed points of reference have been selected by international agreement, and devices such as platinum resistance thermometers and thermocouples used to measure temperatures between these fixed points for a practical scale. A description of the International Temperature Scale is given in Tables 7.301 and 7.302(A). A useful reference pertaining to practical temperature problems is *Temperature, Its Measurement and Control in Science and Industry*, Vol. 1, 1948, Vol. 2, 1955, and Vol. 3, 1962, prepared under the Auspices of the American Institute of Physics, Reinhold Publishing Co., New York.

Evaluation of Entropy Changes from the Properties of the System. Since entropy is a well-behaved thermodynamic function, its value may be fixed if we specify any two convenient properties, such as T and V or T and P, for a homogeneous equilibrium system of fixed composition and amount. Thus

$$S = f(T, V)$$

$$dS = \left(\frac{\partial S}{\partial T}\right)_V dT + \left(\frac{\partial S}{\partial V}\right)_T dV \qquad (7.307)$$

where the entropy-temperature (constant volume) and entropy-volume (constant temperature) coefficients have comparable meaning to those for energy discussed in Sec. 7.2. It will now be shown how these coefficients may be evaluated in terms of heat capacity and PVT data. For a reversible process in which only $P\,dV$ work and heat are interchanged with the surroundings

$$dQ_{\text{rev}} = dE + P\,dV$$

Since $dQ_{\text{rev}} = T\,dS$, we may write

$$T\,dS = dE + P\,dV \qquad (7.308)$$

Hence

$$dS = \frac{1}{T}dE + \frac{P}{T}dV \qquad (7.309)$$

Now dE may be replaced in Eq. 7.309 by

$$dE = C_V\,dT + \left(\frac{\partial E}{\partial V}\right)_T dV$$

and we obtain

$$dS = \frac{C_V}{T}dT + \frac{1}{T}\left(\frac{\partial E}{\partial V}\right)_T dV + \frac{P}{T}dV$$

or

$$dS = \frac{C_V}{T}dT + \frac{1}{T}\left[\left(\frac{\partial E}{\partial V}\right)_T + P\right]dV \qquad (7.310)$$

Since both Eqs. 7.307 and 7.310 express the entropy change in terms of dT and dV, the coefficients of these independent variables must be identical. Hence

$$\left(\frac{\partial S}{\partial T}\right)_V = \frac{C_V}{T} \tag{7.311}$$

and

$$\left(\frac{\partial S}{\partial V}\right)_T = \frac{1}{T}\left[\left(\frac{\partial E}{\partial V}\right)_T + P\right] \tag{7.312}$$

When the heat capacity is a known function of temperature, entropy changes for constant-volume processes may be calculated by the integral

$$\Delta S_V = \int_{T_1}^{T_2} \frac{C_V}{T} \, dT$$

For volume changes at constant temperature, Eq. 7.312 must be simplified. The second derivative of Eq. 7.312 with respect to temperature at constant volume may be written

$$\frac{\partial}{\partial T}\left(\frac{\partial S}{\partial V}\right)_T = \frac{\partial^2 S}{\partial T \, \partial V}$$

$$= -\frac{1}{T^2}\left(\frac{\partial E}{\partial V}\right)_T + \frac{1}{T}\left(\frac{\partial^2 E}{\partial T \, \partial V}\right) - \frac{P}{T^2} + \frac{1}{T}\left(\frac{\partial P}{\partial T}\right)_V \tag{7.313}$$

However, the term $\dfrac{\partial^2 S}{\partial T \, \partial V}$ may be shown to be equal to $\dfrac{1}{T}\left(\dfrac{\partial^2 E}{\partial T \, \partial V}\right)$ as follows. Since the order of differentiation is immaterial

$$\frac{\partial^2 S}{\partial T \, \partial V} = \frac{\partial}{\partial V}\left(\frac{\partial S}{\partial T}\right)_V = \frac{\partial}{\partial V}\left(\frac{C_V}{T}\right) = \frac{\partial}{\partial V}\left[\frac{1}{T}\left(\frac{\partial E}{\partial T}\right)_V\right]_T = \frac{1}{T}\left(\frac{\partial^2 E}{\partial V \, \partial T}\right) \tag{7.314}$$

Thus Eq. 7.313 requires that

$$\left(\frac{\partial E}{\partial V}\right)_T = T\left(\frac{\partial P}{\partial T}\right)_V - P \tag{7.212}$$

This important result will be recognized as the *thermodynamic equation of state* used in Sec. 7.2 to evaluate the change of energy with volume from *PVT* data. On placing the value of $\left(\dfrac{\partial E}{\partial V}\right)_T$ back in Eq. 7.312, it is seen that

$$\left(\frac{\partial S}{\partial V}\right)_T = \left(\frac{\partial P}{\partial T}\right)_V \tag{7.315}$$

This is a very useful result since the coefficient on the right-hand side can be evaluated from *PVT* data. Thus the general expression for entropy change may be written

$$dS = \frac{C_V}{T} \, dT + \left(\frac{\partial P}{\partial T}\right)_V \, dV \tag{7.316}$$

which can be integrated directly if the two coefficients are known as explicit functions of T and V, respectively. For the special case of an ideal gas of constant-heat capacity, Eq. 7.316 integrates to a simple form

$$\Delta S = C_V \ln \frac{T_2}{T_1} + R \ln \frac{V_2}{V_1} \tag{7.317}$$

ILLUSTRATION.   Show that the efficiency relationships of the Carnot cycle are independent of the equation of state of the fluid employed.

We go through the cycle (Fig. 7.301) for one mole of a hypothetical gas that obeys the equation of state

$$PV^{\frac{1}{2}} = R'T$$

where R' is of course not the usual gas constant, but an arbitrary constant. We have

$$P = \frac{R'T}{V^{\frac{1}{2}}}$$

from which, by use of Eq. 7.212,

$$\left(\frac{\partial E}{\partial V}\right)_T = 0$$

Thus,

$$dE = C_V \, dT = dQ - P \, dV = 0$$

for an isothermal process. For the reversible isothermals

$$Q = \int P \, dV = \int_{V_a}^{V_b} \frac{R'T}{V^{\frac{1}{2}}} \, dV$$

$$Q_2 = 2R'T_2(V_b^{\frac{1}{2}} - V_a^{\frac{1}{2}})$$

and

$$Q_1 = 2R'T_1(V_d^{\frac{1}{2}} - V_c^{\frac{1}{2}})$$

For the reversible adiabats, from Eq. 7.310,

$$dS = \frac{C_V}{T} \, dT + \frac{1}{T} P \, dV = 0$$

or

$$C_V \, dT = -P \, dV = -\frac{R'T}{V^{\frac{1}{2}}} \, dV$$

we then find by integration

$$\int_{T_2}^{T_1} \frac{C_V}{T} \, dT = -2R'(V_c^{\frac{1}{2}} - V_b^{\frac{1}{2}})$$

and

$$\int_{T_1}^{T_2} \frac{C_V}{T} \, dT = -2R'(V_a^{\frac{1}{2}} - V_d^{\frac{1}{2}})$$

The two integrals on the left-hand side are equal and opposite in sign, so by addition

$$2R'(V_a^{1/2} - V_b^{1/2} + V_c^{1/2} - V_d^{1/2}) = 0$$

If we then add the expressions for Q_1/T_1 and Q_2/T_2, we have

$$\frac{Q_1}{T_1} + \frac{Q_2}{T_2} = 2R'(-V_a^{1/2} + V_b^{1/2} - V_c^{1/2} + V_d^{1/2})$$
$$= 0$$

This is the result, Eq. 7.302, which was also shown to hold for a perfect gas.

The entropy may alternatively be expressed as a function of T and P, which is particularly convenient for constant-pressure processes. In this case

$$T\,dS = dE + P\,dV$$

is changed to the form

$$T\,dS = dH - V\,dP$$

or

$$dH = T\,dS + V\,dP \qquad (7.318)$$

since $dE = dH - P\,dV - V\,dP$ (from the defining equation for enthalpy). Following a procedure similar to that just shown, the equalities

$$\left(\frac{\partial S}{\partial T}\right)_P = \frac{C_P}{T} \qquad (7.319)$$

and

$$\left(\frac{\partial S}{\partial P}\right)_T = -\left(\frac{\partial V}{\partial T}\right)_P \qquad (7.320)$$

may be derived. In the derivation of Eq. 7.320, the equation

$$\left(\frac{\partial H}{\partial P}\right)_T = -T\left(\frac{\partial V}{\partial T}\right)_P + V \qquad (7.213)$$

is also derived, analogous to the Eq. 7.212 discussed above. Thus, from the change in temperature and pressure, the change in entropy may be evaluated from

$$dS = \frac{C_P}{T}\,dT - \left(\frac{\partial V}{\partial T}\right)_P dP \qquad (7.321)$$

For an ideal gas of constant heat capacity, Eq. 7.321 integrates to the simple form

$$\Delta S = C_P \ln \frac{T_2}{T_1} - nR \ln \frac{P_2}{P_1} \qquad (7.322)$$

With Eq. 7.316 or 7.321 entropy changes may now be evaluated for any of the processes of the type considered at the end of Sec. 7.2. The one which is more convenient is chosen. For constant-pressure processes, Eq. 7.321 should be used; then a knowledge of C_P as a function of temperature is all that is needed.

ILLUSTRATION.   Show how to derive Eq. 7.214.

By definition

$$H = E + PV$$

Hence

$$\left(\frac{\partial H}{\partial T}\right)_P = \left(\frac{\partial E}{\partial T}\right)_P + P\left(\frac{\partial V}{\partial T}\right)_P$$

and

$$C_P = \left(\frac{\partial E}{\partial T}\right)_P + P\left(\frac{\partial V}{\partial T}\right)_P \tag{i}$$

We must now relate $\left(\dfrac{\partial E}{\partial T}\right)_P$ to C_V. This may be done by comparing two equivalent expressions for the total differential dE, one in terms of T and V as independent variables, and the other with T and P as independent variables.

$$dE = \left(\frac{\partial E}{\partial T}\right)_P dT + \left(\frac{\partial E}{\partial P}\right)_T dP \tag{ii}$$

$$dE = \left(\frac{\partial E}{\partial T}\right)_V dT + \left(\frac{\partial E}{\partial V}\right)_T dV \tag{iii}$$

Since dV is a total differential and may be expressed as a function of T and P,

$$dV = \left(\frac{\partial V}{\partial T}\right)_P dT + \left(\frac{\partial V}{\partial P}\right)_T dP \tag{iv}$$

we may substitute for dV in expression (iii) and obtain

$$dE = \left(\frac{\partial E}{\partial T}\right)_V dT + \left(\frac{\partial E}{\partial V}\right)_T \left[\left(\frac{\partial V}{\partial T}\right)_P dT + \left(\frac{\partial V}{\partial P}\right)_T dP\right] \tag{v}$$

Since (ii) and (v) are equivalent expressions, the coefficients of the independent variables dT and dP must be equivalent. Therefore we may equate the coefficients of dT, which gives the desired relationship

$$\left(\frac{\partial E}{\partial T}\right)_P = \left(\frac{\partial E}{\partial T}\right)_V + \left(\frac{\partial E}{\partial V}\right)_T \left(\frac{\partial V}{\partial T}\right)_P = C_V + \left(\frac{\partial E}{\partial V}\right)_T \left(\frac{\partial V}{\partial T}\right)_P$$

and equation (i) becomes

$$C_P = C_V + \left[\left(\frac{\partial E}{\partial V}\right)_T + P\right]\left(\frac{\partial V}{\partial T}\right)_P \tag{vi}$$

It is seen from Eq. 7.212 that (vi) may be written in the form

$$C_P - C_V = T\left(\frac{\partial P}{\partial T}\right)_V \left(\frac{\partial V}{\partial T}\right)_P \tag{7.214}$$

Entropy from a Molecular Point of View.   The procedures described provide an operational basis for the calculation of entropy changes. A convention for assigning numerical values of the entropy for chemical substances will be described later. A physical meaning of entropy may best be indicated by outlining the procedure by which it is calculated from statistical mechanics. This aspect will be discussed quantitatively in Chapter 11, but it is desirable at the present time to provide some qualitative insight as to the meaning of entropy from a molecular point of view.

Let us recall the statistical analysis in Chapter 5 of the behavior of a large number of molecules. It was concluded that we expect the equilibrium state of a large molecular system to correspond closely to the most probable state. The relative populations of the various energy levels for this most probable arrangement are given by the Boltzmann distribution law.

From a molecular point of view entropy is simply the thermodynamic way of representing the relative probabilities of different possible states of a given system. Statement 4, p. 204, is equivalent to the conclusion that we expect a molecular system to proceed to the most probable distribution. In the free-isothermal expansion of a perfect gas, the molecular explanation of the increase in entropy is that the increase in volume decreases the spacing between adjacent translational quantum levels, as seen in Sec. 6.1, hence making a larger number of levels accessible (within the restriction that the total energy of the system must remain constant). Thus in the expanded state there is a larger number of ways of assigning molecules into the available energy levels. In statistical mechanics this may be described by saying that the thermodynamic probability of the expanded state is greater than that of the compressed state; in classical thermodynamics this corresponds to the statement that the entropy of the expanded state is greater than that of the compressed state.

In classical thermodynamics, for an isothermal reversible change the entropy change is determined by Q_{rev}/T. A direct relationship between entropy and the energy level characteristics of the molecular species involved will be developed quantitatively through use of the partition function in Chapter 11. This relationship provides an important test of theory.

Any change which results in an increase of the total partition function for the particles, i.e., makes more energy levels available, will be found to produce an increase in the entropy; for example, vaporization, expansion, mixing with expansion, dissociation, and increase in temperature, all result in an increase in entropy. For entropy alone to serve as a criterion for spontaneous change, the system as a whole must be isolated; if it is not isolated, changes in the surroundings must also be considered. Even in an isolated system at constant energy and volume all effects associated with a given process must be considered. For example, isothermal vaporization increases entropy, but in an isolated system vaporization must simultaneously cause cooling, which decreases entropy. When an equilibrium balance of these effects is reached, the entropy of the isolated system will have its maximum possible value.

Problems

7.301   An ideal heat engine operates by removing heat from a reservoir (which has $C_P = 5000$ cal deg^{-1}) initially at 200°C, transferring the minimum amount necessary to a cold reservoir (which has $C_P = 2000$ cal deg^{-1}) initially at 0°C. Pressure may be assumed constant.

(a) What will be the final temperature and how much work will have been done by the engine when the two reservoirs reach the same temperature?

(b) What will be the temperature of each reservoir after the engine has done 10,000 cal of work?

7.302   How much mechanical energy must be provided for a reversible ideal refrigerator to change 25 kg of water initially at 25°C to water at 0°C? Assume a constant heat capacity of 1 cal deg^{-1} g^{-1} for liquid water, and the release of heat by the engine to the room at a constant temperature of 27°C. (P is constant.)

(a) Calculate the entropy change of the water.

(b) Calculate the entropy change of the room.

7.303   Evaluate the entropy change of each reservoir in Problem 7.301, part (a). What would be the final temperature in Problem 7.301 if the two reservoirs were allowed to equilibrate spontaneously without involving the engine (i.e., no energy removed from the combined system)? In the latter case, evaluate the total entropy change for the spontaneous process.

7.304   The heat capacity of lead between 0 and 300°C is given in Table 7.201(A). Calculate the change in entropy of 100 grams of lead, cooled from 300 to 0°C under a constant pressure of 1 atm. Describe how this cooling might be effected (a) reversibly, (b) irreversibly. Compare the behavior of the entropy of lead plus its surroundings in the two cases, assuming in each that the heat available is received by an ice-water bath at 0°C.

7.305   An ideal heat engine operates by withdrawing heat from a reservoir at constant temperature of 400°K and releasing heat to a reservoir at constant temperature of 300°K. If the engine makes available 1000 cal of net work, how much heat is received by the cold reservoir?

7.306   Ten grams of N_2 (assume perfect gas behavior) expands freely from a volume of 1 liter to a volume of 5 liters at a constant temperature, 27°C. Calculate the change in entropy of the (a) nitrogen and (b) surroundings.

7.307   Five moles of a perfect gas, $\bar{C}_P = 7$ cal mole^{-1} deg^{-1}, expands adiabatically from a pressure of 10 atm and an initial temperature of 127°C to a final pressure of 5 atm. Calculate the change in entropy if (a) the expansion occurs reversibly, (b) if the expansion is such that 500 joules of work is done during the process.

7.308   Set up an integrated equation showing the change in entropy when 1 mole of a gas changes from 27°C and $P = 10$ atm to 7°C and $P = 1$ atm if $\bar{C}_P = 7 + 0.005T$ cal mole^{-1} deg^{-1} and $\bar{V} = (RT/P) + 0.05$ l. mole^{-1}.

7.309   One mole of a van der Waals gas with $\bar{C}_V = 8.0 + 0.002T$ cal mole^{-1} deg^{-1} ($a = 2.5$ l^2-atm mole^{-2}, $b = 0.04$ l mole^{-1}) expands from a volume of 1 liter at 27°C to a volume of 10 liters at a final temperature of 0°C. Calculate the entropy change for this process. Was this a reversible adiabatic change? If it were adiabatic, how much work was done during the expansion?

7.310   Using heat-capacity data from Table 7.201(A), calculate the difference between the entropy of CO_2 gas at 1 atm at 500°C and at 25°C. Assume $PV = nRT$.

*7.311   Develop the Carnot cycle efficiency relationship for a fluid which is assumed to follow the equation of state $P^{\frac{1}{2}}V = R''T$. (HINT: work with H rather than E.)

4. The Free Energies

The entropy change associated with a process in a constant-energy and constant-volume system serves as a useful criterion for prediction of spontaneous change; however, in many systems of chemical interest it is not convenient to keep the energy and volume constant. Variables such as temperature and pressure, or temperature and volume, are easier to control. For this reason it is found convenient to define two additional thermodynamic properties, the Helmholz free energy, A

$$A = E - TS \tag{7.401}$$

and the Gibbs free energy, F
$$F = H - TS \tag{7.402}$$

The two free energies are related to each other as are H and E, i.e.,

$$F = A + PV \tag{7.403}$$

A is the more convenient function for constant-volume processes, and F for constant-pressure processes. Since the terms on the right of Eqs. 7.401 and 7.402 are all thermodynamic functions of state, the free energies must also be thermodynamic properties; they are extensive properties with values for changes usually expressed in energy units per mole.

The Exact Differentials dF and dA. The characteristic behavior of the free energies will now be developed. From the first and second laws, we may write

$$dE \leq T\, dS - P\, dV \tag{7.404}$$

where the equality is for a reversible process and the inequality for an irreversible (nonequilibrium) process. It should be kept in mind that in the reversible case P may be taken as the internal equilibrium pressure in the system, related to V and T by an equilibrium equation of state. However, in a nonequilibrium process, the pressure term represents the force which determines the pressure-volume work (the only kind of work assumed important at this time) exchanged between the system and its surroundings, and as such has no definite relation to the equilibrium equation of state pressure. Similarly, T may not be well defined in a nonequilibrium system. In the case of a nonequilibrium isothermal expansion, it can be seen that W is less than the reversible work ($P_{ex} < P_{in}$); the energy change and entropy change are independent of path, and hence $dE < T\, dS + W_{irrev}$.

We now may develop similar equations for the free energies. First consider only reversible paths
$$dA = dE - T\, dS - S\, dT$$

Replacing dE by its equivalent from Eq. 7.308

$$dA = T\, dS - P\, dV - T\, dS - S\, dT$$

$$= -P\, dV - S\, dT \tag{7.405}$$

Similarly

$$dF = dH - T\,dS - S\,dT$$
$$= dE + P\,dV + V\,dP - T\,dS - S\,dT$$
$$= T\,dS - P\,dV + P\,dV + V\,dP - T\,dS - S\,dT$$
$$= V\,dP - S\,dT \qquad\qquad (7.406)$$

Thermodynamic Criteria for Spontaneous Change. Equation 7.406 indicates that dF is zero for an equilibrium (reversible) process at constant temperature and pressure. For an irreversible (nonequilibrium, i.e., spontaneous) change, dE, in a derivation analogous to that given for Eq. 7.406, must be replaced by the inequality $dE < T\,dS - P\,dV$, with the result

$$dF < V\,dP - S\,dT \qquad\qquad (7.407)$$

In Eq. 7.407, P and T are to be regarded as the effective values of these intensive properties at the boundary of interaction of the nonequilibrium system with its surroundings and in most instances can be described only with a qualitative "greater or less than" statement. If conditions of restraint are imposed which hold P and T constant, then, for a spontaneous change, Eq. 7.407 indicates that the free-energy change will be negative, i.e., less than zero. This is a useful conclusion. For a spontaneous change $\Delta F_{(T,P)}$ is negative.

It may be observed that neither $V\,dP$ nor $S\,dT$ is an exact differential. The total derivatives $d(PV)$ and $d(TS)$ are exact, and hence the sums $V\,dP + P\,dV$ and $T\,dS + S\,dT$ are exact, but the individual terms in these sums are not exact. As discussed previously, $P\,dV_{\text{irrev}} < P\,dV_{\text{rev}}$; hence it is necessary that $V\,dP_{\text{irrev}} > V\,dP_{\text{rev}}$. Similarly, $T\,dS_{\text{irrev}} > T\,dS_{\text{rev}}$ and $S\,dT_{\text{irrev}} < S\,dT_{\text{rev}}$. Both terms on the right of Eq. 7.407 depend on path; if the path is reversible, Eq. 7.406 applies.

Actually, under proper conditions, any one of the thermodynamic properties may be used as an indication of thermodynamic stability. A system is said to be thermodynamically stable if it is at equilibrium, that is, the system is not expected to move spontaneously (irreversibly) to some new more stable state. The following differential equations indicate the appropriate relationships:

$$dE \leq T\,dS - P\,dV \qquad\qquad (7.404)$$
$$dS \geq dE/T + P\,dV/T \qquad\qquad (7.408)$$
$$dH \leq T\,dS + V\,dP \qquad\qquad (7.409)$$
$$dA \leq -P\,dV - S\,dT \qquad\qquad (7.410)$$
$$dF \leq V\,dP - S\,dT \qquad\qquad (7.411)$$

Thus the energy itself may be used as a criterion for equilibrium if the entropy and volume are held constant throughout the change; similarly the enthalpy, if entropy and pressure are constant, or the entropy, if energy and volume are constant. In practice, experiments may conveniently be conducted at constant temperature and pressure, or volume, but not conveniently at constant entropy or, in many cases, at constant energy. Hence, the free energy quantities are the most useful form. Their behavior will be of principal interest in the case of chemical change or physical change of state, inasmuch as a pure homogeneous substance undergoes no change if both T and P, or T and V, are held constant.

It may seem confusing to write an equation for an exact differential such as dF in the form of Eq. 7.411. F is a thermodynamic function of state; ΔF for any change is fixed and independent of path, reversible or spontaneous. Equation 7.411 simply indicates that, in principle, on integration $V\,dP$ and $S\,dT$ must be treated as line integrals, integrated over the actual path followed by the process. If this path is an equilibrium (reversible) path, the combined result will give the correct value of ΔF; if the path is a nonequilibrium path, the combined result will not represent the value of ΔF but will be larger than the value of ΔF.

Free-Energy Coefficients.   We may now indicate how A and F vary with P, V, and T for a given homogeneous substance. From Eqs. 7.406 and 7.405 for a reversible path, it is seen that

$$\left(\frac{\partial F}{\partial T}\right)_P = -S \tag{7.412}$$

$$\left(\frac{\partial F}{\partial P}\right)_T = V \tag{7.413}$$

$$\left(\frac{\partial A}{\partial T}\right)_V = -S \tag{7.414}$$

$$\left(\frac{\partial A}{\partial V}\right)_T = -P \tag{7.415}$$

Maxwell's Reciprocity Relationships.   The equations used to evaluate the entropy coefficients $\left(\frac{\partial S}{\partial P}\right)_T$ and $\left(\frac{\partial S}{\partial V}\right)_T$ can be derived in a very simple manner from Eqs. 7.405 and 7.406. Since dF is an exact differential, the reciprocity relationship Eq. 7.203 may be applied to Eq. 7.406. Thus

$$\left(\frac{\partial V}{\partial T}\right)_P = -\left(\frac{\partial S}{\partial P}\right)_T \tag{7.320}$$

as shown previously. Also from Eq. 7.405

$$\left(\frac{\partial P}{\partial T}\right)_V = \left(\frac{\partial S}{\partial V}\right)_T \tag{7.315}$$

From Eqs. 7.308 and 7.318, corresponding relationships may be written

$$\left(\frac{\partial T}{\partial V}\right)_S = -\left(\frac{\partial P}{\partial S}\right)_V \tag{7.416}$$

and

$$\left(\frac{\partial T}{\partial P}\right)_S = \left(\frac{\partial V}{\partial S}\right)_P \tag{7.417}$$

Equations 7.320, 7.315, 7.416, and 7.417 are called Maxwell's reciprocity relationships.

Free Energies and Work. For an isothermal change, $\Delta A = \Delta E - T \Delta S$; for a reversible path $\Delta A = \Delta E - Q_{rev} = W_{rev}$; that is, ΔA represents the maximum work which can be done in the process. For this reason ΔA is sometimes called the work function. In an isothermal constant-pressure process, $\Delta F = \Delta A + P \Delta V = W_{rev} + P \Delta V$. Thus, in a similar sense, ΔF is the net work function; it represents the maximum work available less the $P \Delta V$ work ($P \Delta V = -W_{PV}$) which is done in the constant-pressure process.

Variation of Free Energies with Temperature. Alternative expressions to Eqs. 7.412 and 7.414 for the variation of F with temperature at constant pressure and A with temperature at constant volume, which are very useful in chemical applications, may be derived. Since

$$F = H - TS$$

$$\frac{F}{T} = \frac{H}{T} - S \tag{7.402}$$

if we differentiate with respect to temperature at constant pressure, we obtain

$$\left[\frac{\partial (F/T)}{\partial T}\right]_P = \frac{1}{T}\left(\frac{\partial H}{\partial T}\right)_P - \frac{H}{T^2} - \left(\frac{\partial S}{\partial T}\right)_P$$

On substituting C_P for $\left(\dfrac{\partial H}{\partial T}\right)_P$ and C_P/T for $\left(\dfrac{\partial S}{\partial T}\right)_P$, the equation above becomes

$$\left[\frac{\partial (F/T)}{\partial T}\right]_P = \frac{C_P}{T} - \frac{C_P}{T} - \frac{H}{T^2}$$

or

$$\left[\frac{\partial (F/T)}{\partial T}\right]_P = -\frac{H}{T^2} \tag{7.418}$$

or

$$\left[\frac{\partial (F/T)}{\partial (1/T)}\right]_P = H \tag{7.419}$$

If the enthalpy is known as a function of temperature, the right-hand side may be integrated over some temperature interval of interest to obtain the variation of F/T.

Similarly, $A = E - TS$ and

$$\left[\frac{\partial (A/T)}{\partial T}\right]_V = -\frac{E}{T^2} \tag{7.420}$$

or

$$\left[\frac{\partial (A/T)}{\partial (1/T)}\right]_V = E \tag{7.421}$$

For the evaluation of free energy changes accompanying PVT changes of a homogeneous phase, it will usually be found best to evaluate ΔE or ΔH and $\Delta (TS)$ and then obtain ΔA or ΔF from their defining equations such as $\Delta F = \Delta H - \Delta (TS)$. $\Delta (TS)$ represents the difference $T_2 S_2 - T_1 S_1$; only for an isothermal change is this simply $T \Delta S$. It will be necessary to assign numerical values for the entropy before the TS terms can be evaluated.

Variation of Free Energies with Pressure.   Under isothermal conditions $dF = V\,dP$. This takes a simple integrated form for an ideal gas; it must be evaluated from actual PVT data for real gases or for condensed phases. For an ideal gas, $dF = nRT\,dP/P$ and

$$F_2 - F_1 = \Delta F = nRT \ln \frac{P_2}{P_1} \qquad (7.422)$$

Since for an ideal gas isothermal change, $\Delta(PV)$, is 0 and ΔA equals ΔF,

$$A_2 - A_1 = \Delta A = nRT \ln \frac{P_2}{P_1} \qquad (7.423)$$

ILLUSTRATION.   The behavior of the Helmholtz free energy in liquid-vapor equilibrium systems.

The behavior of fluids can be conveniently shown on an A vs. V plot, Fig. 7.401. From Eq. 7.415, the slope is seen to be $-P$. The system changes discontinuously from liquid to gas on the lower curve; the equilibrium vapor pressure is represented by the slope of the line intersecting the curve at two points. The subject of phase equilibria will be considered in detail in Chapter 8.

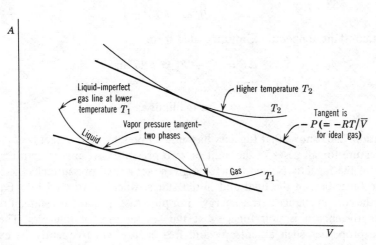

Fig. 7.401   Representation of fluid properties by the Helmholtz free energy, A.

Problems

7.401   One mole of an ideal gas undergoes a free adiabatic expansion from $V = 1$ liter at 25°C to $V = 6$ liters. Calculate ΔF and ΔA.

7.402   Consider a gas which follows the equation of state $\bar{V} = (RT/P) + b$. Calculate ΔF and ΔA when 1 mole is compressed isothermally from a volume of 10 liters to 0.1 liter at 300°K. Assume that b is a known constant.

7.403   Two moles of an ideal gas expands isothermally from an initial volume of 1 liter to a final volume of 5 liters at 25°C. What are the values of ΔF and ΔA for this process? What is the maximum work that could be done in this process? *Repeat the calculation, assuming the gas to follow the van der Waals equation; state your answer in terms of a and b.

7.404   Four grams of oxygen, assumed to be a perfect gas with $\bar{C}_V = 5$ cal deg^{-1} mole^{-1}, is compressed adiabatically from a volume of one liter at 27°C by the irreversible expenditure of 100 joules of work. If the final volume is 0.8 liter, calculate ΔF and ΔA for the process. The initial entropy of oxygen may be assumed known.

7.405   Show that $dH < T\,dS + V\,dP$ for an isothermal spontaneous expansion. Show that $dA < -S\,dT - P\,dV$ in such a case.

7.406   Derive the equation $(\partial H/\partial P)_T = -T(\partial V/\partial T)_P + V$. (Use Eq. 7.320.)

7.407   Use data from Table 7.201(A) to derive an expression for the Gibbs free energy of $Al_2O_3(s)$ at temperature T (between 300 and 1000°K) relative to its free energy at 300°K (P constant at 1 atm). (This equation will contain some integration constants which cannot be evaluated from the limited information given.)

5. Fugacity and Activity

The variation of the free energy of an ideal gas with pressure (at constant temperature) has the simple form of Eq. 7.422. For convenience in handling real gases in a similar way, a property called fugacity, f, is defined by the two equations:

$$dF = nRT\,d\ln f \tag{7.501}$$

or, at constant temperature, in integrated form

$$\Delta F = F_2 - F_1 = nRT\,\ln\frac{f_2}{f_1} \tag{7.502}$$

and

$$\frac{f}{P} = 1, \text{ in the limit as } P \to 0 \tag{7.503}$$

Equation 7.503 shows that fugacity has units of pressure and in fact becomes equal to pressure for all gases in the limit of zero pressure. At any other pressure, the value of the fugacity is such that for a given isothermal pressure change the ratio of the fugacities, in the final and initial states, when substituted into Eq. 7.502, gives the correct change in free energy. For pure gases, a standard state of reference frequently chosen is unit fugacity at the temperature of interest. Thermodynamic properties such as entropy and free energy will frequently be expressed relative to those in the standard state of unit fugacity.

Evaluation of Fugacity.   The problem of evaluating the free energy dependence on pressure of a real gas may now be shifted to the determination of the fugacity. Fugacity is introduced primarily in order to retain the simple form of Eq. 7.422. The relationship between f and P is found as follows: since

$$dF = V\, dP = nRT\, d \ln f$$

then

$$d \ln f = \left(\frac{V}{nRT}\right) dP = \left(\frac{\bar{V}}{RT}\right) dP \qquad (7.504)$$

where $\bar{V}$ is the molar volume.   The fugacity at a given pressure may be evaluated by an integration procedure, using PVT data, starting with $P = 0$ where f and P are equal.   The problem may be conveniently set up by defining a quantity α:

$$\alpha = \frac{RT}{P} - \bar{V} \quad \text{or} \quad \bar{V} = \frac{RT}{P} - \alpha \qquad (7.505)$$

Then

$$d \ln f = d \ln P - \frac{\alpha}{RT} dP \quad \text{or} \quad d \ln \frac{f}{P} = - \frac{\alpha}{RT} dP$$

Since, at $P = 0, f/P = 1$,

$$\ln \frac{f}{P} = \frac{-1}{RT} \int_0^P \alpha\, dP \qquad (7.506)$$

at a given temperature.   The integral may be evaluated graphically or analytically by use of a suitable equation of state.   Thus Eq. 7.506 gives a basis for determining the fugacity at any pressure of interest.   The ratio f/P is called the *fugacity coefficient*

$$\gamma_P = \frac{f}{P} \qquad (7.507)$$

γ_P indicates the deviation from ideal behavior.   It is unity for an ideal gas. Fugacities of nitrogen at various pressures are shown in Table 7.501.

Table 7.501   *Fugacity of Nitrogen, atm**

P, atm	Temperature, °C		
	300	500	800
10	10.04	10.04	10.03
40	40.71	40.66	40.55
100	104.6	104.3	103.5
300	345.9	340.7	332.6
500	640.8	620.0	593.8
700	1003	949.3	890.6
900	1445	1336	1227

* By permission, according to J. Saurel and A. Lecocq, *J. phys. radium*, **20**, 443 (1959).

ILLUSTRATION.   One form of the virial equation of state is

$$P\bar{V} = RT + BP + CP^2 + \cdots$$

Derive an expression for the fugacity coefficient in terms of the virial coefficients B and C, and P at a given temperature.

Using Eq. 7.505,

$$\bar{V} = \frac{RT}{P} + B + CP = \frac{RT}{P} - \alpha$$

or

$$-\alpha = B + CP$$

then

$$\ln \frac{f}{P} = -\int_0^P \frac{\alpha}{RT}\,dP = \int_0^P \left(\frac{B}{RT} + \frac{CP}{RT}\right)dP$$

$$= \frac{BP}{RT} + \frac{CP^2}{2RT}$$

Standard State for Gases.   The standard state of unit fugacity must be regarded as a hypothetical one for real gases, and not a physically real state. Although a pressure may be found at which the fugacity is numerically unity, the actual enthalpy of the gas at this pressure is not the same as the standard-state enthalpy, $\bar{H}^\circ$; the latter is equal to the actual molar enthalpy of the gas at very low pressures. The superscript $^\circ$ will be used to indicate a standard state reference value of any property.

Equation 7.213 shows that the enthalpy of an ideal gas at a given temperature is independent of pressure, $\left(\dfrac{\partial H}{\partial P}\right)_T = 0$. The limiting value of the enthalpy of a real gas at zero pressure (limit) can be shown to be the standard reference value to be associated with unit fugacity. We write

$$\bar{F}^\circ - \bar{F}^* = RT \ln \frac{f^\circ}{f^*} \tag{7.508}$$

where $\bar{F}^\circ$ is the free energy of a gas at the standard fugacity f° ($f^\circ = 1$ atm) and $\bar{F}^*$ is the free energy at f^*, the fugacity at a very small pressure P^* which is so near zero that $f^* = P^*$, Eq. 7.503. Let us write Eq. 7.508 in the form

$$\frac{\bar{F}^\circ}{T} - \frac{\bar{F}^*}{T} = R \ln f^\circ - R \ln f^* = -R \ln f^*$$

since $f^\circ = 1$; if we differentiate both sides with respect to T, at constant pressure P^*, and remember that $\bar{F}^\circ$ is not a function of P, then

$$\frac{d(\bar{F}^\circ/T)}{dT} - \left[\frac{\partial(\bar{F}^*/T)}{\partial T}\right]_{P^*} = -R\left(\frac{\partial \ln f^*}{\partial T}\right)_{P^*}$$

From Eq. 7.418, the left-hand side becomes $-(\bar{H}^{\circ}/T^2) + (\bar{H}^*/T^2)$, and the right-hand side is zero since f^* cannot vary if P^* is held constant. Therefore

$$\bar{H}^{\circ} = \bar{H}^* \tag{7.509}$$

that is, the enthalpy in the hypothetical standard state is the same as that of the real gas in the limit of zero pressure.

Activity. From Eq. 7.502, it is apparent that any two numbers used to characterize initial and final states which are in the same ratio as f_2 and f_1 will serve equally well to calculate the free energy change

$$F_2 - F_1 = RT \ln \frac{f_2}{f_1} = RT \ln \frac{a_2}{a_1}$$

The last equality requires that $a_2 = kf_2$ and $a_1 = kf_1$. Such numbers are commonly used in the thermodynamic treatment of condensed systems. They are called activities. The activity is simply a relative fugacity,

$$a = \frac{f}{f^{\circ}} \tag{7.510}$$

where $1/f^{\circ}$ is a proportionality constant used to establish the relationship between the activity and the fugacity scale. f° is again the fugacity in the standard state which, for the condensed state, is not necessarily chosen as 1 atm. The activity is dimensionless. Its usefulness will become apparent later in the discussion of condensed systems. In situations where measurement of fugacity is impractical, alternative ways of determining the activity will be developed and a state of unit activity will be adopted as a standard against which thermodynamic properties in other states may be compared.

Problems

7.501   For nitrogen at 0°C

$(\bar{V}/RT) \times 10^4$:	196.92	98.46	51.82	31.39	22.45	20.64
P, atm:	50	100	200	400	800	1000

Evaluate the fugacity at each pressure by a graphical method.

7.502   A particular gas follows an equation of state of the form $P\bar{V} = RT + BP$ in a limited PVT range. If B is a given constant, derive the relationship of fugacity to pressure in terms of B. Calculate the change in F when 1 mole of this gas is expanded from 10 to 2 atm pressure at 300°K. Leave the answer in terms of B.

7.503   The equation $f/P = P/P_{\text{ideal}}$ has sometimes been used to estimate fugacities, where P_{ideal} is the pressure the gas would exert if it were to be ideal but with the same molar volume as the real gas at pressure P. Show that this relationship results if $f/P \approx 1$ so $\ln (f/P) \approx (f/P) - 1$ and an equation of state of the form of Eq. 7.221 is assumed.

7.504   The vapor pressure of liquid water at 25°C is 23.76 mm Hg. If water vapor is ideal, what is the activity of water vapor at 1 mm pressure at 25°C if the standard state is taken as the equilibrium vapor pressure at 25°C?

7.505   If the activity of a gas is increased by 50 per cent at 27°C, what is the corresponding change in free energy in calories per mole? If the gas is ideal, what is the corresponding change in ΔH and ΔS?

6. Multicomponent Systems;   the Chemical Potential

If the composition and amount of material in a system are variables, the extensive thermodynamic properties are functions of the number of moles of each component, n_i, in addition to the usual variables, such as T and P. Strictly speaking, only the mass of each component, instead of n_i, need be specified. Thermodynamics is independent of assumed molecular constitution. However, it is customary in chemical thermodynamics to represent the quantity in moles (i.e., gram-formula weights). For example, we must now write

$$F = f(T,P,n_1,n_2, \ldots n_i)$$

In differential form, the total change of F with T, P, and composition takes the form

$$dF = \left(\frac{\partial F}{\partial T}\right)_{P,n_j} dT + \left(\frac{\partial F}{\partial P}\right)_{T,n_j} dP + \left(\frac{\partial F}{\partial n_1}\right)_{T,P,n_j} dn_1$$
$$+ \left(\frac{\partial F}{\partial n_2}\right)_{T,P,n_j} dn_2 + \cdots + \left(\frac{\partial F}{\partial n_i}\right)_{T,P,n_j} dn_i \quad (7.601)$$

The subscript n_j indicates that the number of moles of all components, except any one indicated inside the partial derivative coefficient, remains constant. Hence the first two coefficients have the same meaning designated earlier: $\left(\frac{\partial F}{\partial T}\right)_{P,n_j} = -S$, now the total entropy of the particular mixture represented, and $\left(\frac{\partial F}{\partial P}\right)_{T,n_j} = V$, the total volume. Coefficients of the form $\left(\frac{\partial F}{\partial n_i}\right)_{T,P,n_j}$ are called *partial molar free energies*. Such a quantity is dependent on the composition of the mixture and represents the contribution, per mole, of that component to the total free energy of the mixture for the particular composition represented by n_i and n_j. It is frequently given the symbol $\bar{F}_i$, although because it is also fundamentally related to all other thermodynamic properties and is a widely used function in the study of mixtures, $\bar{F}_i$ has been given a special name, the chemical potential μ_i. Equation 7.601 becomes

$$dF = -S\,dT + V\,dP + \mu_1\,dn_1 + \mu_2\,dn_2 + \cdots + \mu_i\,dn_i \quad (7.602)$$

The relationship of μ_i to other thermodynamic properties will now be shown by an alternative derivation of Eq. 7.602.

General Definition of Chemical Potential.   Consider the total energy of a closed (but expandable) system which is a mixture as a function of S and V, the natural variables (e.g., Eq. 7.308 or 7.404), and the number of moles of each component of the mixture. If any of these variables is changed, e.g., some of the components may be interconvertible, the change in total energy may be represented in the differential form:

$$dE = \left(\frac{\partial E}{\partial S}\right)_{V,n_j} dS + \left(\frac{\partial E}{\partial V}\right)_{S,n_j} dV + \left(\frac{\partial E}{\partial n_1}\right)_{S,V,n_j} dn_1$$

$$+ \left(\frac{\partial E}{\partial n_2}\right)_{S,V,n_j} dn_2 + \cdots + \left(\frac{\partial E}{\partial n_i}\right)_{S,V,n_j} dn_i$$

or

$$dE = T\,dS - P\,dV + \left(\frac{\partial E}{\partial n_1}\right)_{S,V,n_j} dn_1 + \left(\frac{\partial E}{\partial n_2}\right)_{S,V,n_j} dn_2$$

$$+ \cdots + \left(\frac{\partial E}{\partial n_i}\right)_{S,V,n_j} dn_i \qquad (7.603)$$

Now, since $dF = dE + P\,dV + V\,dP - T\,dS - S\,dT$ for any given closed (but expandable) system, we may use Eq. 7.603 as an expression for dE for our mixture and write the equation

$$dF = -S\,dT + V\,dP + \left(\frac{\partial E}{\partial n_1}\right)_{S\,V,n_j} dn_1 + \left(\frac{\partial E}{\partial n_2}\right)_{S,V,n_j} dn_2$$

$$+ \cdots + \left(\frac{\partial E}{\partial n_i}\right)_{S,V,n_j} dn_i \qquad (7.604)$$

On comparing Eqs. 7.602 and 7.604, it is seen that μ_i must be equal to $\left(\dfrac{\partial E}{\partial n_i}\right)_{S,V,n_j}$.

A similar treatment with other thermodynamic functions will show that the chemical potential may be expressed in any of the following equivalent forms

$$\mu_i = \left(\frac{\partial F}{\partial n_i}\right)_{T,P,n_j} = \left(\frac{\partial E}{\partial n_i}\right)_{S,V,n_j} = \left(\frac{\partial H}{\partial n_i}\right)_{S,P,n_j} = \left(\frac{\partial A}{\partial n_i}\right)_{T,V,n_j}$$

$$= -T\left(\frac{\partial S}{\partial n_i}\right)_{E,V,n_j} \qquad (7.605)$$

For this reason we give μ_i a general name rather than identifying it with any particular thermodynamic function. In the study of systems at constant temperature and pressure, μ_i is closely identified with the Gibbs free energy. In the case of a pure substance, the chemical potential is simply the Gibbs free energy per mole, $\bar{F}_i$.

Formulas of the form of Eq. 7.603 are *homogeneous* of the first degree with the *capacity factors* (extensive properties, e.g., S, V, n_i) as independent variables. Mathematically a function $z = f(x,y, \ldots)$ is homogeneous to the nth degree if replacement of x by kx, y by ky, etc., leads to k^n times the original function. In this case $n = 1$, which corresponds to the physical fact that multiplying the size of the system by any factor without changing any of the intensive variables (T, P, mole fractions, etc.) results in extensive properties which are larger by the same factor. Mathematically we may then apply Euler's theorem of homogeneous functions, which for the first degree takes the form

$$v\left(\frac{\partial f}{\partial v}\right)_{w,x,y} + w\left(\frac{\partial f}{\partial w}\right)_{v,x,y} + x\left(\frac{\partial f}{\partial x}\right)_{v,w,y} + y\left(\frac{\partial f}{\partial y}\right)_{v,w,x} + \cdots = f(v,w,x,y\cdots)$$

As applied to Eq. 7.603, for a binary mixture, let $v = S$, $w = V$, $x = n_1$, $y = n_2$, and $f(v,w,x,y) = E$; hence from Euler's theorem we may immediately write

$$E = TS - PV + n_1\mu_1 + n_2\mu_2$$

Since $F = E + PV - TS$, it is apparent that $F = n_1\mu_1 + n_2\mu_2$ or in general

$$F = \sum_i n_i\mu_i \tag{7.606}$$

The latter corresponds physically to integration of Eq. 7.602 under conditions of constant temperature, pressure, and composition. Under these restrictions the chemical potential is constant and the total free energy is proportional to the size of the system.

Chemical Potential in Terms of Fugacity and Activity. The chemical potential of a pure substance is just the molar free energy. We may write Eq. 7.502 in the form

$$\mu_2 - \mu_1 = RT\ln\frac{f_2}{f_1} \tag{7.607}$$

or in terms of the activity

$$\mu_2 - \mu_1 = RT\ln\frac{a_2}{a_1} \tag{7.608}$$

For an ideal gas, the chemical potential bears a simple relationship to the pressure

$$\mu_2 - \mu_1 = RT\ln\frac{P_2}{P_1} \tag{7.609}$$

or in differential form

$$d\mu = RT\,d\ln P \tag{7.610}$$

Other Partial Molar Thermodynamic Quantities. In the study of mixtures it is also useful to define partial molar quantities for the other thermodynamic properties. The partial molar enthalpy is defined by

$$\bar{H}_i = \left(\frac{\partial H}{\partial n_i}\right)_{T,P,n_j} \tag{7.611}$$

and similarly, the partial molar entropy is

$$\bar{S}_i = \left(\frac{\partial S}{\partial n_i}\right)_{T,P,n_j} \tag{7.612}$$

and partial molar volume is

$$\bar{V}_i = \left(\frac{\partial V}{\partial n_i}\right)_{T,P,n_j} \tag{7.613}$$

etc. The partial molar quantities are functions of composition. At any specified composition they represent the contribution of each mole of the ith substance to the total value of that property of the mixture as a whole. An equation of the form of Eq. 7.606 can be written in each case, for example,

$$V = \sum_i n_i \bar{V}_i \tag{7.614}$$

ILLUSTRATION.   Determination of partial molar volumes in aqueous NaCl.

I. M. Klotz (*Chemical Thermodynamics*, Prentice-Hall, Englewood Cliffs, N.J., 1950) gives the following expression for the volume of a solution of sodium chloride in water at 25°C at 1 atm pressure as a function of the number of moles of NaCl, n_2, in 1000 grams of H_2O (i.e., n_1 is constant at 55.51 moles):

$$V = 1001.38 + 16.6253n_2 + 1.7738n_2^{3/2} + 0.1194n_2^2 \text{ cm}^3$$

To evaluate the partial molal volumes of NaCl and H_2O in various solutions we simply differentiate this expression according to Eq. 7.613

$$\bar{V}_2 = \left(\frac{\partial V}{\partial n_2}\right)_{T,P,n_1} = 16.6253 + \tfrac{3}{2}(1.7738)n_2^{1/2} + (2)(0.1194)n_2 \text{ cm}^3 \text{ mole}^{-1}$$

From $\bar{V}_2$ and V, $\bar{V}_1$ may be calculated from Eq. 7.614

$$\bar{V}_1 = \frac{V - n_2\bar{V}_2}{n_1} \text{ cm}^3 \text{ mole}^{-1}$$

The student may solve for actual numerical values.

Chemical Potential in Mixtures.   An equation analogous to Eq. 7.609 may be written to show the dependence of the chemical potential of a component of a mixture of ideal gases on its partial pressure. Since $\left(\dfrac{\partial F}{\partial P}\right)_T = V$ and $\mu_i = \left(\dfrac{\partial F}{\partial n_i}\right)_{T,P,n_j}$, we find from second derivatives that

$$\left[\frac{\partial}{\partial n_i}\left(\frac{\partial F}{\partial P}\right)_T\right]_{T,P,n_j} = \left(\frac{\partial V}{\partial n_i}\right)_{T,P,n_j} = \bar{V}_i = \left[\frac{\partial}{\partial P}\left(\frac{\partial F}{\partial n_i}\right)_{T,P,n_j}\right]_{T,n_j} = \left(\frac{\partial \mu_i}{\partial P}\right)_{T,n_j}$$

i.e.,

$$\left(\frac{\partial \mu_i}{\partial P}\right)_{T,n_j} = \bar{V}_i \tag{7.615}$$

Equation 7.615 is valid for any mixture. It takes a particularly simple form for an ideal gas mixture since

$$V = \sum \frac{n_i RT}{P}$$

and

$$\left(\frac{\partial V}{\partial n_i}\right)_{T,P,n_j} = \bar{V}_i = \frac{RT}{P} \tag{7.616}$$

At constant T and composition, from Eq. 7.615,

$$d\mu_i = RT\frac{dP}{P} \tag{7.617}$$

Since $P = (n_1 + n_2 + n_3 + \cdots)RT/V$ for an ideal gas mixture, we may write $P = \sum_i c_i RT$, where $c_i = n_i/V$; c_i is also equal to $n_i P/n_t RT$, where n_t is the total number of moles, or we may write $c_i = X_i P/RT$, where X_i is the mole fraction. If we differentiate the latter expression at constant composition and temperature, we obtain

$$dc_i = \frac{X_i\,dP}{RT}$$

from which it becomes apparent that $dc_i/c_i = dP/P$. Thus Eq. 7.617 may be written

$$d\mu_i = \frac{RT\,dc_i}{c_i}$$

or in integrated form

$$\mu_i' - \mu_i = RT\ln\frac{c_i'}{c_i} \tag{7.618}$$

A similar expression may be used for real mixtures in which the activity, suitably determined to correct for nonideal characteristics, replaces the concentration.

It is convenient to define the partial pressure P_i of a gas in an ideal mixture by the equation

$$P_i = c_i RT$$

or

$$P_i = X_i P \tag{7.619}$$

It should be noted that the partial pressure is not a partial molar property. Equation 7.618 may then be written in the form

$$\mu_i' - \mu_i = RT\ln\frac{P_i'}{P_i} \tag{7.620}$$

In a real gas mixture we may retain the simple form of Eq. 7.620 by use of the fugacity

$$\mu_i = \mu_i^\circ + RT\ln f_i \qquad (f_i^\circ = 1) \tag{7.621}$$

In the limit of zero total pressure, the fugacity f_i is identical to the partial pressure P_i. At higher pressures, f_i must be determined experimentally in a manner similar to that discussed in Sec. 7.5 for a pure gas. In the present case at constant T and n_i, Eqs. 7.615 and Eq. 7.621 take the differential form

$$d\mu_i = RT\,d\ln f_i = \bar{V}_i\,dP \tag{7.622}$$

where $\bar{V}_i$ represents the partial molar volume, $\left(\dfrac{\partial V}{\partial n_i}\right)_{T,P,n_j}$. Once $\bar{V}_i$ has been determined, the quantity $\alpha_i = (RT/P) - \bar{V}_i$ may be evaluated and the fugacity

f_i evaluated from the equation

$$\ln f_i = \ln X_i + \ln P - \frac{1}{RT}\int_0^P \alpha_i \, dP \tag{7.623}$$

analogous to Eqs. 7.505 and 7.506; X_i is the mole fraction of component i. If the gases mixed are quite similar, it is sometimes assumed that Eq. 7.623 reduces to a form similar to Eq. 7.619 with f_i in place of P_i

$$f_i = X_i f \tag{7.624}$$

where f is the fugacity component i would have if it were a pure gas at total pressure P.

The variation of the chemical potential with temperature, at constant pressure is determined by the partial molar entropy or, alternatively, by the partial molar enthalpy. Following a procedure analogous to that used to develop Eq. 7.615, we may show that

$$\left(\frac{\partial \mu_i}{\partial T}\right)_{P,n_j} = -\bar{S}_i \tag{7.625}$$

$$\left[\frac{\partial(\mu_i/T)}{\partial(1/T)}\right]_{P,n_j} = \bar{H}_i \tag{7.626}$$

where $\bar{S}_i$ and $\bar{H}_i$ are defined by Eqs. 7.612 and 7.611, respectively. The usefulness of the chemical potential, and of these relationships for determining its variation with temperature and partial pressure, or concentration, will become apparent in the following chapters.

Problems

7.601   Prove that $\mu_i = (\partial H/\partial n_i)_{P,S,n_j}$.

7.602   Calculate the change in chemical potential when an ideal gas is compressed from 1 to 10 atm of pressure at 400°C.

7.603   At pressures below 1 atm, a certain gas may be assumed ideal. At 50 atm pressure, its fugacity is 47.6 atm. Calculate the change in chemical potential of this gas if it is compressed from 0.5 atm to 50 atm pressure at 300°K.

7.604   Derive Eqs. 7.625 and 7.626.

7.605   What is the partial molar volume of nitrogen in a perfect gas mixture in which the partial pressure of N_2 is 0.2 atm, the partial pressure of O_2 is 0.4 atm, and the partial pressure of argon is 0.1 atm? Assume that these are the only gases present and that $t = 25°C$.

7.606   If this mixture in Problem 7.605 is compressed at constant composition to a total pressure of 10 atm, calculate the change in the chemical potential of N_2. ($t = 25°C$.)

7.607   Calculate the total change in free energy when 1 liter of the mixture described in Problem 7.605 is prepared from the pure gases, each initially at 1 atm pressure. ($t = 25°C$.)

7.608   Thirty weight per cent H_2SO_4 solution has a density of 1.2185 g ml^{-1}, and 31 per cent solution a density of 1.2267 g ml^{-1}. Calculate the mean value of the partial molar volume of water at these concentrations.

7. Review Problems

7.701   Forty grams of CO_2 expands reversibly and at constant temperature of 100°C from a volume of 7 liters to 10 liters. Calculate Q, W, ΔE, ΔH, ΔS, ΔF, and ΔA if the gas is ideal.

What would be the value of the above quantities if the expansion took place between the same volume limits but adiabatically and against zero external pressure (same initial temperature)?

7.702   Three moles of a van der Waals gas, with $a = 5$ liters^2 atm mole^{-2} and $b = 0.0010$ liter mole^{-1}, undergoes an isothermal expansion at 300°K from a volume of 8 liters to a volume of 40 liters. If 600 cal of heat is absorbed, evaluate W, ΔE, ΔH, ΔS, ΔA, and ΔF.

7.703   Evaluate $\left(\dfrac{\partial E}{\partial V}\right)_T$, $\left(\dfrac{\partial H}{\partial P}\right)_T$, and $C_P - C_V$ for a gas that obeys the equation of state $P(\bar{V} - b) = RT$.

7.704   An ideal heat engine operates by adding heat to a reservoir ($C_P = 5000$ cal deg^{-1}) initially at 20°C, and removing heat from a mixture of ice and water. How much work would be required to freeze an additional 1000 grams of ice, and what would be the final temperature of the reservoir?

*7.705   One kilogram of water, originally melted ice at 0°C and at the 14,000-foot level of Mt. Rainier, reaches the ocean at 7°C without doing any work. Calculate the ΔS for the water and for the surroundings, and the total entropy change. State assumptions.

7.706   Calculate the entropy change when 1 mole of oxygen is heated at 1 atm from 25 to 100°C. Do the same for acetone vapor. Use heat capacity tables in the Appendix.

7.707   Use data from the tables (Appendix) to derive an expression for the enthalpy, entropy, and Gibbs free energy of MgO relative to values of these quantities at 298°K. The entropy of MgO at 298°K can be taken to be 6.4 cal deg^{-1} mole^{-1}.

*7.708   Derive an expression for the fugacity of a gas which obeys the equation of state $P\bar{V} = RT(1 + B/\bar{V})$. HINT: Integrate Eq. 7.504 by parts.

*7.709   Use data in Table 7.501 and the Appendix to calculate the free energy change of nitrogen on going from 10 atm and 300°C to 900 atm and 800°C. The entropy of N_2 at 300°K and 1 atm may be taken to be 46 cal mole^{-1} deg^{-1}. Assume $f = 1$ when $P = 1$ to a sufficient degree of approximation.

7.710   Prove that $\mu_i = \dfrac{\partial A}{\partial n_i}$. What variables must be held constant?

7.711   The volume of an aqueous solution of sulfuric acid in water may be represented by the equation quoted by Aston and Fritz (General References):

$$V = 1001.8 + 35.35 n_{H_2SO_4} + 0.863 n_{H_2SO_4}^2 \text{ cm}^3$$

The number of moles of water is held constant at 55.51. Calculate the partial molar volume of H_2SO_4 in this solution as a function of $n_{H_2SO_4}$. Calculate the partial molar volume of water as a function of $n_{H_2SO_4}$. Evaluate these partial molar quantities, and the density of the solution at $n_{H_2SO_4} = 2$.

General References

Aston, J. G., and J. J. Fritz, *Thermodynamics and Statistical Thermodynamics*, John Wiley and Sons, New York, 1959.

Fermi, Enrico, *Thermodynamics*, Dover Publications, New York, 1936.

Guggenheim, E. A., *Thermodynamics: An Advanced Treatment for Chemists and Physicists*, North Holland Publishing Co., Amsterdam, 1957.

Hougen, O. A., K. M. Watson, and R. A. Ragatz, *Chemical Process Principles*. Part II: *Thermodynamics*, Second Edition, John Wiley and Sons, New York, 1959.

Klotz, I. M., *Chemical Thermodynamics*, Prentice-Hall, Englewood Cliffs, N.J., 1950.

Lewis, G. N., M. Randall, K. S. Pitzer, and L. Brewer, *Thermodynamics*, Second Edition, McGraw-Hill Book Co., New York, 1961.

Margenau, H., and G. M. Murphy, *The Mathematics of Physics and Chemistry*, Second Edition, D. Van Nostrand, Princeton, N.J., 1956.

Rossini, F. D., Editor, *Experimental Thermochemistry*, prepared under the auspices of the International Union of Pure and Applied Chemistry, Interscience Publishers, New York, 1956.

Zemansky, M. W., *Heat and Thermodynamics*, Fourth Edition, McGraw-Hill Book Co., New York, 1957.

Chapter Eight

Phase Equilibria

In this chapter systems in which equilibrium is established between two or more phases will be discussed. Thermodynamics provides a basis for prediction of the behavior of such systems from properties of the pure constituents. We begin by formulating the phase rule.

1. The Phase Rule

A phase is a macroscopic homogeneous portion of a system. Since all gases are completely miscible, there can never be more than one gas phase; however, a number of independent liquid or solid phases may be formed. We will now consider the number of phases which can coexist and the relationship of the properties of each component to the equilibrium behavior of the system.

Number of Components. A phase may be composed of several components; in thermodynamics the number of components C represents the smallest number of distinct chemical substances required to form the phase. We need not consider as distinct components all the various ionic or molecular species which may be an inherent part of a chemical substance. For example, water may be considered a single component, even though in pure liquid water species such as OH^-, H_3O^+, and hydrogen-bonded polymers of varying complexity are undoubtedly present; such species are formed by equilibrium processes (reactions) characteristic of water and are an inherent part of its properties. The phase rule, like all basic thermodynamic relationships, is independent of assumptions pertaining to the particulate nature of matter. The extensive thermodynamic properties of a phase are generally fixed by specifying two parameters, such as temperature and pressure, and the composition in terms of the number of grams (more conveniently, moles) of each of the components necessary to formulate it. To fix the values of the chemical potentials, or of any other intensive thermodynamic property, in a phase only $\underline{C} - 1$ composition variables need be given. Intensive properties depend only on relative numbers of moles and not on total amount. Fixing $\underline{C} - 1$ mole fractions, for example, necessarily fixes the mole fraction of the last component. Intensive properties, particularly the chemical potential, will be of primary interest in the thermodynamic analysis of phase equilibria.

ILLUSTRATION.   Find the number of components necessary to fix the thermodynamic properties of each of the following equilibrium mixtures at a given T and P in a single phase.

(a) $Ca^{++}CO_3^=$ (as a solid ionic mixture),
Since electroneutrality must apply,

$$\sum Ca^{++} = \sum CO_3^=$$

Thus only the amount of one component need be specified. In general, the number of species present less the number of independent equalities (or equilibrium relationships) gives the minimum number of components.

(b) CO_2, H_2O, HCO_3^-, H^+, OH^-, $CO_3^=$, H_2CO_3 in solution
Seven species are listed; however, the following equalities or equilibria must exist simultaneously:

(1) $CO_2 + H_2O \rightleftarrows H_2CO_3$
(2) $H_2CO_3 \rightleftarrows H^+ + HCO_3^-$
(3) $HCO_3^- \rightleftarrows H^+ + CO_3^=$
(4) $H_2O \rightleftarrows H^+ + OH^-$
(5) Σ (positive charges) $= \Sigma$ (negative charges)
Number of components $= 7 - 5 = 2$.
Any other equilibrium, e.g.,
(6) $CO_3^= + H_2O \rightleftarrows HCO_3^- + OH^-$
can be formulated from those listed, e.g., (4) $-$ (3) $=$ (6). Of course, (6) could be given in place of (3) or (4). No fewer than the five relations shown are sufficient; however, any five independent relationships may be chosen.

If we apply a further restriction—for instance, that the total amount of CO_2, including its related forms, is equal to the total amount of H_2O, including its related forms, or that the total number of carbon atoms in all compounds is one half the total number of hydrogen atoms in all compounds—then the system becomes a one-component system. This is the same as specifying that we start with equal molar amounts of CO_2 and H_2O, corresponding to the single formula H_2CO_3.

_____

When several phases are in equilibrium, the total number of components for the whole system can be obtained by adding together the minimum number of components necessary to specify the properties of each phase and subtracting the number of independent phase equilibrium and fixed concentration relationships. For example, $NH_4Cl(s)$, when heated, vaporizes as a mixture of $HCl(g)$ and $NH_3(g)$ in equimolar amounts. With the composition of the vapor fixed, it is effectively a one-component phase. Hence pure $NH_4Cl(s)$ and its equilibrium vapor is a one-component system. On the other hand, when pure $CaCO_3$ is heated, the equilibrium $CaCO_3(s) = CaO(s) + CO_2(g)$ is established. Three phases are in equilibrium; each phase may be considered pure with one component; but, since there is only one equilibrium reaction between phases, we must consider this a two-component system. The same result is obtained if all three species are assumed present in all three phases, since we then must have seven independent equilibrium relationships between phases. Here we have no concentration equalities, even though $n_{CO_2} = n_{CaO}$.

The Chemical Potential and Phase Equilibrium. If several phases are in equilibrium at a fixed temperature and pressure, the transfer of dn_i moles of any component from one phase to another does not change the total free energy of the multiphase system. This may be seen from Eq. 7.406, derived for a reversible process for a closed (fixed amount of material) system

$$dF = V\,dP - S\,dT \qquad (7.406)$$

If T and P are constant, then the sum of the free energy changes in each of the various phases, when a transfer of dn_i moles of component i from one phase to another occurs under equilibrium conditions, must be zero. For each phase, α, $\cdot\beta$, etc., at constant T and P, we may write, from Eq. 7.602,

$$dF_\alpha = \left(\sum_i \mu_i\,dn_i\right)_\alpha$$

hence for all phases

$$dF = \overset{\text{all phases}}{\underset{\alpha,\beta,\ldots}{\sum}} dF_\alpha, \ldots = \overset{\text{all phases}}{\underset{\alpha,\beta,\ldots}{\sum}} \left(\sum_i \mu_i\,dn_i\right)_\alpha \ldots = 0 \qquad (8.101)$$

For simplicity consider only the transfer of dn_i moles of component i between two phases, in which case, to conserve matter, $-(dn_i)_\alpha = +(dn_i)_\beta$. The free energy change for such a transfer may be written

$$dF_i = [\mu_{i(\beta)} - \mu_{i(\alpha)}]\,dn_i$$

Since dn_i is not restricted to zero, the only general way the condition expressed in Eq. 8.101 can be satisfied is for

$$\mu_{i(\alpha)} = \mu_{i(\beta)} \qquad (8.102)$$

This requirement can be shown to extend over all phases in a multiphase equilibrium: the chemical potential of each component must be the same in all phases coexisting at equilibrium.

Equation 8.102 restricts the manner in which the temperature, pressure, and composition can be varied. First, consider a one-component system, such as H_2O, in which equilibrium exists between liquid and gas. The chemical potential of water must be the same in the two phases. The chemical potential changes with

T and P in a unique way in each phase. Remember that for a pure substance the chemical potential is just the molar Gibbs free energy. From Eqs. 7.625 and 7.615 we may write

$$\left(\frac{\partial \mu_g}{\partial T}\right)_P = -\bar{S}_g \tag{8.103}$$

$$\left(\frac{\partial \mu_g}{\partial P}\right)_T = \bar{V}_g \tag{8.104}$$

$$\left(\frac{\partial \mu_l}{\partial T}\right)_P = -\bar{S}_l \tag{8.105}$$

$$\left(\frac{\partial \mu_l}{\partial P}\right)_T = \bar{V}_l \tag{8.106}$$

$\bar{S}$ and $\bar{V}$ represent the molar entropy and molar volume, respectively, of the phase indicated. The entropy and volume of the gas phase are much larger than the

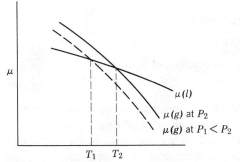

Fig. 8.101   Chemical potentials of liquid and vapor phases.

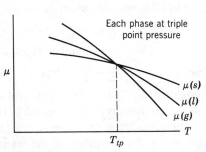

Fig. 8.102   Liquid, solid, and vapor chemical potentials at triple point pressure.

corresponding values for the liquid phase, so the chemical potential of the vapor is more dependent on T and P than the chemical potential of the liquid. The relationship is illustrated schematically in Fig. 8.101. Each of the lines represents the variation of chemical potential with temperature at a particular pressure. Since the molar volume of the liquid is very small, the chemical potential of the liquid does not change appreciably with the total pressure in the system. However, the chemical potential of the gas is markedly dependent on its pressure and can be the same as that of the liquid at a particular temperature only at a certain pressure. When we impose the condition of phase equilibrium on the system, a loss in the number of degrees of freedom occurs. T and P cannot both be chosen arbitrarily; only one value of P is possible for any arbitrarily chosen temperature.

If phase equilibrium in a one-component system is extended to three phases, then the chemical potential must be the same in all three phases. Intersection of the three curves will occur only at a unique temperature and pressure for each substance, called a *triple point*, illustrated schematically in Fig. 8.102.

Gibbs Phase Rule. Variation of the composition of a phase provides a way in which the chemical potentials of its components can be changed at constant T and P. The number of degrees of freedom, symbol $\underline{F}$ (intensive variables), possible in a closed equilibrium system composed of $\underline{C}$ components and $\underline{P}$ phases is conveniently summarized as follows.

The total number of degrees of freedom will be T, P, and the composition variables. The only composition variables which need to be considered will be those of the $\underline{C}$ components; hence there are $\underline{C} - 1$ composition variables for each phase. The total number of variables for all phases will be $\underline{P}(\underline{C} - 1) + 2$. Each component may be considered present in each phase, and the $+2$ corresponds to the temperature and pressure.

From this total number of variables we must subtract the number lost because the chemical potential of each component must be the same in each of the equilibrium phases. This requires an equality of the form of Eq. 8.102 for each component in each pair of phases; hence for $\underline{P}$ phases we have $\underline{C}(\underline{P} - 1)$ independent restrictions.

Thus the net number of degrees of freedom is

$$\underline{F} = \underline{P}(\underline{C} - 1) + 2 - \underline{C}(\underline{P} - 1)$$

$$= \text{number of variables} - \text{number of restrictions}$$

or $$\underline{F} = \underline{C} - \underline{P} + 2 \qquad\qquad (8.107)$$

Equation 8.107, known as the Gibbs phase rule, provides a convenient summary of the limitations to be expected in the study of phase equilibria.

Questions such as the presence or absence of a component in any particular phase, or the inclusion of the walls of the container as a separate phase, are automatically taken care of by the phase rule. Thermodynamically, every component must be present in every phase; however, for a gas in an iron cylinder, for example, the mole fraction of iron in the vapor phase at room temperature is so small that for practical purposes it may be neglected as a vapor component. Neglect of iron in the vapor reduces the number of vapor composition variables by 1; at the same time the number of restrictions required by the equality of vapor and solid chemical potentials is also reduced by 1 by neglect of the equilibrium between $Fe(s)$ and $Fe(g)$, and the net number of degrees of freedom is thus the same as though both these terms had been included. Similarly, if the principal components of interest in the system are not significantly soluble in the walls of the container, the latter may be considered a separate phase of one component. Inclusion of the container in the phase rule would simply increase $\underline{C}$ by 1 and also $\underline{P}$ by 1; again the net effect is no change in the number of degrees of freedom. In practice it is necessary to include as variables only those components whose concentrations have a significant influence on the values of the chemical potentials of other components in any of the equilibrium phases of the system.

ILLUSTRATION. Find the number of degrees of freedom for a closed one-component system when, for a fixed amount of material, (a) only one phase exists, e.g., gas;   (b) two phases are in equilibrium;   (c) three phases are in equilibrium.

The answer to (a) is 2, from Eq. 8.107. The answer to (b) is 1 and corresponds to a fixed vapor pressure at each temperature where liquid and vapor are in equilibrium. The answer to (c) is zero; there is no freedom in specifying the values of T and P at the triple point.

Problems

8.101   Indicate the number of components in each of the following systems:
(a) An aqueous solution of Na^+ and Cl^-.
(b) An aqueous solution of sodium acetate. List important ionic and molecular species present.
(c) An equimolar mixture of hydrogen and iodine gas at sufficiently high temperature so they are in equilibrium with HI gas.
(d) An equilibrium mixture of $FeBr_2(s)$, $FeBr_2 \cdot H_2O(s)$, and H_2O gas.
(e) An equimolar mixture of $FeBr_2$ and H_2O [consider an equilibrium as in (d)].
8.102   Construct a diagram similar to Fig. 8.102 for H_2O, showing schematically the relationship of $\mu(g)$, $\mu(l)$, and $\mu(s)$ at $P = 1$ atm in each case. Mark the normal freezing point and normal boiling point. Discuss the stability of the various phases of water at various temperatures in terms of this diagram.
8.103   A phase equilibrium system is found invariant when five phases coexist. How many components must be present?
8.104   A research paper reports that substances A and B form two different solid solution phases. As the total composition of the system is changed at a constant T and P, the composition of each of the solid coexisting phases is also reported to change. Was this investigator dealing with an equilibrium system? Explain what would be observed if the system were at equilibrium.

2. One-Component Systems

Phase Diagrams.   For a one-component system, a phase diagram is usually a plot of pressure against temperature. The behavior of water is shown in a limited region in Fig. 8.201. The lines represent equilibrium between phases and thus establish the fixed relationship between pressure and temperature. The areas between these lines correspond to regions in which only a single phase exists and in which T and P may be varied independently. Equilibrium between any two phases can exist only if the value of P for a particular T falls on the line dividing the areas, e.g., liquid and gas. The three phases coexist only at the point of intersection of these three lines. This triple point is invariant, $\underline{F} = 0$, in accordance with the phase rule.

At high pressures a number of different crystalline forms (different phases) of ice have been observed. Only limited information is available, so the phase diagram (Fig. 8.202) is not complete. Numerous triple points are shown. More than three independent phases cannot coexist in equilibrium in a one-component

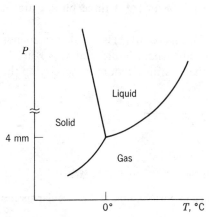

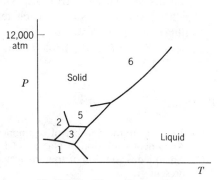

Fig. 8.201   Schematic representation of phase diagram for water in vicinity of triple point.

Fig. 8.202   Phase diagram for water at high pressures (schematic).

system; $\underline{F}$ cannot be less than zero. In Fig. 8.202 four triple points which involve ice (3) are shown.

The phase diagram for sulfur (Fig. 8.203) shows three triple points; 1, between rhombic and monoclinic solid sulfur and the vapor; 2, between monoclinic solid, liquid, and vapor; 3, between rhombic solid, monoclinic solid, and liquid sulfur.

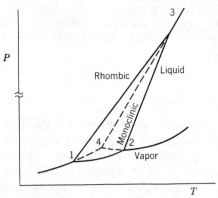

Fig. 8.203   Schematic phase diagram for sulfur.

Monoclinic, rhombic, liquid, and vapor cannot all be in simultaneous equilibrium. The solid-state transition between rhombic and monoclinic occurs at point 1; if it were possible to superheat the rhombic form, a triple point would be expected at point 4 between rhombic, liquid, and gaseous sulfur. Two phases may coexist along the solid lines when T and P are in the proper relationship.

Clapeyron Equation. The equality of the chemical potentials in two equilibrium phases α and β provides a way of determining the relationship of T and P (the curves in the phase diagram) from the thermodynamic properties of the phases. At equilibrium

$$\mu_\alpha = \mu_\beta$$

If T is changed slightly and equilibrium re-established at the new temperature, the pressure must change in such a way as to make the chemical potentials again equal at the new equilibrium point. Hence $d\mu_\alpha = d\mu_\beta$. For a pure substance each of these changes may be represented by an equation of the form $d\mu = -\bar{S}\,dT + \bar{V}\,dP$. Hence

$$-\bar{S}_\alpha\,dT + \bar{V}_\alpha\,dP = -\bar{S}_\beta\,dT + \bar{V}_\beta\,dP$$

This equation may be rearranged to the form

$$(\bar{S}_\beta - \bar{S}_\alpha)\,dT = (\bar{V}_\beta - \bar{V}_\alpha)\,dP$$

or

$$\frac{dP}{dT} = \frac{\Delta\bar{S}}{\Delta\bar{V}} = \frac{\Delta S}{\Delta V} \qquad (8.201)$$

Equation 8.201 is the Clapeyron equation. $\dfrac{\Delta S}{\Delta V}$, the change in entropy over the change in volume for the phase transition, represents the slope of the equilibrium P vs. T curve at a given point.

Since the two phases are in equilibrium, ΔH is Q_{rev} for the reversible transition at the given T and P. Thus Eq. 8.201 may also be written

$$\frac{dP}{dT} = \frac{\Delta H}{T\,\Delta V} \qquad (8.202)$$

The Clapeyron equation may be applied to any phase equilibrium. It predicts, for example, how the freezing point of water will vary with pressure. Since the molar volume of ice is larger than that of liquid water, whereas the enthalpy (also entropy) of the liquid is larger than that of the solid, the ratio on the right of Eq. 8.201 or 8.202 is negative, and hence dP/dT is negative. An increase in the pressure will cause a decrease in the equilibrium melting temperature. The effect may be predicted quantitatively from Eq. 8.201 or 8.202; however, both the entropy change and volume change must be known as functions of T and P before Eq. 8.201 can be integrated properly.

ILLUSTRATION.   From the density of water and ice at 0°C and atmospheric pressure, estimate the freezing point of water at 100 atm pressure by assuming $\bar{V}_s$ and $\bar{V}_l$ remain constant, $\Delta H_{\text{fus}} = 80$ cal g^{-1} (assume this value to be temperature independent).

From values of the densities,

$$d_{H_2O}(\text{liq}) \cong 1 \text{ g cm}^{-3}, \qquad \bar{V}_l = 18.0 \text{ cm}^3 \text{ mole}^{-1}$$

$$d_{H_2O}(\text{ice}) = 0.917 \text{ g cm}^{-3}, \qquad \bar{V}_s = 19.65 \text{ cm}^3 \text{ mole}^{-1}$$

From Eq. 8.202

$$\frac{dP}{dT} = \frac{\Delta H}{T\,\Delta V} = \frac{(-1440 \text{ cal mole}^{-1})(41.3 \text{ cm}^3 \text{ atm cal}^{-1})}{T(19.65 - 18.0) \text{ ml deg mole}^{-1}}$$

$$= \frac{-59{,}472}{T(1.65)} = \frac{-36{,}043}{T} \text{ atm deg}^{-1}$$

and

$$dP = -\frac{dT}{T}(36{,}043)$$

hence

$$P_2 - P_1 = -36{,}043 \ln \frac{T_2}{T_1}$$

$$-\frac{99}{36{,}043} = \ln T_2 - \ln 273.2$$

and thus,

$$\ln T_2 = -0.00275 + 5.61020$$

$$= 5.60745$$

$$T_2 \cong 272.5, \quad \text{i.e.,} \quad T_1 - T_2 \cong 0.7°C$$

An accurate treatment should include consideration of the dependence of molar volumes and heat of fusion on temperature and pressure.

Clausius-Clapeyron Equation. The Clapeyron equation is particularly useful in the study of vaporization equilibria and leads to an expression for the variation of vapor pressure with temperature. In cases where moderate accuracy is sufficient, Eq. 8.202 may be changed to a more convenient form by making the following assumptions: (1) the molar volume of the liquid or solid condensed phase may be neglected relative to that of the vapor at moderately low vapor pressures; (2) the vapor follows the perfect gas law. With these two assumptions, $\bar{V}_g - \bar{V}_c$ (the difference in molar volumes of the gas and condensed phases) may be replaced by RT/P and the Clapeyron equation becomes

$$\frac{dP}{dT} = \frac{P\,\Delta\bar{H}}{RT^2}$$

or

$$\frac{d \ln P}{dT} = \frac{\Delta\bar{H}}{RT^2} \tag{8.203}$$

or

$$\frac{d \ln P}{d(1/T)} = -\frac{\Delta\bar{H}}{R} \tag{8.204}$$

$\Delta\bar{H}$ is now the enthalpy of vaporization per mole. Equation 8.203 or 8.204 is known as the Clausius-Clapeyron equation.

The enthalpy change on vaporization is a rather large number. Its variation with T (related to the difference between vapor and liquid heat capacities) and P is relatively small. $\Delta\bar{H}_{vap}$ is frequently assumed constant over small temperature intervals. In this case the Clausius-Clapeyron equation integrates to the very simple form

$$\ln P = -\frac{\Delta\bar{H}}{RT} + C \tag{8.205}$$

or, as a definite integral,

$$\ln \frac{P_2}{P_1} = -\left(\frac{\Delta \bar{H}}{R}\right)\left(\frac{1}{T_2} - \frac{1}{T_1}\right) \tag{8.206}$$

Thus measurement of the vapor pressure at two temperatures gives sufficient information for the calculation of a mean heat of vaporization. In practice, experimental error is reduced by measurement of the vapor pressure at a series of temperatures. The slope of the $\ln P$ vs. $1/T$ line is $-\Delta \bar{H}/R$, as seen from Eq. 8.204. Alternatively, knowledge of the heat of vaporization and the vapor pressure at one temperature may be used to calculate the vapor pressure at other temperatures.

ILLUSTRATION.   The heat of vaporization of water is 539 cal g^{-1}. If this value is assumed independent of T and P, calculate the vapor pressure of water at 80°C from the fact that the normal boiling point is 100°C.
From Eq. 8.206

$$\log_{10} P_2 = -\frac{(539)(18)}{2.3(1.99)}\left(\frac{1}{353.2} - \frac{1}{373.2}\right)$$

When only the boiling point is known, Trouton's rule, which states that $\dfrac{\Delta \bar{H}_{vap}}{T_{bp}} = $ 21, is sometimes used to obtain a rough estimate of the vapor pressures of "normal" organic liquids at various temperatures. The theoretical basis for this useful approximation will be discussed in Sec. 11.2.

ILLUSTRATION.   The normal boiling point of benzene is 80.2°C. If Trouton's rule is assumed valid, estimate the vapor pressure of benzene at 25°C.
From Eq. 8.206

$$\log_{10} P_2 = -\frac{(21)(353.4)}{2.3(1.99)}\left(\frac{1}{298.2} - \frac{1}{353.4}\right)$$

since

$$\Delta \bar{H} = (21)(353.4) \text{ cal mole}^{-1} \text{ deg}^{-1}$$

For an accurate treatment of vapor pressure data, the Clapeyron equation in its exact form must be used. Vapor pressures measured with good precision (as a function of temperature) are frequently correlated empirically in an equation of the form $\ln P = A/T + B \ln T + CT^2 + \cdots$. This information can be related to the heat of vaporization through the Clapeyron equation, which may be changed to the form

$$\frac{d \ln P}{dT} = \frac{1}{P}\frac{dP}{dT} = \frac{1}{P}\frac{\Delta H}{T(V_g - V_c)} \tag{8.207}$$

Care must be taken to employ consistent units. If vapor pressures are large, it may be necessary to consider the dependence of enthalpy on P as well as T.

The dependence of vapor pressure on temperature for some common substances is illustrated in Fig. 8.204.

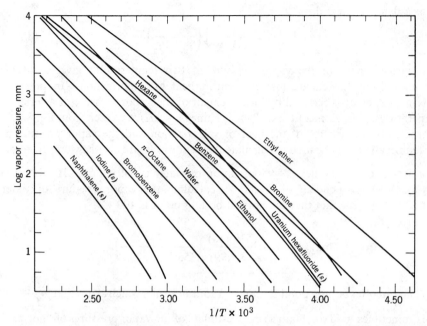

Fig. 8.204   Log P vs. $1/T$ plot. Some deviation from the linear relationship expected from Eq. 8.205 can be seen. (By permission from F. Daniels and R. A. Alberty, *Physical Chemistry*, John Wiley and Sons, New York, 1961.)

ILLUSTRATION.   Beattie, Levine, and Douslin *J. Am. Chem. Soc.*, **73**, 4431 (1951) measured the vapor pressure of *n*-pentane from 100°C to the critical point, 197°C.   The results may be represented by the equation

$$\log_{10} P_{\text{atm}} = 3.75245 - 1225.96 T^{-1} + 8.0684 \times 10^{-4} T$$

Show how to evaluate the heat of vaporization of normal pentane at 400°K.
   Changing to natural logarithms and differentiating,

$$2.303 \log_{10} P_{\text{atm}} = \ln P_{\text{atm}}$$

$$\frac{d \ln P_{\text{atm}}}{dT} = (2.303)(1225.96) T^{-2} + (2.303)(8.0684 \times 10^{-4})$$

From the Clapeyron equation

$$\frac{d \ln P}{dT} = \frac{1}{P} \frac{dP}{dT} = \frac{1}{P} \frac{\Delta H}{T \, \Delta V}$$

Thus

$$\Delta H = PT^{-1} \Delta V (2.303)(1225.96) + (2.303)(8.0684 \times 10^{-4})(PT \, \Delta V)$$

where P may be evaluated from the expression for $\log P$; $T = 400°$; ΔV may be evaluated from equation of state data for the vapor and from density data for the liquid at the temperature and pressure of interest.

If the assumption is made that $\bar{V}_g - \bar{V}_l \cong \bar{V}_g = RT/P$, then

$$\Delta H = R(2.303)(1225.96) + RT^2(2.303)(8.0684 \times 10^{-4})$$

Vaporization of solids may be treated in the same manner. The enthalpy change on vaporization of a solid is called the *heat of sublimation*. The difference between the heat of sublimation and the heat of vaporization of the liquid at the triple point is the *heat of fusion* (Fig. 8.205). The latter may also be determined from a

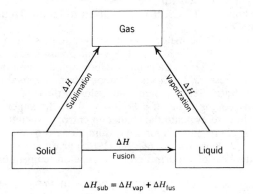

$$\Delta H_{sub} = \Delta H_{vap} + \Delta H_{fus}$$

Fig. 8.205 ΔH relationships.

measurement of the variation of melting temperature with pressure, although in practice it is obtained with better accuracy by calorimetric methods. Some vaporization and fusion data are given in Table 8.201(A).

*Table 8.201   Vaporization and Fusion Data for Some Elements and Compounds**

Subst.	t_{bp},°C	$\Delta \bar{H}^\circ_{vap}$, kcal mole^{-1}	$\Delta \bar{S}^\circ_{vap}$, cal mole^{-1} deg^{-1}	t_{mp},°C	$\Delta \bar{H}^\circ_{fus}$, kcal mole^{-1}	$\Delta \bar{S}^\circ_{fus}$, cal mole^{-1} deg^{-1}
O_2	-182.97	1.630	18.07	-218.76	0.106	1.95
H_2O	100.00	9.717	26.04	0.00	1.4363	5.258
Cl_2	-34.06	4.878	20.40	-101.0	1.531	8.89

The complete Table 8.201(A) will be found in the Appendix.

* From *NBS Circ.* 500, 1952.

Problems

8.201   The vapor pressure of CCl_4 is 843 mm at 80°C and 621 mm at 70°C. Calculate the mean value of $\Delta \bar{H}_{vap}$ in this temperature interval. What is $\Delta \bar{S}$ for vaporization at the normal boiling point?

8.202   Between 20 and 70°C the vapor pressure of mercury is given by the equation $\log_{10} P_{mm} = 10.53 - 0.848 \log_{10} T - 3328\, T^{-1}$. The density of liquid mercury is 13.529 g ml^{-1} at 27°C. If the vapor is assumed ideal, calculate $\Delta \bar{H}$ and $\Delta \bar{S}$ for the vaporization of mercury at 27°C.

8.203   If the densities of liquid and solid bismuth are 10.004 and 9.673 g cc^{-1}, respectively, at the normal melting point, 270°C, and the heat of fusion is 12.6 cal g^{-1}, find the expected melting point under 100 atm pressure.

8.204 n-Hexane boils at 68.7°C. If it is assumed to follow Trouton's rule, estimate its vapor pressure at 27°C.

8.205   In the vicinity of the melting point the vapor pressure above solid $TaBr_5$ is given by $\log_{10} P_{mm} = 12.571 - 5650 T^{-1}$. The vapor pressure above the liquid is given by $\log_{10} P_{mm} = 8.171 - 3265 T^{-1}$. Calculate the boiling point and triple point temperatures, the triple point pressure, the heats of vaporization, sublimation, and fusion, and the entropies of vaporization, sublimation, and fusion at the triple point temperature.

8.206   The normal boiling point of a liquid is 70°C. Its vapor pressure at 25°C is 150 mm Hg. Show how to evaluate the change in entropy when the liquid vaporizes at 70°C from this data. State any important assumptions (do not use Trouton's rule).

8.207   Scott et al. [J. Phys. Chem., 66, 911 (1962)] give the following expression for the dependence of the heat of vaporization of toluene on temperature between 298 and 410°K:

$$\Delta H_{vap} = 11,637 - 4.823 T - 1.260 \times 10^{-2} T^2 \text{ cal mole}^{-1}$$

The normal boiling point of toluene is 383.8°K. Develop an equation from which the vapor pressure of toluene may be calculated at any temperature within this interval if it is assumed that toluene vapor is an ideal gas.

8.208   T. E. Jordan (Vapor Pressures of Organic Compounds, Interscience Publishers, New York, 1954) gives the following data for normal propane:

t,°C:	−42.07	−25.6	1.4	26.9	58.1	78.7	94.8
P_{atm}	1	2	5	10	20	30	40

Plot $\ln P$ vs. $1/T$ and see whether it is reasonable to assume the simple result predicted by Eq. 8.205. Use Eq. 8.204 to estimate the heat of vaporization at 25°C. Indicate data needed and search for them in the literature to determine the heat of vaporization at 25°C, using Eq. 8.207.

8.209   Calculate the entropy of vaporization at the normal boiling point for CCl_3Br. According to Jordan (loc. cit.), $\log_{10} P_{mm} = 7.64 - 8240/4.576T$.

8.210   From the vapor pressure of water at its freezing point, taken as 4 mm Hg, and the data in Table 8.201(A), estimate values for the vapor pressure of liquid water at 20°C and for ice at −10°C.

3. Multicomponent Systems

General Treatment of Chemical Potential.   The presence of two or more independent components of varying miscibility increases the possible complexity of phase equilibrium systems. Before examples of phase diagrams are presented, the general thermodynamic treatment of mixtures will be extended.

Consider first the behavior of ideal mixtures for which Eq. 7.619 may be written

$$P_i = X_i P \qquad (7.619)$$

Since the gases are assumed ideal, each component acts independently and its fugacity is identical to its partial pressure; the dependence of the chemical potential of component i on fugacity is given by the equation

$$\mu_i - \mu_i^\circ = RT \ln \frac{f_i}{f_i^\circ} = RT \ln \frac{P_i}{P_i^\circ} \qquad (8.301)$$

$$= RT \ln f_i = RT \ln P_i \qquad (8.302)$$

analogous to Eqs. 7.607 and 7.609, where μ_i is the chemical potential at f_i, and μ_i° is the standard chemical potential at the standard fugacity $f_i^\circ = 1$ atm.

If a pure gas is condensed reversibly and isothermally, no change in free energy, i.e., change in its chemical potential, occurs. Hence $\mu_g - \mu_l = RT \ln f_g/f_l = 0$, where f_g is the fugacity of the gas in equilibrium with the liquid; the liquid fugacity f_l must then be equal to the fugacity of the equilibrium vapor. The fugacities in condensed phases are defined in this way.

If the liquid phase is a solution, the chemical potential of each component may still be represented by an equation of the form of Eq. 8.301, where f_i is now the fugacity of i in the liquid solution, μ_i is its chemical potential and f_i° is the fugacity of i in its chosen standard state; f_i° is usually not selected as unity. From the definition of activity, Eq. 7.510,

$$\mu_i = \mu_i^\circ + RT \ln a_i \qquad (8.303)$$

For liquid solutions f_i° is frequently chosen as the fugacity of the pure liquid; then $a_i = 1$ for the pure liquid. In such a case a_i for the ith component in a solution is the ratio of f_i to the fugacity of the pure liqid, f_i°. Since f_i° is not always chosen as the fugacity of the pure liquid, we will use the symbol $f_i^\square$ to designate this latter fugacity. In many cases f_i° will be set equal to $f_i^\square$; $f_i^\square$ will always have the same meaning, however, regardless of the choice for f_i°.

Ideal Solutions; Raoult's Law. The chemical potential in idealized solutions is related to the composition in a very simple way. A condensed phase *ideal solution*, whether liquid or solid, is a mixture which obeys Raoult's law. This law may be expressed in the form

$$f_i = X_i f_i^\square \qquad (8.304)$$

or if the vapors are ideal

$$P_i = X_i P_i^\square \qquad (8.305)$$

where $f_i^\square$ (or $P_i^\square$) is the fugacity (or pressure) pure component i would have if it were in the same state (e.g., liquid) under the same total P at the same T as the mixture. If the standard state for activity is taken as the pure liquid phase, then Raoult's law indicates that the activity may be taken as the mole fraction. In actual experiment a solvent is always observed to approach the behavior predicted by Raoult's law as the concentration of the solute approaches zero. If the actual fugacity in a real solution is larger than that predicted by Raoult's law, the solution is said to show *positive* deviation from ideal behavior; if f_i is less, the solution is said to show *negative* deviation. Positive deviations are frequently observed when dissimilar substances are mixed and may lead to immiscibility. Negative deviations occur when the molecules of the two components attract each other and may lead to intermediate compound formation. If Raoult's law can be applied, the chemical potential bears a simple relationship to the mole fraction

$$\mu_i = \mu_{i(f)}^\circ + RT \ln f_i = \mu_{i(f)}^\circ + RT \ln X_i + RT \ln f_i^\square$$

or we may define the standard state as unit mole fraction and let

$$\mu_{i(X)}^\circ = \mu_{i(f)}^\circ + RT \ln f_i^\square,$$

so that

$$\mu_i = \mu_{i(X)}^\circ + RT \ln X_i \qquad (8.306)$$

where the subscripts (f) and (X) indicate standard states of $f^\circ = 1$ and $X^\circ = 1$, respectively, and $f_i^\square$ is a constant at any given T and P. The theoretical basis for Raoult's law will be discussed in Chapter 12.

ILLUSTRATION.   The vapor pressure of pure 2-propanol at 24°C is 40 mm Hg. Assume vapor and liquid phases to be ideal.

(a) If the total pressure above liquid 2-propanol in a closed vessel is 1 atm, find the mole fraction of 2-propanol in the vapor phase.

(b) Find the fugacity of 2-propanol in a liquid solution of 50 grams 2-propanol and 50 grams n-propanol at 24°C.

(c) Find the activity of 2-propanol in the solution described in (b) if (1) pure liquid is taken as the standard state, (2) $f^\circ = 1$ atm.

(d) Find the change in chemical potential of 2-propanol when solution (b) is made from the pure components.

The answers are as follows:

(a) From Eq. 8.305, $X = 40/760$.

(b) Since the molecular weights of 2-propanol and n-propanol are the same, $X_{2\text{-prop}} = 0.5$. Since the solution is ideal, $f_i = X_i f_i^\square = 20$ mm.

(c) (1) Activity = mole fraction; hence $a = 0.5$. (2) Since $a = f_i/f_i^\circ$, $a = 20/760$.

(d) From Eq. 8.306 $\mu - \mu^\circ = RT \ln 0.5 = -(1.987)(297.2)(2.303)(0.301)$ cal mole^{-1}.

Pressure-Composition Relations for an Ideal Solution.   With Eqs. 8.305 and 8.306 it is relatively easy to make a quantitative prediction of the behavior of phase equilibrium situations between ideal mixtures in terms of the properties of the pure components. We consider the behavior of a two-component system. A condensed ideal mixture obeys Raoult's law, and if the vapors behave as perfect gases,

$$P_t = P_1 + P_2 = X_1 P_1^\square + X_2 P_2^\square \tag{8.307}$$

where $P_1^\square$ and $P_2^\square$ are the vapor pressures of the pure components at the given temperature, and the mole fractions represent the composition of the condensed phase. This behavior is illustrated in Fig. 8.301. The composition of the vapor may also be derived by combining Dalton's law with Raoult's law. Let $P_1 = X_1' P_t$, where X_1' represents the composition of the vapor phase in equilibrium with the

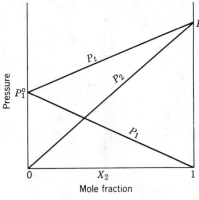

Fig. 8.301 Composition-pressure relationship for a system which follows
Raoult's law.

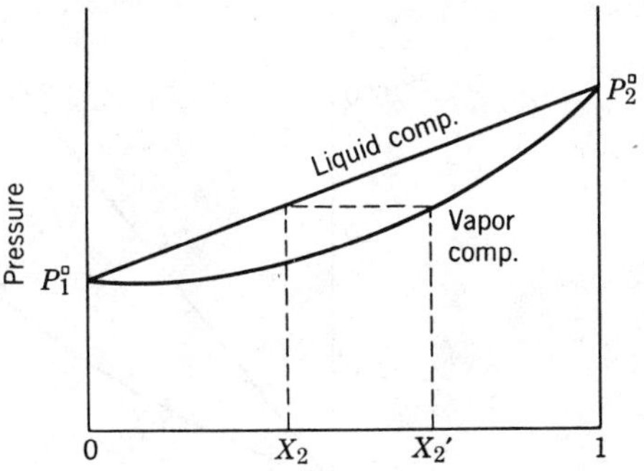

Fig. 8.302 Liquid-vapor composition
relationship for an ideal solution.

condensed phase. The following relationship may be derived for the vapor composition (only component 1 and 2 in system):

$$P_t = \frac{P_1^\square P_2^\square}{P_1^\square - X_1'(P_1^\square - P_2^\square)} \tag{8.308}$$

It may be shown that the vapor phase is always richer in the more volatile component. If the pure two components have the same vapor pressures, the vapor and liquid compositions will be identical over the whole composition range.

The vapor-liquid composition relationship is illustrated schematically in Fig. 8.302. The intersection of any horizontal line with the two curves (the line corresponds to a particular total pressure) gives the composition of the phases in equilibrium. An example of a real system which closely approaches ideal behavior is shown in Fig. 8.303.

Thermodynamic Properties of Ideal Solutions. Raoult's law leads to simple expressions for the thermodynamic properties of a mixture relative to those of the pure components. The free energy of formation of an ideal solution from the pure components is obtained by summing the change in chemical potentials of the constituents. In the solution the chemical potential is given by Eq. 8.306 and that

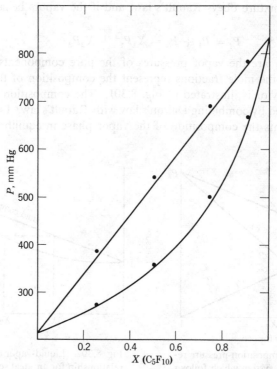

Fig. 8.303   Comparison of experimental data of M. M. Newcome and G. H. Cady (solid points) with ideal solubility curves (solid lines) for the *cyclo*-C_5F_{10}, *n*-C_6F_{14} system at 25°C [data from *J. Am. Chem. Soc.*, **78**, 5216 (1956)].   The system is remarkably close to ideal in its behavior.

of the pure liquid is $\mu_{i(X)}^{\circ}$; hence for an ideal mixture, formed at constant temperature and pressure

$$\Delta F_{\text{mixing}} = \sum_i n_i RT \ln X_i = \sum_i n_i(\mu_{i(X)} - \mu_{i(X)}^{\circ}) \tag{8.309}$$

The negative value of ΔF_{mixing} shows that we may expect two or more components to mix spontaneously if they form an ideal solution.   It may also be seen from Eq. 8.309 that Raoult's law predicts no change in enthalpy on forming an ideal mixture

$$\left(\frac{\partial \frac{\Delta F_{\text{mix}}}{T}}{\partial \frac{1}{T}} \right)_{P, X_i} = \Delta H_{\text{mix}} = 0 \tag{8.310}$$

Hence the entropy change for ideal mixing is

$$\Delta S_{\text{mix}} = -R \sum_i n_i \ln X_i \tag{8.311}$$

ILLUSTRATION. The vapor pressure of heptane at 42°C is 102 mm Hg. The vapor pressure of 2-methyl pentane at 42°C is 405 mm.

(a) Calculate the total pressure above a binary liquid mixture at 42°C containing 10 grams of each of these two components.

(b) Find the mole fraction of heptane in the vapor phase.

(c) Find the free energy of mixing when this solution is formed from the pure components.

The answers are:

(a) Molecular weight of heptane $= 100$, of 2-methyl pentane $= 86$; therefore

$$X_h = \frac{10/100}{10/100 + 10/86} \; ; \quad X_{2mp} = \frac{10/86}{10/86 + 10/100}$$

From Raoult's law

$$P_t = X_h(102) + X_{2mp}(405) \text{ mm Hg}$$

(b) Applying Eq. 8.308,

$$P_t = \frac{(102)(405)}{102 - X'_h(102 - 405)}$$

Solve for $X'_h =$ mole fraction of heptane in vapor phase.

(c) From the expression for the free energy of mixing

$$\Delta F = \frac{10}{100} RT \ln X_h + \frac{10}{86} RT \ln X_{2mp}$$

Colligative Properties in Two-Component Systems. From the behavior of chemical potential we may predict the so-called colligative properties of solutions: the freezing point, boiling point, solvent vapor pressure, and osmotic pressure.

Boiling Point Equilibria. Consider the simple case of a solution of a nonvolatile solute. The chemical potential of the solvent in the vapor phase must be equal to that in the liquid solution when the two phases are in equilibrium. Thus

$$\mu_1(g) = \mu_1(l) = \mu_1^\circ(l) + RT \ln a_1 \tag{8.312}$$

where

$$a_1 = \frac{f_1(l)}{f_1^\circ(l)}$$

with the solvent represented as component 1. On dividing Eq. 8.312 by T and differentiating with respect to temperature, we obtain, at fixed P,

$$\frac{d[\mu_1(g)/T]}{dT} - \frac{d[\mu_1^\circ(l)/T]}{dT} = \frac{R \, d \ln a_1}{dT} \tag{8.313}$$

At the normal boiling point, $\mu_1(g) = \mu_1^\circ(g)$, since $f = 1$ atm if vapor is assumed a perfect gas. Since $\mu_1^\circ(g)$ now refers to the chemical potential of the pure gas, and $\mu_1^\circ(l)$ to pure liquid, the two terms on the left, according to Eq. 7.418, are $-\bar{H}_1^\circ(g)/T^2$ and $-\bar{H}_1^\circ(l)/T^2$, respectively, and we may write

$$\frac{\bar{H}_1^\circ(l) - \bar{H}_1^\circ(g)}{T^2} = \frac{R\, d \ln a_1}{dT} = \frac{-\Delta \bar{H}_{1\,\text{vap}}^\circ}{T^2} \tag{8.314}$$

If the solution is assumed ideal, the activity may be replaced by the mole fraction; furthermore, over a small temperature interval the enthalpy of vaporization may be assumed independent of temperature. Under these conditions, Eq. 8.314 integrates to the limiting form

$$\ln X_1 = \frac{\Delta \bar{H}_{1\,\text{vap}}^\circ}{R}\left(\frac{1}{T} - \frac{1}{T_0}\right) \tag{8.315}$$

in which T_0 is the normal boiling point of the pure solvent; X_1 is unity for equilibrium at T_0 and hence $\ln X_1$ is zero for this limit.

Since the solvent is found to conform to Raoult's law in very dilute solutions, Eq. 8.315 can actually be used when X_2 is small. As X_1 approaches unity, $\ln X_1$ may be replaced by $(X_1 - 1) = -X_2$, as seen by the series form

$$\ln x = (x - 1) - \frac{(x-1)^2}{2} + \frac{(x-1)^3}{3} + \cdots$$

valid when $2 > x > 0$. Thus, as $X_2 \to 0$, Eq. 8.315 assumes the limiting form

$$X_2 = \frac{\Delta \bar{H}_{1\,\text{vap}}^\circ \theta_b}{RT_0^2} \tag{8.316}$$

where TT_0 has been replaced by T_0^2, and $T - T_0$, the boiling point elevation, has been indicated by θ_b. Thus a measured value of θ_b directly indicates the mole fraction of solute. It is customary to define a boiling-point-rise constant characteristic of the solvent in terms of the effect to be expected for a solution of given molal concentration. Equation 8.316 may be changed to the form

$$m = \frac{1000\,\Delta \bar{H}_{1\,\text{vap}}^\circ}{RT_0^2 M_1}\,\theta_b \tag{8.317}$$

or $\theta_b = \lambda_b m$, where λ_b is the molal boiling point constant,

$$\lambda_b = \frac{RT_0^2 M_1}{1000\,\Delta \bar{H}_{1\,\text{vap}}^\circ}$$

and where m is the molal concentration of the solute, and M_1 the molecular weight of the solvent. The rise in boiling point depends not on the nature of the solute in the very dilute concentration range but only on its concentration. Thus measurement of the boiling point rise produced by a known weight of solute in a given amount of solvent provides information about the molecular weight of the solute. It should be emphasized that Eq. 8.313 is valid for all real solutions, whereas the subsequent equations involve the stated assumptions which limit their applicability for nonideal solutions to the very dilute range. Table 8.301 gives values of λ_b for several solvents.

Table 8.301 *Freezing and Boiling Point Constants*

Substance	λ_f (fp, °C)	λ_b (bp, °C)
Acetic acid	3.90 (17)	2.93 (118)
Benzene	5.1 (5.6)	2.64 (80.2)
Camphor	40.0 (180)	...
Ethanol	...	1.23 (78.3)
Naphthalene	6.8 (80)	...
Toluene	...	3.37 (110.6)
Water	1.86 (0)	0.514 (100)

Vapor Pressure Equilibria. Solvent vapor pressures may be predicted at any temperature. In the dilute range, Raoult's law leads to the result

$$P_1 = X_1 P_1^{\square} = (1 - X_2) P_1^{\square}$$

Hence the vapor pressure lowering is $P_1^{\square} - P_1 = X_2 P_1^{\square}$; the fractional lowering is directly proportional to the mole fraction of the solute

$$X_2 = \frac{P_1^{\square} - P_1}{P_1^{\square}} = \frac{\Delta P_1}{P_1^{\square}} \tag{8.318}$$

where ΔP_1 is the amount by which the vapor pressure is reduced. The vapor pressure lowering can be related to the molal concentration if desired. The variation of $P_1^{\square}$ with T is presumed known from solvent vapor pressure data, so Eq. 8.318 may be used at any temperature.

A schematic diagram, similar to Fig. 8.101, is useful in visualizing the behavior of the chemical potentials in solution relative to equilibrium characteristics, as shown in Fig. 8.304. When a solute is added to the liquid phase, the chemical potential at a given temperature is reduced (Eq. 8.303) because a_i, which is based on X_i, is less than unity in the solution. Hence, for equilibrium between the vapor and the liquid, the chemical potential of the vapor must also be reduced, corresponding to a reduction of its pressure, until the two curves intersect. The amount by which the vapor pressure must be reduced is calculated by Eq. 8.318.

Freezing Point Equilibria. Freezing point equilibria may be considered in the same way as the boiling point case. We will consider only the case in which the solid separating is component 1, pure solid solvent. When pure solid solvent is in equilibrium with a liquid solution the solution is at its freezing point, the chemical potentials of the solvent must be identical in the two phases, and hence

$$\mu_1^\circ(s) = \mu_1(l) = \mu_1^\circ(l) + RT \ln a_1 \tag{8.319}$$

Differentiation of this expression with respect to temperature leads to the relationship, at fixed P,

$$\frac{d \ln a_1}{dT} = \frac{\Delta \bar{H}_{1\,\text{fus}}^{\circ}}{RT^2} \tag{8.320}$$

where $\Delta \bar{H}_{1\,\text{fus}}^{\circ}$ is $\bar{H}_1^{\circ}(l) - \bar{H}_1^{\circ}(s)$, the enthalpy of fusion of pure solvents. On applying Raoult's law for the solvent (in very dilute solution) and assuming the heat of

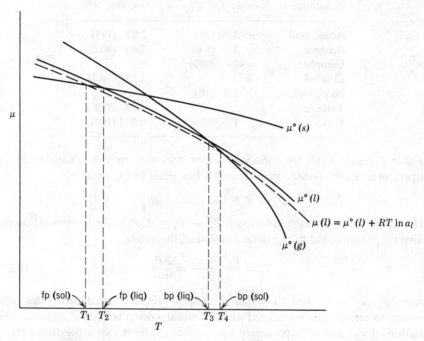

Fig. 8.304 Schematic representation of relationship of chemical potentials of a given substance: as a pure solid (under 1 atm) $\mu^{\circ}(s)$; as a pure liquid (under 1 atm) $\mu^{\circ}(l)$; as a gas (ideal) at 1 atm, $\mu^{\circ}(g)$; and in a liquid solution in which a_l is its activity, $\mu(l)$. It may be seen that the freezing point of the solution $[\mu^{\circ}(s) = \mu(l)]$ at T_1 lies below that of the pure liquid $[\mu^{\circ}(s) = \mu^{\circ}(l)]$ at T_2; and the normal boiling point of the pure liquid $[\mu^{\circ}(l) = \mu^{\circ}(g)]$ at T_3 lies below that of the solution $[\mu(l) = \mu^{\circ}(g)]$ at T_4.

fusion constant over the small temperature interval near the melting point, Eq. 8.320 may be integrated to

$$\ln X_1 = \frac{-\Delta \bar{H}_{1\,\text{fus}}^{\circ}}{R} \left(\frac{1}{T} - \frac{1}{T_0} \right) \tag{8.321}$$

where T_0 is the melting point of pure solvent. Again, this may be changed to the form

$$X_2 = \frac{\Delta \bar{H}_{1\,\text{fus}}^{\circ} \theta_f}{RT_0^2}$$

where θ_f is now $T_0 - T$, the freezing point lowering, and $T_0^2 \cong TT_0$.

In terms of molal concentration units m,

$$\theta_f = \left(\frac{RT_0^2 M_1}{1000\,\Delta\bar{H}_{1\,\text{fus}}^\circ}\right) m = \lambda_f m \qquad (8.322)$$

The approximations in deriving Eq. 8.322 are similar to those for Eq. 8.317. The constant term in parentheses in Eq. 8.322 may be evaluated for a given solvent to give the molal freezing-point-lowering constant λ_f, again independent of the nature of the solute. Equation 8.322 has received wide use for the determination of the molecular weight of dissolved substances. Very careful measurements of the freezing point are required, however, and the simplified form of Eq. 8.322 applies only at very low concentrations for which the freezing point depression is small.

ILLUSTRATION. Calculate the value of the freezing-point-lowering constant, λ_f, for water, given $\Delta H_{\text{fus}} = 79.7$ cal g^{-1} at T_0, 273.2°K.

$$\lambda_f = \frac{RT_0^2 M_1}{1000\,\Delta\bar{H}_{1\,\text{fus}}^\circ} = \frac{(1.987)(273.2)^2(18)}{(1000)(18)(79.7)} = 1.86 \text{ deg molal}^{-1}$$

Osmotic Equilibrium. Osmotic equilibrium may also be explained in a relatively simple manner. If a solution is separated from the pure solvent by a semi-

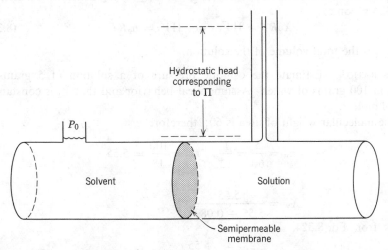

Fig. 8.305 Schematic representation of an osmotic pressure apparatus. For an actual experimental set-up see, for example, B. H. Zimm and I. Myerson, *J. Am. Chem. Soc.*, **68**, 911 (1946); or R. H. Wagner in A. Weissberger, Editor, *Technique of Organic Chemistry*, Third Edition, Interscience Publishers, New York, 1959.

permeable wall (Fig. 8.305) which permits passage only of solvent, equilibrium may be established by application of pressure to the solution so as to make the chemical potential of the solvent the same in the solution as for the pure liquid. If the solution and solvent are maintained at the same temperature, then the necessary increase in total pressure on the solution side can be calculated from the relationship

$$\mu_1 = \mu_1^\circ + RT \ln a_1 + \int_{P_0}^{P} \bar{V}_1 \, dP = \mu_1^\circ$$

which may be understood as follows. $\bar{V}_1$ represents the partial molar volume of the solvent in the solution (Eq. 7.613). The variation of the chemical potential with pressure is given by $d\mu_1 = \bar{V}_1 \, dP$ (Eq. 7.615) at constant temperature. Hence, for osmotic equilibrium, it is necessary that

$$-RT \ln a_1 = \int_{P_0}^{P} \bar{V}_1 \, dP \qquad (8.323)$$

This relation takes a particularly simple form for an ideal solution, or for a real solution in the dilute region where Raoult's law applies. For such a case, $\bar{V}_1$ may be set equal to the molar volume of the pure solvent, and $a_1 = X_1$. If it is assumed that the compressibility of the liquid is negligible i.e., that $\bar{V}$ remains constant with applied pressure, Eq. 8.323 then becomes

$$-RT \ln X_1 = \bar{V}_1(P - P_0) \qquad (8.324)$$

where P_0 is the pressure on the pure solvent side. $P - P_0$ may be called the osmotic pressure, Π. In the very dilute range, $\ln X_1 \cong -X_2$, as shown earlier, and Eq. 8.324 becomes

$$X_2 RT = \Pi \bar{V}_1 \quad \text{or} \quad \Pi V_t = n_2 RT \qquad (8.325)$$

where V_t is the total volume of the solution.

ILLUSTRATION.   Estimate the osmotic pressure of a solution of 5 grams of urea in 100 grams of water. Assume ideal behavior and that $\bar{V}_1$ is constant at 18 ml mole^{-1}.

The molecular weight of urea is 60; therefore

$$n_u = \frac{5}{60} = \frac{1}{12}, \quad n_w = \frac{100}{18} = 5.55$$

and

$$X_w = \frac{5.55}{5.55 + 0.083}$$

Thus, from Eq. 8.324,

$$-RT \ln \frac{5.55}{5.55 + 0.083} = 18\Pi$$

Solve for Π.

Equation 8.325 involves an additional approximation which is not necessary; the student may see if use of this equation introduces significant error.

Equations 8.323, 8.324, and 8.325 show that osmotic pressures become very large even for solutions of moderate concentration. For example, a 0.1m (molal) solution of sucrose has an osmotic pressure of 2.47 atm. Osmotic pressure is an important factor in the ability of large trees to draw water to great heights; the osmotic pressure is limited in a practical sense by the strength of the cell walls and the rate at which osmotic equilibrium can be approached. Osmotic pressure is of great significance in biological systems.

Remarks. Any of the colligative properties can be used to obtain molecular weight information about the solute. In rigorous form, the equations based on activity, e.g., Eqs. 8.314, 8.320, and 8.323, constitute important methods for determination of the actual activity of the solvent in the solution. Detailed discussion of the methods for handling these equations in integrated form can be found in reference books on this important subject. We cannot describe the procedures fully here but will point out an additional important relationship, called the Gibbs-Duhem equation, which involves the chemical potential.

Gibbs-Duhem Equation. The Gibbs-Duhem equation provides a basis for calculating the activity of the solute from the activity of the solvent in a binary solution. It has been shown that for a constant temperature and pressure the total free energy of a homogeneous phase may be expressed as

$$F_{T,P} = \sum_i n_i \mu_i \tag{7.606}$$

In particular, for a binary mixture, we have

$$F_{T,P} = n_1 \mu_1 + n_2 \mu_2$$

Differentiation of this relationship leads to

$$dF_{T,P} = \mu_1 \, dn_1 + \mu_2 \, dn_2 + n_1 \, d\mu_1 + n_2 \, d\mu_2$$

If this equation is compared with Eq. 7.602 at constant T and P,

$$dF_{T,P} = \mu_1 \, dn_1 + \mu_2 \, dn_2$$

it follows that Eq. 8.326 must be valid

$$(n_1 \, d\mu_1 + n_2 \, d\mu_2 = 0)_{T,P} \tag{8.326}$$

This is known as the Gibbs-Duhem relation. In general form

$$\sum_i (n_i \, d\mu_i)_{T,P} = 0 \tag{8.327}$$

Equation 8.327 is a useful relationship; two applications will be mentioned briefly.

Since $d\mu_i = RT \, d\ln a_i$, we may write Eq. 8.326 in the following forms for binary mixtures at constant T and P:

$$n_1 \, d\ln a_1 + n_2 \, d\ln a_2 = 0$$

or, dividing by the total number of moles,

$$X_1 \, d\ln a_1 + X_2 \, d\ln a_2 = 0 \tag{8.328}$$

Hence

$$d\ln a_2 = -\frac{X_1}{X_2} d\ln a_1 \tag{8.329}$$

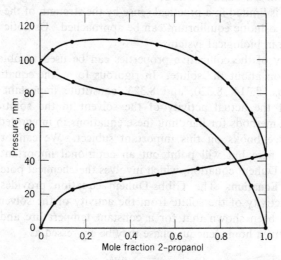

Fig. 8.306   Partial and total vapor pressures for the system 2-propanol-benzene at 25°C. Points are experimental (A. L. Olsen and E. R. Washburn, *J. Phys. Chem.*, **41**, 457 (1937). Curves are calculated, using the Gibbs-Duhem equation, by S. D. Christian, *J. Chem. Ed.*, **39**, 523 (1962), and figure is taken therefrom with permission.

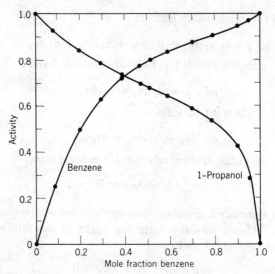

Fig. 8.307   Activity as a function of mole fraction for the system benzene-1-propanol at 45°C. Points are experimental (I. Brown and F. Smith, *Aust. J. Chem.*, **12**, 407 (1957). Curves are calculated by S. D. Christian, *J. Chem. Ed.*, **39**, 523 (1962), and figure is taken therefrom by permission.

If a_1 has been determined as a function of concentration by study of colligative properties, for example, then by a suitable integration procedure, values of a_2 may also be obtained from Eq. 8.329 (see Figs. 8.306 and 8.307).

A second application takes the form of the Duhem-Margules equation.

Duhem-Margules Equation and Henry's Law.   Equation 8.328 may be expressed in a derivative form, T and P constant

$$X_1 \frac{d \ln a_1}{dX_1} + X_2 \frac{d \ln a_2}{dX_1} = 0$$

or

$$X_1 \frac{d \ln a_1}{dX_1} = X_2 \frac{d \ln a_2}{dX_2}, \quad \text{since } dX_1 = -dX_2$$

or

$$\left(\frac{\partial \ln a_1}{\partial \ln X_1} \right)_{T,P} = \left(\frac{\partial \ln a_2}{\partial \ln X_2} \right)_{T,P} \tag{8.330}$$

or, alternatively,

$$\left(\frac{\partial \ln f_1}{\partial \ln X_1} \right)_{T,P} = \left(\frac{\partial \ln f_2}{\partial \ln X_2} \right)_{T,P} \tag{8.331}$$

Equation 8.330, or 8.331, is known as the Duhem-Margules equation. These two equations apply under constant temperature and pressure conditions. However, no assumptions, such as ideal solutions, have been made in their development. If a real solution is studied in the composition range where Raoult's law applies for the solvent, then the left-hand side of Eq. 8.330 is unity. Hence, the right-hand side must also be unity under these conditions, that is, it is necessary that

$$f_2 = k_2 X_2 \tag{8.332}$$

where k_2 is a constant at a particular T and P. However, nothing requires k_2 to be related to the fugacity of the pure solute in any known way, so Eq. 8.332 is not necessarily Raoult's law but is a more general form called Henry's law. Henry's law is frequently presented as an empirical rule that the solubility of gases in very dilute solutions is proportional to the gas pressure above the solution, $P_2 = k_2 X_2$ where k_2 is called the Henry's law constant. A comparison of Raoult law and Henry law behavior for Br_2 in CCl_4 is shown in Fig. 8.308.

We cannot expect Henry's law to be valid unless the concentration of solute is very small. If a gas were to form an ideal solution with the solvent, then Henry's law constant, k_2, would be the same as the Raoult law constant, $f_2^\square$. The latter is the fugacity (approximately the vapor pressure) which the pure solute in the liquid form would have at the temperature of interest. From this we may see the reason for the ideal solution rule that the solubility of a series of similar gases at a fixed pressure increases as their normal boiling points increase, i.e., as $f_2^\square$ decreases. Furthermore, the ideal solubility of a given gas at a constant pressure decreases as T increases ($f_2^\square$ increases as T increases). The variation of ideal solubility with temperature may be predicted with Eq. 8.315. We may simply replace subscript 1 by 2. The same result is obtained if Raoult's law is applied directly at each temperature. These are ideal solution rules and are a poor approximation for gases dissolving in solvents with which they interact strongly, such as NH_3 in water.

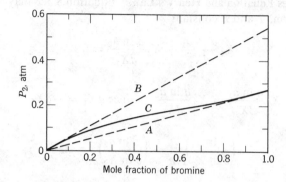

Fig. 8.308   Vapor pressure of bromine above carbon tetrachloride solutions (by permission from Lewis, Randall, Pitzer, and Brewer, *Thermodynamics*, Second Edition, McGraw-Hill Book Co., New York, 1961). The line labeled B represents Henry's law behavior (the slope 0.54 is Henry's law constant). The line labeled A is Raoult's law behavior, $p_2^{\square} = 0.28$ ($t \approx 25°C$). The actual vapor pressures follow line C. The activity of CCl_4 in these mixtures can be calculated with the aid of the Gibbs-Duhem relation.

A somewhat similar generalization may be made about the solubility of solids in liquids. For an ideal solution, Eq. 8.321 for solvent takes the same form for the solute, e.g.,

$$\ln X_2 = \frac{-\Delta \bar{H}_{2\,(\text{fus})}}{R} \left(\frac{1}{T} - \frac{1}{T_0} \right) \tag{8.333}$$

If the melting point T_0 of the pure solute is high, then its ideal solubility X_2 tends to be low, and vice versa.

A similar discussion is not applicable to ideal liquid solutions. On an ideal basis, substances which are both liquids at the temperature of interest will be completely miscible; no two-phase solubility equilibrium exists.

Ideal solution relationships closely approximate the behavior of real systems only for mixtures of chemically similar substances and in practice may be applied to the solvent when the solute is at low concentrations. The equations in which activity has been used have general validity; if we are interested in predicting actual amounts of solute dissolved at equilibrium, we must determine the relationship of activity to concentration.

Henry's law shows that the activity of the solute may be set proportional to the concentration in the very dilute range, where f_2 is proportional to concentration. This assumption will frequently be made in the study of equilibria in dilute solutions.

Problems

8.301   At 42°C the vapor pressure of hexane is 300 mm Hg and of heptane is 100 mm Hg. A particular mixture of the two substances has a total vapor pressure of 200 mm. Calculate the composition of the liquid and vapor phases if the mixture is assumed ideal.

8.302   Calculate the total change in free energy when 1 mole of liquid hexane is mixed with sufficient heptane to form the liquid mixture described in Problem 8.301.

8.303   The normal boiling point of ethyl bromide is 38.4°C. Predict the ideal solubility of C_2H_5Br in a liquid at 38.4°C when the partial pressure of C_2H_5Br above the solution is 100 mm Hg.

8.304   The vapor pressure of pure C_2H_5Br at 20°C is 387.0 mm Hg. Predict the ideal solubility of C_2H_5Br at 20°C when its partial pressure above the solution is 100 mm Hg.

8.305   Use the data in Problems 8.303 and 8.304 to predict the boiling point of a solution of a nonvolatile solute at 1.5 molal in C_2H_5Br as a solvent.

8.306   Assuming the heat of vaporization of water to be independent of temperature in the vicinity of 100°C (9720 cal $mole^{-1}$), calculate the activity of water relative to pure water as the standard state in a solution at its boiling point of 100.30°C (solute nonvolatile).

8.307   If the heat of fusion of water is 79.71 cal g^{-1}, calculate the temperature at which ice will begin to freeze from the solution described in Problem 8.306. Assume that the activity coefficient is independent of temperature.

8.308   Assuming the heat of fusion of camphor to be temperature independent and 1800 cal $mole^{-1}$ at its normal freezing point of 178°C, calculate the temperature at which pure solid camphor is in equilibrium with an ideal liquid solution in which the mole fraction of camphor is 0.95.

8.309   The chemical potential of water in a certain solution at 25°C is less than that of pure water by 100 cal. (a) What osmotic pressure is this solution capable of generating (assume $\bar{V}_1$ constant at 18 ml)? (b) What is the difference between the vapor pressure of water above this solution and that of pure water (23.76 mm)?

8.310   The heat of fusion of benzene is 30.3 cal g^{-1} at its normal freezing point of 5.6°C. A certain solution contains 0.64 gram of an organic substance in 50 grams of benzene and begins to freeze at 5.11°C. What is the molecular weight of the solute?

8.311   A certain dilute aqueous solution has a freezing point of -0.0372°C. Calculate the vapor pressure of water above this solution at 25°C ($P^{\square} = 23.76$). Calculate the osmotic pressure of this solution at 25°C. State any necessary assumptions. $\Delta \bar{H}_{fus}$ and $\bar{V}_1$ are to be assumed known.

8.312   The activity of water in a certain solution is 0.72. Calculate the osmotic pressure which this solution can develop at 25°C. Assume that $\bar{V}_1 = 18$ ml and is constant.

8.313   Estimate all the colligative properties of a $0.5m$ solution of sucrose in water (for vapor pressure and osmotic pressure, use 25°C). ΔH°_{fus} and ΔH°_{vap} are to be assumed given.

8.314   The melting point of naphthalene is 79.9°C, and its heat of fusion is 35.6 cal g^{-1}. Estimate the molal concentration of a saturated solution of naphthalene in benzene at 25°C.

Phase Diagrams for Two-Component Systems. We now summarize phase equilibrium behavior in two-component systems by presenting some representative phase diagrams. Only a sample of the many different effects observed can be given.

For a two-component system, the phase rule takes the form $\underline{F} = 4 - \underline{P}$. An invariant system has four phases in equilibrium; coexistence of three phases allows one independent variable; two phases allow two variables; and a single phase allows three variables, e.g., T, P, and composition. For simplicity, two-component phase diagrams are usually presented at constant pressure or constant temperature, so that a two-coordinate plot suffices. If one variable is held constant, the phase rule becomes $\underline{F} - 1 = 3 - \underline{P}$. An invariant point now corresponds to the intersection of three lines, just as in diagrams for one-component systems.

Solid-Liquid and Solid-Solid Equilibria. A thermodynamic explanation for the depression of the freezing point of a solution has been given in the preceding

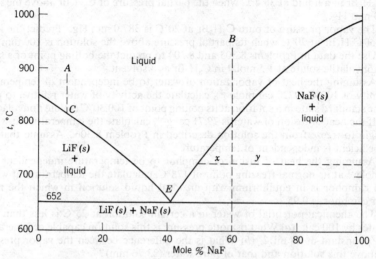

Fig. 8.309 System LiF-NaF, according to A. G. Bergman and E. P. Dergunov, *Compt. rend. acad. sci. U.S.S.R.*, **31**, 755 (1941). A simple eutectic; no intermediate compound formed; no solid solutions formed.

section. Figure 8.309 for the LiF-NaF system illustrates in the form of a phase diagram a simple kind of behavior. No intermediate compounds are formed. Pure solid LiF separates first when melts containing from 0 to 40 mole per cent NaF in LiF are cooled. Pure solid NaF separates first from melts containing from 40 to 100 mole per cent NaF. The initial freezing point for any given melt composition falls on the curved line(s) which limits the area marked "liquid." At a particular liquid composition and temperature corresponding to a point on this line, a two-phase equilibrium can exist between solid and liquid phases; the system is then monovariant (P is already constant). The liquid must have the indicated composition at each temperature when it is in equilibrium with the solid phase.

Tie Lines. When the system is at a temperature and overall composition which fall inside one of the areas marked "liquid + solid," it consists of an equilibrium mixture of two phases. For example, at 700°C and 20 mole per cent NaF overall, one has a mixture of pure solid LiF and a liquid containing about 33 mole per cent NaF (67 mole per cent LiF). A horizontal line drawn at the temperature in question, called a tie line, will intersect two lines. One point of intersection gives the composition of the liquid phase, and the other, the solid phase; in this example, the solid is a pure substance. A simple graphical method may be used to determine the relative amounts of the two equilibrium phases for a given total composition. For example, a tie line is drawn on Fig. 8.309 at 725°C; for a mixture of composition B, two phases, solid NaF and a liquid (50 mole per cent NaF), coexist at this temperature. The tie line is divided into two parts by the vertical line B. It may be verified that

$$\frac{\text{No. moles solid NaF}}{\text{No. moles of liquid}} = \frac{x}{y}$$

This principle may be applied to any two-phase area in any phase diagram.

ILLUSTRATION.   Show that, for a tie line divided as on Fig. 8.309,

$$\frac{x}{y} = \frac{\text{No. moles solid phase}}{\text{No. moles liquid phase}}$$

for a mixture of substances A and B, with the added feature that the solid separating may also be a solution. All percentages are mole percent here.

Let $y = \%$ B in solid phase $- \%$ B overall;
$\quad x = \%$ B overall $- \%$ B in liquid phase.
Then

$$\% \text{ B in solid} = \frac{\text{moles B in solid}}{\text{total moles solid}} = \frac{B_s}{m_s}$$

$$\% \text{ B in liquid} = \frac{\text{moles B in liquid}}{\text{total moles liquid}} = \frac{B_l}{m_l}$$

$$\% \text{ B overall} = \frac{B_s + B_l}{m_s + m_l}$$

Thus

$$\frac{x}{y} = \frac{\% \text{ B overall} - \% \text{ B in liquid}}{\% \text{ B in solid} - \% \text{ B overall}}$$

$$= \frac{\dfrac{B_s + B_l}{m_s + m_l} - \dfrac{B_l}{m_l}}{\dfrac{B_s}{m_s} - \dfrac{B_s + B_l}{m_s + m_l}} = \frac{B_s(m_l) - B_l(m_s)}{B_s(m_l) - B_l(m_s)} \left[\frac{m_s(m_s + m_l)}{m_l(m_s + m_l)} \right]$$

$$= \frac{m_s}{m_l}$$

Eutectic Point. The point of intersection E (Fig. 8.309) of the two curves defining the liquid region and the solid tie line is called the eutectic point (652°C, 40% NaF). A liquid of this composition freezes by forming two separate solid phases simultaneously, pure NaF and LiF. Hence, when the eutectic mixture freezes, three phases coexist in the system and the system is invariant. Changes in temperature or composition cannot occur until at least one of the phases disappears.

When any mixture with a phase diagram similar to that of Fig. 8.309 is cooled, the last drop of liquid to freeze will always have the eutectic composition; only at the eutectic point will the two solids separate simultaneously. Freezing at any other composition will result in separation of only one solid phase. The tie line drawn on the phase diagram at the eutectic temperature "ties" together the compositions of the various phases which may coexist at this temperature.

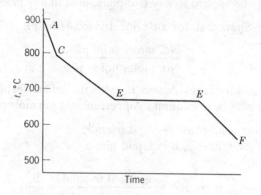

Fig. 8.310   Idealized cooling curve.

Cooling Curves. Experimental evidence for the lines drawn on the phase diagram can be obtained by analysis of the equilibrium phases; however, a much simpler method can be used if the diagram is not too complex and equilibria are established rapidly. A cooling curve gives the temperature as a function of time when the sample is cooled (usually a constant temperature gradient is maintained between the sample and its surroundings). The cooling curve for a mixture of LiF and NaF starting at point A, Fig. 8.309, might be expected to look something like that shown in Fig. 8.310. From A, the cooling rate is determined by the rate of heat transfer and the heat capacity of the liquid mixture. At C, the cooling rate changes because, when the temperature of the system is lowered further, some solid LiF separates and its heat of fusion must also be conducted away. A change in slope will be observed at this point which defines its position on Fig. 8.309. This is not an invariant point, however, and the freezing point of the solution drops continuously as LiF is removed. Cooling at the new rate will continue until the eutectic point is reached. At the eutectic, E, NaF also begins to separate and the fall in temperature will stop until all the liquid phase solidifies. The temperature between E and F will drop at a different rate, related now to the heat capacity of the solid mixture. Thus, the cooling curve for this particular mixture indicates the temperature C at which solid first begins to separate and the temperature E of the eutectic point. By observing cooling curves at composition intervals across the diagram, we may establish the dependence of the initial freezing point as a function of composition. If the eutectic stop temperature is the same for all mixtures, then the phases separating are pure substances. In more complex diagrams to be discussed later, cooling curves take different shapes and, unless equilibrium is established rapidly, may not give sufficient information to define the diagram accurately.

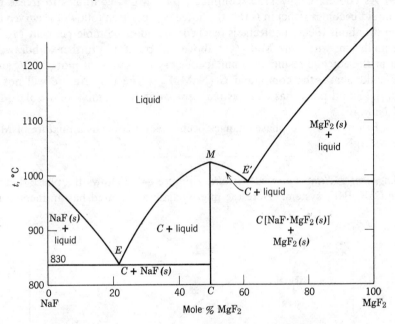

Fig. 8.311   System NaF-MgF$_2$, according to A. G. Bergman and E. P. Dergunov, *Compt. rend. acad. sci. U.S.S.R.*, **31**, 755 (1941), illustrating formation of an intermediate compound. Two simple eutectics; no solid solutions.

Congruent Melting Compound. Figure 8.311 shows the appearance of the phase diagram when the two pure substances form an intermediate compound with a congruent melting point M, where the solid compound melts to form a liquid phase which has the same composition as the solid. In the NaF-MgF$_2$ system, the intermediate compound has the formula NaMgF$_3$. Two eutectic points are observed, E between NaF and NaMgF$_3$, and E' between NaMgF$_3$ and MgF$_2$. If the diagram is divided at the composition of the compound, each half is similar to Fig. 8.309 and the interpretation in each of these halves is similar to that described for Fig. 8.309. If a liquid containing exactly 50 mole per cent NaF is cooled, the solid phase obtained will be NaMgF$_3$ and complete solidification will occur at the melting point of the compound, indicated by the position M in the liquid composition curve. The student may predict the nature of the equilibrium phases coexisting when various melts are cooled in this and in subsequent phase diagrams.

ILLUSTRATION. Describe the phase changes encountered when a mixture of composition 80 per cent MgF_2 and 20 per cent NaF is cooled slowly from 1200 to 750°C.

(a) There is a single uniform liquid phase until T reaches about 1135°C, when pure solid MgF_2 begins to freeze out.

(b) As cooling below 1135° continues, pure MgF_2 continues to freeze out; the liquid becomes richer in NaF; the liquid composition follows the curved line.

(c) At about 1000°, a eutectic is reached; liquid $\approx$ 65 mole per cent MgF_2 is in equilibrium with pure MgF_2 just above this point, but further withdrawal of heat at the eutectic results in simultaneous crystallization of more MgF_2 and a new solid phase, the compound C ($NaMgF_3$). The temperature will not fall until the liquid phase has disappeared, separating into a mixture of solid MgF_2 and $NaMgF_3$.

(d) Below 1000°, no phase changes occur. Solid cools as a mixture of MgF_2 and $NaMgF_3$.

Incongruent Melting Point; Peritectic. Figure 8.312 shows the phase diagram for the CaF_2-BeF_2 system. Here the intermediate compound has an incongruent

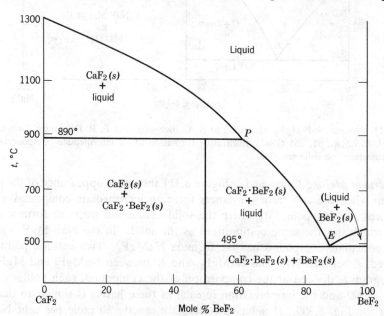

Fig. 8.312 CaF_2-BeF_2 system. The compound $CaF_2 \cdot BeF_2$ is unstable at temperatures above 890°C; it is said to have an incongruent melting point. [According to Counts, Roy, and Osborn, *J. Am. Ceram. Soc.*, **36**, 12 (1953).]

melting point; that is, when melting occurs, the liquid has a composition different from that of the compound and a new solid phase is also formed. At 890°, $CaBeF_4$ melts by the following process

$$CaBeF_4(s) \underset{\text{freezing}}{\overset{\text{melting}}{\rightleftharpoons}} CaF_2(s) + \text{liquid (40 mole \% } CaF_2, \text{ 60 mole \% } BeF_2)$$

Hence, during this transition, we have three different phases in equilibrium and the system is at an invariant point. This equilibrium point (tie line drawn at 890°, liquid composition at point P) is called a peritectic, and the melting reaction (or reverse on freezing) is called the peritectic reaction.

ILLUSTRATION. Describe the changes which occur on cooling or heating mixtures of BeF_2 and CaF_2.

If melts containing less than 50 mole per cent BeF_2 are cooled, Fig. 8.312, freezing will first form CaF_2. As cooling continues, the peritectic freezing reaction will begin at point P. In this case, all the liquid will freeze to a mixture of solid CaF_2 and $CaBeF_4$ at P. If the original melt contains exactly 50 per cent CaF_2, then CaF_2 and liquid will disappear simultaneously at P and the remaining solid will be pure $CaBeF_4$. If the original melt contains from 50 to 60% BeF_2, all the $CaF_2(s)$ will be consumed in the peritectic reaction and further cooling will result in an equilibrium between $CaBeF_4$ and liquid. This equilibrium, with gradually changing liquid composition, will continue down to the eutectic point E, where an invariant point will be observed as pure BeF_2 begins to separate.

These changes are simply reversed when solid mixtures are heated.

Solid Solutions. Figure 8.313 illustrates the appearance of the phase diagram when the solids crystallize as solid solutions, that is, as uniform solid phases of two or more components. A solid solution is a single phase; it is homogeneous. As melts containing less than about 33 mole per cent MgF_2 are cooled, a solid solution separates which is richer in LiF than the liquid phase with which it is in equilibrium. The composition of the solid phase is indicated by drawing a tie line at the temperature of interest; its point of intersection with the *solidus* line AB (which defines the limiting composition observed for the solid phase) indicates the composition of the solid solution, and the other end, the composition of the equilibrium liquid phase. A similar behavior is observed on the MgF_2-rich side. No solid solution can be formed with composition between approximately 30 and 40 mole per cent MgF_2. At the eutectic point E, equilibrium exists between two different solid solutions, one with about 30 mole per cent and the other with about 40 mole per cent MgF_2, and a liquid phase with about 33 mole per cent MgF_2. Since three phases are in equilibrium, this will be an invariant point. After the liquid has completely solidified, the solids may be cooled. In this case the composition of the solid phases changes rapidly with temperature; the compositions are defined at each temperature by the intersection of a tie line CD through the two-solid-phase area with the composition boundary. By the time the temperature

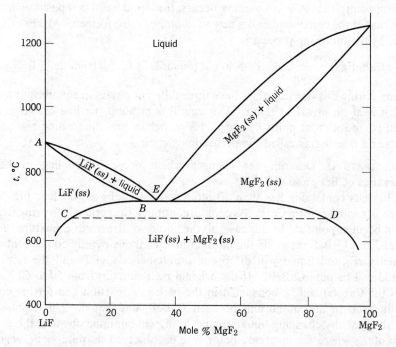

Fig. 8.313   LiF-MgF$_2$ system, showing single eutectic and limited solid solution formation [according to Counts, Roy, and Osborn, *J. Am. Ceram. Soc.*, **36**, 15 (1953)]. LiF(*ss*) represents a solid solution of MgF$_2$ in LiF; its composition can vary from 0 to ~35 mole % MgF$_2$. Similarly MgF$_2$(*ss*) is a solid solution.

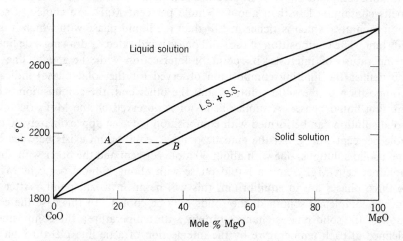

Fig. 8.314   CoO-MgO system. Complete miscibility in solid and liquid phases. [According to H. V. Wartenburg and E. Prophet, *Z. anorg. allgem. Chem.*, **208**, 379 (1932).]

falls to 600°C the LiF phase contains only about 3 mole per cent MgF_2 and the MgF_2 phase only about 6 mole per cent LiF.

In Fig. 8.314, the two components form a complete series of liquid and solid solutions. The solid phase has a different composition from that of the liquid; the compositions of the two mixtures which coexist in equilibrium are indicated by the intersection of the tie line, e.g., *AB*, at any temperature with the curves shown. Addition of MgO to CoO raises the melting point of the latter. The appearance of this diagram suggests that both liquid and solid solutions are not far from ideal

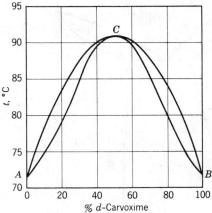

Fig. 8.315 The *d*- and *l*-carvoxime system (by permission from F. H. MacDougall, *Thermodynamics and Chemistry*, John Wiley and Sons, New York, 1939).

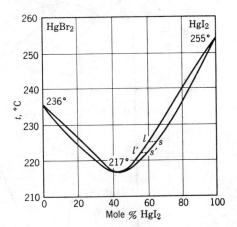

Fig. 8.316 The $HgBr_2$-HgI_2 system (by permission from F. H. MacDougall, *Thermodynamics and Chemistry*, John Wiley and Sons, New York, 1939).

in character, that is, the activity of each component in both phases is nearly proportional to its mole fraction. In some cases, deviation from ideal behavior may be so pronounced as to result in a maximum or a minimum in the melting point curve. The diagram will then look like that illustrated in Fig. 8.315 or 8.316. In these examples the melting points of the two pure components are quite close and any appreciable nonideality in solutions of the two will lead to a maximum or minimum. A thermodynamic proof will be given later to show why the two phases must have the same composition at the maximum or minimum of the curve.

Such a maximum or minimum might be expected if the two components form an intermediate compound. However, the maximum or minimum itself is not proof of the existence of such a compound. If the composition at which the maximum occurs is independent of pressure, then it is probably associated with a compound. Such a test would require very large pressure changes to be meaningful in the freezing point case and is usually not applied. The pressure test is useful in the study of vapor-liquid mixtures; for the solid-state problem, an X-ray examination of the crystal structure provides more reliable evidence.

ILLUSTRATION. In Fig. 8.317, the phase diagram proposed for the Ti_2O_3-TiO_2 system illustrates the behavior when the two components have only limited miscibility in the solid state and also form an intermediate compound. Describe the phases encountered when a melt consisting of 40 per cent TiO_2 and 60 per cent Ti_2O_3 is slowly cooled.

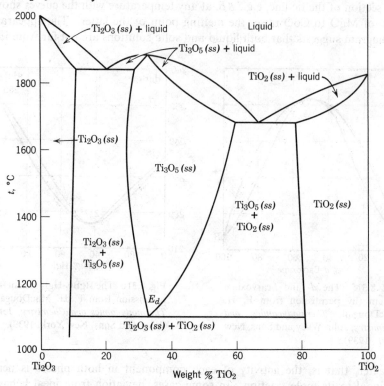

Fig. 8.317 Ti_2O_3 system (according to Devries, Roy, and Osborn, Penn. State School of Mineral Industries, *Eighth Quart. Progr. Rept.*) April 1–June 30 (Appendix I, p. 72, 1953).   *ss* indicates solid solution; the associated formulas have no exact meaning relative to composition.

The interpretation of this diagram follows according to the principles illustrated earlier in simpler cases. A novel feature in Fig. 8.317 is the existence of a eutectoid (invariant) point, E_d. Here the solid solution, identified for convenience by the formula $Ti_3O_5(ss)$, although it should be understood this phase and the other solid solutions have a variable composition, is in equilibrium with $TiO_2(ss)$ and $Ti_2O_3(ss)$. At temperatures below this point (about 1100°) $Ti_3O_5(ss)$ does not exist in equilibrium systems. The behavior of the system on cooling a sample of the solid solution $Ti_3O_5(ss)$ is analogous to that on cooling a liquid mixture toward its eutectic point.

(a) Melt begins to freeze at about 1880°C; solid solution phase labeled $Ti_3O_5(ss)$ separates; initial composition about 35 per cent TiO_2.

(*b*) As cooling continues, the $Ti_3O_5(ss)$ separating becomes richer in TiO_2. At about 1800°, freezing of liquid will be complete. The last drop of liquid to freeze will have a composition corresponding to about 54 per cent TiO_2.

(*c*) Further cooling of the uniform solid solution $Ti_3O_5(ss)$ [composition corresponding to 40 per cent TiO_2, 60 per cent Ti_2O_3] will result in no phase change until about 1200°. At this point separation of $TiO_2(ss)$ ($\sim$ 80 per cent TiO_2) should begin.

(*d*) Further cooling will change the composition of the two solid phases until the eutectoid point E_d (1100°) is reached.

(*e*) Withdrawal of heat at E_d results in disappearance of the $Ti_3O_5(ss)$ phase and formation of more $TiO_2(ss)$ (81 per cent TiO_2) and a new phase $Ti_2O_3(ss)$ (16 per cent TiO_2).

(*f*) After disappearance of the Ti_3O_5 phase further cooling will occur, with slight changes in the composition of the two solid phases. The diagram is not well defined below this point.

In principle, any of the effects discussed in liquid-solid equilibrium systems may also be encountered in systems in which all phases are solid. Diffusion of particles in the solid phase is frequently very slow, and long periods of time may be required for equilibrium to be established. Solubility of solids in each other is generally less than that observed for liquids or solids dissolved in liquids. Statements such as those made with reference to Fig. 8.309, namely, that only pure solid phases separate, are idealized. They mean that, with reference to the composition scale shown, the amount of impurity to be found in the solid phase is negligible. However, even very small traces of impurity may have an important effect on certain properties of the phase; for example, transistors and similar devices may be based on the properties of phases in which the amount of "impurity" is negligible by ordinary standards.

Immiscibility in the Liquid Phase. When immiscibility occurs in the liquid phase, a two-phase area in the liquid region will appear on the phase diagram. Figure 8.318 shows such behavior, together with the solid-liquid phase relationships, for a situation in which no solid solution or compound formation occurs. The *critical solution temperature* is that temperature T_X above which liquid immiscibility is not observed at any concentration. Some liquid systems show a minimum critical solution temperature. The nicotine-water system is a classic example of a system in which both a minimum and a maximum critical solution temperature is observed.

Ternary Systems. For systems containing three components the phase rule becomes $\underline{F} = 5 - \underline{P}$. Even at constant temperature and pressure a coordinate system is needed on which independent variation of the amount of each component can be shown. A triangular diagram is commonly used, as shown in Fig. 8.319. At constant temperature and pressure, phase relationships can conveniently be shown. A two-phase equilibrium system will be univariant and will be represented

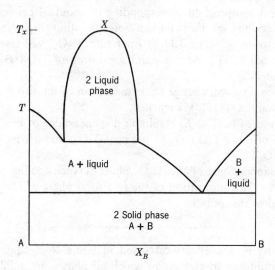

Fig. 8.318 **A system in which a liquid miscibility gap occurs.**

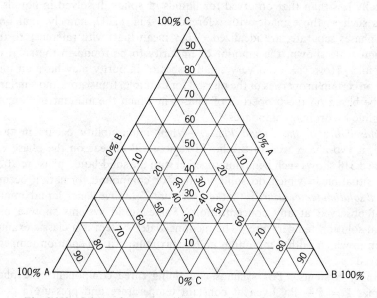

Fig. 8.319 Scheme for representing composition of a ternary system.

by a line on this diagram. If three phases coexist, the system is invariant (T and P both constant); this may correspond to a point on the diagram (intersection of three lines) or to an area bounded by three lines. Some features of relatively simple systems are illustrated in Figs. 8.320 and 8.321. When combinations of the various effects discussed for binary systems occur in systems of three or more components, the number of variations in the appearance of the phase diagrams

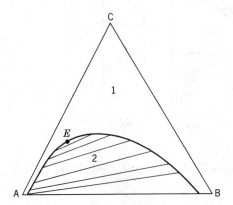

Fig. 8.320   A case of partial miscibility in a three-component system. 1 designates one phase; 2, two phases with tie lines showing relative composition of equilibrium phases. E is the isothermal critical point or plait point; e.g., C_2H_5OH, H_2O, benzene.

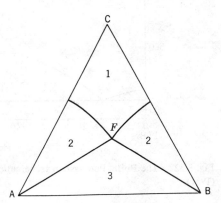

Fig. 8.321   Three components; A and B have limited solubility in C. Any point in area 3 corresponds to a three-phase (invariant) system, solids A and B and saturated solution F. In areas marked 2, solid A (or solid B) is in equilibrium with saturated solution.

becomes very large. The background provided in this chapter should assist the student in understanding any particular system which becomes of interest.

Problems

8.316   In Fig. 8.322 the phase diagram for the $PbBr_2$-PbO system is shown. Four intermediate compounds are observed, one with an incongruent melting point and the other three with congruent melting points. No solid solution is observed. Label this diagram and predict the phases which coexist in equilibrium as melts of various compositions are cooled.

8.317   Draw cooling curves to be expected when liquid mixtures of NaF and LiF containing 35, 40, and 90 mole per cent NaF, respectively, are cooled. See Fig. 8.309.

8.318   Using Fig. 8.309, estimate the ratio of solid LiF to LiF in the liquid phase for a mixture at 700°C where the overall composition is 20 mole per cent NaF.

(a) Use the tie line.

(b) Deduce the answer, using arithmetic.

8.319   What maximum amount of pure NaF can be recovered by crystallization from 200 grams of a melt which is 60 mole per cent NaF? Assume that eutectic occurs at 40 mole per cent NaF. See Fig. 8.309.

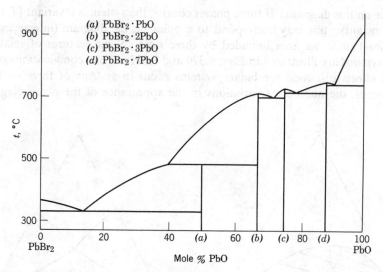

Fig. 8.322   The PbBr₂-Pbo system (schematic). See L. M. Knowles, *J. Chem. Phys.*, **19**, 1130 (1951).

8.320   Describe the phase equilibria encountered when an equilibrium mixture with overall composition of 40 mole per cent MgF_2 and 60 mole per cent NaF is heated from 800 to 1100°C.

8.321   List the phase equilibria encountered when a mixture of 60 per cent MgF_2 and 40 per cent LiF is cooled from 1200 to 600°C.

8.322   Describe carefully and quantitatively the nature of a mixture of 75 mole per cent MgO and 25 per cent CoO at 2600°C.

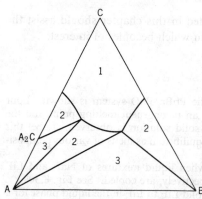

Fig. 8.323   A three-component system with binary compound formation. This system is similar to that in Fig. 8.321 except that A and C form a compound, A_2C, which crystallizes out over the indicated interval.

8.323   Describe the phase changes expected when a 20 per cent B, 80 per cent A mixture is cooled through the region shown in Fig. 8.318.

8.324   List the phases in equilibrium in each of the areas in Fig. 8.323. Specify the composition of the liquid phase carefully in each case.

4. Liquid-Vapor Equilibria

When a liquid mixture of two substances A and B of differing volatilities is allowed to establish equilibrium with its vapor phase, it is to be expected that the vapor and liquid phases will have different compositions, e.g., Fig. 8.401. The phase diagram is of considerable value as a means of predicting the amount of enrichment

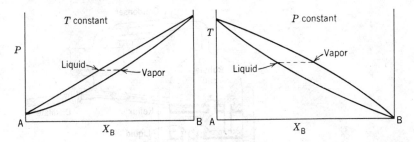

Fig. 8.401   Liquid-vapor diagrams.

which takes place on fractional distillation. It is frequently more convenient to represent boiling points as a function of composition rather than total vapor pressure, although either diagram gives the same information. The relationship between the two is shown schematically in Fig. 8.401. A tie line at any particular value of T indicates the composition of the equilibrium liquid and vapor phases. If it is desired to separate the two components as completely as possible, a distillation column in which liquid-vapor equilibrium can be established successively at various temperatures is necessary, as illustrated in Fig. 8.402. For example, if the liquid is of such composition that it boils initially at T_1, the vapor will be richer in B, as indicated by the tie line; if this vapor phase is allowed to condense and the liquid formed again fractionally vaporized, the boiling point will lie at T_2 with the vapor phase again richer in B; if this is condensed again, etc., it is seen that after a sufficient number of steps the vapor will finally be nearly pure B. A one-step separation can occur on a plate of a fractionation column, e.g., Fig. 8.403; the number of plates (separation steps) required to give the desired fractionation depends on the shape of the phase diagram. The effectiveness of a given fractionation column is indicated by the number of *theoretical plates* corresponding to the number of separation steps which it effects.

Azeotropic Mixtures. If the boiling points of the two components of a mixture are moderately similar and the system shows sufficient deviation from Raoult's law, the vapor-liquid phase diagram may show a maximum or a minimum boiling point. Such diagrams are illustrated schematically in Figs. 8.404 and 8.405, and for actual cases in Fig. 8.406, and are seen to resemble Figs. 8.315 and 8.316. Maximum or minimum boiling mixtures are called *azeotropes*. An argument based on Eq. 8.331 shows that the composition of the two phases must be identical at the point of maximum or minimum. For simplicity let us assume that the vapors

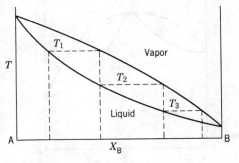

Fig. 8.402 Composition changes on fractional distillations.

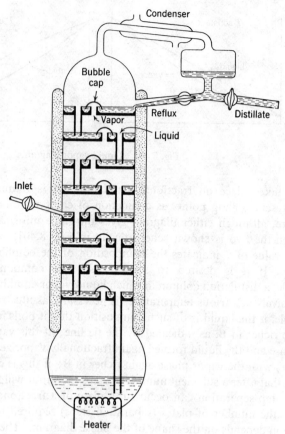

Fig. 8.403   An equilibrium distillation column (by permission from F. Daniels and R. A. Alberty, *Physical Chemistry*, John Wiley and Sons, New York, 1961).

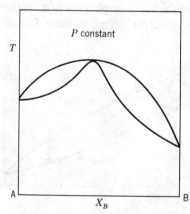

Fig. 8.404   Maximum boiling intermediate mixture.

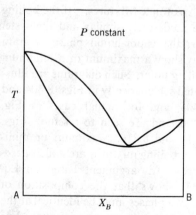

Fig. 8.405   Minimum boiling intermediate mixture.

may be treated as ideal gases. The total pressure is the sum of the partial pressures,

$$P_t = P_a + P_b$$

At the maximum (or minimum)

$$\frac{dP_t}{dX_a} = \frac{dP_a}{dX_a} + \frac{dP_b}{dX_a} = 0 \qquad (8.401)$$

The Duhem-Margules equation, 8.331 may be written in the form

$$\frac{X_a}{P_a}\frac{dP_a}{dX_a} + \frac{X_b}{P_b}\frac{dP_b}{dX_a} = 0$$

hence

$$\frac{dP_b}{dX_a} = -\frac{X_a}{X_b}\frac{P_b}{P_a}\frac{dP_a}{dX_a}$$

and Eq. 8.401 takes the form

$$0 = \frac{dP_a}{dX_a}\left(1 - \frac{X_a P_b}{X_b P_a}\right)$$

Since dP_a/dX_a is never found to be zero, the quantity in parentheses must be zero at the azeotropic concentration. Since, from Eq. 7.619

$$\frac{P_b}{P_a} = \frac{X_b'}{X_a'}$$

where the primed mole fractions correspond to the composition of the vapor, it can be seen that the mole fractions must be equal in the two phases. The ideal solution rule that the vapor phase is richer in the more volatile component must be modified for systems which form azeotropic mixtures.

Azeotropic mixtures are not uncommon. Water and hydrogen chloride form an azeotropic mixture with a maximum boiling point of 108.6°C at 760 mm Hg pressure, when the weight per cent of HCl is 20.222. When a more dilute solution of hydrochloric acid is distilled, the concentration of HCl gradually increases (the fraction of water in the vapor is greater than that in the liquid) until the azeotrope is reached. Further distillation does not change the composition as vapor and liquid phases are identical. This is a method of preparing standard HCl solutions.

The principles of the preceding paragraphs may be used to predict the behavior on either side of the maximum, or of a mixture with a minimum boiling point. Ethyl alcohol and water form an azeotrope with a minimum boiling point of 78.15°C (95.57 per cent ethanol). This composition represents the limit of purification that can be expected by fractional distillation of ethanol-water mixtures.

The two components of a binary mixture may interact strongly to form an intermediate compound. It is possible that formation of such an intermediate compound may result in a phase diagram similar in appearance to that obtained when an azeotropic mixture is formed. The two cases can be distinguished, however, by the fact that the azeotrope composition varies with the total pressure, whereas such a variation will not be observed if the mixture is a true compound.

For azeotropic data on a large number of systems, see L. H. Horsley, *Azeotropic Data*, Advances in Chemistry Series, American Chemical Society, 1952. Examples of actual mixtures are shown in Fig. 8.406.

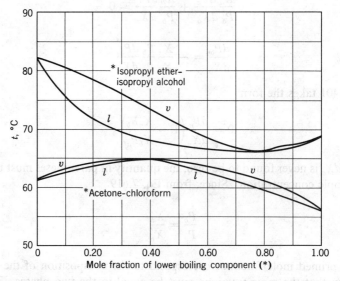

Fig. 8.406 Saturation temperature of binary systems (at 1 atm pressure), showing maximum (acetone-chloroform) and minimum (isopropyl-ether-isopropyl alcohol) boiling azeotropic mixtures (by permission from O. A. Hougen and K. M. Watson, *Chemical Process Principles*, Part II, John Wiley and Sons, New York, 1947).

Distillation of Immiscible Liquids. When two liquid phases coexist in a binary system at constant temperature and total pressure, the system is invariant and the partial pressure of each component in the vapor phase is fixed. Distillation of such a mixture will result in removal of the two components in a mole ratio corresponding to their relative partial pressures. As distillation continues, the composition of each liquid phase will remain unchanged but the relative amounts of the two phases will change until one disappears. Steam distillation is frequently used to carry over organic substances immiscible in liquid water. The effective boiling point of the mixture is less than that of either component, since the sum of the partial pressures is now equal to the atmospheric pressure against which the boiling takes place.

Problems

*8.401   The compounds C_2H_5OH and CH_3OH boil at 78.4 and 64.7°C, respectively. At 20°C, their vapor pressures are 44.5 and 88.7 mm. Assuming that their mixtures are ideal solutions, construct the liquid-vapor phase diagram and determine the minimum number of stages in a distillation column necessary to separate a sample containing 95 per cent CH_3OH from an initial mixture which is 95 per cent C_2H_5OH (mole %).

8.402   Calculate the volume of water to be added to the HCl-H_2O azeotropic mixture to prepare $3N$ HCl ($d = 1.05$ g ml^{-1}).

*8.403   Calculate the temperature at which α-bromotoluene will steam-distill if the atmospheric pressure is 756 mm, and determine its mole fraction in the distillate. The vapor pressure of α-bromotoluene is 10 mm at 73.4°C and 40 mm at 104.8°C. Express vapor pressures in the form $\ln P = AT^{-1} + B$ and use a graphical solution; the heat of vaporization of water may be taken to be 540 cal g^{-1}.

5. Review Problems

8.501   Draw a schematic diagram showing the proper relationship of the chemical potential of a given substance as (a) a gas at 1 atm, (b) a pure liquid under 1 atm pressure, and (c) a liquid in an ideal solution in which the mole fraction is 0.5. Show chemical potentials as function of temperature. State what conclusion may be drawn about the expected boiling point of the solution relative to that of the pure liquid, if the solute is assumed to be nonvolatile. Explain briefly.

8.502   Calculate the vapor pressure of CCl_4 at 90°C from the data given in Problem 8.201.

8.503   Use the data in Table 8.201(A) to estimate the vapor pressure of silver at room temperature. Discuss approximations involved.

8.504   Apply the Clapeyron equation to a gas-liquid equilibrium, if the molar volume of the liquid is $\bar{V} = b$, and the gas obeys the equation of state $P(\bar{V} - b) = RT$.

8.505   Calculate the vapor pressure of solid NH_3 at −85°C from data in Table 8.201(A).

8.506   Most of the $\Delta \bar{S}_{vap}$ values in Table 8.201(A) are between 17 and 25. Explain the outstanding exception, that of sulfur.

8.507   The vapor pressure of carbon tetrachloride at 50°C is 314 mm, that of benzene is 271 mm. If they form an ideal solution, calculate the composition of the gas and liquid phases if the total pressure is 290 mm.

*8.508   Calculate the activity coefficient of carbon tetrachloride in bromine when $X = 0.5$. Estimate quantities from Fig. 8.308 and perform a rough graphical integration based on Eq. 8.329.

8.509   In a two-component solution assume the fugacity of one component is given by the expression

$$\log \frac{f_1}{f_1^{\square}} = \log X_1 + \beta(1 - X_1)^2$$

where β is a constant. Find an expression for $\log (f_2/f_2^{\square})$.

8.510   Estimate the ideal solubility of carbon tetrachloride in chloroform at −30°C [see Table 8.201(A)].

8.511   What would be the osmotic pressure in a tree if the concentration of impermeable solutes in the sap was 1 molal? Express pressure in feet of water. $T = 300°K$.

8.512   Describe the phase equilibria encountered when:

(a) A liquid containing 20 mole per cent BeF_2 (80 per cent CaF_2) is slowly cooled from 1300 to 400°C.

(b) A 55 mole per cent BeF_2 liquid mixture is cooled.

(c) A 50 mole per cent BeF_2 mixture is heated from 400 to 1300°C.

(d) An 80 mole per cent BeF_2 mixture is cooled from 1300 to 400°C.

8.513   Figure 8.311 shows the behavior of the $NaF-MgF_2$ system. If the stable compound $NaF \cdot MgF_2$ were to have an incongruent melting point at 1000°C and 40 per cent MgF_2, instead of the actual behavior, show how the phase diagram would appear.

8.514   Show that Eq. 8.331 requires the solute to obey Henry's law if the solvent obeys Raoult's law.

General References

Daniels, F., and R. A. Alberty, *Physical Chemistry*, Second Edition, John Wiley and Sons, New York, 1961.

Findlay, A., A. N. Campbell, and N. O. Smith, *The Phase Rule and its Applications*, Dover Publications, New York, 1951.

Horsley, L. H., *Azeotropic Data*, Advances in Chemistry Series, American Chemical Society, 1952.

Hougen, O. A., and K. M. Watson, *Chemical Process Principles*, Vol. II, John Wiley and Sons, New York, 1947.

Levin, E. M., H. F. McMurdie, and F. P. Hall, *Phase Diagrams for Ceramists*, American Ceramic Society, 1956.

Lewis, G. N., M. Randall, K. S. Pitzer, and L. Brewer, *Thermodynamics*, Second Edition, McGraw-Hill Book Co., New York, 1961.

MacDougall, F. H., *Thermodynamics and Chemistry*, Third Edition, John Wiley and Sons, New York, 1939.

Weissberger, A., Editor, *Technique of Organic Chemistry*, Interscience Publishers, New York, 1959.

Wetmore, F. E. W., and D. J. LeRoy, *Principles of Phase Equilibria*, McGraw-Hill Book Co., New York, 1950.

Chapter Nine

Thermodynamic Properties

of Chemical Substances

In this chapter, conventions are described for the assignment of numerical values of the thermodynamic properties of chemical substances. These numbers can be used in a simple way to evaluate changes in thermodynamic properties associated with the transformation of a set of isolated reactants to a set of isolated products.

1. Changes in Thermodynamic Properties Accompanying Phase Transformations

Consider the change in thermodynamic properties accompanying a phase change. The two phases may be regarded as different parts of the system, with a discontinuous change in energy, entropy, heat capacity, and similar extensive properties as material is transferred from one phase to the other. For example, the total enthalpy of a one-component heterogeneous system depends on the amount of each phase as well as on T and P. It proves simpler to treat each phase independently in the manner described in Chapter 7 and the transition as a separate event.

Energy and Enthalpy. The vaporization of water at constant temperature and pressure may be represented as follows

$$H_2O(1 \text{ mole, liq, } 373°K, 1 \text{ atm}) \rightarrow H_2O(1 \text{ mole, gas, } 373°K, 1 \text{ atm})$$

Q_P, the amount of heat necessary to maintain constant temperature as the vaporization is carried out at constant pressure, is equal to the enthalpy change. Then

$\Delta \bar{E}$ may be calculated from $\Delta \bar{H} = \Delta \bar{E} + \Delta(P\bar{V})$. Note that $\bar{V}_1$ is the molar volume of liquid water and $\bar{V}_2$ is the molar volume of water vapor at the specified temperature and pressure.

If the vaporization occurred spontaneously into an evacuated space, but from the same initial to the same final state, ΔH and ΔE would have the same values as above, since they are functions of state. The heat absorbed Q would now equal ΔE, not ΔH, since no work is done in such a free evaporation. Values of $\Delta \bar{E}$ and $\Delta \bar{H}$ are usually tabulated in units of calories or kilocalories (kcal) per mole.

All phase transformations may be considered in the same way. A calorimetric device may be used to measure the heat associated with the change. As shown in Chapter 8, measurement of the vapor pressure as a function of temperature also provides information from which ΔH and ΔS can be evaluated for a vaporization process. It is apparent from the first law that values for condensation must be numerically equal but opposite in sign to values for vaporization.

Entropy.   The entropy change associated with a phase change can be evaluated from Q_{rev}/T. The standard transition temperature, the normal boiling point, melting point, etc., is that temperature at which the transition occurs reversibly under a pressure of 1 atm. It is instructive to note that at equal pressures (or also at constant volume) the entropy of the phase stable at higher temperatures is always higher than that of the phase stable at lower temperatures. Vaporization leads to a large increase in entropy, around 21 eu at the normal boiling point for many organic liquids (Trouton's rule, Chapter 8); see Table 8.201(A). The abbreviation eu stands for entropy units, energy per degree mole, with the energy usually expressed in calories. The entropy associated with the melting of a solid is $\Delta H_{\text{fus}}/T_{\text{mp}}$, at the normal melting point.

If the entropy change is to be evaluated for a spontaneous change of phase, such as the freezing of a supercooled liquid, a path must be considered whereby the same process can be carried out reversibly. The entropy change for a reversible path can be evaluated from Q_{rev}.

ILLUSTRATION.   Given the heat of fusion of water at the melting point, 0°C, and the heat capacity of liquid and solid water, calculate the change in entropy for the spontaneous solidification of liquid water at $-5°C$.

The process may be carried out by the following reversible path:

$$H_2O(\text{liq, } 268°K) \rightarrow H_2O(\text{liq, } 273°K); \quad \Delta S = \int_{268}^{273} C_P(\text{liq}) \, dT/T$$

$$H_2O(\text{liq, } 273°K) \rightarrow H_2O(\text{ice, } 273°K); \quad \Delta S = Q_{\text{rev}}/273 = -\Delta H_{\text{fus}}/273$$

$$H_2O(\text{ice, } 273°K) \rightarrow H_2O(\text{ice, } 268°K); \quad \Delta S = \int_{273}^{268} C_P(\text{ice}) \, dT/T$$

The sum of these three reactions gives the direct change of interest.

Free Energy.   The Gibbs free energy shows a particularly simple behavior for phase changes. Under reversible conditions at constant T and P, $\Delta F = 0$ in accordance with Eq. 7.406, and as may also be seen from the defining relation $\Delta F = \Delta H - T\,\Delta S$; under reversible conditions $T\,\Delta S = Q_{rev}$, and at constant pressure $Q_{rev} = Q_P = \Delta H$. The phase equilibrium at constant T and P may be considered a balance between the effects of enthalpy and entropy. Vaporization, for example, leads to a large increase in entropy, but at the same time an increase in enthalpy of the system.

If conditions are such that a phase change occurs spontaneously at constant temperature and pressure, ΔF is negative in accordance with the prediction of Eq. 7.407.

ILLUSTRATION.   Calculate ΔF for the spontaneous liquefaction of supercooled water vapor at 95°C, at 1 atm pressure

$$H_2O(\text{gas}, 368°\text{K}, 1\ \text{atm}) \rightarrow H_2O(\text{liq}, 368°\text{K}, 1\ \text{atm})$$

Assume that water vapor behaves as an ideal gas and that the equilibrium vapor pressure of water at 368°K is 634 mm Hg. Let us consider the transformation of 1 mole. ΔF may be evaluated by summing the following steps.

$$H_2O(\text{gas}, 368°\text{K}, 1\ \text{atm}) \rightarrow H_2O(\text{gas}, 368°\text{K}, 634\ \text{mm}) \tag{1}$$

$$\Delta \bar{F}_1 = RT \ln \frac{634}{760}$$

$$H_2O(\text{gas}, 368°\text{K}, 634\ \text{mm}) \rightarrow H_2O(\text{liq}, 368°\text{K}, 634\ \text{mm}) \tag{2}$$

$$\Delta \bar{F}_2 = 0$$

$$H_2O(\text{liq}, 368°\text{K}, 634\ \text{mm}) \rightarrow H_2O(\text{liq}, 368°\text{K}, 1\ \text{atm}) \tag{3}$$

$$\Delta \bar{F}_3 = \int_{634}^{760} \bar{V}\,dP = \bar{V}(\Delta P)$$

$\Delta \bar{F}_3$ is a very small number, since the molar volume of liquid water, assumed not to change with the small change in pressure, is very small. Hence $\Delta \bar{F}_1$ (negative) is the only significant term.

Problems

9.101   How much mechanical energy must be provided for an ideal refrigerator to change 25 kg of water, initially at 25°C, to ice at 0°C? Assume a constant heat capacity of 1 cal deg^{-1} g^{-1} for liquid water and a heat of fusion of ice of 80 cal g^{-1}, and the release of heat by the engine to the room at a constant temperature of 27°C.

9.102   One kilogram of ice at 0°C is dropped into 5 kg of liquid water initially at 80°C. Assuming no external heat loss and the characteristics of water given in Problem 9.101, calculate the total entropy change as internal equilibrium is established.

9.103   One gram of steam at 373°K condenses to 1 gram of liquid water at 373°K. If $\Delta \bar{H}_{vap} = 9700$ cal mole^{-1} with both phases at their equilibrium vapor pressure at 373°K, calculate the entropy change of the water. What is the entropy change of the surroundings if the process occurs reversibly? What would be the entropy change in the (a) water, (b) surroundings, if 1 gram of steam were condensed rapidly by the irreversible expenditure of 3 l-atm of work? Assume $T = 373°K$ and $PV = nRT$ (for steam).

9.104 A small capsule containing 1 mole of liquid water under a total pressure of 1 atm at its normal boiling point is placed inside an evacuated vessel of sufficient capacity to just hold 1 mole of water vapor at 1 atm at its normal boiling point. If the temperature is held constant at this value, calculate $\Delta \bar{F}$ and $\Delta \bar{A}$ for the process which occurs when the small capsule is broken. Which property is the proper one to consider as a criterion for spontaneous change in this case? Explain.

9.105 Prove that ΔS is positive for the transition from one phase to another as temperature is raised at constant volume.

2. Thermochemistry;   Standard Heat of Formation

The heat associated with chemical changes may be measured to evaluate ΔH and ΔE. Again the nature of the initial and final states and the amount of material undergoing change must be clearly defined. The chemical convention that a symbol or formula stands for one gram mole is adopted; the enthalpy change tabulated corresponds to complete conversion of the reactants to products. The general subject of energy and enthalpy changes of chemical reactions is called thermochemistry. Since a chemical change generally involves different numbers of moles for the various reactants and products, we will not use the bar over the symbol for the enthalpy change of a reaction. The amount of material undergoing reaction will be indicated in the associated equation, or in the units of ΔH, e.g., kcal mole^{-1} of a specified reactant or product.

Consider the combustion of carbon as an example.

$$\text{C(graphite, 25°C, 1 atm)} + \text{O}_2\text{(gas, 25°C, 1 atm)} \rightarrow \text{CO}_2\text{(gas, 25°C, 1 atm)}$$

The value of Q when this reaction is carried out under constant pressure is equal to the enthalpy change; for each mole of CO_2

$$\Delta H = -94{,}050 \text{ cal mole}^{-1} = \Delta E + \Delta(PV)$$

In this case

$$\Delta(PV) = \sum_{\text{prod}} PV - \sum_{\text{react}} PV$$

Since the molar volume of graphite is very small, $P\bar{V}$ for graphite may be ignored relative to the $P\bar{V}$ terms for the gases without introducing appreciable error. This is generally true for condensed phases. If oxygen and carbon dioxide are assumed to behave as perfect gases, $\Delta(PV)$ takes a simple form $\Delta n_g (RT)$, where Δn_g represents the change in moles of gas; since T is the same in the initial and final states, $\Delta(n_g RT)$ will have a nonzero value only if Δn_g is not zero. In the present case Δn_g is also zero, so $\Delta E = \Delta H$.

In most cases, combustion reactions may be studied more conveniently in a constant-volume (bomb) calorimeter. The measured Q then represents ΔE, as no work is done in the process. Even though intermediate temperatures may rise to quite high values, the total heat measured, after the products have been brought back to the final temperature indicated in the chemical equation, represents ΔE for the reaction. ΔE depends only on the specified initial and final states. A great deal of thermochemical data, particularly for organic compounds, has been obtained through the study of combustion reactions. Since heats of vaporization are quite large, it is important to note whether the heat of combustion refers to gaseous or condensed states.

Hess's Law.   If any reaction is represented as a sum of several steps, for each of which the change in enthalpy is known, the enthalpy change for the overall reaction must be the sum of the enthalpy changes of the individual steps. This follows from the first law, although it is frequently referred to as Hess's law of thermochemistry, which was proposed independently in 1840. It may be illustrated by the following sequence at 25°C with each considered as a gas at 1 atm pressure:

$$CH_4(g) + \quad Cl_2(g) \rightarrow CH_3Cl(g) + \quad HCl(g) \qquad \Delta H_1 = -25,600 \text{ cal}$$
$$CH_3Cl(g) + \quad Cl_2(g) \rightarrow CH_2Cl_2(g) + \quad HCl(g) \qquad \Delta H_2 = -23,400 \text{ cal}$$
$$CH_2Cl_2(g) + \quad Cl_2(g) \rightarrow CHCl_3(g) + \quad HCl(g) \qquad \Delta H_3 = -25,000 \text{ cal}$$
$$CHCl_3(g) + \quad Cl_2(g) \rightarrow CCl_4(g) \quad + \quad HCl(g) \qquad \Delta H_4 = -23,500 \text{ cal}$$

$$CH_4(g) + 4Cl_2(g) \rightarrow CCl_4(g) \quad + 4HCl(g) \qquad \Delta H_5 = \sum_1^4 \Delta H_{rx} = -97,500 \text{ cal}$$

The sum of the enthalpy changes of the four reactions written must equal that which would be observed directly for the fifth reaction. It also follows that, if any reaction is written in the reverse direction, the enthalpy change is equal but opposite in sign to that for the forward reaction.

It should be apparent that a similar summation can be performed for any exact thermodynamic property, E, F, A, S, C_P, etc.

Heat of Formation.   To simplify the recording of thermochemical data, a standard heat of formation of each substance is tabulated. The heat of formation is the enthalpy of the chemical substance minus that of the elements of which it is composed. To tabulate a definite numerical value, defined standard states have been adopted by international agreement. The heat of formation will be designated by the symbol ΔH_{for}.

Standard States.   *Solids:* pure stable crystalline form under 1 atm pressure.

Liquids: pure liquid under a total pressure of 1 atm; if the boiling point of the liquid is above the temperature of interest, the liquid is usually chosen as the standard rather than the vapor.

Gases: the gas standard state is hypothetical; that is, it is not possible to find a real gas pressure at which all the thermodynamic properties of the gas have their standard state values. For a perfect gas the standard state for all properties is 1 atm pressure. $\bar{H}$ for a perfect gas is not dependent on pressure, hence the standard state definition of a perfect gas is straightforward. For a real gas, the standard enthalpy (and related properties such as the heat capacity) is the limiting value at zero pressure (see Sec. 7.5), whereas the standard free energy (and similarly for related properties which are concentration dependent, such as entropy) is the value of $\bar{F}$ at unit fugacity. When the standard state of a gas is designated in an equation, it will be done by writing $f° = 1$. This should be understood to mean that all thermodynamic properties have their standard state values. Although a real gas pressure may be found at which the numerical value of the fugacity is unity, this condition does not correspond to the standard state in all respects, since the real gas enthalpy at this pressure will not be the same as the zero-pressure enthalpy value. Hence the standard state for a real gas is well defined but not physically realizable. Standard state values can be converted to real values by the methods discussed in Chapter 7.

The standard state may be defined differently in the study of solutions. The conventions described above are used for pure substances.

Standard Heat of Formation. The standard heat of formation is the enthalpy change on conversion of the elements, each initially in its standard state, to the compound of interest, finally brought to its standard state. The elements are taken as a starting point and are assigned a heat of formation of zero at all temperatures; this is strictly a term of reference and has no meaning relative to the absolute enthalpy of the element or to formation of molecular forms of the element from separate atoms, atoms from subatomic particles, etc. As an example, the standard heat of formation of liquid water at 25°C, -68.32 kcal mole^{-1}, is actually the enthalpy change for the reaction

$$H_2(g, 25°C, f° = 1 \text{ atm}) + \tfrac{1}{2}O_2(g, 25°C, f° = 1 \text{ atm}) \rightarrow$$

$$H_2O \text{ (liq, 25°C, under 1 atm)}$$

As indicated above, $\bar{H}°$ for the gases is equal to $\bar{H}*$, where $P* \approx 0$ (Sec. 7.5). Table 9.201(A) lists standard heats of formation for a number of common substances at 25°C. A superscript $°$ on $\Delta H°_{\text{for}}$ indicates that the value corresponds to the change from the reactants, each initially in its standard state, to the product in its standard state.

We have referred to the enthalpy of formation as the heat of formation. This is a common usage but rather unfortunate because the value of the heat Q depends on

Table 9.201   Standard Enthalpies of Formation, at 25°C, $\Delta H°_{\text{for}}$, kcal mole^{-1}*
(Ions are in aqueous solution)

Substance	$\Delta H°_{\text{for}}$	Substance	$\Delta H°_{\text{for}}$	Substance	$\Delta H°_{\text{for}}$
Al^{3+}	-125.4	$C_6H_6(g)$	19.82	$NH_3(g)$	-11.04
$Al_2O_3(\alpha)$	-399.09	$CCl_4(l)$	-33.3	NH_4^+	-31.74
$SbCl_3$	-91.34	$CS_2(l)$	21.0	$NHO_3(l)$	-41.40

The complete Table 9.201(A) will be found in the Appendix.

* From *NBS Circ.* 500.

the manner in which the change is carried out. The term heat of reaction or heat of formation arose because the enthalpy has commonly been called the heat content of a substance, an undesirable practice since heat is not a thermodynamic property like H. However, such tabulated heats of reaction represent the heat exchanged with the surroundings when the reaction is carried out at the given temperature and at constant pressure throughout; under these conditions, the heat is truly a measure of the enthalpy change.

Calculation of ΔH for Chemical Reactions.   From heats of formation, Table 9.201(A), the enthalpy change for any reaction may be calculated at the temperature of reference; $\Delta H^{\circ}_{\text{reaction}} = \sum_{\text{prod}} n_p \Delta H^{\circ}_{\text{for}} - \sum_{\text{reac}} n_r \Delta H^{\circ}_{\text{for}}$. The proper number of moles of each component must be included. Thus, the heats of formation replace the absolute enthalpies of the substances, which are unknown, for purposes of evaluating the heat of reaction. A path may be imagined in which the reactants are dissociated to their elements, for which heats are the negative of the heats of formation, and the elements then allowed to recombine to form the products. The sum of these reactions gives the change of interest; the arbitrary convention concerning zero heat of formation of the elements cancels.

ILLUSTRATION.   Calculate ΔH° at 25°C for the reaction

$$\text{NaOH}(s) + \text{HCl}(g) \rightarrow \text{NaCl}(s) + \text{H}_2\text{O}(l)$$

The change in enthalpy may be obtained by summation of the following thermochemical equations [data from Table 9.201(A)]:

$\text{NaOH}(s) \rightarrow \text{Na}(s) + \frac{1}{2}\text{O}_2(g) + \frac{1}{2}\text{H}_2(g)$	$\Delta H^{\circ} = -\Delta H^{\circ}_{\text{for}}(\text{NaOH})$	$= \quad 102,000 \text{ cal}$
$\text{HCl}(g) \rightarrow \frac{1}{2}\text{H}_2(g) + \frac{1}{2}\text{Cl}_2(g)$	$\Delta H^{\circ} = -\Delta H^{\circ}_{\text{for}}(\text{HCl})$	$= \quad 22,020$
$\text{Na}(s) + \frac{1}{2}\text{Cl}_2(g) \rightarrow \text{NaCl}(s)$	$\Delta H^{\circ} = \Delta H^{\circ}_{\text{for}}(\text{NaCl})$	$= -98,230$
$\text{H}_2(g) + \frac{1}{2}\text{O}_2(g) \rightarrow \text{H}_2\text{O}(l)$	$\Delta H^{\circ} = \Delta H^{\circ}_{\text{for}}(\text{H}_2\text{O})$	$= -68,320$

$\text{NaOH}(s) + \text{HCl}(g) \rightarrow \text{NaCl}(s) + \text{H}_2\text{O}(l); \quad \Delta H^{\circ} = \sum_{\text{prod}} \Delta H^{\circ}_{\text{for}} - \sum_{\text{reac}} \Delta H^{\circ}_{\text{for}} \quad = -42,530 \text{ cal}$

Note that on addition of thermochemical equations cancellation of terms, equivalent to the addition of algebraic equations, occurs. Although it is not necessary to write out the detailed reactions as is done in this example, in effect this is what we do on calculation of the heat of any reaction from the heats of formation of the compounds involved. We need not be concerned with the feasibility of a reaction. For example, even though benzene is not prepared by direct reaction of carbon and hydrogen in their standard states, the heat of formation of benzene represents the enthalpy of benzene relative to the elements as indicated by the change

$$6\text{C}(\text{graphite}) + 3\text{H}_2(\text{gas}) \rightarrow \text{C}_6\text{H}_6(\text{liq}); \quad \Delta H^{\circ}_{\text{for 298°K}} = 11,718 \text{ cal mole}^{-1}$$

The positive value shows that the enthalpy of benzene is larger than the sum of the enthalpies of the elements of which it is composed.

The enthalpy change can be calculated for a given reaction at some temperature other than the one at which heats of formation have been tabulated if heat capacity data for all the substances involved are available.

ILLUSTRATION. Calculate the standard enthalpy change of the reaction

$$H_2(g) + Cl_2(g) \rightarrow 2HCl(g)$$

at 500°C from the standard heat of formation at 25°C and the heat capacities of hydrogen, chlorine, and hydrogen chloride (as functions of temperature) in this temperature interval.

In the following equations, $f° = 1$ atm in all cases.

(1) $H_2(g, 298°K) + Cl_2(g, 298°K) \rightarrow 2HCl(g, 298°K)$

$$\Delta H_1^\circ = 2\Delta H_{\text{for}}^\circ(HCl) = -44{,}040$$

(2) $2HCl(g, 298°K) \rightarrow 2HCl(g, 773°K)$

$$\Delta H_2^\circ = 2\bar{H}°(HCl)_{773} - 2\bar{H}°(HCl)_{298} = 2\int_{298}^{773} \bar{C}_P^\circ(HCl)\, dT$$

(3) $H_2(g, 773°K) \rightarrow H_2(g, 298°K)$

$$\Delta H_3^\circ = \bar{H}°(H_2)_{298} - \bar{H}°(H_2)_{773} = \int_{773}^{298} \bar{C}_P^\circ(H_2)\, dT$$

(4) $Cl_2(g, 773°K) \rightarrow Cl_2(g, 298°K)$

$$\Delta H_4^\circ = \bar{H}°(Cl_2)_{298} - \bar{H}°(Cl_2)_{773} = \int_{773}^{298} \bar{C}_P^\circ(Cl_2)\, dT$$

---

(5) $H_2(g, 773°K) + Cl_2(g, 773°K) \rightarrow 2HCl(g, 773°K)$

By summation

$$\Delta H_5^\circ = \sum_1^4 \Delta H_{rx}^\circ$$

Expression of ΔH as a Function of Temperature; Kirchhoff's Equations. The result of the above Illustration may be written

$$\Delta H_{773}^\circ = \Delta H_{298}^\circ + \int_{298}^{773} \Delta C_P^\circ\, dT$$

where ΔC_P° represents the difference between the total heat capacity of the products and the total heat capacity of the reactants. Coefficients of similar powers of temperature in C_P equations [Table 7.201(A)] may be combined to obtain an equation $\Delta C_P^\circ = 2\bar{C}_p^\circ(HCl) - \bar{C}_p^\circ(H_2) - \bar{C}_p^\circ(Cl_2)$ which takes the form

$$\Delta C_P^\circ = \Delta a + \Delta b T + \Delta c T^{-2} + \cdots \tag{9.201}$$

and a single integration performed. The enthalpy change at the higher temperature is still called the heat of formation of HCl, that is, the elements are assigned zero heat of formation at each temperature.

This treatment is general and may be applied to any reaction by using a combined heat capacity equation, $\Delta C_p^\circ = \sum\limits_{prod} n_p \bar{C}_p^\circ - \sum\limits_{reac} n_r \bar{C}_P^\circ$; hence

$$\Delta H_T^\circ = \Delta H_{298}^\circ + \int_{298}^T \Delta C_P^\circ \, dT \tag{9.202}$$

or in differential form

$$d \, \Delta H^\circ = \Delta C_P^\circ \, dT \tag{9.203}$$

Equation 9.202 or 9.203 is known as Kirchhoff's equation. Equation 9.203 may be integrated to the form

$$\Delta H_T^\circ = \Delta H_*^\circ + \Delta a T + \tfrac{1}{2} \Delta b T^2 - \Delta c T^{-1} + \cdots \tag{9.204}$$

where ΔH_*° is an integration constant which may be evaluated if the heat of reaction is known at any temperature. Such an equation should be used only in the limited temperature range for which the empirical heat capacity constants are valid.

If the enthalpy change is desired under conditions other than the standard state, for example at high pressures, the standard value is first calculated at the temperature of interest; then, by adding appropriate equations in which the pressure is changed at constant temperature for each component, ΔH may be calculated under the desired conditions.

If over the temperature interval a change in phase of one or more of the components of the reaction occurs, Kirchhoff's equation is applied in steps. The equation derived in terms of the heat capacity of the low-temperature form is used up to the temperature at which the transition occurs, a separate value added for the enthalpy of transition, and a new ΔC_P equation derived using the heat capacity of the high-temperature form in conjunction with other data. For example, for sulfur

$S(rh) + O_2(g) \rightarrow SO_2(g), \quad \Delta H_T^\circ = \Delta H_*^\circ + \Delta a T + \tfrac{1}{2} \Delta b T^2$ (below transition temperature)

$S(rh) \rightarrow S(m); \quad \Delta H^\circ = \bar{H}^\circ(\text{monoclinic}) - \bar{H}^\circ(\text{rhombic}) = \Delta \bar{H}^\circ$ (transition)

$S(m) + O_2(g) \rightarrow SO_2(g), \quad \Delta H_T^\circ = \Delta H_*^{\circ\prime} + \Delta a' T + \tfrac{1}{2} \Delta b' T^2$ (above transition temperature)

An alternative method of representing enthalpy data at various temperatures is to tabulate values of $\bar{H}_T^\circ - \bar{H}_{298}^\circ$, or $\bar{H}_T^\circ - \bar{H}_0^\circ$ ($\bar{H}_0^\circ$ represents the value of $\bar{H}^\circ$ at $T = 0°K$.) These relative enthalpy functions can be evaluated by integration of heat capacity equations or, as will be discussed in Chapter 11, from partition functions evaluated from molecular structure information. The change in enthalpy for any given reaction at temperature T may then be evaluated from the relative enthalpy functions and a knowledge of the value of ΔH_{298}° or ΔH_0°, respectively.

$$\Delta[n(\bar{H}_T^\circ - \bar{H}_{298}^\circ)] = \Delta H_T^\circ - \Delta H_{298}^\circ$$

Tables of data in this form are quite extensive e.g., *JANAF Thermochemical*

Tables, prepared under the auspices of the Joint Army-Navy-Air Force Thermo-chemical Panel by the Thermal Laboratory of the Dow Chemical Company, Midland, Michigan.

Bond Energies. Chemists are interested in associating the change in energy observed in a given chemical process with the breaking of old and the formation of new chemical bonds. Although thermodynamics is not dependent on atomic or molecular models of chemical reaction, it is informative to consider the relation-ship of enthalpy changes to these theories. A system of assigning bond energies has been developed which is useful as an indication of chemical bond strength and as a means of estimating enthalpy changes for reactions which have not been studied experimentally. It is important to assess the significance of these bond energies carefully to distinguish what is exact thermodynamic information and what involves a semiempirical use of thermodynamic data.

The bond dissociation energy of a diatomic gas molecule (as defined in Chapter 4) allows us to assign values for the standard heats of formation of free gaseous atoms. Similar values may be given for atoms of elements normally in the condensed state if vaporization and dissociation energy data are available. Many thermo-chemical tabulations include standard enthalpies of formation of atoms, that is, the standard enthalpy change on formation of free gaseous atoms from an element in its normal thermodynamic standard state. Some representative values are given in Table 9.202.

Table 9.202   Standard Enthalpies of Formation of Atoms, kcal mole^{-1}, at 25°C*

H	52.1	C	171.7	Na	26.0	Mg	35.9
O	59.2	F	18.3	K	21.5	Ni	101.6
N	112.9	Cl	29.0	Ca	46.0	Fe	96.7
S	53.2	Br	26.7	Ba	42.0	Cr	80.5
P	75.2	I	25.5	Al	75.0	Ag	69.1

* Taken largely from *NBS Circ.* 500, 1952.

For elements which occur normally as simple diatomic gas molecules, we may write, for example,

$$Cl_2(g) \rightarrow 2Cl(g), \quad \Delta H^\circ = 2(29.0) = 58 \text{ kcal}$$
$$H_2(g) \rightarrow 2H(g), \quad \Delta H^\circ = 2(52.1) = 104.2 \text{ kcal}$$

For diatomic compounds, additional data from Table 9.201(A) must also be used to obtain bond dissociation energies, for example,

$$CO(g) \rightarrow C(g) + O(g), \quad \Delta H^\circ = 171.7 + 59.2 - (-26.4) = 257.3 \text{ kcal}$$

Actually these are bond enthalpies; however the difference between ΔE and ΔH is zero at 0°K, and is small, usually less than the uncertainty of the bond energy, relative to the magnitude of these quantities at ordinary temperatures. Hence they are generally called bond energies.

Bond energies are particularly useful in estimating thermochemical properties in organic chemistry. It is frequently necessary to use average or mean values. For example, an average value for the C—H bond is assigned as follows for methane:

$$C(graphite) + 2H_2(g) \rightarrow CH_4(g) \qquad \Delta H° = -17.89 \text{ [Table 9.201(A)]}$$
$$4H(g) \rightarrow 2H_2(g) \qquad \Delta H° = -208.4 \text{ (Table 9.202)}$$
$$C(g) \rightarrow C(graphite) \quad \Delta H° = -171.7 \text{ (Table 9.202)}$$

$$C(g) + 4H(g) \rightarrow CH_4(g) \qquad \Delta H° = -398.0 \text{ kcal}$$
$$\text{Average C—H:} \quad \Delta H° = -99.5 \text{ kcal}$$

Bond energies are reported as positive quantities, i.e., for the dissociation of the bond. In a molecule like methane, the actual bond dissociation energy $D(C—H)$ for dissociation of a hydrogen atom is different for each successive step. This may be shown by reference to data discussed by J. A. Bell and G. B. Kistiakowsky, *J. Am. Chem. Soc.*, **84**, 3417 (1962):

$$CH_4 \rightarrow CH_3 + H, \quad D(CH_3—H) = 102$$
$$CH_3 \rightarrow CH_2 + H, \quad D(CH_2—H) = 105 \pm 3$$
$$CH_2 \rightarrow CH + H, \quad D(CH—H) = 108 \pm 3$$
$$CH \rightarrow C + H, \qquad D(C—H) \quad = 82.7$$
$$\text{Average} = 99.5 \text{ kcal}$$

Hence for polyatomic molecules we must clearly distinguish average bond energy from bond dissociation energy.

Once an average value for the C—H bond has been assigned, thermochemical data may be used to assign energies to other bonds; for example, data for methanol and water may be used to fix values for the O—H bond and for the C—O single bond. This type of treatment may be extended and a table of apparent bond energies compiled. Actually each bond energy is affected to some degree by the environment of the bond in the molecule; if allowance is not made for this, only a rough approximation is obtained for the enthalpy of the overall molecule relative to the free atoms of which it is composed by the addition of average bond energies. More elaborate systems of bond energies have been developed which include environmental factors and which provide a reasonably accurate method of estimating the thermochemical properties of organic molecules. Table 9.203 presents some simple average values. For a more extensive treatment, see e.g., G. J. Janz, *Estimation of Thermodynamic Properties of Organic Compounds*, Academic Press, New York, 1958.

Bond energies for simple diatomic molecules can be calculated from Tables 9.201(A) and 9.202. When the molecular energies predicted by summing bond

Table 9.203   Approximate Average Bond Strengths, ΔH, kcal mole^{-1} at 25°C*

		C—N	72.8		C—S	65
C—H	99.5	C=N	147		N—N	39 (hydrazine)
O—H	110.6 (H$_2$O)	C≡N	212.6		N—O	53 (nitrates)
N—H	93.4 (NH$_3$)	C—O	85.5 (general)		Be—Cl	109
Si—H	76 (SiH$_4$)	C=O	176 (aldehydes)		B—C	89
S—H	83 (H$_2$S)	C=O	179 (ketones)		S—F	68
C—C	82.6	C—F	116 (CF$_4$)		Si—Cl	91
C=C	145.8 general use	C—Cl	78.2 (CCl$_4$)		Sn—Cl	76
C≡C	199.6	C—Cl	81 (general)			

* Taken largely, by permission, from T. L. Cottrell, *The Strength of Chemical Bonds*, Butterworths Scientific Publications, London, 1958.

energies deviate significantly from actual experimental values, one concludes that the bond characteristics in the compound in question differ materially from those in the reference compound.

Reactions in Solution. The enthalpy change on formation of a solution of a given substance is the *integral heat of solution*. This heat is generally dependent on the concentration of the solution formed; the composition is usually represented on a mole basis. For example,

$$H_2SO_4(l, 25°C) + 100H_2O(l, 25°C) \rightarrow H_2SO_4(100H_2O, 25°C), \quad \Delta H = -17,680 \text{ cal}$$

that is, the integral heat of solution of 1 mole of sulfuric acid in 100 moles of water to form a 0.5551m solution is $-17,680$ cal, where $P = 1$ atm is to be understood. The magnitude of the enthalpy change for such a process is determined by experiment. From values for various concentrations heats of dilution may be determined; thus, from Table 9.204(A)

$$H_2SO_4(100H_2O) + 100H_2O \rightarrow H_2SO_4(200H_2O)$$

has an enthalpy change of -230 cal.

Table 9.204   Integral Heats of Solution at 25°C, kcal mole^{-1}*

Moles of Water per Mole of Solute	Integral Heat of Solution				
	H$_2$SO$_4$	HCl	NaOH	NH$_4$Cl	NaCl
∞	−22.99	−18.003	−10.246	3.62	0.930
20,000	−21.42	−17.978	...	...	...
5,000	−20.18	−17.952	−10.196	3.652	0.972

> The complete Table 9.204 will be found in the Appendix.

* From *NBS Circ.* 500.

From data for various compounds, we may calculate the heat of reactions in solution.

ILLUSTRATION.   Calculate ΔH for the process

$$NaOH(100H_2O) + HCl(100H_2O) \rightarrow NaCl(201H_2O)$$

By summing a number of thermochemical equations, based on data in Tables 9.201(A) and 9.204(A)

$NaOH(s) \rightarrow Na(s) + \frac{1}{2}H_2(g) + \frac{1}{2}O_2(g)$	$\Delta H_1 = -\Delta H_{for}^{\circ}(NaOH) =$	102,000 cal
$NaOH(100H_2O) \rightarrow NaOH(s) + 100H_2O$	$\Delta H_2 =$	10,110
$HCl(g) \rightarrow \frac{1}{2}H_2(g) + \frac{1}{2}Cl_2(g)$	$\Delta H_3 = -\Delta H_{for}^{\circ}(HCl) =$	22,020
$HCl(100H_2O) \rightarrow HCl(g) + 100H_2O$	$\Delta H_4 =$	17,693
$Na(s) + \frac{1}{2}Cl_2(g) \rightarrow NaCl(s)$	$\Delta H_5 = \Delta H_{for}^{\circ}(NaCl) =$	$-98,230$
$NaCl(s) + 201H_2O \rightarrow NaCl(201H_2O)$	$\Delta H_6 =$	1,016
$H_2(g) + \frac{1}{2}O_2(g) \rightarrow H_2O(l)$	$\Delta H_7 = \Delta H_{for}^{\circ}(H_2O) =$	$-68,320$

$$NaOH(100H_2O) + HCl(100H_2O) \rightarrow NaCl(201H_2O) \qquad \Delta H = \sum_1^7 \Delta H_{rx} = -13,711 \text{ cal}$$

In some reference tables (e.g., Bichowsky and Rossini, General References), heats of formation in various amounts of water have been tabulated; for example

$$Na(s) + \frac{1}{2}Cl_2(g) + 201H_2O(l) \rightarrow NaCl(201H_2O); \quad \Delta H = -97,214 \text{ cal}$$

which is the sum of ΔH_5 and ΔH_6 in the above illustration. Such a tabulation reduces the number of thermochemical equations which must be written to evaluate the heat of a reaction in solution. In this illustration, if the heats of reaction of the aqueous solutions of NaOH and HCl, respectively, were measured and all other enthalpy changes were known except ΔH_1, for example, the unknown heat of formation $-\Delta H_1$ could thereby be determined. Heat-of-solution measurements have been found a convenient way to determine many heats of formation.

Integral Heat of Formation of an Infinitely Dilute Solution. As the amount of water relative to the amount of solute is increased, the integral heat of solution approaches a limiting value described as the integral heat of solution at infinite dilution. The latter may be represented by the symbol (∞aq). For sulfuric acid,

$$H_2SO_4(l) \rightarrow H_2SO_4(\infty aq); \quad \Delta H = -22,990 \text{ cal}$$

This limiting value is determined by extrapolation. It is of particular interest in relation to the heats of formation assigned to ions.

Heats of Formation of Ions. Very dilute solutions of strong electrolytes can be treated from a thermochemical view as mixtures of ions. By adopting an additional convention, it is possible to tabulate standard heats of formation of individual ions, Table 9.201(A). The procedure will be illustrated for the chloride ion. Consider the reactions

$$\frac{1}{2}H_2(g) + \frac{1}{2}Cl_2(g) \rightarrow HCl(g); \quad \Delta H_{for}^{\circ} = -22,020 \text{ cal}$$

and

$$HCl(g) \rightarrow H^+(\infty aq) + Cl^-(\infty aq), \quad \Delta H^\circ = -18,003 \text{ cal}$$

The sum of these two changes gives

$$\tfrac{1}{2}H_2(g) + \tfrac{1}{2}Cl_2(g) \rightarrow H^+(\infty aq) + Cl^-(\infty aq), \quad \Delta H^\circ = -40,023 \text{ cal}$$

Thus

$$\Delta H^\circ(H^+) + \Delta H^\circ(Cl^-) = -40,023 \text{ cal}$$

with the standard states of the ions defined as their characteristic enthalpies at infinite dilution. It has been agreed arbitrarily to assign to the hydrogen ion a standard heat of formation of zero. Its real value is some unknown constant, which, in the evaluation of the heat of reactions involving ions, cancels out in any event. Hence this convention, like that of the zero heat of formation for the elements, does not introduce uncertainty in applying the data. The use of hydrogen as a reference standard is related to the convention adopted in tabulating single electrode potentials.

Similarly, from heats of other reactions or of solution, values for other ions may be established. For example, the heat of neutralization of a strong acid by a strong base in very dilute solution is found, independent of the acid or base used, to be $-13,360$ cal mole^{-1}; this heat is assigned to the reaction

$$H^+(\infty aq) + OH^-(\infty aq) \rightarrow H_2O(l)$$

hence

$$-13,360 = -68,320 - \Delta H^\circ(OH^-) - \Delta H^\circ(H^+)$$

Thus,

$$\Delta H^\circ(OH^-) = -54,960 \text{ cal}$$

Then, from the integral heat of solution to form NaOH(∞aq) and the heat of formation of the hydroxide ion, a heat of formation of $-57,280$ cal may be assigned to the Na$^+$ ion. In this manner, a table of values has been established for the various ions.

Ionic enthalpies may be used to evaluate the heats of reactions of ions and compounds in the usual way. For example,

$$Ag^+(\infty aq) + Cl^-(\infty aq) = AgCl(s)$$

is found from Table 9.201(A) to have a heat of reaction of $-15,657$ cal. When very dilute ionic solutions are mixed, no heat change is observed unless precipitation of a slightly soluble compound or formation of associated ion pairs or molecules (weak electrolyte) occurs. Measured heats of solution must be used to evaluate enthalpy changes for reactions at moderate or high concentration. Ionic enthalpies vary with concentration; standard heats of formation are applicable only at very low concentrations. In this respect, the choice of a standard state is somewhat analogous to that adopted for gases. Ionic enthalpies and their variation with concentration and temperature are of considerable importance in the study of solutions of electrolytes.

Reactions under Adiabatic Conditions. The heat liberated in many chemical reactions is large relative to the heat capacities of the products. If such reactions occur rapidly, conditions approximate those of an adiabatic process in which heat is not exchanged with the surroundings. In such cases, the products of the reaction may be raised to a very high temperature by the liberated energy. The temperatures established in flames of burning gas may be approximated from a knowledge of the heat of combustion. If it is assumed that all the energy released is used to raise the temperature of the specified products, the maximum value attainable can be calculated from the total heat capacity of the products. If temperatures reach very high values, dissociation of the products of the combustion reaction may need to be considered; nonequilibrium states frequently occur. For an example see *Thermochemical Calculations*, R. R. Wenner, McGraw-Hill Book Co., New York, 1941, Ch. XI.

If a reaction of a combustion or decomposition type occurs almost instantaneously, and hence virtually adiabatically, as in the detonation of TNT, the high temperature of the gaseous products generates a tremendous pressure and an explosion results. A prediction of the magnitude of the effects expected can be made through application of the first law.

Problems

9.201 (a) For the vaporization of water, $\Delta \bar{H}^{\circ}_{373^{\circ}K} = 9720$ cal mole^{-1}. What is the value of the energy change on vaporization of water at $373^{\circ}K$ if the vapor is assumed to be a perfect gas? The density of liquid water at $373^{\circ}K$ is 0.958 g cm^{-3}.

(b) If a capsule containing 10 grams liquid water initially under 1 atm pressure is broken inside an evacuated flask of sufficient volume so all the liquid vaporizes and the final pressure of water vapor (perfect gas) is 1 atm, calculate ΔH, ΔE, Q, and W for the process. T remains constant throughout, $373^{\circ}K$.

9.202 Using information in Problem 9.201 and assuming C_P for liquid water to be temperature independent at 1 cal g^{-1} deg^{-1}, calculate the difference in the enthalpy of a mole of water vapor at $373^{\circ}K$ at 1 atm pressure and the enthalpy of a mole of liquid water at $298^{\circ}K$ at 1 atm pressure.

9.203 Assume perfect behavior for the gases and use data from Table 9.201(A) to evaluate ΔH and ΔE for the following reactions at 25°C:

$$2CO(g) + O_2(g) \rightarrow 2CO_2(g)$$
$$4HCl(g) + O_2(g) \rightarrow 2H_2O(g) + 2Cl_2(g)$$
$$C_2H_5OH(g) + 3O_2(g) \rightarrow 2CO_2(g) + 3H_2O(g)$$
$$2C_6H_6(l) + 15O_2(g) \rightarrow 12CO_2(g) + 6H_2O(g)$$

9.204 Write out detailed thermochemical equations, so as to illustrate the meaning of the heat of formation of each compound and show how the measured heat of the reaction

$$H_2SO_4(l) + 2NaOH(s) \rightarrow Na_2SO_4(s) + 2H_2O(l)$$

together with the heats of formation of $H_2SO_4(l)$, $NaOH(s)$, and $H_2O(l)$ can be used to determine the heat of formation of $Na_2SO_4(s)$.

9.205 The heat of combustion of 1 gram of benzoic acid in a constant-volume bomb calorimeter at 25°C is -6300 cal. The heats of formation of $CO_2(g)$ and $H_2O(l)$ are given in Table 9.201(A). Show how to use this information to calculate the heat of formation of benzoic acid.

9.206   Use data from the tables to calculate ΔH for the following reactions (substances in standard states unless otherwise indicated, $T = 298.2°K$):

$$SO_3(g) + H_2O(l) \rightarrow H_2SO_4(l)$$
$$SO_3(g) + 101\,H_2O(l) \rightarrow H_2SO_4(100\,H_2O)$$
$$Ag^+(\infty aq) + NO_3^-(\infty aq) \rightarrow AgNO_3(s)$$
$$4HCl(g, 1000°K + O_2(g, 1000°K) \rightarrow 2Cl_2(g, 1000°K) + 2H_2O(g, 1000°K)$$
$$H_2SO_4(25\,H_2O) \rightarrow H_2SO_4(4\,H_2O) + 21\,H_2O(g)$$

9.207   Use data from Tables 9.201(A) and 7.201(A) to calculate the difference between the standard enthalpy of $H_2O(g)$ at $1000°K$ and its standard enthalpy at $298°K$. Calculate the difference between the standard heat of formation of $H_2O(g)$ at $1000°K$ and its standard heat of formation at $298°K$.

*9.208   If CO_2 is assumed to be a van der Waals gas, with $a = 3.6\ l^2\text{-atm mole}^{-2}$ and $b = 0.0428$ liter mole^{-1}, calculate the enthalpy of 5 grams of $CO_2(g)$ at 50 atm pressure and 25°C, relative to the elements carbon and O_2 in their standard states at 25°C.

9.209   Suppose that the integral heat of solution of Na_2O in 50 moles of water has been measured. Write the necessary thermochemical equations to illustrate how this information, together with a knowledge of the heats of formation of NaOH and H_2O and heat of solution of NaOH in water, may be used to determine the heat of formation of Na_2O.

9.210   From Tables 9.201(A) and 9.202, give the bond energy for the nitrogen molecule, the NO molecule, and the HCl molecule, and the average bond energy for the carbon–oxygen bond in the CO_2 molecule and the oxygen–hydrogen bond in the H_2O molecule.

9.211   From data in Tables 9.202 and 9.203, estimate the standard enthalpy of formation of normal propyl alcohol, acetone, and dimethyl ether.

9.212   Show how to use data in Table 9.201(A) for ethane and methane and data in Table 9.202 to derive a value for the carbon–carbon single-bond energy. Use similar data for methane and ethylene to derive a value for the carbon–carbon double-bond energy. State important assumptions.

9.213   From the average oxygen–hydrogen bond energy in water and the assumption that the bond dissociation energy for the OH molecule is 102 kcal mole^{-1}, calculate the actual bond dissociation energy for the removal of one hydrogen atom from a water molecule.

9.214   Calculate, from data in the tables, ΔH for the reactions
(a) $HCl(25\,H_2O) + NaOH(25\,H_2O) \rightarrow NaCl(51\,H_2O)$.
(b) $H_2(g) + S + 2O_2(g) + 15\,H_2O(l) \rightarrow H_2SO_4(15\,H_2O)$.
(c) The heat of formation of the sulfate ion.

9.215   Develop an equation which expresses the standard enthalpy change for the reaction

$$CH_4(g) + 2O_2(g) \rightarrow CO_2(g) + 2H_2O(g)$$

as a function of temperature over the interval 298 to $1000°K$; use data from Tables 7.201(A) and 9.201(A).

*9.216   Estimate the maximum flame temperature which can be reached by burning methane in a mixture of 15 per cent oxygen and 85 per cent N_2. Indicate any assumptions which may lead to serious error.

3. The Third Law; Standard Entropies of Chemical Substances

The entropy of a pure substance in a single phase at constant pressure varies with temperature in a manner determined by C_P/T. Heat capacities of all substances when measured at temperatures approaching absolute zero are observed to approach zero. This experimental observation is in accord with the Debye theory of heat capacity of solids (Chapter 5), which gives a limiting relation

$$C_V = \text{const } T^3 \qquad (5.423)$$

at temperatures near absolute zero; C_V and C_P may be considered virtually identical and $C_V = C_P$ in the limit as $T \to 0$. The proportionality constant is different for each substance. Hence, it is possible to evaluate the relationship of the entropy of substances at ordinary temperatures to the value at absolute zero by integration of the equation

$$S_T = S_0 + \int_0^T \frac{C_P}{T}\, dT \qquad (9.301)$$

It will be observed from the Debye equation that C_V/T approaches zero as T approaches zero.

   The Third Law.   In Chapter 7 it was pointed out that, according to Eq. 7.302, in the limit as T_1 approaches absolute zero an infinite amount of work must be done to remove a finite amount of heat from the cold reservoir. An idealized system might be conceived, however, in which the heat capacity approaches zero at low temperatures in such a way that the second law alone does not rule out the possibility of reaching absolute zero. However, the *unattainability of absolute zero* is stated as a general principle, as a law of experience, and is known as the third law of thermodynamics. The essence of this principle was presented by Nernst in 1906 and called by him a *heat theorem*. The supporting evidence is now so great that, like the first and second laws, the third law is accepted as generally valid. Evidence comes only in a minor way from attempts to produce very low temperatures and principally from an associated conclusion concerning the limiting value of the entropy at absolute zero. From various considerations (e.g., see, p. 225, Fowler and Guggenheim, *Statistical Thermodynamics*, Cambridge University Press, 1939) it has become apparent that all *perfectly ordered crystalline substances* ("perfect" meaning no randomness in structure) may be assigned zero entropy at absolute zero. The value of this sweeping generalization (an alternative statement of the third law) will become apparent in subsequent developments. With this assumption and the Debye equation, Eq. 5.423, it is possible to evaluate *absolute entropies* of chemical substances by integration of Eq. 9.301; S_0 is given a value of zero for all perfectly ordered crystalline substances.

   ILLUSTRATION.   Evaluation of absolute entropy from experimental data.
   Figure 9.301 shows data from which the third-law absolute entropy of oxygen may be evaluated [from results of W. F. Giauque and H. L. Johnston, *J. Am. Chem. Soc.*, **51**, 2300 (1929)]. The graph is of such a form that the area under the curves is related to the increase in entropy over the temperature interval

covered. Evaluation of the entropy of the gas at its normal boiling point proceeds as follows:

	Contribution to $\bar{S}$
0–14°K (extrapolation)	0.54 cal mole^{-1} deg^{-1}
14–23.66° (area)	1.500
Transition at 23.66°	0.948
Solid II, 23.66–43.76°	4.661
Transition at 43.76°	4.058
Solid I, 43.76–54.39°	2.397
Entropy of fusion (54.39°)	1.954
Liquid, 54.39–90.13°	6.462
Entropy of vaporization (gas at 1 atm)	18.07
Total $\bar{S}_{90.13°K}$	40.59

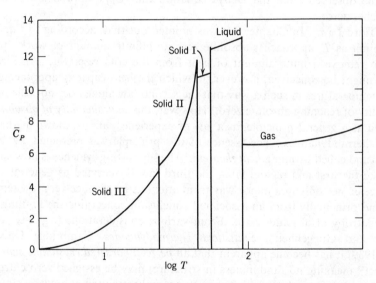

Fig. 9.301   Heat capacity of oxygen as a function of temperature. Various crystalline modifications exist. (By permission from Lewis, Randall, Pitzer, and Brewer, *Thermodynamics*, Second Edition, McGraw-Hill Book Co., 1961.)

Standard Entropies. Standard entropies of substances at 25°C are tabulated in Table 9.301(A) for use in thermodynamic calculations. If phase transitions occur between 0 and 298.2°K, these contributions must be added in the evaluation of the standard entropy as shown in the oxygen case. For future reference Table 9.301(A) includes values for ions in aqueous solution. As in the enthalpy case these are based on an arbitrary convention, assigning H^+ ion at unit activity, based on molal concentration, a standard entropy of zero.

Table 9.301   Some Standard Entropies at 25°C, $\bar{S}°$, cal mole^{-1} deg^{-1}
(Ions are in aqueous solution)

Ar	36.98	CH$_4$	44.50	HI	49.31	NH$_4$Cl	22.6
Al	6.77	C$_2$H$_6$	54.85	Fe	6.49	O$_2$	49.00
Al^{3+}	−74.9	C$_3$H$_8$	64.51	Fe^{++}	−27.1	H$_2$O(l)	16.72

The complete Table 9.301(A) will be found in the Appendix

Entropies in Table 9.301(A) represent values characteristic of each substance in its standard state, as defined in Sec. 9.2, and are given the symbol $\bar{S}°$. Standard entropies of gases are values for the hypothetical perfect-gas state at 1 atm, i.e., at $f° = 1$ atm. The standard entropy may be calculated from the experimental third-law value for the gas at very low pressure by use of the perfect-gas equation to bring the entropy to the corresponding value at 1 atm. The actual experimental values at 1 atm will be slightly different because of gas imperfections.

As an example of the determination of the standard entropy at 190.97°K, we may cite the work of Valentine, Brodale, and Giauque on trifluoromethane. Their data provide the results summarized in Table 9.302.

*Table 9.302   The Entropy of Trifluoromethane,
cal deg^{-1} mole^{-1}**

	Contributions to entropy, $\bar{S}$
0–15°K (extrapolation)	0.67
15–117.97° (graphical integration)	17.50
Fusion, 970/117.97	8.22
117.97–190.97 (graphical integration)	9.71
Vaporization, 3994/190.97	20.91
Entropy of CHF$_3$ gas at boiling point, 190.97°K	57.01
Corr. to ideal gas, $\Delta S = -2b'P/T^3$	0.17
Entropy of ideal CHF$_3$ gas at boiling point	57.18
$\bar{S}°$ from molecular data at 190.97°K	57.23

* By permission from Valentine, Brodale, and Giauque, *J. Phys. Chem.*, **66**, 395 (1962).

The correction to ideal gas behavior at the normal boiling point may be made by considering two changes

(1) real gas (1 atm) → real gas (at P^*, a pressure so small that the entropy is the same as it would be for an ideal gas)

(2) real gas (ideal at P^*) → ideal gas (1 atm)

From the dependence of entropy on pressure at constant temperature, Eq. 7.320, we may write

$$\Delta S_{\text{corr to ideal gas}} = \Delta S_1 + \Delta S_2$$

$$= \left[\int_1^{P^*} - \left(\frac{\partial V}{\partial T} \right)_P dP \right]_{\text{real}} + \left[\int_{P^*}^1 - \left(\frac{\partial V}{\partial T} \right)_P dP \right]_{\text{ideal}}$$

$(\partial V / \partial T)_P$ must be evaluated from the equation of state for the real gas and is R/P for an ideal gas. Valentine, Brodale, and Giauque used the simplified Berthelot equation of the form $P\bar{V} = RT + b'P/T^2$ for trifluoromethane, with a value of $b' = -6 \times 10^5$ cal atm^{-1} deg^2 mole^{-1}. Hence we may write

$$\Delta \bar{S}_{\text{corr}} = \int_1^{P^*} \frac{-R}{P} dP - \int_1^{P^*} \frac{2(6 \times 10^5)}{T^3} dP - \int_{P^*}^1 \frac{R}{P} dP$$

$$= \frac{-12 \times 10^5}{(190.97)^3} (P^* - 1) = 0.17 \text{ cal deg}^{-1} \text{ mole}^{-1}$$

since $P^* \approx 0$. The comparison at the end of Table 9.302 shows the entropy calculated from molecular structure data by a method to be described in Chapter 11. The close agreement is an example of experimental verification of the third law.

Imperfect Crystals and Solid Solutions. Imperfect crystals may be considered similar to mixtures in the sense that there is some uncertainty as to the location of the various molecular or ionic components. Such a situation leads to a contribution to the entropy analogous to an entropy of mixing. Crystal imperfection may arise for a number of reasons; we will mention only a few. NO (also CO) is a classic example of a molecule in which the two atoms are sufficiently similar that some degree of disorder is frozen into the crystal as it is cooled; the difference in energy between an "NO" orientation and an "ON" orientation is not sufficiently great to fix the molecule one way or the other. If the NO and ON orientations are considered equally probable, the entropy effect associated with this uncertainty can be considered the same as the ideal entropy of mixing of two components in equal molar amounts. Hence, from Eq. 8.311

$$\Delta \bar{S}_{\text{mole of mixture}} = -R \ln 0.5 = R \ln 2$$

The heat capacities of crystals with the ordered and random oriented molecules are virtually the same, and no evidence for an entropy of "mixing" in the random form would be observed in a measurement of its heat capacity from the vicinity of $0°$K to high temperatures; that is, the entropy of mixing remains in the crystal as it is cooled to the vicinity of $0°$K and must be assigned to the crystal at $0°$K. If it is not, the entropy evaluated from C_P data for the imperfect crystal will be found too small and will not agree with that determined by independent means.

As another example, we may consider certain ionic crystals of the type of M_2O_3.

In an idealized octahedral coordination of six oxide ions around M^{3+} there are three equivalent positions for each two metal ions. Hence the crystal may be thought of as an ideal mixture of one third holes and two thirds M^{3+}, if a completely random arrangement were possible. Since the location of the metal ions is not definite, such a crystal is not expected to have zero entropy at $0°K$.

Glasses (supercooled liquids) do not have well-defined structures and have some residual entropy at $0°K$.

It will be recognized that nearly all natural substances are isotopic mixtures. However, isotopic composition remains constant in most ordinary chemical changes and need not be considered. Hence an entropy associated with isotopic mixing is not included in the standard entropy values. For this and other reasons to be discussed in Chapter 11 the latter are frequently called *practical* entropies.

Tests of the Third Law. The Third Law may be tested by comparing the entropy change which it predicts for any transformation with that observed experimentally at moderate or high temperatures. For example, it is possible to supercool certain crystalline forms, which normally undergo a transition to a more stable modification, below their transition temperatures. If the heat capacities of both forms, I (stable at low temperatures) and II (stable at high temperatures but capable of being supercooled to the vicinity of absolute zero), are measured from the vicinity of absolute zero to the transition temperature, then the entropy of each form may be evaluated from Eq. 9.301 at the transition temperature. The entropy of the high-temperature form equals that of the low-temperature form plus the entropy of transition, measured from the reversible heat of transition. Such a relationship does not, of course, prove that $S_0 = 0$ but requires only that both forms have the same entropy at absolute zero. A similar test may be made for chemical transformations and a similar conclusion drawn; that is, all perfectly ordered pure chemical substances may be assigned the same entropy at absolute zero. Further evidence will be indicated later (Chapter 11) to suggest why this value has been taken as zero.

Entropy Changes for Chemical Processes. Entropy changes for chemical transformations may be handled in a similar manner to enthalpy changes. An equation is written carefully defining the nature of the initial and final states. ΔS represents the change in entropy when isolated reactants are completely converted into isolated products; if these substances are in their standard states, the entropy change is labeled $\Delta S°$. For example,

$$H_2(g) + \tfrac{1}{2}O_2(g) \rightarrow H_2O(g), \quad \Delta S°_{\text{for}(298)} = -10.6 \text{ eu}$$

Such an entropy change can be calculated from the standard entropies of the substances involved, Table 9.301(A). It will be shown in Chapter 10 that a study of the equilibrium characteristics of a reaction may also be used to determine its entropy change.

Since the entropy change of each of the substances involved in a reaction may be expressed as a function of temperature from heat capacity data, a general expression may be written to indicate how the entropy change for a reaction varies with temperature. The procedure is the same as that outlined in detail in the development of a similar equation for enthalpy, Sec. 9.2, and leads to an expression of the form

$$\Delta S^\circ_{T_2} = \Delta S^\circ_{T_1} + \int_{T_1}^{T_2} \Delta C^\circ_P \frac{dT}{T} \tag{9.302}$$

The calculation of the entropy change for the spontaneous freezing of liquid water at 268°K in an Illustration in Sec. 9.1 is actually of this form.

The measured entropy change for a reaction is frequently used to determine the absolute entropy of one of the participating substances. When all standard entropies are independently known, a comparison of the measured ΔS and the value predicted by absolute values constitutes a check of the validity of the third-law postulate.

The basis for assigning standard entropies is clearly different from that used for enthalpies. According to the third law, entropies of pure substances are always zero or positive. The elements are assigned values in the same way as compounds and are not used as zero reference points as in the case of enthalpies. However, ΔS for any reaction may still be combined with ΔH to calculate ΔF, since the reference convention cancels out for the overall change.

Problems

9.301   If the entropy change for the reaction

$$Fe_2O_3(s) + 6HCl(g) \rightarrow 2FeCl_2(s) + 3H_2O(g) + Cl_2(g)$$

is -43.2 eu at 25°C, show how this value and data from Table 9.301 can be used to determine the absolute entropy of $FeCl_2(s)$.

9.302   A certain liquid obeys Trouton's rule. What will be the total entropy change if 1 mole of the liquid initially under 1 atm pressure is allowed to vaporize into an evacuated container of such a volume that the final pressure is 100 mm Hg, if the temperature remains constant at the boiling point?

9.303   When perfect gases are mixed together, the thermodynamic properties of each are unaffected by the presence of the other:

(a) Develop an equation for the change in entropy when 1 mole of an ideal gas A at initial pressure P is mixed with 1 mole of ideal gas B at an initial pressure P (T constant) (1) if the final total pressure of the mixture is P, and (2) if the final pressure of the mixture is $2P$.

(b) Develop a general equation for the entropy of mixing in terms of mole fractions in the final mixture, when the final total pressure of the mixture is the same as the initial pressure of each of the component gases before mixing (T constant).

9.304   Using heat capacity data from Table 7.201(A), calculate the difference between the standard entropy of formation of CO_2 gas at 500°C and at 25°C. Compare your answer with Problem 7.310.

*9.305   From data for C_2H_5OH in Tables 9.201(A) and 9.301(A), find the value of the vapor pressure of liquid ethanol at 25°C from entropy considerations. HINT: consider the processes:

C_2H_5OH(liq, 1 atm total pressure) → C_2H_5OH (ideal gas at equil. vapor pressure)
C_2H_5OH(ideal gas at equil. vapor pressure) → C_2H_5OH (ideal gas at 1 atm)
C_2H_5OH(liq, 1 atm total pressure) → C_2H_5OH(ideal gas at 1 atm)

Indicate assumptions. Compare your answer with vapor pressure reported in any handbook.

9.306   From data in Tables 9.201(A) and 9.301(A), find values for $\Delta H°$ and $\Delta S°$ at 25°C for:

(a) $Na_2CO_3(s) + 2HCl(g) \rightarrow 2NaCl(s) + H_2O(g) + CO_2(g)$
(b) $CO_3^=(aq) + 2H^+(aq) \rightarrow CO_2(g) + H_2O(l)$

4. Standard Free Energies of Formation

Numerical values for the free energies of chemical substances can be calculated from standard enthalpy and entropy data. The free energy of formation represents the change in F when the compound in question is formed from the elements. F is tabulated rather than A. Thus the free energy of formation of $HCl(g)$

$$\tfrac{1}{2}H_2(g) + \tfrac{1}{2}Cl_2(g) \rightarrow HCl(g)$$

is determined by the sum $\Delta F_{for} = \Delta H_{for} - T\,\Delta S_{for}$. As for enthalpy, the numerical value of ΔF_{for} is assigned to the compound. The elements have zero free energy of formation by convention. It must be kept clearly in mind that the ΔS is for the formation reaction and is not just the standard entropy of the compound (HCl above).

Like $\Delta H°$ and $\bar{S}°$, standard free energies of formation are usually tabulated at 25°C. The standard states of pure substances are those described in Sec. 9.2. The standard for gases is unit fugacity. For condensed phases, the standard state is described as one in which the activity is unity, usually the pure phase. For example, the standard free energy of formation of sodium chloride, represented by $\Delta F_{for}°(NaCl)$, is the free energy change for the reaction

$$Na(s, a = 1) + \tfrac{1}{2}Cl_2(g, f = 1) \rightarrow NaCl(s, a = 1)$$

at the temperature of interest. If the standard free energy of formation is negative, this means that at constant temperature and pressure the elements in their standard states would be expected to react spontaneously to form the compound in its standard state. We have no way of knowing from thermodynamics whether the reaction will proceed at a measurable rate, however. Also, it is possible that intermediate mixtures which have a lower free energy than either pure reactants or products may be formed. Such mixtures will be discussed in Chapter 10. If the tendency to react under other conditions of activity or fugacity is of interest, the appropriate equations may be added to the standard reaction to find the change under the new conditions. The free energy associated with these changes is given very simply in the form $\Delta F = nRT \ln a_2/a_1$ for each component, although the determination of the correct activity in the new state may not be simple.

ΔF **as a Function of Temperature.** The variation with temperature of the standard free energy change for a reaction may be calculated from heat capacity and heat of formation data.

Equation 7.418,

$$\left[\frac{\partial(F/T)}{\partial T}\right]_P = -\frac{H}{T^2} \tag{7.418}$$

may be applied to each substance and the terms combined to give the differential equation,

$$\frac{d(\Delta F^\circ/T)}{dT} = -\frac{\Delta H^\circ}{T^2} \tag{9.401}$$

The superscript degree indicates each substance must be in its standard state. ΔH° is expressed as a function of temperature,

$$\Delta H^\circ = \Delta H^\circ_* + \Delta a T + \tfrac{1}{2}\Delta b T^2 + \cdots \tag{9.204}$$

Thus

$$\frac{d(\Delta F^\circ/T)}{dT} = -\frac{\Delta H^\circ_*}{T^2} - \frac{\Delta a}{T} - \tfrac{1}{2}\Delta b \cdots \tag{9.402}$$

and

$$\frac{\Delta F^\circ}{T} = \frac{\Delta H^\circ_*}{T} - \Delta a \ln T - \tfrac{1}{2}\Delta b T \cdots + I \tag{9.403}$$

where I is an integration constant, or

$$\Delta F^\circ = \Delta H^\circ_* - \Delta a T \ln T - \tfrac{1}{2}\Delta b T^2 \cdots + IT \tag{9.404}$$

The integration constant I may be determined if ΔF° is known at some temperature in the interval over which the equation is applicable. This interval is determined by the heat capacity equations, that is, the range of validity of the constants a, b, etc.

Note that differentiation of Eq. 9.404 with respect to temperature gives an expression for the entropy change of the reaction as a function of temperature,

$$\frac{d\,\Delta F^\circ}{dT} = -\Delta S^\circ \tag{9.405}$$

analogous to Eq. 7.412. Free energy data are frequently summarized for a given reaction in the form of Eq. 9.404, with numerical constants given, thus including the enthalpy, heat capacity, and entropy characteristics. The ΔS° equation, Eq. 9.405, also includes the integration constant I. Thus, I may be evaluated from standard entropies.

From standard free energies of formation for all the participating substances in any reaction, ΔF° for the reaction is

$$\Delta F^\circ = \sum_{\text{prod}} n_p\,\Delta F^\circ_{\text{for}} - \sum_{\text{reac}} n_r\,\Delta F^\circ_{\text{for}} \tag{9.406}$$

at the temperature of interest.

ΔF° may also be calculated from values of ΔH° and ΔS°

$$\Delta F^\circ = \Delta H^\circ - T \Delta S^\circ \tag{9.407}$$

Free energy data at various temperatures are also widely reported in the form of a *relative free-energy function*, $(\bar{F}^\circ - \bar{H}_0^\circ)/T$. The reason for this form will be made apparent in Chapter 11. This function varies smoothly with temperature and intermediate values can easily be interpolated; values are usually given at intervals of several hundred degrees. It will be observed that

$$\frac{\bar{F}^\circ - \bar{H}_0^\circ}{T} = \frac{\bar{H}^\circ - \bar{H}_0^\circ}{T} - \bar{S}^\circ$$

Hence the relative free energy function can be evaluated from relative enthalpy data and entropy data and also from partition functions (Chapter II). The change of the relative free energy function permits evaluation of ΔF° if ΔH_0°, the enthalpy change for the process at absolute zero, is known. The use of such functions obviates the need for integrating heat capacity equations and will be illustrated and discussed further in Chapter 11.

Problems

9.401 One kilogram of ice at 0°C is put into 1 kg of liquid water at 100°C. Calculate the change in F and A which occurs as the system comes to equilibrium. Data for water, $\bar{C}_P$, $\bar{S}_{298°K}^\circ$, $\bar{V}$, and the enthalpy of fusion may be assumed known constants. P remains constant at 1 atm.

9.402 The heat capacity of cadmium is $\bar{C}_P^\circ = 5.46 + 2.466 \times 10^{-3} T$ cal mole^{-1} deg^{-1} in the temperature interval 298 to 600°K. $S_{298°K}^\circ = 12.3$ eu. Calculate the difference in the molar free energy of cadmium at 298 and at 600°K under a constant pressure of 1 atm.

9.403 Given only the heat capacity of liquid water over the temperature interval 0 to 100°C and the absolute entropy of liquid water at 298°K, show how to calculate the difference between the Gibbs free energy of 1 mole of water vapor at 100°C and 1 mole of ice at 0°C, both at 1 atm pressure.

9.404 Using data in Tables 7.201(A), 9.201(A), and 9.301(A) evaluate the standard free energy of formation of $H_2O(l)$ (a) at 25°C, and (b) at 100°C. Assume $H_2O(l)$ has a constant value of C_P of 1 cal g^{-1} in this temperature interval.

9.405 Using standard entropy, heat of formation and heat capacity data, set up an equation of the form of Eq. 9.404 for the free energy of formation of $SO_3(g)$. All constants in the equation should be evaluated.

9.406 The vapor pressure of pure water at 25°C is 23.76 mm Hg. If the vapor pressure of water at 25°C above a particular solution is 21.9 mm Hg, what is the activity of water in the solution if pure water is taken as the standard state? What is the difference in the molar free energy $(\bar{F})$ of pure liquid water and its molar free energy in such a solution?

9.407 Consider the reaction

$$N_2(g) + 3H_2(g) \rightarrow 2NH_3(g)$$

Use data from Tables 7.201(A), 9.201(A), and 9.301(A) to derive a general expression for ΔF° for this reaction as a function of temperature.

9.408   If, for a certain process, $\Delta F° = 20{,}000 + 6T \log_{10} T - 10.0T$, what is the value of $\Delta H°$ and of $\Delta S°$ at $500°K$?

9.409   Use data in Tables 9.201(A) and 9.301(A) to evaluate $\Delta F°$ for $Na_2CO_3(s)$ at $25°C$.

5. Review Problems

9.501   A small bulb initially containing 1 gram of liquid water is shattered inside an evacuated vessel of such volume that the final pressure of water vapor is 100 mm. The temperature is maintained at $100°C$ throughout the experiment. Evaluate ΔF, ΔA, and ΔS. Assume that water vapor is a perfect gas.

9.502   A small bulb containing 20 grams of water is shattered at $100°C$ in a evacuated vessel of volume 20 liters. Evaluate ΔF, ΔA, and ΔS for the isothermal process.

9.503   Use the tables in the appendix to calculate ΔH_{298} and $\Delta S°_{298}$ for the following reactions:

$$SO_2(g) + \tfrac{1}{2}O_2(g) \rightarrow SO_3(g)$$
$$C(gr) + \tfrac{1}{2}O_2(g) \rightarrow CO(g)$$
$$H^+(\infty aq) + OH^-(\infty aq) \rightarrow H_2O(l)$$
$$SO_3(g) + 2NaOH(\infty aq) \rightarrow Na_2SO_4(\infty aq) + H_2O(l)$$
$$H_2SO_4(\infty aq) + 2NaOH(\infty aq) \rightarrow Na_2SO_4(\infty aq) + 2H_2O(l)$$

9.504   Obtain $\Delta F°$ as a function of temperature for the gaseous reaction

$$\tfrac{1}{2}N_2 + \tfrac{1}{2}O_2 \rightarrow NO$$

9.505   Obtain $\bar{F}°_T - \bar{F}°_{298}$ for NO as a function of temperature.

9.506   Evaluate the enthalpy of formation of I_2 gas from iodine atoms at $25°C$.

*9.507   Calculate the maximum hypothetical temperature obtainable in an oxyacetylene torch. Why is this temperature not obtained in practice?

9.508   What would be the entropy of an ideal solution of CCl_4 ($X = 0.4$) and $CHCl_3$ ($X = 0.6$) at the absolute zero, if such a solution were cooled rapidly enough so that it did not separate?

9.509   A bulb containing 18 grams of water is shattered in a vessel of 35 liters containing 40 grams of gaseous argon. The temperature is maintained at $100°C$. Calculate ΔS for the process; assume water vapor and argon are perfect gases.

9.510   If, for a certain process, $\Delta F° = 3000 + 5T \ln T - 15T$, calculate $\Delta H°$ and $\Delta S°$ as functions of temperature.

9.511   If, for a certain process, $\Delta H° = 43{,}600 - 8.0T + 0.002T^2$, express $\Delta F°$ and $\Delta S°$ as functions of temperature if $\Delta S° = 35$ cal deg^{-1} mole^{-1} at $298°K$.

9.512   The entropy of vaporization of a liquid to form a gas is

$$\Delta \bar{S}° = 17 - 10 \ln \frac{T}{90}$$

If the boiling point is $90°K$, obtain an expression for the vapor pressure of the liquid. Calculate $\Delta \bar{F}°$ for vaporization, as a function of temperature. Calculate $\Delta \bar{S}$ for vaporization under equilibrium conditions at $80°K$.

General References

Bichowsky, F. R., and F. D. Rossini, *The Thermochemistry of the Chemical Substances*, Reinhold Publishing Corp., New York, 1936.

Cottrell, T. L., *The Strengths of Chemical Bonds*, Butterworths Scientific Publications, London, 1958.

Fowler, R. H., and E. A. Guggenheim, *Statistical Thermodynamics*, Cambridge University Press, Cambridge, England, 1939.

JANAF Thermochemical Tables, Joint Army-Navy-Air Force Thermochemical Panel, Thermal Laboratory of the Dow Chemical Co., Midland, Mich.

Janz, G. J., *Estimation of Thermodynamic Properties of Organic Compounds*, Academic Press, New York, 1958.

Lewis, G. N., M. Randall, K. S. Pitzer, and L. Brewer, *Thermodynamics*, Second Edition, McGraw-Hill Book Co., New York, 1961.

Rossini, F. D., Editor, *Experimental Thermochemistry*, prepared under the auspices of the International Union of Pure and Applied Chemistry, Interscience Publishers, New York, 1956.

Wagman, D. D., W. H. Evans, S. Levine, and I. Jaffey, *NBS Circ.* 500, 1952, and supplements published in the *Journal of Research* of the National Bureau of Standards.

Wenner, R. R., *Thermochemical Calculations*, McGraw-Hill Book Co., New York, 1941.

Chapter Ten

Chemical Equilibrium

We are now prepared to discuss chemical equilibrium in terms of the thermo-dynamic properties of the participating components.

1. General Principles

For a reversible change at constant temperature and pressure, $dF_{T,P} = 0$. As applied to Eq. 7.602

$$\left(\sum_i \mu_i \, dn_i \right)_{T,P} = 0 \tag{10.101}$$

For a closed system in which a chemical change occurs, the change in number of moles of each constitutent is determined by the stoichiometry of the reaction, e.g.,

$$aA + bB + \cdots \rightarrow cC + \cdots$$

When $c \, dn$ moles of C are formed, $a \, dn$ moles of A disappear, etc., so at equilibrium Eq. 10.101 becomes

$$c\mu_C \, dn + \cdots - a\mu_A \, dn - b\mu_B \, dn - \cdots = 0$$

This requires that

$$c\mu_C + \cdots - a\mu_A - b\mu_B + \cdots = 0 \tag{10.102}$$

Equation 10.102 represents any number of reactants and products. The equilibrium state is characterized by the particular set of concentrations needed to satisfy Eq. 10.102. To determine these we must know how the chemical potential changes with the composition, Eqs. 7.607 and 7.608, and the relative values of the chemical potentials of the pure components. The variation of chemical potential with composition will be reviewed briefly.

Chemical Potential in Mixtures. Ideal gas mixtures were discussed in Sec. 8.3, where it was shown that

$$\mu_i = \mu_i^\circ + RT \ln P_i \tag{8.302}$$

analogous to Eq. 7.609. μ_i° is the standard-state chemical potential of ideal gas i at 1 atm; μ_i is the chemical potential at any other partial pressure P_i. For real gases f_i must replace P_i.

In condensed systems, the activity rather than the fugacity may be used. As defined earlier,

$$a_i = \frac{f_i}{f_i^\circ} \tag{7.509}$$

where f_i° is the fugacity in the chosen standard state. Hence

$$d\mu_i = RT \, d \ln f_i = RT \, d \ln a_i \tag{10.103}$$

In condensed systems, it is customary to relate the activity to a convenient concentration unit, e.g., the mole fraction. If the pure component is chosen as the standard state, f_i° is then the fugacity of the pure component. For Raoult's law (ideal) behavior

$$\mu_i = \mu_{i(X)}^\circ + RT \ln X_i \tag{8.306}$$

Alternatively, the activity may be identified with concentration, e.g., molarity or molality. Solute mole fraction, molarity, and molality approach a direct proportional relationship at very low concentrations

$$X_2 = \frac{n_2}{n_1 + n_2} = \frac{c}{\dfrac{1000\rho - cM_2}{M_1} + c} = \frac{m}{\dfrac{1000}{M_1} + m} \tag{10.104}$$

Here X_2 is the mole fraction, n_1 and n_2 are the number of moles of solvent and solute, respectively, c is the concentration of solute in moles per liter, ρ is the density of the solution, m is the molal concentration of solute, and M_1 and M_2 are the molecular weights of the solvent and solute. However, the various concentration units are not in a simple constant proportion at higher concentrations; the type of concentration unit on which the activity is based must be clearly specified because unity activity corresponds to quite different states (i.e., ideally unit concentration) for each choice of concentration.

Activity Coefficients. In real solutions deviation of the activity from the concentration unit on which it is based is indicated by the activity coefficient, a number, determined experimentally, by which the concentration unit must be multiplied to obtain the correct activity. Thus $a_X = \gamma_X X$, or $a_m = \gamma_m m$, or $a_c = \gamma_c c$. It may be shown that the following relationship exists between the various activity coefficients

$$\gamma_X = \gamma_m(1 + 0.001mM_1) = \gamma_c \frac{[\rho + 0.001c(M_1 - M_2)]}{\rho_0} \qquad (10.105)$$

where ρ is the density of the solution, and ρ_0 the density of the pure solvent. Thus, determination of the activity coefficient on any concentration basis gives sufficient information to calculate the other activity coefficients. To derive Eq. 10.105 we must remember that the activities based on different concentration units are proportional but not equal, e.g., $a_X = ka_m$. At infinite dilution the proportionality constant k can be evaluated; for example, the usual choice of standard state is such that $\gamma_X = \gamma_m = 1$ at zero concentration; hence $(a_X = X)_{\lim_{X \to 0}}$, $(a_m = m)_{\lim_{m \to 0}}$, and $\left(X_2 = \dfrac{M_1 m}{1000}\right)_{\lim_{X_2 \to 0} \, \lim_{m \to 0}}$. Thus $k = M_1/1000$, and we may write

$$a_X = \gamma_X X = \gamma_m m \frac{M_1}{1000}, \quad \text{or} \quad \gamma_X = \gamma_m\left(m + \frac{1000}{M_1}\right)\frac{M_1}{1000}$$

which is equivalent to the first relationship in Eq. 10.105.

We will not discuss here how activities may be determined experimentally for nonideal solutions when direct measurement of fugacities is not practical. A number of suitable methods exist, some of which were indicated in Chapter 8; others will be given in Chapter 12. We shall assume that activities at various concentrations can be determined and proceed to illustrate their use in free energy and equilibrium constant expressions. Frequently, the simplifying assumption will be made that the solutions formed are ideal.

Problems

10.101 (a) If at a particular temperature the density of a $5M$ aqueous solution of a substance of molecular weight 100 is 1.289, calculate the molality and the mole fraction.

(b) If γ_m for this solution is 0.242, calculate γ_X and γ_c.

10.102 Calculate the change in chemical potential of each component and the total free energy change when 1 gram of N_2 and 1 gram of O_2, both initially at 1 atm pressure as pure gases at 25°C, are brought together to form a perfect gas mixture at a total pressure of 0.5 atm.

*10.103 Derive the second half of the relationship shown in Eq. 10.105.

10.104 What is the activity of benzene in a mixture of 10 grams of benzene and 10 grams of toluene if it is assumed ideal and if (a) activity is based on mole fraction and the standard state of benzene is taken as $X_b = 1$? (b) activity is based on mole fraction and the standard state is taken as $m_b = 1$?

2. Homogeneous Gas Equilibria

The Free Energy Reaction Isotherm.   Consider a homogeneous gas reaction such as

$$H_2(g, f_{H_2}) + I_2(g, f_{I_2}) \rightarrow 2HI(g, f_{HI})$$

at some constant temperature. The initial state consists of hydrogen at fugacity f_{H_2} and iodine at fugacity f_{I_2}; these substances form HI at fugacity f_{HI}. The change in free energy ΔF accompanying this process is determined by the difference

$$\Delta F = (\sum_{prod} n_i \mu_i) - (\sum_{reac} n_i \mu_i) \tag{10.201}$$

which, for the HI reaction, becomes

$$\Delta F = 2\mu_{HI} - \mu_{I_2} - \mu_{H_2}$$

Each chemical potential may be expressed in terms of its standard value and the fugacity

$$\mu_i = \mu_i^\circ + RT \ln f_i \tag{8.302}$$

Thus

$$\Delta F = 2\mu_{HI}^\circ - \mu_{I_2}^\circ - \mu_{H_2}^\circ + 2RT \ln f_{HI} - RT \ln f_{I_2} - RT \ln f_{H_2}$$

The difference in the standard chemical potentials may be represented by ΔF°; hence the free energy change for the reaction as described is given by the sum of the standard free energy change and terms relating the chemical potential of each component under the given conditions to its standard value

$$\Delta F = \Delta F^\circ + RT \ln \frac{f_{HI}^2}{f_{H_2} f_{I_2}} \tag{10.202}$$

Such an equation is used only at some particular temperature; it has been shown earlier that ΔF° may be calculated at any temperature from its value at a standard reference temperature, together with heat capacity and heat of reaction data. Equation 10.202 is called the free energy reaction isotherm.

The Equilibrium Constant.   The free energy reaction isotherm may be used to find conditions under which the reaction is expected to proceed spontaneously ($\Delta F_{T,P}$ negative) and the conditions which correspond to equilibrium. In the latter case the term containing the ratio of fugacities must have a value which just cancels ΔF° so that $\Delta F_{T,P}$ is zero. This is the necessary condition for the system to be in a state of equilibrium. The quotient of fugacities needed is given by

$$\Delta F^\circ = -RT \ln \left(\frac{f_{HI}^2}{f_{H_2} f_{I_2}} \right)_{equil} \tag{10.203}$$

Since ΔF° has a fixed value at a given temperature, determined by the defined standard states of the reactants and products, the fugacity quotient at equilibrium must similarly have a fixed value. This constant is characteristic of the reaction under consideration at the given temperature at all total pressures or concentrations and is called the equilibrium constant, K_f. The subscript f indicates that this equilibrium constant is based on the standard states defined by fugacities. Thus Eq. 10.203 may be written:

$$\Delta F° = -RT \ln K_f \tag{10.204}$$

A similar treatment may be developed for any reaction of interest. The equilibrium constant will always have the familiar form

$$K_f = \frac{f_C^c \cdots}{f_A^a f_B^b \cdots} \tag{10.205}$$

for a reaction of the general form $aA + bB + \cdots = cC + \cdots$. It should be emphasized that $\Delta F°$ represents the standard free energy change for the reaction from reactants to products, all in their respective standard states, and does *not* represent the free energy change under the equilibrium condition; the latter is zero. However, K_f is determined by the set of fugacities characterizing the equilibrium state. Thus the right- and left-hand sides of Eq. 10.204 refer to different sets of conditions for the reaction. The reaction isotherm may be used to evaluate ΔF for any arbitrary set of fugacities once $\Delta F°$ is known. The equilibrium constant may be used to evaluate the standard free energy change, or, alternatively, the latter may be used to evaluate the equilibrium constant. If reactants and products are mixed under nonequilibrium conditions, spontaneous change is expected until the fugacity quotient reaches the equilibrium value.

ILLUSTRATION. (*a*) Use data from Tables 9.201(A) and 9.301(A) to calculate the equilibrium constant for the reaction $H_2(g) + I_2(g) = 2HI(g)$ at 25°C.
From Table 9.201(A) (note that $I_2(s)$ is standard state for iodine)

$$\Delta H° = 2\Delta H°_{\text{for HI}} - \Delta H°_{\text{for } I_2}(g) = 2(6200) - 14,880$$
$$= 12,400 - 14,880 = -2480 \text{ cal}$$

From Table 9.301(A)

$$\Delta S° = 2\bar{S}°_{HI} - \bar{S}°_{H_2} - \bar{S}°_{I_2}(g) = 2(49.31) - 31.21 - 62.28$$
$$= 5.13 \text{ cal deg}^{-1}$$

Thus

$$\Delta F° = -2,480 - (298.2)(5.13) \text{ cal}$$
$$= -4,010 \text{ cal}$$

and

$$\ln K = +\frac{4010}{(1.987)(298.2)}$$

(*b*) Show how to calculate the equilibrium degree of dissociation of HI if pure HI is placed in known amount in a vessel of known volume and brought to 400°C. Neglect dissociation of I_2 to iodine atoms.

From the thermodynamic properties of hydrogen, iodine, and hydrogen iodide, an equation of the form of Eq. 9.404 may be developed to evaluate ΔF° at any temperature in the interval over which heat capacities have been measured. Thus, from Eq. 10.204, K may be evaluated at any temperature in this range. Assume that the components of the mixture follow the perfect gas law. Then $P_{0(\text{HI})} = n_{0(\text{HI})}RT/V$, where n_0 is the original number of moles of HI placed in the container of volume V, and P_0 is the pressure which HI would exert at temperature T if none of it had dissociated into hydrogen and iodine. From the stoichiometry of the reaction it is seen that the actual pressure of HI at equilibrium will be $P_{\text{HI}} = P_0 - 2P_{\text{H}_2}$, and that $P_{\text{H}_2} = P_{\text{I}_2}$. Thus

$$K = \frac{P_{\text{HI}}^2}{P_{\text{H}_2}P_{\text{I}_2}} = \frac{(P_0 - 2P_{\text{H}_2})^2}{P_{\text{H}_2}^2}$$

which may be solved for P_{H_2} and subsequently for the other partial pressures. The degree of dissociation must then be equal to $2P_{\text{H}_2}/P_0$.

Equilibrium Constants Based on Concentrations.   If it is more convenient, the equilibrium constant may be expressed as an activity quotient. The standard free energy change then is the value characteristic of the chemical change from initial to final states, each at unit activity.

Activities Based on Mole Fraction.   Consider an ideal gas solution in which the activity is taken as the mole fraction. Since $P_i = X_i P_t$, $a_i = X_i = P_i/P_t$, where P_t is the total pressure and P_i the partial pressure of a given substance. On a pressure basis, for a given reaction

$$\Delta F = \Delta F_f^\circ + RT \ln f_q = \Delta F_P^\circ + RT \ln P_q$$

ΔF_f° indicates the standard free energy change for fugacity standard states, and f_q represents the fugacity quotient of the form seen in Eq. 10.202 for the given reaction, which, in the case of perfect gases, may be replaced by the partial pressure quotient P_q. Each partial pressure may be replaced in turn by the product $X_i P_t$, and the equation becomes

$$\Delta F = \Delta F_P^\circ + RT \ln X_q + RT \ln P_t^{\Delta n}$$

If there is no change in the number of moles in the reaction, $P_t^{\Delta n}$ will be unity and the mole fraction quotient will be the same as the pressure quotient; if there is a change in the number of moles, the mole fraction and pressure quotients then differ by a constant amount determined by the fixed total pressure. The equation may then be written

$$\Delta F = \Delta F_X^\circ + RT \ln X_q$$

where

$$\Delta F_X^\circ = \Delta F_P^\circ + RT \ln P_t^{\Delta n}$$

At equilibrium $X_q = K_X$, the equilibrium constant based on mole fraction; hence

$$K_P P_t^{-\Delta n} = K_X \tag{10.206}$$

Thus the mole fraction equilibrium constant is a function of the total pressure if there is a change in the number of moles in the reaction.

If solutions are not ideal, a similar relationship exists between K_f and K_a but the proportionality constant cannot be derived so simply.

ILLUSTRATION.   Find the relationship between K_P and K_X for the equilibrium $2SO_2 + O_2 \rightarrow 2SO_3$ (assume ideal gas behavior) when the total pressure in the system is 10 atm.

For this reaction $\Delta n = -1$. From Eq. 10.206, we have $10K_P = K_X$.

Activities Based on Moles per Liter.   Concentrations in moles per liter may be used as a basis for activity. For an ideal gas mixture, $P_i = n_i RT/V = c_i RT$. The reader may verify, in the same way as for Eq. 10.206, that

$$K_c(RT)^{\Delta n_g} = K_P \tag{10.207}$$

Correspondingly,

$$\Delta F_P^\circ = \Delta F_c^\circ - \Delta n_g RT \ln RT \tag{10.208}$$

Equation 10.208 shows the relationship between the standard free energy change for the reaction occurring with all components at unit pressure (fugacity) and the standard free energy change for the reaction occurring with all components at unit concentration (activity). The latter, of course, is not the same as when the activity is based on mole fraction.

Form of the Free Energy Reaction Isotherm.   Equation 10.202 may also be written

$$\Delta F = \Delta F_a^\circ + RT \ln a_q \tag{10.209}$$

The power to which each of the activity terms in the activity quotient a_q is raised depends on the manner in which the chemical equation is balanced; that is, each activity is raised to the power equal to the coefficient of that component in the balanced equation. However, multiplying the entire chemical equation by 2 or some similar factor will simply raise all powers in the activity quotient by the same factor and give a free energy change larger by the same factor. The free energy change calculated corresponds to the change for the number of moles reacting, as shown by the balanced equation.

The use of the standard free energy change to calculate the actual composition of an equilibrium system is straightforward only in the case where activities bear some simple relationship to concentration-type terms. This may be assumed in the problems at the end of the chapter; the more complicated case of nonideal solutions will be left for a more advanced treatment.

Dependence of the Equilibrium Constant on Temperature.   *The Van't Hoff Equation.*   The fugacity equilibrium constant is independent of total pressure. However, a change in its value is to be expected if the temperature is changed. The relationship of K_f to temperature is fixed by the properties of the standard free energy

$$\Delta F_f^\circ = -RT \ln K_f \tag{10.204}$$

We may write

$$\frac{\Delta F_f^\circ}{T} = -R \ln K_f$$

and

$$\frac{d(\Delta F_f^\circ/T)}{dT} = -R \frac{d \ln K_f}{dT} \tag{10.210}$$

This differentiation is total since neither ΔF_f° nor K_f is pressure dependent. Since

$$\frac{d(\Delta F_f^\circ/T)}{dT} = -\frac{\Delta H_f^\circ}{T^2}$$

it follows that

$$\frac{d \ln K_f}{dT} = \frac{\Delta H_f^\circ}{RT^2} \tag{10.211}$$

Equation 10.211 is the van't Hoff equation.

In general we will not attach a subscript on ΔF° or ΔH° in equations such as 10.204, 10.210, and 10.211. The character of the standard states to be associated with these quantities should be apparent from the basis used for fugacity or activity terms in the associated equilibrium constant. In heterogeneous systems a mixture of activity and fugacity terms may be used.

Integrated Form of the Van't Hoff Equation. The integrated form of Eq. 10.211 depends on the manner in which the standard heat of the reaction varies with temperature. If ΔC_P° may be taken as zero, the enthalpy and entropy changes for the reaction are not temperature dependent, and the integrated van't Hoff equation takes the simple form

$$\ln K = -\frac{\Delta H^\circ}{RT} + C \tag{10.212}$$

C is an integration constant which in this case is simply $\Delta S^\circ/R$. If $\Delta C_P^\circ = 0$, a plot of $\ln K$ vs. $1/T$ gives a straight line, with slope $-\Delta H^\circ/R$. Once the slope has been measured, a value of integration constant can be calculated from each measured value of K and the best average value taken. The Clausius-Clapeyron equation is a special form of Eq. 10.211.

ILLUSTRATION. Show how to correlate equilibrium constant data when ΔC_P° is a function of temperature.

In the general case,

$$\Delta C_P^\circ = \Delta a + \Delta b T + \cdots$$

where Δa, Δb, etc., are determined from empirical equations representing the relative variation of heat capacities of the reactants and products. It has been shown that this equation leads to an expression of the form of Eq. 9.404. Thus

$$-RT \ln K = \Delta H_*^\circ - \Delta a T \ln T - \tfrac{1}{2}\Delta b T^2 - \cdots + IT \tag{10.213}$$

When heat capacity data are available and equilibrium constants have been measured at a series of temperatures, all the experimentally determined quantities of Eq. 10.213 may be grouped on the left-hand side, and this quantity, frequently called Σ, plotted against the reciprocal of the temperature.

$$\Sigma = -R \ln K + \Delta a \ln T + \frac{\Delta b}{2} T + \cdots = \frac{\Delta H_*^\circ}{T} + I$$

A Σ vs. T^{-1} plot will be a straight line, since Σ includes all the temperature-dependent part of ΔH° and ΔS°. The slope of the Σ plot may be used to determine ΔH_*°, which, together with Σ, leads to determination of the best average value of I. Hence the complete thermodynamic characteristics of the reaction may be calculated from equilibrium constant and heat capacity data.

Figure 10.201 shows a plot for the reaction

$$H_2(g) + \tfrac{1}{2}O_2(g) \rightarrow H_2O(g)$$

according to Bares, Cerny, Fried, and Pick. They use equilibrium data of H. Zeise, *Z. Electrochem.*, **43**, 706 (1937), and heat capacities to derive values of $-\Sigma$;

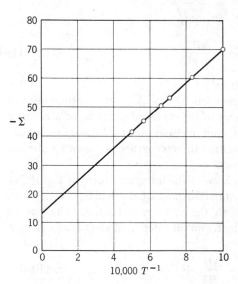

Fig. 10.201 Sigma plot for $H_2(g) + \tfrac{1}{2}O_2(g) \rightarrow H_2O(g)$ between 1000 and 2000°K (by permission from Bares, Cerny, Fried, and Pick, *Collection of Problems in Physical Chemistry*, Addison-Wesley Publishing Co., 1962).

$$-\Sigma = 4.576 \log_{10} K$$
$$+ 8.255 \log_{10} T - 9.405$$
$$\times 10^{-4}T - 4.6925 \times 10^4 T^{-2}$$
$$= -I - \frac{\Delta H_*^\circ}{T}$$

The sigma plot gives $\Delta H_*^\circ = -56,400$ cal and $-I = 13.4$.

Frequently ΔC_P° is quite small compared with the change in enthalpy for the reaction. Hence, over a small temperature interval, a direct plot of $\ln K$ vs. T^{-1} usually gives a good straight line, according to Eq. 10.212. An example is shown in Fig. 10.202.

Le Châtelier's Principle.   The van't Hoff equation gives quantitative meaning to Le Châtelier's principle concerning the effect of temperature on the equilibrium constant. If ΔH° is positive, $\ln K$ increases as T increases; if ΔH° is negative, $\ln K$ decreases as T increases. Similarly, Eq. 10.206 gives a quantitative basis for

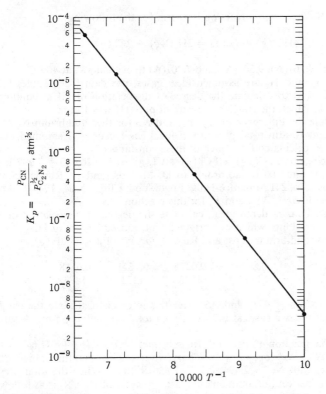

Fig. 10.202   Equilibrium constant K_p for the reaction $\frac{1}{2}C_2N_2(g) \rightarrow CN(g)$ as a function of temperature [constructed from the data of Ruther, McLain, and Scheller, *J. Chem. Phys.*, **24**, 173 (1956)]. Close correspondence to a straight line as predicted by Eq. 10.212 is observed over the temperature interval 1000° to 1500°K.

the effect of pressure on the composition of an equilibrium gas system. Thermodynamics enables us to calculate optimum conditions of T and P for a reaction, as far as the composition of the final equilibrium state is concerned.

Problems

10.201   Calculate the mole fraction, molal, and molar concentrations of a solution containing 20 per cent acetic acid by weight in water, if the density of the solution at 20°C is 1.026 g ml⁻¹.

10.202   (a) If benzene and toluene form an ideal solution, calculate the chemical potential of benzene in a 30 weight per cent benzene solution at 25°C relative to pure benzene as the standard state.

(b) The boiling point of pure benzene is 80.1°C. What will be the vapor pressure of benzene at 80.1°C above the solution described in (a)? Assume ideal gas behavior.

(c) If solution (a) is actually not ideal and γ_X is found to be 0.93 for benzene, what will be the vapor pressure in part (b)?

10.203   Write the free energy reaction isotherm for the following:

$$4HCl(g) + O_2(g) = 2H_2O(g) + 2Cl_2(g)$$

Use data in Tables 9.201(A), 9.301(A), and 7.201(A) to evaluate K_f at 400°C.

10.204   If HI, I_2, and H_2 are assumed ideal gases, use data from Tables 9.201(A), 9.301(A), and 7.201(A) to calculate the degree of dissociation of HI at equilibrium at 400°C in a vessel in which the starting pressure of pure HI was 1 atm.

10.205   Calculate the difference in K_X, K_c, and K_P for the equilibrium $N_2 + 3H_2 = 2NH_3$ at 500°C and 10 atm total pressure, if ideal gas behavior is assumed. Describe the meaning of $\Delta F°$ calculated from each of these constants.

10.206   For the reaction $PCl_5(g) = PCl_3(g) + Cl_2(g)$, $\Delta F° = 20,000 - 7.99T \log_{10} T - 17.27T$ between 400 and 500°K (according to D. M. Yost and H. Russell, *Systematic Inorganic Chemistry*, p. 241, Prentice-Hall, Englewood Cliffs, N.J., 1944). At 450°K calculate the value of $\Delta H°$, $\Delta S°$, and K_f for this reaction.

If the gases may be considered ideal, calculate the degree of dissociation of PCl_5 at 450°K in a 1-liter vessel into which was originally introduced 1 gram of PCl_5.

10.207   For the equilibrium (Yost and Russell, *loc. cit.*) $P_4(g) = 2P_2(g)$

K_f:	0.00645	0.0375	0.1671	0.6118
T, °K:	1173	1273	1373	1473

Determine mean values of $\Delta H°$ and $\Delta S°$ over this interval. Calculate the equilibrium partial pressures of the two gases at 1473°K if their total pressure is 1 atm. Assume ideal gas behavior.

*10.208   For the reaction (Yost and Russell, *loc. cit.*) $\frac{1}{2}N_2(g) + \frac{3}{2}H_2(g) = NH_3(g)$ $\log_{10} K_p = \Delta H_*°/T - \Delta \alpha' \log_{10} T + \Delta \beta'T^2 + I$ over the temperature range indicated in the table below, with $\Delta \alpha' = 2.494$, $\Delta \beta' = 1.856 \times 10^{-7}$. When the total pressure is 10 atm, the volume per cent of ammonia in a $3:1$ mixture of $H_2 : N_2$ is as follows:

%NH_3:	14.73	3.85	1.21	0.49	0.23
°C:	300	400	500	600	700

Develop expressions for $\Delta F°$, $\Delta H°$, and $\Delta S°$ for the reaction as functions of temperature with all constants evaluated (ideal gas behavior assumed).

10.209   From Fig. 10.202, determine values of $\Delta F°$, $\Delta H°$, and $\Delta S°$ for the dissociation of cyanogen at 1200°K. What is the degree of dissociation at a total pressure of 10^{-12} atm? At 1 atm? Assume perfect gas behavior.

10.210   From the expression for Σ given in the Illustration on p. 313 for the formation of water vapor, write expressions as functions of temperature for $\Delta C_P^°$, $\Delta H°$, $\Delta F°$, and $\Delta S°$ for the reaction. Use values of $\Delta H_*°$ and I given in the Illustration.

3. Heterogeneous Chemical Equilibria

Heterogeneous systems in which the equilibrium encompasses substances in two or more phases have been considered at some length in Chapter 8, but we now summarize a few points concerning heterogeneous equilibria which involve chemical change. Equations 10.202 and 10.204 may be applied just as in the homogeneous case, except that some of the fugacity terms are now controlled by the requirement of phase equilibrium.

Gas-Solid Systems. Consider the reaction

$$CaCO_3(s) = CaO(s) + CO_2(g)$$

in which it may be assumed that the solids are pure independent phases; the chemical potentials of $CaCO_3$ and CaO may be conveniently referred to each pure solid as its standard state. Thus the reaction isotherm becomes

$$\Delta F = \Delta F^\circ + RT \ln f_{CO_2} = \mu^\circ_{CO_2} + RT \ln f_{CO_2} + \mu^\circ_{CaO} - \mu^\circ_{CaCO_3}$$

Since pure solids are defined as the solid standard state, they are assigned unit activity at each temperature; the equilibrium constant at all temperatures is simply

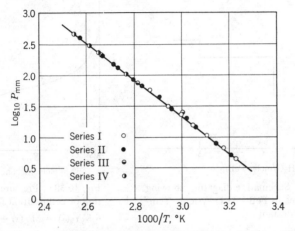

Fig. 10.301 Decomposition pressures in the system $LiHF_2(s) \rightleftharpoons LiF(s) + HF(g)$ [by permission from E. F. Westrum and G. A. Burney, *J. Phys. Chem.*, **65**, 344 (1961)].

the equilibrium fugacity of CO_2. This is the thermodynamic basis for the omission of concentration or pressure terms for pure condensed phases from the equilibrium constant expression.

Similarly, for the decomposition of solid NH_4Cl (assume that HCl and NH_3 show perfect gas behavior),

$$NH_4Cl(s) = HCl(g) + NH_3(g)$$
$$\Delta F^\circ = -RT \ln K = -RT \ln P_{NH_3} P_{HCl}$$

The activity of $NH_4Cl(s)$ remains constant at unity and does not appear in the expression for the equilibrium constant. This is reflected in the meaning of ΔF° for the reaction. The product of the NH_3 and HCl pressures must be constant at any given temperature; if we introduce an excess of either, the other will be reduced by the same proportion.

Figure 10.301 shows a plot of the equilibrium pressures of $HF(g)$ over $LiHF_2(s)$ and $LiF(s)$, as determined by E. F. Westrum, Jr., and G. A. Burney [*J. Phys. Chem*, **65**, 344 (1961)]. The various series correspond to measurements with different mole ratios of the solids in the system (varied from 15 to 93 mole per cent LiHF$_2$). Within the accuracy of the data, no evidence for formation of solid solutions is seen, that is, the ratio of the activities of the two solids remains constant. The enthalpy change on dissociation of LiHF$_2$ to LiF and HF is 13.7 $\pm$ 0.3 kcal mole^{-1} over the range 300 to 375°K.

Equilibrium characteristics can be used conveniently to detect phase changes in heterogeneous systems. For example, FeBr$_2$ forms a number of hydrates, including FeBr$_2 \cdot$H$_2$O, FeBr$_2 \cdot$2H$_2$O, and FeBr$_2 \cdot$4H$_2$O. Since the FeBr$_2$–H$_2$O

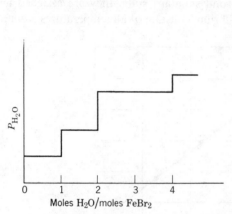

Fig. 10.302 Schematic diagram showing phase changes in FeBr$_2$–H$_2$O system. Temperature is constant.

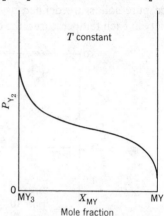

Fig. 10.303 Pressure as a function of composition for

$$MY_3(s) \rightarrow MY(s) + Y_2(g)$$

when MY$_3$ and MY form ideal solid solutions.

system is a two-component one, no more than three condensed phases can coexist in equilibrium with water vapor at a given temperature and total pressure, and when these four phases are present the system is invariant. If only two solid phases are present and the equilibrium reaction corresponds to

$$FeBr_2 \cdot 4H_2O(s) = FeBr_2 \cdot 2H_2O(s) + 2H_2O(g)$$

then the temperature can be varied, but the pressure is a fixed constant for each given temperature. When a new phase appears, the system becomes invariant. T and P cannot be changes unless one of the phases disappears. The observed equilibrium pressures as a function of moles of water at a given temperature may be used to detect the phase changes; in the absence of solid solution formation the behavior of such a system is illustrated in Fig. 10.302. The changes in thermodynamic properties for each reaction in the step-wise hydration can be calculated from equilibrium constant data.

Solid Solutions in Heterogeneous Equilibrium Systems.   If the condensed phases in a heterogeneous chemical equilibrium system are not of fixed composition, the activities of the components are variables and must be included in the equilibrium constant expression. The behavior may be illustrated for a simple case, which is analogous in form to the $CaCO_3$-CaO-CO_2 system but in which it will be assumed that the two solids form an ideal solid solution.

$$MY_3(s) = MY(s) + Y_2(g)$$

so

$$K = \frac{X_{MY}P_{Y_2}}{X_{MY_3}}, \quad \Delta F^\circ = -RT \ln K$$

ΔF° refers to conversion of pure solid MY_3 to pure solid MY and Y_2, an ideal gas at 1 atm. In the equilibrium system MY_3 and MY dissolve in each other. A plot of the pressure of Y_2 at various compositions of the solid phase is shown in Fig. 10.303. The change in pressure is in marked contrast to that of the $CaCO_3$ system, where solid solutions are not formed and the pressure of CO_2 is a fixed constant at a given temperature. In no real system is it correct to state that the condensed phases are completely immiscible; however, the limits of solubility may be so close to unit mole fraction of the component in excess that its activity may be assumed unity. If in such a case the solute is also present as a nearly pure phase, its equilibrium activity and also its chemical potential must be identical in both solid phases. Hence the phase in which its concentration is very low is an extremely nonideal solution. The solute activity coefficient must be very large; $a_2 = \gamma_2 X_2 = 1$, although X_2 is nearly zero. A similar behavior of γ_1 may occur in the phase near $X_2 = 1$.

Distribution of a Solute between Two Liquid Phases. One further example of a heterogeneous equilibrium will be mentioned briefly, the distribution of a solute between two immiscible solvents, of importance in purification procedures. Again, such a distribution equilibrium is determined by the behavior of the chemical potential; that is, at equilibrium the chemical potential of the solute in the two phases must be identical. The situation is analogous to vaporization equilibrium solubility, freezing point equilibria, etc.

Consider the distribution of iodine between CCl_4 and water. At equilibrium the chemical potential of iodine in water (w) is

$$\mu_{I_2} = \mu_{I_2(w)}^\circ + RT \ln a_{I_2(w)}$$

and in CCl_4, abbreviated as (c)

$$\mu_{I_2} = \mu_{I_2(c)}^\circ + RT \ln a_{I_2(c)}$$

Since the two chemical potentials must be equal, the right-hand sides of these equations can be equated

$$\mu^\circ_{(w)} - \mu^\circ_{(c)} = RT \ln \frac{a_{(c)}}{a_{(w)}}$$

Although the absolute values of the standard chemical potentials in each solvent are not known, they are constants and their difference must be a constant. Thus the ratio of the activities in the two immiscible solvents must be an equilibrium constant, called a *distribution constant*. Once it is determined, the manner in which any given amount of solute will distribute itself between two given volumes of immiscible solvents can easily be found when the relationship between activity and concentration is known.

The situation is somewhat more complicated if different kinds of reactions occur in the two solvents—for example, the solute may partially associate into double molecules in one solvent; it may not associate in the other but may be partially ionized. The distribution principle still applies to any given species, such as the monomer (undissociated); the presence of other forms of the solute in a given solvent will tend to increase the total amount of solute found in that phase. The final distribution may be calculated if the various reaction equilibrium constants are known.

Problems

Use data from Tables 7.201(A), 9.201(A), and 9.301(A) where necessary.

10.301   Calculate the equilibrium decomposition pressure of $NH_4Cl(s)$ at 25°C.

10.302   Calculate the partial pressures of HCl and HBr in the equilibrium system

$$AgCl(s) + HBr(g) = AgBr(s) + HCl(g)$$

at 25°C (assume $P_{HCl} + P_{HBr} = 1$ atm) (*a*) if no solid solution occurs; (*b*) if ideal solid solution occurs and the solid mole fraction of AgCl is 0.95.

*10.303   Calculate the temperature at which the decomposition pressure of CO_2 above $CaCO_3(s)$ and $CaO(s)$ is 1 atm. A graphical solution may be convenient.

10.304   Calculate the partial pressure of $H_2(g)$ in an equilibrium mixture of

$$CuO(s) + H_2 = Cu(s) + H_2O(g)$$

at 500°K if ΔC_P is assumed zero and the initial pressure of H_2O at 500°K (before reaction) was 1 atm (no H_2 initially present).

10.305   If for the reaction (according to S. H. Maron and C. F. Prutton, *Principles of Physical Chemistry*, the Macmillan Co., New York, 1958)

$$H_2S(g) + I_2(s) = 2HI(g) + S(rh)$$

K_P is 1.33×10^{-5} atm at 60°C, calculate $\Delta F°$ for H_2S at 298°K. Assume $\Delta C_P = 0$ for the reaction. (Data from Table 9.201(A) and $\Delta F_{HI}°$ at 298°K may be used.)

10.306   Estimate the equilibrium oxygen pressure above CuO and copper at 600°K.

10.307   For the reaction (according to S. H. Maron and C. F. Prutton, *loc. cit.*

$$2NaHCO_3(s) = Na_2CO_3(s) + CO_2(g) + H_2O(g)$$

$\Delta H° = 29,230 + 9.15T - 12.75 \times 10^{-3}T^2$ and $\Delta F_{298}° = 7000$ cal. Determine $\Delta F°$, $\bar{S}°$, and $\Delta H°$ for $NaHCO_3(s)$ at 298°. Calculate the decomposition pressure above $NaHCO_3$ at 500°K.

10.308   The distribution coefficient C_A/C_B of substance X between solvents A and B is 18, where C is the concentration in moles per liter. Calculate the way in which 0.2 mole of X will distribute itself between 50 ml of A and 10 ml of B.

4. Review Problems

*10.401   E. van Beek-Visser [*J. Chem. Phys.*, **29**, 1358 (1958)] published the following partial pressure data for nitrogen-oxygen systems at high temperature ($P_t = 1$ atm).

°K	N_2	O_2	O	N	NO	NO_2
2000	0.784	0.208	3.63×10^{-4}	8.04×10^{-10}	7.837×10^{-3}	1.05×10^{-5}
2500	0.774	0.196	7.46×10^{-3}	2.60×10^{-7}	2.256×10^{-2}	1.58×10^{-5}
3000	0.747	0.160	5.194×10^{-2}	1.22×10^{-5}	4.145×10^{-2}	1.74×10^{-5}
3250	0.724	0.126	0.102	5.32×10^{-5}	4.804×10^{-2}	1.54×10^{-5}
3500	0.698	0.087	0.166	1.876×10^{-4}	4.967×10^{-2}	1.16×10^{-5}
3750	0.675	0.051	0.228	5.596×10^{-4}	4.598×10^{-2}	7.32×10^{-6}
4000	0.659	0.026	0.274	1.462×10^{-3}	3.913×10^{-2}	4.06×10^{-6}
4400	0.646	0.0082	0.312	5.462×10^{-3}	2.793×10^{-2}	1.34×10^{-6}
5000	0.627	0.0017	0.329	2.655×10^{-2}	1.667×10^{-2}	3.3×10^{-7}

Calculate K_p for the following gaseous equilibria at about 500°C intervals and determine graphically a mean $\Delta H°$ for each. How closely does the behavior approach Eq. 10.212?

(a) $N_2 + O_2 \rightleftarrows 2NO$.
(b) $NO + \frac{1}{2}O_2 \rightleftarrows NO_2$.
(c) $O_2 \rightleftarrows 2O$.
(d) $N_2 \rightleftarrows 2N$.

Determine, as accurately as possible from the data given, values of $\Delta F°$, $\Delta S°$, and $\Delta H°$ at 3000°K for each of the reactions above.

*10.402   M. L. Perlman and G. K. Rollefson [*J. Chem. Phys.*, **9**, 362 (1941)], published data leading to the following results for the reaction $I_2(g) \rightleftarrows 2I(g)$:

°K	K_p
1274	0.168
1173	0.480×10^{-1}
1073	1.09×10^{-2}
973	1.80×10^{-3}
872	1.84×10^{-4}

Calculate the degree of dissociation of $I_2(g)$ at 1000°K if the total pressure of I_2 and I in the system is (a) 1 atm, (b) 10^{-3} atms. Evaluate $\Delta H°$ and $\Delta S°$ at 1000°K. Compare your value of $\Delta H°_{1000}$ with the value of $\Delta H°_0$, reported as 35,514 cal. What does your result indicate for the value of $\Delta(H° - H°_0)$ for this reaction at 1000°K?

10.403   Determine the slope (graphically) in Fig. 10.301 and confirm the value of $\Delta H°$ cited. Evaluate $\Delta S°$ and $\Delta F°$ for the reaction at 300°K.

10.404   Show that the phase rule prohibits the coexistence of $FeBr_2(s)$, $FeBr_2 \cdot H_2O(s)$, and $FeBr_2 \cdot 2H_2O(s)$ and water vapor all in equilibrium (assume solid phases are pure) except at a fixed temperature and pressure, analogous to a triple point for a one-component system.

10.405   From data in the tables in the Appendix, calculate the equilibrium decomposition pressure of oxygen above MgO at 25°C.

10.406   An organic substance is partially dimerized when dissolved in benzene; $K_1 = m^2/d = 0.02$, where m and d represent the moles per liter of monomer and dimer, respectively. In benzene-water systems $K_2 = m/C = 5$, where C is the concentration of solute monomer in water. If 100 ml of benzene is equilibrated with 50 ml of water solution of this compound (originally $0.2M$) what will be the final concentration of solute in the water layer?

General References

Bares, J., C. Cerny, V. Fried, and J. Pick, *Collection of Problems in Physical Chemistry*, Addison-Wesley Publishing Co., Reading, Mass., 1962.

Daniels, F., and R. A. Alberty, *Physical Chemistry*, John Wiley and Sons, New York, 1961.

Glasstone, S., *Thermodynamics for Chemists*, D. Van Nostrand Co., Princeton, N.J., 1947.

Klotz I. M., *Chemical Thermodynamics*, Prentice-Hall, Englewood Cliffs, N.J., 1950.

Lewis, G. N., M. Randall, K. Pitzer, and L. Brewer, *Thermodynamics*, Second Edition, McGraw-Hill Book Co., New York, 1961.

Maron, S. H., and C. F. Prutton, *Principles of Physical Chemistry*, Third Edition, the Macmillan Co., New York, 1958.

Sheehan, W. F., *Physical Chemistry*, Allyn and Bacon, Boston, 1961.

Sillen, L. G., P. W. Lange, and C. O. Gabrielson, *Problems in Physical Chemistry*, Prentice-Hall, Englewood Cliffs, N.J., 1952.

Wenner, R. R., *Thermochemical Calculations*, McGraw-Hill Book Co., New York, 1941.

Chapter Eleven

Statistical Thermodynamics

In Chapters 5 and 6 some equations have been developed that have an easily recognizable thermodynamic content, such as the expressions for specific heat. It was necessary to be somewhat inexact because the thermodynamic definitions had to be anticipated. Now that we have developed a thermodynamic method, we can return to the statistical method to give meaning at the molecular level to thermodynamics. Thermodynamic notation will help us to consolidate the statistical approach so far developed and to extend it somewhat further.

1. Connection between Statistical Mechanics and Thermodynamics

Pressure, Volume, Number, and Temperature. The definitions of pressure, volume, and number of molecules in the two disciplines are intuitive in nature. Whatever is obscure about these common notions in either is equally obscure in both. The notion of pressure can be extended down to smaller and smaller samples by statistical methods, but here we are interested in molar properties. Temperature has been rigorously defined by the derivation of the perfect gas law by a statistical method, followed by the identification of the perfect-gas-law T with that defined by the Carnot cycle.

Natural Variables. All the statistical derivations have been made at constant volume and energy or constant volume and temperature. With the choice of independent variables V, T, and N, the Helmholtz free energy A is the appropriate criterion for equilibrium. We shall be interested in F and E also. The logical assertion, already anticipated in Chapter 5, that the average energy $\bar{\epsilon}$ obtained from statistical mechanics can be identified with the thermodynamic energy E will be made. If the former is per molecule, and the latter per mole, the two are then connected by the equation

$$\bar{E} = N\bar{\epsilon} \tag{11.101}$$

where N is Avogadro's number. In addition we shall need to remember that

$$R = Nk$$

where Avogadro's number is the conversion factor between the molar gas constant and Boltzmann's constant.

The Free Energy. We now write down equations from thermodynamics and statistical mechanics:

$$P = -\left(\frac{\partial A}{\partial V}\right)_T \tag{7.415}$$

$$P = NkT\left(\frac{\partial \ln Z}{\partial V}\right)_T \tag{6.303}$$

$$E = \left[\frac{\partial(A/T)}{\partial(1/T)}\right]_V \tag{7.421}$$

$$\bar{\epsilon} = \frac{E}{N} = -\left[\frac{\partial \ln Z}{\partial(1/kT)}\right]_V \tag{5.320}$$

All these equations have been derived in the preceding chapters, as indicated by their numbers; they are gathered together here simply for convenience. They can all be true at once if we can make the identification

$$-\frac{A}{kT} \overset{?}{=} \ln Z^N \tag{11.102}$$

In order to establish that this formula is almost, but not quite, correct, we shall investigate the special case of noninteracting systems, where Z does not depend on N, the number of particles, but does depend on V and T (for example, the partition function for a perfect gas molecule). Then we can compute the chemical potential per molecule, $\dot{\mu}$

$$-\frac{\dot{\mu}}{kT} = -\frac{1}{kT}\left(\frac{\partial A}{\partial N}\right)_{V,T} \overset{?}{=} \ln Z \tag{11.103}$$

This result is clearly wrong because the chemical potential at constant volume and temperature certainly depends on N. For example, for the case of a perfect gas, from Eq. 7.609

$$\mu = \mu^\circ + NkT \ln P \tag{11.104}$$

If we introduce the perfect gas law $PV = NkT$ to convert this equation to the variables N, V, and T we obtain the result

$$\frac{\mu}{kT} = \frac{\mu°}{kT} + \ln \frac{kT}{V} + \ln N \qquad (11.105)$$

Also, if we compute the Gibbs free energy F from Eq. 11.103 by means of Eq. 7.606 for one component we find by comparison with Eq. 11.102

$$F = N\mu \overset{?}{=} A \qquad (11.106)$$

This result is clearly wrong because F is not equal to A for a perfect gas. We must thus look for a different definition of A in terms of Z, but one that is still similar to Eq. 11.102.

Formula for Free Energy.   Formula 11.102 may be considered the result of integration of a pair of the preceding equations. Like any integration, it should have a constant of integration included. But since these are partial integrations, the constant may be a function of those variables held constant. Two integrations, however, are available, one with respect to V and the other with respect to T. Only N has been left a constant in both integrations. The constant of integration is thus a function of N alone. The amended Eq. 11.102 is then

$$-\frac{A}{kT} = N \ln Z + f(N) \qquad (11.107)$$

We must now choose an $f(N)$ that gives the correct form of Eq. 11.105. The correct choice is equivalent to dividing Z^N by $N!$

$$-\frac{A}{kT} = \ln \frac{Z^N}{N!} \qquad (11.108)$$

We shall justify this choice in Sec. 11.4. With the use of Stirling's approximation this expression becomes

$$-\frac{A}{kT} = N \ln Z - N \ln N + N \qquad (11.109)$$

The chemical potential for an ideal system is now given by the expression

$$-\frac{\mu}{kT} = \ln Z - \ln N \qquad (11.110)$$

which has the required dependence on N.

Absolute Values.   The student will note that the expression for the Helmholtz free energy A is written in such a way as to imply that the absolute value of A is fixed; this result is contrary to the thermodynamic assertion that functions such as A, F, and H share with the energy E an indefinite origin E_0 that may contain for one thing the relativistic energy of formation of the elements. Thus we usually write $E - E_0$. However, the meaning of the absolute value for the free energy in Eq. 11.108 is that this is the free energy associated with the particular type of motion covered by the particular partition function written. For example, if Z is a purely translational partition function, the A calculated is the contribution to A from translation; in this sense only is it an absolute quantity.

Gibbs Free Energy; Perfect Gas Law.   We can compute F from μ (Eq. 11.110) for noninteracting systems as before

$$F = N\mu = -NkT \ln Z + NkT \ln N \qquad (11.111)$$

When we compare this result with the expression for A from Eq. 11.108

$$A = -NkT \ln Z + NkT \ln N - NkT \qquad (11.112)$$

we find that

$$PV = F - A = NkT \qquad (11.113)$$

This is a proof that the perfect gas law applies to any system where the partition function is independent of N.

The Standard Free Energy.   To make full use of the thermodynamics developed in the previous four chapters, we must make a precise definition of the standard free energy $F°$ in terms of the partition function. We have adjusted the additive constant that is a function of the number of particles; we must now concern ourselves with the purely constant term which we may write in thermodynamic notation as $F_0° = E_0° = H_0°$, the enthalpy at the absolute zero. It must be pointed out that, while Eq. 11.108 for A is generally true for any system, Eq. 11.111 is applicable only to ideal systems because, in the derivation of Eq. 11.110, Z was assumed independent of the value of N, when $N \ln Z$ was differentiated. There will be a factor V in the partition function whenever Eq. 11.111 is applicable. For example, in the partition function for a polyatomic perfect gas, this factor V is contributed by the translational partition function, and there are no other volume-dependent factors in the rest of the partition function. To take specific cognizance of this, we will write the partition function as

$$Z = \phi V \qquad (11.114)$$

where ϕ represents all the partition function except the volume and has the unit volume^{-1}. We shall also deal specifically with a mole of substance and assign the value of Avogadro's number to N. We shall also fix the pressure at 1 atm so that $V = RT = NkT$. Note that here Boltzmann's constant k must be in cm³-atm deg^{-1}. With these assignments in mind we can write a very special version of Eq. 11.111:

$$F° - F_0° = -RT \ln \phi kT \qquad (11.115)$$

$$= -RT \ln \frac{Z}{N}$$

In Sec. 11.3 we shall use this formula to calculate chemical equilibrium constants.

Problems

11.101   Derive Eq. 11.107 by integration of Eqs. 7.415, etc.

11.102   Express all the thermodynamic functions in terms of Z. Write out explicit formulas for gaseous (*a*) argon, (*b*) HCl.

11.103   If $Z_{\text{trans}} = \dfrac{(2\pi mkT)^{3/2}V}{h^3}$, show that Eq. 11.109 leads to the perfect gas law for a monatomic gas.

2. Liquids

The general features of the liquid state and its relationship to the solid and gaseous states have been described in Sec. 8.2, Fig. 8.201. The central feature is of course the triple point. The solid-gas line from this point terminates tangent to the T axis at $P = 0$. The solid-liquid line continues upward indefinitely for simple substances with closest packing in the solid. However, the liquid-gas line terminates at the critical point, P_c, T_c, above which there is no distinction between

Table 11.201   Some Properties of Condensed Gases*

Property	Gas										
	He	Ne	Ar	Kr	Xe	H_2	CH_4	NH_3	N_2	O_2	F_2
Density (0°C, 1 atm), gl⁻¹	0.179	0.90	1.78	3.75	5.90	0.090	0.718	0.770	1.25	1.43	1.70
Boiling point (1 atm), °K	4.3 (26 atm)	27.3	87.4	120.3	165.0	20.4	111.7	239.8	77.4	90.2	85.1
Melting point (1 atm), °K	0.9	24.4	83.9	116.0	161.4	13.9	89.2	195.4	63.3	54.8	53.6
Vapor density (bp), gl⁻¹	16.0	9.50	5.90	8.30	9.71	1.33	1.80	0.891	4.61	4.61	...
Liquid density (bp), gl⁻¹	125	1200	1390	2400	3100	70	424	682	804	1142	1512
Vapor pressure (solid at mp), mm Hg	<0.02	323	516	549	612	54	70	45.2	96.4	2.0	0.12
Heat of vaporization (bp), cal/g⁻¹	~5	20.8	38.9	25.8	23.0	108.0	122	327	47.6	50.9	40.9
Heat of fusion (mp), cal/g⁻¹	<1.0	4.0	6.7	3.9	3.3	14.0	14.5	80	6.1	3.3	3.2
C_p (10°C, 1 atm), cal/g⁻¹°C	(−180°C) 1.25	Approx. 0.25	0.125	Approx. 0.06	Approx. 0.04	3.39	0.528	0.523	0.248	0.218	0.180
C_p/C_v (10–15°C, 1 atm)	(−180°C) 1.66	1.64	1.67	1.68	1.66	1.41	1.31	1.31	1.40	1.40	...
Critical temperature °K	5.3	44.4	150.7	209.4	289.7	33.3	190.6	405.5	126.0	154.8	144.2
Critical pressure atm	2.3	26.8	48.0	54.3	58.2	12.8	45.7	111.5	33.5	49.7	55.0

* Collected by the Linde Co., and reproduced by permission.

liquid and gas. Fixing P and T at the critical values also fixes the volume at V_c. These fixed points serve to characterize the particular liquid and are listed in reference works. (See Table 11.201.)

A statistical thermodynamic treatment of liquids has as its objective the prediction of these and similar properties. We would like to be able to write a partition function for a liquid in a reasonably simple form, and with it to determine the value of the chemical potential for use in thermodynamic relationships, However, a liquid or a dense gas cannot be treated as an assembly of independent particles, and for this reason the partition function Z is a function of N at constant V, and of course PV no longer equals NkT. Except at fairly low density and high temperature, where the virial coefficients in Eq. 6.510 can be evaluated to a sufficient extent and accuracy, approximations and empirical rules are all that we can present.

Before proceeding further, a useful semiempirical principle will be discussed. It is found that the properties of various liquids and gases are very similar if they are compared in what is referred to as *corresponding states*, that is, states in which pairs of reduced variables, to be defined in the following paragraphs, of the two substances in question are the same.

Reduced Variables.   What are the parameters characterizing molecular interactions that are so important in determining the properties of a liquid? If we look back at the Lennard-Jones potential, Eq. 6.509, we see that there are two characteristic parameters for a substance whose molecules obey this potential. They are r^*, a steric term, and ϵ^*, an energy term.

Not all substances are composed of molecules that obey this law, but within a given class of molecules one might suggest that a similar two-parameter equation of somewhat different form might apply. For the family of rare gases, the Lennard-Jones potential itself gives a fair description of molecular interactions.

In the condensed phase, there are two other parameters that might be used to characterize the substance and that are related in a general way to r^* and ϵ^*. The steric one may be taken as the molar volume at $T = 0°K$, and the energy one is the (extrapolated) enthalpy of vaporization at $0°K$, a measure of the energy necessary to separate the molecules.

The critical constants of the substance, P_c, V_c, and T_c, are also found to be useful parameters which are related to the nature of molecular interactions. These are the properties most commonly used to define the reduced variables for a given substance; the Lennard-Jones parameters or the molar volume and enthalpy of vaporization may be used to define alternate sets. The method is as follows.

We can render the experimental variables P, V, and T dimensionless by division of each one by the corresponding critical values. We thus define the reduced variables

$$P_r = \frac{P}{P_c} \tag{11.201}$$

$$T_r = \frac{T}{T_c} \tag{11.202}$$

and

$$V_r = \frac{V}{V_c} \tag{11.203}$$

If we plot the reduced pressure against the reduced volume for a particular value of the reduced temperature, the curve obtained is virtually the same for a whole group of similar gases. For example, the isotherm data for argon are plotted in terms of these variables in Fig. 11.201. These curves may be used to predict properties of other gases, using only their critical constants. Some data for other gases are given in Table 11.201.

If we render the variables P, V, and T dimensionless by dividing by combinations of the Boltzmann constant and the molecular parameters ϵ^* and r^*, another set

of reduced variables is obtained. This set behaves in the same general manner as
that defined by the critical constants, though not numerically the same.

$$P_r' = \frac{Pr^{*3}}{\epsilon^*} \tag{11.204}$$

$$T_r' = \frac{kT}{\epsilon^*} \tag{11.205}$$

and

$$V_r' = \frac{V}{r^{*3}} \tag{11.206}$$

In the theoretical expressions for P as a function of V and T, the characteristic
energy is always in a ratio with kT. For example, it is that way in the simple but

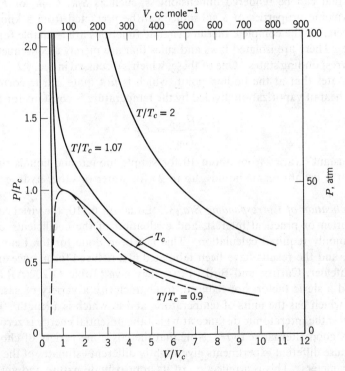

Fig. 11.201 Isotherm data for argon, reduced (data from F. Din, Editor, *Thermodynamic
Functions of Gases*, Vol. II, Butterworths Scientific Publication; London, 1956).

related expression for the second virial coefficient, Eq. 6.511, if Eq. 6.509 is substituted for the energy. Similarly, volume elements can always be divided by r^{*3}.
The result for any of the sets of reduced variables will be in the form

$$P_r' = \Phi(T_r', V_r') \tag{11.207}$$

where the function $\Phi(x,y)$ contains no parameters and is the same function for all gases that have the same *form* for their potential, even though the scale constants may be quite different.

Corresponding States. As a consequence of this fact, we would expect that when the data were reduced according to Eqs. 11.201 to 11.203, or 11.204 to 11.206, all gases with a similar potential function would fit on the same diagram (e.g. Fig. 11.201). This is true of the heavier rare gases, argon, krypton, and xenon, and what is known about radon. Neon is slightly off, and helium far off, from agreement because of quantum effects. A state is said to correspond to another when two of the reduced variables of one state have the same value for the second state. If the third variable has the same reduced value, the law of corresponding states is obeyed.

The third quantity is not restricted to P, V, or T. It can be any thermodynamic function that can be rendered dimensionless, such as S/k, C_V/k, or F/kT. The thermodynamic properties of a substance can be predicted from a knowledge of its parameters if the complete thermodynamic functions are available for a similar substance. There are isolated laws and rules that are merely a consequence of the law of corresponding states. One of these, which is discussed in Sec. 8.2, is Trouton's rule. It states that at the boiling point, which is not quite a true corresponding state, the heat of vaporization divided by the temperature is constant for all liquids

$$\frac{\Delta \bar{H}_{vap}}{T_{bp}} = C_T \tag{11.208}$$

This "constant" varies from about 10 for simple monatomic liquids through 20 or so for the usual organic liquids, up to 25 for water or other hydrogen-bonded liquids.

An Application of Corresponding States. Equation 6.510, the virial equation of state, is often of practical interest, and evaluation of the coefficients B, C, etc., is a commonly required calculation. This has been done for the Lennard-Jones potential, and the results have been tabulated in a reduced form, once and for all, by Hirschfelder, Curtiss, and Bird. First, they give [Table 11.202(A)] an energy factor and a steric factor, not reduced, to characterize a variety of gases. These are ϵ^*/k, which has the units of temperature, and σ, which is a length. They have chosen for σ the interatomic distance at which the potential energy is zero, which is an equally good alternative to r^*. Note that there is some variety of choice in the table because different experiments give slightly different estimates of the Lennard-Jones parameters. This is a reflection of its approximate nature and gives a good idea of the accuracy to be expected (a few per cent).

The procedure is to select values of these parameters for the particular gas under study. Then a reduced temperature is calculated from the equation

$$T^* = kT/\epsilon^* \tag{11.209}$$

This is the ordinary temperature divided by the energy parameter. In Table 11.203(A) the reduced second virial coefficient B^* is given as a function of this T^*.

Table 11.202 Force Constants for the Lennard-Jones (6-12) Potential*

Force constants are given here for a number of substances which are polar and/or nonspherical and hence are not described by the Lennard-Jones potential. These constants along with the tabulated functions based on the Lennard-Jones potential may, however, be useful for purposes of calculations until the theory needed for describing complex molecules has been developed.

Gas	ϵ^*/k, $^\circ K$	σ, Å	$b_0 = \frac{2}{3}\pi N\sigma^3$, cc/mole^{-1}
Noble gases			
Ne	35.60	2.749	26.21
	34.9	2.78	27.10
Ar	119.8	3.405	49.80
	122	3.40	49.58

The complete Table 11.202(A) will be found in the Appendix.

Table 11.203 The Second Virial Coefficient for the Lennard-Jones (6-12) Potential*

$$B(T) = b_0 B^*(T^*)$$
$$T^* = kT/\epsilon^*$$
$$b_0 = \frac{2}{3}\pi N\sigma^3$$

T^*	B^*	T^*	B^*
0.30	−27.88	2.00	−0.63
0.35	−18.75	2.10	−0.55
0.40	−13.80	2.20	−0.48
0.45	−10.75	2.30	−0.42

The complete Table 11.203(A) will be found in the Appendix.

* Adapted by permission from Hirschfelder, Curtis, and Bird, *Molecular Theory of Gases and Liquids*, John Wiley and Sons, New York, 1954.

This reduced coefficient is then converted to a regular dimensioned coefficient by means of the equation

$$B(T) = \tfrac{2}{3}\pi\sigma^3 B^*$$ (11.210)

As written, the result has the dimensions of cubic angstroms per molecule. It can easily be converted to cubic centimeters per mole to give the molar virial coefficient

$$B(T) = N \times 10^{-24} \tfrac{2}{3}\pi\sigma^3 B^*$$
$$= b_0 B^*$$ (11.211)

in cubic centimeters per mole. For convenience, all the constants have been collected in the new steric parameter b_0, which is also tabulated in Table 11.202(A). $B(T)$ is ready for practical use in the molar equation of state

$$PV = RT[1 + B(T)/V]$$ (11.212)

Similar tables exist for the third virial coefficient, the zero-pressure Joule-Thomson coefficient (Sec. 7.2) and a variety of transport properties, such as viscosity.

ILLUSTRATION.   The second virial coefficient of argon at 100°K.

We find from Table 11.202(A) that one value of ϵ^*/k for argon is 119.8°. Thus $T^* = 100/119.8 = 0.836$. From Table 11.203(A) we find the closest value to be $B^* = -3.36$. In Table 11.202(A) we have $b_0 = 49.8$ cc. Thus the second virial coefficient for argon at 100°K in molar units is

$$B = 49.8 \times (-3.36) = -167 \text{ cc mole}^{-1}$$

Partition Function for a Liquid.   Many attempts have been made to write a manageable partition function for a liquid; most of these are beyond the scope of this treatment. A rather simple, if also rather inadequate, partition function is called the smoothed-potential free-volume model. We assume that the molecules in the liquid are subject to a potential energy of constant value $-\chi_0$, caused by the average van der Waals attraction of the neighbors. In the simplest case χ_0 is set equal to the heat of vaporization of the liquid per molecule at the temperature in question. We further assume that the molecules move freely in a little volume v set by the nearest neighbors around them. Outside this volume the potential is infinite; inside it has the constant value $-\chi_0$. Thus the molecules move like a gas in this tiny volume; we therefore write a partition function for a gas in this volume, and weighted by the Boltzmann factor for the potential energy

$$Z_l = \frac{e^{+\chi_0/kT}(2\pi mkT)^{3/2}v}{h^3}$$ (11.213)

In plainest terms, the *free volume* v is adjusted to agree with experiment. The values of the so-called free volume so obtained are reasonable. Notably, the theory of Lennard-Jones and Devonshire, based on a refinement of this model, has given calculated values of the free volume in fair agreement with the values adjusted to fit experiment.

We shall make no further attempt to write down a specific partition function for a liquid but shall simply bear in mind that Z_l is much more complicated than Z_g; in particular it depends on N as well as V and T.

Problems

*11.201 Express the van der Waals equation of state in reduced form.

11.202 Calculate Trouton's constant for argon, C_6H_6, CH_4, H_2O, helium, NH_3, and H_2.

11.203 Determine by substitution in the Lennard-Jones potential the relation between the two characteristic distances $r*$ and σ. (Cf. Problem 6.610.)

11.204 Plot the reduced $B*$ against $T*$ and explain the (qualitative) shape of the curve.

11.205 Calculate the second virial coefficient of CH_4 at $300°K$.

11.206 Calculate the temperatures at which the various rare gases are apparently ideal, i.e., $B = 0$.

11.207 Calculate the temperatures at which the rare gases have the fugacity equal to the pressure over the range where the equation of state, Eq. 11.212, applies.

*11.208 Calculate the free volume in liquid argon at (a) the boiling point, (b) the melting point.

3. Partition Functions and Equilibrium

Expression for K_P. If we consider the general chemical reaction in the gas phase

$$aA + bB = cC + dD \qquad (11.301)$$

we can sum up contributions to the standard free energy change of reaction by the use of Eq. 11.115. We may write

$$\underbrace{\sum n_p(F° - F_0°)}_{prod} - \underbrace{\sum n_r(F° - F_0°)}_{reac} = \Delta F° - \Delta F_0°$$

$$-\frac{\Delta F°}{RT} = c \ln \phi_C + d \ln \phi_D + (c + d - a - b) \ln kT$$
$$- a \ln \phi_A - b \ln \phi_B - \frac{\Delta F_0°}{RT} \qquad (11.302)$$

Then, from Eq. 10.204,

$$K_P = \left(\frac{RT}{N}\right)^{\Delta n} \left(\frac{\phi_C^c \phi_D^d}{\phi_A^a \phi_B^b}\right) e^{-\Delta F_0°/RT} \qquad (11.303)$$

where $\Delta n = c + d - (a + b)$. In the pre-exponential part, R is in cm^3-atm deg^{-1}.

Expressions for K_c, $K_{N'}$, and K_N. If we wish to express the equilibrium constant in terms of concentration, rather than partial pressure, from Eq. 10.207 we observe that

$$K_c = K_P(RT)^{-\Delta n} = N^{-\Delta n} \frac{\phi_C^c \phi_D^d}{\phi_A^a \phi_B^b} e^{-\Delta F_0°/RT} \qquad (11.304)$$

The equilibrium constant in terms of molecules per unit volume N_A', etc., takes the simple form

$$K_{N'} = \frac{\phi_C^c \phi_D^d}{\phi_A^a \phi_B^b} e^{-\Delta F_0^\circ/RT} \tag{11.305}$$

but if the equilibrium constant is defined in terms of the number of molecules in any arbitrary volume V, we must put the V back in the partition function to obtain the expression

$$K_N = \frac{Z_C^c Z_D^d}{Z_A^a Z_B^b} e^{-\Delta F_0^\circ/RT} \tag{11.306}$$

In all these equations the quantity ΔF_0° occurs; this is the same as the enthalpy change of reaction at the absolute zero.

Application of the Equation for K_P. We shall now consider the application of the statistical thermodynamic method to a simple equilibrium. We shall be concerned with the actual computations, and therefore we include the factor 2.3 to convert natural logarithms to Briggsian logarithms. It will be convenient to use an expression for K_P in terms of Z. From Eq. 11.303

$$K_P = \left(\frac{RT}{NV}\right)^{\Delta n} \frac{Z_C^c Z_D^d}{Z_A^a Z_B^b} e^{-\Delta F_0^\circ/RT} \tag{11.307}$$

If Z for each substance is evaluated for 1 mole at a partial pressure of 1 atm, $V = RT$ in each case (with R in cm³-atm deg⁻¹) and Eq. 11.307 becomes

$$K_P = N^{-\Delta n} \frac{Z_C^c Z_D^d}{Z_A^a Z_B^b} e^{-\Delta F_0^\circ/RT} \tag{11.308}$$

Equation 11.308 takes a reasonably simple form for reactions in which the Z's can be evaluated in terms of the molecular constants listed earlier, such as molecular weights, M, and moments of inertia, I. For example, for the reaction $H_2 + 2DI = 2HI + D_2$ at 25°C

$$\log_{10} K_P = -\frac{\Delta F_0^\circ}{2.3RT} + \tfrac{3}{2} \log_{10} \frac{M_{HI}^2 M_{D_2}}{M_{H_2} M_{DI}^2} + \log_{10} \frac{I_{HI}^2 I_{D_2}}{I_{H_2} I_{DI}^2} \tag{11.309}$$

ΔF_0° can be determined from spectroscopic measurements. The ratio of the vibration partition functions is almost unity at room temperature and hence may be omitted. Thus the equilibrium constant can be evaluated without need for the usual kind of thermodynamic measurements.

The equilibrium constant is composed of a Boltzmann factor, $e^{-\Delta F_0^\circ/RT}$, multiplied by the ratio of the partition function terms. The latter depend on the number and spacing of the available energy states in the alternate forms, i.e., reactants compared to products.

The Relative Free Energy Function. Because of the importance of statistical methods as a means of calculating thermodynamic properties of simple gas molecules, it has become common practice to tabulate data in a form called the "relative free energy function," as mentioned briefly in Chapter 9,

$$\frac{\bar{F}^\circ - \bar{H}_0^\circ}{T} \quad \text{or} \quad \frac{F^\circ - F_0^\circ}{T} \tag{11.310}$$

which, as seen in Eq. 11.115, bears a simple relationship to the partition function. If values of this function are tabulated for each of the substances, then for a reaction the difference between the free energy functions of the products and reactants in the usual sense.

$$\sum_{\text{prod}} n_p \left(\frac{\bar{F}^\circ - \bar{F}_0^\circ}{T} \right) - \sum_{\text{reac}} n_r \left(\frac{\bar{F}^\circ - \bar{F}_0^\circ}{T} \right) = \frac{\Delta F^\circ}{T} - \frac{\Delta F_0^\circ}{T} \qquad (11.311)$$

To evaluate ΔF°, ΔH_0° must be known. This can be obtained from the "relative enthalpy functions," $\bar{H}^\circ - \bar{H}_0^\circ$ or alternatively $(\bar{H}^\circ - \bar{H}_0^\circ)/T$ (which can also be calculated from partition functions), if the heat of reaction is known at some one temperature:

$$\sum_{\text{prod}} n_p (\bar{H}^\circ - \bar{H}_0^\circ) - \sum_{\text{reac}} n_r (\bar{H}^\circ - \bar{H}_0^\circ) = \Delta H^\circ - \Delta H_0^\circ \qquad (11.312)$$

Values of free energy functions and relative enthalpy functions are given for a number of substances in Table 11.301(A). Heat capacity data may also be used to calculate these functions:

$$\left(\frac{\bar{F}^\circ - \bar{H}_0^\circ}{T} \right) = \frac{\bar{F}^\circ - \bar{H}^\circ}{T} + \frac{\bar{H}^\circ - \bar{H}_0^\circ}{T}$$

$$= \frac{\bar{H}^\circ - \bar{H}_0^\circ}{T} - \bar{S}^\circ = \frac{1}{T} \int_0^T \bar{C}_P^\circ \, dT - \int_0^T \frac{\bar{C}_P^\circ}{T} \, dT \qquad (11.313)$$

This is frequently done for condensed phases to give all data of interest in the same form.

Values of these functions can be conveniently interpolated to obtain results at temperatures intermediate to those given in Table 11.301(A).

Table 11.301   Selected Values of Relative Free-Energy and Enthalpy Functions*

			T, °K		
	298.16°	400°	600°	800°	1000°
Relative Free Energy Functions, $-\left(\dfrac{\bar{F}^\circ - \bar{H}_0^\circ}{T} \right)$, cal mole^{-1} deg^{-1}					
H_2	24.423	26.422	29.203	31.186	32.738
O_2	42.061	44.112	46.968	49.044	50.697
Relative Enthalpy Functions, $\dfrac{\bar{H}^\circ - \bar{H}_0^\circ}{T}$, cal mole^{-1} deg^{-1}					
H_2	6.7877	6.8275	6.8825	6.9218	6.9658
O_2	6.942	6.981	7.132	7.320	7.497

> The complete Table 11.301(A) will be found in the Appendix.

* By permission from *Selected Values of Physical and Thermodynamic Properties of Hydrocarbons and Related Compounds*, American Petroleum Institute, 1953.

ILLUSTRATION.   Calculate K_P for the reaction $2CO + O_2 = 2CO_2$ at $1000°K$. To calculate ΔH_0° first calculate ΔH_{298}° from Table 9.201(A):

$$\Delta H_{298}^\circ = 2(-94.05) - 0 - 2(-26.42)$$
$$= -135.26 \text{ kcal} = -135,260 \text{ cal}$$

Then from the second half of Table 11.301(A)

$$(\Delta H_{298}^\circ - \Delta H_0^\circ)/298 = 2(7.506) - 2(6.951) - 6.942$$
$$\Delta H_{298}^\circ - \Delta H_0^\circ = -1740 \text{ cal}$$

whence

$$\Delta H_0^\circ = 1740 - 135,260$$
$$= -133,520 \text{ cal}$$

From the first half of Table 11.301(A)

$$-(\Delta F_{1000}^\circ - \Delta H_0^\circ)/1000 = 2(54.109) - 2(48.860) - 50.697$$
$$= -40.20$$
$$\Delta F_{1000}^\circ - \Delta H_0^\circ = +40,200 \text{ cal}$$
$$\Delta F_{1000}^\circ = -93,320 \text{ cal}$$

and since

$$-RT \ln K_P = \Delta F^\circ$$

we have

$$-1.987 \times 1000 \times 2.303 \log_{10} K_P = -93,320$$

and

$$K_P = 2.5 \times 10^{20} \text{ atm}^{-1}$$

(since $\Delta n = -1$, the unit is atmospheres^{-1}).

Problems

*11.301   For the dissociation $I_2(g) = 2I(g)$, $\Delta H_0^\circ = 35,480$ cal. For I_2, the moment of inertia is 743×10^{-40} g cm^2, $\omega = 214$ cm^{-1}, $Z_{el} = 1$. For monatomic iodine, $Z_{el} = 4$. Calculate the degree of dissociation of I_2 at $1000°C$ when the total pressure in the system is 1 atm.

11.302   Use free energy functions and relative heat content data from Table 11.301(A) to calculate the equilibrium constant for the reaction

$$C_2H_4(g) + H_2(g) = C_2H_6(g)$$

at $400°K$. The standard heats of formation of ethylene and ethane at $298.16°K$ are available in Table 9.201(A).

11.303   Make a similar calculation for the reaction

$$N_2(g) + O_2(g) = 2NO(g)$$

at $450°C$. (NOTE: the functions must be interpolated.)

4. Justification of the $N!$ Term; Distinguishability

We have not yet justified the use of Eq. 11.108 for A, more than to observe that without this equation thermodynamics and statistical mechanics fail to agree.

Distinguishability. We can be reasonably certain that we have derived the correct partition function Z_{trans} for a single atom in a volume V, and that the quantities calculated from this partition function are the average values over a long period of time. Now we might suppose that these averages would also apply to the problem of N noninteracting particles in the same volume. We have learned how to write a total partition function as the product of separate partition functions for the independent degrees of freedom (Eq. 5.313). We might therefore anticipate that the partition function for N particles might be $Z \times Z \times \cdots = Z^N$, as in Eq. 11.102, which we know is incorrect. To show what the difficulty is, let us write part of the product for only two molecules, and two energy levels, ϵ_1 and ϵ_2

$$Z \times Z = (\cdots e^{-\epsilon_1/kT} \cdots + e^{-\epsilon_2/kT} \cdots)(\cdots e^{-\epsilon_1/kT} \cdots + e^{-\epsilon_2/kT} \cdots)$$
$$= \cdots e^{-2\epsilon_1/kT} + 2e^{-(\epsilon_1+\epsilon_2)/kT} + \cdots$$

We get only one term from both particles in the same level but two terms for one in each level. This corresponds to the distinction in the second case, of the first particle in the first level, and the second in the second, or on the other hand, the first particle in the second level, and the second in the first. But does this really correspond to a physical distinction in the case of identical particles, such as electrons? The principles of quantum mechanics require that, since there is no recognizable difference in the two arrangements, they be counted only once. One way we could do this is to divide the whole partition function by 2. But this would weight the double occupancy term by $\frac{1}{2}$, which is incorrect.

Particles and Levels in the Classical Region. If we calculate the total number of energy levels with energy less than kT at $273°K$ for a volume of 22.4 liters, it emerges that the number of levels is vastly in excess of Avogadro's number. From this it is clear intuitively that not many levels on the average will be doubly occupied, and that these occurrences will be of negligible importance in the average properties. Therefore, under these circumstances it is permissible to correct the partition function for two particles by dividing it by 2. But we must remember that this step requires a vast excess of states over particles.

If there are more than two particles, the student can easily see that the number of terms in the partition function that are excess in that they refer to indistinguishable configurations increases rapidly. For example, for three particles we have the product

$$(\cdots e^{-\epsilon_1/kT} \cdots + e^{-\epsilon_2/kT} \cdots + e^{-\epsilon_3/kT} \cdots)$$
$$\times (\cdots e^{-\epsilon_1/kT} \cdots + e^{-\epsilon_2/kT} \cdots + e^{-\epsilon_3/kT} \cdots)$$
$$\times (\cdots e^{-\epsilon_1/kT} \cdots + e^{-\epsilon_2/kT} \cdots + e^{-\epsilon_3/kT} \cdots)$$
$$= \cdots + 6e^{-(\epsilon_1+\epsilon_2+\epsilon_3)/kT} \cdots$$

where the term corresponding to all three particles in different energy levels occurs six, or 3!, times. For N particles, if no two particles are in the same level, the factor is $N!$; in this classical region, we must therefore divide the partition function by $N!$ to get a correct enumeration. This is a justification for Eq. 11.108, which gives the free energy for N particles in terms of the partition function for one particle.

Formula for the Entropy; the Sackur-Tetrode Equation. Since we now have a formula for E, Eq. 5.320, and for A, Eq. 11.112, it is easy to determine S from the definition for A, Eq. 7.401, which gives

$$S = \frac{E - A}{T} = -Nk \ln N + Nk \ln Z + N\frac{\bar{\epsilon}}{T} + Nk \qquad (11.401)$$

We have written this down in general, but it is most instructive to take the case of one mole of a perfect monatomic gas. $\bar{\epsilon}$ is $\frac{3}{2}kT$, and the partition function of a perfect gas is given by Eq. 6.115. For this case we find

$$\frac{S}{Nk} = \frac{\bar{S}}{R} = \frac{3}{2} \ln \frac{2\pi mkT}{h^2} + \ln \bar{V} - \ln N + \frac{5}{2} \qquad (11.402)$$

All the constants in this equation are known, and therefore it at least purports to be an absolute entropy. This equation can also be written in terms of the pressure, because $P\bar{V} = NkT$:

$$\frac{\bar{S}}{R} = \frac{5}{2} \ln T + K_s + \frac{3}{2} \ln M + \frac{5}{2} - \ln P \qquad (11.403)$$

in which M is the molecular weight of the gas, and K_s is the same for all gases. In this form Eq. 11.403 is known as the Sackur-Tetrode equation. It applies to real rare gases in the normal range of temperature and pressure, where they are nearly ideal.

The Third Law and the Sackur-Tetrode Entropy. If we obtain the entropy change ΔS, based on experiment and extrapolated to absolute zero, for the process $Ar(s,\ T = 0^\circ K) \to Ar(g,\ STP)$ the result agrees within experimental error with the number calculated from Eq. 11.402. Thus, if we believe Eq. 11.402 is absolute, we conclude that the entropy of crystalline argon is zero at absolute zero. At this stage the student will not be surprised with this result, because he will realize that Eq. 11.402 is the entropy associated with translation, and that except for the onset of translation any other source of entropy in the argon, such as isotopic mixing, is the same before and after vaporization. Thus Eq. 11.402 is not really absolute, but the absolute value of a definite part or contribution to the total entropy, associated with the partition function for translation. However, before the clarification of the role of statistical mechanics in chemistry a great deal of attention was given to the purely thermodynamic content of this agreement. It served as a confirmation for the assertion, often identified with the third law of thermodynamics, that the value zero could be assigned to the entropy of perfectly crystalline substances at the absolute zero.

Statistical Weight and Entropy.   Before we interpret further the result of the preceding paragraphs we will look back at Eq. 5.203, which defines the statistical weight. It is now clear that, as it stands, Eq. 5.203 is probably inapplicable to a gas of identical particles. In fact, if all the molecules are in different levels, it too overestimates the weight by a factor of N!. We should then use the modified weight

$$W = \prod_i \frac{1}{N_i!} \tag{11.404}$$

Since the new weight function differs from Eq. 5.203 only by a constant factor, N!, the maximization procedure will again give the Boltzmann distribution law.

With the use of Stirling's approximation, we find from Eq. 11.404

$$\ln W = -\sum_i N_i(\ln N_i - 1) \tag{11.405}$$

If we go ahead and substitute the values of N_i that maximize W, from Eq. 5.231

$$N_i = \frac{N}{Z} e^{-\epsilon_i/kT} \tag{11.406}$$

we can examine the value of $\ln W_{\text{max}}$. We find that

$$\ln W_{\text{max}} = -N \ln N + N \ln Z + \frac{N\bar{\epsilon}}{kT} + N \tag{11.407}$$

When this result is compared with Eq. 11.401, we observe the very simple result

$$\frac{S}{k} = \ln W_{\text{max}} \tag{11.408}$$

This equation, called the Boltzmann-Planck equation, has been used as an intuitive connection between statistical mechanics and thermodynamics. However, there are logical difficulties with it. We have been discussing a perfect gas with many more levels than particles. If we look back at Eq. 11.404, our revised weight, we see that, if N_i is always zero or one, W is constant at unity. We thus conclude that, if Eq. 11.408 holds, $S = 0$. We thus have two values for the entropy, zero and Eq. 11.402. This is a fundamental problem of statistical mechanics, and we must refine our techniques to solve it.

Discussion of Earlier Derivation; Localized Systems.   If we examine the first derivation of the Boltzmann law in Sec. 5.2, we can see that the procedure is not at all applicable to gas particles in the classical region of more states than particles. The populations N_i are mostly all zero, and occasionally unity. Therefore W is invariably one, and it is doubtful what it means to maximize it. In addition, Stirling's approximation is superficially inapplicable to such small numbers.

The derivation, Eqs. 5.232 et seq., is better, logically. It avoids maximizing W and substitutes averaging; Stirling's approximation is applied only to the reference system of harmonic oscillators. The result is limited, however, to a single system which can accept its energy in one nondegenerate way. This is certainly not true for a mole of gas. The derivations in Chapter 5 are really applicable to the sort of system where distinguishability is not a problem. A group of harmonic oscillators attached to some framework is a good example of such a system. We can clearly distinguish between an oscillator here, specified by its coordinates, and one there with another set of coordinates. Hence there is a meaning to ϵ_i being in the first oscillator rather than the second. Such systems are called localized systems.

When we turn to N particles free to move in the same volume, however, a different derivation is necessary, at least in its underlying assumptions. We shall give this derivation in an elementary manner that preserves many of the mathematical steps of Eqs. 5.203 *et seq.*

Problems

11.401   Evaluate the Sackur-Tetrode constant K_s numerically.

11.402   Sketch the thermodynamic functions A, F, E, H, PV, and S as functions of temperature as the absolute zero is approached.

11.403   Calculate the translational entropy of N_2 at 298°K and 1 atm. Compare your answer with the total entropy [Table 9.301(A)].

5. Quantum Statistics

The result that Eq. 11.404 led to unit statistical weight for all relevant states has the essence of quantum statistics in it. The rule for finding the average properties in quantum statistics is very simple; the first step is to write all the distinguishable wave functions for N particles. If we give these wave functions the symbols $\Psi_1, \Psi_2, \ldots, \Psi_i, \ldots$, the total energy or value of any property associated with an operator can be found for each of the N-particle eigenfunctions by the use of Eq. 2.701. Then we assert as a fundamental principle that the states corresponding to each N-particle eigenfunction are all equally probable. This is, of course, subject to the limitations of the problem, such as constant volume, energy, or number of particles.

For the case of N electrons in a box, we can combine the individual single-particle translational eigenfunctions with the spin eigenfunctions to obtain any number of different single-particle eigenfunctions. That is, with eigenfunctions of the type of Eq. 2.407 *et seq.*, with symbols $\psi_1, \psi_2, \ldots, \psi_j, \ldots$ and the spin eigenfunctions α and β, we can construct sets of complete single-particle eigenfunctions such as

$$\phi_1 = \psi_i\alpha, \quad \phi_2 = \psi_j\beta, \ldots, \quad \phi_N = \psi_k\alpha \qquad (11.501)$$

which are all different.

From these N functions, we can construct a Slater determinant like Eq. 3.409. We will indicate by the notation $\phi_5(3)$ that the fifth eigenfunction is written as a function of the coordinates of the third electron, etc.

The normalized and antisymmetrical wave function for N particles is then

$$\Psi_i = (N!)^{-\frac{1}{2}} \begin{vmatrix} \phi_1(1) & \phi_1(2) & \cdots & \phi_1(N) \\ \phi_2(1) & \phi_2(2) & \cdots & \phi_2(N) \\ \cdots & \cdots & \cdots & \cdots \\ \phi_N(1) & \phi_N(2) & \cdots & \phi_N(N) \end{vmatrix} \qquad (11.502)$$

We can obtain as many different N-particle wave functions as we desire by taking a different set of single-particle wave functions, as in Eq. 11.501. Note, however, that if two of these functions are identical, then two rows of the determinant Eq. 11.502 are identical, and the determinant vanishes.

Note that only one determinant can result from a specific choice; a different order of writing the chosen ϕ_i functions, for instance, simply corresponds to interchanging rows in the determinant, which does not change the value of the determinant. The choice of N different states corresponds to single-particle occupancy of each state. If less than N different states are chosen, two or more particles would have to occupy one or more of the states, and as we have seen the Slater determinant would vanish identically; multiple occupancy of any state is forbidden. Furthermore, if the choice of each state is equally probable in making up the set of N states, then all possible resulting N-particle states (wave functions Ψ_i) will occur with equal probability.

Fermi-Dirac Rules. In our attempt to justify Boltzmann statistics as applied to particles in a box, we were forced to seek conditions that allowed us to neglect double occupancy of states. We know from Eq. 11.502, which embodies the Pauli exclusion principle, that for electrons such double occupancy is forbidden.

We will now develop a distribution law which allows single occupancy with equal probability in any state but forbids double occupancy. This case is called the Fermi-Dirac statistics or F-D or just Fermi statistics. Particles which obey the rule are called fermions and include protons and certain other particles as well as electrons.

Simple Derivation. We want to be able to use Stirling's approximation, so we shall utilize the fact that translational energy levels are very close together compared with the average kinetic energy of the particles. At most, a given state such as $\psi_i\beta$ can be occupied by a single particle; however, we shall lump together a group of these wave functions with nearly the same energy level and treat them as a single degenerate level. We shall assume that all the wave functions for individual particles have been grouped into a series of closely spaced energy levels with degeneracy G_j. G_j must be large enough to be used in Stirling's formula for $G_j!$ but small enough so that the energy span is much less than kT. Suppose that in a particular group there are N_j particles. We shall also make the group of states big enough so that $N_j!$ can be approximated well by Stirling's formula.

At first sight it might appear that under certain circumstances the energy levels might be so widely spaced as to forbid this grouping. However, since we are primarily interested in the entropy and other bulk thermodynamic properties, and since the energy levels of a particle in a box can be made more closely spaced by taking a larger box, we have only to assert that the quantity of material and size of the box are large enough to make the grouping into G_j levels possible. The number of ways of distributing N_j particles among G_j levels, with a maximum of one per eigenstate is

$$W_j = \frac{G_j!}{(G_j - N_j)!\, N_j!} \tag{11.503}$$

The student can see that this is so by thinking of putting N_j numbered discs in G_j boxes with G_j choices for the first, $G_j - 1$ for the second, etc., and then dividing by $N_j!$ because the discs are to be considered indistinguishable. The total weight is the product of all the weights over the j groups:

$$W = \prod_j W_j = \prod_j \frac{G_j!}{(G_j - N_j)!\, N_j!} \tag{11.504}$$

We are now in a position where we have made all the numbers big enough to apply the method of Chapter 5 with assurance. We proceed with Eq. 11.504 in place of 5.203. Analogous to Eq. 5.207 we now have

$$\ln W = \sum_j \left[(N_j - G_j) \ln \left(\frac{G_j}{N_j} - 1 \right) + G_j \ln \frac{G_j}{N_j} \right] \tag{11.505}$$

The same conditions for conservation of energy and particles apply as before, except that the subscript j refers to groups of eigenstates instead of individual ones. By means of the method of undetermined multipliers we find as an alternate distribution law to Eq. 5.217

$$\frac{N_j}{G_j} = (e^{+\alpha+\beta\epsilon_j} + 1)^{-1} \tag{11.506}$$

Since the ratio of N_j to G_j is the average population of one state (always less than unity), and since the states in group G_j are very close together and weighted equally, this ratio is really the population of a single level, j. Thus, if we now set $G_j = 1$, N_j becomes the population of a single level.

   The Classical Limit. Before we discuss the application of Eq. 11.506 to electrons, we will use a limiting form of this equation to clear up the difficulties about $\ln W_{\max}$ raised in Sec. 11.4. By grouping the eigenstates we have made it possible to use Stirling's approximation with confidence. If we now return to the limiting case of many more states than particles to occupy these states, we imply that

$$N_j \ll G_j \tag{11.507}$$

for all groups. Under this condition the Fermi-Dirac rules are operative only in that unit weight is attached to each single occupancy. Although the Pauli exclusion principle will still apply to fermions in this classical limit, multiple occupancy of eigenstates is inherently unimportant, so any results subject to the limitation 11.507 will be applicable to any gas of indistinguishable particles. We might anticipate that a simplification is possible because, if the exponent in Eq. 11.506 is very large for all energy levels, the $+1$ which is added to it can be neglected. We then get

$$\frac{N_j}{G_j} = e^{-\alpha}e^{-\beta\epsilon_j} \tag{11.508}$$

which has the same form as Eq. 5.217, the Boltzmann law. We thus have a classical limit. Notice that, if the exponential term in Eq. 11.506 is very large, then its reciprocal in 11.508 is very small, that is, the average population of each individual level is very small. This is just what we have asserted in the condition 11.507. It can be shown more explicitly by writing out the limiting form of Eq. 11.505 when the condition holds. We rearrange it to read

$$\ln W = \sum_j \left[N_j \ln \left(\frac{G_j}{N_j} - 1 \right) - G_j \ln \left(\frac{G_j}{N_j} - 1 \right)\left(\frac{N_j}{G_j} \right) \right] \tag{11.509}$$

The first term to be summed contains the logarithm of a very large number; the second, the logarithm of a number close to unity. Suppose that $N_j = 10^{10}$ and $G_j = 10^{20}$; then to a good approximation

$$\ln \left(\frac{G_j}{N_j} - 1 \right) = \ln \frac{G_j}{N_j} \quad \text{and} \quad \ln \left(1 - \frac{N_j}{G_j} \right) = -\frac{N_j}{G_j}$$

hence

$$\ln W = \sum_j N_j \left(1 + \ln \frac{G_j}{N_j} \right) \tag{11.510}$$

This weight is equivalent in form to Eq. 11.405 and would lead to a form of Boltzmann statistics that differs from Eq. 11.406 only in that it contains the artificial degeneracies G_j; the most probable distribution is

$$N_j = G_j \frac{N}{Z} e^{-\epsilon_j/kT} \tag{11.511}$$

This distribution substituted into Eq. 11.510 gives Eq. 11.407 again, and thus the Boltzmann-Planck equation, Eq. 11.408.

By means of a weight taken over grouped levels, which considers the approximate or "coarse-grained" energy distribution of the particles, rather than the exact eigenvalue and eigenfunction of each particle, we obtain a correct value of the entropy without the incorrect use of Stirling's approximation on zero and one. Note that the values of the G_j's do not enter the result; the only requirement is that the numbers be sufficiently large.

Identification of α and β. In the special case of the classical limit we can identify β with $1/kT$ by deriving the perfect gas law. The partition function is written in slightly different form

$$Z = \sum_j G_j\, e^{-\beta\epsilon_j} \tag{11.512}$$

Grouping the levels and summing over the groups is exactly the same operation as summing over the individual levels, since in any case the summation is replaced by an integration to obtain the classical partition function for a gas. Then, with Eq. 6.303 for the pressure, the identification can be accomplished.

If we then sum N_j from Eq. 11.508, we obtain the expression for the total number of particles:

$$N = \sum_j N_j = \sum_j G_j \, e^{-\alpha} e^{-\beta \epsilon_j} = e^{-\alpha} Z \qquad (11.513)$$

from which we find by solving for α

$$\alpha = -\ln N + \ln Z \qquad (11.514)$$

By comparison with Eq. 11.110 we see that

$$\alpha = -\frac{\mu}{kT} \qquad (11.515)$$

In the next section we will give a more general discussion that links β with temperature and α with the chemical potential for the Fermi-Dirac distribution as well.

General Relation between ln W_{max} and Thermodynamics.   We now present an analysis that makes a general connection between ln W_{max}, α and β, and the thermodynamic quantities such as S, μ, and T.   In the derivation of either type of statistics, Fermi-Dirac or classical, there occurs an addition process of the type of Eq. 5.216, which in general can be written

$$\sum_i (-\delta \ln W_{max} + \alpha \, \delta N_i + \beta \epsilon_i \, \delta N_i) = 0 \qquad (11.516)$$

Previously, we have substituted the appropriate W in terms of the values of N_i, and with the use of Stirling's approximation we have found the distribution law. However, we can make some deductions from this equation without committing ourselves to a particular distribution.   We will now consider that not only N_i can vary, but that the energy levels themselves also can vary because some external parameter such as the volume V has been varied.   Then, from Eq. 5.205 for the total energy,

$$dE = \sum_i N_i \, d\epsilon_i + \sum_i \epsilon_i \, dN_i \qquad (11.517)$$

Since ϵ_i depends only on volume, we can write

$$d\epsilon_i = \left(\frac{\partial \epsilon_i}{\partial V}\right) dV \qquad (11.518)$$

However, from Eq. 6.302, we see that this is equivalent to

$$d\epsilon_i = -P_i \, dV \qquad (11.519)$$

or

$$\sum N_i \, d\epsilon_i = -P \, dV \qquad (11.520)$$

Now from Eq. 11.517 we see that

$$\sum_i \epsilon_i \, \delta N_i = dE + P \, dV = \delta Q \tag{11.521}$$

In other words, Eq. 11.517 is the statistical thermodynamic version of the first law of thermodynamics. The summation over the middle term in Eq. 11.516 is easily seen to be

$$\sum_i \alpha \, \delta N_i = \alpha \, dN \tag{11.522}$$

where dN is the thermodynamic variation in the total number of particles. If we then hold the total number of particles constant, the middle term of Eq. 11.516 vanishes, and we obtain

$$\delta \ln W_{max} = \beta \, \delta Q \tag{11.523}$$

Now, since W_{max} is a function of the state of the system and does not depend on path, β is the integration factor that corresponds to $1/T$ in thermodynamics. We have thus established the connection between the thermodynamic temperature and β, which must have the form

$$\beta = \frac{1}{kT} \tag{11.524}$$

where k is a constant. It is thus clear that we must identify W_{max} with entropy in the following manner:

$$\ln W_{max} = \frac{S}{k} + \text{const} \tag{11.525}$$

Equation 11.525 is thus the statistical mechanics version of the second law of thermodynamics. It will be appropriate to set the additive constant equal to zero, as we have anticipated in Eq. 11.408. The factor k of course is Boltzmann's constant, which must be evaluated by reference to the size of the thermometric degree. Fixing the value of the integration constant at zero is the statistical mechanical equivalent of the third law of thermodynamics.

We have attached meaning to all the terms in Eq. 11.516 except the middle one. We can now substitute thermodynamic functions for all the symbols except α. If we substitute Eqs. 11.521, 11.522, 11.524, and 11.525 in Eq. 11.516 and rearrange, we obtain

$$T \, dS = kT\alpha \, dN + dE + P \, dV \tag{11.526}$$

Now from the thermodynamic definition $A = E - TS$ or $E = A + TS$ we have

$$dE = dA + T \, dS + S \, dT \tag{11.527}$$

If we substitute Eq. 11.527 in Eq. 11.526 and solve for dA, we find

$$dA = -kT \, \alpha \, dN - S \, dT - P \, dV \tag{11.528}$$

From this

$$\mu = \left(\frac{\partial A}{\partial N} \right)_{T,V} = -kT\alpha \tag{11.529}$$

which is a general proof of Eq. 11.515.

The Fermi-Dirac Distribution Law. We now return to the unapproximated distribution law, Eq. 11.506. We set $G_j = 1$ and insert the values of α and β to obtain

$$N_j = \frac{1}{e^{(\epsilon_j - \dot{\mu})/kT} + 1} \tag{11.530}$$

where now N_j is always a number between zero and one and is to be regarded as the average occupancy of a single state or the probability that the state is occupied.

It can also be written as

$$N_j = \frac{1}{\lambda^{-1} e^{+\epsilon_j/kT} + 1} \tag{11.531}$$

where we have introduced the absolute activity, defined in terms of $\dot{\mu}$ as

$$\lambda = e^{+\dot{\mu}/kT} \tag{11.532}$$

Behavior at the Absolute Zero. At the absolute zero, the states are filled ($N_j = G_j$) up to a certain energy level, after which the states are completely empty. From Eq. 11.530 it is clear how this happens. The exponent is divided by a vanishing quantity, kT, and thus becomes extremely large and negative at low-energy and extremely large and positive at high-energy levels. Thus N_j changes abruptly from one to zero (per state) at $\epsilon_j = \dot{\mu}$. This value of the energy is given the symbol ϵ^* and called the *Fermi level*.

Both above and below this energy level, if we refer to Eq. 11.502, we see that W_j is unity. Thus we see that at the absolute zero, where the transition from empty to full states is abrupt, the total weight, $W = \Pi_j W_j$, is also unity. This result, although developed here for fermions alone, is a very general one.

For example, the success of the third law of thermodynamics as applied to a particular degree of freedom of motion has as its statistical mechanical basis

$$W_{(T=0°)} = 1 \tag{11.533}$$

This is true of the translational degrees of freedom, for which, at high temperatures, Eq. 11.403 successfully predicts the absolute entropy. For neglected degrees of freedom, such as nuclear ones, all that is required is that the statistical weight due to this source not change as the experimental evaluation of the entropy pursues the path, from near enough to $0°K$ to make Eq. 11.533 hold, to the standard temperature.

Intermediate Temperature Range. At intermediate temperatures, the Fermi-Dirac distribution is harder to handle than the Boltzmann. Roughly speaking, in all the lower levels N_j is almost unity (filled levels); rather abruptly, at ϵ^*, the Fermi level, the levels become almost empty. As the temperature increases, the abrupt change from full to empty broadens out and the smooth curve of the Boltzmann distribution is approached (see example in Fig. 11.601).

ILLUSTRATION.   Find the limiting energy forms of Fermi-Dirac statistics.

At upper and lower limits of the energy, the Fermi-Dirac distribution function becomes quite simple. As long as the energy level is very high, the exponential factor will be much larger than unity. Thus we can see that the high-energy "tail" of the distribution will take the limiting form of Eq. 11.508 for *any* Fermi-Dirac distribution. The requirement can be stated in two equivalent ways: either $\alpha + \beta\epsilon_j \gg 1$, or N_j must be very small compared to unity, that is, the Boltzmann distribution can be used on the particles that are in high-energy levels. Another simplification is possible at the low energies, where N_j is very close to, though not quite, unity. The fraction of empty states is then a small number $1 - N_j = N_h$, the number of "holes" per energy state. If we set $G_j = 1$ and write

$$N_j = \frac{1}{e^{+\alpha+\beta\epsilon_j} + 1} \approx 1$$

we find that

$$1 - N_j = \frac{e^{+\alpha+\beta\epsilon_j}}{e^{+\alpha+\beta\epsilon_j} + 1} \approx e^{+\alpha+\beta\epsilon_j} \ll 1$$

The requirement for this to hold true is of course that $\alpha + \beta\epsilon_j$ be a large *negative* number. In this range, the number of empty states is subject to Boltzmann statistics. Only in the intermediate range must we employ the full Fermi-Dirac distribution function.

This is the reason that we can discuss the properties of atoms with excited electronic states without ever mentioning Fermi-Dirac statistics. We put the exclusion principle directly in the problem by never assigning more than one electron to an individual level; then the slight probability that an electron will be in an excited state is given by a (small) Boltzmann factor. To a good approximation all levels are either empty or full.

Bose-Einstein Statistics. The Fermi-Dirac statistics apparently applies to protons and electrons, but other particles, notably photons and He^4 atoms (called in general bosons), obey a different set of rules known as the Bose-Einstein statistics. In this case multiple occupancy is allowed, with the same weight as single occupancy. The distribution law is

$$N_j = (\lambda^{-1} e^{\beta\epsilon_j} - 1)^{-1} \tag{11.534}$$

It is clear that, for the value of $\lambda = 1$, the population of one level (the lowest) can go toward infinity. This occurs at low temperature and high concentration and is called Bose condensation; something of the kind is apparently responsible for the unusual properties of liquid helium. However, the difficulties in applying the Bose-Einstein statistics are too great for further elaboration here.

Problem

11.501   Determine the classical limiting form of Bose-Einstein statistics.

6. Metals, Insulators, and Semiconductors

The Drude-Sommerfeld Model. It had been realized since 1900 that many properties of a metal could be explained if the metal was regarded as a box that enclosed one or more freely moving electrons per metal atom. However, this model failed to explain the lack of the $\frac{3}{2}R$ contribution to the heat capacity required by the classical theory of free particles. The correct use of Fermi-Dirac statistics overcomes this difficulty and allows a qualitative picture of metals to be presented.

We might expect that the repulsion between the charges on the electrons would be a very important part of the problem and would make the Hamiltonian very hard to handle. However, because of the relatively fixed lattice of the positive metal ions distributed through the volume, the charge of the electrons is largely neutralized. We therefore take as our model an ideal gas of electrons, subject only to the constant internal potential of the metal and to an infinite potential at the edge of the metal. We then apply the Fermi-Dirac distribution law, Eq. 11.506, to this problem.

Energy Levels of the Electron Gas. If we use as quantum numbers l, m, and n, the translational energy levels are given by the expression (see Eq. 3.209)

$$\epsilon = \frac{h^2}{8m_e} \left(\frac{l^2}{a^2} + \frac{m^2}{b^2} + \frac{n^2}{c^2} \right) \tag{11.601}$$

For ϵ constant, this is the equation of an ellipsoid, with l, m, n for the more usual x, y, z; a, b, c are the lengths of the sides of the piece of metal and m_e is the mass of the electron. We are interested only in the positive octant of this ellipsoid because all quantum numbers are positive.

Each lattice point (l, m, n = integral positive numbers) corresponds to a possible energy level with two eigenfunctions of opposite spin. All lattice points lying upon the surface of the octant of the ellipsoid defined by Eq. 11.601 have the energy ϵ. All the lattice points within the octant and up to the surface correspond to available levels with energy equal to or less than ϵ. Each lattice point is at the corner of eight cubes, and there are eight corners to a cube. Thus each lattice point corresponds to a cube of unit volume if we neglect special situations at the surfaces, edges, and corners of the octant. Therefore, at large values of ϵ the volume of the octant is very nearly equal to the number of translational eigenstates of energy less than ϵ. This volume is equal to

$$V_{\text{oct}} = \frac{\pi}{6} \left(\frac{8m_e \epsilon^*}{h^2} \right)^{3/2} abc \tag{11.602}$$

The student will note the similarity of this derivation to the one in Sec. 5.4. If we introduce the spin degeneracy, twice this many states are available to electrons. We can then use this expression to calculate the Fermi level ϵ^*, which is defined as the energy reached if N electrons are all put into the lowest possible energy levels. We replace $2V_{\text{oct}}$ by the number of electrons N, and abc by the physical volume V of the metal containing the N electrons, to obtain

$$N = \frac{\pi}{3} \left(\frac{8m_e \epsilon^*}{h^2} \right)^{3/2} V \qquad (11.603)$$

(The student is particularly cautioned not to confuse the volume of the octant in the lattice space of quantum numbers with the physical volume of the metal.) We then solve for the Fermi level energy to find

$$\epsilon^* = \frac{h^2}{8m_e} \left(\frac{3N}{\pi V} \right)^{2/3} \qquad (11.604)$$

This is the highest energy the electrons would reach if they all went into the lowest levels possible consistent with the Pauli principle.

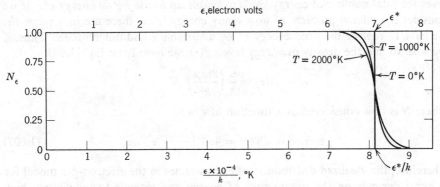

Fig. 11.601   Fermi-Dirac distribution function in copper.

We can insert numerical values in this equation and estimate the magnitude of ϵ^*. If we do so, because the molar volume of a metal and the mass of an electron are so small, the value is very large. For a typical metal such as copper which behaves as if it had one electron free per atom, ϵ^*/k comes out to be of the order of 100,000°K. Such a value means that at room temperature almost all the electrons are in the lowest states, and that above ϵ^* the states are almost empty. We may write the Fermi-Dirac distribution law in the form

$$N_\epsilon = [1 + e^{(\epsilon - \epsilon^*)/kT}]^{-1} \qquad (11.605)$$

where N_ϵ is the population of a single level at a given energy.

This clearly gives the right distribution at the absolute zero, because N_ϵ goes sharply from zero to unity at the Fermi energy. This constant must be replaced by a function of temperature only at temperatures approaching ϵ^*/k, or 100,000°. For copper, the degree of occupancy is shown in Fig. 11.601. The exponential suddenly takes over as the critical energy is reached. The lower the temperature, the more sudden this effect.

Electronic Heat Capacity.   It is clear from Fig. 11.601 that at lower temperatures the electrons do not change level as the temperature is raised, except to a very limited extent. Therefore the energy is constant to a first approximation. It can be shown to be

$$E = N\left[\tfrac{3}{5}\epsilon^* - \chi_0 + \frac{\pi^2 k^2}{4}\left(\frac{T^2}{\epsilon^*}\right)\right] \tag{11.606}$$

The term χ_0 is the potential produced by the metal ions on an electron at rest in the metal. The derivative of Eq. 11.606 with respect to T gives only an extremely small term proportional to T. Because large heat capacity effects are ultimately proportional to T^3 (Eq. 5.423), this contribution is apparent only around 1°K. We have already presented data that show this effect. In Fig. 5.403, the finite intercepts of the metals, as contrasted with the zero intercept for LiF, measure the linear electronic contribution to the specific heat of metals.

Distribution Function for Energy Levels for a Particle in a Box.   Equation 11.603 gives the total number of energy levels available up to the Fermi energy ϵ^*. If we consider the related problem of how many energy levels there are in a range $d\epsilon$, we have to replace the fixed energy ϵ^* by a variable ϵ and differentiate. Thus, if we wish to find the density of energy levels $g(\epsilon)$, we have from Eq. 11.603

$$N(\epsilon) = \frac{\pi}{3}\left(\frac{8m_e\epsilon}{h^2}\right)^{3/2} V$$

where N is now considered as a function of ϵ, and

$$g(\epsilon)\,d\epsilon = dN(\epsilon) = 4\pi V\left(\frac{2m_e}{h^2}\right)^{3/2}\epsilon^{1/2}\,d\epsilon \tag{11.607}$$

Therefore, the idealized distribution of energy states in the electron-gas model for a metal depends on the square root of energy and extends to indefinitely high energy. This may be compared to the similar derivation for the number of frequencies in an elastic solid, Eq. 5.419.

Real Metals and Insulators.   Real materials have some sort of arrangement of the energy levels, like that given by the particle in the box but more complicated. In solids, as distinguished from individual atoms, these levels are usually arranged in continuous bands, with "forbidden" bands lying in between. We have learned from the Fermi-Dirac statistics that the electrons necessary to make the substance electrically neutral fill into these bands until the Fermi level ϵ^* is reached. Where the top of this "Fermi sea" lies determines most of the properties of the material. This corresponds to the observation that in an atom the inner electrons are not as important chemically as the outer few.

The situation of the free electrons in a metal suggested to Fermi an analogy with the ocean (all the electrons) and the top of the ocean (electrons at the Fermi surface). Although composed of water identical with that on the bottom, the surface is the only part of the ocean where wave energy can be excited (where electrons can be excited into slightly higher states by temperature or applied electrical field). Thus the term "Fermi sea" is often applied to the electrons in a metal.

Figure 11.602 serves to make this clear. We plot the number density of levels

$g(\epsilon)$ at any energy against the energy. For a free electron gas this distribution function follows an $\epsilon^{1/2}$ law if plotted against ϵ (Eq. 11.607). In an ideal free electron gas, this curve would continue indefinitely. In the figure we have cut it off to indicate a forbidden band of energies, starting at point ϵ_{co}. If there are just sufficient electrons to fill the allowed band it is found that no metallic conduction

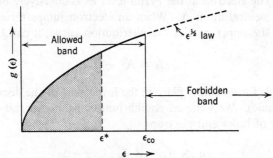

Fig. 11.602   Free electron distribution curve with cut-off.

is possible. On the other hand, if the allowed band is only partially filled, then an electric field of very small strength can excite the electrons slightly and cause metallic conduction.

Semiconductors. The situation in semiconductors is shown in Fig. 11.603. They are really insulators, but with a close empty band above the filled band.

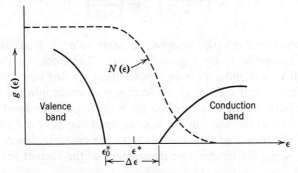

Fig. 11.603   Distribution of energy levels in a semiconductor.

Electrons are promoted up into this level by Boltzmann statistics, and so in the simplest cases a rise in temperature increases the conductivity exponentially. Conductors of this type are called thermal semiconductors. This behavior is contrary to the effect of temperature on metallic conductivity, which usually slowly decreases as the temperature is raised.

The Fermi-Dirac distribution law, Eq. 11.605, is indicated as a broken line on Fig. 11.603. Note that in the lower-energy or valence band the function is nearly unity, corresponding to almost complete occupancy of the available levels. However, the energy gap is depicted as being large enough to make the occupancy of states in the higher or conduction band close to zero. We are thus in the Boltzmann tail or exponential range of the Fermi-Dirac distribution in the valence band. In the energy gap, the Fermi-Dirac function is in an intermediate range, but since there are no available energy states its value is immaterial.

A relatively simple calculation will give the dependence of conductivity on temperature. The electron at the Fermi level ϵ^* is effectively bound to a positive ion to form a neutral atom A. When an electron jumps through the forbidden range $\Delta\epsilon$ into the upper part of the distribution curve, it can be thought of as a reaction

$$A = A^+ + e^-$$

where A^+ stands for an empty place in the lower part of the distribution or a positive vacancy (hole). We write an equilibrium constant for this reaction in terms of the number of holes and electrons

$$\frac{n_e \times n_+}{n_A} = \frac{Z_e Z_+}{Z_A} \exp\left(\frac{-\Delta\epsilon}{kT}\right) \tag{11.608}$$

Now the number of vacancies equals the number of promoted electrons, so $n_e = n_+$; also, whatever the value of n_A, it remains relatively unchanged. We thus find that the number of conduction electrons and also the number of vacancies are given by the expression

$$n_e = \left(\frac{n_A Z_e Z_+}{Z_A}\right)^{\frac{1}{2}} \exp\left(\frac{-\Delta\epsilon}{2kT}\right) \tag{11.609}$$

Now the partition function ratio, whatever its exact value, is relatively insensitive to temperature compared to the exponential part. Therefore, the electrical conductivity of such a semiconductor is an exponentially varying function, containing an energy that is one half the energy of electron promotion into the conductance band. We have implied here that the electrons in the conduction band are carrying the current; however, the holes in the valence band can have a certain mobility in the opposite direction and thus contribute to the current. Since, however, in this example $n_e = n_+$, the temperature dependence of the current will in any case be the same.

The derivation of Eq. 11.609 is essentially based on the Boltzmann distribution law; this is possible because N_j is very small in all the levels in the conduction band. Perhaps a more convincing derivation would use the Fermi-Dirac distribution explicitly. This method gives an equivalent result if proper care is taken to locate the Fermi level. Now by hypothesis enough levels are available to exactly hold the valence electrons, so it would seem that the Fermi level would be just at the top of the valence band, at the point labeled ϵ_0^* in Fig. 11.603. However, since there are no vacancies in the band $\Delta\epsilon$ wide above this energy, we could say that an infinitesimal increase in the number of electrons would put the level at the bottom of the conduction band. The level must be adjusted so that the total number of holes in the valence band equals the number of electrons in the conduction band. This locates the Fermi level in the middle of the empty or forbidden band of energies, as labeled.

Some data are presented in Fig. 11.604. Note that the effect of plotting resistance rather than conductance merely reverses the slope, and that the units of the resistance do not matter, since it is a log plot in that variable.

Intrinsic and Impurity Semiconductors. The inclusion of a small amount of impurity changes the properties of a semiconductor such as silicon very greatly. Since the model we have taken assumes that the number of electrons is just right to exactly fill the valence band level, a small amount of impurity, such as arsenic, which has the wrong number of electrons will drastically change the Fermi level by producing an extra electron which has to be put in the conduction band. A semiconductor without impurity is called an intrinsic semiconductor and is simplest in concept. However, the majority of useful semiconductors have been "tailor made" by the inclusion of impurity. Obviously the situation can rapidly become very complicated and the student is referred to some of the references at the end of the chapter.

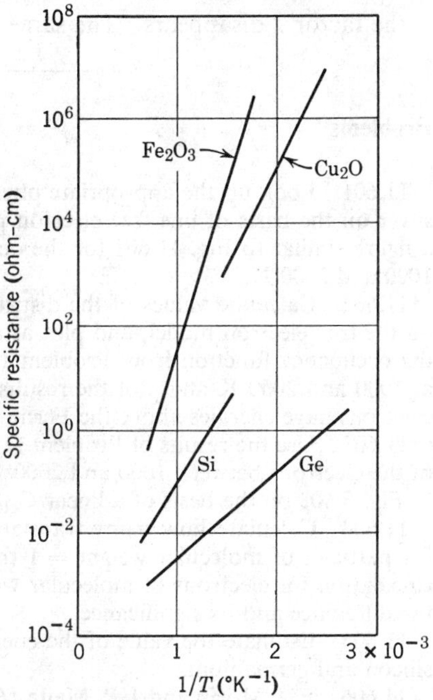

Fig. 11.604 Plot of the log of the resistance vs. $1/T$ for several semiconductors (by permission from C. Kittel, *Introduction to Solid State Physics*, Second Edition, John Wiley and Sons, 1956).

ILLUSTRATION. Analog of Eq. 11.609.

The situation that leads to the factor $\frac{1}{2}$ in the exponent of Eq. 11.609 is a consequence of the dissociative nature of the process $A = A^+ + e^-$ rather than the operation of anything peculiar to Fermi-Dirac statistics or semiconductors.

For example, acetic acid in an unbuffered solution follows the equation

$$HAc = H^+ + Ac^-$$

The equilibrium constant

$$K_a = \frac{[H^+][Ac^-]}{[HAc]}$$

can be written as a ratio of partition functions and an exponential function of the heat of ionization

$$K_a = \frac{Z_{Ac}\text{-}Z_{H^+}}{Z_{HAc}}\, e^{-\Delta H_0^\circ / RT}$$

If we now assume that the concentration of hydrogen ion equals that of acetate ion, the concentration of either one as a function of temperature is of the form

$$[H^+] = \text{const} \times e^{-\Delta H_0^{\circ}/2RT}$$

which is quite analogous to Eq. 11.609.

Of course, in an acetate buffered solution, we do not take a square root, and the factor 2 disappears. The same is true in an impurity semiconductor.

Problems

11.601   Look up the appropriate physical constants and calculate the Fermi level for silver on the basis of one free electron per silver atom. Then calculate values and plot a figure similar to Fig. 11.601 for the occupancy of the levels as a function of energy at 1000 and 2000°K.

*11.602   Calculate values of the distribution function of energy levels for silver based on the free electron model, and plot as a function of energy. Multiply this function by the occupancy function from Problem 11.601 to get the actual distribution of electrons at 1000 and 2000°K and plot the results. By graphical integration, estimate how many electrons have energies above the Fermi level at these temperatures.

*11.603   Use the results of Problem 11.602 to evaluate the average molar heat capacity of the electrons between 1000 and 2000°K. Compare results with the intercept for silver in Fig. 5.403 on the basis of a linear $C_{elec} = aT$.

11.604   Calculate how many translational energy levels there are in a 22.4-liter box for particles of molecular weight $= 1$ that have energy up to $\frac{3}{2}kT$ at STP. Repeat the calculation for electrons of molecular weight $= 1/1800$ in a 22.4-cc box. Comment on the difference and its significance.

11.605   Estimate the value of the energy gap $\Delta\epsilon$ from Figure 11.604 for the elements silicon and germanium.

11.606   F. J. Morin and J. P. Maita [*Phys. Rev.*, **96**, 28 (1954)] give the following conductivity data for a silicon sample. Plot and obtain $\Delta\epsilon$.

$T,°K$	Conductivity, ohm^{-1} cm^{-1}
500	0.03
600	0.2
800	8
1200	80

Do these data agree with those of Fig. 11.604? What can you say about the purity of this sample?

7. Review Problems

11.701   Calculate the second virial coefficient for krypton at $-100°C$.

11.702   Set up an expression for the second virial coefficient for a gas with a box potential:

$$\begin{aligned} \epsilon &= \infty & 0 < r < \sigma_1 \\ \epsilon &= -\epsilon_0^* & \sigma_1 < r < \sigma_2 \\ \epsilon &= 0 & \sigma_2 < r < \infty \end{aligned}$$

11.703 Use free energy functions to calculate an equilibrium constant for the reaction

$$2C + H_2 \rightarrow C_2H_2$$

at 200°C.

11.704 Use free energy functions to calculate the equilibrium constant for the reaction

$$C_2H_6 + C_2H_2 \rightarrow 2C_2H_4$$

at 400°C.

11.705 Calculate the rotational entropy of nitrogen from the standard entropy and the Sackur-Tetrode equation (neglecting vibration). Calculate the moment of inertia at 25°C.

11.706 Calculate the rotational and translational entropy of CO_2 at 25°C. The moment of inertia of CO_2 is 72×10^{-40} g cm^2. Calculate the vibrational entropy by difference.

General References

Davidson, N., *Statistical Mechanics*, McGraw-Hill Book Co., New York, 1962.

Fowler, R. H., and E. A. Guggenheim, *Statistical Thermodynamics*, Cambridge University Press, Cambridge, England, 1939.

Hill, T. L., *An Introduction to Statistical Thermodynamics*, Addison-Wesley Publishing Co., Reading, 1960.

Kittel, C., *Introduction to Solid State Physics*, Second Edition, John Wiley and Sons, New York, 1956.

Mayer, J. E., and M. G. Mayer, *Statistical Mechanics*, John Wiley and Sons, New York, 1940.

Ter Haar, D. *Statistical Mechanics*, Holt, Rinehart, and Winston, New York, 1954.

Chapter Twelve

Solutions

1. Solutions of Nonelectrolytes

Thermodynamic Approach. From an expression for the chemical potentials of the i components in terms of T, P, and X_i, the mole fraction of molecules of the ith kind, we can use the methods of thermodynamics to develop the properties of solutions. For example, according to Eq. 8.306,

$$\mu_i = \mu_i^\circ + RT \ln X_i \tag{8.306}$$

This behavior is approached by any real solution as X_i approaches unity, and serves as the definition of an ideal solution if it holds over the entire range of X_i from zero to one. A similar equation can be written for any solution near $X_i = 0$, only in general the constant μ_i° will be different at the two limits. This can be shown with the use of the relation in Eq. 8.331.

In Eq. 8.306, μ_i° is defined for a particular temperature and pressure; the chemical potential is a function of both T and P, however. If we wish we may write a similar expression in which the pressure dependence of μ_i is explicitly shown. Equation 7.615 shows the pressure dependence of μ_i at constant temperature and composition as

$$d\mu_i = \bar{V}_i \, dP \tag{7.615}$$

If we assume that the liquid partial molar volume $\bar{V}_i$ can be treated as independent of pressure, we may write, for constant temperature and at unit mole fraction,

$$\mu_i = \mu_i^* + P\bar{V}_i$$

or, in a solution to which Eq. 8.306 may be applied,

$$\mu_i = \mu_i^* + P\bar{V}_i + RT \ln X_i \tag{12.101}$$

where now the constant μ_i^* corresponds to the value of μ_i at unit mole fraction and zero pressure (on the liquid). Comparison of Eqs. 8.306 and 12.101 shows that with the stated assumptions $\mu_i^\circ = \mu_i^* + P\bar{V}_i$. It may be pointed out that, in equations such as Eq. 8.302 for gases, the pressure dependence of the chemical potential is explicitly included, and the integration constant, that is, the standard state value $\mu_{i(f)}^\circ$, or $\mu_{i(P)}^\circ$ in the ideal gas case, is not pressure dependent. Because of the behavior of $\bar{V}_i$, the gas-phase chemical potential shows a logarithmic dependence on P, whereas for the condensed state, μ_i approximates a linear dependence on P. The variation of the chemical potential for condensed states with normal atmospheric variations in pressure is generally negligible.

We shall now investigate the statistical mechanical basis of Eq. 12.101.

Partition Function for Dilute or Ideal Solute. The simplest partition function for a mixture of N_i molecules of solute i, etc, and N_0 molecules of solvent would be

$$Z_I = \left(\frac{1}{N_i! \cdots N_0!}\right) Z_i^{N_i} \cdots Z_0^{N_0} \tag{12.102}$$

This expression is just a generalization of the partition function for a group of N identical molecules, being the Nth power of that for a single molecule, but divided by $N!$ (Secs. 11.1 and 11.4). In this equation Z_i is presumed to be independent of N_i but not of V (or P) and T. Division by the factor $N_i! \cdots N_0!$ for the mixture takes the place of division by $N_T!$ in the case of a pure substance. The mixture factor corrects for the indistinguishability of identical particles but leaves in a term corresponding to the contribution to the partition function necessary to account for the mixing of different particles. It may be noted that Eq. 12.102 can be written in the form

$$Z_I = \frac{N_T!}{N_i! \cdots N_0! \, N_T!} \frac{1}{} (Z_i^{N_i} \cdots Z_0^{N_0})$$

Thus $Z_i^{N_i} \cdots Z_0^{N_0}$ takes the place of Z^N (the latter would be used if the mixture were a pure substance consisting of $N = N_T$ particles), and in addition we have the term $N_T!/(N_i! \cdots N_0!)$; the latter provides the extra term needed in expressions for the free energy and entropy to give the contribution indicated by equations such as 8.309 and 8.311.

ILLUSTRATION. Show that, if W in the Boltzmann-Planck equation, Eq. 11.408, is taken as $N_T!/N_A!N_B!$, where $N_T = N_A + N_B$, an entropy of mixing expression of the form of Eq. 8.311 is obtained.

We may write $\ln W = \ln N_T! - \ln N_A! - \ln N_B!$

Applying Stirling's approximation.

$$\ln W = N_T \ln N_T - N_T - N_A \ln N_A + N_A - N_B \ln N_B + N_B$$
$$= N_A \ln N_T + N_B \ln N_T - N_A \ln N_A - N_B \ln N_B$$
$$= -N_A \ln X_A - N_B \ln X_B$$
$$S = k \ln W = -N_A k \ln X_A - N_B k \ln X_B$$
$$= -R(n_A \ln X_A + n_B \ln X_B)$$

If we insert the ordinary Z for translation for the molecules, Eq. 12.102 is the partition function for a mixture of perfect gases and leads to Eq. 7.618. However, if we do nothing but make the assertion that Z_i is independent of N_i and do not limit ourselves to a perfect gas, we can still make some deductions. Analogous to Eq. 11.109 we have

$$A = kT(-N_i \ln Z_i + N_i \ln N_i - N_i + \text{terms independent of } N_i) \qquad (12.103)$$

whence we find by differentiation the chemical potential per molecule:

$$\dot{\mu}_i = \frac{\partial A}{\partial N_i} = \dot{\mu}_i^\circ + kT \ln N_i \qquad (12.104)$$

The quantity $\dot{\mu}_i^\circ$ is now a function of temperature and volume, or pressure. If we recall the equation

$$\frac{\partial \mu_i}{\partial P} = \bar{V}_i \qquad (7.615)$$

we can easily write the corresponding equation per molecule,

$$\frac{\partial \dot{\mu}_i}{\partial P} = \dot{V}_i \qquad (12.105)$$

where $\dot{V}_i$ is the partial volume per molecule, that is, the partial molar volume divided by Avogadro's number. We can integrate this expression to find the $P - V$ dependence of $\dot{\mu}_i$. In the particular case of a liquid solution with the pressure low enough so that the partial molar volume is substantially constant, we find that

$$\dot{\mu}_i = f(N_i, T) + P\dot{V}_i \qquad (12.106)$$

Comparison of Eqs. 12.104 and 12.106 gives the result that

$$\dot{\mu}_i = \dot{\mu}_i^* + P\dot{V}_i + kT \ln N_i \qquad (12.107)$$

where $\dot{\mu}_i^*$ depends only on the temperature. As we have indicated by the dots on top, these μ's and volumes are in terms of the number of molecules. If we convert to moles, Eq. 12.107 becomes equivalent to Eq. 12.101. Thus, the partition function Z_i, Eq. 12.102, is that for an ideal solution.

Any Solution at Low Concentrations and Pressures. If the pressure remains low enough so that the solution is effectively incompressible, at low concentrations

Eq. 12.107 reduces to the ideal form, Eq. 12.101, for all solutions. At low concentrations, the number of molecules N_i in a given volume is directly proportional to the mole fraction X_i, and so going from one unit of concentration to another merely changes the numerical value of μ_i^*. The other requirement is that Z_i be independent of N_i. At low concentrations the energy levels that go into the partition function are determined solely by the interactions of a single solute molecule with the surrounding solvent molecules, and so Z_i does not change with number N_i of solute molecules until there are enough solute molecules so that pair interaction between them becomes a problem. Thus Henry's law is generally true at low enough concentrations (see the discussion in Sec. 8.3).

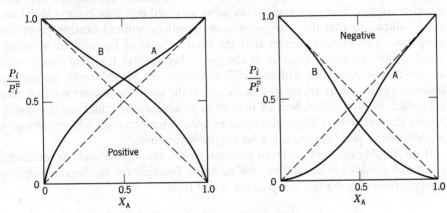

Fig. 12.101   Positive and negative deviations from Raoult's law.

Conditions When Eq. 12.101 Is True over Entire Concentration Range.   For Eq. 12.107 to be equivalent to Eq. 12.101 over the whole concentration range, it is necessary for all the molecules of solute or solvent to be the same size, that is, to have the same constant partial molar volume. Then the number of molecules in a given volume is always the same, and N_i remains proportional to X_i over the entire composition range.

In addition, the partition functions Z_i and Z_0 must be indifferent to the composition of the surrounding molecular environment. In plain language, the molecules of solute and solvent must be quite similar. This is the reason why solutions of chemically similar molecules are usually selected as examples of ideal, Raoult's law solutions. Molecules that are the same except for isotopic substitution are particularly likely to be ideal components of a solution.

Nonideal Solutions.   Relatively few solutions are ideal over the entire concentration range. The usual solution of two components exhibits a vapor pressure behavior such as that pictured in Fig. 12.101. If the vapor pressure is higher than Raoult's law, the deviation is said to be *positive*, and if it is lower, *negative*. A positive deviation means that the two components have a tendency to separate. On the other hand, a negative deviation suggests compound formation, which of course, if it proceeded to completion, would reduce to zero the pressure of one component. This is strictly a qualitative notion, however, and should not be taken too literally. There are many different causes for nonideality, such as dissimilar shapes of molecules, specific forces, freedom of rotation, and dimerization or dissociation of a component. These are in general resistant to expression in terms of a reasonably simple partition function. Remember, however, the very important thermodynamic fact; all solution components obey Raoult's law near $X = 1$ and Henry's law near $X = 0$.

Regular Solutions.   Among the types of nonideality, there is one which can be handled in an approximate manner with simple equations. This is the model of the regular solution. The model assumes that molecules in the solution are quite similar; namely, that they pack in the same way and that they occupy about the same volume, so that they can interchange positions without causing geometric problems. This in turn implies that the total volume of the solution is nearly equal to the sum of the volumes of the pure components. It is also necessary to assume that the molecules, although different in van der Waals' forces, are not too different and that there are no specific forces. If the second restriction on the forces is satisfied, the first is also, because in practice two highly dissimilar van der Waals' liquids (indicated by a large difference in critical temperature) will not dissolve in each other; one becomes a gas before the other melts.

If we simplify the combinatorial problem by the assumption that the molecules are mixed completely at random, the partition function for the regular solution can be written, for the two components A and B, as

$$Z_R = \left(\frac{1}{N_A! \, N_B!}\right) Z_A^{N_A} Z_B^{N_B} \exp\left(\frac{-N_A N_B}{(N_A + N_B)} \frac{w_{AB}}{kT}\right)$$

$$= Z_I \exp\left(-\frac{N_A N_B}{(N_A + N_B)} \frac{w_{AB}}{kT}\right) \tag{12.108}$$

Thus the partition function is the same as that for an ideal solution, except that it is multiplied by an exponential energy term. The factor $N_A N_B/(N_A + N_B)$ is proportional to the random number of A-B neighbors. The w_{AB} term reflects the difference between the A-A and B-B energies, and the alternate two A-B pair energies. It is of course zero for an ideal solution.

We now proceed to calculate the chemical potential for this partition function. We find that

$$A = kT(-N_A \ln Z_A - N_B \ln Z_B + N_A \ln N_A + N_B \ln N_B - N_A - N_B)$$

$$+ \left(\frac{N_A N_B}{N_A + N_B}\right) w_{AB} \tag{12.109}$$

whence the chemical potential per molecule of A is

$$\dot{\mu}_A = \frac{\partial A}{\partial N_A} = kT \ln N_A - kT \ln Z_A + \left[\frac{N_B^2}{(N_A + N_B)^2}\right] w_{AB} \tag{12.110}$$

If we then convert this from numbers of molecules to mole fraction,

$$X_A = \frac{N_A}{N_A + N_B} = \frac{N_A}{N_T} \qquad (12.111)$$

and remember that the total number of molecules N_T is a constant within a given volume of solution, then

$$\mu_A = \mu_A^\circ + kT \ln X_A + (1 - X_A)^2 w_{AB} \qquad (12.112)$$

with a symmetrical expression for the B species. If we now assume that the gas phase is ideal, we can equate chemical potentials in the two phases to obtain the regular-solution replacement for Raoult's law (Eq. 8.305):

$$P_A = P_A^\square X_A \exp \left[(1 - X_A)^2 \frac{w_{AB}}{kT} \right] \qquad (12.113)$$

We can also use Eq. 7.421 on the expression for A, Eq. 12.109, to obtain the energy associated with the partition function. If we then subtract the energy of the pure components, obtained in a similar way, we find for the energy of mixing *if* w_{AB} is independent of T

$$\Delta E_R = \left(\frac{N_A N_B}{N_A + N_B} \right) w_{AB} \qquad (12.114)$$

Since there is by hypothesis negligible volume change on mixing, we can also write $\Delta(PV) = 0$ and

$$\Delta H_R = \Delta E_R \qquad (12.115)$$

Note that for an ideal solution the enthalpy ("heat") of mixing is zero. The entropy of mixing is the same for regular as for ideal solutions:

$$\Delta S = -k(N_A \ln X_A + N_B \ln X_B) \qquad (12.116)$$

It may also be observed that the exponential part of Eq. 12.113 represents the value of the activity coefficient for a regular solution.

Phase Separation and Long-Range Order. We can show by two differentiations of Eq. 12.113 that there is a point of inflection. At this point of inflection $dP/dX = 0$ when $w_{AB}/kT = 2$. This behavior corresponds to a critical point at $X_A = X_B = \frac{1}{2}$ and

$$T_c = \frac{w_{AB}}{2k} \qquad (12.117)$$

Below this temperature, the theory predicts a separation of phases consisting of an A-rich and a B-rich region. Thus, in this sense positive deviation from Raoult's law does eventually lead to an unstable solution and a "tendency to separate." w_{AB} is positive because T must be positive. The behavior Eq. 12.113 for two values of w_{AB}/kT is illustrated in Fig. 12.102.

There is another, quite unexpected, critical point at

$$T_c = -\frac{w_{AB}}{2k} \tag{12.118}$$

if w_{AB} is negative. There can be no question of the solution having a tendency to separate, because now w_{AB} operates in a sense that holds the solution together. We have mentioned previously the fact that negative deviation roughly corresponds to "compound formation." What is happening is that the solution is rapidly

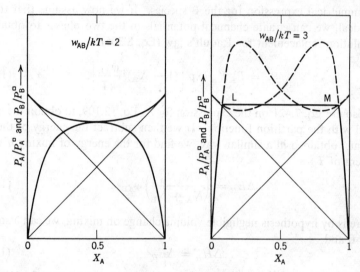

Fig. 12.102 Critical solution temperature and phase separation predicted by Eq. 12.113 (by permission from E. A. Guggenheim and R. A. Fowler, *Statistical Thermodynamics*, Cambridge University Press, 1939).

getting a regular A—B—A—B $\cdots$ character to its arrangement as the temperature is lowered. As this second critical temperature is passed, this alternation is preserved over an indefinite large distance in the lattice.

Although this behavior is predicted by the theory, it is not observed in ordinary solutions. It is an important feature, however, of solid solutions, in particular of certain binary alloys of metals. At low temperature, an X-ray analysis of the structure of the alloy shows a definite alternation in the location of the two kinds of atoms; at a certain temperature this alternation suddenly disappears.

The changes that take place in a solution with a negative value of w_{AB} as the temperature is raised are shown schematically in Fig. 12.103. We will take the case where there are equal numbers of A and B molecules. At the absolute zero, every A molecule is surrounded by B molecules, and vice versa. This order persists for an indefinitely large distance, and every A molecule can be thought of as attached to a lattice with a spacing twice the A—B distance. The same is true for the B molecules. Such an arrangement is described as long-range order. As the temperature is raised to a temperature below the critical one, thermal fluctuations occur, and a few A and B atoms exchange places. These disordered places are isolated from one another, and the majority of A atoms continue to be on one lattice, and the majority of B atoms on the other. The system is still regarded as having long-range order, although it is not perfect. As the critical temperature is passed, these

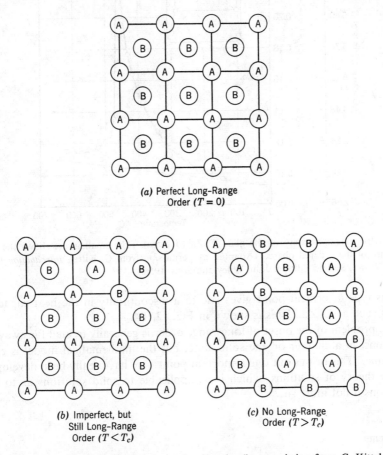

(a) Perfect Long-Range
Order $(T = 0)$

(b) Imperfect, but
Still Long-Range
Order $(T < T_c)$

(c) No Long-Range
Order $(T > T_c)$

Fig. 12.103   Schematic diagrams showing order-disorder (by permission from C. Kittel, *Introduction to Solid State Physics*, Second Edition, John Wiley and Sons, 1956).

lattices suddenly cease to have an excess of A or B molecules, and at this point long-range order is said to be destroyed. However, because the negative value of w_{AB} still favors A—B pairs over A—A or B—B pairs, any A is somewhat more likely to have B neighbors than A neighbors; and so it is said that short-range order is still present in the solution, although the regular pattern of long-range order is gone. Finally, at very high temperature, the effect of w_{AB} is negligible, and no order remains.

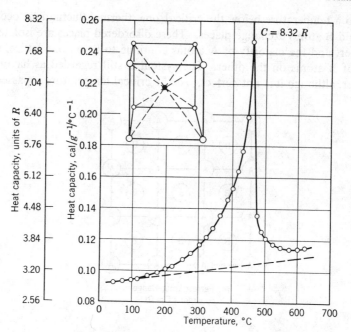

Fig. 12.104 Heat capacity of the alloy CuZn (β brass). The small insert shows the crystal structure of the ordered phase. (Adapted by permission from C. Kittel, *Introduction to Solid State Physics*, Second Edition, John Wiley and Sons, 1956.)

This type of critical point gives rise to a discontinuity in the heat capacity of alloys such as CuZn. This is shown in Fig. 12.104.

The problem of the onset of long-range order is generally treated far away from solutions, in a chapter on the solid state, but the mathematical model is exactly the same. This brings out one important point: we have really been developing a lattice theory of solutions, which is as applicable to solid solutions as to liquid solutions if not more so.

Problems

12.101   Derive Raoult's law, the freezing point depression law, and the osmotic pressure law from the starting point of Eq. 12.101.

12.102   Derive Eq. 12.112, starting from the partition function. Also derive the expression for the chemical potential of the B species, both from the partition function and from Eq. 12.112 and the Gibbs-Duhem equation.

12.103   Derive Eq. 12.113, and make plots of the vapor pressure of A with values of $w_{AB}/kT = -1, 0, +1$, and $+2$.

12.104   Derive Eq. 12.116 from the partial molar entropies and from Eq. 12.109 with 12.115. Which is easier?

12.105   Derive Dalton's law of partial pressures from Eq. 12.102 and the partition function for an ideal monatomic gas.

12.106   Differentiate Eq. 12.113 twice, and find the critical value of w_{AB}/kT.

*12.107   Develop an equation for the vapor pressure of Br_2 above a solution of bromine in CCl_4. Assume that the solution is ideal but that an appreciable degree of dissociation of Br_2 into bromine atoms occurs in the solution. Express the vapor pressure as a function of the apparent mole fraction (if dissociation is ignored), and the dissociation equilibrium constant (assumed known) and the vapor pressure of pure bromine at the temperature of interest.

2. Electrolytes.   Debye-Hückel Theory

Coulomb's Law.   In order to understand the behavior of ions in solution or, for that matter, a variety of other phenomena in chemistry, it is necessary to have an appreciation of the unique type of interaction expressed by Coulomb's law. Ordinary chemical bonding forces are short range. Even the van der Waals' force that holds electrically neutral molecules together falls off with the inverse seventh power of distance. However, as the student will recall from elementary physics, the force between charged particles or, more precisely, point charges falls off with the inverse second power of distance. That is, if we have a point charge at x', y', and z' in rectilinear coordinates, a charge at point x, y, and z is acted on by a force that falls off with the inverse second power of the distance

$$r = +\sqrt{(x - x')^2 + (y - y')^2 + (z - z')^2} \qquad (12.201)$$

The force on the particle at x, y, z may be regarded as a vector, with its direction in the same direction as the vector joining the two charged particles. This second vector $\vec{r}$ has the components $x - x'$, $y - y'$, and $z - z'$. The force vector $\vec{f}$ which points in the same direction diminishes by a factor $1/r^2$ as the distance between the two particles increases; thus to get $\vec{f}$ from $\vec{r}$ it is necessary to divide by r^3. In fact, the equation connecting them in a vacuum is

$$\vec{f} = \frac{q_1 q_2 \vec{r}}{r^3} \qquad (12.202)$$

where q_1 and q_2 are the charges on the point particles. With such a force law particles containing unbalanced charges can exert an influence on other such particles over a relatively long range. Although the magnitude of this force is reduced by the presence of a medium, such as a solvent, the form of the law persists, but with the force divided by the dielectric constant D of the medium if the particles are far enough apart. These long-range forces are responsible for the fact that electrolytes, although completely dissociated into ions, have to be diluted to exceptionally low concentrations before they behave like ideal solutions. For example, at a concentration of 0.01 mole fraction, a solution of sucrose in water is more nearly ideal than a solution of NaCl; at this concentration $LaCl_3$ is very far from ideal (Fig. 12.201).

Extensive Properties.   It is even remarkable that salts and solutions of salts have the ordinary extensive thermodynamic properties. For a contrary example, stellar matter, governed by the force of gravity, which also falls off with the second power of distance, does not fit into the ordinary scheme of extensive and intensive properties, for when the size of a star is doubled the gravitational energy more than doubles. Solely because of the balance between electrical charges (electrical neutrality), although there is a definite net binding energy between charges, this energy can be shown to be proportional to the size of the piece of salt or the volume of the solution at a given concentration. This is far from easy to demonstrate and

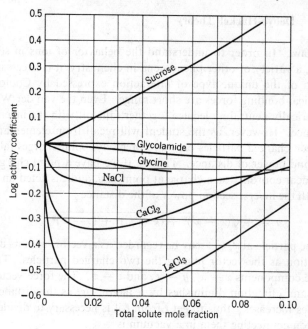

Fig. 12.201   Activity coefficient of various ionic and nonionic solutes in water (by permission from R. H. Robinson and R. A. Stokes, *Electrolyte Solutions*, Second Edition, Academic Press, New York, 1959).

is beyond the scope of our present treatment. Any ordinary way of setting it up involves the difference between two integrals that increase without bound but that nevertheless have a finite difference.

The Potential.   We often speak in a loose manner about the electrical force and the electrical potential; they must be carefully distinguished and also distinguished from the potential energy, discussed in Sec. 2.1. The x component of the mechanical force is related to the potential energy by the expression

$$f_x = -\frac{\partial}{\partial x} V(x, y, z) \tag{2.101}$$

with similar expressions for the y and z force components. A large value of potential energy does not necessarily imply a large value of force; if the potential is large but changes only slowly with the coordinate, the force is small. Conversely, a potential energy may be small but changing rapidly and thus correspond to a large force. Note also that, although $V(x, y, z)$ is a scalar, the force is a vector with components given by the partial derivatives in each dimension in turn, $\partial V/\partial x$, $\partial V/\partial y$, $\partial V/\partial z$. The symbol ∇, called "del," is used to denote the process of making such a vector out of a scalar function of several variables, and in general means the vector operator with the components $\partial/\partial x$, $\partial/\partial y$, and $\partial/\partial z$. Equation 2.101 may thus be written in vector notation

$$\vec{f} = -\nabla V(x, y, z) \tag{12.203}$$

In the treatment of atoms and molecules presented in Chapters 3 and 4, we wrote expressions for the electrostatic potential energy, such as that for an electron and a proton in the hydrogen atom

$$V(r) = -\frac{e^2}{r} \tag{2.108}$$

In the general case of two point charges q_1 and q_2, the potential energy expression is

$$V(r) = \frac{q_1 q_2}{r} \tag{12.204}$$

We may verify that Eqs. 12.202 and 12.204 are consistent by application of 12.203; the operator del applied to $1/r$ gives $-\vec{r}/r^3$; hence

$$\vec{f} = -\nabla V(r) = -q_1 q_2 \nabla\left(\frac{1}{r}\right) = q_1 q_2 \frac{\vec{r}}{r^3} \tag{12.205}$$

it is useful to define a related quantity, the electrical potential ϕ. This quantity Is simply the electrostatic potential energy of a positive point charge of unit magnitude, at a certain point due to the presence of other charges. If we imagine replacing the charge q_1 in Eq. 12.204 by a unit positive charge, then ϕ is given by q_2/r. For the more general case in which q_1 may not be a unit positive charge, Eq. 12.204 may be written

$$V(r) = q_1 \phi$$

The units of ϕ are thus energy units divided by charge units. Note also that, since potential energy is a scalar quantity, the electrical potential is also a scalar quantity.

The Field. Most simply, the field is the force felt by a unit charge, said to be in the field of one or more other charges. If we set $q_1 = 1$ in Eq. 12.205, we obtain the contribution to the field from a single point charge. The total field of these contributions is

$$\vec{E} = \sum_i -q_i \nabla\left(\frac{1}{r_i}\right) \tag{12.206}$$

The unit charge used as a "probe" is supposed not to affect the position of the charges that are generating the field. The field is defined in terms of the potential

$$\vec{E} = -\nabla \phi \qquad (12.207)$$

The Dot Product.   Further Properties of ∇.   The dot product of two vectors is the scalar sum of the product of the x components of the two vectors, plus the product of the two y components, plus the product of the two z components. It is written with a dot: $\vec{A} \cdot \vec{B} = c$. In particular, $\vec{r} \cdot \vec{r} = r^2$, and ∇^2, which means $\nabla \cdot \nabla$, is $\partial^2/\partial x^2 + \partial^2/\partial y^2 + \partial^2/\partial z^2$, a scalar operator.   We can also show that

$$\nabla r = \frac{\vec{r}}{r} \qquad (12.208)$$

and that

$$\nabla \cdot \vec{r} = 3 \qquad (12.209)$$

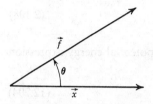

Fig. 12.202   Force acting at an angle θ to a displacement.

ILLUSTRATION.   Show that a constant force of magnitude f, acting at an angle θ to the direction of displacement of a mass m through distance of magnitude x, does an amount of work equal to $-\vec{f} \cdot \vec{x}$, where $\vec{f}$ is the vector representing the force and $\vec{x}$ the displacement (Fig. 12.202).

The work is equal to $-f_x x$, where f_x is the component of the force in the x direction and x is the magnitude of the displacement.   This is exactly equivalent to the statement which defines the dot product—that is, the dot product is the scalar sum of the product of the x components, y components, and z components. In this case we are interested in only one direction.   Hence

$$\vec{f} \cdot \vec{x} = (f \cos \theta)x = f_x x$$

Laplace's Equation.   When a number of charges are distributed in space, such as for a particular configuration of an electrolyte, the potential at any point is given by the sum of the potentials from the various ions, just as the field is the sum of the separate fields, as shown by Eq. 12.206. Of course, if the point in the field happens to coincide with one of the charges, then $1/r_i$ diverges, and the field cannot be determined at this point; the potential is plus or minus infinity. Now, if the definitions of ∇ and ∇^2 are kept in mind, it can be shown by differentiation that

$$\nabla^2 \left(\frac{1}{r}\right) = 0 \qquad (12.210)$$

everywhere except at the point $r = 0$. Therefore, from Eq. 12.206 if we operate on both sides by $\nabla \cdot$

$$\nabla \cdot \vec{E} = 0 \qquad (12.211)$$

because when each of the $1/r_i$ terms is operated on by ∇^2 it gives zero.   Now, together with Eq. 12.206, it appears that the equation for the potential is

$$\nabla^2 \phi = 0 \tag{12.212}$$

which is the fundamental partial differential equation called Laplace's equation. It must be solved to determine the potential of any configuration of charges.

Poisson's Equation. If the charges are divided finely enough or can be considered as "smeared out" by a statistical average, we can speak of a charge density ρ, which is a function of the position in space. We shall use the symbol ρ to represent the charge density at the point x, y, z, and the symbol ρ' to represent the density at the point x', y', z'. The unprimed point is where the field is measured.

To get the total net charge, we integrate over the volume; thus

$$q(V) = \iiint_{\text{all vol}} \rho' \, dx' \, dy' \, dz' \tag{12.213}$$

This integral would be zero over the whole of a balanced electrolyte solution, or $-q_i$ if one ion of charge q_i were held out.

The field is also an integral over the whole volume. This results from the replacement of the sum in Eq. 12.206 by an integral over the distribution function:

$$\vec{E} = - \iiint_{\text{all vol}} \rho' \, \nabla\left(\frac{1}{r}\right) dx' \, dy' \, dz' \tag{12.214}$$

Now we will operate on both sides of this equation with $\nabla\cdot$, which is a function of x, y, and z, and not of x', y', and z'. On the right-hand side, only $\nabla(1/r)$ is a function of x, y, z, so

$$\nabla \cdot \vec{E} = - \iiint_{\text{all vol}} \rho' \, \nabla^2\left(\frac{1}{r}\right) dx' \, dy' \, dz' \tag{12.215}$$

Now at first sight this integral might seem to be zero, and the integrand is zero everywhere except at the point where the field is measured, x, y, z. Near here the value of $\nabla^2(1/r)$ increases without bound as the point is approached because the field is both very large and changes sign, as a unit charge is passed through the origin. A mathematical analysis shows that, if a function of x', y', and z', called f', is so treated, the value of f' at x, y, and z is selected. Thus, including constant terms,

$$\iiint_{\text{all vol}} f' \, \nabla^2\left(\frac{1}{r}\right) dx' \, dy' \, dz' = -4\pi f \tag{12.216}$$

where f stands for the function f' at x, y, z. If we utilize this result, it follows that

$$\nabla \cdot \vec{E} = 4\pi\rho \tag{12.217}$$

or in terms of the potential

$$\nabla^2 \phi = -4\pi\rho \tag{12.218}$$

This result is called Poisson's equation.

Proof of Eq. 12.216.   We offer a proof of this equation for the student who has studied the Gauss divergence theorem, which relates volume integrals such as Eq. 12.216 to surface integrals. We take the special case of a sphere, with center at x, y, z and radius vector $\vec{r}$ (not a constant) and radius r (constant). To any vector $\vec{V}$ we may apply the theorem

$$\iiint_{\text{vol of sphere}} \nabla \cdot \vec{V}\, dx'\, dy'\, dz' = \iint_{\text{surf of sphere}} \vec{V} \cdot d\vec{S}$$

We take the particular vector $\vec{V} = \nabla(1/r)$, for which the theorem becomes

$$\iiint_{\text{vol}} \nabla^2 \left(\frac{1}{r}\right) dx'\, dy'\, dz' = -\left(\frac{1}{r^3}\right) \iint_{\text{surf}} \vec{r} \cdot d\vec{S}$$

using Eqs. 12.202 and 12.205. Now the vector for a surface is normal to the surface and points out. The vector $d\vec{S}$ is infinitesimal and points in the same direction as $\vec{r}$. An integral over $d\vec{S}$ alone would be zero over the sphere, but when two vectors that point in the same direction are multiplied, the result is the product of their scalar lengths. Thus it emerges that

$$-\left(\frac{1}{r^3}\right) \iint \vec{r} \cdot d\vec{S} = -\left(\frac{1}{r^3}\right) \iint r\, dS = -\left(\frac{1}{r^2}\right) \iint dS$$

Now all that remains under the integral sign is the area of a sphere of radius r or $4\pi r^2$. Thus the value of the right-hand side is -4π. Since all this is contributed at the point x, y, z, the sign and magnitude of the constant in Eq. 12.216 are established. Since the contributions to the volume integral are all zero except at the point x, y, z, this constant merely multiplies the value of f' at this point to give $-4\pi f$.

Application to Ions in Solution.   Equation 12.218 applies as it stands to the large-scale potential of a "swarm" or dust of charge points in a vacuum. It will now be applied to the very-small-scale atomic-sized interaction between ions. This is the first of several approximations of the Debye-Hückel theory, and it is the most difficult for us to justify, or even to estimate how wrong it is. In order to use the Poisson equation in solution we must introduce the dielectric constant of the medium (water). It is assumed to be a constant (a second approximation). In terms of the dimensionless dielectric constant D and cgs units, Eq. 12.218 takes the form

$$\nabla^2 \phi = -\left(\frac{4\pi}{D}\right)\rho \tag{12.219}$$

Boltzmann's Factor and the Average Charge Density.   We shall consider a certain ion α, and the average charge density at a distance r measured from its center as origin, with the symbol ρ_r. If there were no energy of interaction between charges, the average charge density would be the same throughout the solution

$$\rho_r = \sum_\beta \frac{q_\beta}{V}$$

where the summation is over all the ions of both charges, contained in the volume of the solution V. Clearly, the charge density would be very small because of the random arrangement of oppositely charged ions. If the volume were large, it would be zero. The effect of the interaction between the charges is to unbalance this charge near the ion α, and this can be represented by a Boltzmann weighting factor; $\exp(-W_{\alpha\beta}/kT)$ containing the interaction energy between ions, $W_{\alpha\beta}$. This energy is a function of the distance r between ions α and β and of the charge on the ions. Debye and Hückel assume it to be

$$W_{\alpha\beta} = q_\beta \phi_r \tag{12.220}$$

where q_β is the charge on ion β, and ϕ_r is the potential at a distance r from ion α. This is an approximation because it neglects the effect on the distribution of the other ions of fixing ion β at r. Then the charge density at a distance r from ion α is

$$\rho_r = \sum_\beta q_\beta \frac{\exp(-q_\beta \phi_r/kT)}{V} \tag{12.221}$$

With this in mind, the Poisson equation becomes

$$\nabla^2 \phi_r = -\left(\frac{4\pi}{DV}\right) \sum_\beta q_\beta \exp(-q_\beta \phi_r/kT) \tag{12.222}$$

This is called the Poisson-Boltzmann equation. If N_i like ions are grouped, it becomes

$$\nabla^2 \phi_r = -\left(\frac{4\pi}{DV}\right) \sum_i N_i q_i \exp(-q_i \phi_r/kT) \tag{12.223}$$

This equation must be solved to find the potential at a distance r from ion α.

Linear Solution of Debye and Hückel. Equation 12.222 is a differential equation in ϕ_r, but in practice it is too difficult to solve. Debye and Hückel expanded the exponential part, after the formula $e^x \approx 1 + x$ with the neglect of higher powers of x. They thus assumed that the potential energy of the ions was small compared to kT. When this approximate expansion is made, the first term that comes from the 1 vanishes

$$\sum_i N_i q_i = 0 \tag{12.224}$$

because the solution is electrically neutral. The term in x gives rise to the linear equation

$$\nabla^2 \phi_r = \kappa^2 \phi_r \tag{12.225}$$

where

$$\kappa^2 = \frac{4\pi}{VDkT} \sum_i N_i q_i^2 \tag{12.226}$$

The solution of Eq. 12.225 is

$$\phi_r = \left(\frac{A}{r}\right) e^{-\kappa r} + \left(\frac{B}{r}\right) e^{+\kappa r} \tag{12.227}$$

The second term must vanish ($B = 0$) for the potential to be finite at an infinite distance from ion α.

The Potential at the Ion α.   It is necessary to assume that the ions are charged in the center and have a finite size; otherwise a positive and a negative ion could come together and release an infinite amount of energy.   So we assume that there is a distance a inside of which there is no other ion but ion α (Fig. 12.203).   Inside this sphere, the potential from the other ions is constant; the only force comes from the potential of the central ion, whose field is $q_\alpha \vec{r}/r^3 D$, up to $r = a$.   Beyond

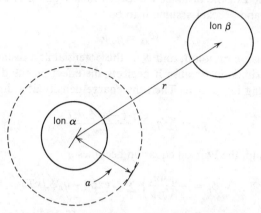

Fig. 12.203   The model for the Debye-Hückel theory.

$r = a$ the field is given by $\vec{E} = -\nabla \cdot \phi_r$.   At $r = a$ the two fields have to be equal. Then, with the use of Eq. 12.227

$$\frac{q_\alpha}{a^2 D} = \frac{1}{a^2} A\, e^{-\kappa a}(1 + \kappa a)$$

which can be used to evaluate the integration constant A.

Alternatively, we may solve for the constant A in Eq. 12.227 by observing that the total charge in the rest of the solution, excluding the single ion α, must be $-q_\alpha$, i.e.,

$$\int_a^\infty \rho_r 4\pi r^2\, dr = -q_\alpha$$

Comparison of Eqs. 12.225 and 12.219 shows that $\rho_r = (-D/4\pi)\kappa^2 \phi_r$, or

$$\rho_r = \frac{-D}{4\pi}\kappa^2\left(\frac{A}{r}\right) e^{-\kappa r}$$

Thus the integral becomes

$$D\kappa^2 A \int_a^\infty r e^{-\kappa r}\, dr = q_\alpha$$

Integration by parts gives

$$A = \frac{q_\alpha e^{\kappa a}}{D(\kappa a + 1)} \tag{12.228}$$

Hence Eq. 12.227 becomes

$$\phi_r = \frac{q_\alpha e^{\kappa a} \, e^{-\kappa r}}{Dr(\kappa a + 1)}$$

We will be particularly interested in the value of the potential when $r = a$. This value is

$$\phi_{r=a} = \frac{q_\alpha}{Da(\kappa a + 1)}$$

The potential at this point may be regarded as made up of two contributions, that from the central ion α and that from the rest of the ions, or *ionic atmosphere*. Since the charge on α is permanently fixed to the ion itself and does not move relative to the ion, it does not contribute to the work of introducing the ion into a solution. The contribution to the potential of the charge on ion α at $r = a$ is q_α/Da. If we subtract this quantity from $\phi_{r=a}$, we obtain the contribution to the potential at $r = a$ for the rest of the ions

$$\phi_\alpha = -\left(\frac{\kappa q_\alpha}{D}\right)(1 + \kappa a)^{-1} \tag{12.229}$$

Since the effect of the central ion has been removed, this is now the potential at the surface of a charge-free cavity of radius a. Such a potential is constant throughout the cavity, and the important result is that this is the potential at $r = 0$ due to the other ions and felt by the ion α. The total potential is infinite, but of course no ion is acted on by its own charge.

Mean Activity Coefficient for the Ions. By a roundabout process of computing the total free energy for all the ions and then taking the derivative of the free energy with respect to the number of a certain kind of ion, it is possible to develop the contribution to the chemical potential of each ion by the electric forces. We shall, however, employ a short cut. We shall compute the electric contribution to the free energy from charging a single ion, α. The charge will be increased from zero to q_α by means of a charging parameter λ which varies from zero to one. The charge at any time is then λq_α. The charge on one ion alone does not affect κ significantly, so the contribution to the free energy from the charging process is the integral of the potential up to this charge,

$$\mu_\alpha^{el} = \int_0^1 \phi_\alpha(\lambda) q_\alpha \, d\lambda = \frac{-\kappa(1 + \kappa a)^{-1}}{D} q_\alpha^2 \int_0^1 \lambda \, d\lambda$$

$$= -\frac{(q_\alpha^2/2D)\kappa}{(1 + \kappa a)} \tag{12.230}$$

We have written the work of charging a single ion in a notation indicating that it measures directly the electrical contribution to the chemical potential of ions of that type. This results directly because the charging process takes place at constant temperature and volume with no other kind of work besides the electrical work of charging the ion; thus

$$\Delta A = -\int S \, dT - \int P \, dV + W_{elec} = W_{elec}$$

at constant T and V. Since the particular ΔA involved is for a single ion, and since $\mu = \Delta A / \Delta N$, and ΔN is 1, the electrical work is a direct measure of the contribution of the electrical forces to μ.

Now, for the solution which would be ideal if it were not for the electrical forces,

$$\mu_i^{\text{total}} = \mu_i^{\text{ideal}} + \mu_i^{\text{el}}$$

From the equations for the chemical potential in terms of concentration and activity coefficients (compare Eq. 8.303)

$$\mu_i^{\text{total}} = \mu_i^\circ + kT \ln \gamma_i c_i$$

and

$$\mu_i^{\text{ideal}} = \mu_i^\circ + kT \ln c_i$$

We have by subtraction, $\mu_i^{\text{el}} = kT \ln \gamma_i$; in particular, for the ions of species α

$$kT \ln \gamma_\alpha = \mu_\alpha^{\text{el}} \tag{12.231}$$

and if there are only plus and minus ions of one type each, the measurable mean activity coefficient is the average of those given by Eq. 12.231 for the two ions,

$$(\nu_+ + \nu_-) \ln \gamma_\pm = \nu_+ \ln \gamma_+ + \nu_- \ln \gamma_- \tag{12.232}$$

where the ν's are the formal number of cations and anions obtained from the salt as its formula is written; thus, for $LaCl_3$, $\nu_+ = 1$ and $\nu_- = 3$.

Combination of Eqs. 12.230, 12.231, and 12.232 gives an experimentally usable result:

$$\ln \gamma_\pm = \frac{(q_+ q_- / 2 DkT)\kappa}{(1 + \kappa a)} \tag{12.233}$$

It is convenient to put these quantities in molar units; to do so we define the ionic strength

$$I = \tfrac{1}{2} \sum_i c_i z_i^2 \tag{12.234}$$

where c_i is in moles per liter, and z_i is in unit ionic charges (-1 for Cl^-, etc.).

In practical units, for water near 20°C, the formula Eq. 12.233 becomes

$$\log_{10} \gamma_\pm = -0.51 z_+ (-z_-) \frac{I^{1/2}}{1 + (a/3.0)I^{1/2}} \tag{12.235}$$

where the distance a is measured in angstroms. This expression can be fitted to data, and the value of a so evaluated examined. It is 3.8 Å for KCl, with similar reasonable values for other salts. However, in some cases unreasonable or even negative values are found, and in general the values obtained are too erratic to fit in with other estimates of ionic size, such as those from X-ray study of the corresponding crystals.

ILLUSTRATION. Calculate the mean ionic activity coefficient for a $0.001M$ solution of $ZnCl_2$ in the vicinity of 20°C, assuming that the Debye–Hückel theory may be applied and that the ion size parameter is 3.0 Å.

A standard value of 3.0 Å for the ion size parameter was proposed by Guggenheim [*Phil. Mag.*, **19**, 588 (1935)] in view of the fact that this value is of the right magnitude; it must be considered a semiempirical constant, and simplifies the form of Eq. 12.235. Small deviations from this value do not have a serious effect on the value of the activity coefficient in the concentration range where the Debye-Hückel theory might be expected to give a reasonable approximation.

Hence
$$I = \tfrac{1}{2}[0.001(4) + 0.002(1)] = 0.003$$

$$\log_{10} \gamma_{\pm} = \frac{-0.51(2)(0.003)^{\frac{1}{2}}}{1 + (0.003)^{\frac{1}{2}}} = -0.0536$$

$$\gamma_{\pm} = 0.886$$

At very low concentrations the value of $(a/3.0)I^{\frac{1}{2}}$ is negligibly small relative to unity, and Eq. 12.235 takes the limiting form

$$\log_{10} \gamma_{\pm} = -0.51 z_{+}(-z_{-})I^{\frac{1}{2}} \tag{12.236}$$

Even for uni-univalent electrolytes, Eq. 12.236 should not be applied at concentrations appreciably above $0.001M$; in this range C_i is virtually equal to m_i.

The limiting law for various electrolytes takes the form

uni-univalent $\log_{10} \gamma_{\pm} = -0.51 I^{\frac{1}{2}} = -0.51 m^{\frac{1}{2}}$

uni-bivalent $\log_{10} \gamma_{\pm} = -1.02 I^{\frac{1}{2}} = -1.77 m^{\frac{1}{2}}$

bi-bivalent $\log_{10} \gamma_{\pm} = -2.04 I^{\frac{1}{2}} = -4.08 m^{\frac{1}{2}}$

This behavior is shown graphically in Fig. 12.204. The approach to this behavior by appropriate electrolytes is remarkable; however, the figure confirms that the theory is a poor approximation at appreciable concentrations.

The Debye-Hückel theory has been extended on a semiempirical basis and used to correlate activity coefficient data in the form

$$\log_{10} \gamma_{\pm} = -A_{\gamma} z_{+}(-z_{-}) \frac{I^{\frac{1}{2}}}{1 + I^{\frac{1}{2}}} + Bm$$

where A_{γ} is a Debye-Hückel constant, and B is an empirical constant fixed by experimental data for the substance in question. Values of B are quite similar for electrolytes of similar type. Extensive tables have been prepared which summarize data for various electrolyte solutions in this form; for example, see Lewis, Randall, Pitzer, and Brewer, *Thermodynamics*, McGraw-Hill Book Co., 1961.

Meaning of Kappa; Limitations of the Debye-Hückel Theory. The value of $\phi_r = (A/r)e^{-\kappa r}$ can be put back into Eq. 12.221 for ρ_r and the result expanded, as in getting Eq. 12.224. The leading term in ρ_r has the same form in r as ϕ_r. If the student will recall the problem of the "most probable" distance of the electron from the nucleus in the $1s$ state of the hydrogen atom, he will see that, although ρ_r is a maximum at $r = 0$, it must be multiplied by the volume of the spherical

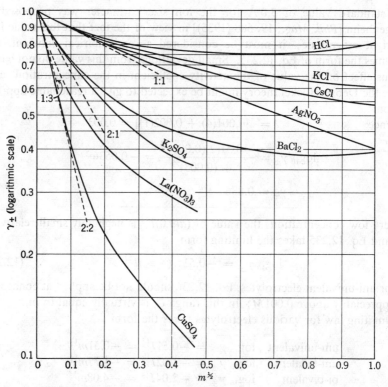

Fig. 12.204   Plot of log $\gamma\pm$ vs. $m^{1/2}$ for electrolytes in aqueous solutions at 25°C; dashed lines drawn with Debye-Hückel limiting slopes (by permission from M. A. Paul, *Principles of Thermodynamics*, McGraw-Hill, New York, 1951).

shell $4\pi r^2/dr$ to obtain the radial density. Then the functional form of the density is $re^{-\kappa r}$, and this function is a maximum at $r = 1/\kappa$. It is clear then why the reciprocal of κ is called the mean thickness of the ionic atmosphere. Because of the exponential fall-off, at several multiples of κ the effect of the central ion is almost zero.

Because of the averaging effect of taking a smooth density, the distance $1/\kappa$ should be much greater than the size of the ions a. In practical units, this means that the concentration of a univalent electrolyte should be considerably below $0.1M$, and correspondingly less for polyvalent systems.

ILLUSTRATION.   What is the apparent "thickness of the ionic atmosphere" for a solution (a) of $0.001M$ HCl and (b) of $0.01M$ HCl?

To solve this problem, we must calculate the value of the distance $1/\kappa$ in terms of the practical units of concentration and ionic strength. We have Eq. 12.226,

$$\kappa^2 = \frac{4\pi}{VDkT}\sum_i N_i q_i^2$$

for κ^2, and Eq. 12.234

$$I = \tfrac{1}{2} \sum_i c_i z_i^2$$

for the ionic strength. These quantities are proportional to each other, at the same temperature and in the same solvent, because

$$c_i = \frac{N_i}{NV}$$

and

$$z_i = \frac{q_i}{|e|}$$

where N is Avogadro's number, and $|e|$ the charge of the electron (absolute value). At $0°C$ and with a dielectric constant for water of 88, this gives

$$\kappa = 0.32 \times 10^8 I^{\frac{1}{2}} \text{ cm}^{-1}$$

or very nearly

$$\frac{1}{\kappa} = \frac{3}{I^{\frac{1}{2}}} \text{ Å}$$

The ionic strength of a uni-univalent electrolyte such as HCl is equal to the concentration. So for part (a)

$$\frac{1}{\kappa} = \frac{3}{(0.001)^{\frac{1}{2}}} = 100 \text{ Å}$$

and for part (b)

$$\frac{1}{\kappa} = \frac{3}{(0.01)^{\frac{1}{2}}} = 30 \text{ Å}$$

These distances are reasonably large, but for $0.1N$ HCl, the value of $1/\kappa$ is 10 Å, which is too small to justify "smearing out" the ionic atmosphere.

Limitations on the Size of the Ion.   It would appear that any restrictions on the Debye-Hückel theory caused by κ could be alleviated by going to lower concentrations. There is, however, another requirement that is not removable by dilution. The expansion that led to Eq. 12.225 requires that $q_\beta \phi_r / kT$ be less than unity to be reasonably correct. In terms of the value of ϕ_r in the simple case where all ions have the charge q, this requires that

$$\frac{q^2}{DakT} < 1 \tag{12.237}$$

which means that the bigger the ions, the better the theory is obeyed. Bjerrum showed how to treat situations where the ions were too small, by counting all ions within the radius where the inequality 12.237 is not satisfied as bound and as thus neutralizing the center ion. Such pairs were counted out of the electrical picture, and the Debye-Hückel theory was applied to those remaining. This refinement, although beyond the scope of this discussion, reintroduces the ideal of partial dissociation of the electrolyte and is quite satisfactory.

Use of the Debye-Hückel Theory. Probably the most important success of the theory is that it provides a basis for understanding the general features of the behavior of electrolytes, as contrasted with nonelectrolytic solutions. The notion of the mean thickness of the ionic atmosphere is particularly useful. Because of the approximations made in the theory, it would be foolish to expect it to apply exactly to real electrolytes. However, in favorable cases where the approximations are good, the theory can be verified by means of experimental tests. In Sec. 12.3 we describe the measurements of electromotive force that have been used to calculate experimental values of activity coefficients for comparison with the Debye-Hückel theory. We therefore defer further the examination of the results to that section.

Weak Electrolytes. Although they were studied and explained before strong electrolytes, weak acids and bases are extreme examples of associated ion pairs in the Bjerrum sense. The acetate ion is not small in an overall sense; nevertheless, it has a binding spot for the H^+ ion, which means that the centers of charge of two ions can get very close together indeed. Thus the Debye-Hückel theory does not apply to acetic acid, even at very high dilutions, until it is realized that the theory should be applied to the free ions alone. Then it is quite satisfactory. Thus weak electrolytes fit into the general picture.

Problems

12.201 Verify Eq. 12.205 by direct differentiation. Prove Eqs. 12.208 and 12.209.

*12.202 Prove by substitution that the first term of Eq. 12.227 satisfies Eqs. 12.225 and 12.219.

12.203 Derive Eq. 12.228, solve for A, and write down the formula for ϕ_r.

12.204 Explain why the ion's self-potential is subtracted from the total potential to obtain the physically significant potential ϕ_α.

12.205 Derive Eq. 12.229.

12.206 Introduce numerical quantities, and verify Eq. 12.235.

12.207 Prove that $\nabla^2(1/r) = 0$.

12.208 Derive Eq. 12.233.

3. Thermodynamics and Electromotive Force

Reactions Involving Ions. In order to produce the flow of electricity at terminals by means of chemical reaction, it is necessary for ions to gain or lose charge. We shall first consider such reactions in the absence of external emf. For example, an oxidation-reduction reaction (in this section ions are in aqueous solution)

$$Cr^{++} + Fe^{3+} = Cr^{3+} + Fe^{++}$$

has an equilibrium governed by the equation

$$\mu_{Cr^{++}} + \mu_{Fe^{3+}} = \mu_{Cr^{3+}} + \mu_{Fe^{++}} \tag{12.301}$$

where each chemical potential can be written in the form

$$\mu_{Cr^{++}} = \mu^{\circ}_{Cr^{++}} + RT \ln a_{Cr^{++}} \tag{12.302}$$

with three other similar expressions for the other ions.

The substitution of these expressions in Eq. 12.301 yields

$$RT \ln K = RT \ln \left(\frac{a_{Cr^{3+}} a_{Fe^{++}}}{a_{Cr^{++}} a_{Fe^{3+}}} \right)$$

$$= -(\mu^{\circ}_{Cr^{3+}} - \mu^{\circ}_{Cr^{++}}) + (\mu^{\circ}_{Fe^{3+}} - \mu^{\circ}_{Fe^{++}}) \tag{12.303}$$

If we knew the difference of values of the various μ°'s, we could then calculate the equilibrium constant.

A similar expression can be set up for the heterogeneous reaction

$$Cu^{++} + Zn = Cu + Zn^{++}$$

for which

$$RT \ln K = RT \ln \left(\frac{a_{Zn^{++}}}{a_{Cu^{++}}} \right) = -(\mu^{\circ}_{Zn^{++}} - \mu^{\circ}_{Zn}) + (\mu^{\circ}_{Cu^{++}} - \mu^{\circ}_{Cu}) \tag{12.304}$$

For purposes of tabulation, all such reaction types can be broken up into half-reactions of the type

$$Cu = Cu^{++} + 2e^{-}$$

with the corresponding equation

$$\mu_{Cu} = \mu^{\circ}_{Cu} = \mu_{Cu^{++}} + 2\mu_e = \mu^{\circ}_{Cu^{++}} + RT \ln a_{Cu^{++}} + 2\mu_e \tag{12.305}$$

Of course, such a division is entirely formal, because we have no way of realizing one half-reaction without a balancing one that preserves electrical neutrality. In the final result for the complete reaction the chemical potential of the electron μ_e cancels out, because of the condition of electrical neutrality.

Ionic Reactions Influenced by EMF.   It is instructive to take a very convenient reaction to begin our analysis of the effect of emf on chemical equilibrium:

$$AgCl(s) + \tfrac{1}{2}H_2(1 \text{ atm}) = Ag(s) + H^+ + Cl^-$$

This reaction can be carried out so that a controlled emf can be applied to it, in a simple manner. A container filled with hydrochloric acid contains two electrodes (Fig. 12.301).

One is a silver wire coated with a layer of silver chloride. The other is a hydrogen electrode, composed of an inert platinum sponge over which hydrogen at 1 atm fugacity is constantly bubbled. The two electrodes are connected by means of copper wire to a potentiometer, and the flow of current is indicated by a galvanometer. The cell is reversible if a small change in applied emf reverses the galvanometer deflection. If then the galvanometer is exactly balanced, thermodynamics

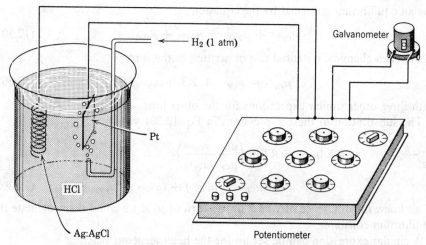

Fig. 12.301   Experimental setup for measurement of cell emf.

can be used to calculate the free energy change involved if the chemical reaction in the cell is specified.

EMF and Free Energy Change.   It is clear from the arrangement in Fig. 12.301 that no reaction can take place when the two electrodes are disconnected. The hydrogen, which should be available to reduce the AgCl, is on the other side of the tank. The following two reactions cannot go independently because of charge generation:

$$\tfrac{1}{2}H_2 = H^+ + e^-$$
$$AgCl + e^- = Ag + Cl^-$$

However, if a wire is available to move the excess electrons from the first reaction to the second, the reaction can proceed. When the cell is balanced with the reversible emf, then the total free energy change is zero. Since P and T are constant, F is the correct free energy, so

$$\Delta F_{\text{total}} = \Delta F_{\text{cell}} + \Delta F_{\text{elec}} = 0 \qquad (12.306)$$

For the reaction as written (transfer of one faraday)

$$
\begin{aligned}
\Delta F_{\text{cell}} &= \sum_i n_i \mu_i \\
&= \mu_{Ag}^\circ + \mu_{H^+} + \mu_{Cl^-} - \mu_{AgCl}^\circ - \tfrac{1}{2}\mu_{H_2}^\circ \\
&= \mu_{Ag}^\circ + \mu_{H^+}^\circ + \mu_{Cl^-}^\circ - \mu_{AgCl}^\circ - \tfrac{1}{2}\mu_{H_2}^\circ + RT \ln a_{H^+} + RT \ln a_{Cl^-} \\
&= \Delta F^\circ + RT \ln a_{HCl} \qquad (12.307)
\end{aligned}
$$

In this equation ΔF° stands for the algebraic sum of the standard chemical potentials, of molar free energies. We have also introduced the activity of HCl

$$a_{HCl} = a_{H^+} a_{Cl^-} \qquad (12.308)$$

Alternatively, we often see defined the mean ionic activity,

$$a_{\pm} = (a_{H^+}a_{Cl^-})^{\frac{1}{2}} \qquad (12.309)$$

Both these definitions avoid the difficulty that it is impossible to measure an individual ion activity. In the general case a_2, the activity of an electrolyte which is directly proportional to fugacity (or pressure on an ideal basis), is related to the mean ionic activity by the expression

$$a_2 = a_{\pm}^{\nu} = a_{+}^{\nu_+}a_{-}^{\nu_-}$$

where ν_+ and ν_- are the number of moles of positive and negative ions, respectively, formed on complete ionization of one mole of electrolyte. $\nu = \nu_+ + \nu_-$.

The mean ionic molality is related to the total molality of the electrolyte m by the expressions

$$m_{\pm}^{\nu} = m_{+}^{\nu_+}m_{-}^{\nu_-}$$

where $m_+ = \nu_+ m$ and $m_- = \nu_- m$.

Hence

$$m_{\pm} = m(\nu_+^{\nu_+}\nu_-^{\nu_-})^{1/\nu}$$

We may write

$$a_2 = \gamma_2 m = a_{\pm}^{\nu} = \gamma_{\pm}^{\nu}m_{\pm}^{\nu} = \gamma_{\pm}^{\nu}m^{\nu}(\nu_+^{\nu_+}\nu_-^{\nu_-})$$

from which the relationship between $\gamma_{\pm}$ and γ_2 can be derived.

$$\gamma_2 = \gamma_{\pm}^{\nu}m^{\nu-1}(\nu_+^{\nu_+}\nu_-^{\nu_-})$$

The mean ionic activity coefficient $\gamma_{\pm}$ is related to individual ionic activity coefficients by the relationship

$$\gamma_{\pm}^{\nu} = \gamma_{+}^{\nu_+}\gamma_{-}^{\nu_-}$$

Now if we return to Eq. 12.306, the electrical part of the free energy is simply equal to the electrical displacement associated with the reaction, which is $n\mathscr{F}$, the Faraday times the number of moles of electrons used in the reaction as written, multiplied by the voltage, $\mathscr{E}$:

$$\Delta F_{elec} = +n\mathscr{F}\mathscr{E} \qquad (12.310)$$

If the Faraday has the value 96,500, the free energy is expressed in joules; however, if the more usual calorie is used, the appropriate value is $\mathscr{F} = 23,052$.

We thus find from Eqs. 12.306, 12.307, and 12.310 that

$$\Delta F_{cell} = -n\mathscr{F}\mathscr{E} \qquad (12.311)$$

This is the fundamental equation used to connect thermodynamics with reversible emf values. It is obvious, but extremely important to note, that this equation applies solely to reversible reactions at equilibrium. A special case of Eq. 12.311 is used to define a standard emf at unit activity,

$$\mathscr{E}° = -\frac{\Delta F°}{n\mathscr{F}} \qquad (12.312)$$

Then values of $\mathcal{E}^\circ$ for each half-cell reaction can be tabulated and summed algebraically to give the $\mathcal{E}^\circ$ for the total reaction. With the arbitrary convention that the electron has the entropy value $S^\circ = 15.6$ (one half the value for H_2) and the standard enthalpy of formation $\Delta H^\circ_{\text{for}} = 0$, the standard voltage of the hydrogen electrode becomes zero. We then obtain the celebrated electromotive series of the elements and the standard oxidation-reduction potentials for the ions. These tables are an alternative way of storing the data presented in Tables 9.201(A) and 9.301(A) for reactions at the standard temperature of 25°C.

However, in order to emphasize the link with thermodynamics we will calculate emf's directly from the tables of standard enthalpy and entropy. For example, we will do the calculation indicated in Eq. 12.312 at 298°K, using the fact that $\Delta F^\circ = \Delta H^\circ - T\,\Delta S^\circ$ and the established conventions.

ILLUSTRATION.   Calculate $\mathcal{E}^\circ$ for the cell shown in Fig. 12.301, using data from Tables 9.201(A) and 9.301(A).

$$\Delta F^\circ = \mu^\circ_{\text{Ag}} + \mu^\circ_{\text{Cl}^-} + \mu^\circ_{\text{H}^+} - \mu^\circ_{\text{AgCl}} - \tfrac{1}{2}\mu^\circ_{\text{H}_2}$$

$$= 1000[0 + (-40.02) + 0 - (-30.36) - 0]$$

$$- 298(10.2 + 13.17 + 0 - 22.97 - 15.6)$$

$$= -5130 \text{ cal mole}^{-1}$$

whence, since $n = 1$,

$$\mathcal{E}^\circ = \frac{5130}{23,052} = 0.2225 \text{ volt}$$

The tabulated and measured voltage for this cell at unit activity is 0.222 volt.

Effect of Concentration on EMF.   Suppose that we connect two of these cells (Fig. 12.301) in series, with the external connections made to the two hydrogen electrodes (Fig. 12.302). We shall assume that the activity of HCl in one is a_1, and in the other a_2. If we write the two reactions as

$$\text{AgCl}(s) + \tfrac{1}{2}\text{H}_2(1 \text{ atm}) = \text{Ag}(s) + \text{HCl}(a_1)$$

and

$$\text{Ag}(s) + \text{HCl}(a_2) = \text{AgCl}(s) + \tfrac{1}{2}\text{H}_2(1 \text{ atm})$$

we see by addition that the net reaction is

$$\text{HCl}(a_2) = \text{HCl}(a_1)$$

which is to say that the effect of operating the cell is to transfer HCl from one activity to another; the emf depends on a concentration difference, and so the cell is called a concentration cell. If we write ΔF for this cell, we find that $\Delta F^\circ = 0$ and

$$\Delta F = RT \ln \left(\frac{a_1}{a_2}\right) \tag{12.313}$$

from which we find $\mathcal{E}^\circ = 0$ and

$$\mathcal{E} = \frac{RT}{n\mathcal{F}} \ln \left(\frac{a_2}{a_1}\right) \tag{12.314}$$

For this case, of course, $n = 1$.

We should remark here that, if $\mathcal{E}$ is positive (that is, if ΔF is negative), the reaction is a spontaneous one as written. Negative values of $\mathcal{E}$ indicate that the reaction will go in the opposite direction to the one written. We therefore conclude that with

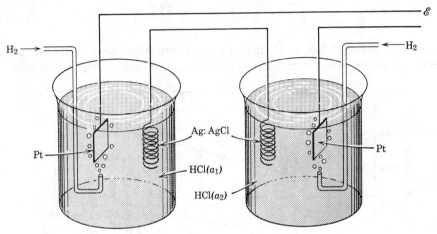

Fig. 12.302   Concentration cell.

$a_2 > a_1$ the current will flow spontaneously in such a direction to approach the condition $a_2 = a_1$.

EMF and Activity Coefficients.   One of the most important uses of emf measurements is the experimental evaluation of the activity coefficients for electrolytes. We shall take as an example the H_2-AgCl cell, as it is used to determine the activity of HCl in solution. At first sight we might think to write

$$a_{HCl} = \gamma_{HCl} m_{HCl} \tag{12.315}$$

and expect γ to go to unity as the molarity goes to zero. However, a plot of the fugacity of HCl gas over a solution of hydrochloric acid (Fig. 12.303) shows that the Henry's law region is not reached; as the molarity in the solution goes to zero, the curve becomes tangent to the $f = 0$ line, which means that γ_{HCl} goes to zero,

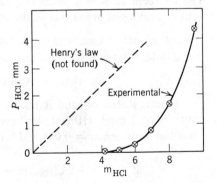

Fig. 12.303   Fugacity of aqueous HCl.

not unity. This is so because we are not considering the correct species in the solution as it goes to infinite dilution. We should be interested in $m_{Cl^-} = m_{H^+}$, to which the "formal" concentration m_{HCl} is also equal. This behavior suggests the expression based on Eqs. 12.308 and 12.309,

$$a_{HCl} = a_{H^+}a_{Cl^-} = a_{\pm}^2 = \gamma_{\pm}^2 m_{\pm}^2 \tag{12.316}$$

If we now make this substitution in Eq. 12.307 we obtain

$$\Delta F = \Delta F^\circ + 2RT \ln m\gamma_{\pm} \tag{12.317}$$

or in terms of emf

$$\mathscr{E} = \mathscr{E}^\circ - \frac{2RT}{n\mathscr{F}} \ln m - \frac{2RT}{n\mathscr{F}} \ln \gamma_{\pm} \tag{12.318}$$

If we look at Eq. 12.235, we see that at low concentration, log γ should vary as the square root of I, the ionic strength, which is the same as saying that it varies with the

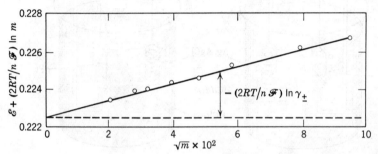

Fig. 12.304   Plot to obtain $\mathscr{E}^\circ$ and log γ.

square root of m. We therefore plot the experimental data in the form

$$\mathscr{E} + \frac{2RT}{n\mathscr{F}} \ln m \text{ vs. } m^{\frac{1}{2}}$$

The intercept at $m = 0$ yields $\mathscr{E}^\circ$, whereas the deviation from this emf yields the activity coefficient at various values of m (Fig. 12.304).

ILLUSTRATION.   Calculate activity coefficients for HBr in aqueous solutions from emf data. Show how to evaluate ΔS° for the process

$$H_2(g) + AgBr(s) = Ag(s) + H^+ + Br^-$$

Hetzer, Robinson, and Bates, have reported emf values for the following cell: Pt; $H_2(g, 1 \text{ atm})$, HBr(m), AgBr(s); Ag(s), between 0 and 50°C and at concentrations between $m = 0.005$ and 0.1. Plots of

$$\mathscr{E}^{\circ\prime} = \mathscr{E} + 2k \log_{10} m - 2k \left[\frac{A\sqrt{m}}{1 + Ba^*\sqrt{m}}\right] = \mathscr{E}^\circ - 2k\beta m$$

against m are shown in Fig. 12.305 where A and B are constants evaluated from the Debye-Hückel theory, a^* is the ion size parameter (taken as 4.4 Å), and $k = 2.3RT/\mathscr{F}$. From this graph the following expression for $\mathscr{E}^\circ$ as a function of

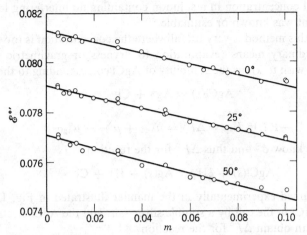

Fig. 12.305   Plots of $\mathscr{E}^{\circ\prime}$ as a function of m at 0, 25, and 50°. The best straight line was established by least-squares methods using only the points at $m < 0.1$. [By permission from Hetzer, Robinson, and Bates, *J. Phys. Chem.*, **66**, 1424 (1962).]

the centigrade temperature, t, was developed:

$$\mathscr{E}^{\circ} = 0.07109 - 4.87 \times 10^{-4}(t - 25) - 3.08 \times 10^{-6}(t - 25)^2$$

Hence, using Eq. 12.318, values of the activity coefficient may be evaluated.

m	$\gamma_{\pm}(0°C)$	$\gamma_{\pm}(25°C)$	$\gamma_{\pm}(50°C)$
0.005	0.932	0.930	0.926
.02	.884	.879	.874
.05	.845	.838	.831
.10	.817	.808	.797

To evaluate ΔS°, we use the following relationships:

$$\Delta F^{\circ} = -n\mathscr{F}\mathscr{E}^{\circ}$$

$$\frac{d\Delta F^{\circ}}{dT} = -\Delta S^{\circ} = n\mathscr{F}\frac{d\mathscr{E}^{\circ}}{dT} = n\mathscr{F}\frac{d\mathscr{E}^{\circ}}{dt}$$

Hence we need only differentiate the expression above, which gives $\mathscr{E}^{\circ}$ as $f(t)$. From the standard entropies of the elements and of AgBr, and the entropy convention for H^{+} and ΔS°, we may determine the standard entropy of the bromide ion.

EMF and Solubility.   Since the emf of a cell depends on concentration, it is clear that, if the other factors are known, concentrations can be determined by emf measurements. For example, the cell we have been discussing could be used to estimate the HCl concentration in a solution containing no interfering ions, if the activity coefficient was known or estimable.

In particular, this method is very useful where the concentration is too low to be measured by ordinary means (evaporation to dryness or gravimetric analysis). Suppose that we wish to know the solubility of AgCl corresponding to the reaction

$$AgCl(s) = Ag^+ + Cl^-$$

for which

$$-RT \ln K_{sp} = \Delta F° = \mu°_{Ag^+} + \mu°_{Cl^-} - \mu°_{AgCl} \tag{12.319}$$

Now we already know $\mathscr{E}°$ and thus $\Delta F°$ for the reaction

$$AgCl(s) + \tfrac{1}{2}H_2 = Ag(s) + H^+ + Cl^-$$

$\Delta F°$ can be obtained experimentally in the manner illustrated in Fig. 12.304. If we replace the HCl in the cell by a soluble silver salt, and the AgCl electrode by a silver wire, we can obtain $\Delta F°$ for the reaction

$$H^+ + Ag(s) = Ag^+ + \tfrac{1}{2}H_2$$

from a similar plot. The sum of these two experimental $\Delta F°$'s gives the $\Delta F°$ corresponding to the solubility product, Eq. 12.319. Alternatively, if thermodynamic tables are available, the $\Delta F°$ can be calculated directly.

Problems

12.301   Calculate the hypothetical emf at unit activity for the reaction of Eq. 12.304. Devise a feasible way of realizing this emf.

12.302   Repeat the calculations on p. 382, with HBr and AgBr substituted.

*12.303   From the following data, find $\mathscr{E}°$ for the cell in Fig. 12.301. Obtain values for the activity coefficient for HCl and compare them with Eq. 12.235. Attempt to evaluate a. Is the value reasonable?

m_{HCl}	Cell, volts
0.003215	0.52052
.004488	.50384
.005619	.49257
.007311	.47948
.009138	.46860
.011195	.45861
.013407	.44974
.01710	.43783
.02563	.41824
.05391	.39222
.1238	.34199

12.304   Calculate the solubility product for AgCl directly from thermodynamic tables. Calculate $\mathscr{E}°$ for the cell with hydrogen and silver wire electrodes used to find this solubility product experimentally ($t = 25°C$).

4. Review Problems

12.401   Calculate the "thickness of the ionic atmosphere" in a $0.0005M$ aqueous solution of hydrochloric acid, $D = 78.5$ (at $25°C$).

12.402   The equilibrium vapor pressure of HCl above a $4m$ aqueous solution is 2.395×10^{-5} atm at $25°C$. The mean ionic activity coefficient in this solution is 1.76. Calculate the vapor pressure to be expected above a $0.001m$ solution of HCl at $25°C$, assuming, in the latter case, that the Debye-Hückel theory may be applied. (NOTE: $a_{HCl} = kP_{HCl} = a_{H^+}a_{Cl^-} = a_{\pm}^2$.)

12.403   Calculate the change in the chemical potential of NaCl on dilution of a $0.004M$ solution to a concentration of $0.001M$ at $25°C$. Assume that the Debye-Hückel theory may be applied at both concentrations, with $a = 3$ Å.

12.404   For the Ag,AgBr(s), Br^- electrode $\mathscr{E}^0$ is -0.0713 volt, and for the Ag,Ag^+ electrode it is -0.7995 volt (at $25°C$). Show how to use these data to calculate the solubility of AgBr(s) in water at $25°C$.

12.405   The emf of a cell composed of a hydrogen electrode and a $Hg,Hg_2Br_2(s)$, Br^- electrode immersed in a hydrogen bromide solution, designed to study the reaction

$$\tfrac{1}{2}H_2(g) + \tfrac{1}{2}Hg_2Br_2(s) = Hg(l) + H^+ + Br^-$$

in the vicinity of room temperature may be represented by the equation

$$\mathscr{E}^° = 0.1397 - 8.1 \times 10^{-5}(t - 25) - 3.6 \times 10^{-6}(t - 25)^2$$

where t represents the temperature in degrees centigrade [W. D. Larson, *J. Am. Chem. Soc.*, **62**, 764 (1940)]. Show how the entropy and enthalpy of formation of the bromide ion can be evaluated from this equation, given $\bar{S}^°$ for H_2, Br_2, Hg, and Hg_2Br_2, and the standard enthalpy of formation of Hg_2Br_2, all at $25°C$.

12.406   The solubility of $AgIO_3$ is 1.77×10^{-4} mole liter^{-1} at $25°C$. Use data provided in Problem 12.404 and the solubility to evaluate $\mathscr{E}^°$ for the Ag,$AgIO_3(s)$, IO_3^- electrode.

*12.407   A cell of the type illustrated in Fig. 12.301 gave the emf's listed below when the electrodes were immersed in an electrolyte solution containing propionic acid, sodium propionate, and sodium chloride, each component at the concentration m [data according to H. S. Harned and R. W. Ehler, *J. Am. Chem. Soc.*, **55**, 2379 (1933)].

$m \times 10^3$	$\mathscr{E}$	$m \times 10^3$	$\mathscr{E}$
4.90	0.648	18.7	0.613
8.72	.633	25.6	.605
12.8	.623	31.8	.600

(a) Write the cell reaction.

(b) Write the general expression for the emf of the cell as a function of the activities of the ions involved in the electrode processes.

(c) Show how an extrapolation method could be used to determine an accurate value of the ionization constant of propionic acid.

12.408   Use data from Tables 9.201(A) and 9.301(A) to determine the solubility of FeS.

12.409   For the Fe,Fe^{++} electrode $\mathscr{E}^°$ is 0.440, and for the Fe^{++},Fe^{3+} electrode $\mathscr{E}^°$ is -0.771. What must be the value for the Fe,Fe^{3+} electrode?

General References

Fowler, R. H., and E. A. Guggenheim, *Statistical Thermodynamics*, Cambridge University Press Cambridge, England, 1939.

Guggenheim, E. A., *Mixtures*, Oxford University Press, Oxford, England, 1952.

Hildebrand, J. H., and R. L. Scott, *Solubility*, Fourth Edition, Reinhold Publishing Co., New York, 1962.

Robinson R. A., and R. H. Stokes, *Electrolyte Solutions*, Second Edition, Academic Press, New York, 1959.

Chapter Thirteen

Transport and Rate Processes

1. Collisions in Gases

The Mean Free Path. It is a matter of some interest and importance to find the length of the path traveled by a molecule between two collisions and also to find the number of collisions between the molecules in unit time. There is a distribution of free path lengths traveled by a molecule between collisions, corresponding to the random nature of gas molecule motions.

Consider a beam of molecules starting out at the same point and all traveling in the $+x$ direction while passing through a gas of the same molecules at a concentration of N' molecules per cubic centimeter. How many molecules survive in the beam without collision after a distance x has been traveled?

As was shown in Fig. 6.502, the target area of a single hard sphere molecule of diameter σ is $\pi\sigma^2$. Let I be the intensity of the beam at a distance x from the origin of the beam. This intensity falls off from an initial intensity I_0 because of collisions. In a slice of gas (Fig. 13.101a) of unit cross section and thickness dx, there are present $N'\,dx$ molecules which have total cross section equal to $\pi\sigma^2 N'\,dx$. The chance of a beam molecule experiencing a collision in the distance dx is given by the ratio of the target area to the whole unit area. Thus the average decrease in intensity is the product of this factor and I, or

$$-dI = I(\pi\sigma^2 N'\,dx) \tag{13.101}$$

If $I = I_0$ when $x = 0$, integration of Eq. 13.101 gives

$$I = I_0 e^{-\pi\sigma^2 N' x} = I_0 e^{-x/\lambda} \tag{13.102}$$

where the constant $\pi\sigma^2 N'$ has been designated as $1/\lambda$. The average length of path $\bar{x}$ may be shown to be λ as follows:

$$\bar{x} = \frac{\int_{I_0}^{0} - x\,dI}{\int_{I_0}^{0} - dI}$$

and, by use of Eqs. 13.101 and 13.102, this becomes

$$\bar{x} = \frac{\pi\sigma^2 N' I_0 \int_{0}^{\infty} x e^{-\pi\sigma^2 N' x}\,dx}{\pi\sigma^2 N' I_0 \int_{0}^{\infty} e^{-\pi\sigma^2 N' x}\,dx}$$

$$= \frac{1}{\pi\sigma^2 N'} = \lambda$$

From Eq. 13.102, it is seen that when x has the value λ, then I is I_0/e. Lambda, the "mean free path," is inversely proportional to the concentration of molecules present in the gas phase, and to the cross section of the molecules. The above

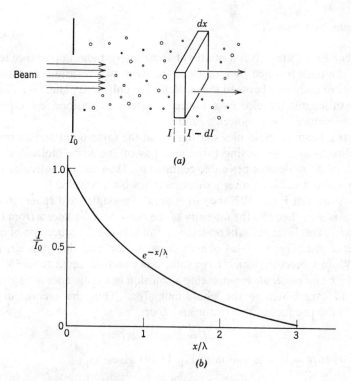

Fig. 13.101   Fraction of molecules in the beam as a function of relative distance traveled.

equation is numerically exact only for very fast molecules; otherwise relative speeds of the colliding molecules must be used. Consider the molecule that is not moving at all. It will eventually be hit by some moving molecule, so that its mean free path is zero. The mean free path must be reduced by a factor of $(2)^{1/2}$ for this reason, and the correct expression is

$$\lambda = \frac{1}{(2)^{1/2}\pi\sigma^2 N'} \tag{13.103}$$

Mean Free Path and Collision Number.   If we divide the mean free path of the molecule (Eq. 13.103) by its average speed (Eq. 6.206), we obtain the average time between collisions. The number of collisions made by a single molecule per second is the reciprocal of this time. The total collision number for N' molecules of type A per unit volume is

$$\mathscr{Z}_{AA} = 2^{3/2}N_A'^2\sigma^2\left(\frac{2\pi kT}{m}\right)^{1/2}$$

This result should actually be divided by a factor of 2, the *symmetry number*, since every collision has been counted twice, each collision being shared by two molecules. In addition, this equation for $\mathscr{Z}_{AA}$ is not quite correct, in that the relative speeds of the colliding molecules must be taken into account. The correct derivation, which is quite lengthy, leads to

$$\mathscr{Z}_{AA} = N_A'^2\sigma^2\left(\frac{2\pi kT}{\mu}\right)^{1/2} \tag{13.104}$$

where the 2 was divided out and the relative speeds are accounted for by replacing m by the reduced mass of the colliding particles,

$$\mu = \frac{m}{2}$$

In Eq. 6.502 for collisions between unlike molecules, the symmetry factor of 2 did not appear because we considered only the collisions of molecules of type A with those of type B,

$$\mathscr{Z}_{AB} = 2[N_A'N_B'][\sigma_{AB}^2]\left[\left(\frac{2\pi kT}{\mu}\right)^{1/2}\right] \tag{6.502}$$

where $\mu = m_A m_B/(m_A + m_B)$ and $\sigma_{AB}^2 = [(\sigma_A + \sigma_B)/2]^2$.

Mean Free Path and Transport.   An ideal gas of point molecules, which make no collisions except with the wall, is quite unlike a real gas. Mixing would take place between two ideal gases at molecular speeds, whereas in a real gas relatively slow diffusion is observed; at 1 atm, λ is of the order of 10^{-5} cm. The molecules move in randomly directed steps of this order of magnitude. Only at low pressures ($\sim 10^{-2}$ mm Hg) do the steps reach the order of 1 cm in length. For this reason, gases at higher pressures can often be treated like continuous fluids, with local values of density, temperature, and momentum, even though they are not in macroscopic equilibrium.

Transport of mass is considered in the phenomenon called diffusion; transport of energy in thermal conduction; and transport of momentum in viscosity. The same sort of mechanism transports energy and momentum as well as mass; we therefore pause and consider the general process of motion by random steps. The assumption that these steps are really random is fundamental and is often called the *assumption of molecular chaos*. Our discussion of these phenomena will apply especially to gases.

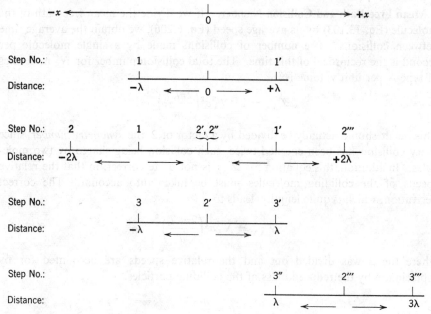

Fig. 13.102   A one-dimensional random walk. Only half the possibilities for step 3 are illustrated; steps from initial positions 2 and 2″ are omitted.

Mean Free Path and the Random Walk.   The phenomenon of the irregular and random motions of colloidal particles, termed Brownian motion, exemplifies random fluctuations at molecular dimensions, and is a graphic illustration of a three-dimensional random walk. Consider the analogous one-dimensional problem. Suppose that a walker (molecule) in the x-coordinate direction takes steps of average size λ, the mean free path. Assume that the walker makes a random choice of motion in the $+x$ and $-x$ direction on each step. Then we wish an expression for the distance traveled from the starting point after a given number of steps (Fig. 13.102). After one step, $x_1 = \pm\lambda$ or

$$x_1^2 = \lambda^2$$

After two steps, the walker will be either at 0 or $\pm 2\lambda$ or, on the average,

$$\overline{x_2^2} = \frac{2 \cdot 0^2 + 2(2\lambda)^2}{4} = 2\lambda^2$$

After three steps, the walker will be at $\pm\lambda$ or $\pm3\lambda$ from the origin or, on the average,

$$\overline{x_3^2} = \frac{3\cdot(\lambda)^2 + (3\lambda)^2}{4} = 3\lambda^2$$

where, for simplicity in Fig. 13.102 and in the average just computed, only half the possible steps were used because of the symmetry of the motions. After n steps, by induction,

$$\overline{x_n^2} = n\lambda^2 \quad \text{or} \quad \left(\overline{x_n^2}\right)^{\frac{1}{2}} = n^{\frac{1}{2}}\lambda \tag{13.105}$$

The student will find if he considers the four- or five-step problem that small displacements are more probable than large ones. In fact, if n steps have been taken, where n is a large number, the probability that the wanderer should be a distance $k\lambda$ from the origin is

$$p(k) = \text{const } e^{-(k\lambda)^2/2n\lambda^2} = \text{const } e^{-k^2/2n} \tag{13.106}$$

For a given (even or odd) n, k can assume only even or odd values. This equation is another instance of a Gaussian distribution (Sec. 6.2); the constant is $(2/\pi n)^{\frac{1}{2}}$. Also

$$\overline{k^2} = \frac{\displaystyle\int_0^\infty k^2 e^{-k^2/2n}\, dk}{\displaystyle\int_0^\infty e^{-k^2/2n}\, dk} = n$$

which gives back Eq. 13.105, i.e., $\overline{k^2}\lambda^2 = \overline{x_n^2} = n\lambda^2$.

The derivation of Eq. 13.105 neglected the actual variation of step sizes, i.e., free path lengths. In addition, because of the phenomenon of *persistence of velocities*, the probability of a step being in either the $+x$ or $-x$ direction after a given step is not $\frac{1}{2}$ each. This problem may be readily handled by use of the binomial distribution law. However, the rigorous treatment of these problems is a matter of considerable complexity, and we will be content here with Eq. 13.105 and the conceptual insights that its derivation affords.

The random walk problem has many interesting applications. For example, if two iodine atoms are produced in solution by action of light, $I_2 \xrightarrow{h\nu} 2I$, and if the atoms move away from each other, the chance of their coming together again may be treated as a three-dimensional random walk problem. Another application is the problem of the average distance between the two ends of a polymer molecule, such as a polyethylene chain: each unit of the chain is a step; only certain angles (109°) between successive steps are permitted; and part of the volume of the space is excluded in the random walk if it was once passed through, i.e., is occupied by earlier links of the chain. We shall encounter still another application later in this chapter.

ILLUSTRATION.   In an experiment dealing with the determination of the magnetic moment of the proton by an atomic beam technique, Rabi, Kellog, and Zacharias

[*Phys. Rev.*, **46**, 157 (1934)] reduced the pressure of H_2 in their system (25°C) to $\sim 5 \times 10^{-7}$ mm. The beam traveled a distance of 30 cm between collimation and the detector. Find the fractional depletion of the beam because of collisions.

Now if we assume Eq. 13.103 applies, $\lambda = 1/(2)^{1/2}\pi\sigma^2 N'$; if $\sigma_H \simeq \sigma_{H_2} \simeq 3.0$ Å, we have (with use of the conversion factors in the Illustration on p. 157)

$$\lambda = 1/1.4 \times 3.14 \times (3 \times 10^{-8})^2 \times (5 \times 10^{-8} \times 13.6$$
$$\times\ 980/1.38 \times 10^{-16} \times 298)$$

$$= 1.6 \times 10^4 \text{ cm}$$

Then,

$$I = I_0 e^{-30/1.6 \times 10^4} = I_0 e^{-0.0019} = 0.998\ I_0$$

In later work, distances traveled by the beam were raised to several meters. The student may satisfy himself that the beam intensity remained high. The above intensity is an upper limit since the cross section for knocking an atom out of the beam is higher than that used.

Problems

13.101   In an ordinary Thermos bottle at room temperature, the distance between the walls is ~ 0.5 cm. What must be the pressure of air between the walls of the bottle so that a molecule of N_2 should just travel on the average from one wall to the other without a collision ($\sigma_{N_2} \simeq \sigma_{O_2} \simeq 3.5 \times 10^{-8}$ cm)?

13.102   How many gas-phase collisions does a molecule of N_2 make per second under the conditions of Problem 13.101 (*a*) with other N_2 molecules? (*b*) with O_2 molecules?

* 13.103   A child meandering toward school makes on the average one step forward for every step backward; he takes ten steps per minute. Find the probability that in half an hour the child will have (*a*) progressed 100 steps forward to school; (*b*) made no forward progress.

2. Diffusion

Diffusion Coefficient.   Simple pressure differences in a pure fluid give rise to hydrodynamic flow, as in the movement of butane gas along a tube to the nozzle of a burner, or the stirring of a gas with a paddle wheel. The existence of concentration gradients in a fluid of two or more components gives rise to a net molecular flow called diffusion.

Consider a binary gas mixture of A and B at constant pressure such that N'_A and $(N'_A + dN'_A)$ molecules cc^{-1} of component A are at positions x and $x + dx$ in the x direction. Then as a consequence of random molecular motions there is a net flow of molecules of component A in the $+x$ direction which is proportional to the concentration gradient of A,

$$\mathscr{N}_A = -\mathscr{D}\frac{\partial N'_A}{\partial x} \tag{13.201}$$

where, if $\mathcal{N}_A$ is in molecules cm^{-2} sec^{-1}, then $\mathcal{D}$, the diffusion coefficient defined by Eq. 13.201 called Fick's law, has units cm^2 sec^{-1}.

We represent this situation in Fig. 13.201, where the case of constant concentration gradients is illustrated for the condition of constant pressure, i.e., $N'_A + N'_B = N'$ molecules cc^{-1} everywhere. This condition ensures that, *if only random molecular motions enter*, the gradient of the B concentration is equal and opposite in sign to that of A, i.e., $\partial N'_A/dx = -\partial N'_B/dx$, and $-\mathcal{N}_A = \mathcal{N}_B = -\mathcal{D}\,\partial N'_B/dx$.

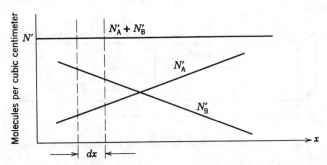

Fig. 13.201   A simple case of concentration gradients in a mixture with $N' =$ constant.

We may find the time dependence of the concentrations as follows. Consider two planes of unit area perpendicular to the x axis and separated by the distance dx. Then the rate at which A accumulates between the planes is simply the difference between the rates of entry and departure of A from this region

$$\frac{\partial N'_A}{\partial t}\, dx = (\mathcal{N}_A)_x - (\mathcal{N}_A)_{x+dx} = (\mathcal{N}_A)_x - \left[(\mathcal{N}_A)_x + \frac{\partial(\mathcal{N}_A)_x}{\partial x}\, dx\right]$$

and

$$\frac{\partial N'_A}{\partial t} = -\frac{\partial(\mathcal{N}_A)_x}{\partial x} = -\frac{\partial}{\partial x}\left[-\mathcal{D}\left(\frac{\partial N'_A}{\partial x}\right)\right] = \mathcal{D}\left(\frac{\partial^2 N'_A}{\partial x^2}\right) \qquad (13.202)$$

with a similar expression for diffusion in the y and z directions. The last equality in Eq. 13.202 is valid if $\mathcal{D} \neq \mathcal{D}(x)$, that is, $\mathcal{D}$ is not a function of concentration.

In three dimensions, Eq. 13.202 takes the form

$$\frac{\partial N'_A}{\partial t} = \mathcal{D}\left[\frac{\partial^2 N'_A}{\partial x^2} + \frac{\partial^2 N'_A}{\partial y^2} + \frac{\partial^2 N'_A}{\partial z^2}\right]$$

$$= \mathcal{D}\nabla^2 N'_A \qquad (13.203)$$

Equation 13.202 and 13.203 are particular forms of the *equation of continuity* which applies to many other phenomena, including the temperature in heat conduction and the electric potential in an ionic solution. If the left side of Eq. 13.203 is zero, the resulting form is Laplace's equation (Eq. 12.212). Equation 13.203 is called Fick's second law.

In general, the species A and B will not have the same diffusion coefficient, so that, although $\partial N'_A/\partial x = -\partial N'_B/\partial x$, $\mathscr{N}_A \neq \mathscr{N}_B$ in general. If the concentration N' is to remain constant, there must in addition be a net velocity $v_{\mathscr{G}}$ of the gas as a whole, that is, a mass motion of the gas arising out of the diffusive transport, so that the condition for constant pressure is

$$\mathscr{N}_{\text{A tot}} + \mathscr{N}_{\text{B tot}} = \mathscr{N}_A + \mathscr{N}_B + N'v_{\mathscr{G}} = 0 \qquad (13.204)$$

where the subscript "tot" represents the total net flow. We shall return to this equation shortly.

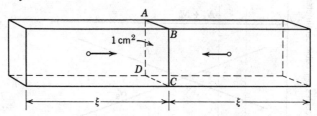

Fig. 13.202   One-dimensional diffusion of molecules in a box.

Diffusion and Mean Free Path.   We now relate diffusion to the concept of mean free path. $ABCD$ is a plane of unit cross section perpendicular to the x-coordinate direction (Fig. 13.202). Let τ be a mean time such that molecules within a distance ξ to the right of the plane, which are walking in the $-x$ direction, pass the plane, while molecules within a distance ξ to the left of the plane, which are wandering in the $+x$ direction, pass the plane. Of course, only half of the molecules in each compartment move in the prescribed direction. Then, if the average concentration of A molecules in the box on the left is N'_A, the average concentration in the box on the right is $N'_A + \xi(\partial N'_A/\partial x)$, since the centers of the two boxes, each of volume ξ cc, are ξ cm apart. The net number of molecules diffusing in the positive x direction in time τ is simply one half of the difference in numbers of molecules in each compartment,

$$-\left[\tfrac{1}{2}\xi\left(N'_A + \xi\frac{\partial N'_A}{\partial x}\right) - \tfrac{1}{2}\xi N'_A\right] = -\frac{\xi^2}{2}\cdot\frac{\partial N'_A}{\partial x}$$

where the $\tfrac{1}{2}$ factor allows for the molecules moving in the "wrong" direction. The number being transferred across the unit plane per second is

$$\mathscr{N}_A = -\mathscr{D}_A\frac{\partial N'_A}{\partial x} = -\frac{\xi^2}{2\tau}\frac{\partial N'_A}{\partial x} \qquad (13.205)$$

whence

$$\mathscr{D}_A = \frac{\xi^2}{2\tau} \quad \text{or} \quad \xi^2 = 2\tau\mathscr{D}_A \qquad (13.206)$$

an equation given over 50 years ago by Einstein.

We had previously

$$\overline{x_n^2} = n\lambda^2 \qquad (13.105)$$

for the mean-square displacement after n steps. If we identify the mean-square displacement $\overline{x_n^2}$ with ξ^2 of the preceding equation, then

$$\overline{x_n^2} = n\lambda^2 = 2\tau \mathscr{D}_A$$

and

$$\mathscr{D}_A = \frac{n\lambda^2}{2\tau} = \tfrac{1}{2}\bar{c}_A\lambda \qquad (13.207)$$

where $\bar{c}_A$ is the mean speed of the molecules and $\tau = n\lambda/\bar{c}_A$. In three dimensions, Eq. 13.206 becomes

$$\text{mean-square displacement} = 6\tau \mathscr{D}_A \qquad (13.208)$$

The derivation of Eq. 13.207 is by no means rigorous. The relation shows that λ, hence σ^2, the molecular cross section, may be determined from diffusion measurements. $\mathscr{D}_A$ is inversely proportional to the pressure of a gas, since λ varies in that way. The temperature dependence of $\mathscr{D}_A$ is more complex than might be surmised from the equation; this will be clarified in Sec. 13.3.

Following from Eq. 13.204, we see that the total transport of A and B across a unit plane per second is actually

$$\mathscr{N}_{A\,tot} = \mathscr{N}_A + N'_A v_\mathscr{D}; \quad \mathscr{N}_{B\,tot} = \mathscr{N}_B + N'_B v_\mathscr{D}; \quad \text{and} \quad v_\mathscr{D} = \frac{-(\mathscr{N}_A + \mathscr{N}_B)}{N'}$$

$$(13.209)$$

For the diffusion of molecules of A, the *observed* diffusion coefficient $\mathscr{D}$ corresponding to Eq. 13.204 is given in general by the expression

$$\mathscr{N}_{A\,tot} = -\mathscr{D}\frac{\partial N'_A}{\partial x} \qquad (13.210)$$

with a similar one for $\mathscr{N}_{B\,tot}$. We have, on substitution of Eqs. 13.205 and 13.209,

$$\mathscr{D} = \frac{N'_B}{N'}\mathscr{D}_A + \frac{N'_A}{N'}\mathscr{D}_B \qquad (13.211)$$

and with use of Eq. 13.207,

$$\mathscr{D} = \frac{1}{2N'}(N'_B\bar{c}_A\lambda_A + N'_A\bar{c}_B\lambda_B) \qquad (13.212)$$

where the λ quantities are the mean free paths of components A and B.

Problems

13.201   Obtain Eq. 13.208 by using the relations of a right-angle triangle.

13.202   (a) Calculate the relative magnitudes of $\mathscr{D}_X$ (X = He, Ne, Ar, Kr, C_8H_{18}), given σ_X = 2.6, 2.8, 3.4, 3.8, 10 Å, respectively, at any pressure and temperature.
(b) Find the absolute magnitude of $\mathscr{D}_{He}$ at 10^{-1}, 10, and 10^3 mm Hg at 300°K.

3. Viscous Flow

Viscosity Coefficient.   Consider the situation when two portions of a nonideal gas (fluid) move relative to one another or, in general, when the velocity of mass motion of the fluid in a particular direction x is a function of the z position in the fluid (Fig. 13.301). Then the liquid is being sheared. The transport of momentum between two planes in a direction z perpendicular to the flow, is accompanied by a frictional force which acts in opposition to the shearing of the liquid,

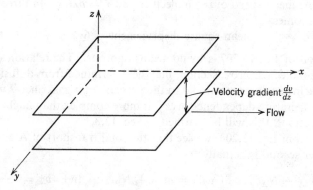

Fig. 13.301   Shearing of a fluid.

since slow-moving molecules which diffuse to a faster-moving plane slow the latter down, and vice versa. The *force per unit area* (Fig. 13.301) in the flow direction exerted on the slower plane is

$$f = \eta \frac{dv}{dz} \tag{13.301}$$

an equation similar in form to the defining equation for $\mathscr{D}$ dealing with mass transport (Eq. 13.201). The constant η defined by Eq. 13.301 is called the viscosity coefficient. If η is very large a large force is required to shear the fluid. For example, shearing of a gel or a glass, as opposed to a "thin" fluid, would require a large value of f.

By considering the details of the momentum transport one may arrive at the equation

$$\eta = \frac{\rho \bar{c} \lambda}{2} \tag{13.302}$$

where ρ is the density of the fluid. Evidently, as follows from either Eq. 13.301 or Eq. 13.302, η has units of gram cm^{-1} sec^{-1}, called the *poise* in honor of Poiseuille, a pioneer in this field.

For a gas mixture of molecules of similar mass and cross section, such as N_2 and O_2, then

$$\eta = \frac{\eta_A \lambda_A'}{\lambda_A} + \frac{\eta_B \lambda_B'}{\lambda_B} + \cdots \tag{13.303}$$

where the λ' quantity is the mean free path of the component in the mixture, and λ is what the value would be for the pure gas at its partial pressure.

Viscosity Coefficient and Pressure. Since ρ is directly, and λ inversely, proportional to the concentration of gas, η is independent of pressure. Actually η tends to decline at low pressures because of the increasing importance of the phenomenon of slippage, that is, the failure of gas molecules which collide with a wall, or falling marble, etc., depending on the experimental setup used to establish a velocity gradient, to acquire the velocity of the object in question.

Viscosity Coefficient and Temperature. At constant gas volume, Eq. 13.302 predicts an *increase* in η with rise of temperature ($\bar{c}$ increases). The actual rise at low temperature is more rapid than the $T^{1/2}$ factor in $\bar{c}$. In fact, the variations of $\mathcal{D}$ and η with temperature provide excellent sources of information on the approximations of the hard sphere model, inasmuch as these properties depend intimately on molecular collisions. Although Eq. 13.103 for mean free path asserts that λ is independent of temperature, in practice it is found that λ increases with T. This finding depends on the fact that, although the hard sphere model allows for the existence of repulsive forces (albeit not in quantitatively correct fashion), the model ignores the existence of attractive forces of the form

$$f_a = -\frac{\partial \epsilon_a}{\partial r} = \frac{K_a'}{r^n} \tag{13.304}$$

where, from Eq. 6.506, n is commonly set equal to 7. The existence of attractive forces causes collisions which would not otherwise occur. The decreasing importance of these forces at higher temperature has been taken into account by a number of semiempirical equations. An equation by Sutherland, which has survived some 70 years as a useful approximation at intermediate temperatures, is

$$\lambda = \frac{\lambda_\infty}{1 + C/T} \tag{13.305}$$

where C is constant and λ_∞ is the limiting value of λ. C is related to the intermolecular attractive potential, $C \propto K_a'/\sigma^{n-1}$, where σ is the mean molecular diameter; $C = 78$, 170, 170, 335 for helium, argon, CH_4, C_5H_{12}, respectively (compare Table 6.501).

We may also write

$$\eta = \frac{\frac{1}{2}\rho \bar{c} \lambda_\infty}{1 + C/T} \tag{13.306}$$

Actually the repulsive potential (Eq. 6.507) will at high temperature tend to produce the opposite type of T dependence (i.e., C negative), and more complex expressions should be written.

In any case the study of the temperature dependence of λ, $\mathscr{D}$, η, etc., leads to information on the form of the molecular force field and to evaluation of gas imperfection constants, such as the second virial coefficient.

ILLUSTRATION. The determination of intermolecular potential parameters from the temperature dependence of viscosity.

C. P. Ellis and C. J. C. Raw [*J. Chem. Phys.*, **30**, 574 (1959)] have measured the viscosity of several gases over a wide range of temperature. Some of their data for N_2 and NO is given in Table 13.301.

Table 13.301   Viscosity Coefficients η (g cm^{-1} sec^{-1}) for N_2 and NO

N_2

t, °C:	699.5	747.7	795.8	847.2	893.0	497.5	1000.2		
$\eta \times 10^7$:	3916	4017	4119	4216	4374	4461	4582		

NO

t, °C:	100.8	192.5	301.8	404.1	498.3	599.8	701.0	804.7	901.6
$\eta \times 10^7$:	2223	2659	3130	3483	3842	4152	4472	4753	4986

Now Eq. 13.306 may be written in the form

$$\eta = \text{const} \frac{T^{\frac{1}{2}}}{(1 + C/T)}$$

since $\bar{c}$ depends on $T^{\frac{1}{2}}$, and on rearranging, $T + C = \text{const } T^{\frac{3}{2}}/\eta$. $T^{\frac{3}{2}}/\eta$ vs. T was used by Ellis and Raw to evaluate the empirical Sutherland constant, C, which is a measure of the maximum attractive interaction between two molecules. Values found by them in this way are given in Table 13.302.

Table 13.302   Evaluation of C and ϵ^*/k from Temperature Dependence of Viscosity**

Gas:	N_2	NO	BF_3	SiF_4	SF_6
C, °K:	104	124	196	224	243
ϵ^*/k, °K:	91.5	119	178	147	259

* From C. P. Ellis and C. V. C. Raw, *J. Chem. Phys.*, **30**, 574 (1959).

The data are preferably described with use of the Lennard-Jones 6-12 potential (Eq. 6.509). In terms of the parameters of this potential, it can be shown that an equation of form similar to that just given also applies, that is,

$$\eta = \text{const} \frac{T^{\frac{1}{2}}}{\left[r^{*2}\Omega\left(\frac{kT}{\epsilon^*}\right)\right]}$$

where Ω is a tabulated quantity which is a function of the reduced temperature, $T_r' = kT/\epsilon^*$ (Eq. 11.205), and thus depends on the properties of the colliding molecules. By a trial and error process, ϵ^*/k (and also r^*) was evaluated by these authors from the data (Table 13.302).

In general ϵ^* and C are seen to increase with molecular complexity. The student may consult the reference of Chapter 6 to Hirschfelder, Curtiss, and Bird for further discussion. He may confirm the values of C tabulated for N_2 and NO by plotting the data.

_____

Problems

13.301   Repeat Problem 13.202 for η_X.

13.302   Plot the calculated relative variation of the viscosity coefficient for helium, and also for C_5H_{12}, from 0 to 500°C against $T^{\frac{1}{2}}$. Also plot a reference curve for $C = 0$.

13.303   Write down an approximate expression which will give a more correct dependence of $\mathscr{L}_{AA}$ on temperature than is afforded by Eq. 13.104.

4. Thermal Conduction

Existence of a temperature gradient in a fluid gives rise to transport of energy. Thus in analogy with the other transport quantities

$$Q = -\kappa_t \frac{dT}{dx} \tag{13.401}$$

where Q is the amount of heat energy carried across unit plane perpendicular to the x axis per second when the gradient is dT/dx. The expression for κ_t, the specific thermal conduction constant, is

$$\kappa_t = 1.25 \, \rho \bar{c} \lambda c_V \tag{13.402}$$

so

$$\kappa_t = \tfrac{5}{2}\eta c_V \tag{13.403}$$

where c_V is the specific heat at constant volume. κ_t has units of g cm sec^{-3} deg^{-1}.

These expressions hold for monatomic gases with translational degrees of freedom only. For polyatomic molecules a modified relation holds,

$$\kappa_t = C'\eta c_V \quad (C' < \tfrac{5}{2}) \tag{13.404}$$

Problems

* 13.401   Plot the relative heat gain per unit time against pressure for a Thermos flask containing liquid N_2, and having 0.5 cm between the walls, as the inner space is evacuated by factors of 10 in the pressure starting at 10 mm air and going down to 10^{-5} mm; see Problem 13.101 and discuss the failure of Eq. 13.402 at lower pressures here.

   13.402   Calculate the specific thermal conductivity of (a) argon and (b) helium at 1 atm and 30°C. See Problem 13.202 for σ values.

5. Transport Phenomena in Solutions of Electrolytes

Ions in electrolyte solutions serve to transport charge. While they have randomly directed velocities of the order of 10^4 cm sec^{-1}, characteristic of translational motion around room temperature, the mean free path in the liquid state is very short (Sec. 14.8). The net migration velocity under the influence of an applied electric field of 1 volt cm^{-1} is only of the order of 10^{-4} cm sec^{-1}, which is very small compared to the velocity of the random motions.

A large number of data on the conductivity of various electrolytes is available. We shall briefly describe the manner in which data are tabulated and some of the general conclusions drawn from them.

Conductance, Ionic Mobility, and Transference Numbers. The *specific conductance* κ_{sp} of a solution is defined as

$$\kappa_{sp} = \frac{A}{R} \text{ ohm}^{-1} \text{ cm}^{-1} \qquad (13.501)$$

where R is the measured resistance of a cell filled with the solution and A is a cell constant dependent on cell geometry (electrode area, distance between electrodes, etc.). The *equivalent conductance* Λ is

$$\Lambda = \frac{\kappa_{sp}}{c} \qquad (13.502)$$

where c is concentration in equivalents per cubic centimeter ($1/c$ is the volume containing one equivalent). Λ (dimensions cm^2 ohm^{-1} equiv^{-1}) can be considered to be the sum of the conductances of the positive and negative ions. Kohlrausch's law of independent migration of ions asserts that, at infinite dilution, the contribution of each ion is independent of the nature of its partner and may be tabulated as an ionic property for the particular solvent medium,

$$\Lambda^0 = \lambda_+^0 + \lambda_-^0 \qquad (13.503)$$

At finite concentrations the ionic conductances may be added to give the total equivalent conductance, but the individual values depend on the ionic partner as well as concentration.

The *ionic mobility* is defined as the ionic velocity in centimeters per second under a potential gradient of 1 volt cm^{-1} and is related to the conductance by

$$u_+ = \lambda_+/\mathscr{F} \qquad (13.504)$$

where $\mathscr{F}$ is the faraday.

The relative amount of current transported by a particular ion is represented by a transport or transference number, defined as

$$t_+ = \frac{\lambda_+}{\Lambda} \qquad (13.505)$$

Note that $t_+ + t_- = 1$. The transference number can be determined experimentally. The Hittorf method is based on determination of concentration changes in the vicinity of each electrode caused by passage of a direct current through the electrolyte. Cations migrate toward the cathode and (for simple electrolysis) are removed from the cathode compartment by the electrode reduction; anions move toward the anode and are similarly removed by the anode oxidation. The net result is a decrease of solute from the cathode compartment of $Q/\mathscr{F} - Qt_+/\mathscr{F} = Qt_-/\mathscr{F}$ equivalents, and, similarly, $Qt_+/\mathscr{F}$ equivalents of solute from the anode compartment; Q is the number of coulombs of electricity passing through the cell. In the moving boundary method an indicator is used to follow the migration of ions; in some cases solutions with different refractive indices form a boundary which can be followed visually. The student may refer to the General References for details of such methods.

Ionic mobilities, transference numbers, ionic conductances, and equivalent conductances are all interrelated. Our attention will be focused primarily on conductivity. Conductance varies with temperature and with concentration. Some limiting ionic conductances at infinite dilution are shown in Table 13.501. The variation with concentration for some representative salts is shown in Fig. 13.501. It will be observed that in dilute solution Λ decreases with concentration. Kohlrausch observed that at very low concentrations, for strong electrolytes,

$$\Lambda = \Lambda^0 - \mathscr{B}c^{1/2} \qquad (13.506)$$

where $\mathscr{B}$ is a constant; a plot such as Fig. 13.501 should be linear in the vicinity of zero concentration. Onsager and others have applied the Debye-Hückel theory to the problem of predicting the value of the constant $\mathscr{B}$ in Eq. 13.506. The treatment appears to be successful at very high dilutions. In such a treatment, one has the problems associated with the Debye-Hückel development with the added complication of deformation of the ionic atmosphere, which is moving in the opposite direction of the central ion, and of frictional forces associated with motion of the ions through the solvent medium. These problems make a theoretical treatment at concentrations above $0.001 M$ (or even lower for ions carrying more than unit charge) very difficult; semiempirical equations, which are extensions of the limiting law, are used to correlate conductance data at higher concentrations.

It will be observed (Table 13.501) that the hydrogen and hydroxide ions have unusually high mobilities compared to other ions in aqueous solution. This is believed to be the result of a different mechanism for transferring charge; a proton may jump from one water molecule to another by an exchange mechanism, which gives a high effective mobility. If the proton originates from a hydronium ion,

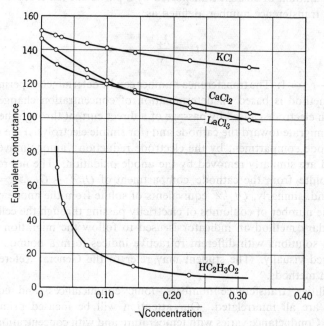

Fig. 13.501 Equivalent conductance as a function of concentration (by permission from F. Daniels and R. A. Alberty, *Physical Chemistry*, Second Edition, John Wiley and Sons, 1962).

H_3O^+, the transfer of H^+ effectively occurs; if it originates from H_2O, the proton transfer effectively moves an OH^-, as indicated schematically below.

proton migration, H^+ transferred to right

proton migration, OH^- transferred to left

The mobilities of the other ions bear some relationship to their size, which is

Table 13.501 Limiting Ionic Equivalent Conductances in Water at 25°C*

Ion	λ^0	Ion	λ^0
H^+	349.8_1	OH^-	198.3
Li^+	38.6_8	F^-	55.4
Na^+	50.10	Cl^-	76.35
K^+	73.50	Br^-	78.14
Rb^+	77.8_1	I^-	76.8_4
Cs^+	77.2_6	N_3^-	69
Ag^+	61.9_0	NO_3^-	71.46
Tl^+	74.7	ClO_3^-	64.6
NH_4^+	73.5_5	BrO_3^-	55.7_4
$CH_3NH_3^+$	58.7_2	IO_3^-	40.5_4
$(CH_3)_2NH_2^+$	51.8_7	ClO_4^-	67.3_6
$(CH_3)_3NH^+$	47.2_5	IO_4^-	54.5_5
NMe_4^+	44.9_2	ReO_4^-	54.9_7
NEt_4^+	32.6_6	HCO_3^-	44.5_0
NPr_4^+	23.4_2	Formate	54.5_9
NBu_4^+	19.4_7	Acetate	40.9_0
NAm_4^+	17.4_7	Bromoacetate	39.2_2
$(CH_3)_3(C_6H_5)N^+$	34.6_5	Chloroacetate	42.2_0
$CH_2OH \cdot CH_2 \cdot NH_3^+$	42.2_3	Cyanoacetate	43.4_2
Be^{++}	45	Fluoroacetate	44.3_9
Mg^{++}	53.0_5	Iodoacetate	40.6_0
Ca^{++}	59.50	Propionate	35.8
Sr^{++}	59.4_5	Butyrate	32.6
Ba^{++}	63.6_3	Benzoate	32.3_8
Cu^{++}	53.6	Picrate	30.39
Zn^{++}	52.8	$SO_4^=$	80.0_2
Co^{++}	55	$C_2O_4^=$	74.1_5
Pb^{++}	69.5	$CO_3^=$	69.3
La^{3+}	69.7	$Fe(CN)_6^{3-}$	100.9
Ce^{3+}	69.8	$P_3O_9^\equiv$	83.6
Pr^{3+}	69.6	$Fe(CN)_6^{4-}$	$110._5$
Nd^{3+}	69.4	$P_4O_{12}^{4-}$	$93._7$
Sm^{3+}	68.5	$P_2O_7^{4-}$	$95._9$
Eu^{3+}	67.8	$P_3O_{10}^{5-}$	109
Gd^{3+}	67.3	$[Co(NH_3)_6]^{3+}$	101.9
Dy^{3+}	65.6	$[Co_2tri\text{-}en_3]^{6+}$	$68._7$
Ho^{3+}	66.3	$[Ni_2tri\text{-}en_3]^{4+}$	$52._5$
Er^{3+}	65.9		
Tm^{3+}	65.4		
Yb^{3+}	65.6		

* By permission from R. A. Robinson and R. H. Stokes, *Electrolyte Solutions*, Second Edition, Academic Press, 1959.

determined by the degree of hydration in many cases. The alkali-metal cations have mobilities in inverse order of their crystallographic size; the Li^+ ion may be expected to be strongly hydrated and appears effectively larger than Cs^+, for example. The mobilities of the simple bivalent cations are quite similar. Stoke's law, which relates the force f applied to macroscopic particles and the velocity v attained in a medium of viscosity η to the radius of the particle r,

$$f = 6\pi\eta rv \tag{13.507}$$

appears to correlate the size and behavior of very large ions, but not those of usual dimensions.

The Temperature Dependence of Conductivity. The effect of temperature appears largely associated with the change of solvent viscosity. The product $\lambda^0\eta^0$ is roughly constant; see Fig. 13.502. Some variation of this product may be expected if the effective size, i.e., degree of hydration, changes with temperature.

Applications. In addition to information about the size and interaction of ions, conductivity measurements provide useful data for a variety of other purposes: concentrations at which marked changes in the ionic composition occur may be detected; the general level of conductivity provides evidence for the kinds and concentrations of ions present; equilibrium constants may be determined. We shall conclude this section by describing the determination of the ionization constant of a weak electrolyte by conductance measurements.

It will be observed in Fig. 13.501 that the equivalent conductance of acetic acid falls off with increasing concentration much more rapidly than that of the strong electrolytes. This rapid fall-off is due to association of ions to form acetic acid molecules. Weak electrolytes generally show this behavior; the limiting value for the conductances at zero concentration must be determined from individual ionic conductances, measured for compounds of the ions involved which are strong electrolytes, e.g., hydrochloric acid and sodium acetate. If the ionic conductances were not a function of concentration, the degree of ionization α of acetic acid could be calculated from the simple relationship

$$\alpha = \frac{\Lambda}{\Lambda^0} \tag{13.508}$$

This is the simple Arrhenius theory for the conductivity of weak electrolytes. Actually we may write $\alpha = \Lambda/\Lambda_i$, where Λ_i is the equivalent conductance of a hypothetical fully ionized solution of acetic acid in which the ionic interactions are the same as one in which each ion concentration is αc. R. A. Robinson and R. H. Stokes (General References) have used an expression of the form

$$\Lambda_i = \Lambda^0 - \frac{(B_1\Lambda^0 + B_2)\sqrt{\alpha c}}{1 + Ba\sqrt{\alpha c}} \tag{13.509}$$

B, B_1, and B_2 are Debye-Hückel-Onsager theory constants; a is the ion-size factor of Eq. 12.228. The approximate value of $\alpha = \Lambda/\Lambda^0$ is used first to get a tentative value of Λ_i; then α is re-evaluated from Λ/Λ_i and a new Λ_i calculated; these successive approximations to α converge rapidly. Table 13.502 is presented by Robinson and Stokes. The ionization equilibrium constant K_a is calculated from the formula

$$K_a = \frac{\alpha^2 \gamma_{\pm}^2 c}{1 - \alpha}$$

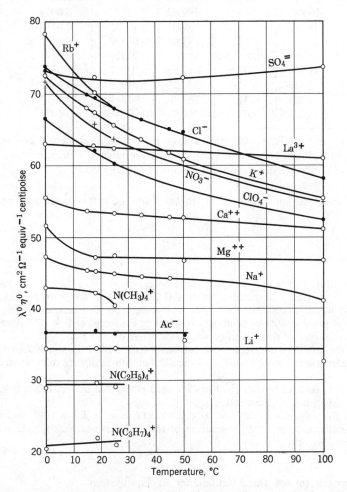

Fig. 13.502   Variation of the product $\lambda^0 \eta^0$ with temperature (by permission from R. A. Robinson and R. H. Stokes, *Electrolyte Solutions*, Academic Press, 1959).

with the mean ionic activity coefficient evaluated from the Debye-Hückel theory. The various equilibrium constant values are within experimental error at concentrations less than 0.006 mole liter^{-1}; at higher concentrations, neglect of the activity coefficient of the undissociated molecules, failure of Eq. 13.509, etc., contribute to the fall-off. To eliminate such uncertainties, the true thermodynamic equilibrium

Table 13.502   Calculation of Ionization Constant of Acetic Acid at 25°*

c	Λ_{obs}	$\Lambda/\Lambda^0 \approx \alpha$	Λ_i	$\Lambda/\Lambda_i = \alpha$	$-2 \log \gamma_{\pm}$	$K_a \times 10^5$
0.00002801	210.38	0.5384	390.13	0.5393	0.0039	1.753
0.00011135	127.75	0.3270	389.81	0.3277	0.0061	1.754
0.0002184	96.493	0.2470	389.62	0.2477	0.0074	1.752
0.0010283	48.146	0.1232	389.05	0.12375	0.0113	1.751
0.002414	32.217	0.0825	388.63	0.08290	0.0141	1.752
0.005912	20.962	0.0537	388.10	0.05401	0.0178	1.750
0.02	11.566	0.0296	387.16	0.02987	0.0241	1.740
0.05	7.358	0.0188	386.27	0.01905	0.0302	1.726
0.1	5.201	0.0133	385.46	0.013493	0.0357	1.700
0.2	3.651	0.0093	384.54	0.009494	0.0420	1.653

* By permission from R. A. Robinson and R. H. Stokes, *Electrolyte Solutions*, Second Edition, Academic Press, New York, 1959; based on conductivity measurements of D. A. MacInnes and T. Shedlovsky, *J. Am. Chem. Soc.*, **54**, 1429 (1932).

constant is taken as the value of K_a in the limit of extrapolation to zero concentration.

Problems

Data from Table 13.501 may be used where necessary.

13.501   The resistance of a cell containing 0.02N KCl was found to be 473.5 ohms. κ_{sp} for the solution is 0.002768 ohm^{-1} cm^{-1}. Evaluate the cell constant. The specific conductance of good quality conductivity water is of the order of 1×10^{-6} ohm^{-1} cm^{-1}. What is the resistance of this cell filled with conductivity water?

13.502   Calculate the equivalent conductance for 0.02M KCl. Evaluate the ratio Λ/Λ°.

13.503   Calculate the ionic mobility of the calcium ion at infinite dilution in aqueous solution.

13.504   Calculate transference numbers for each of the ions in very dilute solutions of KCl, NaCl, CaCl$_2$, Na$_2$SO$_4$, respectively.

13.505   If the ionization constant of chloroacetic acid is 1.5×10^{-3}, estimate the equivalent conductance of a 0.01N solution of the acid (assume that simple Arrhenius theory may be applied).

6. The Approach to and the Maintenance of Equilibrium

Role of Collisions. In Chapter 6, we developed the properties of a gas in terms of an ideal model which barred collisions, except with the wall of the confining vessel. If the appropriate distribution function of velocities were changed, say by a reversible adiabatic expansion, to one characteristic of a lower temperature, the excess momentum of the molecules must be removed during the process. This comes about because of the fact that the retreating wall does not return all the momentum to the gas molecule that collides with it.

This model allows no exchange of momentum between molecules, however. If a hot gas and a cold gas flowed into a single large container they would have a double distribution function that was a simple average, rather than one characteristic of a new intermediate temperature. Actually, gases rapidly equilibrate by collision between molecules.

Dynamic Equilibrium and Boltzmann's H Function. The energy in a group of molecules in contact is constantly being shifted around among the various molecules. It is difficult to show, but reasonable to assert, that a series of collisions in a nonequilibrium system results in a more probable distribution of energy than obtained before the collisions took place, on the average. When the equilibrium distribution is attained or closely approached, these same collisions do not operate to make the distribution any less probable. The nature of the individual collisions does not change at equilibrium, however, because an individual collision has no equilibrium or nonequilibrium quality. The only thing that can be considered from a statistical or a thermodynamic point of view is the average behavior of a large number of collisions. Boltzmann studied the average value of the log of the distribution function $f(u, v, w)$, which is called the Boltzmann H function,

$$H = \overline{\ln f} = \iiint\limits_{-\infty}^{\infty} f \ln f \, du \, dv \, dw \tag{13.601}$$

This H is not to be confused with the enthalpy. H is constant if f does not change. If the distribution function f is time dependent, then H is also a function of time. The Maxwellian distribution is the only equilibrium one. Boltzmann showed that collisions always operate so that this function can never increase, i.e.,

$$\frac{dH}{dt} \leqslant 0 \tag{13.602}$$

From the molecular standpoint this corresponds to the fact that entropy can only increase, in a nonequilibrium process, or stay constant, in isolated systems. The entropy can be extended conceptually to nonequilibrium systems by the definition

$$S = -\text{const } H \tag{13.603}$$

One can show that this equation is true at equilibrium; if Maxwell's distribution is substituted in Eq. 13.601, the equivalent of Eq. 11.402 for the entropy is produced. Away from equilibrium, Eq. 13.603 can be used in principle to *define* a value of S.

Rates of Activation and Deactivation of Molecules. According to the Maxwell distribution law, a small but finite proportion of molecules has speeds, and hence amounts of energy, greater than the average or greater than any finite amount specified. How does a molecule get an amount of energy greater than average? One answer is that the molecule may acquire it by a single very rare collision of the type where one of the participants goes off with a major share of the energy. If a molecule is to end up with a great excess of energy, it must have many such rare collisions. Also, the more energy it gets, the greater the chance that on subsequent collisions it will lose the energy that it previously had gathered. This situation may usefully be considered as a complicated, one-dimensional random walk problem along the energy coordinate (Fig. 13.601). The average step size, $\bar{\lambda}_+$, for positive movement (the direction of increasing energy) may be set approximately constant when the molecule is at energies well above the average—corresponding to the fact that the molecule collides most frequently with molecules having energy near the average. The average step size for movement to the left $\bar{\lambda}_-$ increases with increase in the energy of the molecule—corresponding to the

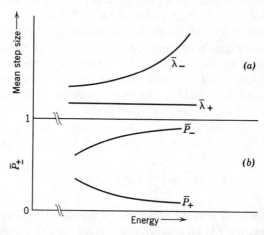

Fig. 13.601   Qualitative representation of some parameters of a random walk along the energy coordinate. (a) Variation of $\bar{\lambda}_\pm$ with energy. (b) Variation of $\overline{P}_\pm$ with energy.

larger amounts of energy which the molecule has available to lose. Similarly, the average probability $\overline{P}_-$ that a given encounter of the excited molecule will lead to a leftward negative step increases with increase in its energy, while the average probability for a positive step $\overline{P}_+$ must correspondingly decline, since $\overline{P}_+ + \overline{P}_- = 1$.

It is for these reasons that high-energy molecules become rarer, as an exponential function of the energy they bear, when looked at from a dynamic point of view. Equation 13.106 assures us of the exponential form.

In connection with the kinetics of chemical reactions, we often wish to know the rate at which molecules of a certain very high energy are produced by collision. We may obtain this by considering the reverse process, that is, how fast the molecules leave this state of high energy, because at equilibrium the rates of production and destruction of "hot" molecules by collisional processes are equal. This is an instance of "detailed balancing," which we shall encounter again in Sec. 14.2. Virtually every collision of a hot molecule will be a deactivating one, i.e., $\overline{P}_- \rightarrow 1$ (Fig. 13.601), because, on a random statistical basis, it is highly unlikely that the rare hot molecule will hit another hot molecule; it will most probably hit a cold molecule and, on the average, lose much of its excess energy, since λ_- is large at very high energy. If N'^* is the concentration of hot molecules and $(N' - N'^*) \approx N'$ is the concentration of cold molecules, the number of collisions between the two species is, from Eq. 6.502,

$$\mathscr{Z}_{A^*A} = 4N'^*N'\sigma_{A^*A}^2 \left(\frac{\pi kT}{m}\right)^{\frac{1}{2}} \tag{13.604}$$

where half the molecular mass has been inserted for the reduced mass, as defined for equal masses.

We can then use the Maxwell-Boltzmann distribution to calculate N'^* and thus the actual rate of activation *and* deactivation *at equilibrium*. In addition, if we assume that a change in the rate of deactivation of hot molecules, say by chemical reaction, does not affect the rate of activation, we can still use the *equilibrium* rate of deactivation to calculate the rate of activation of molecules even though the actual value of N'^* is no longer the equilibrium value.

The student will note that in kinetic problems many more assumptions enter than in the chapters dealing with equilibrium properties. There is no general theory of nonequilibrium processes comparable in scope to thermodynamics.

ILLUSTRATION. One possible way in which molecules might share energy on collision would be on a random statistical basis. Consider vibrational energy only, for the case where the molecules in a bath are all diatomic harmonic oscillators of frequency v, at a temperature such that $kT = 2hv$. What is the total probability, on a collision between two molecules having internal energy above the zero-point level of $2hv$ and $10hv$, respectively, that the "hotter" molecule will gain energy?

For the assumed random statistical model of probabilities for energy transfer, all possible outcomes are equally probable. These are:

	Molecule 1	Molecule 2
Initial energy before collision	$2hv$	$10hv$
Final energy after collision, any of	0	12
	1	11
	2	10
	3	9
	4	8
	5	7
	6	6
	7	5
	8	4
	9	3
	10	2
	11	1
	12	0
Sum	$78hv$	$78hv$
Average outcome	$6hv$	$6hv$

It is evident that there are only 2 chances in 13 that molecule 2 will gain energy, and only 4 chances in 13 that either molecule will acquire more than 10 hv in the collision.

Although the *average* outcome of the collision is to produce two molecules each having energy of $6hv$, the student will note that this collisional energy-transfer model is quite different from one (which we may call the "averaging model") in which the energy of the colliding molecules is simply averaged, i.e., molecule 1: $2hv \rightarrow 6hv$; molecule 2: $10hv \rightarrow 6hv$; where $(2 + 10)/2 = 6$.

If the temperature is raised so that the average bath molecule has energy $4hv$, the student may easily show that the chance of the hotter molecule acquiring more energy than $10hv$ on collision with an average bath molecule is now raised to 4/15 on the random model.

Problems

* 13.601   Show with use of the "averaging model" of collisional energy transition probabilities, just described in the Illustration, that in a system which obeys this model no molecule may have zero energy at equilibrium. Graph the form of the energy distribution that would arise for such a system of colliding molecules at equilibrium. What can you conclude about such a model?

13.602   For 1 atm of helium at 300°K, find graphically the rate at which new atoms having speeds in the range 8.05×10^3 to 8.09×10^3 m sec^{-1} are produced per cc sec^{-1}.

13.603   For 1 atm of HCl ($v = 2800$ cm^{-1}) in a bath at 300°K what is the rate of production of new molecules having vibrational energy greater than $6hv$?

* 13.604   Equation 13.601 may be written in short form as $H = \int f \ln f \, d\tau$, where $d\tau$ is the volume element. At equilibrium, $\delta H = \int (\ln f + 1) \, \delta f \, d\tau = 0$. Use the method of undetermined multipliers, together with the additional constraints on f,

$$\int f \, d\tau = N; \quad \delta N = 0$$

$$\int \tfrac{1}{2} m(u^2 + v^2 + w^2) f \, d\tau = \bar{E}; \quad \delta \bar{E} = 0$$

to show that f must have the form of Maxwell's function, Eq. 6.103.

7. Reaction Rate Laws; Order of Chemical Reactions

In this section we introduce some formal aspects of the quantitative treatment of "chemical transport," that is, the conversion of reactants into new chemical species. Equation 13.101 governing the mean free path is of the form

$$\frac{dy}{dt} = ky \tag{13.701}$$

This is a first-order linear differential equation and is a very simple instance of a rate law. Chemical reaction rates and other rate phenomena frequently depend on time in a more complex manner. The *order* of a chemical reaction is defined as the sum of the exponents of the concentration factors which appear in the rate expression for the reaction. Consider a given reaction for which the rate of production of products is given by the expression

$$\frac{dC_{\mathrm{Pr}}}{dt} = k C_A^a C_B^b C_C^c$$

where C_A, etc., are the concentrations of reactants; then the order of the reaction is $\sum_i (\text{exponent})_i = a + b + c$.

The order of a reaction may not be directly deduced from the balanced stoichiometric equation for the reaction, except in the special important cases described in Chapter 14. Our objective in this chapter is simply to classify reactions with respect to the dependence of rate on concentrations of reactants and on time, in a mathematical sense, with no consideration of *why* they are thus dependent. The rate laws to be described apply to "irreversible" reactions under conditions of constant volume and constant temperature. These are the conditions that prevail when a reaction proceeds slowly in a closed container in a bath. The expressions appropriate for constant-pressure systems, or for adiabatic conditions, will not be considered; the former frequently involve flow systems in which reactants flow through a furnace and products are collected; the latter arise in fast reactions (an explosion is an extreme case) or in systems where heat transport to the walls, whether by stirring or by thermal conduction, is not efficient, as in some polymerization reactions.

Constant Rates; "Zero-Order" Reactions.   We start with the simplest case of constant rate of consumption of a reactant with time. Thus for the reaction $A \rightarrow \mathrm{Pr}$,

$$\frac{dC_{\mathrm{Pr}}}{dt} = k C_A^0 = k. \tag{13.702}$$

Since the rate of increase of the concentration of Pr is to be a constant, C_A in Eq. 13.702 must be raised to the zero power. The conventional units of k are conc sec^{-1}.

There are not many good examples of this type of reaction; oxygen at constant pressure will attack the planar face of graphite ($C + O_2 \rightarrow CO_2$) at a constant rate until the latter is consumed. Many chemical examples are experimental artifacts. Thus the dissolution of a zinc rod arranged vertically so that its end just maintains contact with an acid solution of constant concentration

$$Zn + 2H^+ \rightarrow Zn^{++} + H_2$$

will proceed according to Eq. 13.702. This is an instance of a *heterogeneous* reaction, i.e., one that involves more than one phase. The hydrogenation of liquid vegetable oils to make margarine, in the presence of a solid platinum catalyst, is another instance. By contrast, *homogeneous* reactions involve only a single phase. There is no known instance of a homogeneous zero-order gas reaction.

Integration of Eq. 13.702 gives

$$C_{\text{Pr}} = \not{k}t + \text{const} \tag{13.703}$$

If $C_{\text{Pr}} = 0$ at $t = 0$, then the constant term is zero. The rate laws Eq. 13.702 and 13.703 are illustrated for a particular reaction in Fig. 13.701. Increase of the initial concentration (amount) of reactant, C_{A_0}, simply prolongs the time taken until it is all consumed. The time taken until half the reactant is consumed, i.e., when $C_{\text{Pr}} = C_{A_0}/2$, is from Eq. 13.703 simply

$$t_{\frac{1}{2}} = \frac{C_{A_0}}{2\not{k}} \tag{13.704}$$

Transport and rate processes

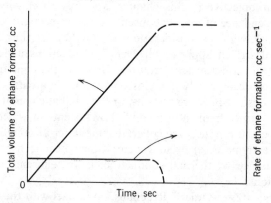

Fig. 13.701 Illustration of the rate law for a zero-order reaction: decomposition of solid silver methyl [*J. Phys. Chem.*, **63**, 1523 (1959)].

and the initial amount of material divided by the rate of reaction gives the total time it takes for the reaction to go to completion; C_{A_0} and $\not{k}$ must of course have the same concentration units.

First-Order Reactions. We note that Eq. 13.701 is linear and first order in y, i.e., y is raised to the first power, and hence corresponds to a first-order reaction. Such a process may be characterized by an extent-of-completion parameter a, which obeys the differential equation

$$\frac{da}{dt} = -\frac{a}{\tau} \tag{13.705}$$

The constant τ is called the relaxation time of the process. The quantity a is any parameter accessible to measurement that indicates the extent of reaction; it could be the change in length of a sample of plastic, stretching under a load, or the pressure of a gas which is being depleted by effusion, or the amount of radioactive nuclei of an element still not decomposed. The only requirement is that a be selected so that $a = 0$ at $t = \infty$; otherwise the solution diverges. If, at $t = \infty$, a reaches some constant value a_f, the equation may apply to the difference, $a - a_f$.

There are many examples of first-order reactions in the gas phase and in solution. These include processes such as

$$C_3H_6 \text{ (cyclopropane)} \rightarrow C_3H_6 \text{ (propylene)}$$
$$C_4H_8 \text{ (cyclobutane)} \rightarrow 2C_2H_4$$
$$2N_2O_5 \rightarrow 4NO_2 + O_2$$
$$C^{14} \rightarrow N^{14} + e \,(\beta \text{ particle)}.$$

as well as the time-honored example, the inversion (hydrolysis) of sucrose. For chemical reactions, such as A → Pr, there is a common notation on concentration in wide use which will be adopted. The initial concentration of reactant is designated as a and the change of concentration to time t as x; thus

$$\frac{dx}{dt} = k(a - x) \tag{13.706}$$

The units of k, the first-order *specific rate constant*, are sec^{-1}. Integration of Eq. 13.706 after separation of variables gives

$$\int_0^x \frac{dx}{(a - x)} = k \int_0^t dt$$

or

$$\ln \frac{a}{(a - x)} = kt \tag{13.707}$$

Another form of Eq. 13.707 is

$$a - x = ae^{-kt}, \quad \text{or} \quad C_A = C_{A_0} e^{-kt} \tag{13.708}$$

The change of concentration with time, the relaxation phenomenon, is governed by the *time-rate law*, Eq. 13.707 or 13.708.

If the elapsed time is designated as $t_{1/2}$ when $x = a/2$, then

$$t_{1/2} = \frac{\ln 2}{k} \tag{13.709}$$

that is, $t_{1/2}$ is independent of initial concentration. Also, the plot of $\ln [a/(a - x)]$ vs. t (Fig. 13.702) is linear and has slope equal to k; a plot of $\ln (a - x)$ vs. t is linear, and has slope equal to $-k$ and intercept $\ln a$. These are characteristic criteria of first-order reactions.

It is noted again that the equations above were derived for an irreversible process. If the back reaction Pr → A occurred simultaneously, the rate law would be somewhat altered, as we shall see in Chapter 14, but even in this case the above expressions would hold near the beginning of the reaction when x is negligibly small.

ILLUSTRATION.   Time-rate law for a first-order reaction.

The dehydrochlorination of *n*-propyl chloride

$$CH_3CH_2CH_2Cl \rightarrow CH_3CH{=}CH_2 + HCl$$

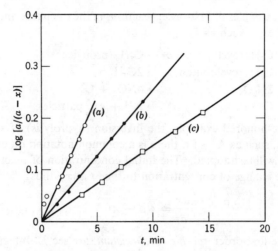

Fig. 13.702   Plot of log $[a/(a - x)]$ vs. t from data for the reaction n-PrCl $\rightarrow$ C$_3$H$_6$ + HCl, at three temperatures: (a) 744.3°K; (b) 735.3°K; (c) 723.4°K [by permission from Barton, Head, and Williams, *J. Chem. Soc.*, 2039 (1951)].

has been studied, and the dependence of the concentrations on time is shown in Fig. 13.702. The data have intercept zero, and slopes equal to $k/2.303$. For the highest temperature, where the rate constant is largest, the initial data do not lie on the line as well as for the lower temperatures; this suggests that experimental error may have arisen in making the first few measurements at very short elapsed time of reaction.

Now Eq. 13.708 has the form of a distribution function since it expresses the fraction of molecules $(a - x)/a$ which have "lived" to time t as e^{-kt}. We may ask, what is the average life expectancy $\bar{t}$ of a molecule? It is simply

$$\bar{t} = \frac{\displaystyle\int_0^\infty t e^{-kt}\, dt}{\displaystyle\int_0^\infty e^{-kt}\, dt}$$

These are standard integrals and yield the value

$$\bar{t} = \frac{1}{k} = \tau \tag{13.710}$$

This illustrates the meaning of the mean lifetime, or relaxation time, as that time during which the quantity has decayed to $1/e$ of its original value; since $e^{-kt} = 1/e$. The relation to Eq. 13.102 for free path length is immediately evident.

ILLUSTRATION.   An example of first-order processes.

Suppose that two radioactive elements in a mixture were counted simultaneously, and that they decomposed with independent rate constants, k_1 and k_2;

also one was not the parent of the other or any other radioactive product. Then the total count rate would be $A_1 + A_2 = A$. A plot of the log of the activity should show a break if the two constants are sufficiently different. In Fig. 13.703 the straight line *b* represents the decay of the long-lived isotope. It is extrapolated back in time with confidence that the decay is first order. At large values of *t*, curve *a* for the composite activity coincides with *b* because the short-lived isotope is almost gone. Then, in the early time of the experiment, the

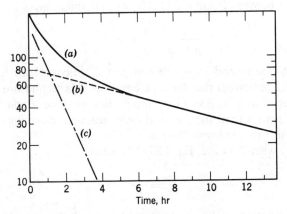

Fig. 13.703   Analysis of composite decay curve: (*a*) composite decay curve, (*b*) longer-lived component, (*c*) shorter-lived component (by permission after G. Friedlander and J. W. Kennedy, *Introduction to Radioactivity*, John Wiley and Sons, New York).

extrapolated activity (line *b*) is subtracted from *a* to give the first-order straight-line plot for the short-lived isotope, line *c*. The slopes of the two lines give k_1 and k_2. The fact that line *c* comes out straight supports the assumption of first-order decay. [Note that subtraction of *c* from *a* cannot be carried out directly (linearly) on the plot because of the log scale.]

The student may now obtain (rough) values of $t_{1/2}$ for both elements from Fig. 13.703 ($t_{1/2} = 8$ hr; 0.8 hr).

Behavior such as this was demonstrated by Segré, Halford, and Seaborg [*Phys. Rev.*, **55**, 321 (1939)] in the separation of Br^{80} isomers having different half lives.

Second-Order Reactions.   For the reaction $2A \rightarrow Pr$, or $A + B \rightarrow Pr$, we have the simple second-order rate law

$$\frac{dx}{dt} = k(a - x)^2 \tag{13.711}$$

for the case of equal initial concentrations of A and B. Classic examples include the hydrolysis of esters, e.g., ethyl acetate to give acetic acid and ethyl alcohol

$$CH_3CO_2C_2H_5 + H_2O \rightarrow CH_3CO_2H + C_2H_5OH$$

and the synthesis of urea in solution

$$NH_4^+ + CNO^- \rightarrow (NH_2)_2CO$$

Important gas-phase examples are

$$H_2 + I_2 \rightarrow 2HI$$

and

$$2N_2O \rightarrow 2N_2 + O_2$$

Integration of t between 0 and t, and x between 0 and x, gives

$$\frac{1}{a - x} - \frac{1}{a} = kt \tag{13.712}$$

where the units of the second-order rate constant k are conc^{-1} sec^{-1}.

Equation 13.712 prescribes that the time course of this second-order reaction is such that the plot of $(a - x)^{-1}$ vs t is a straight line of slope k and intercept $1/a$. Equation 13.711 asserts that, for a second-order reaction, doubling of concentrations in the system will quadruple the rate.

At the time $t_{1/2}$, when $x = a/2$, Eq. 13.712 becomes

$$t_{1/2} = \frac{1}{ka} \tag{13.713}$$

and $t_{1/2}$ increases as the initial concentration decreases. Since we have now seen that $t_{1/2}$ is proportional to a, a^0, and a^{-1} for zero, first-, and second-order reactions, respectively, we may induce the general relation

$$t_{1/2} \propto a^{1-n} \tag{13.714}$$

where n is the order of the reaction.

The rate law for a second-order reaction is somewhat more complicated if A and B are not present in equal initial concentrations. Then

$$\frac{dx}{dt} = k(a - x)(b - x) \tag{13.715}$$

and integration gives

$$\frac{1}{b - a} \ln \frac{a(b - x)}{b(a - x)} = kt \tag{13.716}$$

The plot of $\ln [a(b - x)/b(a - x)]$ vs. t is a straight line.

Pseudo-Order Reactions.   Consider the reaction $A + B \rightarrow Pr$, in which one of the reactants is present in large excess, e.g., H_2O in the hydrolysis of esters. If $a \gg b$, then $(a - x) \simeq a$ for all values of x, and the rate law Eq. 13.715 takes the form

$$\frac{dx}{dt} \simeq ka(b - x) = k'(b - x) \tag{13.717}$$

The "constant" quantity $(a - x) \simeq a$ is absorbed into k'. Thus this reaction appears formally first order and is said to be pseudo-first order. It should be noted, however, that the apparent first order of the reaction refers to its time course (the way in which concentrations vary in time), or "time order," and not to the dependence of the rate on concentration, or "concentration order," which still remains second order. Thus the doubling of *all* initial concentrations quadruples the initial rate, since not only is *b* doubled but also k' becomes $2k'$ (equal $2ka$). The pseudo-first-order rate constant k' has dimensions sec^{-1}, since it is the product of the second-order constant k ($conc^{-1} sec^{-1}$) and a concentration term. Where appropriate, a first-order constant may be converted to a second-order rate constant by division by a concentration term.

The solution of a zinc bar in hydrochloric acid described earlier is really pseudo-zero order.

The difference between the time order and the concentration order is characteristic of all pseudo-order reactions and is found also for many heterogeneous reactions. Still another important instance arises in connection with catalyzed reactions, where the rate of reaction may depend on the concentration of a catalyst which remains constant in time; for example, the rate of hydrolysis of acetonitrile to acetamide,

$$CH_3CN + H_2O \xrightarrow{H^+} CH_3CONH_2$$

is proportional to hydrochloric acid concentration below $1M$ HCl, and hydrogen ions are not consumed by this reaction.

Third-Order Reactions. For the reaction $3A \rightarrow Pr$ or $A + B + C \rightarrow Pr$, the rate law takes the form

$$\frac{dt}{dx} = k(a - x)^3 \tag{13.718}$$

when the initial concentrations of A, B, and C are equal. Integration gives

$$kt = \frac{1}{2}\left[\frac{1}{(a - x)^2} - \frac{1}{a^2}\right] \tag{13.719}$$

and the units of k are $conc^{-2} sec^{-1}$. These equations reveal the expected concentration dependence of the rate and also the variation of reactant concentration with time.

If A, B, and C are not present at equal concentrations, the rate law is more complicated, as would also be the case for the reaction $2A + B \rightarrow Pr$, whether or not A and B were initially at the same concentration.

Instances of third-order reactions include

$$2NO + O_2 \rightarrow 2NO_2$$

$$3H \rightarrow H_2 + H$$

An overall reaction may be third order even if the reaction equation is not one of the simple model types described above—whether it is ostensibly simpler, say $A \rightarrow Pr$, or apparently more complex, say $A + 2B + 3C + 4D + \cdots \rightarrow Pr$. The complicated reaction

$$KClO_3 + 6Fe^{++} + 6H^+ \rightarrow KCl + 6Fe^{3+} + 3H_2O$$

for example, is found to be kinetically third order. In many instances, it is possible to designate a single (slow) step in the complex scheme which largely determines the observed order.

We shall not be concerned with reactions (to be found in solution only) having order greater than three.

Remarks. Ambiguity in the definition of rate, in the case where unequal numbers of moles or reactants and products are involved in the overall stoichiometric equation, is avoided by the following convention agreed on by the International Union of Pure and Applied Chemistry in 1957. For the reaction

$$\nu_A A + \nu_B B + \cdots \rightarrow \nu_L L + \nu_M M + \cdots$$

where the ν quantities are integral numbers, the rate is defined as

$$\text{rate} = -\frac{1}{\nu_A}\frac{dC_A}{dt} = -\frac{1}{\nu_B}\frac{dC_B}{dt} = \frac{1}{\nu_L}\frac{dC_L}{dt}, \quad \text{etc.}$$

In summary, it should be kept in mind that order represents an empirical finding, although one which may actually be quite understandable, reasonable, and even predictable in some cases. The real significance of the experimental determination of order is the insight that it may afford into the overall mechanism of the process in question. Apart from that, the determination of order and the appropriate rate law in a given instance also provides a very useful and convenient summarizing statement about the rate of reaction. The systematic development of rate expressions for reactions of varying order and complexity will be taken up later.

Problems

13.701   Graphite is oxidized in air in a furnace at the rate of 10^{-6} mole cm^{-2} sec^{-1}. How many pounds of graphite would be oxidized in 1 hr if a constant surface of 1 ft^2 were exposed?

13.702   For the isomerization of p-tolyl isocyanide to p-tolunitrile the following data were obtained [*J. Phys. Chem.*, **63**, 1793 (1959)]:

A (190°C)		B (220°C)	
Time, min	Nitrile, %	Time, min	Nitrile, %
9.0	17.5	2.50	27.5
14.0	27.0	2.60	29.0
19.0	35.0	3.55	37.5
25.0	43.0	4.55	46.0

From sets A and B find the respective values of k in sec^{-1}, and calculate $t_{1/2}$, $t_{1/4}$, $t_{3/4}$, and $t_{15/16}$ for set A.

13.703   The catalytic decomposition of SbH_3 at 25°C gave the following results. Calculate k by any expression so far encountered. What do you conclude about order?

t, min:	2.0	4.0	6.0	12.0	16.0	24.0
% reaction:	11.8	22.0	30.6	57.4	70.8	89.3

13.704   The half life for decomposition of nitrous oxide is found to vary with initial pressure as follows. Find the order.

P, mm:	58	140	282	292	356
$t_{1/2}$, sec:	810	469	300	260	213

13.705   In the inversion of an acid solution of sucrose at 25°C, the reaction was followed by studying the changing angle of polarization of the solution. Assuming that α is linear in concentration of sucrose, find the order, k, and $t_{1/2}$.

t, min:	0	30	90	150	330	630	∞
α, deg:	46.75	41.00	30.75	22.00	2.75	−10.00	−18.75

13.706   Acetaldehyde decomposes stoichiometrically when heated as follows:

$$CH_3CHO \rightarrow CH_4 + CO$$

The following was observed by C. N. Hinshelwood and W. K. Hutchison, *Proc. Roy. Soc.* (*London*), **A111**, 380 (1926). Find the order and k.

t, sec:	0	42	105	190	310	480	840
P, mm:	360	394	434	474	514	554	604

13.707   A second-order rate constant has the dimensions cm^3 molecules^{-1} sec^{-1}. What conversion factors are required to express k in units of liters molecules^{-1} sec^{-1}; liters mole^{-1} sec^{-1}; atm^{-1} sec^{-1}?

13.708   Obtain Eq. 13.719 and show that $t_{1/2} = \frac{3}{2}(1/ka^2)$.

* 13.709   Find the order and the approximate values of k from the data giving the decrease of pressure with time for several runs for the reaction [C. N. Hinshelwood and T. E. Green, *J. Chem. Soc.*, **128**, 730 (1926)]

$$2NO_2 + H_2 \rightarrow N_2O + H_2O(g)$$

	Initial Conditions		ΔP, mm				
Run	P_{NO_2}, mm	P_{H_2}, mm	30 sec	60 sec	90 sec	120 sec	180 sec
1	300	404	31	55	71	82	95
2	310	302	27	48	63	73	87
3	232	313	18	32	43	52	63
4	110	316	4	8	11	15	22
5	299	117	16	29	39	46	54

8.   Review Problems

13.801   (*a*)   If the appropriate diameter of helium is 2.6 Å, calculate the mean free path at 10^{-12}, 10^{-6}, and 1 mm Hg pressure, and 25°C.

(*b*)   If the residual pressure in interstellar space is $\sim 10^{-30}$ cm Hg at a temperature of $\sim 5°K$, calculate λ and see whether helium atoms are likely to collide in traveling from the sun to the nearest star (~ 4 light-years away).

13.802   What is the physical meaning of the rise of viscosity with mean free path? What would be the viscosity of a truly ideal (point mass) gas?

13.803   Calculate collision number, viscosity, average speed, and diffusion constant for the gas in Problem 13.801a at 1 mm.

* 13.804   Thermal conductivity detectors are used in gas chromatography; a wire, which is one arm of a Wheatstone bridge, is cooled by thermal conduction by surrounding gas. Consider that, in the detector of a gas chromatographic analysis apparatus, half of the helium carrier gas in the detector cell is replaced first by methane, then by propane, and finally by pentane as these materials, in an equimolar mixture under analysis, are successively eluted from the chromatography column. This causes an imbalance of the detector because of the change in thermal conductivity of the gas in the cell. Calling the sensitivity for methane unity, speculate on the magnitude of the errors which arise by assuming the detector has equal mole-sensitivity for all three substances.

13.805   Determine Λ^0 for CsCl, $CaCl_2$, Na_2SO_4, $LaCl_3$, $CaSO_4$ aqueous solutions. Suggest how molar conductance measurements indicate ionic types in solution.

13.806   If saturated silver chloride solution has a specific conductance of 1.8×10^{-6} ohm^{-1} cm^{-1} (corrected for the contribution of the water used), estimate the value of the solubility and solubility product constant for AgCl.

13.807   Predict the shape of a conductance curve constructed by plotting the specific conductance of 50 ml of a $0.1N$ solution of acetic acid against the volume of $1N$ NaOH added in a titration experiment.

13.808   Use the Maxwell distribution to compute Boltzmann's H function for a perfect gas. Compare this result with the Sackur-Tetrode equation for S (Chapter 11).

* 13.809   Calculate the rate in moles l^{-1} sec^{-1} at which molecules having energy of $\sim 30kT$ are produced in argon gas at STP. The energy range is kT kcal. Use Table 11.202(A).

13.810   Find several examples of zero-order processes, not necessarily chemical reactions.

* 13.811   If a spherical particle burned uniformly at the same rate as in Problem 13.701, how long would it take to burn a 1-cm-diameter particle? (Density is 2.25 g cm^{-3}.)

13.812   Suppose that every water molecule striking a cold surface condensed, and that the water vapor was maintained (in an otherwise empty space) at its equilibrium pressure at room temperature. Express the rate of condensation in cubic centimeters of liquid per cm^2 second.

13.813   Starting with Eq. 13.708 and expressing it as a distribution function in the differential form,

$$\frac{dC}{C_0} = -k_1 e^{-k_1 t}\, dt$$

show again that $\bar{t} = 1/k$.

13.814   Integrate Eq. 13.715 by means of partial fractions.

* 13.815   If measurements of a reaction were started only after the lapse of time t_1 and the formation of x_{t_1}, obtain the modified form of Eq. 13.707 that applies.

* 13.816   What happens to Eq. 13.716 as $b \rightarrow a$? Show that it becomes identical with Eq. 13.712.

13.817   Show that the integrated form of the rate law

$$\frac{dx}{dt} = k(a - 2x)^2(b - x)$$

is

$$kt = \frac{1}{(2b - a)^2} \left[\frac{2x(2b - a)}{a(a - 2x)} + \ln \frac{b(a - 2x)}{a(b - x)} \right]$$

General References

Benson, S. W., *The Foundations of Chemical Kinetics*, McGraw-Hill Book Co., New York, 1960.

Frost, A. A. and R. G. Pearson, *Kinetics and Mechanism*, Second Edition, John Wiley and Sons, New York, 1961.

Hirschfelder, J. O., C. F. Curtiss, and R. B. Bird, *Molecular Theory of Gases and Liquids*, John Wiley and Sons, New York, 1954.

Kennard, E. G., *The Kinetic Theory of Gases*, McGraw-Hill Book Co., New York, 1938.

Present, R. D., *Kinetic Theory of Gases*, McGraw-Hill Book Co., New York, 1958.

Robinson, R. A., and R. H. Stokes, *Electrolyte Solutions*, Academic Press, New York, 1959.

Taylor, H. S., Editor, *A Treatise on Physical Chemistry*, Second Edition, D. van Nostrand Co., Princeton, N.J., 1931.

Chapter Fourteen

Chemical Kinetics

1. Introduction

The study of the rates and mechanisms of chemical reactions is known as chemical kinetics. Although the topics considered here are drawn from the field of chemical reactions, the general principles and methods that have been developed have found applications to other rate processes far afield—all the way from the behavior of theater patrons lined up in a queue to the combination of atomic nuclei in a star. Rate studies shed light on the way in which molecules behave in the course of breaking chemical bonds and in forming new ones; in clarifying this dynamic process, most of the varied techniques (Chapter 16) used to obtain direct information about the structures of stable molecules are not applicable.

The rates of reaction, except in special instances, are not directly related to thermodynamic functions of state of reactants and products. An example of this is the stability of a mixture of gaseous hydrogen and oxygen at room temperature, despite an enormous $-\Delta F$ value for the transformation to H_2O; by contrast, aqueous H^+, i.e. (H_3O^+), and OH^- combine "instantly" to form water, despite the appreciably smaller value of $-\Delta F$ for this process.

What determines the rate, in one theory of rate processes, are the properties of the reactants and of an intermediate transition state of higher free energy than the reactants or products; what is relevant is a knowledge of the thermodynamic properties of the reactants and of the transition state, or activated complex as it is called (Fig. 14.101). Although it is usually practicable to measure the

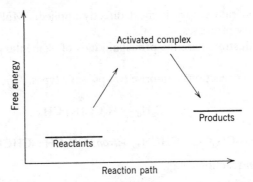

Fig. 14.101   Schematic diagram of free energy changes associated with the reaction process.

thermodynamic functions of the reactants, it is not so for the transient, activated complex. The methods of statistical mechanics are used in order to calculate the properties of the activated complex; the latter will be designated as X^*.

In this chapter we will concentrate largely on homogeneous reactions in the gas phase, with only a brief consideration of liquid-phase behavior.

2. Molecularity and Elementary Reactions

Molecularity. A simple classification of chemical reactions may be made according to the number of reactant entities, molecules or atoms, that group together to form the activated complex. This number is called the *molecularity* of the reaction; it must be an integral number.

For a *unimolecular* reaction, $A \rightarrow X^* \rightarrow Pr$, which takes place exactly as written, only one molecule of reactant enters into the activated complex. For a *bimolecular* reaction, we may have

$$2A \rightarrow X^* \rightarrow Pr \quad \text{or} \quad A + B \rightarrow X^* \rightarrow Pr$$

If three molecules enter the activated complex, the reaction is called *trimolecular*.

In order to calculate the rate of a reaction from theory we must know the mechanism, and hence the molecularity, so that we may be able to make reasonable assumptions about the structure and properties of the activated complex.

Elementary Reactions. Actually most overall reactions (for example, the oxidation of methane) are complex and involve more than a single, simple, one-step process. Inspection of the overall chemical equation for a reaction will not suffice to determine the mechanism concerned. Of fundamental importance, antecedent to the study of complex processes, are a knowledge and understanding of the general characteristics of the various possible simple, one-step "type reactions" which compose complicated overall reactions. Such simple reactions, *each of whose mechanisms is given by the simplest stoichiometric chemical equation* for the reaction, are called elementary reactions. It is to the calculation of their rates that reaction rate theory is most directly applied. Molecularity is defined only for elementary processes.

It is useful to illustrate here the principal kinds of elementary reactions that can occur.

(*a*) Unimolecular reactions comprise two possible types. These are *isomerization* reactions, e.g.,

$$\text{cyclo-}C_3H_6 \rightarrow H_3CCH\!\!=\!\!CH_2$$

or

$$\text{cis-}CH_3CH\!\!=\!\!CHCH_3 \rightarrow \text{trans-}CH_3CH\!\!=\!\!CHCH_3$$

and *decomposition* reactions, e.g.,

$$N_2O_5 \rightarrow NO_2 + NO_3$$

and

$$C_2H_6 \rightarrow 2CH_3$$

(*b*) Bimolecular reactions may be classified somewhat more arbitrarily. There are *decomposition* reactions, e.g.,

$$2HI \rightarrow H_2 + I_2$$

as well as *exchange* or *displacement* reactions, e.g.,

$$D + H_2 \rightarrow HD + H$$

and

$$Na + C_2H_5Cl \rightarrow NaCl + C_2H_5$$

Another type, *association* reactions, are the reverse of a unimolecular decomposition, e.g.,

$$2NO_2 \rightarrow N_2O_4$$

and

$$2CH_3 \rightarrow C_2H_6$$

(*c*) There are few if any examples of genuine trimolecular gas-phase reactions. The most plausible is probably the association of atoms to give molecules

$$3H \rightarrow H_2 + H$$

or

$$3I \rightarrow I_2 + I$$

and, possibly,

$$2I + He \rightarrow I_2 + He$$

A large number of ostensibly trimolecular reactions, such as

$$2I + I_2 \rightarrow 2I_2$$

may actually proceed as follows:

$$I + I_2 \rightarrow I_3$$

$$I_3 + I \rightarrow 2I_2$$

in which case two consecutive bimolecular reactions take place, one an association and the other a displacement; the reaction is only trimolecular in a formal sense in terms of initial reactants.

The reason for the paucity of gas-phase trimolecular examples, and the complete absence of reactions of higher molecularity, is not that such reactions do not or cannot occur, but simply that they cannot be detected in competition with other more efficient (usually bimolecular) processes which give rise to the same or other products.

Order and molecularity are identical for homogeneous elementary reactions, but this identity does not hold in general. Thus, if $A \rightarrow Pr$ and the rate law is $d\,Pr/dt = k C_A^0 = k$, so that the reaction proceeds with constant rate, it is zero order; this evidently cannot correspond to zero molecularity. Again, while molecularity is constrained to be integral, the order need not be so if the exponents of the concentration terms are not integers, as happens in complex reactions.

Principle of Detailed Balancing. When a forward reaction and its reverse are included in a reaction scheme, say,

$$C_2H_6 \rightleftharpoons 2CH_3$$

an equilibrium state may result. In such cases, the principle of detailed balancing requires that the reverse reaction written be exactly the microscopic reverse of the forward one and involve the same activated complex. In general, when equilibrium is established, it is a requirement of the principle that all reactions be exactly balanced, or microscopically balanced, by the rate of the equivalent reverse process. This was the case in the example of Chapter 13 on the production and removal, by collisions, of energized molecules in a gas. If this principle is not observed, false equilibrium equations will be obtained. The principle does not necessarily apply to systems away from equilibrium.

As an example, the equilibrium $Br_2 \rightleftharpoons 2Br$ can be maintained by two alleged mechanisms. A bimolecular dissociation caused by collision may be balanced by a trimolecular recombination,

$$Br_2 + Br \rightarrow 3Br$$
$$3Br \rightarrow Br_2 + Br$$

Or a unimolecular dissociation can be followed by a bimolecular recombination:

$$Br_2 \rightarrow 2Br$$
$$2Br \rightarrow Br_2$$

Either one will give a correct equilibrium constant, with bromine atom concentration proportional to $C_{Br_2}^{1/2}$, where C_{Br_2} is the equilibrium concentration of molecules. However, if the forward part of one scheme is falsely balanced by the backward half of the other, the correct equilibrium constant expression will not be produced.

In general, any mechanism correctly formulated will produce the correct equilibrium expressions; thus thermodynamics gives no information about mechanism.

Problems

14.201   What are the molecularity and type of the following elementary reactions?
(a) trans-CH_3CH=$CHCH_3$ → cis-CH_3CH=$CHCH_3$

(b) $2C_2H_4$ → C_4H_8 (c) N_2O_4 → $2NO_2$
(d) $H + C_2H_4$ → C_2H_5 (e) $C_2H_4 + C_3H_6$ → C_5H_{10}
(f) $3H$ → $H_2 + H$ (g) $H^+ + CH_4$ → CH_5^+

14.202   Does the statement that the following elementary reactions are among those
that occur in a hydrocarbon system violate the principle of detailed balancing?

$$2CH_3 → C_2H_6$$
$$C_2H_6 → C_2H_5 + H$$
$$C_2H_5 → CH_3 + CH_2$$
$$CH_2 + H → CH_3$$

14.203   How would the situation be modified if the statement in Problem 14.202 were
altered so that the reactions listed were specified to be the only ones that occur?

3. Theoretical Expressions for the Specific Rate Constants of Bimolecular Reactions

Bimolecular reactions prove to be simpler than unimolecular reactions and are
important for the understanding of the latter. They are therefore treated first.

Collision Theory.   *Rate Expression.*   We consider the treatment of the collision
theory, which had been given definitive formulation by M. Trautz and W. C. M.
Lewis before 1920. For a bimolecular reaction to take place, the reacting atoms or
molecules must collide. If the molecules rebound with conservation of total
translational energy, the collision is termed *elastic*; if translational energy in
converted into rotational or vibrational energy, the encounter is described as
inelastic.

For the case of hard spheres, only double collisions are possible because the
process of collision is instantaneous, and the collision is over before a third
molecule can hit. Thus, if we imagine three billiard balls in a triple collision, then
what is apparently a single click is a click-click, and thus two double collisions.
Although real molecules are not hard spheres and a double collision is actually of
finite duration, the probability of a triple collision in a gas is still, in general,
relatively reduced. We shall return to this subject later in the consideration of
trimolecular reactions.

For the reaction $A + B →$ Pr, the rate law is

$$\frac{dC_{Pr}}{dt} = k_{bi}C_A C_B$$

and, if concentrations are expressed in units of molecules per cubic centimeter,

$$\text{rate} = \frac{dN'_{Pr}}{dt} = k_{bi}N'_A N'_B$$

The number of collisions per cubic centimeter per second made between molecules of type A and those of type B was given earlier as

$$\mathscr{Z}_{AB} = 2[N'_A N'_B][\sigma^2_{AB}]\left[\left(\frac{2\pi kT}{\mu}\right)^{1/2}\right] \simeq 10^{-10} N'_A N'_B \text{ molecules cc}^{-1}\text{ sec}^{-1} \quad (6.502)$$

If collision always resulted in reaction, then the rate dN'_{Pr}/dt would equal $\mathscr{Z}$. Every reaction would then proceed at a large rate which, at a particular temperature, would vary only because of changes in σ and μ from case to case.   Then

$$\frac{dN'_{Pr}}{dt} = \mathscr{Z} = \mathscr{z}N'_A N'_B \quad (14.301)$$

where $k_{bi} = \mathscr{z}$ and is numerically equal to the collision number $\mathscr{Z}_{AB}$ at unit concentration of reactants.

For most reactions, not all collisions are fruitful. Only those collisions having a certain relative translational energy along the line of centers of the collision partners in excess of some minimum critical value, ϵ_c, characteristic of the particular reaction, can lead to reaction. The collision theory proposes that $\mathscr{z}$ must be multiplied by the fraction $e^{-\epsilon_c/kT}$, a Boltzmann factor, to give the specific rate of these energetic collisions. We shall attempt to show below that this expression is reasonable. From this standpoint, the rate constant has the theoretical form

$$k_{bi} = \mathscr{z}e^{-\epsilon_c/kT} = 2\sigma^2\left(\frac{2\pi kT}{\mu}\right)^{1/2} e^{-\epsilon_c/kT}$$

$$= 2\sigma^2\left(\frac{2\pi kT}{\mu}\right)^{1/2} e^{-E_c/RT} \quad (14.302)$$

for unlike collision partners. For the reaction $2A = Pr$, as was seen in Chapter 13, the collision number and k_{bi} are reduced by the symmetry factor 2.

ILLUSTRATION.   A triumph of the collision theory was the agreement it gave with the experimental results of M. Bodenstein for the hydrogen iodide reaction. Bodenstein [Z. physik. Chem., **29**, 295 (1899)] obtained for the reaction $2HI \overset{k_1}{\underset{k_2}{\rightleftharpoons}}$ $H_2 + I_2$ the following specific rate constants.

T, °K:	781	716	700	683	666	647
$k_1 \times 10^3(22.4$ 1 mole^{-1} min^{-1}):	105.9	6.70	3.10	1.37	0.588	0.230
$k_2(22.4$ 1 mole^{-1} min^{-1}):		3.58	0.375	0.172	0.0659	0.0379	0.0140

We shall verify the approximate agreement between simple collision theory and the data of Bodenstein for a specific case.

Consider the data for k_1 at 700° and 647°K in order to evaluate E_c from Eq. 14.302.

$$\frac{k_{700}}{k_{647}} = \left(\frac{700}{647}\right)^{\frac{1}{2}} \left(\frac{\exp\left(-E_c/700R\right)}{\exp\left(-E_c/647R\right)}\right)$$

and neglecting the small effect due to the first factor on the right, then

$$\frac{3.10}{0.230} = \exp\left(\frac{E_c}{R} \times \frac{53}{700 \times 647}\right)$$

and

$$E_c = 44.0 \text{ kcal mole}^{-1}$$

Then, $k_{700} = \mathcal{Z} \exp\left(-44,000/1.987 \times 700\right)$ is the theoretical value, where $\mathcal{Z} = \sigma^2(2\pi kT/\mu)^{\frac{1}{2}}$, and a round estimate for the kinetic collision cross section of σ_{HI} is 5.0×10^{-8} cm. So, multiplying k and μ by N,

$$\mathcal{Z} = 25.0 \times 10^{-16}\left(\frac{2 \times 3.142 \times 8.317 \times 10^7 \times 700}{128/2}\right)^{\frac{1}{2}} \text{cc molecule}^{-1} \text{ sec}^{-1}$$

$$= 25.0 \times 10^{-16} \times 7.56 \times 10^4 \text{ cc molecule}^{-1} \text{ sec}^{-1}$$

$$= 1.89 \times 10^{-10} \times 6.023 \times 10^{23} = 11.4 \times 10^{13} \text{ cc mole}^{-1} \text{ sec}^{-1}$$

and

$$k_{700} = 11.4 \times 10^{13} e^{-31.75}$$

$$= 1.85 \text{ cc mole}^{-1} \text{ sec}^{-1}$$

as the result from theory.

For comparison we have the measured value:

$$k_{700} = 3.10 \times 10^{-3} \text{ in units of } 22.4 \text{ l. mole}^{-1} \text{ min}^{-1}$$

$$= 3.10 \times 10^{-3} \times 22,400/60 = 1.16 \text{ cc mole}^{-1} \text{ sec}^{-1}$$

The agreement may be considered satisfactory.

The student may use the data of Bodenstein and plot $\ln k$ vs. $1/T$ to obtain E_{c1} and E_{c2}. From these he may deduce the heat of reaction.

Energy Distribution Functions.   Before we examine the meaning of the exponential part of Eq. 14.302 we consider some specific forms which energy distribution functions may take.

In Chapter 6, it was shown that for motion in the x direction a velocity distribution function could be converted to a speed distribution function,

$$\frac{dN_c}{N} = 2\left(\frac{m}{2\pi kT}\right)^{\frac{1}{2}} e^{-mc^2/2kT} dc \tag{6.123}$$

where the energy in the exponent involves a single square term, c^2. We may readily convert this distribution back to an energy distribution function with use of the relations,

$$\epsilon_1 = \tfrac{1}{2}mc^2, \quad d\epsilon_1 = mc \, dc$$

and

$$dc = \frac{d\epsilon_1}{mc} = \frac{d\epsilon_1}{(2m\epsilon_1)^{\frac{1}{2}}}$$

where the subscript 1 refers to one square term. Then

$$\frac{dN_{\epsilon_1}}{N} = F(\epsilon_1) \, d\epsilon_1 = 2\left(\frac{m}{2\pi kT}\right)^{\frac{1}{2}} \frac{1}{(2m\epsilon)^{\frac{1}{2}}} e^{-\epsilon_1/kT} \, d\epsilon_1$$

$$= \left(\frac{1}{\pi kT}\right)^{\frac{1}{2}} \epsilon_1^{-\frac{1}{2}} e^{-\epsilon_1/kT} \, d\epsilon_1 \tag{14.303}$$

which is already normalized, since the original speed distribution function was normalized.

The average translational energy in one square term follows the equipartition law and is

$$\bar{\epsilon}_1 = \int_0^\infty \epsilon F(\epsilon_1) \, d\epsilon_1$$

$$= \int_0^\infty \left(\frac{\epsilon}{\pi kT}\right)^{\frac{1}{2}} e^{-\epsilon_1/kT} \, d\epsilon_1 = \tfrac{1}{2}kT$$

The same result was derived earlier in Chapter 6 by taking the velocity distribution as the starting point.

Now for translational motion in two dimensions x and y, we can derive the speed distribution function,

$$\frac{dN_c}{N} = \frac{mc}{kT} e^{-mc^2/2kT} \, dc \tag{14.304}$$

If we change the variable again from c to ϵ_2, we obtain for energy in two square terms ($c^2 = u^2 + v^2$),

$$\frac{dN_{\epsilon_2}}{N} = F(\epsilon_2) \, d\epsilon_2 = e^{-\epsilon_2/kT} \frac{d\epsilon_2}{kT} \tag{14.305}$$

The average translational energy in two square terms is

$$\bar{\epsilon}_2 = \int_0^\infty \epsilon F(\epsilon_2) \, d\epsilon_2 = kT$$

As we saw earlier in Chapter 6, this is also the classical limit of the average energy for one vibrational degree of freedom of the harmonic oscillator, which also has two square terms in the classical Hamiltonian,

$$\mathcal{H}(p,x) = \frac{p^2}{2m} + \frac{kx^2}{2} \tag{2.115}$$

The fraction of molecules which have energy equal to or greater than ϵ_c in two square terms is found simply from Eq. 14.305 as the incomplete integral,

$$\int_{\epsilon_c}^{\infty} e^{-\epsilon_2/kT} \frac{d\epsilon_2}{kT} = e^{-\epsilon_c/kT} \tag{14.306}$$

The generalization of the results in Eqs. 14.303 and 14.305 to the form of the distribution function of energy in n square terms is

$$F(\epsilon_n)\, d\epsilon_n = \frac{1}{\left(\dfrac{n}{2} - 1\right)!} \left(\frac{\epsilon_n}{kT}\right)^{(n/2)-1} e^{-\epsilon_n/kT} \frac{d\epsilon_n}{kT} \tag{14.307}$$

It follows that substitution of $n = 1$ and $n = 2$ in Eq. 14.307 gives back Eqs. 14.303 and 14.305, respectively; note that $(-\tfrac{1}{2})!$ has the value $\pi^{1/2}$.

The equilibrium fraction $B(\epsilon)$ of molecules which have energy in excess of ϵ_c in n square terms is

$$B(\epsilon) = \int_{\epsilon_c}^{\infty} F(\epsilon_n)\, d\epsilon_n = \sum_{(n/2)=1}^{n/2} \frac{1}{\left(\dfrac{n}{2} - 1\right)!} \left(\frac{\epsilon_c}{kT}\right)^{(n/2)-1} e^{-\epsilon_c/kT} \tag{14.308}$$

If the condition

$$\epsilon_c \gg \left(\frac{n}{2} - 1\right) kT$$

holds, then only the last term in the summation is important, and

$$B(\epsilon) = \frac{1}{\left(\dfrac{n}{2} - 1\right)!} \left(\frac{\epsilon_c}{kT}\right)^{(n/2)-1} e^{-\epsilon_c/kT}$$

For $n = 2$, Eq. 14.308 reduces to Eq. 14.306.

Energy Requirement for Bimolecular Reactions.   In connection with the collision theory expression Eq. 14.302, a relative translational energy quantity ϵ_c entered. It may be shown now that it is the relative translational energy along the line of centers which appears in this problem, and not the total relative translational energy. Figure 14.301 describes a collision between atoms, or molecules, A and B, treated as spheres. Consider two-dimensional motion in the plane of the paper. It is evident that, although the total relative velocity of A and B perpendicular to the line of centers of the collision pair is large, the component of the relative velocity parallel to the line of centers is small; the molecules suffer a collision of low intensity which is independent of the magnitude of the perpendicular component and equivalent to a head-on collision of total velocity equal only to the parallel component (Fig. 14.302). This is the life-saving feature of the landing on a slope by a ski-jumper.

For three-dimensional motion, there are two perpendicular components of the relative velocity (at right angles to each other so that one points out of the paper, in terms of Fig. 14.301) and one parallel component.

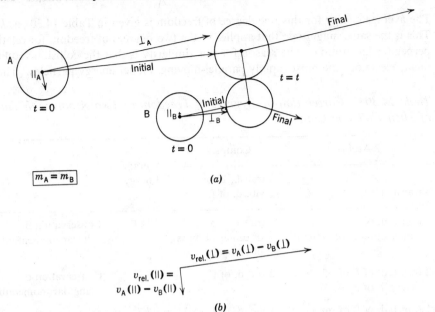

$$m_A = m_B$$

(a)

$$v_{\text{rel.}}(\perp) = v_A(\perp) - v_B(\perp)$$

$$v_{\text{rel.}}(\parallel) = v_A(\parallel) - v_B(\parallel)$$

(b)

Fig. 14.301 (a) Composition and (b) sum of initial velocities perpendicular ($\perp$) and parallel ($\parallel$) to the line of centers of the collision pair.

Consider now the overall description of the process which occurs when two atoms form a diatomic collision complex. Initially, the two atoms possess a total of six (translational) degrees of freedom (Table 14.301). The complex has only three translational degrees of freedom, but there are two rotational and one vibrational degree of freedom. Thus three translational degrees of freedom of the atoms become the two rotations and the vibration of the collision complex. The rotations may be considered to arise from the two mutually perpendicular components of the relative velocity perpendicular to the line of centers (with conservation of angular momentum), while the vibrational degree of freedom may be identified with the component of the relative velocity parallel to the line of centers. The three degrees of translational freedom of the complex as a whole ensure conservation of linear momentum.

We wish now to examine more carefully the energy distribution that applies for the degree of freedom of relative translational energy parallel to the line of centers.

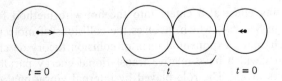

Fig. 14.302 Effective collision process of Fig. 14.301.

The average energy for this one degree of freedom is given in Table 14.301 as kT. This is the same magnitude that applies to the two degrees of freedom for relative perpendicular motion. The reason for this similarity is that the collision requirement selects out the most rapidly parallel-moving, higher-energy particles. These

Table 14.301   Correlation of Degrees of Freedom of Two Atoms with Those of Their Collision Complex

2 Atoms	Complex 3 transl., 2 rot., 1 vib. d. of f.	Average Energy	Remarks
6 transl. d. of f.			
3 transl. d. of f. of center of mass of system	3 transl. d. of f. of center of mass of complex	$\frac{3}{2}kT$	Conservation of linear momentum
2 transl. d. of f. of rel. vel. $\perp$ l. of c.	2 rot. d. of f.	kT	Conservation of angular momentum
1 transl. d. of f. of rel. vel. $\parallel$ l. of c.	1 vib. d. of f.	kT	

therefore make a contribution to the total number of collisional encounters which exceeds their simple proportion in the gas. A similar situation was encountered previously in Chapter 6 in connection with the derivation of Eq. 6.306. There, the distribution function for molecules moving in the x direction which collided with the wall of the container was indicated as

$$\frac{dN}{N} = \text{const. } uf(u)\, du$$

The factor u in the distribution function weights the higher velocities of the molecules relative to the wall and shifts the distribution function for *colliding* molecules to greater velocities (energies) than apply for the function $f(u)$ for *all* the molecules of the gas. The above distribution function is identical in form, apart from constants which would be canceled on normalization, to Eq. 14.304 for molecular speed in two degrees of freedom. This is what makes appropriate the Boltzmann factor $e^{-\epsilon_c/kT}$ in Eq. 14.302, which is the incomplete integral above ϵ_c given in Eq. 14.306.

This interesting effect also enters into the hot-wire method for heat capacity measurement, in Sec. 6.4, which involves the collisions of molecules with a wire.

Thus the Boltzmann exponential term of collision theory describes the fraction of collision pairs which have relative translational energy parallel to the line of centers in excess of ϵ_c. The role played by internal vibrational excitation of the colliding species is still obscure.

Modified Collision Theory.   Equation 14.302 is the form that the simple collision theory takes.   Assuming that the magnitude of $\mathscr{z}$ is not greatly changed for solutions, this equation may also be applied to solution reactions.   That it cannot be adequate in general for the *average* rate constant, k, may be simply demonstrated as follows. For the reversible bimolecular reaction

$$A + B \underset{k_r}{\overset{k_f}{\rightleftharpoons}} C + D$$

we have the equilibrium constant K in terms of the average specific rate constants,

$$K = \frac{k_f}{k_r} = \frac{\mathscr{z}_f e^{-E_f/RT}}{\mathscr{z}_r e^{-E_r/RT}} \simeq e^{-\Delta H/RT}$$

i.e., $\ln K \simeq -\Delta H/RT$, where to the first approximation $\mathscr{z}_f$ and $\mathscr{z}_r$ cancel, and $(E_r - E_f) = \Delta H$, the heat of reaction.   But the above relation for $\ln K$ is of the right form in general only if the entropy change ΔS is zero.   This is inherent in the assumptions of the simple collision theory.   We will be able to see its meaning in more detail shortly.   In many instances, such as the Menschutkin reaction for the formation of quaternary ammonium salts.

$$RX + R_3'N \rightarrow RR_3'NX$$

the simple theory gave an overestimate of the rate.   By 1930 the expression had been modified by C. N. Hinshelwood and E. A. Moelwyn-Hughes by insertion of a "probability factor" $\mathscr{P}$, usually less than unity.   This factor allows for collisions with the right energy but the wrong orientation of the reactants, or for "steric hindrance" or other factors which might reduce the rate.   Therefore

$$k = \mathscr{P}\mathscr{z}e^{-E_c/RT} \tag{14.309}$$

In principle, this $\mathscr{P}$ factor should be deducible semiquantitatively, or at least qualitatively, from the nature of the reaction.

Comparison with the Arrhenius Equation; the Arrhenius Activation Energy.   A mathematical expression for the temperature dependence of the specific reaction constant was given by Arrhenius in 1889:

$$k = Ae^{-\epsilon_a/kT} \tag{14.310}$$

where A, the pre-exponential factor, frequently termed the *frequency factor*, is independent of temperature;   and ϵ_a is called the Arrhenius activation energy. Comparison of Eq. 14.309 with the Arrhenius equation suggests an interpretation of the frequency factor, namely $A = \mathscr{P}\mathscr{z}$, and of ϵ_a.   To maintain A as a temperature-independent constant, we define ϵ_a in a way analogous to the thermodynamic equation that relates the heat of reaction to an equilibrium constant (Chapter 9),

$$\epsilon_a = \frac{-d \ln k}{d(1/kT)} \tag{14.311}$$

From this definition and Eq. 14.302

$$\epsilon_a = \epsilon_c + \frac{kT}{2} \tag{14.312}$$

where the quantity ϵ_a is an observed experimental quantity defined by Eq. 14.311. Since $\frac{1}{2}kT$ is not independent of temperature, the $\ln k$ vs. $1/T$ plot (Fig. 14.303) will depart slightly from linearity. The $\frac{1}{2}kT$ term, which enters from the variation of collision number with temperature, is in the nature of an experimental artifact which could be eliminated by studying the temperature coefficient of the rate constant under conditions such that y was maintained invariant. Alternatively, a plot of $\ln (k/T^{1/2})$ vs. $1/T$ may be used.

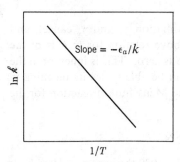

Fig. 14.303   An Arrhenius plot of the rate constant vs. $1/T$.

The form of the plot of the logarithm of the rate constant vs. the reciprocal temperature is familiar from thermodynamics, as in the Clausius-Clapeyron and van't Hoff equations (Chapters 8 and 10). The magnitude of the Arrhenius energy is independent of the units of k.

Absolute Rate Theory.   *Potential Energy Surfaces.*   When a group of atoms comprising several molecules form a complex and rearrange into new molecules, the potential energy of the system is a complex function of the various interatomic distances. For most reactions a multidimensional drawing to show the corresponding potential energy surface would be required.

For the reaction $H + H\text{—}H \rightarrow H\text{—}H + H$, which can be followed with isotopes, the situation is simpler. For the particular case where all the reactant atoms are in a line (colinear), the potential energy surface can be represented in two dimensions by means of lines of equal potential (common on relief maps), shown in Figs. 14.304 and 14.305. If the atoms are numbered 1, 2, 3, in order, the pertinent distances are r_{12} and r_{23}. When the first distance is large and the second is near the H—H distance in H_2, atom 1 is free and atoms 2 and 3 are bound. When both distances are a little in excess of the H—H distance, and equal, the configuration is a linear complex located at the highest point (marked x) in the "mountain pass" between products and reactants. This saddle point in the pass is the region of existence of the activated complex whose ground state energy is thereby determined. Then, finally, when r_{23} is large and r_{12} small the stabilized products have formed.

H. Eyring and M. Polanyi described a semiempirical method for calculating such energy surfaces. If the mathematical techniques of quantum mechanics were improved, we could, in principle, construct the potential energy surfaces for all possible reactions. Thus we could calculate the potential energy and molecular properties of the activated complex. Since this is not possible in practice in scarcely any cases, potential energy surfaces are most useful for their contribution

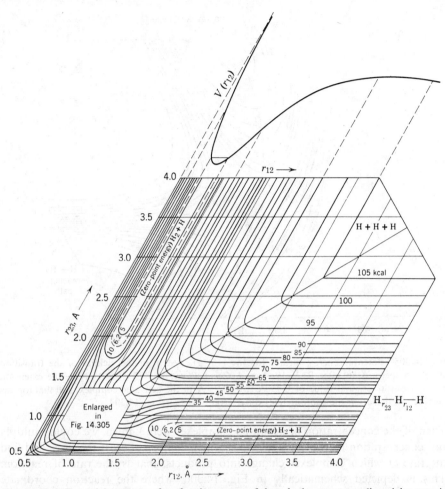

Fig. 14.304   Potential-energy surface for the system of three hydrogen atoms [based by permission on Eyring, Gershinowitz, and Sun, *J. Chem. Phys.*, **3**, 786 (1935)]; the elevation at the top of the figure shows $V(r_{12})$ as a function of r_{12}, for $r_{23} = \infty$, and is a Morse-type potential for H_2 (Fig. 4.105).

to a qualitative understanding of the reaction process. The activation energy to be entered into rate calculations is taken as an experimental finding. Some success is had in computing the properties of the activated complex (moments of inertia, vibration frequencies, etc.) from semiempirical generalizations about molecular binding (Chapter 16), together with reasonable kinds of assumptions about which bonds in the activated complex are stretched or contracted relative to the reactants (i.e., tending to become half-bonds or half-formed bonds, etc.), and by how much.

   The Eyring-Polanyi Equation.   Consider the reaction process in terms of the general bimolecular scheme,

$$A + B \rightarrow X^* \rightarrow Pr$$

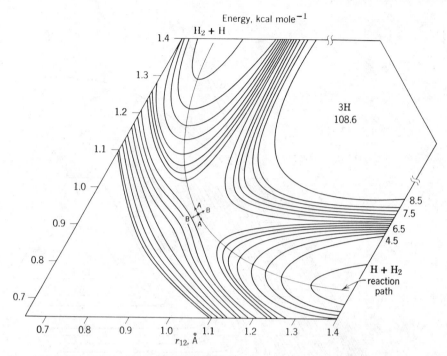

Fig. 14.305 Potential energy surface for the $H + H_2$ system in the vicinity of the transition state x [by permission after R. E. Weston, *J. Chem. Phys.*, **31**, 892 (1959)]. Note the extension of r_{H_2} from its original value of 0.75 Å to ∼0.95 Å in the activated complex, and that for this detailed recalculation the contour lines differ from those of Fig. 14.304.

Then, if the concentration of activated complexes were known, we could multiply this concentration by the average rate at which complexes cross the pass, and find the rate at which complexes change into products, that is, the rate of reaction. This is depicted schematically in Fig. 14.306, where the reaction coordinate corresponds to the reaction path line of Fig. 14.305. Motion across the top of the pass (A–A; compare Fig. 14.305) is represented as a translation along the reaction coordinate, which is therefore to be considered as flattened out at the maximum; motion in the perpendicular direction (B'–B of Fig. 14.305) corresponds to an ordinary vibration as in a normal molecule. We now proceed with the two parts of the calculation: (1) calculation of the concentration of complexes, and (2) calculation of the rate at which they become products.

In all of this, the Born-Oppenheimer approximation (Chapter 4) is assumed to hold, so that only the lowest-energy electronic surface enters into consideration.

PART ONE. H. Eyring and M. Polanyi took as their model the condition that the complex X*, although of transient existence with a lifetime of ∼10^{-13} sec, i.e., the time of molecular vibrations, nonetheless is otherwise to be considered as a sort of normal species which may be handled as though in equilibrium with the reactants. This does *not* mean, however, that the transition state is merely the same thing as an "unstable" species, such as a radical. The mathematical consequence of the postulate is that we may write

$$K^* = \frac{N'_{X^*}}{N'_A N'_B} \qquad (14.313)$$

where the N' terms are concentrations in molecules per cubic centimeter, and K^* is an equilibrium constant. Throughout this discussion we shall take the standard state of concentration as 1 molecule cm^{-3}. Then, as in Eq. 11.305,

$$K^* = \frac{\phi_{X^*}}{\phi_A \phi_B} e^{-\Delta E_0/RT} \qquad (14.314)$$

where ϕ, Eq. 11.114, is the partition function; ΔE_0 is the molar difference in zero-point energy of reactants and complex; ϕ_{X^*} is written for the zero of energy of its own potential well at the top of the pass.

On equating Eqs. 14.314 and 14.313 and rearranging, we obtain

$$N'_{X^*} = \frac{\phi_{X^*}}{\phi_A \phi_B} e^{-\Delta E_0/RT} N'_A N'_B$$

The additional assumption is made for the activated complex that its degree of freedom of motion along a reaction coordinate, x', which in a normal molecule would be a vibration, may be replaced by an additional one-dimensional translation over the flat top of the pass. On factoring this extra translational partition function out of ϕ_{X^*}, we have

$$N'_{X^*} = \frac{\frac{1}{2}(2\pi\mu^* kT)^{1/2}\Delta x'}{h} \frac{\phi'_{X^*}}{\phi_A \phi_B} e^{-\Delta E_0/RT} N'_A N'_B \qquad (14.315)$$

where $\Delta x'$ symbolizes an element of length (whose magnitude will not concern us) of the flat top of the pass; μ^* is the effective mass of the reacting system in its

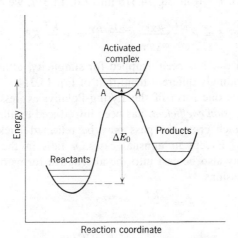

Fig. 14.306 Profile of reaction path.

motion along the pass; ϕ'_{X*} is in all other respects a normal molecule partition function except that one vibrational partition function is now absent; the factor of $\frac{1}{2}$ arises because only complexes traveling in the forward (products) direction enter into consideration. The concentration of complexes in the reaction path is $\rho(N'_{X*}) = N'_{X*}/\Delta x'$.

PART TWO. The rate of reaction also depends on the average velocity $\bar{v}*$ with which complexes travel over the barrier to give products. Therefore the rate is given by

$$\text{rate} = \bar{v}*\rho(N'_{X*})$$

$$= \frac{\bar{v}*(2\pi\mu*kT)^{1/2}}{2h} \frac{\phi'_{X*}}{\phi_A\phi_B} e^{-\Delta E_0/RT} N'_A N'_B \tag{14.316}$$

The specific rate constant is

$$k = \frac{\text{rate}}{N'_A N'_B} = \bar{v}* \frac{(2\pi\mu*kT)^{1/2}}{2h} \frac{\phi'_{X*}}{\phi_A\phi_B} e^{-\Delta E_0/RT} \tag{14.317}$$

We had previously for velocity in one dimension

$$f(v)\,dv = \left(\frac{m}{2\pi kT}\right)^{1/2} e^{-mv^2/2kT}\,dv \tag{6.112}$$

Then in the present case, since we consider only complexes with forward velocity,

$$\bar{v}* = \frac{\int_0^\infty v* e^{-\mu* v*^2/2kT}\,dv*}{\int_0^\infty e^{-\mu* v*^2/2kT}\,dv*} = \left(\frac{2kT}{\pi\mu*}\right)^{1/2} \tag{14.318}$$

and the normalizing factor in the denominator is also taken only over molecules having $+v*$.

If we substitute for $\bar{v}*$ from Eq. 14.318 into Eq. 14.317, we obtain

$$k = \kappa \frac{kT}{h} \frac{\phi_{X*}}{\phi_A\phi_B} e^{-\Delta E_0/RT} = \kappa \frac{kT}{h} K* \tag{14.319}$$

where the prime on ϕ'_{X*} has been dropped for simplicity, although remembered, and $K*$ is correspondingly different from that of Eq. 14.314.

Equation 14.319 is one form of the Eyring-Polanyi expression; the factor κ, the so-called *transmission coefficient*, has been introduced to allow for the fact that some complexes which cross the pass may be reflected back before becoming stabilized products. Except in unusual cases, κ falls in the range 0.5 to 1.0. Equation 14.319 may also be cast into the alternative forms of the absolute rate theory (ART) expressions,

$$k = \kappa \frac{kT}{h} e^{-\Delta F*/RT} \tag{14.320}$$

$$= \kappa \frac{kT}{h} e^{\Delta S*/R} e^{-\Delta H*/RT} \tag{14.321}$$

from the relation between ΔF^* and K^* (Eq. 10.204) and between ΔF^* and ΔH^* and ΔS^* (Eq. 9.407).

Fundamental criticism has been made of the postulate of equilibrium of the activated complex, treated as a pseudonormal molecule. These objections, which were well understood* by the authors of ART, refer both to the equilibrium aspect and to the activated complex concept. More rigorous theories reduce, for certain limiting approximations, frequently of good validity, to a form similar to ART. We shall continue here to exploit ART as a remarkably accurate and simple method of calculating the rates of many chemical reactions, and of providing useful insights. Reactions involving hydrogen atom or proton movement as part of the reaction mechanism tend to be inadequately dealt with on this basis, and a more correct quantum mechanical treatment may be necessary; this is referred to again later on.

Explicit Forms of k for Various Bimolecular Reactions. We consider now several cases involving varying complexity of reactants. The development follows closely the contributions of H. Eyring and his coworkers.

(*a*) A and B are atoms. The simplest case is the bimolecular reaction between atoms to form a diatomic molecule. Such a process is extraordinarily inefficient because the energy of combination of the atoms must be dissipated or the molecule almost inevitably decomposes again. The transmission coefficient, κ, here is close to zero. For the reaction $2H \rightarrow H_2$, κ is $\sim 10^{-13}$, corresponding to the probability of stabilization of the H_2 molecule by spontaneous emission of radiation. Since H_2 is homonuclear, it has no dipole moment, and the emission probability is low. For the reaction $H + Cl \rightarrow HCl$, κ is much larger, $\sim 10^{-9}$, since heteronuclear HCl does have a dipole moment and higher transition probability (Chapter 4). The rate expressions for these inefficient reactions is quite interesting. We have

$$\phi_A = \frac{(2\pi m_A kT)^{3/2}}{h^3}; \qquad \phi_B = \frac{(2\pi m_B kT)^{3/2}}{h^3} \tag{14.322}$$

$$\phi_{X^*} = \frac{[2\pi(m_A + m_B)kT]^{3/2}}{h^3} \frac{8\pi^2 I^* kT}{h^2} \tag{14.323}$$

where the symmetry number σ_{X^*} is omitted for simplicity, the moment of inertia is

$$I^* = \mu^* \sigma^{*2} = \frac{m_A m_B \sigma^{*2}}{m_A + m_B} \tag{4.102}$$

and where the single vibration of the complex has gone into the translation along the reaction coordinate.

Calculation of the translational partition function of the complex depends only on its total mass, which is easily known; but its rotational partition function (and vibrational if it were to enter) depends on the structural configuration of the molecule, and thus indirectly on the valence forces and chemical binding of the atoms.

---

* H. Eyring, J. Walter, and G. Kimball, *Quantum Chemistry*, John Wiley and Sons, New York, 1944, Chap. 16.

Substitution of these equations into Eq. 14.319 gives

$$k = \kappa \frac{\dfrac{kT}{h} \dfrac{[2\pi(m_A + m_B)kT]^{3/2}}{h^3} \dfrac{8\pi^2 I^* kT}{h^2}}{\dfrac{(2\pi m_A kT)^{3/2}}{h^3} \dfrac{(2\pi m_B kT)^{3/2}}{h^3}} e^{-\Delta E_0/RT} \qquad (14.324)$$

$$= \kappa 2\sigma^{*2} \left(\frac{2\pi kT}{\mu^*}\right)^{1/2} e^{-\Delta E_0/RT}$$

which is formally the same as the simple collision theory result,

$$k = \mathcal{Z} e^{-E_c/RT} = 2\sigma^2 \left(\frac{2\pi kT}{\mu}\right)^{1/2} e^{-E_c/RT} \qquad (14.302)$$

We may rewrite Eq. 14.324 in symbolic form as

$$k = \kappa \frac{kT}{h} \frac{\phi_t^{*3} \phi_r^{*2}}{\phi_{t_A}^3 \phi_{t_B}^3} e^{-\Delta E_0/RT} \qquad (14.325)$$

where the ϕ's stand for one-dimensional partition functions. If we cancel similar-order-of-magnitude quantities (i.e., cancel powers of like types of partition functions), and drop specific species labels, it is seen that

$$k = \kappa \frac{kT}{h} \frac{\phi_r^2}{\phi_t^3} e^{-\Delta E_0/RT} \qquad (14.326)$$

Then, neglecting κ, we see by comparison with Eq. 14.302 that the magnitude of $\mathcal{Z}$ is

$$\mathcal{Z} \simeq \frac{kT}{h} \frac{\phi_r^2}{\phi_t^3} \qquad (14.327)$$

(b) A is an atom; B is a diatomic molecule: With partition functions written in symbolic form, the rate constant for a linear activated complex is

$$k = \kappa \frac{kT}{h} \frac{\phi_t^{*3} \phi_r^{*2} \phi_v^{*(9-5-1)}}{\phi_{t_A}^3 \phi_{t_B}^3 \phi_{r_B}^2 \phi_{v_B}} e^{-\Delta E_0/RT} \qquad (14.328)$$

The total number of atoms in the complex is three, and corresponds to nine degrees of freedom; it has three ordinary translational and two rotational degrees of freedom; the -1 in the exponent of ϕ_r^* allows for the "lost" vibrational degree of freedom of the complex. The order of magnitude of Eq. 14.328 is then

$$k = \kappa \frac{kT}{h} \frac{\phi_v^2}{\phi_t^3} e^{-\Delta E_0/RT} \qquad (14.329)$$

By comparison of Eq. 14.329 with 14.327 it is immediately evident that the $\mathcal{P}$ factor of collision theory stands in this case for the ratio (apart from κ),

$$\mathcal{P} \simeq \frac{\phi_v^2}{\phi_t^3} \bigg/ \frac{\phi_r^2}{\phi_t^3} = \frac{\phi_v^2}{\phi_r^2} \simeq 10^{-2} \text{ to } 10^{-3}$$

A reaction for which $\mathscr{P}$ is significantly less than unity is said in collision theory to be "slow," the slowness being relative to the prediction of simple collision theory. Such a reaction rate is seen to be quite "normal" from the point of view of ART. One of the simplest examples is the exchange reaction

$$H_2 + D \rightarrow H + HD$$

for which the ART has had reasonable success. The activated complex in this case may be represented as the linear structure.

$$H \cdot \cdot H \cdot \cdot D$$

which has two rotational degrees of freedom, represented by ϕ_r^{*2} in Eq. 14.328. Its four vibrational degrees of freedom correspond (cf. Chapter 4) to the motions,

$H \cdot \cdot H \cdot \cdot D;$	$H \cdot \cdot H \cdot \cdot D;$	$H \cdot \cdot H \cdot \cdot D$
asymmetric stretch	*symmetric stretch*	*bending*
identified roughly as becoming a translation in the reaction coordinate as the H-H bond breaks while the the H-D bond forms	"breathing" mode	doubly degenerate—with another similar vibration perpendicular to the paper

ILLUSTRATION.   The example of hydrogen atom exchange, involving hydrogen atom movement in the reaction coordinate, is presumably one in which a classical treatment of this coordinate may not be fully valid. This may be illustrated, as was done by Kanai [*Progr. Theoret. Phys.*, **4**, 11 (1949)], as follows.

For the reaction $H + H_2 \rightarrow H \cdot \cdot H \cdot \cdot H$ the diameter d of the pass, from the value of Hirschfelder, Eyring, and Topley [*J. Chem. Phys.*, **4**, 170 (1936)], is $\simeq 10^{-9}$ cm. But the de Broglie wavelength of the activated complex, having effective reduced mass close to unity, is

$$\lambda^* = h/\mu^* v^* \simeq 6.7 \times 10^{-27}/(1 \times 4 \times 10^5/6 \times 10^{23})$$

$$\simeq 10^{-8} \text{ cm}$$

where v^* was simply assigned a reasonable order of magnitude, 4×10^5 cm sec^{-1}. So $\lambda > d$; classical considerations are not strictly valid and quantum mechanical tunneling will occur. None the less, the conventional ART calculation may still yield the correct order of magnitude in many such cases. One instance in which tunneling is all-important is the radioactive disintegration of unstable nuclei. Here reactants and products are separated by such an enormous energy barrier that no "thermal" reaction occurs at all (heating does not increase the rate of disintegration at temperatures less than astral); see Sec. 2.4.

(*c*) A and B are polyatomic nonlinear molecules. This is the most complicated case of a bimolecular reaction. Let A and B contain $\mathscr{N}_A$ and $\mathscr{N}_B$ atoms, respectively. The activated complex is nonlinear and possesses three rotational degrees of freedom and hence $[3(\mathscr{N}_A + \mathscr{N}_B) - 6 - 1]$ vibrational degrees of freedom.

$$k = \kappa \frac{kT}{h} \frac{\phi_t^{*3} \phi_r^{*3} \phi_v^{3(\mathscr{N}_A + \mathscr{N}_B) - 7}}{\phi_{t_A}^3 \phi_{t_B}^3 \phi_{r_A}^3 \phi_{r_B}^3 \phi_{v_A}^{3\mathscr{N}_A - 6} \phi_{v_B}^{3\mathscr{N}_B - 6}} e^{-\Delta E_0/RT} \tag{14.330}$$

On simplifying,

$$k = \frac{kT}{h} \frac{\phi_v^5}{\phi_t^3 \phi_r^3} e^{-\Delta E_0/RT} \tag{14.331}$$

This is an order-of-magnitude expression for k, and in this case

$$\mathscr{P} \simeq \frac{\phi_v^5}{\phi_r^5}, \quad \text{a very small number}$$

Reactions of the type $A + BC \rightarrow AB + C$ are said to be *three-center*, corresponding to the activated complex structure, $A \cdot\cdot B \cdot\cdot C$. A and BC may be an atom and a diatomic molecule, as in $D + H_2$ exchange, or more complex species as described in the next subsection. Metathetic reactions or addition reactions $AB + CD \rightarrow$, such as $H_2 + I_2 \rightarrow 2HI$ or $H_2 + H_2C = CH_2 \rightarrow CH_3 - CH_3$, are, said to be *four-center*, corresponding to the activated complex structure,

$$
\begin{array}{c}
A \cdots B \\
\vdots \quad\quad \vdots \\
C \cdots D
\end{array}
$$

ILLUSTRATION.   Following C. E. H. Bawn [*Trans. Faraday Soc.*, **31**, 1536 (1935)], we calculate the rate of association of two complex species, $A + B \rightarrow X^* \rightarrow AB$, as follows.

$$k = \frac{kT}{h} \frac{\phi^*}{\phi_A \phi_B} e^{-\Delta E_0/RT}$$

$$
= \frac{\dfrac{kT}{h} \dfrac{[2\pi(m_A + m_B)kT]^{3/2}}{h^3} \dfrac{8\pi^2 (8\pi^3 I_1^* I_2^* I_3^*)^{1/2}(kT)^{3/2}}{\sigma_{X^*} h^3}}{\dfrac{(2\pi m_A kT)^{3/2}}{h^3} \dfrac{(2\pi m_B kT)^{3/2}}{h^3} \dfrac{8\pi^2(8\pi^3 I_1 I_2 I_3)_A^{1/2}(kT)^{3/2}}{\sigma_A h^3} \dfrac{8\pi^2(8\pi^3 I_1 I_2 I_3)_B^{1/2}(kT)^{3/2}}{\sigma_B h^3}}
$$

$$
\times \frac{\prod\limits^{i} (1 - e^{-h\nu_i^*/kT})^{-1} e^{-\Delta E_0/RT}}{\prod\limits^{j} (1 - e^{-h\nu_{Aj}/kT})^{-1} \prod\limits^{k} (1 - e^{-h\nu_{Bk}/kT})^{-1}}
$$

The expressions in $I_1 I_2 I_3$ are the partition functions for three degrees of freedom of rotation of an asymmetric rotor, where the I quantities are principal moments of inertia; other expressions are familiar.

To obtain an approximate value of the equation, Bawn set all $I_i \sim 10^{-39}$ g cm², and all values of

$$(1 - e^{-h\nu/kT})^{-1} \simeq 1 \text{ at } 300°K.$$

The resulting $\mathscr{P}$ value was $\simeq 10^{-6}$.

Examples of such processes considered by Bawn are the reactions

$$2NO_2 \rightarrow N_2O_4$$
$$CH_3 + CH_3 \rightarrow C_2H_6$$
$$CH_3 + C_2H_5 \rightarrow C_3H_8$$
$$2C_4H_6 \text{ (butadiene)} \rightarrow C_8H_{12}$$

Simpler reactions,

$$H_2 + C_2H_4 \rightarrow C_2H_6$$
$$I_2 + C_2H_4 \rightarrow C_2H_4I_2$$

were calculated to have $\mathscr{P}$ factors around 10^{-2} to 10^{-3}.

The student may determine the changes in the values for $\mathscr{P}$ that result for the last two reactions on replacing the approximations given above by more exact values for $\phi_r^2(H_2)$ and $\phi_r^2(I_2)$ and for $\phi_v(H_2)$ and $\phi_v(I_2)$ (see Table 4.101(A) for molecular constants).

Comparison of Rate Theories with Experiment.   Absolute rate theory provides us with an interpretation of the values of $\mathscr{P}$ which arise in the collision theory treatment. This is exemplified by the following reactions of progressively increasing complexity:

1. $H + H \rightarrow H_2$, $\mathscr{P} = 1$ in principle (although the reaction doesn't "go" because of the circumstance that the H_2 molecule formed reacts back right away, i.e., $\kappa \simeq 0$).
2. $H + C_2H_6 \rightarrow H_2 + C_2H_5$, $\mathscr{P} \simeq 10^{-1}$ to 10^{-2}
   $H + H_2C{=}CH_2 \rightarrow C_2H_5$, $\mathscr{P} \simeq 10^{-1}$ to 10^{-2}
3. $CH_3 + C_2H_6 \rightarrow C_2H_5 + CH_4$, $\mathscr{P} \simeq 10^{-3}$ to 10^{-4}
   $C_2H_5 + H_2C{=}CH_2 \rightarrow C_4H_9$, $\mathscr{P} \simeq 10^{-3}$ to 10^{-4}

However, many exceptions to the general trends may be found. In Table 14.302 are examples of reactions which display $\mathscr{P}$ values less than those of more complex species, or different from those of similar species. In collision theory, geometry and steric factors must be invoked to explain the $\mathscr{P}$ factors and the "slowness" of the reaction with increasing complexity of A and B.

It should not be thought that all such simple ART calculations agree with experiment. The reaction

$$C_2H_5 + C_2H_5 \rightarrow C_4H_{10}$$

has a characteristic rate that is very close to the simple collision theory prediction, and much larger than the ART calculation made in the preceding Illustration. The discrepancy, it turns out, is explained by the fact that the activated complex should actually involve more rotational degrees of freedom and fewer vibrational degrees of freedom than were allowed for in the model of Eq. 14.330. In general, it is very important in the application of the theory to make a correct appraisal of the contribution of rotational degrees of freedom, because of the large difference

Table 14.302   Calculated Pre-exponential Factors for Some Bimolecular Reactions*

Reaction	Temp., °K	Pre-exponential Factors (10^{12} cc mole^{-1} sec^{-1})			Activation Energy, kcal mole^{-1}	$\mathscr{P}$
		Experimental	Absolute Rate Theory	Collision Theory		
1. $NO + O_3 \rightarrow NO_2 + O_2$	215	0.80	0.44	47	2.5	0.017
2. $NO_2 + O_3 \rightarrow NO_3 + O_2$	295	5.9	0.14	63	7.0	0.094
3. $NO_2 + F_2 \rightarrow NO_2F + F$	320	1.6	0.12	59	10.4	0.027
4. $NO_2 + CO \rightarrow NO + CO_2$	665	12	6.0	74	31.6	0.16
5. $2NO_2 \rightarrow 2NO + O_2$	565	1.8	4.5	43	26.6	0.042
6. $NO + NO_2Cl \rightarrow NOCl + NO_2$	310	0.83	0.84	71	6.9	0.012
7. $2NOCl \rightarrow 2NO + Cl_2$	475	9.4	0.44	59	24.5	0.16
8. $NOCl + Cl \rightarrow NO + Cl_2$	310	11.4	4.4	57	1.1	0.20
9. $NO + Cl_2 \rightarrow NOCl + Cl$	600	4.0	1.2	93	20.3	0.043
10. $F_2 + ClO_2 \rightarrow FClO_2 + F$	240	0.035	0.082	47	8.5	0.0007
11. $2ClO \rightarrow Cl_2 + O_2$	375	0.058	0.010	26	0.0	0.0022
12. $COCl + Cl \rightarrow CO + Cl_2$	315	400	1.8	65	0.83	6.1

* By permission, after Herschbach, Johnston, Pitzer, and Powell, *J. Chem. Phys.*, **25**, 736 (1956).

in magnitude between rotational and vibrational partition functions. We may think of this as a discrepancy which arose because we have erroneously excluded many possible configurations of the activated complex.

The general success of ART, when properly applied, may be seen from the calculation for various reactions of the pre-exponential part of the rate constant, given in Table 14.302. This demonstrates that the theory is greatly superior to the collision theory, for which the examples constitute favorable cases since they involve small molecules. Only the last reaction fails to agree adequately, and the experimental data should be rechecked.

More Exact Treatment of Reaction Rates.   The two theories that have been described above have been the most important, in both the historical and the practical sense, that have been given. In more recent years, several more sophisticated treatments have been made, along with closer examination of the quantum mechanical foundations. Some of these considerations emphasize the formal analogies of chemical reaction with compound nucleus formation and the scattering phenomena of nuclear physics. In one extension of the collision theory approach, particularly suited for nonadiabatic systems (i.e., those for which electronic transitions are involved so that the Born-Oppenheimer approximation is poor), the detailed quantum states of the colliding particles are specified, and a detailed reaction cross section, analogous to the scattering cross section just mentioned, is formally defined. For suitable assumptions and approximations, the Eyring-Polanyi equation, Eq. 14.319, may be obtained. Alternatively, in one simple form, the rate constant becomes

$$k = 2\left(\frac{2}{\pi\mu kT}\right)^{1/2} \int_0^\infty \epsilon C(\epsilon)\, e^{-\epsilon/kT}\, \frac{d\epsilon}{kT} \tag{14.332}$$

where $C(\epsilon)$ is the reaction cross section, a function of the relative kinetic energy ϵ, and μ is the reduced mass. A particular postulated form of $C(\epsilon)$,

$$C(\epsilon) = 0, \qquad\qquad\qquad \epsilon < \epsilon_c$$
$$C(\epsilon) = \pi\sigma^2[1 - (\epsilon_c/\epsilon)], \qquad \epsilon \geq \epsilon_c$$

leads to the simple collision theory, Eq. 14.302.

Fast Reactions.   The experimental study of bimolecular reactions has usually been made in the way tacitly indicated in some of the problems encountered so far. The reactants are mixed in some conventional vessel and reaction proceeds; from time to time the system is analyzed by the measurement of any convenient physical property, such as density, color intensity, or dielectric constant; or samples are removed and analyzed by chemical reactivity (oxidizing or reducing power, acidity, etc.). It is evident that this procedure is suitable only if the reaction is not over in less than 1 sec, or even several minutes, so that the experimenter has the time to mix reactants and remove successive aliquot samples without serious errors in the measured elapsed reaction time. In the period since 1930 several techniques have been devised for the measurement of the rate constants of gas and solution reactions which are complete in less than 1 sec or even 1 msec. Such reactions are arbitrarily called "fast" for practical reasons unconnected with theory. Some of the experimental methods will be briefly indicated.

Diffusion Flame Method.   M. Polanyi and coworkers devised a useful method for the study of metal atom reactions of the type

$$Na + CH_3Cl \rightarrow NaCl + CH_3$$

$$K \; + HBr \; \rightarrow KBr + H, \text{etc.}$$

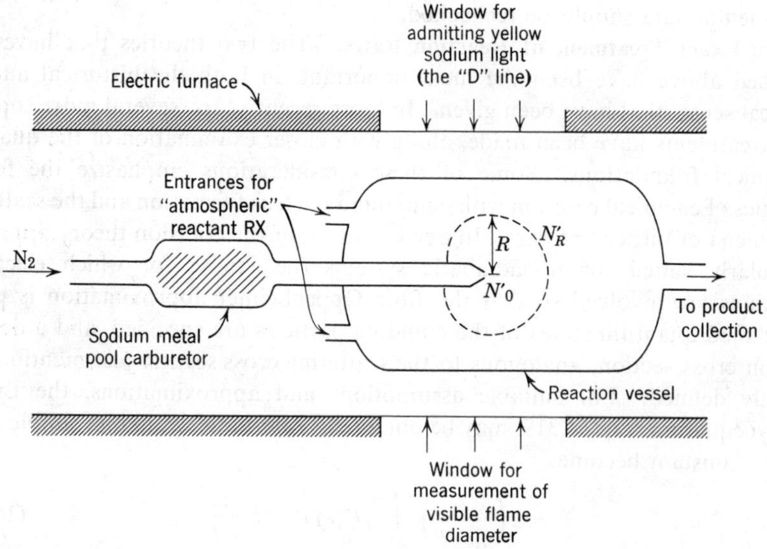

Fig. 14.307   Top view of a schematic arrangement of a sodium diffusion flame apparatus.

The atoms, usually sodium, are picked up in a stream of nitrogen (Fig. 14.307) at their saturation vapor pressure and are carried to a nozzle of radius r_0, from which they diffuse into the halide reactant gas and react. The equation of continuity, for sodium transport by diffusion only, is simply

$$\mathscr{D}\nabla^2 N'_{Na} - k N'_{Na} N'_{hal} = 0 \tag{14.333}$$

This is Eq. 13.203 with $\partial N'_{Na}/\partial t$ set equal to zero, and with a term in sodium consumption by reaction with "hal" added. The condition in which the change with time of the sodium concentration at any point in the reaction vessel is zero is called a *steady state* condition. The symmetrical diffusion of sodium vapor from the nozzle gives a spherical "flame" which is made visible by illumination with light from a sodium lamp; this causes the sodium atoms to fluoresce and, after the lapse of a little time so that constant concentrations are established, gives rise to a steady flame. As the sodium vapor diffuses it reacts and eventually becomes sufficiently depleted at a distance R from the nozzle, at a concentration N'_R, so that it can no longer be detected by the eye or by a photocell detector. For the boundary conditions that

$$N'_{Na} = 0, \text{ at infinite distance from the nozzle,}$$

and

$$N'_{Na} = N_0, \text{ the concentration at the nozzle,}$$

the solution of Eq. 14.333 gives

$$N'_R = \frac{N'_0 r_0}{R} e^{-(\text{\textsl{k}} N'_{hal} R^2 / \mathscr{D})^{\frac{1}{2}}} \tag{14.334}$$

From measurements of N'_0, N'_R, r_0, R, N'_{hal}, and a knowledge of the diffusion coefficient $\mathscr{D}$, the rate constant $\text{\textsl{k}}$ may be calculated.

Refinements of this treatment have been given. The method has also been extended to other reactants, e.g., amines and boron trihalides

$$NH_3 + BF_3 \rightarrow H_3N \cdot BF_3$$

This reaction is not thermoneutral, and by the measurement of temperatures in various regions with thermocouple probes the relevant geometry of the flame is determined from these steady-state values.

The specific rate constants measured may be of the order of $10^{-1}\mathcal{z}$ to $10^{-5}\mathcal{z}$, where $\mathcal{z}$ is the specific collision rate, and correspond to "reaction times" of a fraction of a second. Sometimes the rates are expressed as "collision yields," that is, the inverse of the average number of collisions of A and B required for reaction; these values are the fractional coefficients of $\mathcal{z}$ just given.

If one attempted to mix these reactants in conventional fashion, the reaction would be over before the mixing was completed.

References

Garvin, D., V. P. Guinn, and G. B. Kistiakowsky, *Discussions Faraday Soc.*, **17**, 32 (1954).
Polanyi, M., *Atomic Reactions*, Williams and Norgate, London, 1932; E. Warhurst, *Quart. Revs.*, **5**, 44 (1951).

Fast Mixing and Flow Systems. Techniques have been devised for the high-speed mixing, in a fraction of a second, of liquid or gaseous reactants. The mixture can then be made to flow at a known high rate down a tube (Fig. 14.308). If one of the reactants A is colored, that is, has an absorption band, or some other useful property, its rate of consumption may be followed as a function of time by scanning along the length of the flow tube with a suitable detector, say a phototube calibrated against known concentrations of A. Studies of fast solution reactions and of fast gas reactions which utilize this experimental scheme have been made.

Alternatively, it is unnecessary to make the reaction time correspond to a physical distance traveled down a tube. A detection device, whether a simple photocell or infrared spectrometer, with a response time of a millisecond, say,

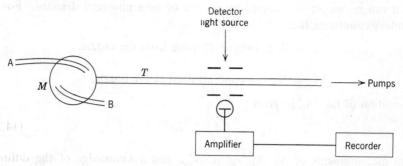

Fig. 14.308   Schematic diagram showing high-speed tangential mixer M in which A and B come together before flowing down tube T or flowing into a reactor-analysis cell.

feeds into a recording oscillograph. The reactants are mixed and expanded quickly into a monitored cell, and the variation of the signal with time is recorded. In this way rapid gas reactions, such as

$$NO + O_3 \quad \rightarrow NO_2 + O_2$$

$$NO + NO_2Cl \rightarrow NOCl + NO_2$$

have been studied.

References

Johnston, H. S., *Discussions Faraday Soc.*, **17**, 14 (1954).
Roughton, F. J. W., *Proc. Roy. Soc.* (*London*), **A155**, 269 (1936).

Flash Photolysis. The problem of rapid mixing is avoided in quite another experimental arrangement (Fig. 14.309). A precursor to reaction is mixed at leisure with a reactant and then a second reactant is generated *in situ* in the reactor in a time of the order of 10^{-2} to 10^2 msec. Norrish has successfully used this technique to study reactions such as

$$O + NO_2 \rightarrow O_2 + NO \tag{a}$$

$$O + CH_4 \rightarrow OH + CH_3 \tag{b}$$

$$Cl + O_2 \quad \rightarrow ClO + O \tag{c}$$

For reaction a, pure NO_2 is both a reactant and the precursor of the oxygen atom. For reactions b and c, CH_4 and O_2, and Cl_2 and O_2, are initially mixed. The rapid discharge of a high-capacity condenser bank sending thousands of joules of energy through a flash tube causes the dissociation of NO_2, O_2, or Cl_2 into atoms which initiate reaction. After this, the rate of reaction may be monitored by some rapid photodetection system similar to those just mentioned.

The reactant has also been produced *in situ* by fast flow of the mixture containing a precursor through a hot furnace and then past an effusion slit leading to a mass-spectrometer ionization chamber (Chapter 17). For example, it is possible to study a reaction such as

$$CH_3 + C_2H_6 \rightarrow CH_4 + C_2H_5$$

where methyl is produced, say, by the flow of a $Hg(CH_3)_2$–C_2H_6 mixture through a short furnace where the precursor, $Hg(CH_3)_2$, breaks down.

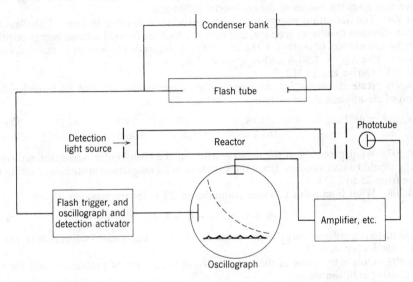

Fig. 14.309   Schematic representation of flash photolysis experimental arrangement. Dashed oscillograph curve is signal; horizontal sawtooth line is time base.

The HO_2 intermediate has been detected in similar manner in a reaction mixture of H_2 and O_2.

The species studied in fast reactions by the above (and other) techniques are frequently not in a state of statistical equilibrium. In some studies, emphasis has been placed on spectroscopic measurements of the transient species produced in these nonequilibrium systems, and such studies have been termed *kinetic spectroscopy*.

References

Eltendon, G. C., *J. Chem. Phys.*, **15**, 455 (1947); J. B. Farmer and F. P. Lossing, *Can. J. Chem.*, **33**, 861 (1955), on mass-spectrometer methods.

Norrish, R. G. W., and N. Basco, *Can. J. Chem.*, **38**, 1769 (1960); *Discussions Faraday Soc.*, **33** (1962), on flash photolysis and kinetic spectroscopy.

Problems

*14.301   Find an expression for the average velocity, $+\bar{u}$, of molecules moving in the $+x$ direction, relative to the average velocity of those that strike the wall while traveling in the $+x$ direction, for a box of O_2 molecules.

*14.302   What happens to the reduced mass for a collision pair as one of the component masses gets much larger than the other? Show that it is clearly wrong to use the ordinary average mass to obtain the collision number.

14.303   Draw a figure that illustrates why it is the mean diameter and not the mean radius that gives the radius of the collisional target area.

14.304   The activation energy for radical association is close to zero. Calculate the relative amounts of ethane, propane, and butane which are formed without energy requirement by association of methyl, CH_3, and ethyl, C_2H_5, radicals present in equal concentrations. Use $r_{CH_3} = 1.90$ Å and $r_{C_2H_5} = 2.25$ Å.

14.305   Derive Eq. 14.312.

14.306   Rate constants for the bimolecular, nitric oxide-catalyzed *cis-trans* isomerization of *cis*-ethylene-d_2 are as follows; evaluate E_a.

k, cm³ mole⁻¹ sec⁻¹:	3.18	6.57	15.7	34.2	70.0
T, °K:	561.2	578.0	600.6	620.5	639.9

14.307   What precision in the determination of the bimolecular Arrhenius activation energy would be necessary to detect the variation in its magnitude in studies covering the range from 25 to 150°C?

14.308   What fraction of collision complexes at 25°C for the reaction

$$A + C_3H_8 \rightarrow HA + C_3H_7$$

would surpass a critical energy requirement E_c of (*a*) 8.8 kcal mole⁻¹ when A is H, (*b*) 8.0 kcal mole⁻¹ when A is D.

14.309   Obtain the value of the ratio k_H/k_D in the system of Problem 14.308 for $t = 627$°C using collision theory.

14.310   Plot the distribution function of Eq. 14.303 and obtain graphically, by measuring areas, the fraction of systems in which the energy exceeds (*a*) $\frac{1}{2}kT$, (*b*) $2kT$. Do the same for the function of Eq. 14.305. Assume some convenient temperature.

14.311   Compare the fraction of molecules at 27°C that have energy in excess of 100 kcal mole⁻¹ for the cases $n = 2$, $n = 10$, where n is the number of square terms that enter.

14.312   Show that $kT/h \simeq 10^{13}$ sec⁻¹.

14.313   What is the physical explanation of the nonappearance of the length of the barrier top in the final expression of the Eyring-Polanyi equation?

*14.314   For the reaction of H_2 and I_2 at 250°C via a planar complex,

$$H_2 + I_2 \rightarrow \begin{matrix} H \cdots I \\ \vdots \vdots \\ H \cdots I \end{matrix} \rightarrow 2HI$$

obtain an expression for (*a*) the specific rate constant in terms of symbolic partition functions, (*b*) the $\mathscr{P}$ factor.

*14.315   Given the following distances, $d(H_2) = 0.74$ Å, $d(I_2) = 2.66$ Å, $d(H—H) = 0.92$ Å, $d(H—I) = 2.0$ Å, and $d(I—I) = 3.0$ Å, deduce moments of inertia and calculate the value of $\mathscr{P}$, in Problem 14.314, in terms of the ratio of vibrational partition functions.

(NOTE: For a planar molecule, $I_A + I_B = I_C$, where I_C is the moment about the principal axis perpendicular to the plane.)

*14.316   Find the value of σ^2 required to fit the simple collision theory value of the pre-exponential factor in Table 14.302 for reactions 5 and 7. From these quantities, deduce the value of σ_{F_2} and of σ_{Cl} (see Eq. 6.501) from the data given for reactions 3 and 8.

14.317   In a sodium-diffusion-flame study of RX at a temperature of 275°C, with $N_0' = 2 \times 10^{-3}$ mm Hg, $r_0 = 0.2$ cm, and a halide partial pressure of 0.4 mm Hg, R is found to be 2 cm under viewing conditions such that $N_R' = 1.2 \times 10^{-6}$ mm. Given $\sigma^2 = 20$ Å^2, calculate $\mathscr{D}$ and find the rate constant k. NOTE: N' is given in pressure units.

4. Unimolecular Reactions; Theoretical Rate Expressions

Collision Theory; the Lindemann-Christiansen Mechanism. The formulation of specific rate constant expressions for unimolecular gas reactions at one time posed a paradox. On the one hand, being first order, $t_{1/2}$ was believed to be independent of the pressure of the reacting gas. On the other hand, since the collision theory stressed the importance of collisions in the activation process, it appeared that the rate of collision, and of reaction, should decline with pressure decrease. The resolution of this difficulty follows.

The average reactant molecule that will subsequently undergo decomposition becomes energized ("hot") by a series of lucky collisions which constitute a random walk along the energy coordinate. The final activation step occurs when two unactivated molecules collide, and one of them acquires an energy in excess of the critical value, ϵ_c. Virtually every collision of an activated molecule deactivates it. The molecule has a chance to decompose between the collision that activates it and the one that deactivates it. However, there is a time-lag or relaxation time for decomposition, which characterizes the probability that some of the internal energy should cause the weakest bond to become stretched and break.

These three steps, activation, deactivation, and reaction, constitute the mechanism which was proposed independently in 1921–1922 by F. Lindemann and by J. A. Christiansen to explain the fact that, although activation is an elementary bimolecular process and hence second order, the observed order of an elementary unimolecular reaction is the first:

$$A + M \xrightarrow{k_1} A^* + M \qquad (1)$$
$$A^* + M \xrightarrow{k_2} A + M \qquad (2) \qquad\qquad (14.401)$$
$$A^* \xrightarrow{k_3} Pr \qquad (3)$$

A is the reactant. The asterisk represents a critically energized molecule and *not* an activated complex, and M is any molecule of A or of added inert gas such as helium or H_2. The net rate of the reaction is the rate of step 3, which is unimolecular. The bimolecular steps 1 and 2 are not conventional chemical reactions but merely represent the collisional relaxation processes which bring about thermal equilibrium. The concentration of A^* at any time is at most that small equilibrium fraction of all A molecules, as given by Eq. 14.308.

Now, the rate of production of A* is virtually balanced by the rates of deactivation (Sec. 13.6) and reaction of A*, so

$$k_1 C_A C_M = k_2 C_{A*} C_M + k_3 C_{A*} \tag{14.402}$$

This is the *steady-state* equation for A*. Thus we obtain

$$C_{A*} = \frac{k_1 C_A C_M}{k_2 C_M + k_3} \tag{14.403}$$

and

$$-\frac{dC_A}{dt} = k_3 C_{A*} = \frac{k_1 k_3 C_A C_M}{k_2 C_M + k_3} \tag{14.404}$$

There are three pressure regions of interest. At *very high pressure* of the gas, $k_2 C_M \gg k_3$ (where k_2 is just $\mathscr{y}$ as in Sec. 13.6) and Eq. 14.404 reduces to

$$-\frac{dC_A}{dt} = \frac{k_1 k_3 C_A}{k_2} = k_\infty C_A \tag{14.405}$$

where k_∞ is the observed, first-order specific rate constant at the high-pressure limit.

At *very low pressure*, $k_2 C_M \ll k_3$ and Eq. 14.404 becomes second order

$$-\frac{dC_A}{dt} = k_1 C_M C_A$$
$$= k_0 C_A \tag{14.406}$$

where, if $C_A \ll C_M$, C_M may be treated as constant and k_0 is an observed first-order specific rate constant at the low-pressure limit. But, since k_0 depends on the first power of C_M, this reaction is better called pseudo-first order; that is, it is first order as far as the variation with time of C_A is concerned (the "time order"), but it is second order for the variation of the rate with the initial pressures of A and M (the "concentration order").

At *intermediate pressure*, $k_2 C_M \simeq k_3$, and Eq. 14.404 may be rearranged slightly as

$$-\frac{dC_A}{dt} = \frac{k_1 k_3 C_M}{k_2 C_M + k_3} C_A = k_{uni} C_A \tag{14.407}$$

Again, if $C_A \ll C_M$, then at a given pressure of M, C_M is effectively a constant and the reaction is again pseudo-first order.

At any value whatsoever of the pressure, the reaction is unimolecular.

Inspection of the foregoing equations shows that $k_\infty > k_{uni} > k_0$; that is, k_{uni} declines monotonically with decrease of pressure, where k_{uni} is the observed first-order rate constant (Fig. 14.401). The experimental verification of the predicted fall-off by Hinshelwood (1926) for propionaldehyde was a great stimulus to further study. The fall-off has been well verified in a number of cases, including these reactions:

$$N_2O_5 \quad \rightarrow NO_2 + NO_3$$

$$H_2\underset{H_2}{\overset{H_2}{\bigtriangledown}} \rightarrow CH_3CH{=}CH_2$$

$$CH_3NC \rightarrow CH_3CN$$

The physical meaning of the fall-off is the following. As $P \rightarrow \infty$, the concentration C_{A*} is just that Boltzmann equilibrium fraction, $B(\epsilon)$, given by Eq. 14.308. At lower pressures, "bleed-off" of A* by reaction becomes comparable with the rate

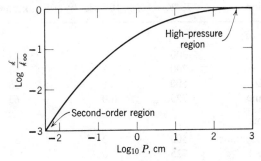

Fig. 14.401   Fall-off for unimolecular isomerization of CH_3NC (230°C) [*J. Am. Chem. Soc.*, **84**, 4215 (1962)].

of collisional deactivation and C_{A*} drops below its equilibrium fraction as given by Eq. 14.403. As $P \rightarrow 0$, deactivating collisions become so infrequent that every activated molecule reacts; C_{A*} drops very markedly and the observed rate becomes just the rate of activation (Eq. 14.406).

Some Experimental Observations; the Energy Requirement for Unimolecular Reactions. We had $k_\infty = k_1 k_3 / k_2$ (Eq. 14.405). Experimentally (Table 14.401), it is found that the Arrhenius equation,

$$k_\infty = \frac{k_1 k_3}{k_2} = Ae^{-(\epsilon_a/kT)}, \quad \text{is} \quad \sim 10^{13} e^{-(\epsilon_a/kT)} \text{ sec}^{-1}.$$

(In some cases, $A > 10^{13}$ sec^{-1} has also been found; we consider this later.) At one time it was thought that k_1/k_2 which is just $B(\epsilon)$, corresponded to the term $e^{-\epsilon_a/kT}$, while k_3 was the reaction frequency, $\sim 10^{13}$ sec^{-1}. Such an interpretation is at best only adequate for diatomic molecules. It was proposed by Hinshelwood (1926) that a proper formula for k_1/k_2 involves the recognition that reacting molecules have s internal vibrational degrees of freedom ($2s$ square terms) in which to accumulate energy, as in Eq. 14.308.

ILLUSTRATION.   H. S. Johnston and R. L. Perrine [*J. Am. Chem. Soc.*, **73**, 4782 (1951)] give the value of $k = k_0/C_M$ for the low-pressure decomposition of N_2O_5

at 27°C as 1.27×10^5 cc mole^{-1} sec^{-1}. We examine the correspondence of this value with the theoretical expression (Eq. 14.308, in which s replaces $n/2$)

$$k = \frac{k_0}{C_M} = \mathscr{Z} \left[\frac{1}{(s-1)!} \left(\frac{\epsilon_c}{kT} \right)^{s-1} e^{-\epsilon_c/kT} \right]$$

These workers found that $E_c = 24.7$ kcal mole^{-1}, where $RT = 1.99 \times 300 = 0.6$ kcal mole^{-1}. Now the maximum number of vibrational degrees of freedom in N_2O_5 is $(3 \times 7) - 6 = 15$. Actually the effective value of s seems to be around 10, so that at 27°C we have $E_c/9\,RT = 24.7/5.4 = 4.6$; although the required

Table 14.401   Some Experimental Data on Unimolecular Reactions

Reaction	T, °K	A_∞, 10^{13} sec^{-1}	E_∞, kcal mole^{-1}
Decomposition of:			
1. N_2O_5	300	5	23
2. C_2H_5Br	700	3	54
3. C_3H_7ONO	500	20	38
4. Cyclobutane	725	400	63
Isomerization of:			
1. Methyl isocyanide	500	2	38
2. cis-Butene-2	725	6	63
3. Cyclopropane	760	200	65

condition for simplification of Eq. 14.308 is not fully satisfied, the next term of the series contributes only 1/4.6 as much, and we may obtain a good order-of-magnitude result from the simple approximate expression.

With the use of $\sigma = 3$ Å, as adopted by Johnston and Perrine, we have, by a calculation illustrated earlier, $\mathscr{Z} = 9 \times 10^{13}$ cc mole^{-1} sec^{-1}.

Then
$$k_1 = 9 \times 10^{13} \left(\frac{1}{9!} \left(\frac{24.7}{0.6} \right)^9 e^{-24.7/0.6} \right)$$

$$= 9 \times 10^{13} \times \frac{1}{3.6 \times 10^5} \times (41.2)^9 \times 1.23 \times 10^{-18}$$

$$= 1.05 \times 10^5 \text{ cc mole}^{-1} \text{ sec}^{-1}$$

The agreement is satisfactory; but it should be kept in mind that s was really used as an adjustable parameter to give a fit. The student may calculate the consequences of changing the assumed value of s by ± 2.

Since the value of k_1/k_2 given by use of Eq. 14.308 is much greater than $e^{-\epsilon_c/kT}$, it follows that k_3 is much less than $\sim 10^{13}$ sec^{-1}. In general, $k_3 \ll 10^{13}$ sec^{-1} because it takes time for the internal energy to become optimally distributed and for bond rupture to occur.

General Expressions for k_{uni}. Equation 14.404 is a great simplification of the true situation. We may rewrite the specific rate constant expression for molecules with energy above ϵ_c in a particular energy range ϵ to $\epsilon + d\epsilon$ as follows:

$$(k_{uni})_\epsilon = \left(\frac{k_1 C_M k_3}{k_2 C_M + k_3}\right)_\epsilon = [F(\epsilon)]\left(\frac{\mathscr{z} C_M}{\mathscr{z} C_M + k_3}\right)(k_3) \tag{14.408}$$

We see that the rate constant is the product of three factors: (a) the *equilibrium* fraction of molecules which are in the required energy range; (b) the correction of this fraction for the molecules in (a) actually present in the steady state; and (c) k_3, their rate of decomposition.

We consider two formulations of k_3.

1. The Hinshelwood model has been employed above; k_3 was taken as a constant, and it was then possible to integrate k_1/k_2 independently from ϵ_c to ∞ to obtain Eq. 14.308.

2. The O. K. Rice–H. C. Ramsperger–L. S. Kassel model asserts that k_3 is a function of the energy with the following classical statistical form:

$$k_3(\epsilon) = \mathscr{A}\left(\frac{\epsilon - \epsilon_c}{\epsilon}\right)^{s-1} \tag{14.409}$$

where $\mathscr{A}$ is a frequency of intramolecular energy interchange, $\sim 10^{13}$ sec^{-1}. The rate constant with the use of Eq. 14.408 is

$$k_{uni} = \frac{1}{(s-1)!}\int_{\epsilon_c}^{\infty}\left(\frac{\epsilon}{kT}\right)^{s-1}e^{-\epsilon/kT}\frac{1}{1 + \dfrac{\mathscr{A}}{\mathscr{z} C_M}\left(\dfrac{\epsilon - \epsilon_c}{\epsilon}\right)^{s-1}}\mathscr{A}\left(\frac{\epsilon - \epsilon_c}{\epsilon}\right)^{s-1}\frac{d\epsilon}{kT}$$

$$= \frac{\mathscr{A}}{(s-1)!(kT)^s}\int_{\epsilon_c}^{\infty}\frac{(\epsilon - \epsilon_c)^{s-1}e^{-\epsilon/kT}\,d\epsilon}{1 - \dfrac{\mathscr{A}}{\mathscr{z} C_M}\left(\dfrac{\epsilon - \epsilon_c}{\epsilon}\right)^{s-1}} \tag{14.410}$$

which must be integrated by numerical methods. For $P \rightarrow 0$, k_3 drops out (Eq. 14.406), and the two formulations become identical.

For small molecules ($s = 3$ to 5), such as N_2O and NOCl, k_3 may be $> 10^{10}$ for reasonable values of ϵ; for large molecules ($s \sim 15$ to 20), such as cyclobutane and dimethylcyclobutane, k_3 may be as small as 10^5 sec^{-1}. The pressure at which $k_3(\epsilon)$ becomes much greater or less than $k_2 C_M$ thus depends on the complexity of the molecule A in general. The sample range of k_3 illustrates the practical limitations: it is not feasible to investigate k_0 for very large molecules, or k_∞ for very small molecules.

The classical statistical formulations given above, although widely used, have the value here mainly of mathematical and expository simplicity. Vibrational degrees of freedom properly involve quantum statistics. For a model of a molecule consisting of s degenerate coupled oscillators at a level of energy $jh\nu$, for which

$\epsilon_c = mh\nu$, Eq. 14.409 becomes

$$k(j) = \mathscr{A} \frac{(j - m + s - 1)!\, j!}{(j - m)!\, (j + s - 1)!}$$

(14.411)

Unfortunately, most molecules are not so simple and the more exact treatment becomes complex.

Unimolecular Reactions and Energy Transfer. Equation 14.409 assumes that internal energy is rapidly and randomly distributed within the molecule; that is, the relaxation time for this intramolecular process is much less than the relaxation time for decomposition of the activated molecule. Comparison of theory and experiment seems to justify this postulate.

A second assumption implicit in the above equations is that activated molecules are deactivated on every collision; that is, intermolecular energy transfer is very efficient. This means, by application of microscopic reversibility, that activated molecules arise by collisions of unactivated molecules—the latter being always present in equilibrium amounts since they suffer no depletion by chemical reaction—and do not arise from collisions of activated molecules of lesser energy. Evaluation of k_0 and comparison with the theory provide a good test of this assumption. So far, the evidence indicates that it is reasonably valid for complex polyatomic molecules, but not for diatomic molecules.

Absolute Rate Theory Treatment. We consider the application of the Eyring-Polanyi treatment for the high-pressure case, where the assumption of equilibrium between reactant A and complex X*

$$A \rightarrow X^* \rightarrow Pr$$

is a particularly good one. The transition state treatment has been extended to the fall-off region but we need not consider it here. Then,

$$k_\infty = \kappa \frac{kT}{h} \frac{\phi^*}{\phi_A} e^{-\Delta E_0/RT}$$

(14.412)

and we have for an order-of-magnitude expression,

$$k_\infty = \kappa \frac{kT}{h} \frac{\phi_t^{*3} \phi_r^{*3} \phi_v^{*3n-7}}{\phi_{t_A}^3 \phi_{r_A}^3 \phi_{v_A}^{3n-6}} e^{-\Delta E_0/RT}$$

(14.413)

$$= \kappa \frac{kT}{h} \frac{1}{\phi_{v_A}} e^{-\Delta E_0/RT}$$

(14.414)

For T very high, $\phi_v = (1 - e^{-h\nu/kT})^{-1} \simeq \dfrac{kT}{h\nu}$ (14.415)

For T very low, $\phi_v \simeq 1$ (14.416)

so that we have

$$(h\nu \ll kT), \quad k_\infty = \kappa \nu e^{-\Delta E_0/RT}$$

(14.417)

$$(h\nu \gg kT), \quad k_\infty = \kappa \frac{kT}{h} e^{-\Delta E_0/RT}$$

(14.418)

In either case, $k_\infty \sim 10^{13}\, e^{-\Delta E_0/kT}$, if $\kappa \sim 1$.

Absolute rate theory thus supplies a meaning and the correct magnitude of the Arrhenius A factor, and interprets the significance of the Arrhenius activation energy. The observed value E_a is thus numerically equal to the molar difference in the zero-point energies of the reactant and the activated complex, that is, to the critical energy, E_c. (kT/h is temperature dependent, but we are ignoring this here.)

In some exceptional instances A may be much less than 10^{13}, as in the decomposition of N_2O, where $A \sim 10^{11}$ was found; these exceptions are reasonably attributed to special restrictions associated with changes of electronic state during the course of the reaction, or to the fact that terms such as ϕ_r^* / ϕ_{r_A} may not exactly cancel. The latter reason also accounts for values of $A \sim 10^{15}$ to 10^{17} (Table 14.401) which have been found, and which may be associated with loosening of molecular binding in the activated complex, resulting in enhanced values of ϕ_r^* and ϕ_v^*.

The Critical Increment. From the expressions given earlier we see that the Arrhenius A factors formally take the following values in the classical theory:

$$P = \infty: \quad A \sim 10^{13} \text{ sec}^{-1}$$

$$P = 0: \quad A \sim \mathscr{z} \frac{1}{s!} \left(\frac{\epsilon_c}{kT} \right)^{s-1} \text{conc}^{-1} \text{sec}^{-1}$$

In the latter case, A shows a marked temperature dependence.

The observed activation energies obtained from $d \ln k/dT$ assume the values:

$P = \infty: \quad \epsilon_a = \epsilon_c$

$P = 0: \quad \epsilon_a \simeq \epsilon_c - (s-1)kT$ (neglecting the temperature dependence of $\mathscr{z}$)

A number of years ago, R. C. Tolman pointed out that the correct descriptive term to be applied to the observed activation energy is the *critical increment*, that is, the average extra energy which must be added to the average reactant molecules (in the relevant degrees of freedom) in order to convert them to average reacting molecules. In some cases this increment is numerically identical with the minimum energy ϵ_c that a reactant molecule must possess in order to react. This is the case for bimolecular reactions and for unimolecular reactions at high pressures.

For unimolecular reactions studied in the usual way with thermal collisional excitation of the molecules, the value of ϵ_c/kT customarily lies in the range 35 to 45 (Table 14.401).

Shock Wave Studies. Any of the conventional or fast experimental methods already mentioned in connection with bimolecular reactions may also be used for unimolecular reactions. Still another, the shock wave method, has been used to study fast unimolecular and bimolecular reactions.

The shock wave technique involves the very rapid heating of a gas or mixture of gases by adiabatic compression to temperatures as high as several thousands of degrees. Since a conventional piston would have to travel faster than a bullet in some cases to heat the gas fast enough and high enough, another, more practical arrangement is used, as in Fig. 14.402. The compartment D contains a gas, such as H_2 or helium (having intrinsically high molecular speeds), at a high pressure, say

2 to 5 atm; alternatively D contains a mixture such as $H_2 + O_2$ which is exploded. In either case, when the membrane M is ruptured, the gas in S is compressed by the shock wave which is produced and which travels through it at speeds in excess of the velocity of sound in the unshocked gas.

The generation of the shock wave may be understood in terms of the figure as follows. An initial part of the compressional pressure impulse is shown in 1. Successive impulses travel with the velocity of sound, v_s, through the already heated gas at progressively higher speeds (regions 2 and 3), since $v_s = (\gamma kT/m)^{1/2}$

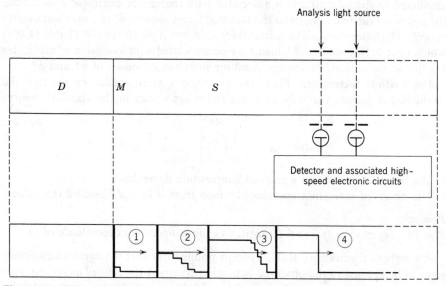

Fig. 14.402 Schematic representation of a shock wave apparatus. D is driver gas section, usually of metal; M is rupturable membrane; S is shocked gas section, frequently a glass pipe. One or more light beams, pressure-sensitive (piezoelectric) gauges, and other sensing device are used to monitor the pressure wave and chemical changes in the gas.

where γ is the heat capacity ratio. The steps eventually catch up with the leading one and form a discontinuous pressure front, shown in region 4, whose thickness is only a few mean free paths. After passage of the front through the detector light beam, in 10^{-6} to 10^{-8} sec depending on conditions, the heated gas in the light path reacts "at leisure."

In this way, the decomposition of N_2O_4,

$$N_2O_4 \rightarrow 2NO_2$$

was studied. The formation of the brown NO_2 product may be followed by the decreasing transmission of blue light, as measured with a fast phototube over a period of 50 to 100 μsec.

The isomerization of *cis*-butene-2 (and other gases) has been studied to 1000 to 1250°K. The results correspond well to extrapolation of the data of Table 14.401, at 725°K, by means of the Arrhenius equation.

It is evident that the shock wave technique is also useful for investigating processes such as intermolecular energy transfer. The shocked molecules, say O_2, are excited to high rotational and vibrational states; and their relaxation to lower energy states by transfer of energy to other species (e.g., helium atoms) may be studied. The decomposition of diatomic molecules such as H_2 and O_2 has been extensively investigated.

References

Britton, D., N. Davidson, and G. Schott, *Discussions Faraday Soc.*, **17** (1954), on N_2O_4 decomposition.

Lifshitz, A., S. H. Bauer, and E. L. Resler, *J. Chem. Phys.*, **38**, 2056 (1963), on high-temperature shock-wave studies.

Problems

14.401   If A is a diatomic molecule with $\nu = 5 \times 10^{13}$ sec^{-1}, and if 20 quanta are required as a minimum for activation, how many molecules are in this state, at equilibrium, relative to the ground state? What fraction of all molecules has 20 or more quanta at equilibrium? (Take $T = 300°$ and $3000°K$.)

14.402   Show from Eq. 14.407 that the plot of $1/k_{uni}$ vs. $1/C_M$ is a straight line.

*14.403   Explain why the second-order rate constant, defined as k_{obs}/C_M, falls off as the pressure *increases* from 0 to ∞.

14.404   If k has declined for CH_3NC isomerization so that $k/k_\infty = 0.5$ at $P = 70$ mm Hg ($t = 230°C$), calculate the value of k_3 on the Hinshelwood model at this pressure ($\sigma = 4.5$ Å).

14.405   Compare the magnitude of k_0 given by use of Eq. 14.308 with a simple collision theory prediction, for the case $E_c = 50$ kcal mole^{-1}, $t = 400°C$, $s = 5$ (compare Problem 14.311).

*14.406   Show that at very high energies, where $(j - m + s - 1) \simeq (j - m)$ and $(j + s - 1) \simeq j$, Eq. 14.411 assumes the form of Eq. 14.409.

14.407   Show that $\phi_v = (1 - e^{-h\nu/kT})^{-1}$ has magnitude of the order of unity at low temperatures and rises to significant magnitude at $1500°K$, given that $\nu = 5 \times 10^{13}$ sec^{-1}.

*14.408   If $\mathscr{A} = 2 \times 10^{13}$ sec^{-1} and $E_c = 50$ kcal mole^{-1}, find the required energies in order that $k_3(\epsilon)$ may be both as large as 10^{10} and as small as 10^4 sec^{-1} for the cases $s = 4$, $s = 15$. Do this *both* for the classical case and for a degenerate oscillator having ν as in Problem 14.407.

14.409   Estimate the magnitude of the rate constant for *cis*-butene-2 isomerization at $1200°K$ (see the discussion above).

5. Trimolecular Reactions

Collision Theory.   The calculation of the rates of trimolecular reactions by collision theory suffers from the difficulty of quantitatively defining three-body collisions. The probability that a three-body collision complex should occur may be estimated from the ratio of the molecular diameter σ to the mean free path λ

(Fig. 14.501). At 1 atm pressure λ is $\sim 10^{-5}$ cm, and since molecular diameters σ are $\sim 10^{-8}$ cm a trimolecular collision will occur once for every thousand bimolecular collisions. To make a more precise specification of $\mathscr{Y}_{\text{tri}}$ requires knowledge of the effective lifetime, τ, of the bimolecular collision complex, which in turn depends on the force field for molecular interaction. The order of magnitude of τ is 10^{-12} to 10^{-13} sec, which corresponds to the time required for a collision complex to execute a single cycle of the motion of the newly formed "bond" and to dissociate. Such a magnitude also arises if we assume that the effective radius of a molecule, the intrusion within which by another molecule defines a collision, extends over a distance of the order of a molecular diameter. Then

$$\tau \sim r_{\text{eff}}/c_r \sim 10^{-8}/10^4 \text{ to } 10^{-8}/10^5 = 10^{-12} \text{ to } 10^{-13} \text{ sec}$$

where c_r is the average relative speed of the two molecules at 300°K. These estimates lead to $\mathscr{Y}_{\text{tri}} \sim 10^{-33}$ cc² molecule⁻² sec⁻¹.

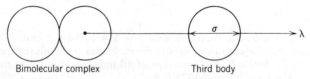

Bimolecular complex   Third body

Fig. 14.501   Representation of trimolecular collision probability.

The rate of recombination of oxygen atoms in the presence of argon has been measured and found by Harteck and coworkers to be $\sim 10^{-33}$ cm⁶ molecule⁻² sec⁻¹ from 300 to 3000°K. For the recombination of iodine atoms at 300°K in the presence of inert gas molecules such as H_2, helium or argon

$$2I + M \rightarrow I_2 + M$$

k is found to be of the order of 3×10^9 l² mole⁻² sec⁻¹ from flash photolysis and shock wave studies (see Problem 14.501) with a slightly *negative* activation energy. For more complex inert gases, such as $n\text{-}C_5H_{12}$, benzene, and CCl_4, k rises to 10^{10} to 10^{11} l² mole⁻² sec⁻¹. For I_2 as the inert gas, k takes the value at 300°K of 2×10^{12} l² mole⁻² sec⁻¹, with a considerably enhanced *negative* activation energy. Similar results exist for the recombination of bromine atoms. The I_2-inert gas results indicate successive two-body collisions of the type

$$I + I_2 \rightleftarrows I_3$$
$$I_3 + I \rightleftarrows 2I_2$$

where I_3 is an intermediate species which has a lifetime considerably longer than those of the transient collision complex previously considered, and whose lifetime is shortened by back-decomposition if its energy, i.e., the energy of I and I_2, is increased by raising the temperature. This gives rise to the negative activation energies observed here and in related studies.

The recombination of n-hexyl radicals in the presence of an inert gas, represented as

$$2\,n\text{-}C_6H_{13} \rightarrow n\text{-}C_{12}H_{26}^*$$
$$n\text{-}C_{12}H_{26}^* + M \rightarrow n\text{-}C_{12}H_{26} + M$$

involves an "unstable" intermediate, $C_{12}H_{26}^*$, whose characteristic lifetime may begin to be of the order of seconds.

It is obvious that in a few cases there is really no clear-cut distinction between a trimolecular process and two successive bimolecular processes.

Absolute Rate Theory. The treatment of trimolecular reactions by ART is less ambiguous and avoids the semantic problems raised by collision theory. For the reaction of atoms

$$A + B + C \rightarrow Pr$$

we have

$$\mathcal{k} = \kappa \frac{kT}{h} \frac{\phi^*}{\phi_A \phi_B \phi_C} e^{-\Delta E_0/RT} \qquad (14.501)$$

For $\Delta E_0 = 0$ and $\kappa = 1$, this reduces for a linear complex to an order of magnitude which is the same as that obtained previously by collision considerations.

$$\mathcal{k} = \frac{kT}{h} \frac{\phi_r^2 \phi_v^3}{\phi_t^6} \simeq 10^{-33} \text{ cc}^2 \text{ molecule}^{-2} \text{ sec}^{-1} \qquad (14.502)$$

Whether or not the intermediate two-body complex has a considerable lifetime, Eq. 14.501 retains its validity.

Reactions such as iodine atom recombination, or nitric oxide reactions such as

$$2NO + O_2 \rightarrow 2NO_2$$

(which involves the NO_3 intermediate and its further reaction with another molecule of NO), both show negative activation energy; in both cases ΔE_0^* is approximately zero. If the detailed partition functions are inserted in Eq. 14.501 for ϕ_r and ϕ_t, we have, with neglect of the vibrational functions,

$$\mathcal{k} = \frac{kT}{h} \frac{m_*^{3/2}}{m_{NO}^3 m_{O_2}^{3/2}} \frac{\dfrac{8\pi^2 IkT}{h^2}}{\left[\dfrac{(2\pi kT)^{1/2}}{h}\right]^6} = \frac{\text{const}}{T} \qquad (14.503)$$

so $\mathcal{k}$ varies inversely with the temperature. More complex reactant molecules, having rotational degrees of freedom, increase the magnitude of the inverse temperature dependence.

Problems

14.501 Convert $\mathcal{k}$ in cm⁶ molecules⁻² sec⁻¹ to $\mathcal{k}$ in l² mole⁻² sec⁻¹.

*14.502 Would $\mathcal{k}$ be smaller or larger than the value given by Eq. 14.502 if (a) the activated complex were nonlinear? (b) the reactants were diatomic?

*14.503   Obtain a rough estimate for the magnitude of k in Eq. 14.503.

14.504   Verify the last sentence in Sec. 14.5.

*14.505   If for the reaction $2NO + O_2 \rightarrow 2NO_2$ the value of ΔE_0 were 0.3 kcal mole^{-1}, find the observed value E_a for the range -78 to $100°C$.

6. Rate Laws for Combinations of Elementary Reactions

So far we have been concerned with the nature and characteristics of the various elementary reactions. Some or all of the following combinations of elementary reactions are of most frequent occurrence in complex reactions. We shall briefly consider the form of the rate laws that apply, and then in Sec. 14.7 show in a few illustrative cases how our knowledge of elementary processes contributes to an understanding of complex reactions.

Reversible Reactions.   The reactions treated so far have been irreversible. If reactions are appreciably reversible, one has the condition of *opposing* reactions. Various situations are possible:

(a) First order–first order, e.g., *cis*-butene-2 $\rightleftarrows$ *trans*-butene-2.

(b) First order–second order, e.g., $C_4H_9Br \rightleftarrows C_4H_8 + HBr$.

(c) Second order–first order, e.g., $H_2 + C_2H_4 \rightleftarrows C_2H_6$, or the reverse of example b.

(d) Second order–third order, e.g., $I_2 + Ar \rightleftarrows 2I + Ar$.

It will suffice here to consider the simplest of these, the first order–first order case. For $A \underset{k_2}{\overset{k_1}{\rightleftarrows}} B$, we have

$$\frac{dx}{dt} = k_1(a - x) - k_2 x \tag{14.601}$$

At equilibrium when $x = x_e$,

$$\frac{dx}{dt} = 0 = k_1(a - x_e) - k_2 x_e \tag{14.602}$$

whence

$$k_2 = \frac{k_1(a - x_e)}{x_e} \tag{14.603}$$

and on substituting for k_2 in Eq. 14.601, we have on reduction

$$\frac{dx}{dt} = k_1 \frac{a}{x_e}(x_e - x) \tag{14.604}$$

The resemblance to Eq. 13.706 is immediately evident, so that we may write,

$$k_1 t = \frac{x_e}{a} \ln \frac{x_e}{x_e - x} \tag{14.605}$$

Simultaneous Reactions.   A substance may disappear by two or more *parallel,* concurrent processes.   Thus we may have

$$CH_3CH_2CH_2CH_3 \rightarrow CH_3CH_2CH{=}CH_2 + H_2 \qquad (a)$$
$$\rightarrow CH_3 + {\cdot}CH_2CH_2CH_3 \qquad (b)$$
$$\rightarrow 2CH_3CH_2{\cdot} \qquad (c)$$

The nitration of benzene to give, simultaneously, *m-, o-,* and *p*-dinitrobenzene is a familiar example.   If one reaction predominates it is termed the *principal reaction,* and other minor reactions are called *side reactions.*   Various combinations of order are possible.   If one or more reactions are reversible as well, the situation becomes even more complicated.   Wegscheider pointed out many years ago that, if a substance reacts simultaneously by processes of the *same* order, than the ratio of the amounts of the products formed will be constant and independent of the extent of reaction.   Otherwise, the ratio will vary with the degree of completion of the reaction.

For the simplest case of two first-order, irreversible concurrent reactions, for example,

$$CH_3CHBrCH_2CH_3 \xrightarrow{k_1} CH_2{=}CHCH_2CH_3 + HBr$$
$$\xrightarrow{k_2} CH_3CH{=}CHCH_3 + HBr$$

one has

$$\frac{dx}{dt} = k_1(a - x) + k_2(a - x)$$
$$= (k_1 + k_2)(a - x)$$

Thus

$$(k_1 + k_2)t = \ln \frac{a}{a - x} \qquad (14.606)$$

and the total reaction is similar to a single first-order process with rate constant equal to $(k_1 + k_2)$.

Consecutive Reactions.   Still another complication of the kinetic rate laws arises if one or more intermediates intervene between the reactants and the products of interest.   This occurs in the formation of acetic acid by hydrolysis of acetonitrile:

$$CH_3CN \xrightarrow{H_2O} CH_3CONH_2 \xrightarrow{H_2O} CH_3CO_2H + NH_3$$

The formation of trinitrobenzene from benzene is another instance.

The more complex combinations of various kinetic orders are not amenable to exact analytical treatment, and mathematical approximation and numerical methods, or simplification of the experimental conditions in practice, is used to make the problems tractable.

Consider the simplest system of two consecutive, irreversible first-order reactions

$$A \xrightarrow{k_1} B \xrightarrow{k_2} C$$

Reverting for clarity to the notation used earlier in this chapter, we have

$$-\frac{dC_A}{dt} = k_1 C_A, \quad \text{and} \quad C_A = C_A^\circ e^{-k_1 t} \tag{14.607}$$

$$\frac{dC_B}{dt} = k_1 C_A - k_2 C_B \tag{14.608}$$

$$\frac{dC_C}{dt} = k_2 C_B \tag{14.609}$$

$$C_A^\circ = C_A + C_B + C_C \tag{14.610}$$

The crux of this problem is the calculation of the concentration of the intermediate, C_B, at time t. From Eq. 14.608 with 14.607 we have

$$\frac{dC_B}{dt} + k_2 C_B = k_1 C_A^\circ e^{-k_1 t} \tag{14.611}$$

This is a linear differential equation with constant coefficients the solution of which is

$$C_B = \frac{k_1 C_A^\circ}{k_2 - k_1} (e^{-k_1 t} - e^{-k_2 t}) \tag{14.612}$$

From Eqs. 14.612 and 14.609, dC_C/dt is readily found, while from Eq. 14.610, $C_C = C_A^\circ - C_A - C_B$ is obtained.

Two extreme cases may occur. (a) If $k_2 \gg k_1$, the intervention of the intermediate is of no kinetic consequence and the system will behave like A → C. (b) If $k_2 \ll k_1$, B will accumulate in the system and the curve of C production with time will show a pronounced *induction period*; that is, the formation of C lags far behind the disappearance of A, and as far as production of C is concerned, we have in effect started off with pure B. For $k_2 \sim k_1$, intermediate behavior is observed. The hydrolysis of a dilute solution of acetonitrile to give acetic acid in aqueous hydrochloric acid is pseudo-first order and exemplifies the whole range of

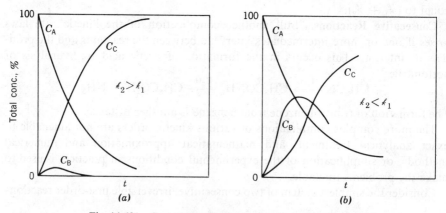

Fig. 14.601 Consecutive first-order reactions, A → B → C.

Table 14.601 Hydrolysis of Propionitrile to Give Propionic Acid

HCl, N	Temp., °C	Analyt. Method*	Observed $k \times 10^2$, hr^{-1}						k_1/k_2
			% Propionic Acid Formed†						
			10–20	20–30	30–40	40–50	50–60	60–70	
4.00	99.7	A	39.2	40.0		39.7	40.1	39.7	1/300
		AA	39.7	38.8	39.1	39.8	38.8		
6.48	50.0	A	2.00	2.52		3.42	3.55	3.59	1/10
		AA	3.53	3.51	3.52	3.51	3.48		
8.47	59.6	A	16.9		23.4	32.6	32.7	32.8	3/1
		AA	122	122	122	117	123	121	

* A = analysis for propionic acid only. AA = analysis for both propionic acid and propionamide; gives total amount of nitrile reacted.

† Given to indicate the region of reaction percentage concerned.

possible behavior with a variation from $k_1 \ll k_2$, in moderately concentrated acid (4N), to $k_1 \gg k_2$, in highly concentrated acid (12N).

The markedly S-shaped curve for C_C in Fig. 14.601b is characteristic of an induction period, which is barely evident in Fig. 14.601a. For $k_2 \ll k_1$, the C_C curve would lie on the abscissa.

ILLUSTRATION. The data of C. A. Winkler *et al.* [*Can. J. Research*, **B20**, 69 (1942)] illustrate the behavior for propionitrile (Table 14.601). The reactions involved are

$$C_2H_5CN \xrightarrow[H_2O]{k_1} C_2H_5CONH_2 \xrightarrow[H_2O]{k_2} C_2H_5CO_2H + NH_3, \quad \text{with HCl catalyst}$$

It is evident that at 4.00N acid scarcely any induction period can be seen within experimental error. At 6.48N acid the induction period is significant, but after 30 to 40 per cent reaction the k values found from analyses for final product (A) have converged to the true value. At 8.47N, the k values from A analyses have also converged after 40 to 50 per cent reaction, but to a final value which is *not* the rate of hydrolysis of nitrile but is close to (although a little less than) the rate of hydrolysis of propionamide!

The student may calculate the maximum percentage concentration of propionamide that arises in the three systems.

Complex Reactions. Many reactions constitute a complicated assembly of various types of elementary and simple combination processes previously described. Nuclear disintegration schemes provide many examples of simultaneous and consecutive first-order reactions. In many instances, these reactions may be too difficult to unravel in a satisfactory way, and rate laws, if stated, will be gross approximations valid only under certain conditions. A considerable amount of research may be required to elucidate the nature of the events taking place. Thus, in the combustion of gasoline and hydrocarbons, great effort has already been devoted (and more will be required) to clarifying the nature and role of the various aldehydic, oxy-, and peroxy- intermediates formed, even in the early stages of reactions, and of various degradation steps.

Problems

14.601 Write down some further examples of the combination reactions listed above.

14.602 For the reaction $trans$-CHD=CHD $\rightleftarrows$ cis-CHD=CHD, for which $x_e = \frac{1}{2}a$, the following data were obtained at 521°C [J. $Chem$. $Phys$., **23**, 315 (1955)]:

t, min:	7.0	9.0	11.0	13.0	16.0	20.0
% cis:	6.1	8.0	9.3	11.4	13.3	15.7

Find the value of k_1 in sec^{-1} for each time given, and calculate a best overall value.

14.603 Compare the values of k_1 in Problem 14.602 with those that result from the use of Eq. 13.707.

*14.604 Obtain from Eq. 14.601 the integrated form

$$k_1 t = \frac{1}{\gamma} \ln \frac{a}{a - \gamma x}$$

where $\gamma = (k_1 + k_2)/k_1$.

14.605 Given Eq. 14.612, calculate the maximum concentration of C_B that can occur. Show that it is

$$(C_B)_{max} = C_A^\circ (k_2/k_1)^{k_2/(k_1 - k_2)}$$

and that it occurs at

$$t_{max} = \frac{1}{k_2 - k_1} \ln \frac{k_2}{k_1}$$

7. Stationary Chain Reactions

The Steady State Approximation. Many complex reactions involve intermediates which occur at very low, almost vanishingly small, concentration. Highly unstable intermediate molecules fit into this category, as do also very reactive species such as atoms or radicals which destroy themselves by fast reaction. The quantitative treatment and interpretation of complex reactions are greatly facilitated by use of the steady state, or stationary state, assumption suggested by Christiansen and by Polanyi and Herzfeld in 1919. The approximation is used that $dR/dt \simeq 0$, relative to those of stable species, where R is the intermediate. This approximation was already used in Sec. 14.4. From this assumption a set of simultaneous algebraic equations is obtained, equal in number to the number of intermediates to which the postulate is applied, which may be solved to eliminate the concentrations of the intermediates in terms of concentrations of stable species.

The general conditions necessary to make the approximation valid may be seen by reconsideration of the first-order consecutive reaction scheme

$$A \xrightarrow{k_1} B \xrightarrow{k_2} Pr$$

On applying the steady state assumption to B, we have

$$\frac{dC_B}{dt} = 0 = k_1 C_A - k_2 C_B \tag{14.701}$$

or

$$C_B = \frac{k_1 C_A}{k_2} = \frac{k_1 C_A^o}{k_2} e^{-k_1 t} \tag{14.702}$$

An exact solution of the differential equation without the steady state simplification was

$$C_B = \frac{k_1 C_A^o}{k_2 - k_1} (e^{-k_1 t} - e^{-k_2 t}) \tag{14.612}$$

Two conditions must be imposed on Eq. 14.612 in order to cause it to reduce to Eq. 14.702:

1. $k_2 \gg k_1$; this will reduce Eq. 14.612 to the form

$$C_B = \frac{k_1 C_A^o}{k_2} (e^{-k_1 t} - e^{-k_2 t}) \tag{14.703}$$

and ensures that the concentration of the intermediate is very small relative to the concentration of stable species. It is not, however, a sufficient condition.

2. $t \gg 1/k_2$; this brings Eq. 14.703 to the form of Eq. 14.702, since it ensures that

$$e^{-k_1 t} \gg e^{-k_2 t} \tag{14.704}$$

and sufficient time has elapsed since the start of the reaction so that the intermediate is in the steady state, i.e., is in "quasi equilibrium" with stable species.

The approximation $dR/dt \simeq 0$ does *not* mean that the concentration of R is a constant throughout the reaction. It *does* mean, for example, in Eq. 14.701, where we have

$$k_2 C_B = k_1 C_A - \frac{dC_B}{dt} \tag{14.705}$$

that dC_B/dt is negligible in comparison with the quantity $k_1 C_A$, when the steady state conditions hold.

The Hydrogen-Bromine Reaction. If the intermediates in a complex reaction are involved in a cyclic process whereby they are constantly removed and then re-formed by reactions which *in toto* give rise to consumption of reactant and production of products, the phenomenon is called a *chain reaction*. One of the simplest, earliest, and best examples of such a reaction is

$$H_2 + Br_2 \rightarrow 2HBr$$

which was studied quantitatively by Bodenstein and Lind in 1907. The following reaction scheme applies:

$$Br_2 + M \quad \rightarrow 2Br \ + M \quad \text{(chain initiation)} \tag{1}$$

$$Br \ + H_2 \ \rightarrow HBr + H \quad \text{(chain propagation)} \tag{2}$$

$$H \ + Br_2 \ \rightarrow HBr + Br \quad \text{(chain propagation)} \tag{3}$$

$$H \ + HBr \rightarrow Br \ \ + H_2 \quad \text{(chain retardation)} \tag{4}$$

$$2Br + M \quad \rightarrow Br_2 \ + M \quad \text{(chain termination)} \tag{5}$$

Inspection of the mechanism reveals that bromine and hydrogen atoms are consumed and regenerated, with the production of product, in cyclic fashion by steps 2 and 3. They are the *chain carriers*.

For the above reaction, the chain-carrier concentrations quickly rise to a maximum and then slowly decay again to zero as the reaction proceeds to completion. This is characteristic of the *stationary chain* process. By contrast, in the water reaction $H_2 + \frac{1}{2}O_2 \rightarrow H_2O$, the concentrations of the chain carriers, such as hydrogen atoms, increase continuously and rapidly with time, because removal of a chain carrier by reaction gives rise to an average of more than one replacement. The reaction is termed *branching chain*, and the characteristics, which were developed by N. Semenoff, frequently include explosions. Nuclear explosions represent the most dramatic instance of branching chain processes.

Both stationary and branching chain processes may be recognized by some or all of the following characteristics: (*a*) an induction period; (*b*) peculiar non-integral kinetic order; (*c*) sensitivity of the rate to impurities, including oxygen (which may consume or produce chain carriers); (*d*) sensitivity of the rate to pressure, the shape of the reactor, packing of the reactor by "inert" solids, etc., which drastically affect the rate of initiation and termination processes; (*e*) explosions.

In addition to oxidation reactions, many other reactions, such as polymerization of olefins, hydrocarbon decompositions, and chlorinations, may display such behavior.

We illustrate the steady state method now for the hydrogen-bromine case. Application of the steady state approximation with use of the reaction scheme given above provides two equations from which the concentrations of the intermediates, bromine and hydrogen may be obtained:

$$\frac{dC_{Br}}{dt} \simeq 0 = 2k_1 C_{Br_2} C_M - k_2 C_{Br} C_{H_2} + k_3 C_H C_{Br_2} + k_4 C_H C_{HBr} - 2k_5 C_{Br}^2 C_M \tag{a}$$

and

$$\frac{dC_H}{dt} \simeq 0 = k_2 C_{Br} C_{H_2} - k_3 C_H C_{Br_2} - k_4 C_H C_{HBr} \tag{b}$$

From (*b*):

$$C_H = \frac{k_2 C_{Br} C_{H_2}}{k_3 C_{Br_2} + k_4 C_{HBr}} \tag{c}$$

From $(a) + (b)$: $0 = 2k_1 C_{Br_2} C_M - 2k_5 C_{Br}^2 C_M$

or

$$C_{Br} = \left(\frac{k_1 C_{Br_2}}{k_5}\right)^{1/2} \tag{d}$$

Substitution of (d) into (c) also will give C_H in terms of stable species C_{H_2}, C_{Br_2}, and C_{HBr}. Now

$$\frac{dC_{HBr}}{dt} = k_2 C_{Br} C_{H_2} + k_3 C_H C_{Br_2} - k_4 C_H C_{HBr} \tag{e}$$

Substitution of (c) and (d) into (e) gives

$$\frac{dC_{HBr}}{dt} = \frac{2(k_1/k_5)^{1/2} k_2 C_{Br_2}^{3/2} C_{H_2}}{C_{Br_2} + (k_4/k_3) C_{HBr}} \tag{14.706}$$

which is the expression found empirically by Bodenstein and Lind. It is convenient to write also

$$\frac{dC_{HBr}}{dt} = \frac{2(k_1/k_5)^{1/2} k_2 C_{Br_2}^{1/2} C_{H_2}}{1 + k_4 C_{HBr}/k_3 C_{Br_2}} \tag{14.707}$$

At $t = 0$ and $C_{HBr} = 0$,

$$\left(\frac{dC_{HBr}}{dt}\right)_{t=0} = 2\left(\frac{k_1}{k_5}\right)^{1/2} k_2 C_{Br_2}^{1/2} C_{H_2} \tag{14.708}$$

which is a $\frac{3}{2}$ total-order rate law. We may define k_{obs} as $2k_1^{1/2} k_2/k_5^{1/2}$.

The form of these expressions corresponds to the chemistry involved: the half-power of C_{Br_2} follows from the equilibrium between bromine molecules and atoms, while the occurrence of C_{HBr} in the denominator expresses its inhibitive effect.

Chain initiation may be brought about by the use of light energy. For example, H_2 and Cl_2 mixtures are stable in the dark at room temperature, but light dissociates Cl_2 and starts the reaction.

The student may well ask two questions. (a) Why are not $2H + M \rightarrow H_2 + M$ and $H + Br + M \rightarrow HBr + M$ termination steps? (b) Why has the inhibiting reverse reaction of step 3, $Br + HBr \rightarrow Br_2 + H$, not been considered? Our knowledge of rate constant expressions already gained earlier for such elementary reactions provides the answers:

(a) The relative rates of the bimolecular propagation steps 2 and 3,

$$Br + H_2 \rightarrow HBr + H \tag{2}$$

$$H + Br_2 \rightarrow HBr + Br \tag{3}$$

determine which of the two chain carriers is of lesser reactivity and is present at higher steady state concentration. Mathematically, this can be seen from relation (c) above, where

$$\frac{C_H}{C_{Br}} = \frac{k_2 C_{H_2}}{k_3 C_{Br_2} + k_4 C_{HBr}} \tag{14.709}$$

At low values of C_{HBr} only reactions 2 and 3 are important (the occurrence of some reaction 4 only tends to lower C_H relatively still further). Since both reactions 2 and 3 involve an atom plus a diatomic molecule, the Arrhenius A for both is not much different from $\mathscr{z}$, and the entropies of activation must be similar. Thus the heat of activation or activation energy will largely determine their relative specific rates. The known bond dissociation energies are $D_0(\text{H—H}) = 103$ kcal mole^{-1}, $D_0(\text{H—Br}) = 87$ kcal mole^{-1}, and $D_0(\text{Br—Br}) = 46$ kcal mole^{-1}. Reaction 2 is at least 16 kcal mole^{-1} *endothermic*, which is the minimum value of ΔE_0; E_a is actually 17 kcal mole^{-1}. Reaction 3 is 41 kcal mole^{-1} exothermic, and $E_a \sim$ 1 kcal mole^{-1}, so the relative rates of steps 2 and 3 will differ by a large factor $(e^{-16,000/RT})$ and $C_{Br} \gg C_H$. Thus termination involves bromine atoms only.

In the $H_2 + Cl_2$ reaction, the attack on H_2 by chlorine is more efficient than by bromine since $D(\text{HCl}) = 101$ kcal mole^{-1}. The resulting reduced concentration of chlorine makes a termination step $2Cl + M \rightarrow Cl_2 + M$ much slower, with the consequence that the chain steps, $H_2 + Cl$ followed by $Cl_2 + H$, have "infinite" length, and cause a "thermal" explosion because of the rapid rise of temperature for this exothermic process.

(b) The relative rates of the reverse of reaction 2 (which is reaction 4) and the reverse of reaction 3, which are both of the same type as before, are determined largely by ΔE_0 for the same reasons given above. Reaction 4 is 16 kcal mole^{-1} exothermic and involves an activation energy of ~ 1 kcal mole^{-1}, while from the data already given, the reverse of step 3 has $E_a = 42$ kcal mole^{-1} and is hopelessly slow. So reaction 4 competes effectively with reaction 3 and HBr is a retarder for this reason, but the reverse of 3 cannot compete with reaction 2.

In the H_2–Cl_2 reaction, HCl is not an inhibitor, since the activation energy is much larger for abstraction of hydrogen from HCl by hydrogen than it was from HBr. Sometimes dirt on the walls is an inhibitor and reacts with the chlorine preferentially, thus stopping the chains. O_2 impurity is an inhibitor and removes hydrogen by association to form HO_2 in what may be called a three-body process with zero activation energy. This reaction, however, does not preponderate over $H + Cl_2$, for which $E_a \simeq 3$ kcal mole^{-1}, because of the low $\mathscr{z}$ value of trimolecular processes. It cannot compete effectively with $H + Br_2$, for which $E_a \simeq 1$ kcal mole^{-1} only, and the hydrogen bromide reaction is not inhibited by O_2.

The Rice-Herzfeld Mechanisms. An important instance of stationary chain reactions is provided by the thermal decomposition of organic compounds. In 1929, F. Paneth demonstrated that unstable free radicals occurred on the pyrolysis of organic compounds (Fig. 14.701). For example, $Pb(CH_3)_4$ was produced on pyrolysis of acetone and passage of the decomposition products over a lead mirror following the furnace. F. O. Rice and K. F. Herzfeld (1934) put forward some mechanisms to explain how the observed behavior of organic decompositions, including first-order findings, could occur by a complex radical scheme.

Consider the following reaction scheme, in which M stands for a stable molecule and R for a highly reactive radical:

$$M_1 \xrightarrow{k_1} R_1 + M_2 \tag{1}$$

$$R_1 + M_1 \xrightarrow{k_2} R_1H + R_2 \tag{2}$$

$$R_2 \xrightarrow{k_3} R_1 + M_3 \tag{3}$$

$$R_1 + R_2 \xrightarrow{k_4} M_4 \tag{4}$$

Step 1 is chain initiation by unimolecular decomposition of M_1. Since $k_1 \sim 10^{13} e^{-E_1/RT}$, k_1 is very small because E_1 is of the order of magnitude of the dissociation energy D for bond rupture, e.g., $D(C\!-\!C) \simeq 80$ kcal mole^{-1} (Table

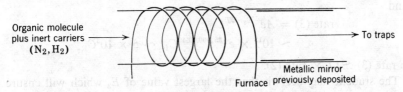

Organic molecule plus inert carriers (N_2, H_2) → ... → To traps

Metallic mirror
Furnace previously deposited

Fig. 14.701 Schematic Paneth-type experiment.

9.203). Steps 2 and 3 are chain propagation. The bimolecular rate constant k_2 may be characterized as $k_2 \simeq \mathscr{P} z e^{-E/RT}$, where we found $\mathscr{P} \simeq 10^{-4}$ for such a reaction type, and E_2 is experimentally found to be $\simeq 10$ kcal mole^{-1}. Step 3 is again a unimolecular decomposition and $k_3 \simeq 10^{13} e^{-E_3/RT}$. If $E_3 \simeq D_3$ is very large, k_3 would be very small. This would mean a very inefficient chain process and would imply $C_{R_2} \gg C_{R_1}$; chain termination would have to be $2R_2 \rightarrow (R_2)_2$ rather than the given reaction 4. For rate 3 to be comparable with rate 2, so that 4 is reasonable, E_3 must be $\leqslant 40$ kcal mole^{-1}. The higher value of E_3 relative to E_2 is permissible for comparable magnitudes of the rates of 2 and 3, because the former depends on the concentration of M_1 as well as R_1, while 3 does not.

The concentrations of R_1 and R_2 may be eliminated by solution of the simultaneous equations

$$\frac{dC_{R_1}}{dt} \simeq 0 = k_1 C_{M_1} - k_2 C_{R_1} C_{M_1} + k_3 C_{R_2} - k_4 C_{R_1} C_{R_2} \tag{14.710}$$

$$\frac{dC_{R_2}}{dt} \simeq 0 = k_2 C_{R_1} C_{M_1} - k_3 C_{R_2} - k_4 C_{R_1} C_{R_2} \tag{14.711}$$

Summing,

$$0 = k_1 C_{M_1} - 2k_4 C_{R_1} C_{R_2} \tag{14.712}$$

Substitution for C_{R_2} from Eq. 14.711 in 14.712 yields finally

$$C_{R_1} \simeq \left(\frac{k_1 k_3}{2k_2 k_4} \right)^{1/2} \tag{14.713}$$

Then for the rate of disappearance of reactant we have

$$-\frac{dC_{M_1}}{dt} = k_1 C_{M_1} + k_2 C_{R_1} C_{M_1} = k_1 \left[1 + \left(\frac{k_2 k_3}{2 k_1 k_4} \right)^{1/2} \right] C_{M_1} \qquad (14.714)$$

which is a first-order rate law.

ILLUSTRATION.   Find the relative magnitudes of steps 2 and 3, given $E_2 =$ 10 kcal, $E_3 = 35$ kcal, and M_1 present at 76 cm Hg ($t = 546°C$).
      Now,

$$\text{rate (2)} = \mathscr{P} \mathdefault{z} e^{-E_2/RT} C_{M_1} C_{R_1}$$

$$\simeq 10^{-4} \times 10^{14} \times e^{-10,000/2 \times 819} C_{M_1} C_{R_1} \text{ moles cc}^{-1} \text{ sec}^{-1}$$

$$\simeq 10^{-4} \times 10^{14} \times e^{-6.1} \times 1.5 \times 10^{-5} C_{R_1}$$

$$\simeq 3 \times 10^2 C_{R_1} \text{ moles cc}^{-1} \text{ sec}^{-1}$$

And

$$\text{rate (3)} = A e^{-E_3/RT} C_{R_2}$$

$$\sim 10^{13} \times e^{-35,000/1640} C_{R_2} \sim 5 \times 10^3 C_{R_2}$$

so rate (3) $\simeq 17 \times$ rate (2).
      The student may see whether the largest value of E_3 which will ensure rate (2) $< (5) \times$ rate (3) (at a pressure of M_1 of 10 cm) exceeds 40 kcal mole^{-1} appreciably.

Chain Length.   Equation 14.714 shows that the rate is the sum of the first step plus a later chain portion.   The ratio

$$\text{CL} = \frac{k_1 C_{M_1} + k_2 C_{R_1} C_{M_1}}{k_1 C_{M_1}} = 1 + \left(\frac{k_2 k_3}{2 k_1 k_4} \right)^{1/2} \qquad (14.715)$$

gives a measure of the chain length of the reaction.
      Observed Activation Energy.   The value of E_1 was indicated to be ~ 80 kcal mole^{-1} in many cases, while on the other hand E_a is found experimentally to be less.   This is explained as follows.   For long chains we simplify Eq. 14.714 as

$$-\frac{dC_{M_1}}{dt} = \left(\frac{k_1 k_2 k_3}{2 k_4} \right)^{1/2} C_{M_1} = k_{obs} C_{M_1} \qquad (14.716)$$

Then, recalling the general Arrhenius equation $k = A e^{-E/RT}$, and substituting into Eq. 14.716 for each k factor, we have

$$E_a = E_{obs} = \tfrac{1}{2}(E_1 + E_2 + E_3 - E_4)$$

Using $E_1 = 80$, $E_2 = 10$, $E_3 = 35$, $E_4 = 0$ kcal mole^{-1}, $E_{obs} = 62$ kcal mole^{-1}, which is 18 kcal mole^{-1} below E_1.
      Other Reaction Orders.   The proper termination step might be $2R_1 \rightarrow (R_1)_2$ or $2R_2 \rightarrow (R_2)_2$, depending on the relative rates of steps 2 and 3.   If $E_3 = 40$ kcal mole^{-1}, the latter would be favored.   On the other hand, if E_3 is low, ~ 20 kcal

mole^{-1} corresponding to low stability, then $2R_1$ is favored and different observed order would result.

ILLUSTRATION. The decomposition of acetone, although somewhat more complex, is closely related to the above scheme.

$$CH_3COCH_3 \rightarrow CH_3\cdot + \cdot COCH_3 \tag{1}$$
$$\cdot COCH_3 \rightarrow CH_3\cdot + CO \tag{2}$$
$$CH_3\cdot + CH_3COCH_3 \rightarrow CH_4 + \cdot CH_2COCH_3 \tag{3}$$
$$\cdot CH_2COCH_3 \rightarrow CH_3\cdot + CH_2{=}CO \tag{4}$$
$$CH_3\cdot + \cdot CH_2COCH_3 \rightarrow C_2H_5COCH_3 \tag{5}$$

The pyrolysis of acetone on a hot wire is in fact a convenient laboratory method for the preparation of ketene.

General Remarks. It is now believed that, although radical chain processes are a prominent feature of most organic molecule decompositions, not all reactions necessarily involve radical intermediates; internal molecular rearrangement processes may also occur. Thus one may have

$$C_2H_6 \rightarrow 2CH_3\cdot$$
$$\rightarrow C_2H_4 + H_2$$

It is possible to inhibit the chain process, and either favor molecular rearrangement processes or assist in isolation of the first radical initiation step by adding free radical "traps." Propylene, NO, and toluene have been widely used to trap and quench free radicals, e.g.,

$$CH_3\cdot + NO \rightarrow CH_3NO \rightarrow \text{other molecules of no concern}$$
$$CH_3\cdot + C_6H_5CH_3 \rightarrow CH_4 + C_6H_5CH_2$$

where the benzyl radical is a relatively unreactive radical that usually dimerizes. The toluene-carrier technique of M. Szwarc has been widely applied.

Branching Chains. The water formation reaction is an example of a branching chain process. A plausible mechanism is

H_2	$\rightarrow 2H$	(initiation)
$H + O_2$	$\rightarrow OH + O$	(branching propagation)
$O + H_2$	$\rightarrow OH + H$	(branching propagation)
$H + O_2$	$\rightarrow HO_2$	(propagation)
$HO_2 + H_2$	$\rightarrow H_2O + OH$	(chain transfer)
$HO_2 + \text{wall impurity}$	$\rightarrow \text{destruction}$	(termination)
$H + \text{gas impurity}$	$\rightarrow \text{destruction}$	(termination)

Although the fourth and fifth steps give rise to no increase in total number of chain carriers, the second and third steps double the number of carriers and cause *branching* of subsequent processes. The quantitative treatment of branching chain processes was given first by Semenoff in 1927.

The above system may be idealized as

$$M_1 \xrightarrow{k_1} 2R_1 \tag{1}$$

$$R_1 + M_1 \xrightarrow{k_2} \alpha R_2 \tag{2}$$

$$R_2 + M_1 \xrightarrow{k_3} R_1 + M_2 \tag{3}$$

$$R_1 + \text{wall} \xrightarrow{k_s} M_3 \tag{4}$$

$$R_1 + M_4 \xrightarrow{k_g} M_5 \tag{5}$$

Equation 2 is a branching reaction with $\alpha > 1$. Step 4 represents heterogeneous destruction of the chain carrier at the wall surface, while step 5 is some gas-phase homogeneous termination step. Thus the rate of the reaction and its characteristics may well depend on the geometry of the vessel, packing, etc.

If we assume that the steady state treatment applies, then

$$C_{R_1} = \frac{2k_1 C_{M_1}}{(1 - \alpha)k_2 C_{M_1} + k_s + k_g C_{M_4}}$$

$$C_{R_2} = \frac{2\alpha k_1 k_2 C_{M_1}/k_3}{(1 - \alpha)k_2 C_{M_1} + k_s + k_g C_{M_4}} \tag{14.717}$$

The rate of consumption of reactant M_1 is then

$$-\frac{dC_{M_1}}{dt} = k_1 C_{M_1} + k_2 C_{R_1} C_{M_1} + k_3 C_{R_2} C_{M_1}$$

$$= \left[k_1 + \frac{2k_1 k_2 C_{M_1} + 2\alpha k_1 k_2 C_{M_1}}{k_s + k_g C_{M_4} - (\alpha - 1)k_2 C_{M_1}} \right] C_{M_1} \tag{14.718}$$

and, neglecting the term in k_1, the slow initiation step,

$$-\frac{dC_{M_1}}{dt} = \frac{2k_1 k_2 (1 + \alpha) C_{M_1}^2}{k_s + k_g C_{M_4} - (\alpha - 1)k_2 C_{M_1}} \tag{14.719}$$

From Eq. 14.718 it is seen that:

(a) If $\alpha = 1$, i.e., no branching, the equation is perfectly well-behaved and

$$-\frac{dC_{M_1}}{dt} = \frac{4k_1 k_2 C_{M_1}^2}{k_s + k_g C_{M_4}} \tag{14.720}$$

(b) If $\alpha > 1$, the magnitude of the denominator of Eq. 14.719 becomes smaller as α increases, or as $(k_s + k_g C_{M_4})$ decreases. Eventually, for a critical value of α given by

$$\alpha = 1 + \frac{k_s + k_g C_{M_4}}{k_2 C_{M_1}} \tag{14.721}$$

the denominator is zero and the rate infinite, that is, explosion occurs. Since the number of chain carriers increases without limit, the steady state method is not applicable to describe the explosion.

When and if explosion occurs thus depends strongly on k_s and $k_g C_{M_4}$. k_s depends on vessel shape; k_g varies with pressure. This explains the occurrence of "explosion limits," which depend on pressure and temperature, vessel geometry, and nature of the wall surface.

Problems

14.701   Find the rate law for production of ketene from the mechanism for acetone pyrolysis.

*14.702   Given $D(F\text{—}F) = 38$ kcal mole^{-1}, $D(I\text{—}I) = 36$ kcal mole^{-1}, $D(H\text{—}F) = 133$ kcal mole^{-1}, and $D(H\text{—}I) = 76$ kcal mole^{-1}, what features different from the hydrogen bromide reaction might you expect for the hydrogen fluoride and hydrogen iodide reactions, neglecting any other complicating factors? Is the hydrogen iodide reaction a chain process?

14.703   Obtain the expression for the disappearance of Br_2, in the $H_2 + Br_2$ reaction and evaluate its magnitude at $t = 0$ in terms of HBr production.

14.704   Show that Eq. 14.713 may be readily obtained by the recognition that the term $(k_4 C_{R_1} C_{R_2})$ in Eq. 14.711 is negligible, since it involves two very low concentrations.

14.705   Given $E_4 \sim 0$ and $k_4 \simeq y$, apply Eq. 14.715 to calculate the chain length, using the other values suggested in the text for k_1, k_2, and k_3.

14.706   Use the steady state method to show that in the Rice-Herzfeld scheme $2R_2 \rightarrow (R_2)_2$ for termination leads to 0.5 order, and $2R_1 \rightarrow (R_1)_2$ leads to 1.5 order, in the rate law for disappearance of M.

*14.707   Evaluate E_{obs} from Eq. 14.708 and your knowledge of reactions 1, 2, and 5.

14.708   Why would lowering total pressure have opposite effects on the importance of heterogeneous and of homogeneous termination steps in branching chain reactions?

8. Solution Reactions

Comparison with Gas-Phase Reaction. Much of the theoretical treatment previously given for gases may be readily extended to solution reactions. A number of gas reactions, particularly unimolecular ones, proceed in nonpolar solvents with only slightly changed rates and values of the Arrhenius parameters. The decomposition of N_2O_5 in carbon tetrachloride and the isomerization of pinene and of p-tolyl isocyanide in hydrocarbon solvents are examples. For the isocyanide, the rate at 200°C is $k = 4.5 \times 10^{-4}$ sec^{-1} in Nujol solvent, and the high-pressure gas value, $k_\infty = 7.5 \times 10^{-4}$ sec^{-1}, differs by less than a factor of 2. For the gas, $E_a = 33.8$ kcal mole^{-1} and $A = 10^{12.5}$ sec^{-1}, in solution, $E_a = 36.8$, $A = 10^{13.7}$ sec^{-1}. These values actually differ by scarcely more than the possible experimental error.

Important rate differences, however, are frequently found in polar solvents where solute-solvent interaction occurs; the reactant is frequently called the *substrate*. Also, while gas-phase thermal reactions almost invariably involve neutral species, a great variety of solution reactions in polar solvents are ionic in character. Some or all of the reactants, the activated complex, or the product may be ions; in less polar solvents, ion pairs have been shown to be of particular importance in reaction mechanisms. Acid-base homogeneous catalysis reactions, of which there are only a few gas-phase examples, are preponderantly ionic in mechanism and are an important class of solution reactions.

Ionic reactions are virtually absent in the gas phase because of the large free energy of formation of ions in the absence of a polar solvent. C. A. Winkler has shown that the Menschutkin reaction

$$R_3N + R'X \rightarrow [R_3R'N]^+X^-$$

which involves ionic intermediates and products, and which proceeds homogeneously in polar solvents, becomes heterogeneous in nonpolar solvents and proceeds only on the highly polar glass wall. This is also the nature of many, but by no means all, instances of heterogeneity in gas-phase reactions.

We shall not consider the extensive subject of the mechanisms of solution reactions and of acid-base catalysis. The student may consult the references cited at the end of this section. Later, we shall discuss briefly some physical chemical aspects of these reactions related to the dielectric constant property of the solvent and to the ionic strength of the solution. First, however, we shall examine the definition of collision number in solution.

Collisions and Encounters. The rate of collisions in solution between two species, in the absence of an interaction potential, is given roughly, although not exactly, by $\mathscr{Z}_{AB}$ for gases (Eq. 6.502). Furthermore, although the number of such collisions is roughly the same, they are no longer randomly distributed. Two molecules A and B which collide in solution tend to be trapped together in a solvent cage, as suggested by J. Franck and E. Rabinowitch, and experience multiple collisions; such an *encounter* is terminated by diffusion apart of A and B. *Secondary* encounters of A and B are very important. Caging can be demonstrated in several ways. One way involves the composition of the products formed when free radicals or atoms are produced in solution in the presence of a scavenger; methyl or other radicals can be produced in pairs in close proximity to each other, i.e., in *geminate* fashion, as by the decomposition of acetyl peroxide

$$(CH_3CO-O-)_2 \rightarrow 2\dot{C}H_3 + CO_2$$

or of azoalkyls

$$R-N{=}N-R \rightarrow 2\dot{R} + N_2$$

It is almost impossible to prevent formation of ethane by methyl recombination even in the presence of relatively large concentrations of very efficient scavengers such as I_2,

$$\dot{C}H_3 + I_2 \rightarrow CH_3I + I$$

To inhibit recombination completely it is necessary to make the solvent the scavenger.

Studies of geminate and secondary recombination may be related to information about the appropriate diffusion coefficient $\mathscr{D}$ of the solute. Experimentally, the use of inert gases at variable high pressures provides more control of the diffusion coefficient $\mathscr{D}$ than does the use of different solvents and simulates condensed phase behavior.

For the calculation of collision numbers of solute and solvent molecules, a different approach from the gas-phase treatment is appropriate. Since any molecule in the solvent is surrounded by N_s neighbors, a molecule will have changed half its neighbors by the time τ it has diffused to a new adjacent site at a distance which is a little greater than its own diameter, σ, because of the lattice imperfection and "free volume" of the liquid (Chapter 11). A rough idea of the free volume is given by the volume increase observed when many solids (not water) melt, say ~ 10 per cent. From Eq. 13.208 we have as a crude estimate

$$6\tau\mathscr{D}_{AS} \simeq \sigma^2 \tag{14.801}$$

where $\mathscr{D}_{AS}$ refers to the substrate A in the solvent S. Since in time τ the number of encounters made is $N_s/2$, the specific rate of encounters by one molecule is

$$\mathscr{L}'_{AS} \simeq \frac{6\mathscr{D}_{AS}N_s}{2\sigma^2} = \frac{3\mathscr{D}_{AS}N_s}{\sigma^2} \text{ sec}^{-1} \tag{14.802}$$

N_s has the maximum value of 12 (Chapter 15) for hexagonal close packing. If the mole fraction of reactant B in the solvent is X_B, where $X_B \ll 1$, then the rate of encounters of a molecule of A with other solute molecules B is

$$\mathscr{L}'_{AB} \simeq \frac{3\mathscr{D}_{AS}N_s X_B}{\sigma^2} \tag{14.803}$$

The above rough description contains implicit assumptions regarding the randomness of diffusive events and the absence of an attractive potential to describe the interaction of A. More refined treatments and discussion are described in the References.

ILLUSTRATION.   Find the approximate duration of an encounter by A with a solvent molecule.

Consider some reasonable, but arbitrarily specified, properties of the system. From Eq. 14.801,

$$\tau = \frac{\sigma^2}{6\mathscr{D}_{AS}}$$

Let $\sigma = 6 \times 10^{-8}$ cm; then from Eq. 13.207

$$\mathscr{D}_{AS} \simeq 0.5\bar{c}_{AS}\lambda$$

where λ, the mean free path, is of the order of 3 per cent of σ, and where $\bar{c}_{AS}$ is the mean relative speed. At 300°K, for appropriate values of m_A and m_S, $\bar{c}_{AS} \simeq 10^4$ cm sec^{-1}.

Then

$$\mathscr{D}_{AS} \simeq 0.5 \times 10^4 \times 1.8 \times 10^{-9} \simeq 10^{-5} \text{ cm}^2 \text{ sec}^{-1}$$

and

$$\tau \simeq 36 \times 10^{-16}/6 \times 10^{-5} = 6 \times 10^{-11} \text{ sec}$$

Since A changes only half its neighbors, in time τ, the duration of each encounter is $\sim 2 \times 6 \times 10^{-11} \simeq 10^{-10}$ sec.

The number of collisions made by a molecule with the molecules of the "walls" of the solvent cage is $\sim 10^4/1.8 \times 10^{-9} = 5.5 \times 10^{12}$ sec^{-1}, and in 10^{-10} sec is ~ 550.

The student may find roughly the number of encounters and collisions made by A with B if X_B is 0.01.

References

Franck, J., and E. Rabinowitch, *Trans. Faraday Soc.*, **30**, 120 (1934).
Herk. C., M. Feld, and M. Szwarc, *J. Am. Chem. Soc.*, **83**, 2998 (1961).
Noyes, R. M., *Progr. in Reaction Kinetics*, **1**, 129 (1961).

Absolute Rate Theory and the Brønsted-Bjerrum Equation. The consideration of gas reactions assumed ideal behavior. For solution reactions such an assumption is scarcely realistic. Equation 14.319,

$$k = \kappa \frac{kT}{h} K^* = \kappa \frac{kT}{h} \frac{N'^*}{N'_A N'_B} \tag{14.319}$$

becomes for solutions

$$k_s = \kappa \frac{kT}{h} K_s^* \frac{\gamma_A \gamma_B}{\gamma^*} \tag{14.804}$$

where

$$K_s^* = \frac{a^*}{a_A a_B} = \frac{N'^* \gamma^*}{N'_A N'_B \gamma_A \gamma_B} \tag{14.805}$$

and a represents activity. The ideal state is defined as that corresponding to solute behavior at infinite dilution, for which the coefficients γ are unity; hence

$$k_s = k_{0s} \frac{\gamma_A \gamma_B}{\gamma^*} \tag{14.806}$$

where k_{0s} is the rate constant at infinite dilution. This equation was first derived in another manner by J. N. Brønsted and by N. Bjerrum in the early twenties.

The gas-phase rate may be related to k_s through Henry's law relation between gaseous pressure and solution concentration of the reactants. For unimolecular reactions, especially, if A and A* are very similar, k and k_s may also be similar in magnitude, as found previously.

In general, heats of activation for reaction in solution, ΔH_s^*, are related to those in the gas phase by the differences in heats of solution of the reactants and activated complex. An important factor in determining this is the relative degree of solvation of reactants and complex. If both reactants and products are of low polarity, and hence the complex is also of low polarity (since it will resemble usually either reactants or products), there is little change in ΔH^*. If the complex is more solvated than the reactants, then ΔH_s^* is lower than ΔH^*, and vice versa.

Parallel changes in the entropy of activation, ΔS^*, occur. When the complex is more solvated than the reactants, $\Delta H_s^* < \Delta H^*$; this means relative loss of translational degrees of freedom of the "bound" solvent molecules and a decreased value of ΔS_s^* relative to ΔS^*.

Such parallel changes are of common occurrence and are partially compensatory.

Ionic Reactions; Variation of Ionic Strength of Solution.   Consider the reaction

$$A^{z_A} + B^{z_B} \rightarrow X^{*(z_A + z_B)} \rightarrow Pr$$

where z_A, z_B are charges of any magnitude and sign. The Debye-Hückel expression for the activity coefficients of the various ions γ_i, which is similar in form to Eq. 12.235 for the experimentally accessible quantity $\gamma_{\pm}$, is

$$\ln \gamma_i = \frac{-C_1 z_i^2 I^{1/2}}{1 + C_2 I^{1/2}} \tag{14.807}$$

where C_1 and C_2 are constants. For the limiting dilution case (Eq. 12.236),

$$\ln \gamma_i \simeq -C_1 z_i^2 I^{1/2}$$

On substituting Eq. 14.807 in Eq. 14.806, written in the form

$$\ln k_s = \ln k_{0s} + \ln \gamma_A + \ln \gamma_B - \ln \gamma^*$$

there is obtained

$$\ln k_s = \ln k_{0s} + C_1 I^{1/2}[(z_A + z_B)^2 - z_A^2 - z_B^2]$$
$$= \ln k_{0s} + 2C_1 I^{1/2} z_A z_B \tag{14.808}$$

At 25°C, for aqueous solution,

$$\log k_s = \log k_{0s} + 1.02 I^{1/2} z_A z_B \tag{14.809}$$

or, more accurately,

$$= \log k_{0s} + \frac{1.02 z_A z_B I^{1/2}}{1 + 2 I^{1/2}} \tag{14.810}$$

Reaction between an Ion and a Neutral Molecule.   In this case $z_B = 0$, and in the above approximation, $k_s = k_{0s}$ and is independent of ionic strength. This is valid only in the limiting region and for molecules having no dipole moment.

The ionic strength may be altered by addition of inert salts; the resulting behavior was termed the *primary* salt effect by Brønsted. An example of an ion-molecule reaction is shown in Fig. 14.801 for the hydrolysis of γ-butyrolactone in aqueous solution. The quantity $\log k/k_0$ is actually found to depend linearly on I at high values, but the effect is small and irregular; the uni-univalent inert electrolytes NaCl and NaClO$_4$ actually give opposite effects.

Reaction between Two Ions. The rates of reactions between two ions are strongly influenced by the charges on the ions. Compare, for example,

$$NH_4^+ + CNO^- \rightarrow (NH_2)_2CO \tag{1}$$

and

$$ClO_2^- + ClO_2^- \rightarrow ClO^- + ClO_3^- \tag{2}$$

In the first reaction there is an attractive coulombic energy term which tends to

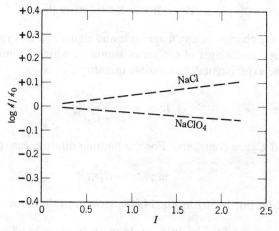

Fig. 14.801   Plot of logarithm of the relative rate of hydrolysis of γ-butyrolactone in various salt solutions. (Adapted by permission from A. Frost and R. G. Pearson, *Kinetics and Mechanism*, Second Edition, John Wiley and Sons, 1961.)

lower ΔH^*, while in the second case the result is the opposite. However, it turns out that an even more important effect influences ΔS^*. For reaction 1 the charge on the activated complex is zero, and its solvation, i.e., ordered solute-solvent structure, is reduced relative to the reactants; ΔS^* tends to be large. In reaction 2, the activated complex bears a double charge and the degree of solvation is considerably enhanced relative to the reactants, so that ΔS^* declines. Glasstone, Laidler, and Eyring show that in water, for which $D = 80$, the effect on the rate should be an increase of a factor of ~ 100 for each decrease of the product $z_A z_B$ by one unit.

The variation of rate with increase of ionic strength is described by Eq. 14.810. It predicts a positive effect on the rate if A and B have charges of the same sign, and a negative effect if they are of opposite sign. It should be understood that D is to be constant for all values of I. The value k_0 refers to a particular D value.

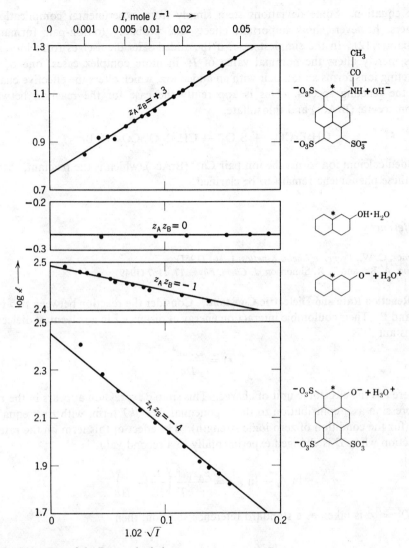

Fig. 14.802 Test of the Brønsted relation:

$$\log k = \log k_0 + z_A z_B \frac{1.02 \sqrt{I}}{1 + 2 \sqrt{I}}$$

[adapted by permission from A. Weller, *Progr. in Reaction Kinetics*, **1**, 205 (1961)]; in connection with the $z_A z_B = 0$ plot, note the lesser values of ionic strength relative to Fig. 14.801.

Successful applications of Eq. 14.810 include the one of Fig. 14.802 for acid-base reactions of excited organic ions (the details of which are unimportant here). The predicted zero effect, when $z_A z_B = 0$, should be noted. There are, however, many cases in which the effects observed upon addition of electrolyte do not conform to the equation. Some deviations stem simply from experimental complications; others, however, show important effects due probably to ion-pair formation (Chapter 12). In the simplest case, if the added salts themselves form ion-pairs this merely alters the nominal value of I; in more complex cases, one of the reacting ions forms an ion pair with an added ion, which alters the effective charge of the reacting species. This is apparently the case for the reaction between bromacetate ($BrAc^-$) and thiosulfate,

$$CH_2BrCO_2^- + S_2O_3^= \rightarrow CH_2(S_2O_3)CO_2^= + Br^-$$

Added calcium ion forms the ion pair $Ca^{++}(BrAc^-)$, which is the reactant. Many of these phenomena remain to be clarified.

References

Davies, C. W., *Progr. in Chem. Kinetics*, **1**, 161 (1961).
Olson, A. R., and T. R. Simonson, *J. Chem. Phys.*, **17**, 1167 (1949).

Reaction Rate and Dielectric Constant. Consider the reaction between two ions A and B. Their coulombic interaction energy at distance r in a solvent of dielectric constant D is

$$V(r) = \frac{z_A z_B e^2}{Dr} \tag{14.811}$$

where e is the electronic unit of charge. This simple expression appears in the rate expression as a contribution to the exponential $\Delta H^*/kT$ term, with r set equal to r^* (for the condition of zero ionic strength). The effect of this term on the rate of reaction when D is changed experimentally to a second value is

$$\ln k_0 - \ln k_0' = \frac{z_A z_B e^2}{r^* kT} \left(\frac{1}{D_2} - \frac{1}{D} \right)$$

If $D' = \infty$ is taken as a standard reference solution, then

$$\ln k_0 = \ln k_0^\infty - \frac{z_A z_B e^2}{r^* kT D} \tag{14.812}$$

an equation due to G. Scatchard (1930). The plot of $\ln k_0$ against $1/D$ should be a straight line of slope $(-z_A z_B \times \text{const})$. If z_A and z_B have the same sign, then as D increases k_0 increases; and if the signs are unlike, the effect of increase of D is to decrease k_0. Experimentally, k_0 is found by extrapolation in each solvent from finite concentration to $I = 0$. Figure 14.803 illustrates the effect for two reactions for which $z_A z_B = 2$ and -2, respectively.

Fast Solution Reactions; Relaxation and Other Methods. The examples of ionic reactions mentioned above were fairly slow processes. By contrast, there are ionic reactions which occur so fast that the observed rate may be governed by diffusion, e.g.,

$$H^+ + OH^- \rightarrow H_2O$$
$$Ag^+ + Cl^- \rightarrow AgCl$$

M. Eigen has measured the rates of reactions which are complete in a time of 10^{-9} sec or less. The method involves a sudden small disturbance of a system in equilibrium, and the measurement of the rate at which the system relaxes back to the equilibrium condition. When a system is very near to equilibrium, the rate at

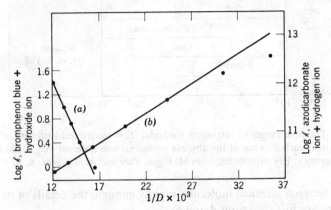

Fig. 14.803   Relation between rate constant and dielectric constant (by permission from A. Frost and R. G. Pearson, *Kinetics and Mechanism*, Second Edition, John Wiley and Sons, 1961).

(a) Bromphenol blue + hydroxide (Amis and LaMer)

$$BPB^= + OH^- \rightarrow BPB\ OH^{\equiv}$$

(b) Azodicarbonate + hydrogen ion (King and Josephs)

$$N_2(CO_2)^= + H^+ \rightarrow HN_2(CO_2)^-$$

which it approaches equilibrium is taken to be proportional to the free energy displacement from equilibrium. For a perturbation from equilibrium, given as Δn in concentration,

$$\frac{d\,\Delta n}{dt} = -k\,\Delta n$$

where $1/k = \tau$ is the relaxation time.

Several methods for rapidly disturbing equilibrium ionic systems have been used (Fig. 14.804): (1) periodic pressure variation associated with sound absorption; (2) periodic electric field variation; (3) temperature jump caused by a brief high-voltage impulse.

By these methods rate constants have been measured for a number of processes such as

(1) $H^+ + OH^- \rightarrow H_2O$; $k = 1.5 \times 10^{11}$ l mole^{-1} sec^{-1}
(2) $H^+ + SO_4^= \rightarrow HSO_4^-$; $k = 10^{11}$ l mole^{-1} sec^{-1}
(3) $NH_4^+ + OH^- \rightarrow NH_3 \cdot H_2O$; $k = 4 \times 10^{10}$ l mole^{-1} sec^{-1}

Nuclear magnetic resonance phenomena (Chapter 16) have also been applied to the measurement of fast reactions. For example, the rapid transfer of the proton to NH_3 from H_2O in reaction 5 (cf. reaction 3) causes its resonance properties to appear as characteristic of neither NH_4^+ or H_2O. Similarly, if the proton is

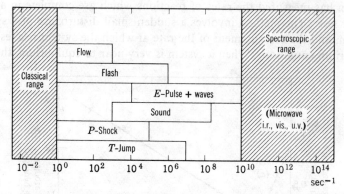

Fig. 14.804 The time ranges of relaxation methods: E = electric field strength, P = pressure, T = temperature, each division of the abscissa represents one order of magnitude in reciprocal time (or frequency). [By permission, from M. Eigen, *Pure and Appl. Chem.*, **6**, 97 (1963).]

exchanged between identical molecules rapidly enough, the details of its molecular environment are lost (reactions 4 and 6).

(4) $H_2O + H_3O^+ \rightarrow H_3O^+ + H_2O$

(5) $NH_3 + H_2O \rightarrow NH_4^+ + OH^-$

(6) $NH_4^+ + NH_3 \rightarrow NH_3 + NH_4^+$

Problems

14.801   The unimolecular decomposition of N_2O_5 has been studied in gas phase and various solvents [H. Eyring and F. Daniels, *J. Am. Chem. Soc.*, **52**, 1472 (1930)]. Compare the enthalpy changes due to solvation in the solvents nitromethane, bromine, propylene dichloride, and nitric acid, using the following data:

Solvent	$k \times 10^5$, sec^{-1}	E, kcal mole^{-1}	T, °C
Gas	1.65	24.7	20
Nitromethane	1.53	24.5	20
Bromine	2.15	24.0	20
Propylene dichloride	7.37	28.0	45
Nitric acid	1.97	28.3	45

14.802   Find the approximate number of encounters per second of a solute molecule with other solute molecules in a solution of mole fraction 0.001 at room temperature. The properties of the solution are as given in the Illustration on p. 479.

14.803   Calculate $\log k - \log k_0$ for the acid-catalyzed decomposition reaction of H_2O_2, a reaction of type, $z_A z_B = -1$ (i.e., $H_2O_2 + H^+ + Br^-$), at pH = 6, 4, and 2 in water, for (a) 0.1 and (b) 0.001 molar concentration of bromide ions.

14.804   Svirbely et al. [J. Am. Chem. Soc., **60**, 330, 1613 (1938)] give the following data for the reaction

$$NH_4^+ + OCN^- \rightarrow (NH_2)_2CO$$

in glycol-water solvent mixtures at 30°C. By an appropriate plot, evaluate r^*. Find the energy of interaction of ion pairs per mole, at the critical configuration in water, if $D = 76.7$ is used.

D:	76.7	63.5	60.0	55.0	50.0	45.0
$k_0 \times 10^2$:	0.62	1.13	1.40	1.91	2.65	3.78

References

Amis, E. S., *Kinetics of Chemical Change in Solution*, The Macmillan Co., New York, 1949.
Eigen, M., *Discussions Faraday Soc.*, **17**, 194 (1954), on fast reactions.
Moelwyn-Hughes, E. A., *Kinetics of Reactions in Solutions*, Second Edition, Oxford University Press, 1946.

9. Review Problems

14.901   What are the first two translational energy levels of the activated complex, treated as a particle in a box, for motion along the reaction coordinate? Let the molecular weight of the complex be 100 atomic mass units, and the length of the pass be 0.5 Å.

*14.902   A molecule of a gas at 0°C which consists of single oscillators of frequency 1000 cm^{-1} has an energy of 100 quanta. Find the probability on a statistical basis that the next collision (a) can possibly cause gain of energy, (b) will cause gain of energy if the collision partner has one quantum.

14.903   What is the maximum amount, on the RRK model, by which the critical increment could differ from the critical energy for the decomposition of diazomethane, CH_2N_2, at 300°C at low pressures?

14.904   The Hinshelwood theory predicts that $k_2 C_M \ll k_3 \ll k_2 C_{M'}$ should span a pressure range of a factor of 10^4, if the inequality signifies an observable ratio of 100:1. For CH_3NC the actual range exceeds a factor of 10^6. What can you say about the effective range of $k_3(\epsilon)$ values?

*14.905   Write Eq. 14.404 as a sum of two terms for two specified energies $C_A^*(\epsilon_1)$ and $C_A^*(\epsilon_2)$. Given that at equilibrium, $C_A^*(\epsilon_1)/C_A^*(\epsilon_2) = 10:1 = k_1(\epsilon_1)/k_1(\epsilon_2)$, and also that $k_3(\epsilon_1)/k_3(\epsilon_2) = 1:10$, plot $1/k_{uni}$ vs. $1/C_M$.

14.906   The magnitude of y_{tri} was described as $\sim 10^{-33}$ cc^2 molecule^{-1} sec^{-1}. Verify this statement for O_2 gas.

14.907   From the information on p. 462 estimate roughly the lifetime of I_3.

*14.908   Propose a mechanism and a rate expression for $-dC_{Cl_2}/dt$ in the reaction of Cl_2 with H_2, by use of the information on the characteristics of this reaction as they differ from Br_2.

14.909   From the information of Problem 14.702, calculate an approximate value for the specific rate constant k in cc molecule^{-1} sec^{-1} for

$$H + HI \rightarrow H_2 + I \quad \text{and} \quad I + HI \rightarrow H + I_2$$

Assume $E = 0$ for an exothermic step.

14.910   Do the two simultaneous reactions

represent a branching chain process?

14.911   The overall stoichiometry of the decomposition of N_2O_5 is

$$2N_2O_5 \rightarrow 4NO_2 + O_2$$

However, the kinetics show first-order behavior in time and concentration. R. A. Ogg in 1947 proposed the mechanism

$$N_2O_5 \xrightarrow{k_1} NO_2 + NO_3$$

$$NO_2 + NO_3 \xrightarrow{k_2} N_2O_5 \qquad \text{(fast)}$$

$$NO_2 + NO_3 \xrightarrow{k_3} NO + NO_2 + O_2 \quad \text{(slow)}$$

$$NO + N_2O_5 \xrightarrow{k_4} 3NO_2 \qquad \text{(very fast)}$$

Apply the steady state treatment to the concentrations of NO and NO_3 and show that this mechanism results in first-order kinetics.

General References

Benson, S. W., *The Foundations of Chemical Kinetics*, McGraw-Hill Book Co., New York, 1960.

Eyring, H., and E. M. Eyring, *Modern Chemical Kinetics*, Reinhold Publishing Co., New York, 1963.

Friess, S. L., E. S. Lewis, and A. Weissberger, Editors, *Investigation of Rates and Mechanisms of Reactions*, Second Edition, Part I, 1961, and Part II, 1963, Interscience Publishing Co., New York.

Frost, A. A., and R. G. Pearson, *Kinetics and Mechanism*, Second Edition, John Wiley and Sons, New York, 1961.

Glasstone, S., H. Eyring, and K. J. Laidler, *The Theory of Rate Processes*, McGraw-Hill Book Co., New York, 1941.

Hinshelwood, C. N., *Kinetics of Chemical Change*, Fourth Edition, Oxford University Press, Oxford, 1940.

Chapter Fifteen

Scattering and Diffraction;

Crystal Structure

In Chapter 1, we considered some of the aspects of the interaction of matter with electromagnetic radiation such as light and X-rays. We will now return to some special aspects of this problem. We will take up the general problem of scattering, interaction, and diffraction effects, which are responsible for such phenomena as the scattering of visible light, and the X-ray intensity patterns produced by regular crystalline arrays of atoms.

1. Emission and Scattering from an Electric Dipole

In preceding chapters, we considered the definite quantum energy levels responsible for the stability and the spectra of atoms and molecules. In this area, a classical approach is of limited use, because classical models usually predict continuous spectra for simple systems, in contradiction to the experimental facts. Also, the effect of light or other electromagnetic radiation on a molecule has been neglected when the frequency of the light is not equal or nearly equal to the frequency of a spectral line or absorption. We will now consider the classical treatment of light impinging on a molecule at a frequency that is distant from an absorption frequency. At a given point, O, an expression for the amplitude of the electric field of the electromagnetic wave may be written

$$A = A_0 e^{i\omega t} = A_0 \cos \omega t + (iA_0 \sin \omega t) \qquad (15.101)$$

where in the second equality we consider only the real part of the complex function as having any physical meaning. It is for this reason that we use only the cosine term, and not the imaginary sine term generated by the exponential. The angular frequency, ω is related to the normal frequency and wavelength by the equation

$$\omega = 2\pi\nu = \frac{2\pi c}{\lambda} \tag{15.102}$$

The average intensity of such a light beam is proportional to the absolute value of the square of the amplitude. It can be obtained by multiplying A by its complex conjugate and dividing by 8π

$$I = \frac{1}{8\pi} |A^2| = \frac{1}{8\pi} A^*A \tag{15.103}$$

This expression, applied to the amplitude from Eq. 15.101, gives

$$I = \frac{1}{8\pi} (A_0 e^{-i\omega t})(A_0 e^{+i\omega t}) = \frac{1}{8\pi} A_0^2 \tag{15.104}$$

if A_0 is assumed to be real.

If absolute values of the amplitudes and intensity are required, the constant term 8π has to be included. We shall be concerned mostly with relative values of the amplitudes of scattered to incident beams, for which the constant will cancel out.

If the light beam is traveling in a vacuum in a certain direction for a given distance from O represented by the vector $\vec{R}$, the amplitude at $\vec{R}$ is given by the expression

$$A \text{ (at } \vec{R}) = A_0 \exp\left[i\omega(t - |R|/c)\right] \tag{15.105}$$

where c is the velocity of light in vacuum. This equation is for a single source of light in a vacuum; for example, we may take an incident parallel beam, where R is the distance along the beam. When there is more than one source of light, we must combine various terms of this type to obtain the amplitude or intensity at various points.

Coherent and Incoherent Light. In what follows, we shall be concerned mostly with various sources of radiant energy of the same frequency that have a definite phase relation between each other. If the amplitude at a certain point is A_1 from one source and A_2 from another, the total amplitude is

$$A = A_1 + A_2 \tag{15.106}$$

Thus the beams will interfere either constructively or destructively, and the intensity will be the absolute value of the square of the sums of the amplitudes

$$I = \frac{1}{8\pi} |(A_1 + A_2)^2| \tag{15.107}$$

The light from two such sources is said to be coherent.

On the other hand, suppose that one of the sources emitted light with no particular phase relationship with the other, such as light of a different frequency. Then the intensities from each source would be independent, and

$$I = I_1 + I_2 = \frac{1}{8\pi} |A_1^2| + \frac{1}{8\pi} |A_2^2| \qquad (15.108)$$

Such light is said to be incoherent. As a special example, light in two mutually perpendicular planes of polarization, although of the same frequency, cannot interact and thus is incoherent.

Model for the Harmonic Electric Dipole. A real atom contains a number of electrons, which are of small mass and movable enough to respond to a periodic electric field of the type given by Eq. 15.101. We will not consider the details of such a quantum system of many particles. We take as a starting point a very useful model for a molecule interacting with radiation of frequency far from a spectral frequency of the molecule. Consider that a single electron is bound by a harmonic restoring force to a heavy positive charge and can oscillate in such a way that the restoring force is harmonic, and not coulombic. Also assume that the motion is classical, that is, that the quantum number for this vibration is large enough so that we do not have to consider quantum states; the oscillator will thus be assigned an energy that can be effectively a continuous variable. We will characterize the state of the dipole at a given instant by its displacement x from the equilibrium position. The instantaneous dipole moment M is the charge times the displacement

$$M = ex \qquad (15.109)$$

We must obtain an expression for the displacement as a function of time in order to calculate the dipole moment as a function of time. In Sec. 2.2, we considered the motion of a classical harmonic oscillator. If a particle of mass m is restrained by a spring which exerts a force $-kx$ on the particle, the equation of motion $(f = ma)$ is

$$-kx = m \frac{d^2x}{dt^2} \qquad (2.116)$$

and the displacement is given by

$$x = x_0 \cos \left(\frac{k}{m}\right)^{1/2} t \qquad (2.119)$$

That is, if a mass is allowed to oscillate, undisturbed by an outside force, it will vibrate with a frequency characteristic of the oscillator

$$\nu_0 = \frac{1}{2\pi} \left(\frac{k}{m}\right)^{1/2} \qquad (2.120)$$

The subscript zero will be used to indicate the natural frequency of the oscillator, as distinguished from any imposed frequency. The angular frequency, as defined by Eq. 15.102, is

$$\omega_0 = \left(\frac{k}{m}\right)^{1/2}$$

If we use this equation to eliminate the constant k, Eq. 2.116 can be written

$$m\left(\frac{d^2x}{dt^2} + \omega_0^2 x\right) = 0 \tag{15.110}$$

If, however, the particle is an electron in an electric field of the form of Eq. 15.101, it will also be acted on by an outside force of magnitude $-eA$, where e is the electronic charge. The equation of motion is then

$$m\left(\frac{d^2x}{dt^2} + \omega_0^2 x\right) = eA_0 e^{i\omega t} \tag{15.111}$$

Here, the dipole of natural frequency ω_0 is being forced to oscillate with an applied frequency of ω. If we seek a periodic solution of the form $x = (\text{const})e^{+i\omega t}$, we find as the displacement under these conditions the expression

$$x = \left(\frac{A_0 e}{m}\right)\frac{1}{\omega_0^2 - \omega^2}e^{i\omega t} \tag{15.112}$$

The instantaneous moment M is just ex. This equation gives a finite answer as long as we avoid exact resonance ($\omega_0 = \omega$), which corresponds to avoiding the frequency of a spectral line.

ILLUSTRATION.   Solution of Eq. 15.111.

If we look for a steady state solution of the same frequency as the light driving the oscillator, it must be of the form

$$x = Be^{+i\omega t}$$

where B is a constant that may possibly be a complex number. If this equation is inserted in the equation of motion, Eq. 15.111

$$m(-\omega^2 Be^{i\omega t} + B\omega_0^2 e^{i\omega t}) = eA_0 e^{i\omega t}$$

Solving this equation for B, we find

$$B = \frac{A_0 e}{m}\frac{1}{\omega_0^2 - \omega^2}$$

Note that B is real and finite if $\omega_0 \neq \omega$.

Radiation from an Oscillating Electric Dipole.   One of the consequences of Maxwell's electromagnetic theory is that an oscillating electric dipole will produce electromagnetic radiation of a frequency equal to its frequency of vibration. Although a mass without charge will, according to Eq. 2.119, vibrate at a constant amplitude if left to itself, a charged particle will under the same circumstances produce electromagnetic waves. An isolated dipole, vibrating with its natural frequency, will emit all its energy until its amplitude is zero. It will emit energy uniformly around its axis, and, if this is viewed as a polar axis, with maximum density at the equator and no intensity in the polar directions. The explanation is that light waves are a transverse vibration in the ether; the motions of the dipole along the polar axis excite these perpendicular vibrations most effectively in the equatorial plane, and since there is no motion of the dipole at all in the directions perpendicular to the polar axis, no waves are excited in the polar direction. The amplitude of the waves falls off with the factor $\sin \theta$ if θ is the angle from the pole, that is, 90° minus the angle from the equatorial direction. Although we will not give the proof, it is found that the amplitude of the radiation from such a dipole has the form

$$A(\text{dipole}) = \frac{\omega^2 |M|}{c^2 |R|} \sin \theta \exp [i\omega(t - |R|/c)] \qquad (15.113)$$

In addition to constant terms, the amplitude of radiation from the dipole depends on the absolute magnitude of the dipole

$$|M| = (M^*M)^{\frac{1}{2}} \qquad (15.114)$$

and the square of the frequency, as well as the angular factor $\sin \theta$. In the absence of a supply of energy, the dipole will continue to emit energy until $|M| = 0$, when all the energy is used up. This is the difficulty with the classical model of the hydrogen atom; it should continue to emit energy until the electron is on top of the proton instead of finding a stable quantum state such as the $1s$ state. The intensity of the radiation is

$$I(\text{dipole}) = \frac{1}{8\pi} A^*A = \frac{1}{8\pi}\left(\frac{M^*M}{c^4 |R^2|}\right)\omega^4 \sin^2 \theta \qquad (15.115)$$

Note that the intensity depends on the fourth power of the frequency, and of course also falls off with the second power of the distance from the source, $|R^2|$.

As unrealistic as the classical dipole model may seem, it can be used for real molecules under certain circumstances. Take, for example, one of the outer shell electrons in a rare gas atom. Under no external electric field, it can be thought of as being in a fixed energy level, with the next higher energy level very far away. Under the influence of a weak external field, the average position of the electron shifts slightly so that the center of gravity of the electron probability is itself slightly shifted away from the nucleus of the atom. In the absence of an electric field such a distribution would have slightly higher energy than the undisturbed distribution. In the electric field, however, the average displacement of the electron to an unsymmetrical distribution reduces the total energy. Over this very short range of distortion the situation is very similar to the model of an electron on a spring. A very small but continuous change in energy is possible, and so if the energy of the undistorted quantum state is regarded as the zero of energy, the classical model is a quite realistic model for the interaction of the electrons with an electromagnetic field, even though it is not suitable for the interaction of the electrons with the coulomb field of the nucleus. (Compare the treatment of the Stark effect in Sec. 16.3.)

Dipole Scattering of an External Field. We have seen (Eq. 15.112) that an oscillating electric field interacting with an electron will set up an oscillating dipole and also that such a dipole will emit radiation in a symmetrical pattern (Eq. 15.115); such a process takes part of the energy of a plane wave traveling in a forward direction and sends it out in other directions. This is called scattering, as opposed to absorption of radiation, because although the main beam is attenuated, as in absorption, the light appears undiminished if viewed from or integrated over all angles. This is shown in Fig. 15.101.

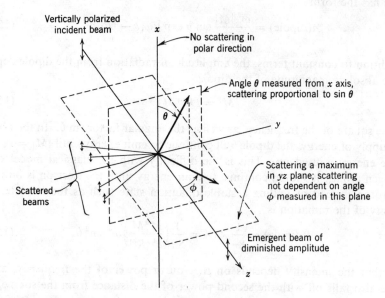

Fig. 15.101   Scattering of a light wave, polarized in the x direction, by a single dipole, located at the origin.

If we insert the value of M from Eq. 15.109 and Eq. 15.112 in Eq. 15.114, we obtain $|M|$. Then, from Eq. 15.113 for the scattered amplitude from a single dipole

$$A(\text{scattered}) = A_0\left(\frac{e^2}{mc^2\,|R|}\right)\left[\frac{1}{(\omega_0/\omega)^2 - 1}\right]\sin\theta \exp\left[i\omega(t - |R|/c)\right] \quad (15.116)$$

Similarly, the intensity of scattered light, from Eq. 15.115, becomes

$$I_s = I_0\left(\frac{e^2}{mc^2}\right)^2\left(\frac{\sin^2\theta}{|R^2|}\right)\left[\frac{1}{(\omega_0/\omega)^2 - 1}\right]^2 \quad (15.117)$$

The intensity of light scattered from a single dipole depends on a number of factors; it is proportional to, first, the intensity of the incident beam I_0; second, a constant factor; third, an angle-distance-of-observation factor; and, finally, a frequency factor.

Examination of Frequency Factor; Rayleigh and Thomson Scattering. For ordinary atoms the lowest electronic frequencies are in the ultraviolet, so if light in the longer-wavelength visible region is allowed to fall on an atom we may assume that $\omega_0 \gg \omega$. This means that the -1 in the brackets can be neglected in Eq. 15.117. Scattering in this region is called Rayleigh scattering, and the intensity is

$$I_s(\text{Rayleigh}) = I_0 \left(\frac{\omega}{\omega_0} \right)^4 \left(\frac{e^2}{mc^2} \right)^2 \frac{\sin^2 \theta}{|R^2|} \qquad (15.118)$$

Such scattering is dependent on the fourth power of the frequency of the incident radiation and also on the strength of the bonding of the electron, as reflected by ω_0^{-4}.

If, on the other hand, short-wavelength light in the form of X-rays is scattered from atomic systems, the condition is now $\omega_0 \ll \omega$. In this case, sometimes called Thomson scattering, the factors in the bracket equal -1, which yields

$$I_s(\text{X-rays}) = I_0 \left(\frac{e^2}{mc^2} \right)^2 \frac{\sin^2 \theta}{|R^2|} \qquad (15.119)$$

which depends neither on the frequency of the radiation nor on the strength of the electron binding.

Note that from Eq. 15.116 Rayleigh scattering has the same sign as the incident amplitude. This means that the scattering is in phase with the incident light, because the frequency of the light is so low that the electron follows the field exactly. On the other hand, for Thomson scattering the factor -1 appears, and we have for the amplitude of the scattered light, from Eq. 15.116

$$A_s(\text{X-rays}) = -A_0 \left(\frac{e^2}{mc^2} \right) \left(\frac{\sin \theta}{|R|} \right) \exp \left[i\omega (t - |R|/c) \right] \qquad (15.120)$$

The minus sign indicates that the emitted light is $180°$ out of phase with the incident light at the origin $R = 0$.

Angular Factor for Unpolarized Light.   In ordinary investigations of scattering, measurements are usually made around a fixed circle, corresponding to the equatorial plane. If we first consider vertically polarized light, as in the preceding paragraphs, intensities around the equatorial angle ϕ are constant, while those up and down the polar angle θ will depend on $\sin^2 \theta$ and be a maximum in the equatorial plane. The scattering envelope, or relative intensity plotted on a polar diagram, will look like a doughnut with a very small hole located in the equatorial plane. There is an axis of symmetry in the polar axis (Fig. 15.102).

Horizontally polarized light is essentially no different; the dipole oscillates in the y direction; but if we retain the same angular coordinates, the intensity becomes a function of ϕ. In the equatorial plane, with ϕ measured from the emergent beam of the incident radiation, radiation is a maximum at $\phi = 0$ and $180°$, and zero in the axis of the vector of polarization, where ϕ equals 90 or $270°$. The amplitude at any angle depends on $\cos \phi$, and the intensity on $\cos^2 \phi$ (Fig. 15.103).

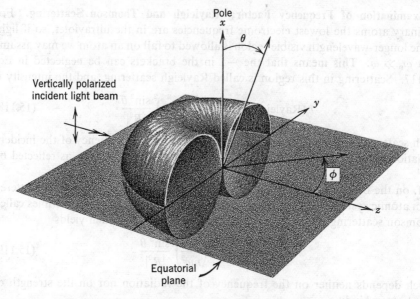

Fig. 15.102 Polar diagram of scattered intensity from vertically polarized incident light. The front half of the distribution has been omitted for clarity; it is identical with that shown and joins smoothly to it. Length of radius vector from origin indicates relative intensity.

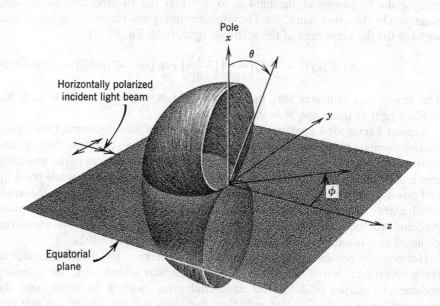

Fig. 15.103 Polar diagram of scattered intensity from horizontally polarized incident light, but in coordinates more appropriate for vertically polarized light. The front half of the distribution has been omitted as in Fig. 15.102. Length of radius vector from origin indicates relative intensity.

The intensity of unpolarized light is the average of the intensity of two polarized beams at 90° to one another. Around the equatorial plane these factors are 1 and $\cos^2 \phi$. Thus for unpolarized light the angular factor is

$$\frac{1 + \cos^2 \phi}{2}$$

Now, since for unpolarized light there is no preferred angle around the axis of propagation, the scattering must be symmetrical about this axis; that is, this

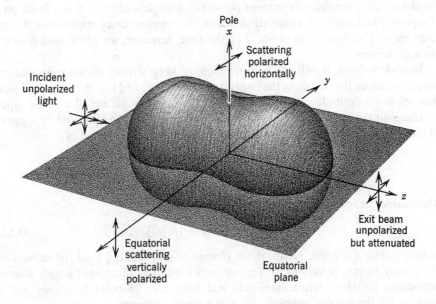

Fig. 15.104   Polar diagram of dipole scattering of unpolarized light.

factor will apply to unpolarized radiation in any plane that includes the axis of propagation. The scattering envelope for this case is dumbbell shape and is shown in Fig. 15.104. Because of its symmetry and orientation, the angular dependence is best expressed in terms of a single angle, called the *scattering angle*, which is the angle any scattered ray makes with the emergent primary beam of incident radiation. We will indicate this angle by the symbol θ_s. It is of course not confined to the equatorial plane, but in that plane is equivalent to ϕ, not θ. We have, nevertheless, used the letter θ to correspond to the customary usage in the scattering literature. We shall also have occasion to use the Bragg reflection angle θ_b, defined by the relation

$$\theta_s = 2\theta_b \tag{15.121}$$

This angle occurs equally naturally in the study of the reflection of X-rays from atomic planes. In terms of the scattering angle θ_s, the angular factor for unpolarized light becomes

$$\frac{1 + \cos^2 \theta_s}{2} \tag{15.122}$$

The Scattering Factor; Relative Amplitudes and Intensities.   Now that we have developed equations for the Rayleigh and X-ray scattering of single-electron dipoles, we will wish to extend these formulas to scattering by real atoms. We do this by introducing another factor, f, into equations such as Eq. 15.116. This is a dimensionless number called the atomic scattering factor, which can be thought of as the effective number of electrons present in a single scatterer. It is a function of frequency and angle of observation but in the simplest cases approaches the real number of electrons in an atom. For the time, however, we will regard it simply as a parameter.

In what follows, it will not be convenient to keep writing all the constants and angular factors that occur in the equations such as Eq. 15.116. We will use instead the relative amplitude produced as compared to the amplitude of a single dipole scatterer at the same angle. These relative quantities will be indicated by a prime. Thus, if we rewrite Eq. 15.116 for a real atom with a given value of f,

$$A = A_0 f \left[\frac{1}{(\omega_0/\omega)^2 - 1} \right] \left(\frac{e^2}{mc^2} \right) \left(\frac{\sin \theta}{|R|} \right) \exp \left[i\omega(t - |R|/c) \right]$$

the relative or reduced amplitude will be written

$$A' = f \exp \left[i\omega(t - |R|/c) \right] \tag{15.123}$$

which is much simpler. Also, if we change to unpolarized light, or change the frequency region, equations for the ordinary amplitude must be changed, whereas equations for the relative amplitude still hold true. Similar equations will be written for the relative intensity, I'. For a single scatterer,

$$I' = f^2 \tag{15.124}$$

Note that the 8π factor (Eq. 15.103) is omitted from the relative intensity expression.

2. Scattering from a Large Number of Centers

We have obtained equations for the scattering from individual scattering centers and now consider how the scattered light from different centers interacts to produce the total scattering observed. If light from two sources arrives at the point of observation in phase, the two sources will reinforce one another in that the amplitudes add to produce a stronger wave; if they are out of phase they will cancel, at least partially. It is therefore important to calculate the phase difference in the radiation from two centers. We shall follow the treatment given by R. W. James.

Phase Difference.   In Fig. 15.201 two scattering centers are indicated as P_1 and P_2. The vector distance between them is indicated as $\vec{r}$. The direction of the incident beam is given by the unit vector $\vec{s}_0$ (unit vector: $\vec{s}_0 \cdot \vec{s}_0 = 1$). We will make the observation at a very large distance R away, whose direction from both centers is given by the unit vector $\vec{s}$. The path difference Δ (not a vector) is the difference between the lengths P_2M and P_1N. These two distances are the projections of the vector $\vec{r}$ on the direction of the scattering vector and the incident vector, respectively. Thus, if we write $\vec{S} = \vec{s} - \vec{s}_0$,

$$
\begin{aligned}
\Delta &= (\vec{r} \cdot \vec{s}_0) - (\vec{r} \cdot \vec{s}) \\
&= -\vec{r} \cdot (\vec{s} - \vec{s}_0) \\
&= -\vec{r} \cdot \vec{S}
\end{aligned}
\tag{15.201}
$$

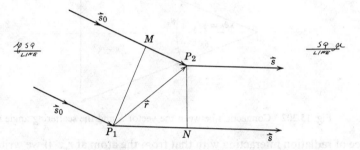

Fig. 15.201   The phase difference Δ from two scattering centers.

The phase difference in angular measure is obtained from this distance by multiplying it by κ, where

$$
\kappa = \frac{2\pi}{\lambda}
\tag{15.202}
$$

If we now make P_1 the origin of a coordinate system and locate other scattering systems by the vector $\vec{r}$, the quantity $-\kappa\vec{r} \cdot \vec{S}$ will be the phase difference between waves scattered at the origin and those originating at $\vec{r}$.

Waves leaving the origin at time t and going to the distant observation station R will reach there at time $|R|/c$ later. If we make this distance an integral number of wavelengths from the origin, the relative amplitude at R is

$$
A' = f_0 e^{+i\omega t}
$$

if the scattering takes place at the origin. However, if the scattering takes place at any other center given by the vector $\vec{r}$, its contribution to the amplitude must include the phase difference in Eq. 15.123

$$
A' = f_0 \exp\left(+i\omega t + i\kappa\vec{r} \cdot \vec{S}\right)
\tag{15.203}
$$

The total amplitude at R is obtained by summing terms like Eq. 15.203 for all points occupied by scattering atoms.

Amplitude and Intensity for N Scatterers.   It thus follows that the total amplitude of scattered radiation from N atoms, each located by a vector $\vec{r}_p$, at the observation point will be

$$A' = e^{+i\omega t} \sum_p f_p \exp\left(+i\kappa\vec{r}_p \cdot \vec{S}\right) \tag{15.204}$$

The relative intensity is obtained from this amplitude by multiplying it by its complex conjugate

$$A'^* = e^{-i\omega t} \sum_q f_q \exp\left(-i\kappa\vec{r}_q \cdot \vec{S}\right)$$

where we have used a different running index q to indicate each atom which is a

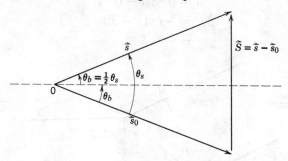

Fig. 15.202   Connection between the vector $\vec{S}$ and the scattering angle θ_s.

source of radiation interacting with that from the atom at r_p. If we write the vector distance between two atoms,

$$\vec{r}_{pq} = \vec{r}_q - \vec{r}_p \tag{15.205}$$

we can write this product as a double sum

$$I' = A'^*A' = \sum_p \sum_q f_p f_q \exp\left(-i\kappa\vec{r}_{pq} \cdot \vec{S}\right)$$

If we separate this sum into the terms where $p = q$ and those where $p \neq q$, we can write it as

$$I' = \sum_p f_p^2 + \sum_{p,q}^{p \neq q} f_p f_q \exp\left(-i\kappa\vec{r}_{pq} \cdot \vec{S}\right) \tag{15.206}$$

because there is no phase factor when $p = q$.

Geometrical Interpretation of the Vector $\vec{S}$.   The vector $\vec{S}$, which is the difference between the unit vectors that identify the incident and the scattered beams, can be associated with the scattering angle θ_s. If we make the geometrical construction in Fig. 15.202 it is apparent that the absolute length of $\vec{S}$ is

$$|S| = 2 \sin\left(\frac{\theta_s}{2}\right) \tag{15.207}$$

Scattering from Centers of Finite Size.   The first use that will be made of Eq. 15.204 is to calculate the effect of the distribution of scattering power over a center of size comparable to the wavelength of the radiation being scattered. We regard a center as being composed of a distribution of point dipole scatterers in a definite arrangement. For this purpose we will consider that the center is located at the origin and has scattering elements located by the vector $\vec{r}_p$. We shall first consider scattering by a shell of point dipoles uniformly distributed over the surface of a sphere of radius r. The summation in Eq. 15.204 will then be replaced by an integral over the surface of the sphere. We will locate the position of a scattering element at $\vec{r}_p$ by the polar angle ψ between the vector $\vec{S}$ and the vector $\vec{r}_p$. We can evaluate the product in the exponent, Eq. 15.204, as

$$\kappa \vec{S} \cdot \vec{r}_p = \left(\frac{2\pi}{\lambda}\right)\left[2 \sin \left(\frac{\theta_s}{2}\right)\right](r \cos \psi) \tag{15.208}$$

If we introduce a parameter that involves the scattering angle and wavelength only

$$\mu = \frac{4\pi \sin (\theta_s/2)}{\lambda} \tag{15.209}$$

we can write the sum, Eq. 15.204, as an integral over the surface element $2\pi r^2 \sin \psi \, d\psi$

$$A' = e^{+i\omega t}\int_0^\pi f_p \exp (i\mu r \cos \psi) \, 2\pi r^2 \sin \psi \, d\psi \tag{15.210}$$

This integral can be evaluated if we treat f_p as a constant over the sphere and remember that

$$d \cos \psi = -\sin \psi \, d\psi$$

$$\int e^{ikx} \, dx = \left(\frac{-i}{k}\right) e^{ikx}$$

and

$$\sin x = \frac{ie^{-ix} - ie^{ix}}{2}$$

The result of the integration is

$$A' = 4\pi r^2 f_p \frac{\sin \mu r}{\mu r} e^{+i\omega t} \tag{15.211}$$

Thus a spherical shell of scattering material contains an angular factor $(\sin \mu r)/\mu r$ in addition to the angular factor $(1 + \cos^2 \theta_s)/2$ that applies to a point scattering center. Now, if r is very small, the sine can be expanded as $\sin x = x$ for small x, and the new factor becomes unity. Thus, in the limit of a sphere small with respect to the wavelength of the radiation, Eq. 15.211 becomes

$$A' = 4\pi r^2 f_p e^{+i\omega t}$$

This limit corresponds to what is effectively a point scatterer. Since $4\pi r^2$ is the area of the sphere, and f_p is the scattering power of a single scatterer, we have obviously set the density of scatterers on the sphere at one per unit area of the sphere.

We have plotted the function $(\sin \mu r)/\mu r$ in Fig. 15.203. For scattering at low angles it is equal to unity, because μ approaches zero when θ approaches zero. It

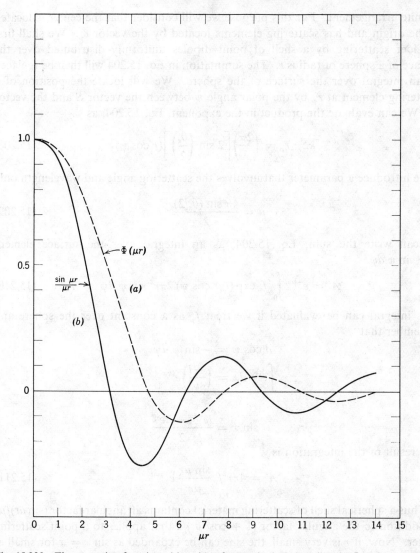

Fig. 15.203   The scattering functions (sin $\mu r)/\mu r$ for a spherical shell (b) and $\Phi(\mu r)$ for a sphere (a) plotted against μr (adapted by permission from R. W. James, *The Optical Principles of the Diffraction of X-rays*, G. Bell & Sons, London, 1948).

begins to fall off rapidly as μr nears unity. Thus a value of μ, which contains only information about the radiation and the angle of observation, allows us to estimate when interference effects are to be expected in a scattering system with a characteristic dimension such as the radius r. The condition is $\mu r \approx 1$ or

$$r \approx \frac{1}{\mu} \tag{15.212}$$

For wide-angle scattering near $90°$ this implies that $r \approx \lambda$, but at scattering angles of only a few degrees, the interference occurs with much larger scatterers only.

We can also compute the scattering from a sphere of uniform density of scattering material throughout its volume. This involves integration of Eq. 15.211 over a range of r from 0 to r_0

$$A' = f_p e^{+i\omega t} \int_0^{r_0} 4\pi r^2 \frac{\sin \mu r}{\mu r} \, dr$$

The value of this integral is

$$A' = \tfrac{4}{3}\pi r_0^3 f_p \Phi(\mu r_0) e^{+i\omega t} \tag{15.213}$$

where $\Phi(\mu r_0)$ is the function

$$\Phi(\mu r_0) = \frac{3}{(\mu r_0)^3} (\sin \mu r_0 - \mu r_0 \cos \mu r_0) \tag{15.214}$$

This function also approaches unity as μr_0 goes to zero, and is otherwise quite similar in behavior to $(\sin \mu r)/\mu r$. It is also plotted in Fig. 15.203. We have included it here because of its importance in the light scattering from large spherical particles. Note that in the limit of small μr_0 Eq. 15.213 reduces to

$$A' = \tfrac{4}{3}\pi r_0^3 f_p e^{+i\omega t}$$

Since the first term in this product is the volume of the scattering sphere, clearly it is implied that the density of scatterers of strength f_p is one per unit volume.

Calculation of the Scattering Factor for X-rays.   For an atom very small compared with the wavelength of the radiation, the scattering factor, f, is just equal to the total number of electrons, Z. However, if the electrons are spread out over a large volume, interference effects will reduce f. If the density of electrons in an atom is spherically symmetrical, then the density can be described in terms of a density function whose integral over the volume is equal to Z. Thus if the function is $\rho(r)$

$$\int_0^\infty 4\pi \rho(r) r^2 \, dr = Z \tag{15.215}$$

The scattering from any shell, at a given value of r, will be given by Eq. 15.211. The value of f_p for a single electron is unity, and the number of electrons in the shell is equal to $4\pi\rho(r)r^2 \, dr$. The total atomic scattering factor f_a as used in the expression

$$A' = f_a e^{+i\omega t}$$

is the integral

$$f_a = \int_0^\infty 4\pi r^2 \rho(r) \frac{\sin \mu r}{\mu r} \, dr \tag{15.216}$$

This integral must be evaluated by a machine calculation or other numerical method from some calculation of the electron density, based on the best atomic wave functions. The result of such a calculation for the sodium atom is presented in Fig. 15.204. For low angles or long wavelengths, f_a approaches $Z = 11$; for

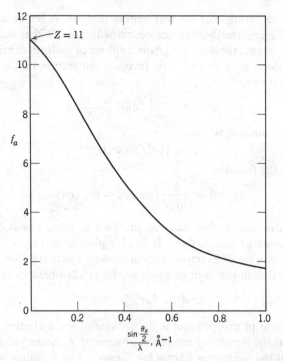

Fig. 15.204   The scattering factor for the sodium atom (by permission from C. Kittel, *Introduction to Solid State Physics*, John Wiley and Sons, 1956).

other conditions the appropriate value of f_a can be read from the graph. Similar information for other atomic scattering centers is given in the *International Tables for the Determination of Crystal Structure* (Borntrager, Berlin, 1935).

Problems

15.201   What is the phase difference between two scattering centers if the scattering is measured very close to $\theta_s = 0$?

15.202   Calculate the reduced intensity of scattering from two centers located one wavelength apart on the axis of the incident beam, as a function of θ_s.

15.203   Evaluate the integral, Eq. 15.210, that leads to the scattering factor for a spherical shell of constant density.

15.204   Write an expression for the scattering factor for X-rays from a hydrogen atom in a ls state. How could this expression be evaluated?

3. Scattering from a Gas; the Polarizability

The simplest application of Eq. 15.206 is to the problem of scattering by a dilute ideal gas, where there is no geometrical order to the arrangement of the atoms. In this case, the phase factors are completely random and cancel each other to a high degree of accuracy. The equation for the reduced intensity, if we assume all the atoms are the same and drop the terms with phase differences, becomes

$$I' = N'f^2 \qquad (15.301)$$

where N' is the number of atoms per cubic centimeter.

Rayleigh Scattering.   If the particles that scatter the light are small compared to the wavelength, the angular scattering is very simple in form.   For unpolarized light, the angular dependence is of the form $1 + \cos^2 \theta_s$.   One point of note is that the light scattered at 90°, where the intensity is lowest, is completely polarized, because only one component of the light is scattered at this angle.   The intensity also depends on the fourth power of frequency, or the inverse fourth power of wavelength.   Thus blue light is scattered much more effectively than red light.   It was in this manner that Lord Rayleigh explained the blue color of the light scattered by the molecules in the atmosphere, and the reddish light that comes directly through from the sun when it is low on the horizon.   He further confirmed his theory by the observation that the blue light is polarized, while the incident beam of direct sunlight is unpolarized.

It remains to evaluate the absolute value of the intensity in terms of measurable quantities.   This involves a discussion of f and ω_0.

The Polarizability.   The polarizability α of an atom in the gas phase can be defined in terms of the dipole moment M caused by a constant electric field E_0

$$M = \alpha E_0 \qquad (15.302)$$

We can obtain the polarizability of a dipole from its equation of motion, Eq. 15.111.   Since the field is static, d^2x/dt^2 is zero, ω is zero, and $A_0 = E_0$; therefore

$$m\omega_0^2 x = eE_0$$

and

$$M = ex = \frac{e^2 E_0}{m\omega_0^2}$$

From Eq. 15.302,

$$\alpha = \frac{e^2}{m\omega_0^2}$$

If there are effectively f dipoles in each atom, we then find

$$\alpha = \frac{fe^2}{m\omega_0^2} \qquad (15.303)$$

This may be further related to measurable quantities if we write down without proof the relationships between polarizability of the atoms α, dielectric constant ϵ of the gas, and its refractive index n:

$$\epsilon = 1 + 4\pi N'\alpha \qquad (15.304)$$

$$\epsilon = n^2 \qquad (15.305)$$

These formulas can be applied to nonpolar molecules in a dilute gas. However, the result, Eq. 15.303, is either largely useless if we leave the magnitudes of the parameters unspecified, or very inaccurate if we make simple guesses for f and ω_0.

Some further insight into the polarizability of an atom can be gained by taking a slightly more realistic model. If Z electrons are uniformly distributed about a nucleus of charge eZ, but confined to a spherical volume of radius r_0, the effect of a field would be to shift the nucleus a distance r from the center of the spherical cloud of electrons. This crude picture of a polarized atom is shown in Fig. 15.301.

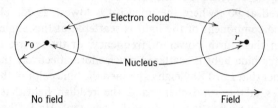

No field   Field

Fig. 15.301   A polarized atom with a spherical cloud of electrons.

In such a situation the dipole moment is the product of the charge eZ and the distance between the nucleus at r and the center of the cloud of electrons at the origin

$$M = eZr \tag{15.306}$$

The field from a spherically symmetrical shell of charge is zero inside the shell so that the nucleus does not feel a force from the electrons beyond r. The electrons within the radius r act as if they were concentrated at the center of the cloud where $r = 0$. The number of electrons within this sphere is $Z(r/r_0)^3$, because the density of charge has been assumed to be uniform within the sphere.

Therefore, from Coulomb's law, the force on the nucleus is

$$f = \frac{q_1 q_2}{r^2} = \frac{-(eZ)[eZ(r/r_0)^3]}{r^2} \tag{15.307}$$

In order to find the external field that would balance this force, we must divide by the charge and change the sign.

$$E_0 = \frac{eZr}{r_0^3} \tag{15.308}$$

From this result and Eq. 15.306, we find

$$\alpha = \frac{M}{E_0} = r_0^3 \tag{15.309}$$

This remarkably simple result states that the polarizability is proportional to the volume of the molecule. It also shows that the unit of polarizability is volume.

In Table 15.301 some values of the polarizability of the rare gases and other spherical molecules are compared with σ^3, the cube of the van der Waals radius of the atom or molecule, divided by 8 because the radius of contact is the diameter of the individual particle (see Eq. 6.501). This crude model predicts polarizabilities that are of the right order of magnitude, especially for the heavier atoms and molecules.

Table 15.301   Polarizability of Gas
Molecules in Units of $Å^3$

Molecule	Polarizability per Molecule	$\sigma^3/8$
He	0.20	2.2
Ne	0.393	2.5
Ar	1.623	4.9
Kr	2.46	5.8
CH_4	2.58	6.9
CCl_4	10.5	25

Absolute Value of Rayleigh Scattering.   Equation 15.303 has one important use as it stands. If we introduce it into Eq. 15.118 to eliminate ω_0, and use Eq. 15.102 to eliminate ω, we can obtain a formula for the scattering in terms of observable parameters. First Eq. 15.118 must be multiplied by f^2N' to introduce the factors from Eq. 15.301. Then, with these substitutions, the formula for the Rayleigh scattering becomes

$$I_s(\text{Rayleigh}) = I_0(2\pi)^4 N'\alpha^2 \left(\frac{1}{\lambda^4}\right) \frac{\sin^2 \theta}{R^2} \qquad (15.310)$$

This result, for vertically polarized light, is independent of φ and depends only on the polar angle θ. For unpolarized light, the corresponding equation is

$$I_s(\text{Rayleigh}) = I_0 8\pi^4 N'\alpha^2 \left(\frac{1}{\lambda^4}\right) \frac{1 + \cos^2 \theta_s}{R^2} \qquad (15.311)$$

Practical Scattering Measurements.   Equation 15.311 will now be put in a form suitable for application to experimental measurements. We have Eqs. 15.304 and 15.305, which relate the polarizability to the measured value of the refractive index of the gas. In addition, the refractive index of a dilute gas is so close to unity that we may replace n^2 by $2n - 1$. Thus

$$\alpha = \frac{n^2 - 1}{4\pi N'} = \frac{n - 1}{2\pi N'} \qquad (15.312)$$

Although absolute intensities are hard to measure, it is relatively easy to determine a ratio of the intensity of scattered light to the incident light at a suitably large distance from the sample. Therefore the Rayleigh ratio is defined in terms of measurable quantities, and we find

$$R(\theta_s) = \frac{I_s R^2}{I_0} = \frac{2\pi^2(n-1)^2}{N'\lambda^4}(1 + \cos^2 \theta_s) \qquad (15.313)$$

If everything in this equation can be considered known but N', the number of molecules per cubic centimeter can be calculated, and thus Avogadro's number evaluated.

Units of the Rayleigh Ratio. One might expect from the name, ratio, that $R(\theta)$ would be dimensionless. This is not the case. Aside from dimensionless quantities, there is a factor $N'\lambda^4$ in the denominator. Since N' is in molecules per cubic centimeter and λ is in centimeters, the unit of $R(\theta)$ is reciprocal centimeters (cm^{-1}). This reflects the fact that the amount of light scattered is proportional to the path-length, as long as the primary incident beam is not attenuated greatly. Thus the ratio should ideally be measured for a pathlength of 1 cm, at a sufficiently large distance R so that the 1 cm of path can be regarded as a point source. This requirement conflicts with the experimental necessity of a longer pathlength and shorter observation distance, in order to make the actual intensity of the light scattered great enough to be accurately measured. This practical requirement makes the definition of the angle of scattering less precise. These difficulties have been met adequately in practice; however, the details are beyond the scope of our treatment.

X-ray Scattering by an Atomic Gas. It might be expected that X-ray scattering from a dilute gas such as argon would follow the simple equation

$$I' = N'f^2 \tag{15.301}$$

and such scattering is indeed found. However, inelastic collisions of the high-energy X-ray photons with the atoms give rise to scattering of radiation of a different frequency from the incident beam, and this must be separated and subtracted from the total scattering to verify the prediction of Eq. 15.301.

In a very dense gas, such as argon compressed to 500 atm, an interesting excluded volume effect is observed. If the gas atoms are treated as hard spheres, there is an excluded volume

$$b' = \tfrac{16}{3}\pi r_A^3$$

for every molecule (see Eq. 6.505). There is then a total excluded volume equal to Nb' for N molecules of the gas. If the gas is so compressed that this excluded volume is an appreciable fraction of the sample, the scattering is reduced, as shown by Debye, in a manner given by the equation

$$I' = N'f^2\left[1 - \left(\frac{2Nb'}{V}\right)\Phi(\mu r_A)\right] \tag{15.314}$$

where Φ is the scattering function for a sphere given in Eq. 15.214 and Fig. 15.203. Now this function is large when the scattering angle is low, where it reaches unity, and falls off rapidly as the scattering angle increases. If $2Nb'$ is equal to one half of the total volume, the low-angle scattering is thus reduced by one half. At higher angles, the angular dependence of the scattering becomes almost the same as for a dilute gas, which falls off rather more slowly with angle. For a dense gas, as contrasted to the same gas dilute, there is thus a maximum at low but not zero angle of scattering. This is the characteristic "halo" effect observed with liquids as well as gases. If the gas is solidified, this halo, which is symmetrical around the incident beam, breaks up into the characteristic diffraction pattern of a crystal exposed to a beam of X-rays.

Problems

15.301   If possible, obtain a Polaroid or other polarizer and look at the light from the blue sky when the sun is low on the horizon. What is the axis of polarization with respect to NSEW? Look at the light in the direction of the sun. (Do not look directly at the sun.) Is it polarized?

15.302   Analyze the units of Eq. 15.302 to show that the units of polarizability are cubic centimeters per molecule. What are the units of the dielectric constant and refractive index?

15.303   Calculate the refractive index of CCl_4 vapor at 10 cm pressure from Eq. 15.309 and from the experimental value of the polarizability.

15.304   Calculate and plot the shape of the scattering envelope as a ratio to the scattering at 0° for angles θ_s from 0 to 180° for argon at 0°C, and at 500 atm, for X-rays of wavelength of 2 Å. Use the equation of state for hard spheres $P(V - Nb') = Nk\bar{T}$ and take Nb' to have the value 30 cc mole^{-1}.

4. Light Scattering from Solutions of Macromolecules

Turbidity.   An ordinary solution of a relatively low-molecular-weight substance appears to the naked eye as a crystal-clear liquid. Careful centrifugation will remove the motes of dust that are present in most solutions made in the open laboratory, and the solution will look clear even in a beam of bright light. But it was a source of some puzzlement to early polymer chemists that solutions of such materials as polystyrene in benzene always look slightly cloudy, no matter how carefully they are cleaned of impurities. Although the solvent can be shown to scatter a certain amount of light, the amount of scattering caused by a high-molecular-weight solute is often many times the scattering of a liquid gas composed of low-molecular-weight compounds. It is this scattering of light that is the inherent cause of the easily apparent turbidity of macromolecular solutions.

The turbidity τ is defined in terms of the reduction in intensity of the incident light beam after traversing a distance x in the turbid medium:

$$\frac{-dI}{dx} = \tau I \tag{15.401}$$

If this expression is integrated, we find

$$I = I_0 e^{-\tau x} \tag{15.402}$$

ILLUSTRATION.   Integration of Eq. 15.401. (Compare Eq. 13.101 *et seq.*)

If we separate the variables

$$\frac{-dI}{I} = \tau \, dx$$

Upon integration between the limits I_0, the incident intensity as it enters the turbid medium where $x = 0$, to its intensity I at point x

$$\int_{I_0}^{I} \frac{dI}{I} = -\tau x$$

Then

$$\ln \frac{I}{I_0} = -\tau x$$

and

$$I = I_0 e^{-\tau x}$$

The reciprocal of the turbidity is the length of turbid medium required to reduce the intensity of a beam to $1/e$ of its initial intensity.

The solution is turbid, not because of the absorption of light, but because the light is scattered out of the incident beam into the scattered beams, which emerge from the solution in all directions. If we write Eq. 15.401 in the form for finite differences and rearrange, we find

$$\frac{-\Delta I}{I} = \tau \, \Delta x$$

This is in the same form as Eq. 15.313, where $-\Delta I$ takes the place of I_s and I takes the place of I_0. If we set $\Delta x = 1$, this corresponds to the unit scattering distance of the Rayleigh ratio. However, the Rayleigh ratio refers to the scattering at a particular angle; in order to get the total effect, the ratio must be integrated over the entire sphere of scattering, at a convenient value of the distance R, which is $R = 1$. At this unit distance, the area element corresponding to the angles of observation is called the solid angle of the sphere. The Rayleigh ratio, Eq. 15.313, can be written in terms of the scattered intensity at right angles, $R(90°)$:

$$R(\theta_s) = R(90°)(1 + \cos^2 \theta_s) \tag{15.403}$$

An element of solid angle over the scattering sphere is $\sin \theta_s \, d\theta_s \, d\phi$, and if we integrate over this angle

$$\tau = \frac{16\pi}{3} R(90°)$$

$$= \frac{8\pi}{3} R(0°) \tag{15.404}$$

The latter expression follows because the extrapolated scattering at 0° is twice that at 90°.

ILLUSTRATION.   Integration of the angular term.
Our problem is to integrate the expression

$$(1 + \cos^2 \theta)(\sin \theta) \, d\theta \, d\phi$$

The limits of θ are from 0 to π, and the limits of the angle around the scattering axis, ϕ, are 0 to 2π. If we let $\cos \theta = x$, the corresponding limits are 1 and -1. We thus have

$$\int_0^\pi \int_0^{2\pi} (1 + \cos^2 \theta) \, d\phi \sin \theta \, d\theta = 2\pi \int_1^{-1} (1 + x^2)(-dx)$$

$$= -2\pi \left(x + \frac{x^3}{3} \right) \Big|_{+1}^{-1} = \frac{16\pi}{3}$$

The value of the constant in Eq. 15.404 is thus established. The units are, of course, the same as for $R(90°)$, per centimeter, since the constant is dimensionless.

Calculation of $R(\theta)$ for a Solute.   Equation 15.313 applies as it stands to scattering centers in a vacuum, that is, the scattering is from a gas in an otherwise empty space. If, on the other hand, scattering centers such as polymer molecules in solution are under consideration, there is a small scattering from the solvent, with the scattering due to the polymer superimposed on this background. In what follows, we shall assume that any background scattering from the solvent has been subtracted. The refractive index of the solution, n, is now considerably larger than unity, so Eq. 15.312 is no longer applicable to the polarizability of a scattering center. However, since the solution is dilute, the refractive index, n, will be very close to the refractive index of the solvent, n_0. We replace Eq. 15.312 by the relationship

$$\alpha = \frac{n^2 - n_0^2}{4\pi N'} \tag{15.405}$$

We will also replace the number of particles per cubic centimeter by the concentration in grams per cubic centimeter, Avogadro's number, and the molecular weight of the solute:

$$N' = \frac{c\mathbf{N}}{M}$$

We thus find that the polarizability per solute molecule is

$$\alpha = \frac{M}{4\pi\mathbf{N}} \frac{n^2 - n_0^2}{c} \approx \frac{M}{2\pi\mathbf{N}} n_0 \frac{\Delta n}{c} \tag{15.406}$$

In this expression $\Delta n/c$ is the refractive index increment and can be measured in a differential refractometer to a high degree of accuracy. If, as we have assumed, the concentration is low, it is a constant of the polymeric material dissolved in a particular solvent. We shall give it the symbol

$$\psi = \frac{\Delta n}{c} \tag{15.407}$$

With these substitutions, Eq. 15.311 becomes, in terms of the Rayleigh ratio at 90° defined as in Eq. 15.313,

$$R(90°) = \frac{2\pi^2 n_0^2 \psi^2}{N\lambda^4} cM = KcM \tag{15.408}$$

Here all the constant factors have been gathered together in the scattering constant K,

$$K = \frac{2\pi^2 n_0^2 \psi^2}{N\lambda^4} \tag{15.409}$$

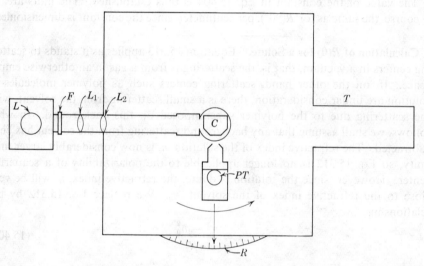

Fig. 15.401 Experimental arrangement for measuring light scattering from solution (*viewed from above*; adapted by permission from Brice Phoenix catalog, *Bull*. BP 1000-B). *C*, semi-octagonal cell; *F*, monochromatic filter; *L*, mercury lamp; L_1, achromatic lens; L_2, plano-cylindrical lens; *PT*, photomultiplier tube; *T*, light-trap tube; *R*, graduated circle.

Note that λ is the wavelength of the light *in vacuo*; it entered the expression from the substitution $\lambda = c/v$, where c is the velocity of light *in vacuo*, not in the medium. The frequency v is of course the same in the vacuum as in the medium.

A similar expression can be written for the turbidity:

$$\tau = \frac{16\pi}{3} KcM = HcM \tag{15.410}$$

where H is simply the constant K multiplied by the factor $16\pi/3$, to change the 90° scattering function into turbidity.

Experimental Measurement of Scattered Light.   Arrangements for the measurement of scattered light include a source of monochromatic light that is passed through a cell containing the solution, and a rotating detector that can be set at angles between 0 and 180° to the incident beam. A typical apparatus is shown in Fig. 15.401. An absolute calibration can be avoided if the particular cell being used is filled first with a sample of known turbidity, and then with the solutions under study. Measurements can be made at different frequencies, but the refractive index increment used in the calculation must be measured at each frequency. Experiments over a wide frequency range are theoretically desirable, but the range is limited in practice by two factors: (1) low-frequency light is scattered and detected much less effectively, and so the experimental error is much more of a problem in the red region than in the blue; (2) most molecules begin to have specific absorptions beyond the range of blue light, and so short wavelengths in the near-ultraviolet region are not generally usable. In practice, a convenient light source to study scattering is the blue mercury lamp line with a wavelength of 4358 Å.

Measurements of turbidity can alternatively be made in the cells of an ordinary spectrophotometer. In such an instrument, the measured quantity is the attenuation of the incident beam as it passes through a known thickness of solution; the turbidity is calculated from Eq. 15.402, with x set equal to the path length in the cell.

Depolarization.   According to the simple Rayleigh theory of light scattering, the light scattered from a wave of given polarization has the same axis of polarization as the incident beam. Thus, light scattered at 90° has an axis vertical to the plane of observation, even if the incident light is unpolarized, because this is the only component of the light scattered at this angle. Experimentally, complete polarization is found for spherically symmetrical scatterers such as argon atoms. However, the light scattered at 90° from molecules that are not spherically symmetrical is often not completely polarized because some of the electronic motion excited by the light transfers energy to other modes of electronic motion, which in turn emit light not polarized in the original direction. For a typical polymer molecule, this depolarized light might amount to 5 per cent of the total. This extra depolarized light should be corrected for, but the correction is usually smaller than some of the other uncertainties of measurement and theory. It is treated further in the article of Doty and Edsall in the General References.

Determination of Molecular Weight.   Equations such as 15.408 form the basis for the determination of molecular weights from light scattering or turbidity measurements. However, in their present form they are still too idealized for direct application. First, in order to apply them at all, the wavelength of the radiation must be in large excess over the largest dimension of the scattering molecule. If it is not, internal interference reduces the scattering in all but the $\theta = 0$ or forward direction. This problem will be dealt with in the next section. However, even if the scattering molecules are small compared with the wavelength of the light, interference between the polymer molecules will affect the scattering. Therefore, in order to obtain a true molecular weight, all measurements must be extrapolated to zero concentration.

In practice, this is accomplished by making reciprocal plots of $Kc/R(90°)$ or Hc/τ against concentration, followed by extrapolation to $c = 0$. The plots take the form

$$\frac{Kc}{R(90°)} = \frac{1}{M} + 2Bc \qquad (15.411)$$

$$\frac{Hc}{\tau} = \frac{1}{M} + 2Bc \qquad (15.412)$$

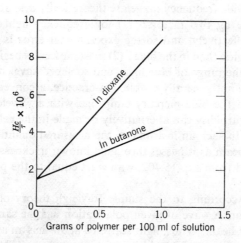

Fig. 15.402   Light scattering from polystyrene in various solvents [by permission from Ewart, Roe, Debye, and McCartney, *J. Phys. Chem.*, **14**, 687 (1946)].

which are linear in concentration and extrapolate smoothly to $c = 0$. The value of the intercept gives $1/M$ and thus the molecular weight. A typical plot is shown in Fig. 15.402.

The slope of the plot, which is equal to $2B$, reflects the intermolecular interactions of the polymer molecules. The constant B is analogous to the second virial coefficient of a gas. Its detailed interpretation requires a more thermodynamic interpretation of scattering than we have given here. Note that it varies in different solvents. However, since extrapolation to $c = 0$ removes its effect, it has no bearing on the determination of molecular weights.

Internal Interference in Light Scattering. When the wavelength of the light scattered is small enough so that internal scattering is an important factor, the angular dependence of the light scattering is no longer given by the factor

$$(1 + \cos^2 \theta_s)/2$$

The Rayleigh ratio now takes the form

$$R(\theta_s) = KcMP(\theta_s)(1 + \cos^2 \theta_s) \qquad (15.413)$$

where $P(\theta_s)$ is a new factor that takes account of the internal interference. It is a dimensionless number that is positive but less than unity, and approaches unity as the wavelength of the light increases and as the scattering angle goes to zero. We have already considered scattering from a sphere, containing a uniform density of scattering matter. The reduced amplitude of scattering is given by Eq. 15.213. Since the angular factor of $(1 + \cos^2 \theta_s)/2$ has been left out of this expression, the only angular dependent part is the factor Φ. Since the scattered intensity is the square of the absolute value of the amplitude, we see by comparison of Eq. 15.413 with Eq. 15.213 that

$$P(\theta_s) = [\Phi(\mu r_0)]^2 \tag{15.414}$$

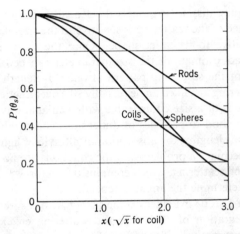

$$x(\sqrt{x} \text{ for coil})$$

Fig. 15.403   Particle scattering factors for spheres, rods, and coils (by permission from P. Doty and J. T. Edsall, *Advances in Protein Chemistry*, Vol. VI, Academic Press, 1951).

We shall now write μr_0 explicitly in terms of θ_s and the diameter of the spheres, $D = 2r_0$, and the definition of μ from Eq. 15.209:

$$\mu r_0 = \frac{2\pi D \sin (\theta_s/2)}{\lambda'} \tag{15.415}$$

Note that λ' is the wavelength of the light in the solution ($\lambda/\lambda' = n_0$). The function for $P(\theta_s)$ has the properties that are required. It falls off toward zero as the size of the particle increases, and finally shows a series of maxima and minima corresponding to diffraction from the large particle. For small particles, or any particle as θ approaches zero, it becomes unity and can be neglected in Eq. 15.413.

Similar problems have been solved for different shapes of large particles. Without writing down the form for the equation, we will present the results graphically, along with those for a sphere. In all cases, we will present $P(\theta_s)$ as a function of a characteristic variable which contains a size parameter as well as an angular and wavelength dependence. In Fig. 15.403, the variable x represents

$$x = \frac{\mu D}{2} \tag{15.416}$$

For the case of a rigid rod of length L and diameter much smaller than L,

$$x = \frac{\mu L}{2} \tag{15.417}$$

For the case of a random coil of a flexible macromolecule, characterized by a root-mean-square average distance R between the ends,

$$x = \frac{\mu R}{6^{1/2}} \tag{15.418}$$

Note that for these quite dissimilar models the general behavior is similar. Thus the angular dependence of the scattering is sensitive to the size of the scatterer, but not particularly sensitive to its exact shape. Once the shape is decided upon, however, a rather exact estimate of the size parameter can be obtained from the angular dependence of the scattering pattern at one wavelength or, equally well, by a study of the scattering at a fixed angle (usually 90°) over a series of wavelengths, as long as the particle is of a size comparable with available wavelengths of light.

This restricts the method to particles of dimensions comparable to visible light because, at shorter wavelengths, the absorption of ultraviolet light in the region of a natural frequency becomes a problem and the equations are no longer valid. At longer wavelengths, the scattering, which contains the factor λ^{-4}, becomes so weak that it is difficult to determine the angular dependence.

These methods can also be extended to the turbidity, measured over a series of wavelengths; an integration of $P(\theta)$ over the scattering envelope is of course involved, but the proper analysis of turbidity of a polymer solution yields the same information about the size of the particles as a study of the scattered light.

Determination of Size by Dissymmetry. Equation 15.413 includes the effect of internal interference but does not take any account of intermolecular interference between the scattering molecules. If we neglect these latter interferences for the moment, we observe that if the particles are small $P(\theta_s) = 1$, and the scattering is symmetrical about the axis of the incident beam, as regards forward and backward scattering. If we observe scattering at 45°, for example, in the forward direction, it is equal to the scattering at 135°, which is in the backward direction, but makes a symmetrical angle of 45° with the incident beam extended backward. If the particles are large enough so that $P(\theta_s)$ is not unity, these intensities will not be equal. Because of the monotonic decline of $P(\theta_s)$ with angle, the scattering in the forward direction will be somewhat greater. We define a dissymmetry ratio,

$$Z = \frac{R(45°)}{R(135°)} = \frac{P(45°)}{P(135°)} \tag{15.419}$$

which is in general equal to or greater than unity. If this ratio is closely equal to unity we can conclude only that the particles are small compared to the wavelength of light. However, if it is substantially larger than unity, it can be used to evaluate the characteristic dimension D, L, or R. Computations based on the value of

$P(\theta_s)$ at 45° and 135° are shown in Fig. 15.404. The dissymmetry ratio Z is plotted against D/λ' for the various shapes, where now D stands for L, or R also where appropriate. In the absence of external interference the experimental dissymmetry can thus be used to obtain D/λ' and thus D. In actual practice, the dissymmetry must be extrapolated to zero concentration to obtain a true value of D.

Extrapolation Method for D and M; the Zimm Plot. In order to obtain a true value of the molecular weight, use can be made of the fact that, for all shapes of particles, $P(\theta_s)$ goes to unity at zero scattering angle. Therefore, at zero scattering angle, a formula such as Eq. 15.411 will be valid for particles of any size. A factor of 2 must be introduced, however, because $\cos^2 0° + 1 = 2$, whereas $\cos^2 90° + 1 = 1$.

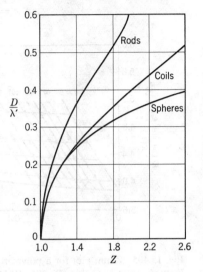

$$\frac{2Kc}{R(0°)} = \frac{1}{M} + 2Bc \qquad (15.420)$$

This expression calls for a second extrapolation to $c = 0$ as well as $\theta = 0$, to finally evaluate the molecular weight, M.

A convenient way of carrying out such an extrapolation on one graph is shown in Fig. 15.405, called a Zimm plot. All values of $R(\theta_s)$ have been divided by $1 + \cos^2 \theta_s$ to reduce them to equivalent values at 90° for symmetrical scattering. Any residual change is due to size effects. In order to spread the points out, they are plotted against the arbitrary function $\sin^2(\theta_s/2) + \text{const} \times c$. The double extrapola-

Fig. 15.404 Dissymmetry as a function of particle diameter and wavelength (by permission from P. Doty and J. T. Edsall, *Advances in Protein Chemistry*, Vol. VI, Academic Press, 1951).

tions to $c = 0$ and $\theta_s = 0$ intercept at the value of $1/M$, when both c and θ_s are zero. If there were no intermolecular interactions, all points would lie on a single line corresponding to $c = 0$. If the particles were so small that there were no internal interference, this line would be horizontal. The slope of the $c = 0$ line reflects internal interference and thus size alone; the slope of the $\theta_s = 0$ line reflects external interference and thus the second virial coefficient of the molecules alone. The intercept of both lines depends on the value of the molecular weight alone. The plot thus serves to separate the three effects, which in any given scattering measurement are all interacting.

Detailed Interpretation of the Zimm Plot. Since $\sin^2 0°$ equals zero, the $\theta_s = 0$ line is effectively plotted against the concentration alone. It is thus to be treated according to Eq. 15.411. The intercept is proportional to the reciprocal of the molecular weight, and the slope gives the virial coefficient directly.

The interpretation of the slope of the $c = 0$ line is not quite so direct. Since $c = 0$, the line is plotted against $\sin^2(\theta_s/2)$ alone. We shall treat the case of spherical particles only, although a more general interpretation is possible. The deviation from a horizontal straight line is caused by the factor Φ^2 alone, and although this does not predict a straight line of finite slope for all angles, an expansion of the function gives a straight-line portion near $\theta_s = 0$ and $\Phi^2 = 1$. If we use the definition of Φ, Eq. 15.214, and of μr_0, Eq. 15.415, as well as the expansions

$$\sin x = x - \frac{x^3}{3!} + \frac{x^5}{5!} + \cdots$$

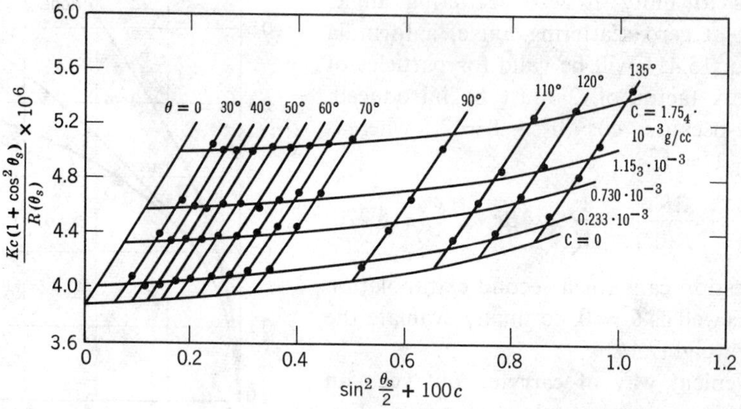

Fig. 15.405   Zimm plot for a polymer in $0.10M$ NaCl [by permission from G. Ehrlich and P. Doty, *J. Am. Chem. Soc.*, **76**, 3764 (1954)].

and

$$\cos x = 1 - \frac{x^2}{2} + \frac{x^4}{4!}$$

we find that

$$\Phi^2 = 1 - \frac{(\mu r_0)^2}{5} + \cdots$$

$$= 1 - \frac{1}{5}\left(\frac{2\pi D}{\lambda'}\right)^2 \sin^2 \frac{\theta_s}{2} + \cdots$$

The reciprocal of this factor, multiplied by the intercept, gives the initial portion of the zero concentration line. Thus the dimensionless ratio of the slope to the intercept at $\theta_s = 0$ is the ratio

$$\frac{1}{5}\left(\frac{2\pi D}{\lambda'}\right)^2$$

which allows the diameter D to be evaluated.

ILLUSTRATION.   Numerical values from Fig. 15.405.

The intercept in Fig. 15.405 is 3.87×10^{-6}, which gives a molecular weight of 258,000. From the slope of the $\theta_s = 0$ line, the second virial coefficient may be calculated and in this case is seen to be 3.2×10^{-4} cm^3 moles g^{-2}. The slope of the $c = 0$ line gives the dimensions of the copolymer. The effective hard sphere radius is 155 Å.

Problems

15.401   The refractive index of butanone at 25°C is 1.3740, and the refractive index increment of the system polystyrene-butanone is 0.219 cm^3 g^{-1}. Given the following turbidities of the solutions of polystyrene in butanone, determined at $\lambda = 5461$ Å:

conc., g/100 ml:	1.0	0.85	0.65	0.35	0.175
τ:	0.0133	0.0125	0.0118	0.0083	0.0052

calculate the molecular weight of the polymer.

15.402   Calculate the degree of dissymmetry which would be shown by spherical particles 1000 Å in diameter dissolved in H$_2$O ($n_0 = 1.33$). Assume blue light of $\lambda = 4360$.

15.403   The molecular weight of tobacco mosaic virus is 44,500,000 dissolved in water. It exhibits an angular dissymmetry of 1.90 with light of $\lambda = 5461$. Calculate its dimensions on the basis of a rod and a sphere. Assume that the molecule has a density of 2 g cm^{-3} to decide which of these models is more realistic.

15.404   From the data in Problem 15.403 calculate the shape of the scattering envelope in a solution of tobacco mosaic virus.

5. Structure of Solids; the Crystal Lattice

We may think of a crystal as a solid composed of atoms arranged in a three-dimensional periodic pattern. The periodic pattern should extend over an interval which is large relative to the unit of periodicity. If the arrangement is not periodic, the detailed structure of a macroscopic piece of solid cannot be solved because of the large number of particles present. We will now describe some general characteristics of the crystalline state and, in Sec. 15.6, the procedure by which X-ray scattering studies may be used to obtain interatomic distances in crystals.

The Crystal Habit. The external appearance of a crystal of a given substance (see Fig. 15.501) usually depends on conditions prevailing during the crystallization process; in general differences are due not to variation in internal structure but to the rate of growth of the various crystal faces. A common example of different crystal habits is the many-varied forms of snow crystals. It is found, however, that each of these externally different forms has the same interfacial angles. This feature of macroscopic crystal structure is characteristic of all materials and is sometimes called the *first law of crystallography*. It suggests some regular internal pattern of the basic building blocks of the crystal. Most common solids are an aggregate of crystallites. Large single crystals are seldom found in nature.

The Crystal Lattice. The structure of a crystal, i.e., the relative positions of the atoms of which it is composed, may be most conveniently described relative to a lattice of points characteristic of the given crystal. Such a point lattice indicates

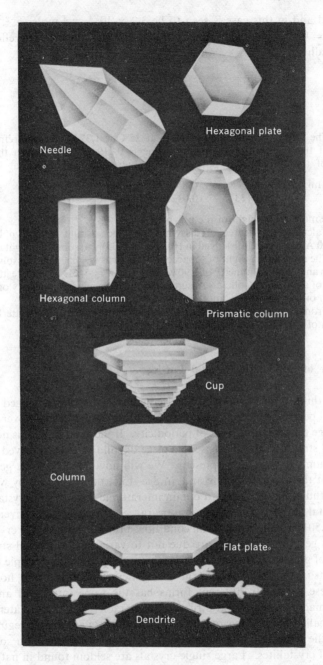

Fig. 15.501 External variations in crystalline forms of ice crystals (by permission, as shown by John A. Day, "Wintry Art in Snow," *Natural History*, Jan. 1962, p. 29).

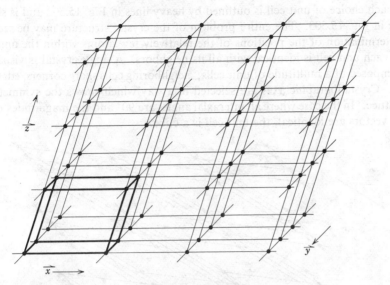

Fig. 15.502   A point lattice.

the existence of a translation repetition pattern, Fig. 15.502. The lattice may be generated from a given point by repeated application of three basic vectors, $\vec{x}$ with magnitude a, $\vec{y}$ with magnitude b, and $\vec{z}$ with magnitude c. The directions of these vectors correspond to what are called the crystallographic axes, Fig. 15.503. The interaxial angles, α for the angle between $\vec{y}$ and $\vec{z}$, β between $\vec{x}$ and $\vec{z}$, and γ between $\vec{x}$ and $\vec{y}$, and the magnitudes a, b, and c, are specific characteristics of each crystalline substance; determination of these quantities constitutes one of the first steps in the elucidation of the crystal structure. The points of the lattice, Fig. 15.502, do not necessarily indicate positions of atoms (although the position of the lattice may arbitrarily be placed so each lattice point corresponds to the position of one of the kinds of atom in the crystal) but are meant to indicate that the environment about any lattice point within the crystal is identical with that about any other lattice point.

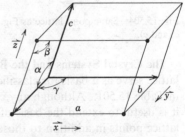

Fig. 15.503   Basic vectors along crystallographic axes. Repeated application of these vectors forms the lattice of Fig. 15.502. Crystallographic angles α, β, γ are shown.

Each crystal may be considered to have a characteristic fixed point lattice. However, it may be easily seen (for example, compare Figs. 15.504 and 15.502) that a given point lattice may be generated by a choice of many different sets of basic vectors, that is, a variety of choices for the crystallographic axes exists.

The Unit Cell.   It will be seen, Fig. 15.502 or 15.504, that the point lattice, generated by application of the basic vectors, may be considered as composed of unit cells.

One such choice of unit cell is outlined by heavy lines in Fig. 15.502 and is shown alone in Fig. 15.503. The entire problem of the crystal structure may be reduced to determination of the positions of the relatively few atoms within the unit cell, since each unit cell is identical with all its neighbors. A single crystal is visualized as composed of a multitude of unit cells; neighboring cells share corners, edges, or faces. Crystallographic axes are selected in a way which shows the symmetry of the lattice. In the case where all interaxial angles are 90° and the magnitudes of the basic vectors are identical, the unit cell is a cube.

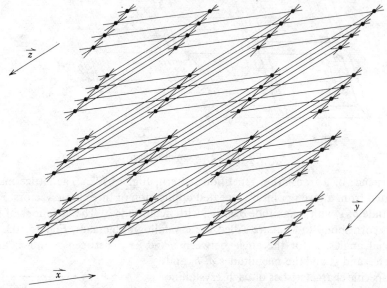

Fig. 15.504   Same point lattice as Fig. 15.502 but with different choice of axes for $\vec{x}$ (and a) and $\vec{z}$ (and c).

The Crystal Systems and the Bravais Lattices.   The characteristics of the point lattice serve as a basis for classification of crystals into one of seven systems, listed in Table 15.501. Although any crystal must belong to one of these seven systems, it is useful to extend the basis of classification to include unit cells which contain lattice points in addition to those at the corners. Cells which contain points only at the corners are called primitive; since each of the corners is shared by eight neighboring cells, a primitive cell contains the equivalent of only one lattice point. Cells which contain additional points are called nonprimitive. Nonprimitive cells are used only if the crystal can thereby be classed in a system of greater symmetry and hence the unit cell described with fewer parameters. Bravais, as early as 1848, showed that the seven basic crystal systems may profitably be expanded, by inclusion of nonprimitive cells, to only fourteen space lattices. The fourteen Bravais lattices are listed in Table 15.501, and the corresponding unit cells are illustrated in Fig. 15.505. The symbols P, I, C, and F are used to indicate primitive, body-centered, centered on one face only, and centered on all faces, respectively. It may

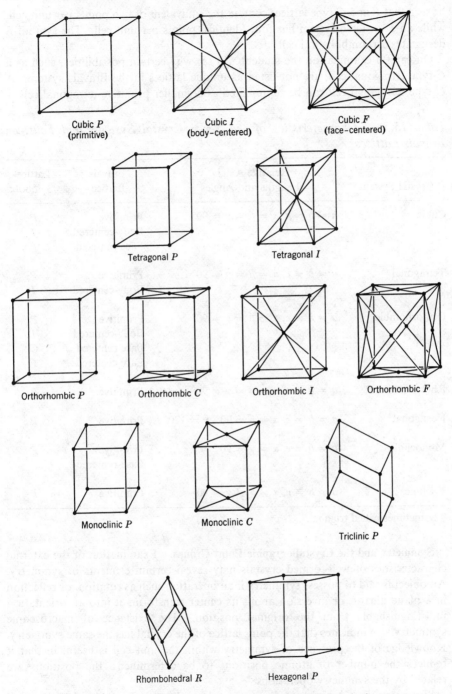

Cubic *P*
(primitive)

Cubic *I*
(body-centered)

Cubic *F*
(face-centered)

Tetragonal *P*

Tetragonal *I*

Orthorhombic *P*

Orthorhombic *C*

Orthorhombic *I*

Orthorhombic *F*

Monoclinic *P*

Monoclinic *C*

Triclinic *P*

Rhombohedral *R*

Hexagonal *P*

Fig. 15.505   Unit cells representative of the fourteen Bravais lattices.

be seen that I- and C-type lattices contain the equivalent of two points per unit cell, while an F-centered system has four identical points per unit cell. The symbol R designates a rhombohedral cell.

On careful examination the student will see why certain possibilities, such as a C-type tetragonal cell, are not listed as unique lattices in the Bravais system. A C-type tetragonal cell can be represented as a smaller primitive tetragonal cell.

Table 15.501   Characteristics of the Seven Crystal Systems and Fourteen Bravais Lattices

Crystal System	Relative Axial Lengths and Angles	Bravais Lattice	Lattice Symbol
Cubic	$a = b = c, \alpha = \beta = \gamma = 90°$	Primitive	P
		Body-centered	I
		Face-centered	F
Tetragonal	$a = b \neq c, \alpha = \beta = \gamma = 90°$	Primitive	P
		Body-centered	I
Orthorhombic	$a \neq b \neq c, \alpha = \beta = \gamma = 90°$	Primitive	P
		Body-centered	I
		Base-centered	C
		Face-centered	F
Rhombohedral*	$a = b = c, \alpha = \beta = \gamma \neq 90°$	Primitive	R
Hexagonal	$a = b \neq c, \alpha = \beta = 90°, \gamma = 120°$	Primitive	P
Monoclinic	$a \neq b \neq c, \alpha = \gamma = 90° \neq \beta$	Primitive	P
		Base-centered	C
Triclinic	$a \neq b \neq c, \alpha \neq \beta \neq \gamma \neq 90°$	Primitive	P

* Sometimes called trigonal.

Symmetry and the Crystallographic Point Groups.   Examination of the external characteristics of well-formed crystals may reveal certain elements of symmetry. An object is said to possess symmetry if an operation such as rotation, or reflection in a plane mirror, or inversion about its center transforms it into an orientation indistinguishable from the original position. The existence of macroscopic symmetry also indicates that the point lattice of the crystal has the same symmetry. Knowledge of the presence of symmetry within the unit cell is useful in that it reduces the number of atomic positions to be determined; the positions are related by the symmetry operations.

Symmetry characteristics are represented by a shorthand notation. The symbol

1 means that no element of symmetry exists. $\overline{1}$ indicates the presence of a center of inversion. 2 designates a two-fold rotation axis, that is, as the object is rotated about this axis, an orientation indistinguishable from the starting position is reached at 180° and, of course, again at 360°. Similarly 3, 4, and 6 indicate the presence of three-fold, four-fold, and six-fold axes with repeat intervals of 120°, 90°, and 60°, respectively. These are the only rotation axes consistent with the required translation repetition pattern of the lattice. *m* indicates a mirror plane, that is, the unit cell may be divided by a plane into two parts which are mirror images. We may also have symmetry based on a combination of rotation and inversion. For example, $\overline{4}$ represents a four-fold rotary inversion axis; in such a case an equivalent orientation results when the object is rotated by 90° and then inverted through the center. Some symmetry operations are illustrated in Fig. 15.506.

Various combinations of these symmetry operations may be present and are then designated by combinations of symbols. For example, 222 represents three mutually

Table 15.502   The 32 Crystal Classes

Crystal System	Symmetry Elements for each of the Various Possible Classes
Triclinic	1, $\overline{1}$
Monoclinic	2, *m*, 2/*m*
Orthorhombic	222, 2*mm*, *mmm*
Tetragonal	4, $\overline{4}$, 4/*m*, 422, 4*mm*, $\overline{4}2m$, 4/*m* 2/*m* 2/*m*
Cubic	23, 432, 2/*m*$\overline{3}$, $\overline{4}3m$, 4/*m* $\overline{3}$ 2/*m*
Hexagonal	6, $\overline{6}$, $\overline{6}m2$, 6/*m*, 6*mm*, 622, 6/*m* 2/*m* 2/*m*
Rhombohedral	3, $\overline{3}$, 3*m*, 32, $\overline{3}2/m$

perpendicular two-fold axes; 2/*m* represents a two-fold axis with a mirror plane perpendicular to that axis. It can be shown that for all the various crystal systems there are only 32 ways of taking the elements of symmetry singly and combining them about a point. Each possible combination is called a crystallographic point group, or a crystal class. The possible classes for each of the crystal systems are listed in Table 15.502. It should be noted that the symbols used to designate the classes do not include all symmetry elements which may be recognized but only the minimum number necessary to characterize the class; in certain cases, alternate symbols might equally well be used, e.g., 3/*m* is equivalent to $\overline{6}$.

The symmetry operations for each of the 32 point groups are illustrated in Fig. 15.507. In addition to the International symbols given in Table 15.502, the corresponding Schoenflies symbols, generally used by spectroscopists to represent the symmetry of molecules, are also indicated. Each diagram shows a set of points

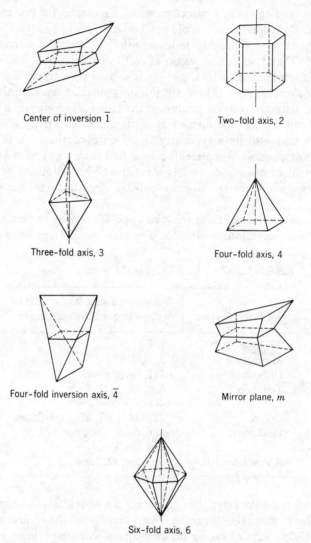

Fig. 15.506 Some symmetry operators as applied to polyhedra.

having the symmetry of the class. The first-named axis is perpendicular to the
plane of the figure.

If crystals are well formed and have enough faces, evidence for assignment to
one of the 32 crystal classes can be obtained by optical examination of the symmetry
and angular relationship of crystal faces. However, it is not possible to distinguish
the various primitive and centered lattices in the same crystal system by optical
means. The latter requires X-ray evidence, as will be explained later.

Space Groups. The symmetry of a finite body (a polyhedron, a molecule, etc.)

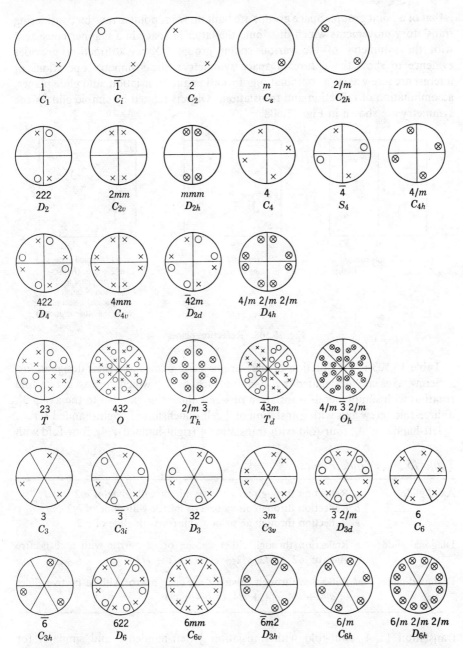

Fig. 15.507 Illustration of the symmetry characteristics for each of the 32 crystal classes. A point above the circle is indicated by ×, below by ○. The number of equivalent points is indicated for each case.

is that of a point group. Space groups are built up from point arrays by considering translatory movements which distribute the latter in space in a manner consistent with the symmetry of the various point groups. X-ray diffraction provides evidence to show the nature of space symmetry; the symmetry operations of interest are screw axes, a combination of rotation and translation, and glide planes, a combination of reflection and translation. Objects related by simple glide plane symmetry are shown in Fig. 15.508.

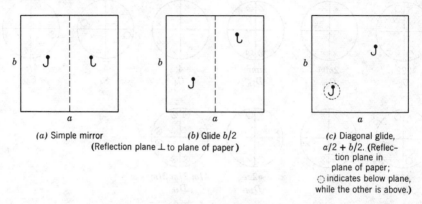

(a) Simple mirror
(Reflection plane ⊥ to plane of paper)

(b) Glide b/2

(c) Diagonal glide, a/2 + b/2. (Reflection plane in plane of paper; ○ indicates below plane, while the other is above.)

Fig. 15.508   Reflection planes.

Table 15.503 is a tabulation of the various glide planes and their designations.
Screw axes are designated by symbols such as 2_1, which means a two-fold rotation with simultaneous translation of $\frac{1}{2}$ cell dimension parallel to the axis; 3_1, a three-fold screw axis with translation of $\frac{1}{3}$ cell dimension (3_1 right-handed screw, 3_2 left-handed); 4_1, four-fold with translation $\frac{1}{4}$ (right-handed); 4_2, four-fold with

Table 15.503   Glide Planes

Axial glide	*a* Reflection through an *xy* or *xz* mirror with glide of *a*/2
	b Reflection through an *xy* or a *yz* mirror with glide of *b*/2
	c Reflection through an *yz* or *xz* mirror with glide of *c*/2
Diagonal glide	*n* Reflection through either *xy*, *xz*, or *yz* mirror with a respective glide of *a*/2 + *b*/2, *a*/2 + *c*/2, or *b*/2 + *c*/2
Diamond glide	*d* Reflection through either *xy*, *xz*, or *yz* mirror with respective glides of *a*/4 + *b*/4, *a*/4 + *c*/4, or *b*/4 + *c*/4

translation $\frac{1}{2}$; 4_3, four-fold with translation $\frac{1}{4}$ (left-handed); and similarly for six-fold screw axes. Several types of screw axes are illustrated in Fig. 15.509.
   These possible elements of space symmetry, applied to the 32 crystal classes, give a maximum of 230 possible combinations. Each one is called a space group. They are described in detail in many books on X-ray crystallography and particularly in

the *International Tables for X-ray Crystallography*. Each crystal must belong to one of the 230 space groups. Table 15.504 lists the space groups for the triclinic and monoclinic systems and the International symbols used to designate the various elements of symmetry. Generally it is necessary to use both optical and X-ray evidence in deciding to which of the space groups a given crystal belongs. The space group is of assistance in the final elucidation of the crystal structure in

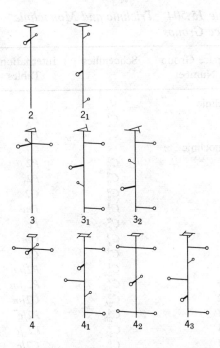

Fig. 15.509   Illustration of repetition pattern for 2-, 3-, and 4-fold screw axes (adapted by permission from *Elementary Crystallography*, M. J. Buerger, John Wiley and Sons, 1956.)

that symmetry may reduce the number of unknowns, atomic positions, to be determined. Physical properties, such as electrical and thermal conductivity, refractive index, and piezoelectric effect, also provide evidence about symmetry.

Crystal Planes and Miller Indices. In both optical and X-ray crystallography the characteristics of crystals are conveniently discussed in terms of planes. The concept of a crystal plane may easily be visualized by reference to the crystal lattice. As shown in Fig. 15.510, plane surfaces may be drawn which contain some of the lattice points (if lattice points are included the plane is said to be *rational*; this is the only type of plane of interest). A large number of planes with different orientations may be drawn. Parallel to any plane there is a whole set of planes which may be generated from it by application of the unit lattice translations. A plane may be represented symbolically by Miller indices, a set of three numbers (hkl), each representing the reciprocal of the axial intercept of the plane in the set closest to but not containing the origin. The intercepts are expressed as fractions of the unit cell length on the x, y, and z axes, respectively. Miller indices are whole numbers. It is more convenient to use the reciprocal of the intercept, since this gives an index of zero if the intercept is infinite, that is, if the plane in question does not intersect a particular axis. Illustrations of the assignment of Miller indices are shown in Figs. 15.510, 15.511, and 15.512.

Table 15.504   Triclinic and Monoclinic Space Groups

Space Group Number	Schoenflies	International Tables
Triclinic		
1	C_1^1	$P1$
2	C_i^1	$P\bar{1}$
Monoclinic		
3	C_2^1	$P2$
4	C_2^2	$P2_1$
5	C_2^3	$C2$
6	C_s^1	Pm
7	C_s^2	Pc
8	C_s^3	Cm
9	C_s^4	Cc
10	C_{2h}^1	$P2/m$
11	C_{2h}^2	$P2_1/m$
12	C_{2h}^3	$C2/m$
13	C_{2h}^4	$P2/c$
14	C_{2h}^5	$P2_1/c$
15	C_{2h}^6	$C2/c$

Orthorhombic	59 space groups
Tetragonal	68 space groups
Rhombohedral	25 space groups
Hexagonal	27 space groups
Cubic	36 space groups

The planes in a set are all equidistant. A given Miller index set may be considered to indicate the plane in the set nearest the origin, or it may be taken to represent the whole set. Indices of some simple planes in a tetragonal crystal are shown in Fig. 15.512.

The plane faces which form the boundaries of macroscopic crystals are in every case found to be part of a set of lattice planes and therefore may be identified by Miller indices.

The interplanar distance for various Miller indices can easily be derived from trigonometry if the unit cell lengths and interaxial angles are known. This spacing

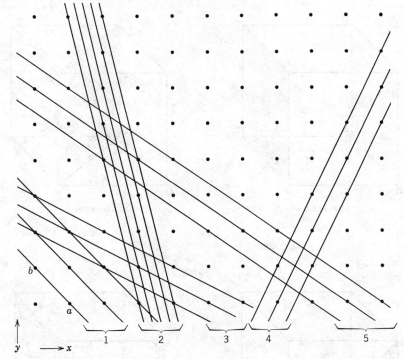

Fig. 15.510   Illustration of assignment of Miller indices in two dimensions.

	Intercepts		Indices
1.	$a,$	b	11
2.	$a,$	$4b$	41
3.	$4a,$	$2b$	12
4.	$-a,$	$2b$	$\bar{2}1$
5.	$9a,$	$6b$	23

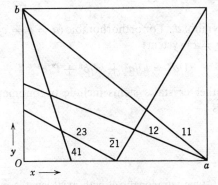

Fig. 15.511   Same planes as Fig. 15.510 within unit (enlarged) cell. The plane within the unit cell, with intercepts equal to the reciprocals of the Miller indices, belongs to the set shown in Fig. 15.510. The interplanar spacing between all members of the set is the same as the shortest distance between the plane nearest the origin and the origin.

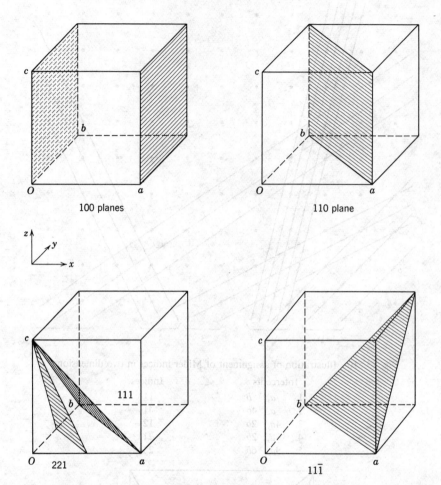

is represented by the symbol d. For orthorhombic $(a \neq b \neq c)$, cubic $(a = b = c)$, and tetragonal $(a = b \neq c)$ systems

$$1/d^2 = h^2/a^2 + k^2/b^2 + l^2/c^2 \qquad (15.501)$$

Expressions for the other crystal systems include trigonometric functions of the crystallographic angles.

Problems

15.501   Construct a C-type tetragonal cell with axial lengths a and c. What are the axial lengths (in terms of a and c) of the simpler tetragonal cell to which this non-primitive choice is related?

15.502   To which of the Bravais lattices is an F-type tetragonal cell equivalent?

15.503   Why isn't the *F*-centered cubic cell eliminated for the same reason as the *F*-centered tetragonal cell?

*15.504   In what crystal system would an *F*-centered cubic cell be classed if it were reduced to a primitive cell? Calculate the crystallographic angles for the primitive cell. What would be the answers for the body-centered cubic case?

15.505   Calculate the shortest distance between lattice points in the body-centered and face-centered cubic lattices (give answer in terms of the unit distance *a*).

15.506   Compare the number of nearest neighbors for each point in the simple, body-centered, and face-centered cubic cases.

15.507   Determine the angle of intersection of a 111 plane and a 001 plane in a cubic system.

15.508   Derive the value for the interplanar spacing of the 111 planes for an orthorhombic crystal if $a = 2b = 3c = 10$ Å.

*15.509   Explain the meaning of the symbols and the symmetry associated with the space group symbol *Pmmm*. Can this space group belong to the monoclinic crystal system? Explain. It appears as a space group for the orthorhombic system but not for the cubic system. Explain.

6. X-ray Scattering from a Crystal Lattice; Some Crystal Structures

Scattering from a Point Lattice.   First consider the scattering of X-rays from a simple idealized crystal in which a single scattering unit, with $f = 1$, is located at each lattice point. We wish to find the combined effect of all scattered wavelets at an observation point R outside the crystal, at a great enough distance that the

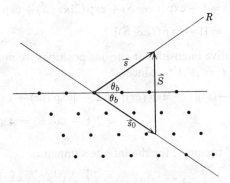

Fig. 15.601   Construction showing the Bragg angle and the vector $\vec{S}$.

vectors from the various lattice points to R all have virtually the same direction. We will assume that each scattered wavelet is not rescattered or absorbed; this proves a reasonable assumption for very small crystals. The following treatment was adapted from that of R. W. James, *The Optical Principles of the Diffraction of X-Rays*, G. Bell and Sons, London, 1948.

Consider the intensity of scattered radiation from a beam s_0, Fig. 15.601, which intersects a given crystal plane of scattering points at angle θ_b. θ_b corresponds to the angle of incidence and of reflection if the plane were considered a reflecting mirror. The scattered wavelets reaching point R from the various points of the lattice may have phase differences. We may apply Eq. 15.204 to obtain the total amplitude

$$A' = \exp(i\omega t) \sum_p \exp(i\kappa \vec{r}_p \cdot \vec{S}) \qquad (15.601)$$

where, as before, $\kappa = 2\pi/\lambda$; $\vec{r}_p$ is the vector to each point of the lattice from the origin, and $\vec{S} = \vec{s} - \vec{s}_0$. It will be recalled (Eq. 15.207) that for the $\vec{S}$ vector $|S| = 2 \sin \theta_b$, where $2\theta_b = \theta_s$, the total angle of scattering. We must now sum over all lattice points.

For each lattice point, $\vec{r}_p$ may be written

$$\vec{r}_p = u\vec{x} + v\vec{y} + w\vec{z} \qquad (15.602)$$

where $\vec{x}, \vec{y}, \vec{z}$ are the basic vectors of the point lattice and u, v, and w are integers, varying from zero to values large enough to give the lattice the dimensions of the crystal. Hence Eq. 15.601 may be written

$$A' = \exp(i\omega t) \sum_{u=0}^{N_x} \exp(i\kappa u\vec{x} \cdot \vec{S}) \sum_{v=0}^{N_y} \exp(i\kappa v\vec{y} \cdot \vec{S}) \sum_{w=0}^{N_z} \exp(i\kappa w\vec{z} \cdot \vec{S}) \qquad (15.603)$$

Each summation is from zero to some large finite number, determined by the crystal dimension; if the upper limit is taken as virtually infinite, each summation is of the form

$$\sum_{u=0}^{\infty} \exp(i\kappa u\vec{x} \cdot \vec{S}) = 1 + \exp(i\kappa \vec{x} \cdot \vec{S}) + \exp(2i\kappa \vec{x} \cdot \vec{S}) + \exp(3i\kappa \vec{x} \cdot \vec{S}) + \cdots$$

$$= [1 - \exp(i\kappa \vec{x} \cdot \vec{S})]^{-1} \qquad (15.604)$$

To calculate the relative intensities at various positions we must multiply A' by its complex conjugate, $I' = A'A'^*$. Since

$$[1 - \exp(-ix)][1 - \exp(ix)] = 2 - [\exp(ix) + \exp(-ix)]$$

$$= 2(1 - \cos x) = 4 \sin^2 \frac{x}{2}$$

the expression for I' becomes, for the infinite summation

$$I' = \frac{1}{64} \left(\sin^2 \frac{\kappa \vec{x} \cdot \vec{S}}{2} \right)^{-1} \left(\sin^2 \frac{\kappa \vec{y} \cdot \vec{S}}{2} \right)^{-1} \left(\sin^2 \frac{\kappa \vec{z} \cdot \vec{S}}{2} \right)^{-1} \qquad (15.605)$$

It may be seen from Eq. 15.605 that I' ranges from a small fraction to very large values; it does not actually become infinite, as indicated by Eq. 15.605, because, for one reason the summation should not have been over an infinite range of u, v, and w. However, I' will have its largest values when $\kappa \vec{x} \cdot \vec{S}/2$, $\kappa \vec{y} \cdot \vec{S}/2$, and $\kappa \vec{z} \cdot \vec{S}/2$ are each integral multiples of π. It is found in practice that the total intensity cannot materially exceed the general scattering background unless each of the three factors in Eq. 15.605 has its maximum values.

If a, b, and c are the unit cell dimensions, i.e., the magnitude of the basic vectors

$\vec{x}$, $\vec{y}$, and $\vec{z}$, and α', β', and γ' are the angles between $\vec{x}$, $\vec{y}$, and $\vec{z}$, respectively, and the vector $\vec{S}$, then each of the factors in Eq. 15.605 will be a maximum if

$$\vec{x} \cdot \vec{S} = (2 \sin \theta_b)(a)(\cos \alpha') = h'\lambda$$
$$\vec{y} \cdot \vec{S} = (2 \sin \theta_b)(b)(\cos \beta') = k'\lambda \qquad (15.606)$$
$$\vec{z} \cdot \vec{S} = (2 \sin \theta_b)(c)(\cos \gamma') = l'\lambda$$

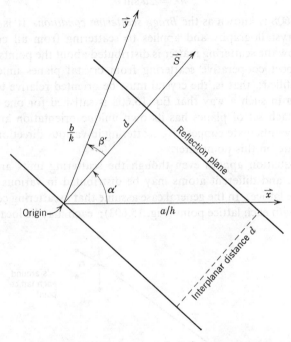

Fig. 15.602   Relationship between $\vec{x}$, $\vec{y}$, $\vec{S}$ and the reflection plane.

where h', k' and l' must be integers (or zero). Each of the equations in Eq. 15.606 can be written in the form

$$(2 \sin \theta_b)(a \cos \alpha')/h' = \lambda$$

It may be seen with the aid of the two-dimensional construction in Figure 15.602 that, for each of the various integral values of h', $(a \cos \alpha')/h'$ corresponds to the distance d between the "reflection" plane and the origin, that is, h' corresponds to the Miller index for the plane in question. Similarly $d = (b \cos \beta')/k'$, where k' corresponds to the Miller index on the y axis and, in the three-dimensional case, $d = (c \cos \gamma')/l'$, where l' corresponds to l. Thus each of the equations reduces to the form

$$2d \sin \theta_b = \lambda \qquad (15.607)$$

which we conclude is the necessary condition for the scattering intensity to have an appreciable magnitude. If h, k, and l have a common factor n, the corresponding reflection may be considered as the nth order of a lattice reflection arising from planes with the set of indices resulting when the common factor is divided out. For example, $d_{100} = 2d_{200}$; the value of θ_b at which a first-order ($n = 1$) reflection (cooperative scattering) for (200) would be observed is the same as that for second-order ($n = 2$) scattering from (100). The general form of the necessary condition for cooperative scattering is

$$n\lambda = 2d \sin \theta_b \tag{15.608}$$

Equation 15.608 is known as the *Bragg scattering condition*. It is an important basic law of crystallography and applies to scattering from all crystal lattices, regardless of how the scattering matter is distributed about the points of the lattice. We cannot expect cooperative scattering from crystal planes unless the Bragg condition is fulfilled; that is, the crystal must be oriented relative to the incident beam of X-rays in such a way that Eq. 15.608 is satisfied for one of the crystal planes. Since each set of planes has its own unique orientation and interplanar spacing, we may anticipate cooperative scattering in various directions and angles. We will elaborate on this point later.

The Bragg equation applies even though the scattering units are atoms with many electrons, and different atoms may be distributed in various ways around the points of the lattice. In the general case assume that i scattering centers (atoms) are associated with each lattice point (Fig. 15.603); each may be located by adding

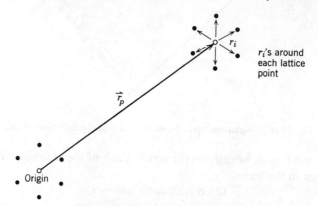

Fig. 15.603   Relationship of $\vec{r}_p$ and $\vec{r}_i$.

an additional vector $\vec{r}_i$ to the vector $\vec{r}_p$. The scattering strength of each center is given by its atomic scattering factor, f_i. Thus the summation of Eq. 15.603 will be modified by the presence of additional terms and will take the form

$$A' = \exp(i\omega t) \sum_p \exp(i\kappa\vec{r}_p \cdot \vec{S}) \sum_i f_i \exp(i\kappa\vec{r}_i \cdot \vec{S}) \tag{15.609}$$

The second term is a constant characteristic of the structure, i.e., the distribution of the atoms around the lattice point (the same for all lattice points), and is called the structure factor, F

$$F = \sum_i f_i \exp(i\kappa\vec{r}_i \cdot \vec{S}) \tag{15.610}$$

Equation 15.610 may be simplified by changing the vector dot product in the exponent to its equivalent in terms of the Miller indices of the reflecting plane in question and the positions of the atoms about the lattice point.

The position of each atom relative to the lattice point is given by $\vec{r}_i$, which may be written

$$\vec{r}_i = u_i\vec{x} + v_i\vec{y} + w_i\vec{z}$$

where u_i, v_i, and w_i are the displacement coordinates from the lattice point in the x, y, and z directions, respectively, in fractions of the unit cell dimensions. When the Bragg reflection condition is satisfied, we see from Eq. 15.606 that

$$\vec{r}_i \cdot \vec{S} = (hu_i + kv_i + lw_i)\lambda$$

and

$$i\kappa\vec{r}_i \cdot \vec{S} = 2\pi i(hu_i + kv_i + lw_i)$$

Hence the structure factor may be written

$$F_{hkl} = \sum_i f_i \exp\left[2\pi i(hu_i + kv_i + lw_i)\right] \tag{15.611}$$

where the summation is taken over all atoms in the unit cell. In Eq. 15.609 diffraction amplitudes distributed about the points of the lattice are summed together. Alternatively, the position of the points of the lattice may arbitrarily be taken to correspond to the position of any one of the atoms in the cell, and the effects of all atoms considered to be the combined effects from a set of parallel point lattices. The contributions from each parallel set will in general not be in phase, however, and the relative intensities of the various Bragg reflections provide information about the distribution of matter in the cell. Observed intensities may be compared with those calculated for an assumed structure from equations based on Eqs. 15.611 and 15.609.

The conditions for cooperative scattering from crystals apply for any form of electromagnetic radiation. However, $n\lambda/2d$ cannot exceed unity ($\sin\theta$ cannot exceed unity). Since the spacing between adjacent planes in crystals is of the order of angstroms, radiation of comparable wavelength must be used if cooperative scattering is to be conveniently observed. It is apparent that cooperative scattering of ordinary visible light can be expected only from planes separated by much larger distances.

Laue Diffraction Patterns. In 1912, von Laue established X-ray diffraction by crystals as an experimental fact. A schematic representation of a diffraction set-up is shown in Fig. 15.604. In the Laue method, white, i.e., polychromatic, X-radiation (ordinarily from a tungsten target) is used with a stationary single crystal. The various crystal planes will produce diffraction spots by selecting the particular component of the incident beam which has a wavelength satisfying the Bragg conditions. An illustration of a Laue photograph is shown in Fig. 15.605, where the diffracted beams have been recorded on a photographic plate. Laue photographs are not as easy to interpret as the following types.

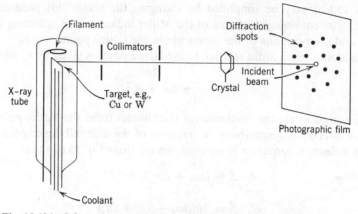

Fig. 15.604   Schematic representation of X-ray diffraction setup for crystals.

Fig. 15.605   Laue pattern of a silicon crystal in approximately the [100] orientation (courtesy of J. Washburn; taken by permission from C. Kittel, *Elementary Solid State Physics*, John Wiley and Sons, 1962).

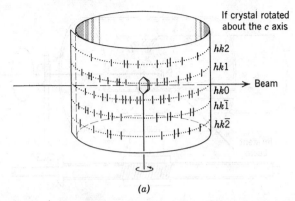

Fig. 15.606a Schematic representation of relationship of beam-crystal-film in the rotation method. One crystal axis is parallel to the rotation axis. Bragg planes parallel to this axis give spots on the equatorial layer line.

Rotation-Oscillation Methods.   In the rotation method, a cylindrical camera is used, and a small crystal, mounted so one of the crystallographic axes is perpendicular to the X-ray beam, is placed in a beam of monochromatic X-rays. With a fixed value of λ, the crystal is rotated to bring its various planes into the proper orientation to satisfy the Bragg condition. The diffraction spots are generated in a series of horizontal rows or layers. Those at the same level as the crystal arise from planes parallel with the vertical rotation axis; those above and below arise from planes inclined to the vertical axis. See Fig. 15.606. The advantage of the rotation method over the Laue method is that each diffraction spot can immediately be assigned one index in accordance with the crystal orientation and layer line location. However, a great many spots are observed, and complete indexing may

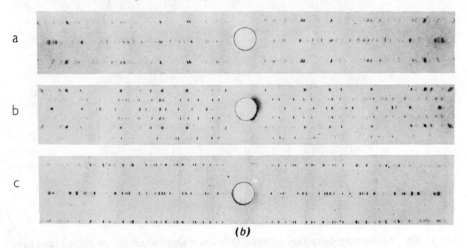

Fig. 15.606b Rotation photograph about three axes of (orthorhombic) mercuric chloride (a) about [100], (b) about [010], (c) about [001] (taken by permission from J. M. Bijvoet, *X-ray Analysis of Crystals*, Butterworth Scientific Publications, London, 1951).

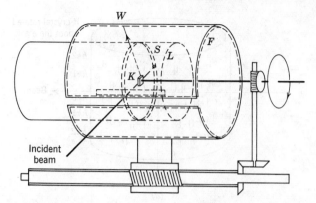

Fig. 15.607   Schematic diagram of Weissenberg apparatus. K = crystal turned about horizontal axis; L = diaphragm with cylindrical slit S through which one layer line passes; W = filmholder with film F displaced in a horizontal direction synchronously with the turning of the crystal. (By permission from J. M. Bijvoet, *X-ray Analysis of Crystals*, Butterworth Scientific Publications, London, 1951.)

still be very difficult or impossible if the crystal has low symmetry and a large unit cell.   Some simplification results if the crystal is oscillated only through small angular displacements, but a better procedure is to use a moving film technique.

   Moving Film Methods.   If the crystal is rotated and the recording film displaced simultaneously in a systematic way, the diffracted beams are spread out in an orderly pattern.   The Weissenberg method (Fig. 15.607) is commonly used; Figs. 15.608 and 15.609 show how rotation spots can be spread out.   From knowledge

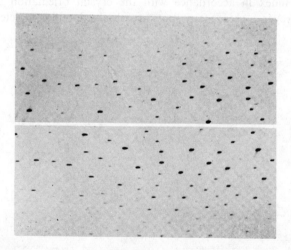

Fig. 15.608   Weissenberg diffraction pattern.   Diffraction spots which fall on curved lines have similar indices, e.g., 101, 102, 103.   (By permission from J. M. Bijvoet, *X-ray Analysis of Crystals*, Butterworth Scientific Publications, London, 1951).

of the camera geometry and the crystal orientation, each diffraction spot can be identified with a particular set of crystal planes.

The Powder Method.   In the rotating single-crystal methods, the motion of the crystals brings the various planes into proper orientation for diffraction. In the

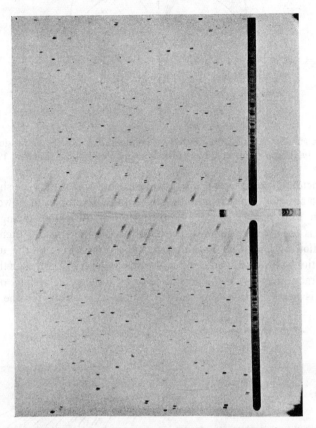

Fig. 15.609 The relation between Weissenberg and rotating-crystal photographs. The main part of the photograph is the Weissenberg record; the darker vertical stripe contains the rotating-crystal record of the same layer, recorded on the same film. A horizontal line may be drawn connecting any Weissenberg spot with the corresponding spot on the rotating-crystal record. Note the intense background in the rotating photograph; on the Weissenberg record this background is spread out over the entire film width and consequently appears much attenuated. (Pectolite, $Ca_2NaSi_3O_8(OH)$, monoclinic; b-axis rotation; Cu $K\alpha$ radiation from hot-cathode x-ray tube, filtered through nickel foil.) (By permission from M. J. Buerger, *X-ray Crystallography*, John Wiley and Sons, 1942.)

powder (Debye-Scherrer) method, the orientations are simultaneously present because the monochromatic beam is directed onto a finely divided, randomly oriented powder. The powdered sample is usually rotated, nevertheless, to help ensure random orientation. With a powder the diffracted rays generate a cone

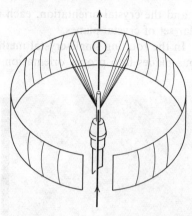

Fig. 15.610 Schematic representation of powder method apparatus (by permission from J. M. Bijvoet, *X-ray Analysis of Crystals*, Butterworth Scientific Publications, London, 1951).

around the incident beam. The powder camera usually is of the type shown in Fig. 15.610, with a strip of film surrounding the sample. Examples of powder patterns are shown in Figs. 15.611 *et seq.* Identification of the planes giving rise to the various lines is only straightforward for relatively simple crystal systems.

Determination of Unit Cell Parameters. The dimensions of the unit cell are fixed by selecting values a, b, and c and α, β, and γ, which will correlate the positions of all the diffraction spots. If the crystal belongs to the cubic system, only a single parameter a is needed. It may be seen from the expressions for the interplanar

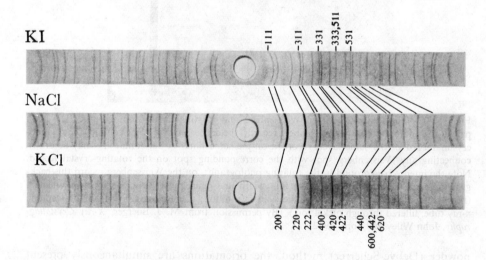

Fig. 15.611 Powder diagrams of KI, NaCl, and KCl. An explanation of the relative intensities will be provided in a following paragraph. (By permission from J. M. Bijvoet, *X-ray Analysis of Crystals*, Butterworth Scientific Publications, London, 1951.)

spacings, Eq. 15.501, that each d, and hence, for a given wavelength, each value of $\sin \theta$, is determined by the cell parameter and Miller indices. The observed value of $\sin \theta$, and hence d, can be calculated from camera geometry and the observed position of the diffraction spot. If an index is assigned to that spot, the cubic cell parameter can be calculated. If the assigned index is correct, the cell parameter will then give d values for the other various planes which must agree with the location of other diffraction spots. The lines of Fig. 15.611 can be indexed in this way. Planes of low indices are those with small values of $\sin \theta$.

For less symmetrical classes, more cell parameters must be determined; at most, six may be necessary. These can be fixed with certainty by observing the relative positions of a large number of diffraction spots; many hundreds may be recorded. Single-crystal rotation and moving film techniques are of considerable assistance in determining the unit cell dimensions; for example, the layer spacings on rotation photographs give the cell dimension for the vertical axis, and crystallographic angles can be determined from the characteristics of Weissenberg patterns. We shall not explain these features in detail or discuss the techniques for indexing various kinds of X-ray patterns.

Intensity of Diffraction Spots.   The relative intensities of the various diffraction spots may be derived by multiplying the amplitude by its complex conjugate. However, the detailed treatment involves a number of factors in addition to those we have discussed. We can only mention briefly some of the more important effects.

A secondary interaction of the diffracted beam with crystal planes, particularly for intense reflections and for large perfect crystals, must be considered. The reflected wave will also meet the Bragg angle scattering conditions for planes above it and hence will be partially scattered back in the direction of the primary beam. The effect of multiple scattering has an important bearing on the form of the final intensity expression and results in an expression which is proportional to the first power of the structure factor rather than the square. However most crystals appear to have a *mosaic* structure; that is, they are composed of small sections, perfect to the extent of several hundreds of planes, but the various sections are not in perfect alignment with each other. Under these conditions the effects of multiple scattering are not significant, and this is usually assumed to be the case.

Some correction may be needed for absorption of the primary and scattered beams in a manner which leads to incoherent scattering. Very small crystals are used so as to minimize the absorption correction.

Vibration of the atoms in the crystal lattice tends to affect the intensity of diffracted beams because motion of the scattering centers modifies the phase relationship of the scattered waves. The magnitude of such motion is temperature dependent and is allowed for by introducing a temperature factor into the expression for each atomic scattering factor. A simple isotropic correction may take the form

$$f = f_0 \exp \frac{-B \sin^2 \theta_b}{\lambda^2} \qquad (15.612)$$

where B is related to the displacement of the atom in its thermal vibrations.

In the usual experimental arrangement, the incident X-ray beam is unpolarized. Therefore, as discussed in Sec. 15.1, there will be an overall factor multiplying the intensity, given by Eq. 15.122. This expression, called the polarization factor, rewritten in terms of the Bragg angle, is

$$p = \frac{1 + \cos^2 2\theta_b}{2} \qquad (15.613)$$

Another important effect, known as the Lorentz factor, L, expresses the relative time the given crystal plane spends in the narrow angular range over which reflection occurs. Perfect crystals are in position for reflection for only a few seconds of arc, though most crystals are mosaics and reflect over several minutes of arc. The Lorentz factor depends on the type of X-ray photograph being taken and the value of θ. For equatorial rotation photographs it is $1/\sin 2\theta$; for other layers $(1/\sin 2\theta) [\cos \theta/(\cos^2 \phi - \sin^2 \theta)^{1/2}]$, where ϕ is the angle between the reflecting plane and the axis of rotation. For powder photographs a factor of the form

$$\frac{1}{\sin^2 \theta_b \cos \theta_b}$$

is used, which also allows for the variation in the size of the cone of reflection with the diffraction angle.

In certain cases, crystal symmetry may be such that diffractions from several different sets of planes are collected at the same spot, in which case the total observed intensity should be divided into the contributions of each of the hkl's involved. This is allowed for by inclusion of a multiplicity factor.

Thus certain of the angular factors depend on the type of diffraction photograph taken, and the detailed form of the intensity relation to the structure factor must be adapted accordingly. If we multiply A', as given by Eqs. 15.609, 15.610, and 15.611 by its complex conjugate, the resulting expression shows that the relative intensities are proportional to the square of their structure factors, F_{hkl}. This result is valid for a crystal which is an aggregate of small mosaic blocks but should be modified to include the Lorentz, polarization, temperature, and absorption factors. We may write

$$I_{hkl} \text{ (relative)} = |F_{hkl}|^2 (L)(p)(\text{TF})(\text{Abs } F) \qquad (15.614)$$

As shown by Eq. 15.611, F_{hkl} can be evaluated if the positions of the atoms and their respective scattering factors are known. Temperature factor (TF) and absorption factor (Abs F) can be calculated or assigned values to fit experimental results; in some circumstances, such as low temperature and very small crystals, these two factors are effectively unity. Hence we may calculate the expected intensity from an assumed structure. If these relative intensities agree with observed values, the assigned structure is assumed correct.

Measurement of Intensities. Intensities may be measured by observation of photographic density on films or, more directly, by use of a quantum counter.

The quantity desired for comparison with the structure factor is the integrated intensity, which is proportional to the area under the curve obtained by plotting photographic density (or beam intensity as indicated by a counter) as a function of angle. Photographic intensities may be put on an absolute basis by comparison with a series of timed exposures of the incident beam or by comparison with reflections from a known standard structure (e.g., sodium chloride).

Summary of Procedure for Determination of a Crystal Structure by X-ray Analysis. The unit cell dimensions and space group are first to be determined. The unit cell dimensions can be obtained from the diffraction angles and assigned indices of the various diffraction spots. An assignment of indices consistent with the entire diffraction pattern must be found.

Optical and X-ray diffraction data provide evidence for the space group assignment. If symmetry based on glide operations is present, certain restrictions will be observed in the class of reflections present; for example, if a diagonal glide plane with component $a/2 + b/2$ is present, only reflections from $hk0$ planes for which $h + k$ is even will be observed. Evidence for the correct assignment of space group can be obtained by examining the pattern for such characteristic absences. Such omissions are a result of the geometry of the selected unit cell and the symmetry associated with it. Convenient forms for the structure factor for each of the space groups have been tabulated in the *International Tables for X-ray Crystallography*.

Intensity data are not needed, other than on a present or absent basis, for unit cell and space group assignment. They are needed, however, for determination of the atomic positions. It is usually more convenient to work with a set of structure factors, F_{hkl}, rather than the intensities themselves. Hence, after proper consideration of angular factors, the square roots of the relative intensities are taken to give a set of observed F's. If the phases of these factors were known, a direct synthesis of the structure could be achieved. In general it is necessary to assume a structure which, after refinement through trial and error calculations, should evolve to one which gives a set of F's in agreement with those observed. Such calculations are greatly facilitated by electronic digital computers.

Electron Density Projections. The electron density in a given volume element in a crystal can be calculated with the aid of a Fourier series expression in which the coefficients are the F_{hkl}'s. Let $\rho(x, y, z)$ be the density of scattering matter at the corresponding point x, y, z within the crystal. The structure of the crystal is periodic parallel to x, y, and z, at distances of a, b, and c, respectively, and the density ρ is related to a Fourier series of the type

$$\rho(x, y, z) = \frac{1}{V} \sum_{h} \sum_{k} \sum_{l}^{\infty}{}_{-\infty} F_{hkl} \exp\left[-2\pi i \left(\frac{hx}{a} + \frac{ky}{b} + \frac{lz}{c} \right) \right] \tag{15.615}$$

For every diffraction line given by the crystal there corresponds a term in the Fourier series, but, from intensity data alone, the phases of the F's are not known. Once these have been determined (by comparison with a proposed structure) the experimental data (intensities) alone can be used to calculate the electron density

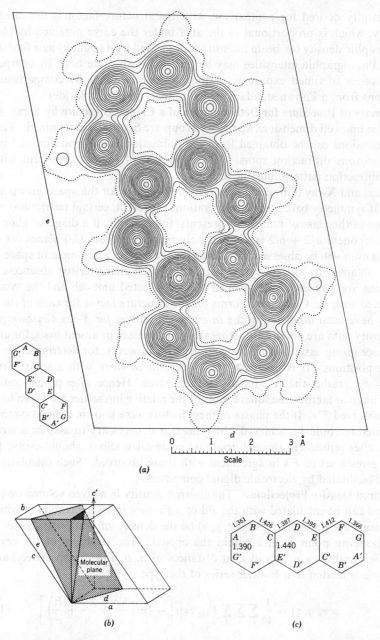

Scale

0   1   2   3 Å

(a)

(b)

(c)

Fig. 15.612   Electron density projection of the anthracene molecule (by permission from Sinclair, Robertson, and Mathieson, *Acta Cryst.*, **3**, 254 (1950). (*a*) A crystal section through the plane of the molecule. Each contour line represents a density increment of $\frac{1}{2}e$ Å^{-3}, the half-electron line being dotted. (*b*) Relation of molecular plane to the crystal axes and unit cell. (*c*) Dimension of the anthracene molecule.

distribution throughout the crystal. The positions of maximum density indicate the location of atoms; see, e.g., Fig. 15.612.

If the crystal has a center of symmetry, Eq. 15.615 reduces to the form

$$\rho(x, y, z) = \frac{1}{V} \sum_{h} \sum_{k} \sum_{\substack{l \\ -\infty}}^{\infty} \pm |F_{hkl}| \cos 2\pi \left(\frac{hx}{a} + \frac{ky}{b} + \frac{lz}{c} \right) \qquad (15.616)$$

Fourier series are very useful in crystallography and, in various forms, assist in the selection of trial structures in the early stages of analysis [see, for example, *Crystal-Structure Analysis*, by M. J. Buerger (General References)].

Examples of Some Simple Structures. To illustrate the behavior of intensities in relation to structure we will consider several simple cases. If an elementary substance were to crystallize in a simple cubic structure, with atoms only at the

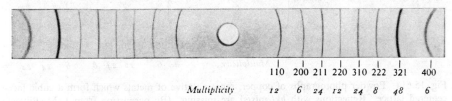

110	200	211	220	310	222	321	400

Multiplicity   *12*   *6*   *24*   *12*   *24*   *8*   *48*   *6*

Fig. 15.613   Powder diagram of tungsten, typical of metals which have a body-centered cubic lattice. Reflections with $h + k + l$ odd are missing. (By permission from J. M. Bijvoet, *X-ray Analysis of Crystals*, Butterworth Scientific Publications, London, 1951.)

lattice points, the structure factor would take a very simple form. For the centro-symmetric case Eq. 15.611 becomes

$$F_{hkl} = \sum f_i \cos 2\pi (hu_i + kv_i + lw_i) \qquad (15.617)$$

In the present case the primitive cube contains the equivalent of only one atom. We may place it at the origin; all other atoms are related by the unit translations; hence $u_i = v_i = w_i = 0$ and F_{hkl} is simply f_a, the atomic scattering factor, and varies only because of the dependence of f_a on θ. We can cite no examples of such a structure, although KCl closely approximates it, as will be explained below.

Many metals crystallize in a body-centered or in a face-centered cubic structure. The body-centered unit cell contains two atoms; one may be placed at the origin and the other at 1/2, 1/2, 1/2. Hence from Eq. 15.617

$$F_{hkl} = f_a[\cos 2\pi(0) + \cos \pi(h + k + l)]$$
$$= f_a[1 + \cos \pi(h + k + l)]$$

In this case, if the sum of the indices is even, $F_{hkl} = 2f_a$; but if the sum is odd, $F_{hkl} = 0$. In Fig. 15.613, a powder pattern of tungsten, no lines for which the sum $h + k + l$ is odd are observed. The extinction of such a class of reflections is evidence for the body-centered lattice. The body-centered cube is basically two interpenetrating simple cubic lattices. For reflections from planes such as 100, scattering from the centered atoms is 180° out of phase with that from atoms at the corners. However, reinforcement occurs for 200, for example; here the inter-planar spacings are one-half the unit cell distance and, for the appropriate Bragg angle, all atoms scatter in phase.

The face-centered cubic unit cell contains the equivalent of four atoms which may be placed at 0, 0, 0; 1/2, 1/2, 0; 1/2, 0, 1/2; 0, 1/2, 1/2. Hence from Eq. 15.617

$$F_{hkl} = f_a[\cos 2\pi(0) + \cos \pi(h + k) + \cos \pi(h + l) + \cos \pi(k + l)]$$

In this case, if the indices are all even or all odd, $F_{hkl} = 4f_a$; but if the indices are mixed (some even and some odd), $F_{hkl} = 0$. This behavior is observed in Fig. 15.614 for copper.

| | | | | 111 | 200 | | 220 | 311 | 222 | 400 | 331 | 420 |
| Multiplicity | | | | 8 | 6 | | 12 | 24 | 8 | 6 | 24 | 24 |

Fig. 15.614 Powder photographs of copper, representative of metals which form a cubic face-centered lattice. Reflections with *hkl* mixed are missing. (By permission from J. M. Bijvoet, *X-ray Analysis of Crystals*, Butterworth Scientific Publications, London, 1951.)

Cesium chloride crystallizes in the cubic system. The lattice resembles a body-centered system in that one type of atom, say cesium, is at the origin and the other, chlorine, is at the center of a cube of cesium atoms (and vice versa). Thus the structure factor expression, similar to that for the body-centered case, becomes

$$F_{hkl} = f_{Cs} + f_{Cl}[\cos \pi(h + k + l)]$$

Reflections from the two types of atoms are in phase if the sum of the indices is even, but out of phase if the sum is odd, i.e.,

$$F_{hkl \text{ odd}} = f_{Cs} - f_{Cl}$$

Thus, in Fig. 15.615, reflections for planes with *hkl* odd are diminished in intensity, but are not absent as in the case of an elementary substance with the same atomic arrangement. The intensity comparisons must include consideration of the powder multiplicity factor.

Sodium chloride crystallizes in a face-centered cubic lattice, Fig. 15.616, which may be visualized as two interpenetrating networks of sodium ions and chloride ions. We may place sodium at 0, 0, 0; 1/2, 1/2, 0; 1/2, 0, 1/2; 0, 1/2, 1/2 and chlorine at 1/2, 1/2, 1/2; 1/2, 0, 0; 0, 1/2, 0; 0, 0, 1/2 (Fig. 15.615). Hence,

$$F_{hkl} = f_{Na}[1 + \cos \pi(h + k) + \cos \pi(k + l) + \cos \pi(h + l)]$$
$$+ f_{Cl}[\cos \pi (h + k + l) + \cos \pi h + \cos \pi k + \cos \pi l]$$

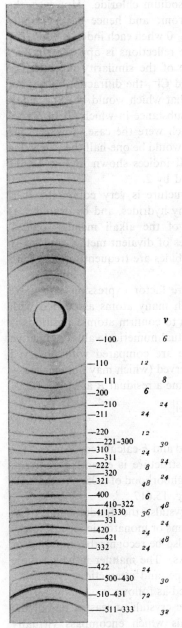

Fig. 15.615 CsCl, which has a simple cubic structure, though similar to body-centered cubic in some respects. Since scattering powers of cesium and chlorine differ, lines for which $h + k + l$ are odd are weakened by the out-of-phase relationship but are not absent. v = multiplicity factor. Relative intensities have suffered in the reproduction process. (By permission from J. M. Bijvoet, *X-ray Analysis of Crystals*, Butterworth Scientific Publications, London, 1951.)

	v
—100	6
—110	12
—111	8
—200	6
—210	24
—211	24
—220	12
—221–300	30
—310	24
—311	24
—222	8
—320	24
—321	48
—400	6
—410–322	48
—411–330	36
—331	24
—420	24
—421	48
—332	24
—422	24
—500–430	30
—510–431	72
—511–333	32

If each index is even, $F_{hkl} = 4f_{Na} + 4f_{Cl}$.

If each index is odd, $F_{hkl} = 4f_{Na} - 4f_{Cl}$.

If indices are mixed in any way, $F_{hkl} = 0$.

This corresponding behavior of intensities is apparent in Fig. 15.611.

Potassium chloride has the same structure as sodium chloride. However, the potassium ion and the chloride ion are isoelectronic and hence have virtually the same scattering factors. Thus, for KCl, $F_{hkl} \cong 0$ when each index is odd. The absence of these reflections is apparent in Fig. 15.611. Because of the similarity in scattering power of K^+ and Cl^-, the diffraction pattern of KCl resembles that which would be expected of a simple cubic substance in which all atoms are the same. If such were the case, however, the unit cell spacing would be one-half the true value for KCl, and all indices shown in Fig. 15.611 would be divided by 2.

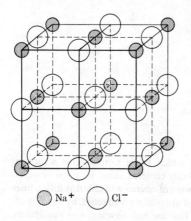

$\bigcirc$ Na$^+$ $\bigcirc$ Cl$^-$

Fig. 15.616   The NaCl structure.

The NaCl structure is very common. It is assumed by many hydrides, and by cyanides as well as halides of the alkali metals; oxides, sulfides, tellurides of divalent metals, and many nitrides and carbides are frequently found with this structure.

While structure factor expressions are more complex for less symmetrical crystal systems with many atoms associated with each lattice point, the use of diffraction intensities to confirm atomic positions is basically the same as shown in these examples. Actual numerical values of relative intensities calculated from the assigned structure are compared with observed values for as many diffraction spots as can be observed (which may number many hundreds). It has become common practice to define a residual R as

$$R = \frac{\sum ||F_{obs}| - |F_{calc}||}{\sum |F_{obs}|} \tag{15.618}$$

as an indicator of the agreement between F-observed and F-calculated. An $R < 0.2$ is generally taken to indicate that the proposed structure is essentially correct. Well-defined structures may give R values in the neighborhood of 0.05. An example of a complex structure (vitamin B_1) is shown in Fig. 15.617.

Particle Interactions in Crystals.   In some crystals, the fundamental units associated with each lattice point are individual atoms or monatomic ions, whereas in others, molecular or ionic groups, which may also be recognizable in liquid or gaseous phases, constitute the basic building blocks. The manner in which these units pack together, determined by their size, shape, and interaction, establishes the crystal structure. Crystals are frequently classed as follows.

(a) *Metallic Crystals.*   The idea that in metallic crystals at least a few of the electrons from each atom may move in orbitals which encompass virtually

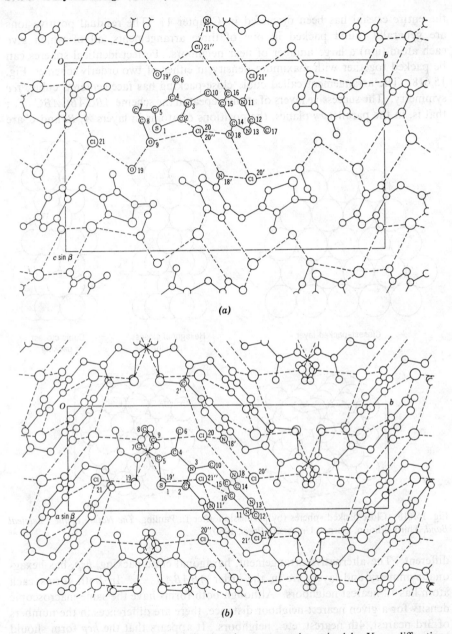

(a)

(b)

Fig. 15.617   An example of an unusually complex structure determined by X-ray diffraction, thiamine hydrochloride (vitamin B_1) [by permission from J. Kraut and H. J. Reed, *Acta Cryst.*, **15**, 747 (1962)].   3039 reflections were observed.   Space group $P2_1/c$ (monoclinic) with $a = 6.99$, $b = 20.59$, $c = 12.73$, and $\beta = 114°$.   Figure shows packing of molecules.   (a) Orthographic projection along a axis; (b) orthographic projection along c axis.   Refinement was continued until $R = 0.08$.

the entire crystal has been discussed in Chapter 11. The residual positive ions are generally found packed in one of three arrangements, all of which give each atom (ion) a large number of near neighbors. Perfect identical spheres can be packed together with maximum density in either of two orderly schemes, Fig. 15.618. The arrangement called cubic close-packing has face-centered cubic, *fcc* symmetry. The successive layers of atoms repeat in the scheme $ABCABCABC\ldots$; that is, in the parallel xy planes, the positions of atoms in layers A, B, and C are

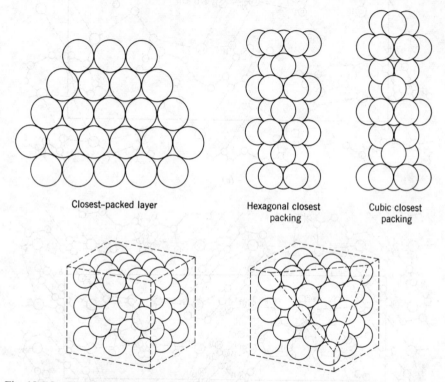

| Closest–packed layer | Hexagonal closest packing | Cubic closest packing |

Fig. 15.618   Close-packed spheres (by permission after L. Pauling, *The Nature of the Chemical Bond*, Third Edition, Cornell University Press, 1960).

different. The alternative arrangement, hexagonal close-packing, *hcp*, has hexagonal symmetry and layers are in the order $ABABAB\ldots$. In both forms each atom has 12 nearest neighbors. Although both forms have the same macroscopic density for a given nearest-neighbor distance, there are differences in the numbers of 3rd nearest, 4th nearest, etc., neighbors. It appears that the *hcp* form should be slightly more stable. Many metals are found with *fcc* structures, however [see Table 15.601(A)]. The third structure found for many metals is the body-centered cubic arrangement, in which each atom has 8 nearest neighbors but 6 more at a distance only about 15 per cent greater. The close-packed structures are also of importance in certain ionic salt-like substances and in the rare gases.

Table 15.601 Crystal Structures of Selected Elements

Element	Structure	Density at 20°C, g cm⁻³	Lattice Constants at Room Temperature a	c or Axial Angle	Atomic Volume, cm³ mole⁻¹	Nearest Neighbor Distance, Å
Aluminum	*fcc*	2.70	4.04		9.99	2.86
Argon	*fcc*	· · ·	5.43 (20°K)			3.83
Barium	*bcc*	3.5	5.01		39	4.34

The remainder of this table will be found in the Appendix as Table 15.601(A).

(b) *Covalent Crystals.* Crystals of the Group IV elements and compounds such as SiC and BN are found in which the atoms are bonded together in a specific fashion which may be associated with the formation of covalent bonds. The diamond crystal is an excellent example; each carbon atom is bonded to 4 neighbors in a tetrahedral three-dimensional array which extends throughout the single crystal. The bonds are similar to those characteristic of carbon in organic molecules. The entire crystal may be considered one gigantic molecule, Fig. 15.619.

(c) *Molecular Crystals.* Here atoms are grouped together in recognizable molecules. Intramolecular distances usually are not materially different from those

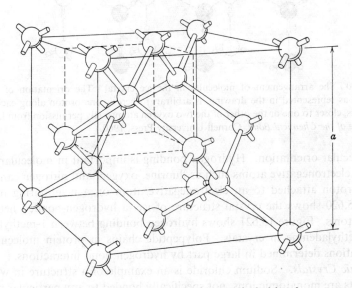

Fig. 15.619 Crystal structure of diamond, showing the tetrahedral bond arrangement. Germanium, silicon, and gray tin have the same structure. (By permission from Shockley and from C. Kittel, *Introduction to Solid State Physics*, John Wiley and Sons, 1956.)

characteristic of the isolated molecule in the vapor phase; for example, the I—I distance is 2.65 Å in the vapor phase and 2.70 Å in the molecular crystal of iodine. Molecules are generally packed together in something approaching a close-packing arrangement. However, they are usually not spherical, and certain relative orientations may maximize the van der Waals interactions between neighbors. Specific interactions, notably hydrogen bond formation, are often responsible for the

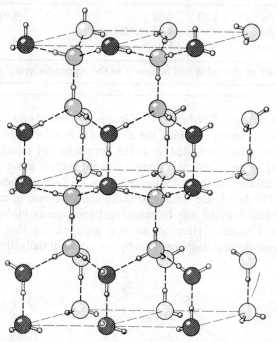

Fig. 15.620 The arrangement of molecules in the ice crystal. The orientation of the water molecules, as represented in the drawing, is arbitrary; there is one proton along each oxygen-oxygen axis, closer to one or the other of the two oxygen atoms. (By permission from L. Pauling, *The Nature of the Chemical Bond*, Cornell University Press, 1960.)

intermolecular orientation. Hydrogen bonding is important in molecular crystals in which electronegative atoms such as fluorine, oxygen, and nitrogen can interact with a proton attached to an electronegative atom on a neighboring molecule. Figure 15.620 shows the crystal structure of ice, a hydrogen-bonded network of oxygen atoms. Figure 15.621 shows hydrogen bonding between 1-methylthymine and 9-methyladenine in crystals. Polypeptide chains in protein molecules have configurations determined in large part by hydrogen bond interactions.

(*d*) *Ionic Crystals.* Sodium chloride is an example of a structure in which the basic units are monatomic ions, not specifically bonded to any particular neighbor but packed together in such a way as to maximize the electrostatic interaction energy for the whole crystal. A reasonably good approximation of the potential energy of an ion in such a crystal, relative to that when the ions are separated at great distances, can be calculated (according to Born) by application of Coulomb's law from an equation of the form

$$V(R) = -\frac{Ae^2z^2}{R} + \frac{Be^2}{R^n} \qquad (15.619)$$

where $V(R)$ is the potential energy of an ion in the crystal, e the electronic charge, z the valence, and R the distance between neighboring oppositely charged ions. A is the Madelung constant, a geometric factor characteristic of the crystal lattice. The Madelung constant allows for all interactions of the ions in the crystal with

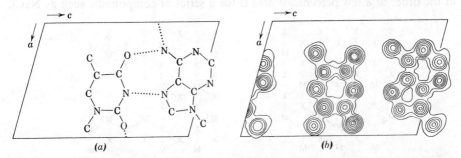

(a)   (b)

Fig. 15.621   The arrangement of atoms in the crystal containing equal numbers of molecules of 1-methylthymine and 9-methyladenine, as determined by Hoogsteen [*Acta Cryst.*, 822 (1959)]. (a) The two molecules with their hydrogen bonds. (b) The contour lines representing levels of electron density, as determined by the intensities of the X-ray diffraction maxima [by permission from L. Pauling, *The Nature of the Chemical Bond*, Cornell University Press, 1960, and Hoogsteen, *Acta Cryst.*, **12**, 822 (1959)].

the given ion in terms of the basic distance R; for example, A is 1.748 for NaCl, 1.763 for a body-centered cubic lattice, CsCl type; etc. B is a repulsion constant and can be determined from R_0, the equilibrium distance of closest approach, by equating attractive and repulsive forces at the equilibrium position:

$$B = \frac{R_0^{n-1}Az^2}{n} \qquad (15.620)$$

which we may solve for B if n is known. The Born exponent, n, can be evaluated from a second derivative of the potential energy, which is related to compressibility of the crystal. n depends on the ion size and ranges from 5 to 12.

The relationship of the lattice energy to other energetic quantities can be seen through the Born-Haber thermochemical cycle. For example, for a metal halide MX

$$MX(c) \xrightarrow{\;U\;} M^+(g) + X^-(g)$$

$$\Delta E^\circ \downarrow \qquad\qquad I \uparrow\downarrow \qquad -EA\uparrow\downarrow$$

$$M(c) + \tfrac{1}{2}X_2(g) \xrightarrow{\;\Delta E_s^\circ + \frac{1}{2}\Delta E_d^\circ\;} M(g) + X(g)$$

Hence

$$U = -\Delta E^\circ + \Delta E_s^\circ + \tfrac{1}{2}\Delta E_d^\circ + I - EA$$

where $U = -NV(R)$ the lattice energy per mole, ΔE° is the energy of formation of $MX(c)$ from the elements in their standard states, I is the ionization potential of the gaseous metal atom, EA is the electron affinity of the halogen atom, ΔE_s° is the sublimation energy of $M(c)$, and ΔE_d° is the dissociation energy of the diatomic halogen gas molecule. Electron affinity is difficult to determine experimentally; attempts have been most successful for some of the halogen atoms. The reliability of the Born expression for the lattice energy for the alkali halides appears to be of the order of a few percent. Where U for a series of compounds, such as NaCl,

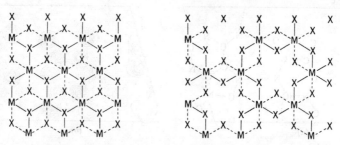

Fig. 15.622   Section of a Sandwich layer (two-dimensional polymer), based on octahedral coordination, in MX_2 and MX_3 compounds, respectively.

KCl, CsCl, is used to calculate values for the EA's of the halogens, reasonably consistent values are obtained [the order of magnitude in kilocalories per mole, is as follows: Cl (88), Br (80), I (71)].

The type of treatment outlined above is applicable only for simple ionic crystals such as the alkali halides. A large number of inorganic substances have basically ionic structures but are not so simple. Compounds of the forms MX_2 and MX_3 frequently form layer-type crystals, Fig. 15.622, in which the halogen ions are essentially in a close-packed array; the metal ions are in octahedral holes, surrounded by an octahedron of the halogen ions, between alternate layers. No molecular groupings corresponding to the simple empirical formula can be seen; in some cases some of the halogens in the octahedral set may be closer than others but these crystals are still considered basically ionic. The sandwich layers interact through van der Waals forces. Many variations of this kind of structure are found in inorganic substances.

Interatomic distances in many ionic crystals are observed to be combinations of approximately additive contributions from the ions involved, so to a certain extent the ions may be regarded as having a fixed size. Table 15.602(A) lists the apparent radii for a number of monatomic ions [according to Pauling (General References)].

Imperfections in Crystals.   A crystal imperfection may be defined as any deviation from the perfect structure based on the point lattice. All actual crystals are more or less imperfect. We shall consider imperfections only briefly to show the

Table 15.602   Crystal Radii and Univalent Radii of Ions

H^-	He	Li^+	Be^{++}	B^{3+}	C^{4+}	N^{5+}	O^{6+}	F^{7+}
2.08		0.60	0.31	0.20	0.15	0.11	0.09	0.07
(2.08)	(0.93)	(0.60)	(0.44)	(0.35)	(0.29)	(0.25)	(0.22)	(0.19)

The remainder of this table will be found in the Appendix as Table 15.602(A).

nature of some defects which have an important effect on such properties as electrical conductivity, solid state diffusion, color, luminescence, and strength.

Nonstoichiometry, i.e., deviation of the composition of the crystal from a simple empirical formula, is not uncommon in oxides. For example, FeO is not found; rather, depending on conditions, the ferrous oxide crystal may range in composition

$O^=$	Fe^{3+}	$O^=$	Fe^{++}	$O^=$	Fe^{++}	$O^=$	Fe^{++}
Fe^{++}	$O^=$	Fe^{++}	$O^=$	Fe^{++}	$O^=$	$Fe^=$	$O^=$
$O^=$	Fe^{++}	$O^=$	(vacancy)	$O^=$	Fe^{3+}	$O^=$	Fe^{++}
Fe^{++}	$O^=$	Fe^{++}	$O^=$	Fe^{++}	$O^=$	Fe^{++}	$O^=$
$O^=$	Fe^{3+}	$O^=$	Fe^{++}	$O^=$	Fe^{++}	$O^=$	Fe^{++}
Fe^{++}	$O^=$	(vacancy)	$O^=$	Fe^{++}	$O^=$	Fe^{++}	$O^=$
$O^=$	Fe^{++}	$O^=$	Fe^{++}	$O^=$	Fe^{3+}	$O^=$	Fe^{++}

Fig. 15.623   Nonstoichiometry in FeO.

from $FeO_{1.04}$ to $FeO_{1.19}$. Such a variation in composition may result from the presence of varying amounts of Fe^{3+} in the crystal; if a number of ferric ions are present, then, to maintain electrical neutrality, one-half this number of vacancies at positions normally occupied by Fe^{++} must occur (Fig. 15.623). A similar behavior is found with NiO. Zinc oxide normally contains more zinc than oxide ions. If zinc atoms occupy sites normally taken by zinc ions, an equivalent number of vacancies in oxide ion sites must exist. A cation ion vacancy can be created in KCl by dissolving a small amount of $CaCl_2$ in it. A replacement of K^+ by Ca^{++} must, to preserve electrical neutrality, also create a vacancy at another K^+ site.

Lattice vacancies may occur in pairs, which does not change the composition of the crystal; that is, a positive ion and a compensating negative ion, perhaps somewhat removed from each other, may be missing from an otherwise perfect crystal. The number of such vacancies is frequently temperature dependent and has a certain equilibrium concentration.

An ion may be located in an interstitial site rather than its normal position, which is left vacant. Such behavior occurs in the silver halides and does not alter the stoichiometry of the crystal. Diffusion of ions into such vacancies to create new vacancies is believed responsible for the conductivity of alkali and silver halide crystals. The electrical conductivity of crystals provides important information about vacancies. If actual ion migration occurs, Faraday's law should relate the quantity of charge transported and the amount of electrode reaction during the flow of current.

Lattice defects can be produced in NaCl or KCl by heating crystals in the presence of alkali metal vapor. When neutral atoms are incorporated into the crystal, negative ion vacancies in corresponding number must also appear. Crystals of KCl become purple in color when small amounts of sodium or potassium atoms

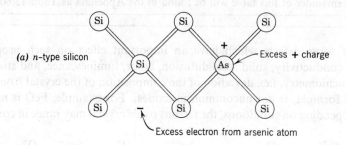

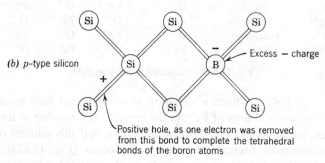

Fig. 15.624 Charges associated with impurity atom in silicon; (*a*) with arsenic impurity an electron is available for conduction; (*b*) with boron impurity a positive hole is available. The type designation is *n* for negative carriers and *p* for positive carriers or holes. The arsenic atom is called a donor atom because on becoming ionized it gives up an electron to the conduction band. The boron atom is called an acceptor atom because on becoming ionized it takes up an electron from the valence band; that is, the ionization of the hole associated with the acceptor corresponds to the addition of an electron to the acceptor, the hole moving to the former state of the valence electron. Many diatomic semiconductors have the zinc blende (ZnS) structure, which may be derived from the diamond structure by decomposing the latter into two *fcc* lattices, the cations (Zn) populating one *fcc* lattice and the anions (S) populating the other. (By permission from C. Kittel, *Introduction to Solid State Physics*, John Wiley and Sons, 1956.)

are present; the defects are called *F* centers (*Farbe*). The characteristic absorption of light is apparently a phenomenon of the crystal rather than of the absorbed atom, as sodium or potassium produces the same effect. It is thought that the absorbed alkali metal atom is ionized with the free electron bound in the negative ion vacancy. Defects can also be produced by other means, e.g., radiation.

Substitution of a Group V or a Group III atom in the crystal lattice of a Group

IV element may produce an impurity semiconductor, discussed briefly in Chapter 11. Arsenic as the impurity atom produces an *n*-type conductor; boron creates a positive hole and a *p*-type conductor. See Fig. 15.624.

For more details on the many interesting effects associated with imperfections in crystals, the student is referred to books such as *Introduction to Solid State Physics*, by Charles Kittel (General References).

Problems

15.601   Verify (use trigonometry and an appropriate diagram) that $d_{hkl} = (a/h) \cos \alpha'$, as asserted in the sentences immediately following Eq. 15.606.

15.602   What is the highest-order diffraction line of 100 which can be observed from a CsCl crystal with copper radiation ($\lambda = 1.54$ Å)? With molybdenum radiation ($\lambda = 0.71$ Å)? $a = 4.12$ Å.

15.603   Plot the product of the Lorentz and polarization factors as a function of θ for an equatorial layer rotation set of planes.

15.604   For cubic NaCl a is 5.64 Å. Calculate the Bragg angle for scattering from 222 planes. Calculate the shortest Na^+—Cl^- distance.

15.605   Calculate the theoretical density of (*a*) NaCl, (*b*) strontium. Show how crystal structure data and measurement of the density can be used to obtain Avogadro's number.

15.606   Strontium crystallizes in a face-centered cubic structure with $a = 6.05$ Å. What is the nearest neighbor distance between strontium atoms?

15.607   Assume that M crystallizes with a simple cubic structure with $a = 4$ Å. Construct the powder pattern to be expected if the crystal film distance is such that 1 mm displacement on the film corresponds to 1° of arc (what is the crystal-film distance?) and X-rays of wavelength 1.54 Å are used.

Repeat this construction if the element crystallizes in a body-centered cubic structure with $a = 6$ Å.

15.608   Explain why lines with *hkl* each odd are relatively more intense in the KI pattern, Fig. 15.611, than in NaCl, with which KI is isomorphous.

15.609   Thallium bromide is isostructural with CsCl and has a value of $a = 3.97$ Å. What is the shortest distance between Tl^+ and Br^- in the crystal?

15.610   Calculate c/a for an ideal hexagonal close-packed structure.

15.611   Diamond forms a face-centered cubic structure (see Fig. 15.619) with atoms at each lattice point and displaced by 1/4, 1/4, 1/4 from each lattice point (8 atoms in the unit cell). Derive the expression for the structure factor and consider the possibility of extinctions for certain classes of reflections. $a = 3.56$ Å. What is the shortest C—C distance?

7. Particle Scattering

Davisson and Germer, in 1927, demonstrated the validity of the de Broglie hypothesis by experimental observation that electrons are diffracted from a crystal of nickel in accordance with diffraction laws for radiation. As found in Problem 1.413 the wavelength to be associated with an electron accelerated by a potential of V volts can be expressed as $(150/V)^{1/2}$ angstroms. The most useful results have been obtained with beams of the order of 50 kev energy ($\lambda \approx 0.05$ Å). Scattering of heavier particles (protons, neutrons, α particles, etc.) has also been observed; electron and neutron diffraction have been most useful as a source of molecular

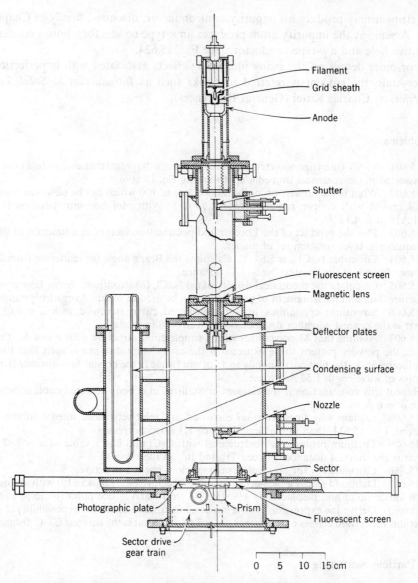

- Filament
- Grid sheath
- Anode
- Shutter
- Fluorescent screen
- Magnetic lens
- Deflector plates
- Condensing surface
- Nozzle
- Sector
- Photographic plate
- Prism
- Fluorescent screen
- Sector drive gear train

0   5   10 15 cm

Fig. 15.701 Electron diffraction apparatus (schematic) for study of scattering by gases [by permission from L. O. Brockway and L. S. Bartell, *Rev. Sci. Instr.*, **25**, 569 (1954)].

structure data. We will only briefly indicate some of the general features of scattering in these two cases.

Electron Diffraction. Because of absorption problems electron diffraction is best suited for study of crystal surfaces or very thin crystal films and for the structure of gas molecules. A schematic diagram of an apparatus used by L. O.

Brockway is shown in Fig. 15.701. An example of a gas diffraction pattern is given in Fig. 15.702. An electron beam passing through a collection of free atoms in a gas would not produce diffraction rings; however, if the beam is scattered by molecules, interference maxima and minima occur which can be associated with the interaction of scattered waves from atoms at fixed distances within the molecules, even though the molecules themselves are distributed and oriented randomly. We can compound the scattered waves vectorially by a method analogous to that

Fig. 15.702   An electron diffraction pattern for $AsBr_3$. Diffraction maxima are shown as light rings and minima as dark rings. The plate was provided by Professors Kenneth Hedberg and Otto Bastiansen, to whom we express our thanks, and was made in Professor Bastiansen's laboratory at the University of Oslo.

developed earlier. The atomic scattering factor for electrons f_{ed} is expressed in the form

$$f_{ed} = \frac{e^2(Z-f)}{2mv^2 \sin^2 \theta_b} \qquad (15.701)$$

where Z is the nuclear charge and f is the X-ray scattering factor. θ_b is one-half the total scattering angle, θ_s. The expression for the relative intensity, above general background, of scattering from randomly oriented gas molecules takes the general form

$$I(\theta) = \sum_i \sum_j (f_{ed})_i (f_{ed})_j \frac{\sin sr_{ij}}{sr_{ij}} \qquad (15.702)$$

where $s = (4\pi/\lambda) \sin \theta_b$, and r_{ij} is the interatomic separation of the various ij pairs of atoms in the molecule. Hence the observed intensity as a function of angle may be compared with that calculated for an assumed model. Equation 15.702 assumes a rigid molecule and no phase shift on scattering. It may be modified to allow for these assumptions. An example of a particularly good fit is shown for CCl_4 in Fig. 15.703. The calculated curve is based on a tetrahedral model with a Cl—Cl distance of 2.887 ± 0.0004 Å and a C—Cl distance of 1.769 ± 0.005 Å.

Accuracy in bond distances of the order of a few tenths of a per cent has been claimed in electron diffraction work. Rotating sectors, Fig. 15.701, are used to increase the relative exposure time for large scattering angles. The number of maxima and minima observed is usually of the order of 12 to 15. This means that no more than five or six parameters, such as bond angles or distances, may usually be treated as variables.

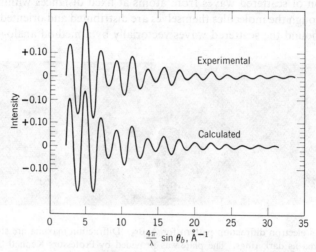

Fig. 15.703 Comparison of calculated and observed intensities for CCl_4 [by permission from Bartell, Brockway, and Schwendeman, *J. Chem. Phys.*, **23**, 1854 (1955)].

Neutron Scattering. Neutrons interact mainly with atomic nuclei, although there may be a significant interaction with the atomic electrons if all electron spins are not paired. Thermal neutrons issuing from an atomic pile will have a distribution of velocities with an average de Broglie wavelength of the order of 1.4 Å. A virtually monochromatic component, with band width of the order of 0.05 Å, can be obtained by impinging a collimated beam on a single crystal, CaF_2, for example, and selecting the corresponding diffraction angle according to the Bragg equation.

The scattered neutron wave may be assumed spherically symmetrical and of the form $-(b/r)e^{i\kappa r}$, where r is the distance of the point of measurement from the origin and b is a complex number called the scattering length. b is related to the scattering cross section σ by

$$\sigma = \frac{\text{scattered neutron current}}{\text{incident neutron flux}} = 4\pi |b^2|$$

The amplitude of the scattered waves may be expressed in terms of scattering cross sections and may be combined according to general scattering theory. Nuclear theory is not presently adequate to provide a full explanation of the magnitudes of the cross sections for the various atoms. Cross sections do not depend on scattering angle, nor do they increase regularly with atomic number as do the X-ray scattering factors. The latter is the main reason for the usefulness of neutron scattering in certain problems. Hydrogen, for example, has a scattering factor comparable to that of other atoms, and hydrogen positions may be determined by neutron diffraction. Isotopes may have quite different neutron cross sections; hence it is possible to distinguish in neutron diffraction work certain atoms which could not be distinguished in X-ray diffraction.

If the scattering atom possesses a magnetic moment, the intensity of scattering in any direction will also depend on magnetic interaction with the neutron spin, and the observed results may give information about the alignment of spins in the crystal lattice. An example is shown in Fig. 15.704.

For a detailed discussion of neutron diffraction, the student is referred to a book such as that by G. E. Bacon (see General References).

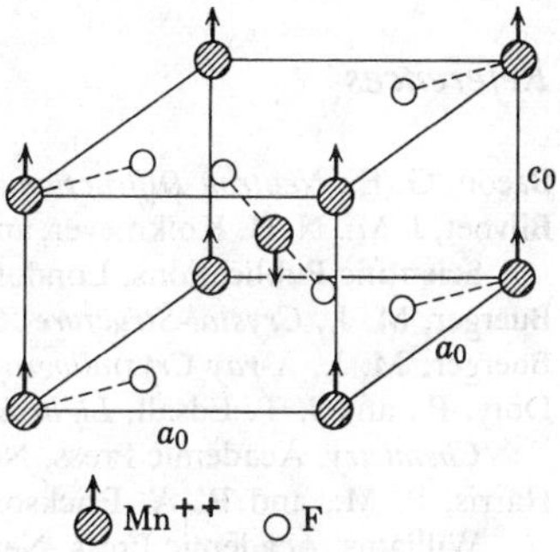

Fig. 15.704   The unit cell of MnF_2, showing the antiferromagnetic arrangement of the magnetic moments of the Mn^{++} ions (Erickson, 1953) (by permission from G. E. Bacon, *Neutron Diffraction*, Oxford University Press, 1955).

8. Review Problems

15.801   Determine a set of correct units for the quantities I_s and I_0 in the Rayleigh ratio, Eq. 15.313.

15.802   Show by algebraic addition of intensities that the angular factor for unpolarized light scattered from a single center is of the form given in Eq. 15.122, and independent of the angle around the incident beam.

15.803   Calculate the scattering factor (Eq. 15.216) if the density function has the form

$$\rho(r) = \text{const} \, (1 - r/b)$$

from $r = 0$ to $r = b$ and zero beyond $r = b$.

15.804   The refractive index increment of a natural polysaccharide dissolved in water is $0.144 \text{ cm}^3 \text{ g}^{-1}$ and $n_0 = 1.33$. At $\lambda = 4360$ Å the following data were obtained. Calculate the molecular weight.

conc, g/100 ml.	0.0540	0.0270	0.0135	
$R(90)°$	1.340	0.650	0.313	

15.805   How many equivalent points arise for the point group D_{6h}? for O_h?

15.806   Construct a two dimensional lattice similar to Fig. 15.511. Show the planes $\bar{1}3, 34, 23, 22$. If the lattice is square with unit dimension a, evaluate the distance between neighboring planes for each of the sets indicated.

15.807   If the radius of the carbon atom in diamond is taken as one-half the shortest C—C distance and the atoms are assumed spherical, calculate the fraction of the volume of the unit cell occupied by carbon atoms. What would be the volume occupied by the same number of atoms if their radius were the same but a close-packed structure were to be assumed?

15.808   Calculate the relative distances of the 8 nearest and 6 next-nearest neighbors in the *BCC* structure for metals. Compare the weighted average distance in the *BCC* structure with the value for 14 nearest atoms (12 equal and 2 farther) in the close-packed structures.

15.809   Eliminate *B* from Eq. 15.619 and derive an expression for the lattice energy per mole of cations for NaCl (assume $n = 8$, $R_0 = 2.8$ Å).

References

Bacon, G. E., *Neutron Diffraction*, Clarendon Press, Oxford, 1955.

Bijvoet, J. M., N. H. Kolkmeyer, and C. H. MacGillavry, *X-ray Analysis of Crystals*, Butterworths Scientific Publications, London, 1951.

Buerger, M. J., *Crystal-Structure Analysis*, John Wiley and Sons, New York, 1960.

Buerger, M. J., *X-ray Crystallography*, John Wiley and Sons, New York, 1942.

Doty, P., and J. T. Edsall, *Light Scattering in Protein Solutions*, Vol. IV of *Advances in Protein Chemistry*, Academic Press, New York, 1951.

Harris, P. M., and R. A. Erickson, in *Methods of Experimental Physics*, Vol. 3, edited by D. Williams, Academic Press, New York, 1962.

James, R. W., *The Optical Principles of the Diffraction of X-rays*, G. Bell and Sons, London, 1948.

Kaspar, J. S., and K. Lonsdale, General Editors, *International Tables for X-ray Crystallography*, The Kynock Press, Birmingham, England.

Kittel, C., *Introduction to Solid State Physics*, Second Edition, John Wiley and Sons, New York, 1956.

McLachlan, D., Jr., *X-ray Crystal Structure*, McGraw-Hill Book Co., New York, 1957.

Moore, W. J., *Physical Chemistry*, Third Edition, Prentice-Hall, Englewood Cliffs, N.J., 1962.

Pauling, L., *The Nature of the Chemical Bond*, Third Edition, Cornell University Press, Ithaca, N.Y., 1960.

Chapter Sixteen

Molecular Spectra and

Resonance Phenomena

In the early chapters, we discussed briefly the electronic spectrum of the hydrogen atom, and rotational and vibrational spectra of diatomic molecules as a means of obtaining the corresponding energy levels. In subsequent chapters, molecular properties such as bond distances, bond energies, and vibration frequencies were used. We now return to a more complete discussion of molecular spectra, from which such molecular properties are obtained. In fact, the study of molecular spectra has been an exceedingly fruitful means of obtaining information about molecular structure and chemical binding. We shall also describe some of the theoretical approaches to chemical binding, as pertains to the electronic spectra of molecules.

Spectra may be termed resonance phenomena, in contrast to phenomena such as scattering (Chapter 15). In the former, the frequency of the radiation corresponds to the difference between two atomic or molecular energy levels; in the latter, the radiation frequency is far from any such energy level difference. In the scattering discussion of Chapter 15, the main interest was in amplitudes, phase shifts, and intensities of the scattered radiation produced by radiation falling on a sample. The effect of the radiation on the sample was discussed briefly on the basis of some simple models. We now return to a further consideration of the effect of electric fields (even of very low frequencies) on atoms and molecules, and molecular dipole moments. Dipole moments are important in the form of the selection rules which determine the spectra.

1. Molecules with Permanent Dipoles

A molecule with an initially symmetrical charge distribution has this distribution distorted in the presence of an electric field to produce a dipole moment, which is zero in the absence of the field. In addition to the field-induced dipole moment many molecules possess a permanent dipole moment that is a consequence of their unsymmetrical molecular structure.

Polar and Nonpolar Molecules.   Atoms such as argon, and molecules such as hydrogen and methane, have a symmetrical distribution of electric charge. Not only are they electrically neutral, in that the total charge on the nuclei is equal and opposite in sign to the total charge of the electrons, but also the centers of gravity of the positive and negative charges, taken separately, coincide. Such molecules are called nonpolar.

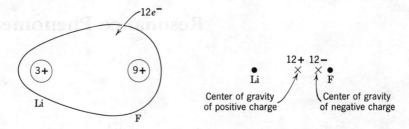

Fig. 16.101   A polar molecule, and a point dipole associated with it. The fluorine is at 1.564 Å from the lithium, $12-$ centers at 1.282 Å, and $12+$ centers at 1.173 Å from the lithium. [Computed from the measurements of Wharton, Klemperer, Gold, Strauch, Gallagher, and Derr, *J. Chem. Phys.*, **38**, 1203 (1963).]

On the other hand, molecules like HCl (gas) and LiF (gas) have a larger density of electrons at the halogen end of the molecule than at the other end. Therefore, the center of gravity of the negative charge does not coincide with the center of gravity of the positive charge on the nuclei.

Representation of a Molecule by a Point-Charge Dipole.   In a real molecule the positive charges are associated with the massive nuclei and thus have a fairly precise location, subject to the orientation of the molecule and the effect of molecular vibration. The electrons, however, are distributed over the whole molecule, with an average density at a given point equal to ψ^2 at that point. For many purposes the electrical distribution of a polar molecule may be represented by a very simple model, a point-charge dipole, analogous to the instantaneous dipole M used in Chapter 15. This model consists of a permanent dipole μ_0, composed of positive and negative charges e_a and $-e_a$ separated by a distance δ. The permanent dipole moment μ_0 is defined as

$$\mu_0 = e_a \delta \qquad (16.101)$$

Thus the value of the dipole moment does not depend on the charge or the distance individually, but on their product alone. For example, the dipole moment associated with twice the charge separated by half the distance has the same value

$$\mu_0 = \frac{\delta}{2}(2e_d) = e_d\delta$$

A real point-charge dipole is associated with some physical charge and physical distance; in many cases it can be replaced by an equivalent ideal dipole with extremely large charges separated by a vanishingly small distance. The relationship between a real molecule and a real point-charge dipole is shown in Fig. 16.101.

Interaction of a Dipole with Fields.   Since a dipole consists of two equal and opposite charges bound together by a rigid molecular frame, it is clear that its behavior in a field will be different from that of the individual charges that comprise it.   The simplest sort of field is that between charged parallel plates of very large

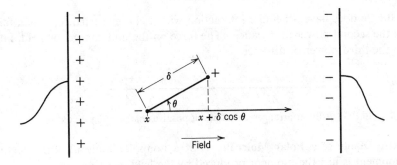

Fig. 16.102   The interaction of a dipole with a constant field (schematic).

size compared to the distance between them.   In such a constant field E_0 a unit positive charge is subject to a force equal to the field.   If the plates are perpendicular to the x axis, the potential energy of the unit positive charge is proportional to the distance x

$$V(x) = -E_0 x + \text{const}$$

If the axis of the dipole is kept at a fixed angle θ to the x axis, Fig. 16.102, the total potential energy of the dipole is of the form

$$
\begin{aligned}
V(x,\theta)(\text{dipole}) &= -E_0[-e_d x + e_d(x + \delta \cos \theta)] + \text{const} \\
&= -E_0 e_d \delta \cos \theta + \text{const} \\
&= -\mu_0 E_0 \cos \theta + \text{const} \qquad (16.102)
\end{aligned}
$$

Thus, as long as the angle that the dipole makes with the field is held constant the potential is constant, and no force acts on the dipole that would cause it to move toward either plate of the condenser.   However, there is an energy of orientation of the dipole, dependent on the angle θ, of the form

$$V(\theta) = -\mu_0 E_0 \cos \theta \qquad (16.103)$$

This can vary from $-\mu_0 E_0$, if the dipole is lined up with the field, to $+\mu_0 E_0$, if the dipole is lined up and opposing the field.

Thus the physical effect of a constant field on a dipole, in the absence of thermal agitation of the molecules, would be to line it up with the field, after which there would be no residual force (torque) on the dipole system.

The interaction of a dipole with the field of a unit positive charge is somewhat more complicated. If the dipole and single charge are lined up as in Fig. 16.103, then Coulomb's law gives

$$V(x) = \frac{e_d}{x} - \frac{e_d}{x - \delta} \tag{16.104}$$

At large values of x compared with δ this reduces to the form

$$V(x) = -\left(\frac{1}{x^2}\right) e_d \delta = -\frac{\mu_0}{x^2} \tag{16.105}$$

Thus a dipole does have a definite interaction with a charged particle, which falls off with the second power of distance. The force on the unit charge, or field, falls off with the third power of distance.

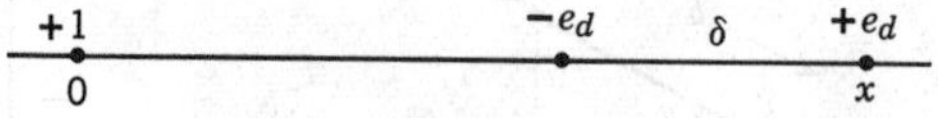

Fig. 16.103   A linear arrangement of a unit positive charge and a dipole.

Effective Dipole of a Polar Molecule.   For a nonpolar molecule the effective dipole moment is just the moment produced by the field

$$M = \alpha E_0 \tag{15.302}$$

The dielectric constant ϵ of a dilute gas is related to the polarizability α by the expression we have used before (Eq. 15.304)

$$\alpha = \frac{\epsilon - 1}{4\pi N'} \tag{16.106}$$

if the molecule is nonpolar. A polar molecule is also affected in the same way by an electric field, but this polarizability is only a part of the dielectric constant.

At very high temperatures, the molecule and its permanent dipole are turning in all directions, with no preferred orientation. Therefore its average effect on the component of the total dipole in a fixed direction is zero. However, at lower temperatures, the electric field tends to orient the dipole parallel to the field in such a way as to achieve a minimum energy. The total component of dipole moment of the molecule is thus made up from the dipole induced by the field, plus the average contribution from the partially oriented permanent dipole. If θ is the angle between the permanent dipole and the field, the total dipole component in the field direction is given by the expression

$$\bar{M} = \alpha_\infty E_0 + \mu_0 \overline{\cos \theta} \tag{16.107}$$

Here, α_∞ is the polarizability due to the movement of the electrons α_E plus a possible contribution α_A due to internal displacements of the atoms caused by the electric field. These two contributions to the total polarizability are in addition to that caused by molecular orientation. Experimentally, α_∞ can be separated from the orientation effect if the temperature is high enough or if the field oscillates rapidly enough so that the average value of $\cos\theta$ is zero. However, in a static field, the total polarizability of a polar molecule will reflect orientation as well as electronic effects. We define the total polarizability, including orientation effects, in a manner analogous to Eq. 15.302

$$\bar{M} = \alpha_{total}E_0 \tag{16.108}$$

This total α should be used in Eq. 16.106 to determine the static-field dielectric constant of a gas of polar molecules. (However, the related equation, Eq. 15.305, is restricted to nonpolar gases because of the relatively high frequency of light.) If we combine Eqs. 16.107, 16.108, and 16.106 we obtain

$$\epsilon - 1 = 4\pi N'\left(\alpha_\infty + \frac{\mu_0\,\overline{\cos\theta}}{E_0}\right) \tag{16.109}$$

The qualitative behavior of this expression is easy to describe. At any temperature the first term in the parentheses is present and corresponds to the slight change in electronic distribution caused by a weak electric field. The second term is due to the physical orientation of the molecule, including the heavy nuclei, which are rotating in all possible degrees of freedom about the center of gravity. If this rotation is sufficiently vigorous (high temperature,) then the average value of $\cos\theta$, which ranges from 1 to -1 as θ varies from zero to π, will be zero. At lower temperatures the orientations will be weighted by a Boltzmann factor,

$$\exp\left(\mu_0 E_0 \frac{\cos\theta}{kT}\right)$$

which contains the energy of orientation of the dipole with or against the field.

In three dimensions, the orientation is specified not only by the angle θ but also by the angle ϕ around the axis of the field. This latter angle, of course, does not affect the energy of the dipole. If we average over all values of the orientation angles, we have the expression

$$\overline{\cos\theta} = \frac{\sum \cos\theta \exp\left(\mu_0 E_0 \cos\theta/kT\right)}{\sum \exp\left(\mu_0 E_0 \cos\theta/kT\right)} \tag{16.110}$$

for the average value of $\cos\theta$. If we replace the summation by an integration over all the angles θ and ϕ, we obtain

$$\overline{\cos\theta} = \frac{\displaystyle\int_0^{2\pi}\int_0^{\pi} \cos\theta \exp\left(\mu_0 E_0 \cos\theta/kT\right)\sin\theta\,d\theta\,d\phi}{\displaystyle\int_0^{2\pi}\int_0^{\pi} \exp\left(\mu_0 E_0 \cos\theta/kT\right)\sin\theta\,d\theta\,d\phi}$$

This integral can be evaluated easily if we observe that the field is always very small compared to the effect of the thermal motions, i.e., $\mu E_0 \ll kT$. The integral over ϕ yields 2π in both numerator and denominator. Then we expand the exponential and keep only the first term in each integral that does not vanish. Thus by using

$$e^x \approx 1 + x$$

and

$$d \cos \theta = -\sin \theta \, d\theta$$

we obtain

$$\overline{\cos \theta} = \frac{\displaystyle\int_{+1}^{-1} \cos \theta [1 + (\mu_0 E_0 \cos \theta / kT)] \, d(\cos \theta)}{\displaystyle\int_{+1}^{-1} [1 + (\mu_0 E_0 \cos \theta / kT)] \, d(\cos \theta)}$$

$$= \frac{\mu_0 E_0}{3kT} \tag{16.111}$$

If we substitute this value of $\overline{\cos \theta}$ in Eq. 16.109 the relation first derived by Debye is obtained

$$\frac{(\epsilon - 1)}{4\pi N'} = \alpha_\infty + \frac{\mu_0^2}{3kT} \tag{16.112}$$

We see, therefore, that when the measured dielectric constant of a gas is substituted in the left-hand side of Eq. 16.112, the result should be a linear function of $1/T$. From the intercept at $1/T = 0$, we can obtain the polarizability of the molecule. If the slope of the line is zero, the molecule is nonpolar; otherwise the slope is equal to $\mu_0^2/3k$, and so the dipole moment of the molecule can be estimated.

Experimental Determination of Dipole Moment in a Gas. For use in the evaluation of data, Eq. 16.112 is usually put in a molar form by multiplying by a factor including Avogadro's number. The quantity that results is called the *molar polarization* with the symbol P. Thus, if we multiply through by the factor $(4\pi/3)N$

$$P = \frac{4\pi}{3} N\left(\alpha_\infty + \frac{\mu_0^2}{3kT}\right) \tag{16.113}$$

where

$$P = \frac{4\pi}{3} N\left(\frac{\epsilon - 1}{4\pi N'}\right) = \frac{1}{3} \frac{N}{N'} (\epsilon - 1) \tag{16.114}$$

Note that N/N' is the ratio of Avogadro's number to the number of molecules actually present in 1 cc when the dielectric constant is measured. P is independent of concentration, whereas the dielectric constant is concentration dependent.

Some results of early measurements, suggested by Debye's equation, are shown in Fig. 16.104. Equation 16.113 is sometimes written

$$P = P_\infty + P_0$$

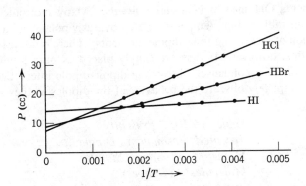

Fig. 16.104   Polarization as a function of $1/T$ for the hydrogen halides [by permission from C. T. Zahn, *Phys. Rev.*, **24**, 400 (1924)].

where P_∞ is the temperature-independent polarization of the molecules, and P_0 is the orientation polarization. Note that in Fig. 16.104, P_∞ is greatest for the molecule with the most electrons, HI, and least for HCl, with HBr in between. This fact reflects the usual behavior of such molecules. However, judging from the slope the temperature-dependent part of P is much more important with HCl than with HI because HCl is a much more polar compound. As before, HBr is in between. These slopes correspond to dipole moments of 1.03, 0.78, and 0.38 for HCl, HBr, and HI, respectively, measured in units of 10^{-18} esu cm per molecule. This unit is often called the *debye*.

Some results for polyatomic molecules are shown in Fig. 16.105. It is clear that the possibly symmetric molecules, CH_4 and CCl_4, have no dipole moment, and thus there is support for the assertion that these molecules are truly symmetric. Table 16.101 summarizes some values of dipole moment.

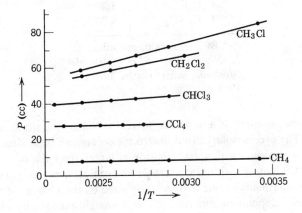

Fig. 16.105   Polarization as a function of $1/T$ for some substituted methanes [by permission from R. Sanger, *Physik. Z.*, **27**, 556 [1926]].

Dipole Moments Obtained in Nonpolar Solvents.   Many molecules which are nonvolatile or unstable at high temperature are obviously polar, and it is desirable to have a method of measuring their dipole moments.   There is no straightforward way of doing this, however.   If they are simply placed as pure liquids or solids between the plates of a condenser, the strong dipole-dipole interactions between the molecules completely obscure the behavior of the dipoles as they would act if

Table 16.101   *Presently Accepted Permanent Dipole Moments of Some Simple Molecules* (Debyes)*

Molecule	μ_0
HF	1.91
HCl	1.08
HBr	0.79
HI	0.38
CO	0.11
N_2O	0.17
COS	0.72
H_2O	1.84
H_2S	0.93
SO_2	1.61
NH_3	1.47
PH_3	0.55
NF_3	0.23
PF_3	1.025
CH_3OH	1.69
$C_6H_5CH_3$	0.37
C_6H_5Cl	1.70
$C_6H_5NO_2$	4.20

* By permission, according to J. W. Smith, *Electric Dipole Moments*, Butterworths, London, 1955.

isolated from one another.   If a nonpolar solvent is found, the situation becomes a little simpler.   The excess polarization due to the solute can be evaluated by difference.   For polar molecules, this contribution is larger than the contribution that would be expected from P_∞ alone, as measured by optical means.   It is then possible to treat the measurements at one temperature alone by the Debye method, if P_∞ is estimated in an independent manner.   This approach avoids any change in the solvent-solute interaction caused by temperature change, and of course avoids the necessity of varying the temperature over a wide range.   However, it is subject to the great limitation that it is impossible to calculate the local field operating on the polar molecule in a dense medium composed of a highly polarizable, (even if nonpolar) liquid.

For a detailed treatment of this problem, the student is referred to the References at the end of the section.

In Table 16.102 the true gas-phase dipole moment is compared with dipole moments of the same material estimated in solution. Considering the difficulties involved, the agreement is remarkably good.

*Table 16.102   Comparison of Some Dipole Moments (Debyes) Obtained from Vapor-Phase and Solution Measurements**

Substance	Gas Phase	CCl_4 Sol'n	CS_2 Sol'n	C_6H_6 Sol'n
Nitrobenzene	4.20	3.92	3.66	3.97
t-Butyl chloride	2.13	2.19	2.01	2.14
Acetonitrile	3.97	3.43	3.21	3.47
Aniline	1.48	1.46	1.42	1.51

* By permission from J. W. Smith, *Electric Dipole Moments*, Butterworths, London, 1955.

The Total Polarization of Real Gases over a Wide Range of Frequencies.   In Chapter 15, we considered the polarizability of nonpolar dilute gases in the range of Rayleigh scattering frequencies, that is, the visible spectrum. There this range was considered, by comparison with X-rays, to be the low-frequency range. Here we are considering the behavior of polar molecules at what we have described as static voltages, or zero frequency. Thus, by comparison, the range of the visible spectrum is the high-frequency range. In actual practice, it is a further complication that electrical measurements of capacitance are much more convenient with a-c than with d-c voltage. Therefore, the theory that we have nominally developed for a static voltage is actually applied to measurements of dielectric constant in the kilocycle or megacycle frequency range. The practical question then arises, Are these frequencies low enough compared with the speed of molecular orientation so that the Debye theory can be applied? This question can be answered if we examine the observed total polarization of a gas over an extremely wide range of frequencies all the way from the ultraviolet region to electric frequencies in the audible range. In order to make a convenient diagram, P is plotted against a logarithmic scale of frequency (Fig. 16.106).

The total polarization can be written as the sum of several frequency-dependent contributions

$$P = P_E + P_A + P_0$$

In the X-ray region (not shown) the polarization is effectively zero. Not even the electrons are in phase with such a high frequency. After passing through the region of ultraviolet absorption ($\omega \approx \omega_0$) we reach the range of the visible spectrum, where only the electronic component P_E makes an appreciable contribution to the polarization. Furthermore, away from resonant frequencies, the contribution of P_E is substantially constant. We then pass through another region of absorption where the motion of the nuclear masses (molecular vibration) is being excited. At lower frequencies still, the field is oscillating so slowly that the molecular distortion it produces adds a component P_A, the so-called atomic polarization. Then, after a period of frequencies that are resonant with the orientation frequencies of the polar

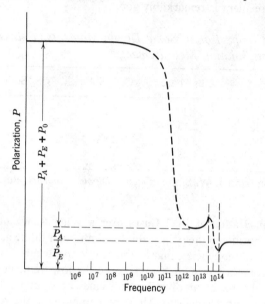

Fig. 16.106   Typical behavior of polarization as a function of frequency for a polar substance (adapted by permission from R. J. W. LeFevre, *Dipole Moments*, Third Edition, Methuen, 1953).

molecules, we enter the true low-frequency region, where dipole orientation adds a final contribution, P_0. The total polarization then remains substantially unchanged down to zero frequency. It is in this region that the Debye equation can be applied to obtain the permanent dipole moment of the molecules.

For monatomic gases such as argon, only P_E is important at all frequencies below the ultraviolet. For nonpolar molecules such as CO_2, although P_0 is always zero, the molecule can still be distorted in an electric field of intermediate frequency, and so only P_E and P_A are present in the total polarization.

However, for a polar molecule such as HCl, all three factors operate and can be separated by a suitable investigation over a wide frequency range. Note that P_∞ obtained from the Debye equation is equal to $P_E + P_A$. In the rest of this chapter, we shall be largely concerned with the ranges of frequency that separate these contributions. The uppermost region is the range of electronic spectra; at the onset of the contribution of P_A we observe molecular vibration spectra and finally, in the third transition region, rotational spectra.

Problems

16.101   Estimate the dipole moments of the molecules in Fig. 16.105.

16.102   Plot the molar polarization of SO_2 as a function of $1/T$ if the polarization P_∞ is 18 $Å^3$ molecule^{-1}.

16.103   Calculate the dipole moment of HCl as if the molecule were completely ionic, with ions at the bond distance (see Chapter 4).

16.104   Explain why the Debye method of measuring dipole moments is very sensitive for large moments but quite inaccurate (on a percentage basis) for small moments.

16.105   The polarization of nitroethane vapor at 415.6 and 484.3°K is 217.3 and 188.6 cc mole^{-1}, respectively, according to E. C. Hurdis and C. P. Smyth [*J. Am. Chem. Soc.*, **64**, 2829 (1942)]. What is the dipole moment of this molecule? Another estimate of P_∞ (from refractive index) is 17.0 cc mole^{-1}. How does this compare with the value from the measurements of Hurdis and Smyth?

References

Böttcher, C. J. F., *Theory of Electric Polarization*, Elsevier, New York, 1952.

Debye, P., *Polar Molecules*, Dover (reprint), New York, 1945.

Fröhlich, H., *Theory of Dielectrics*, Second Edition, Oxford Press, London, 1958.

LeFevre, R. J. W., *Dipole Moments*, Third Edition, Methuen and Co., London, 1953.

Smith, J. W., *Electric Dipole Moments*, Butterworths Scientific Publications, London, 1955.

Smyth, C. P., *Dielectric Behavior and Structure*, McGraw-Hill Book Co., New York, 1955.

2. Selection Rules

In Sec. 16.1, and earlier in Chapter 15, we saw that a good account of the behavior of molecules in the presence of electromagnetic radiation could be achieved with classical models. We had to exclude those regions of frequency where resonance absorption was taking place because what are essentially quantum energy jumps cannot be thoroughly explained without the use of quantum mechanics. We proceed first to develop selection rules, which choose from the many combinations of two energy levels those that can be combined to yield observable spectroscopic lines or bands. Selection rules were used earlier in Sec. 4.2; now that we have described some properties of the dipole moment, it is possible to indicate the origin of such rules.

Dipole Moment Operator.   We shall consider the dipole moment operator for a simple diatomic molecule. In this kind of molecule the dipole moment is always directed along the line joining the two nuclei. We shall allow for the possible variation of the value for the dipole moment of the molecule with internuclear separation by means of a simple linear relationship

$$\mu = \mu_0 + \mu_1 Q \tag{16.201}$$

where Q is the displacement of the interatomic distance from its point of minimum potential energy. Thus Q allows for the distortion of the molecule by molecular vibration.

For convenience, we shall consider the projection of this dipole on the Z axis, because this involves only the angle θ. This projection can be written as

$$\mu_Z = \mu \cos \theta = (\mu_0 + \mu_1 Q) \cos \theta \tag{16.202}$$

The moment μ_0 can be closely identified with the permanent dipole of the molecule; μ_1 can be interpreted as the derivative of the dipole moment with respect to the displacement Q.

The dipole moment operator can be obtained in the usual way (Sec. 2.7) from the dipole moment in terms of components along the three space-fixed axes, X, Y, and Z. We shall write expressions only for the Z component; the other components can easily be written by analogy. The dipole moment contains only coordinates, and no momenta, so the operator has the same form as the classical expression

$$\mathbf{\mu}_Z = \mu_Z = (\mu_0 + \mu_1 Q) \cos \theta \tag{16.203}$$

The expectation value for the Z component of the dipole moment associated with a given state of the molecule characterized by the wave function ψ_i will be given by the expression (Eq. 2.701) integrated over all pertinent coordinates τ

$$\bar{\mu}_Z = \int \psi_i^* \mathbf{\mu}_Z \psi_i \, d\tau \equiv (i \,|\mathbf{\mu}_Z|\, i) \tag{16.204}$$

Note that we have introduced here a shorthand notation for the integral which preserves the essential information about the integration. The empty parentheses and bars ($|$ $|$) have places for the operator symbol and the indices of the wave functions. The bars of course do not mean absolute value.

The Transition Moment Integral.   As a result of the quantum mechanical treatment of a physical system in the presence of electromagnetic radiation, one finds that the intensity of a spectral transition between an initial level i with wave function ψ_i, and a final level f with wave function ψ_f, is proportional to the square of the magnitude of the integral

$$(i \,|\mathbf{\mu}_Z|\, f) = \int \psi_i^* \mathbf{\mu}_Z \psi_f \, d\tau \tag{16.205}$$

where $\mathbf{\mu}_Z$ is the dipole moment operator (Z component). This integral is called the *transition moment integral*. Note that it is similar to Eq. 16.204, except that the wave functions have different indices and thus correspond to different states.

For the time being, we shall assume that the initial and final states, although in different vibrational and rotational states, are both in the ground electronic state, which permits the omission of the unchanged electronic functions from ψ_i and ψ_f. The case of electronic transitions is discussed later in Secs. 16.5 and 16.6. If the pertinent wave functions contain only rotational and vibrational parts, the total wave function may, to a rather good approximation, be written as the product of the two parts

$$\psi_j = \psi_{vj} \psi_{Rj} \tag{16.206}$$

Substituting Eqs. 16.203 and 16.206 into Eq. 16.205 and expanding the terms gives an expression for the transition moment integral,

$$(i \, |\mu_z| \, f) = \mu_0 \left[\int \psi_{Ri}^* \cos \theta \psi_{Rf} \, d\tau_R \right] \left[\int \psi_{vi}^* \psi_{vf} \, d\tau_v \right]$$
$$+ \mu_1 \left[\int \psi_{Ri}^* \cos \theta \psi_{Rf} \, d\tau_R \right] \left[\int \psi_{vi}^* Q \psi_{vf} \, d\tau_v \right] \quad (16.207)$$

This is the fundamental expression for deducing selection rules.

Rotational Selection Rules.   Selection rules are obtained by examination of the terms in Eq. 16.207, for various combinations of initial and final state wave functions. Since the vibrational wave functions (like any set of eigenfunctions) are orthogonal, the first term will vanish unless both the subscripts vi and vf represent the same vibrational state. The other integral in the first term contains the factor $\cos \theta$; its presence causes the integral to become zero, unless the rotational functions have J values which differ by unity. The first term vanishes, then, unless the molecule has a nonvanishing dipole moment ($\mu_0 \neq 0$), unless $\Delta J = \pm 1$, and unless $\Delta v = 0$. Since the rotational energy changes, but not the vibrational energy, these conditions are called the pure rotational selection rules.

ILLUSTRATION.   Show that the rotational integral in Eq. 16.207 is nonvanishing for rotational states with $J = 0$ and $J = 1$.

These functions are the same as s and p atomic orbitals, and, choosing the p_z orbital, we have

$$\int \psi_{Ri}^* \cos \theta \, \psi_{Rf} \, d\tau_R = \int \frac{1}{2\pi^{1/2}} \cos \theta \, \frac{1}{2} \left(\frac{3}{\pi} \right)^{1/2} \cos \theta \sin \theta \, d\theta \, d\varphi$$

since the volume element $d\tau_R$ is $\sin \theta \, d\theta \, d\varphi$. This becomes, on integrating over φ from 0 to 2π,

$$\frac{3^{1/2}}{2} \int_0^\pi \cos^2 \theta \sin \theta \, d\theta = \frac{3^{1/2}}{2} \left[\frac{-\cos^3 \theta}{3} \right]_0^\pi = \frac{3^{1/2}}{2} \cdot \frac{2}{3} = 3^{-1/2}$$

which is not zero.

––––––––––––––––––

The rotational wave functions have the interesting property that any one of them, when multiplied by the $\cos \theta$ factor, may be expressed exactly as the sum of two different rotational wave functions belonging to J values one larger and one smaller than the original function. That is

$$\cos \theta \psi_{R,J} = a\psi_{R,J+1} + b\psi_{R,J-1} \quad (16.208)$$

where $\psi_{R,J+1}$ is a rotational function of the set with rotational quantum number $J + 1$, and similarly for $\psi_{R,J-1}$; and where a and b are constant parameters independent of θ and φ (rotational coordinates), but of course different for different values of J. If this expression is substituted into Eq. 16.207, and one remembers that rotational wave functions are orthogonal, the selection rule for the quantum number J is obtained.

Vibrational Selection Rules. Consider the second term in Eq. 16.207. The rotational factor is exactly the same as in the first term, so that the same selection rule is obtained for the quantum number J. The vibrational factor is now different, and contains the vibrational displacement coordinate which multiplies initial and final vibrational state wave functions. The vibrational wave functions, assumed to be those of the harmonic oscillator, behave toward the coordinate Q in the same fashion as the rotational functions toward $\cos \theta$; that is, for any one of the harmonic oscillator functions, $\psi_v(Q)$,

$$Q\psi_v(Q) = a\psi_{v-1}(Q) + b\psi_{v+1}(Q) \tag{16.209}$$

with similar remarks about the constants a and b. Again, using the orthogonality property, one obtains the selection rule. To summarize, the second term of Eq. 16.207 will be nonvanishing if $\mu_1 \neq 0$, and $\Delta J = +1$ or -1, and $\Delta v = +1$ or -1; these constitute the vibrational selection rules.

Several important limitations should be recognized. First, real molecules are not harmonic oscillators (Sec. 2.2); this is found to introduce additional functions on the right-hand side of Eq. 16.209. Second, the simple linear dependence of μ on Q in Eq. 16.201 is not correct for large displacements. The lowest electronic states of molecules, with only a very few exceptions, dissociate into neutral atoms, which means that the slope must approach zero for large Q. Hence the second term in Eq. 16.207 may also be nonvanishing for $\Delta v = \pm 2, \pm 3$, etc.

These selection rules also apply, of course, to diatomic molecules which were discussed in Chapter 4. For homonuclear diatomic molecules, both μ_0 and μ_1 are zero, and hence they show neither rotational nor vibrational spectra. Heteronuclear diatomic molecules almost invariably have nonzero values of both μ_0 and μ_1, and therefore exhibit both rotational and vibrational spectra. In polyatomic linear molecules, it is possible to have $\mu_0 = 0$ and $\mu_1 \neq 0$; for such molecules rotational spectra are forbidden, but vibrational spectra are allowed; examples are CO_2 and C_2H_2. Note, however, that polyatomic molecules will have several distinct Q's, corresponding to different kinds of vibrations.

Polyatomic linear molecules also have terms in the dipole moment expansion representing components perpendicular to the axis of the molecule; these cannot be permanent (μ_0) type, but must occur multiplied by the appropriate vibrational displacement. For such vibrations, frequently called *bending* vibrations or *perpendicular* vibrations, a similar analysis gives the selection rule

$$\Delta J = 0, \pm 1$$

Nonlinear polyatomic molecules can also be treated by a further extension of these methods, and selection rules determined for both rotational and vibrational transitions. These selection rules will be discussed in connection with the description of rotational and vibrational spectra in the next sections.

Problems

16.201   Show that the p_x and p_y orbitals, used in place of the p_z orbital in the Illustration, give a zero result. This occurs since they correspond to different polarization of the light beam.

16.202   Show that Eq. 16.209 is true, using $v = 1$, and evaluate the constants a and b. Use the equation to determine what must be the functional form for $\psi_3(Q)$ (don't normalize it).

16.203   Write the dipole operator (function of θ and φ) corresponding to the X and Y space-fixed components of the permanent dipole.

16.204   The selection rule on J allows transitions such as $J = 1 \rightarrow 2$. Using the Z component of the dipole, which of the d orbitals gives a nonzero integral with each of the orbitals p_z, p_x, and p_y?

3. Rotational Spectra

A study of rotational spectra in the gas phase is another way of obtaining structural information about molecules. The diffraction methods discussed in Chapter 15 give atomic positions or inter-atomic distances more or less directly; rotational spectra give directly one or more moments of inertia, and interatomic distances by inference from these moments. For calculation of the rotational partition function only the moments of inertia appear in the equations.

Moments of inertia were introduced briefly in Sec. 4.3; we shall begin this section with a more detailed account of moments and products of inertia.

Moments of Inertia.   In classical physics an object which is constrained to rotate about a certain fixed axis, such as the balance wheel of a watch or the crank-shaft of an engine, has a moment of inertia I

$$I = \sum_i m_i r_i^2 \tag{16.301}$$

where the small parts of the object with masses m_i are located at the (perpendicular) distances r_i from the axis of rotation, and the sum is taken over all parts of the rotating object. The moment of inertia is used with the angular velocity of rotation in writing an expression for the kinetic energy of rotation, just as the mass is used with the linear velocity in writing an expression for the kinetic energy of translation. Equation 16.301 is appropriate only for systems composed of a finite number of point masses; an integral is necessary for objects with continuous distribution of mass, as in most macroscopic systems. The sum thus applies to molecules.

Since the rotation of a molecule in the gas phase is not constrained to any fixed axis, several different moments of inertia are needed to describe completely the kinetic energy of rotation. The model for a molecule with $\mathcal{N}$ atoms is taken to be a set of $\mathcal{N}$ point masses fixed in relation to each other, but of course free to move in space by rigid translation and rotation. The mass of each atom, m_i, is regarded as concentrated at a point; this assumption disregards the detailed electronic distributions but is a good approximation. A Cartesian coordinate system is taken with its origin at the center of gravity of the molecule, and also taken to rotate with the molecule; that is, each atom of the molecule has certain fixed x, y, and z coordinates in this axis system (Fig. 4.302). We define the moments of inertia, I_{xx}, I_{yy}, and I_{zz} as well as *products* of inertia I_{xy}, I_{xz}, I_{yz} with respect to this coordinate system by

$$I_{xx} = \sum_i m_i(y_i^2 + z_i^2)$$

$$I_{yy} = \sum_i m_i(x_i^2 + z_i^2) \qquad (16.302)$$

and

$$I_{xy} = \sum_i m_i x_i y_i$$

with similar expressions for I_{zz}, I_{yz}, and I_{xz}. These equations define six different quantities; however, it turns out that only three of them are really independent. If the Cartesian coordinate system is chosen with a different orientation, the moments and products of inertia will generally be different from those obtained with the original orientation. There is, however, a special orientation of the coordinate axes for which all three products of inertia are zero; these axes are called the *principal axes*, and the I_{xx}, I_{yy}, and I_{zz} with respect to these axes are called the *principal moments of inertia* and denoted I_x, I_y, and I_z. The principal moments are obtained from spectroscopic measurements. In some systems the choice of principal axes is obvious or dictated by symmetry; any rotation axis of symmetry must be a principal axis, and a mirror plane must be perpendicular to a principal axis.

In molecules of very low symmetry the choice of principal axes may not be obvious. If the bond angles and distances are all known, the principal axes and principal moments can be computed by a systematic procedure.

ILLUSTRATION.   Determine the moments and products of inertia for a linear symmetrical molecule ABA, in a nonprincipal axis system and in the principal axis system.

Since the masses of the two A atoms are the same and they are at the same distance from B, the center of gravity, the origin of the coordinate system is also at B. In the first coordinate system, let the x axis make an angle of 30° with the molecular axis; assume that the A—B distance is 3, and the mass of A is 6.

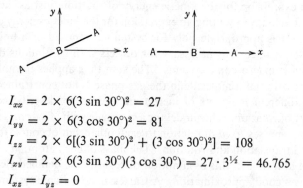

$$I_{xx} = 2 \times 6(3 \sin 30°)^2 = 27$$
$$I_{yy} = 2 \times 6(3 \cos 30°)^2 = 81$$
$$I_{zz} = 2 \times 6[(3 \sin 30°)^2 + (3 \cos 30°)^2] = 108$$
$$I_{xy} = 2 \times 6(3 \sin 30°)(3 \cos 30°) = 27 \cdot 3^{1/2} = 46.765$$
$$I_{xz} = I_{yz} = 0$$

If the molecule makes an angle of $0°$ with the x axis

$$I_{xx} = I_x = 2 \times 6(0)^2 = 0$$
$$I_y = 2 \times 6(3)^2 = 108$$
$$I_z = 108$$
$$I_{xy} = I_{xz} = I_{yz} = 0$$

Rotational Types.   The expression for rotational energy levels of a molecule and the selection rule governing its spectral transitions depend on the rotational type to which the molecule belongs.   The type is determined by relations between the magnitudes of the principal moments of inertia.

For linear molecules, the principal moment about the molecular axis is zero; the other two are nonzero and (necessarily) equal.   One has exactly the same energy expression and selection rules as for the diatomic molecule discussed in Chapter 4

$$\epsilon = \frac{h^2}{8\pi^2 I} J(J + 1) \tag{4.101}$$

$$\Delta J = +1 \text{ or } -1 \tag{4.202}$$

and the rotational quantum number, J, may have values $0, 1, 2, 3, \ldots$.   Because of the equality of the two nonzero principal moments the subscript may be dropped and the moment of inertia may be denoted by I.

For all other rotational types, there is no principal moment equal to zero.   An important type has two of the three moments equal; this is called a *symmetric top* or a *symmetric rotor*; examples are CH_3Cl, cyclopropane, and benzene.   The two equal principal moments are usually called I_B, and the other one I_A.   A molecule may be a symmetric top because of a coincidental combination of atomic masses and positions, but this is quite rare; an example is HCNO.   Usually, a molecule is a symmetric top because of the presence of various kinds of symmetry discussed in Sec. 15.5.   If there is a three-fold or higher rotation symmetry axis in the molecule, it must be a symmetric top; the axis of unique moment of inertia, I_A, must then coincide with the three-fold or higher rotation axis.   A symmetric top molecule may or may not possess a permanent dipole moment.   If the molecule has a mirror plane or a two-fold or higher axis perpendicular to the three-fold or higher rotation axis, it cannot have a dipole moment.   In the absence of such a mirror plane or axis, the molecule may have a dipole moment, but it is directed along the symmetry axis; that is, the molecular dipole has zero components along the other two axes.

Rotational energy levels of the symmetric top are given by the expression

$$\epsilon = \frac{h^2}{8\pi^2 I_B} J(J + 1) + K^2 \left(\frac{h^2}{8\pi^2 I_A} - \frac{h^2}{8\pi^2 I_B} \right) \tag{16.303}$$

The quantum number J may have the same values as before, and the quantum number K the integer values $-J, -J + 1, \ldots, +J$.   The selection rules, which are found by methods similar to those described in Sec. 16.2, depend on which principal axes have a nonvanishing dipole component.

If there is a dipole component parallel to the axis having moment of inertia I_A (three-fold or higher axis), the *parallel* selection rules apply

$$\Delta J = 0, \pm 1; \quad \Delta K = 0 \tag{16.304}$$

If there is a dipole component along either of the axes having moment of inertia I_B (which is impossible in molecules with a three-fold or higher symmetry axis), the *perpendicular* selection rules apply

$$\Delta J = 0, \pm 1; \quad \Delta K = \pm 1 \tag{16.305}$$

Some molecules have all three principal moments of inertia equal; these are called *spherical tops*; examples are CH_4 and SF_6. If there are two or more different rotation axes of three-fold or higher symmetry, the molecule must be a spherical top. But with such high symmetry, the molecular dipole moment must be zero; the selection rules forbid all rotational spectrum transitions.

Finally, there are molecules in which all three of the principal moments are different; these are called *asymmetric tops* or *asymmetric rotors*. It should be noted that asymmetric tops may have some symmetry; planes of reflection and two-fold rotation axes may be present and the molecule still not be a symmetric top. For asymmetric tops there is no general expression for the energy levels (which are related to all three moments of inertia); for each J value, $2J + 1$ distinct levels exist. Extensive numerical tables of these eigenvalues are available to aid in the analysis of rotational spectra of asymmetric rotor molecules. Even simple molecules such as H_2O and O_3 are asymmetric rotors. However, the complexity of the treatment is so great that we can make no further analysis of it.

Determination of Moments of Inertia from Rotational Spectra. The analysis of conventional rotational spectra for linear and symmetrical top molecules with three-fold or higher symmetry axes is done like that for diatomic molecules; see Sec. 4.2. Because of the selection rule $\Delta K = 0$ (parallel selection rules), the transition energies for the symmetrical top are, from Eq. 16.303,

$$\Delta E = \frac{2h^2}{8\pi^2 I_B}(J + 1) = h\nu \tag{16.306}$$

where we assume that I_A and I_B are the same in states J and $J + 1$. The spectrum then is a series of equally spaced lines, with spacing between adjacent lines of

$$\frac{1}{h}\Delta(h\nu) = \Delta\nu = \frac{2h}{8\pi^2 I_B} \tag{16.307}$$

This means that only one of the principal moments, I_B, can be obtained for most symmetric tops. In asymmetric tops, by contrast, it is frequently possible to obtain all three principal moments of inertia. The moments of inertia for most molecules are so large that observation of rotational spectra by means of conventional spectroscopic apparatus is extremely difficult. For this reason, such observations have been largely confined to molecules containing hydrogen or deuterium and one heavier atom, such as H_2O, NH_3, or HCl.

Microwave Spectra. A different experimental approach is also possible. Instead of a black-body source which radiates all frequencies, one may employ electronic tubes (Klystrons, etc.) which are capable of precise oscillations in the range of thousands of megacycles per second or roughly one wave number. Since the source emits only a very narrow range of frequencies, one can dispense with the conventional prism or grating and scan over the spectrum by tuning the source and thereby varying its frequency. This development also results in a very great resolving power.

The radiation emitted by these tubes is usually called microwave, because the wavelengths are in the range of a few millimeters to a few centimeters, which are small compared to conventional radio wavelengths. The term microwave spectroscopy is used for spectroscopic studies in this region. A diagram of a simple microwave spectrograph is shown in Fig. 16.301. The range of frequencies is very limited,

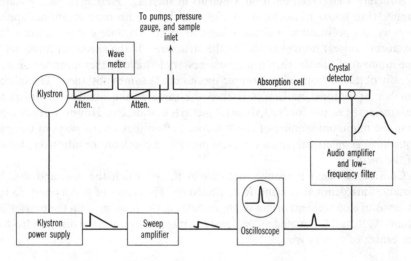

Fig. 16.301   Diagram of a simple microwave spectrograph. Auxiliary equipment is needed for precise determination of frequencies but is not shown in the diagram. (By permission from Gordy, Smith, and Trambarulo, *Microwave Spectroscopy*, John Wiley and Sons, 1953.)

in contrast to conventional spectroscopy, so that it is either inconvenient or even impossible to observe a series of rotational lines for linear molecules and symmetric tops from whose spacing the moment of inertia may be calculated. However, by studying the Stark effect, that is, the shifts and splittings of lines due to the application of a constant electric field, it is usually possible to determine unambiguously the J values of the states involved in a single transition.

In the absence of an electric field, the rotational energy levels of a linear molecule have degeneracy which becomes greater for the higher energy states; see Sec. 4.1. The degeneracy of the level with quantum number J is given by the expression $2J + 1$. A particular allowed rotational transition, such as $J = 4 \rightarrow 5$, is in reality an exact superposition of several different transitions. In the presence of an electric field, the degeneracy of rotational energy levels is partially removed. The appearance of the spectrum is thereby altered; absorption lines are shifted and split into a number of components. If the steady electric field is applied in the same direction as the oscillating electric field of the radiation, which must be polarized, the line corresponding to the $J \rightarrow J + 1$ transition is split into $J + 1$ separate lines. A further discussion of the Stark effect will be given at the end of this section.

For example, a microwave absorption is found at 24,325.92 megacycles sec^{-1} in carbonyl sulfide. Since a steady electric field causes this to spit into two absorption lines, it must be the $J = 1 \rightarrow 2$ transition. Other considerations show that the isotopic species $O^{16}C^{12}S^{32}$ is responsible for the absorption. Use of Eq. 16.306 shows that the moment of inertia for this transition is 1.37975×10^{-38} g cm^2. Note the high degree of precision available by this method.

Structure Determination from Moments of Inertia. *First Method.* Except for symmetrical linear triatomic molecules, which have no pure rotational spectrum anyway, all polyatomic molecules have at least two different parameters (bond distances, angles) needed to define the structure. If the spectrum furnishes only one moment of inertia, then it will be necessary to have further information; this is usually obtained from other isotopic species of the same substance. The minimum number of isotopic molecules is then the same as the number of independent parameters; i.e., two for N_2O, three for methyl chloride, etc. However, study of more than the minimum number of isotopic species furnishes several ways of computing equivalent geometrical parameters and provides a check on the internal consistency of the method.

Consider a linear triatomic molecule ABC, in which the A-B and B-C bond distances are denoted as r and R, respectively. The center of gravity may be found in terms of a convenient origin of coordinates at the A atom, with the masses of the atoms A, B, and C denoted m_1, m_2, and m_3, respectively, and the distance from A to the center of gravity is r_{cg}

$$r_{cg} = \frac{rm_2 + (r + R)m_3}{m_1 + m_2 + m_3} \tag{16.308}$$

where $m_1 + m_2 + m_3$ is M, the molecular mass. The moment of inertia (taken about the center of gravity) then becomes

$$I = m_1 \left[\frac{rm_2 + (r + R)m_3}{M} \right]^2 + m_2 \left[\frac{rm_2 + (r + R)m_3}{M} - r \right]^2$$

$$+ m_3 \left[R + r - \frac{rm_2 + (r + R)m_3}{M} \right]^2 \tag{16.309}$$

and, on simplifying,

$$I = r^2 \frac{m_1(m_2 + m_3)}{M} + 2rR \frac{m_1 m_3}{M} + R^2 \frac{m_3(m_1 + m_2)}{M} \tag{16.310}$$

We have eliminated explicit use of the center-of-gravity coordinates, and the moment is shown clearly as a function of the known atomic masses and the unknown bond distances. The units in this equation are not specified, and any consistent set will be correct. Rather than using cgs units, it is very convenient to use atomic weight units for mass and angstrom units for distance. Then, if the expression $h/8\pi^2 I$ is given in megacycles per second, it can be divided into 5.05531×10^5 in order to obtain I in atomic weight units $\times$ angstroms^2.

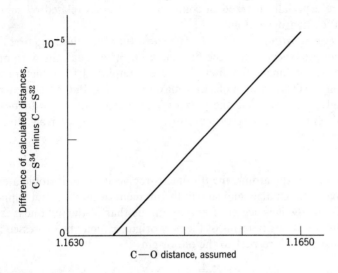

Fig. 16.302   Calculated values of the C—S distance for various assumed values of the C—O distance in carbonyl sulfide, $C^{12}O^{16}S^{32}$ and $C^{12}O^{16}S^{34}$. Note that not the individual C—S distances, but only their difference, has been plotted. This difference becomes zero at a C—S distance of 1.559216 Å, and a C—O distance of 1.16339 Å. For an assumed C—O distance of 1.1650 Å, the C—S distance calculated for the S^{32} isotope is 1.557909 Å.

ILLUSTRATION.   The molecules $O^{16}C^{12}S^{32}$ and $O^{16}C^{12}S^{34}$ have $h/8\pi^2 I$ of 6081.490 and 5932.816 megacycles sec^{-1}, respectively. Determine the C-O and C-S bond distances, given the atomic masses (on the O^{16} scale).

$$O^{16} = 16.00000, \quad C^{12} = 12.00382, \quad S^{32} = 31.98199, \quad S^{34} = 33.97890.$$

Placing the appropriate values in Eq. 16.310, we obtain for the S^{32} molecule,

$$83.12617 = 11.73232r^2 + 17.06110rR + 14.93050R^2$$

and for the S^{34} molecule, with r and R the C—O and C—S distances, respectively,

$$85.20928 = 11.86982r^2 + 17.54239rR + 15.35168R^2$$

An analytical solution could be given, but it is more illuminating to solve these two equations graphically. The value 1.1650 Å is assumed for the C—O distance, as well as several values close to this; the result for each equation is a curve which, for a very short distance, can be treated as a straight line. Since these two lines intersect at a very small angle, we show in Fig. 16.302 the difference between the two lines as a function of the assumed C—O distance. The intersection point occurs at C—O and C—S distances of 1.1634 and 1.5592 Å, respectively.

The use of other isotopic pairs of carbonyl sulfide molecules yields other values of the C—O and C—S distances, which differ slightly from those obtained using the S^{32} and S^{34} molecules. The reason for such differences is found in the slightly different magnitudes of zero-point energy for the various isotopic molecules; such differences are especially marked in comparing molecules related by substitution of deuterium for hydrogen atoms.

The Second or Substitution Method. The substitution method requires a greater number of isotopic species than the first method. The equations were originally derived by J. Kraitchman, but first extensively employed for structure work by C. C. Costain. All types of molecules may be treated, but we consider only a linear molecule oriented along the x axis. The masses and coordinates of the atoms in the center-of-gravity system are denoted m_i and x_i, respectively. The moment of inertia is

$$I = \sum m_i x_i^2 \qquad (16.311)$$

Suppose that one of the atoms, the jth one, is replaced by an isotopic atom. The center of gravity will change, and so will the moment of inertia. But suppose that the coordinate of the new center of gravity minus that of the old one is Δx; then the coordinates of atoms in terms of the new origin, x_i', may be expressed in terms of the coordinates with respect to the old origin

$$x_i' = x_i - \Delta x \qquad (16.312)$$

The new moment of inertia is

$$I' = \sum m_i(x_i')^2 = \sum m_i(x_i - \Delta x)^2 + \Delta m_j(x_j - \Delta x)^2 \qquad (16.313)$$

since the jth atom now has a mass $m_j + \Delta m_j$. Then

$$\Delta I = I' - I = \sum m_i x_i^2 - 2 \sum m_i x_i \Delta x$$
$$+ \sum m_i \Delta x^2 + \Delta m_j(x_j - \Delta x)^2 - \sum m_i x_i^2 \qquad (16.314)$$

But the old origin was at the center of gravity, so

$$\sum m_i x_i \equiv 0 \qquad (16.315)$$

Furthermore, the new center of gravity is found from

$$x_{cg}' = \frac{\sum m_i x_i + \Delta m_j x_j}{M + \Delta m_j} = \Delta x \qquad (16.316)$$

where $M = \sum m_i$, and Eq. 16.316 reduces to

$$x_{cg}' = \frac{\Delta m_j x_j}{M + \Delta m_j} \qquad (16.317)$$

Substituting this result in 16.314 gives

$$\Delta I = \frac{M \, \Delta m_j x_j^2}{M + \Delta m_j} \tag{16.318}$$

This expression makes it possible to compute the center-of-gravity coordinates of the jth atom, using the measured change in moment of inertia and the known change in mass. Applying the method to the previous data for carbonyl sulfide, we find that x_3 for the sulfur atom is 1.0382 Å. The $h/8\pi^2 I$ value for $O^{18}C^{12}S^{32}$ is found to be 5704.83 megacycles sec^{-1}; Eq. 16.318 then gives, using $m_1 = 18.0049$, $x_1 = 1.6820$ Å.

In principle, the coordinate of the carbon atom should be obtained by means of a substitution there, using C^{13} or C^{14}. However, atoms located near the center of gravity give quite small changes in moment of inertia, and a coordinate so calculated has rather large uncertainties. It is preferable to use the center-of-gravity equation, Eq. 16.315, to locate such atoms. In this way we find that $x_2 = 0.5241$ Å; the bond distances are then $r = 1.1579$ Å and $R = 1.5623$ Å.

The distances obtained are denoted r_s. The distances obtained from the first method are denoted r_0, to remind us that they are based upon the ground vibrational state. An analysis for diatomic molecules shows that the r_s distances are closer to the equilibrium distances, i.e., the distance at the minimum of the potential energy curve. For polyatomic molecules the r_s distances show considerably less scatter than the r_0 distances, when there are enough isotopic data to permit evaluation of distances by several distinct molecular combinations.

It should be noted that the number of different isotopic species required for asymmetric rotor molecules is usually less than the number of parameters to be determined, since two or even three of the principal moments may be independent and can often be obtained from spectra. In the water molecule, for example, there are two structural parameters, the bond distance and the HOH angle; but since two of the three moments of inertia are independent, only one isotopic form need be studied.

The Stark Effect. We have, in Sec. 16.1, treated the molecule in the presence of an electric field. The treatment was classical, and the resulting expressions applied to the measurement of molecular dipole moments. It is also possible to determine dipole moments by use of the Stark effect. The interpretation of such experiments requires the application of quantum mechanics, and we shall examine only the case of the linear molecule.

Consider a polar linear molecule in an electric field directed along the Z axis. The classical Hamiltonian contains the usual kinetic energy of rotation, but in addition a potential energy of orientation for the dipole in the field E_0, of the form $\mu_0 E_0 \cos \theta$ (Eq. 16.103). The strength of the field and the molecular moment are usually such as to make this term small compared to rotational energies. The total Hamiltonian operator, obtained as in Chapter 2, is the following

$$H = H_{\text{rot}} - \mu_0 E_0 \cos \theta \tag{16.319}$$

where we have indicated the operator for rotational kinetic energy merely by a symbol. In the absence of an electric field, the functions 3.220 (see also Sec. 4.1) are eigenfunctions of this operator, or

$$H_{\rm rot}\psi_i = \epsilon_i \psi_i \tag{16.320}$$

In the presence of an electric field, however, these functions are no longer eigenfunctions; that is, corresponding to Eq. 16.320 we have

$$H\psi_i = H_{\rm rot}\psi_i - \mu_0 E_0 \cos\theta\psi_i = \epsilon_i\psi_i - \mu_0 E_0 \cos\theta\psi_i$$

This kind of problem is frequently met in quantum mechanics. An actual system is described by a Hamiltonian which is almost, but not quite, that of an exactly soluble problem; the real system differs by a small "perturbation." There is a systematic way of obtaining the energies of the actual system, based on the known energies of the ideal system; this is called *perturbation theory*. The result we shall obtain is the same as that obtained by perturbation theory, though we shall use a variation method to obtain it.

If the second term of Eq. 16.319 is really small, as suggested above, an approximate wave function may be obtained by application of Eq. 4.105. Consider the lowest state, with $J = 0$; its wave function is just a constant. In the presence of an electric field, this function is "spoiled" from being an eigenfunction by a term proportional to $E_0 \cos\theta$. We guess, then, that a better approximate wave function for the lowest state might include the constant ψ_0 plus a small amount of the $J = 1$ eigenfunction $\cos\theta$, or ψ_1. Equation 4.105 then becomes, with δ a small quantity to be determined,

$$\epsilon = \frac{\int (\psi_0 + \delta\psi_1)(H_{\rm rot} - \mu_0 E_0 \cos\theta)(\psi_0 + \delta\psi_1) \sin\theta \, d\theta \, d\phi}{\int (\psi_0 + \delta\psi_1)(\psi_0 + \delta\psi_1) \sin\theta \, d\theta \, d\phi}$$

Expanding this expression and using the orthogonality of ψ_0 and ψ_1, the fact that ψ_0 and ψ_1 are eigenfunctions of $H_{\rm rot}$ and Eq. 16.208, we obtain

$$\epsilon = \frac{\int (\psi_0 + \delta\psi_1)(\epsilon_0\psi_0 + \delta\epsilon_1\psi_1 - \mu_0 E_0 \cos\theta\psi_0 - \mu_0 E_0 \cos\theta \, \delta\psi_1) \sin\theta \, d\theta \, d\phi}{1 + \delta^2}$$

$$= \frac{\epsilon_0 + \delta^2\epsilon_1 - 2\delta\mu_0 E_0 \int \psi_0 \cos\theta\psi_1 \sin\theta \, d\theta \, d\phi}{1 + \delta^2} \tag{16.321}$$

Now to find the best wave function (evaluate δ) we differentiate ϵ and set the derivative equal to zero

$$\frac{\partial\epsilon}{\partial\delta} = 0 = \frac{(1 + \delta^2)\left(-2\mu_0 E_0 \int \cdots + 2\delta\epsilon_1\right) - \left(\epsilon_0 - 2\delta\mu_0 E_0 \int \cdots + \delta^2\epsilon_1\right)2\delta}{(1 + \delta^2)^2}$$

$$\tag{16.322}$$

The integral in Eq. 16.321 has been abbreviated for convenience. If now δ is indeed small, terms containing δ^2 and higher powers may be neglected and the expression solved for δ

$$\delta = \frac{+\mu_0 E_0 \int \psi_0 \cos \theta \psi_1 \sin \theta \, d\theta \, d\phi}{\epsilon_1 - \epsilon_0} \tag{16.323}$$

Upon inserting the values of the functions $\psi_0 = (4\pi)^{-\frac{1}{2}}$, $\psi_1 = \left(\dfrac{3}{4\pi}\right)^{\frac{1}{2}} \cos \theta$, and integrating, we obtain $\delta = 3^{-\frac{1}{2}} \mu_0 E_0/(\epsilon_1 - \epsilon_0)$. The effect of the field is thus to mix one of the excited state $(J = 1)$ wave functions with the ground state function $(J = 0)$:

$$\psi = \psi_0 + 3^{-\frac{1}{2}} \frac{\mu_0 E_0}{\epsilon_1 - \epsilon_0} \psi_1 \tag{16.324}$$

The energy in the presence of the field will then be different from that in the absence of a field; Eq. 16.321 gives, with 16.324,

$$\epsilon = \epsilon_0 - \frac{1}{3} \frac{\mu_0^2 E_0^2}{\epsilon_1 - \epsilon_0} \tag{16.325}$$

The other states also become mixed because of the field, in somewhat similar fashion; the general results are shown in Fig. 16.303. The effect on the spectrum is sketched in Fig. 16.304, showing the $J = 0 \rightarrow 1$ and $1 \rightarrow 2$ transitions in the absence and in the presence of an electric field.

Another effect of this mixing is shown in the expectation value of the dipole moment component along the Z direction. From Eq. 16.204 we have

$$\bar{\mu}_Z = \int \psi_i \mu_0 \cos \theta \psi_i \, d\tau \tag{16.326}$$

In the absence of a field, this gives identically zero for each and every ψ_i. However, in the presence of a field the eigenfunctions become mixed; that is, for the lowest state $\psi = \psi_0 + \delta \psi_1$, the expectation value then becomes

$$\bar{\mu}_Z = \int (\psi_0 + \delta \psi_1) \mu_0 \cos \theta (\psi_0 + \delta \psi_1) \, d\tau$$

which yields

$$\bar{\mu}_Z = \frac{2\mu_0^2 E_0}{3(\epsilon_1 - \epsilon_0)} \tag{16.327}$$

That is, the mixing effect produces a slight polarization of the molecule in the lowest state. It is interesting that this polarization is found only for the lowest state; all higher states are mixed with two other states (i.e., $J = 1$ is mixed with both $J = 0$ and $J = 2$) in such a way that the polarization is still exactly zero. The total Z component of the dipole in 1 cc of a gas is then the component per molecule in the

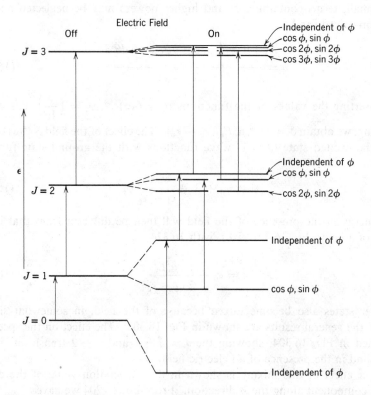

Fig. 16.303   Rotational energy-level diagram for polar diatomic molecule in the absence and the presence of a steady electric field. The scale of energy splittings is greatly enlarged for clarity. The transitions shown are for radiation polarized parallel to the steady electric field. The ϕ angular dependence of the states is also indicated.

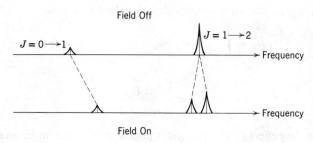

Fig. 16.304   The $J = 0 \rightarrow 1$ and $1 \rightarrow 2$ spectrum transitions of a polar diatomic molecule in the absence and the presence of a steady electric field. Polarizations are as in Fig. 16.303. Note that the splitting of $J = 1 \rightarrow 2$ is symmetrical neither in frequencies nor in intensities.

$J = 0$ state, multiplied by the number of molecules per cubic centimeter in the $J = 0$ state, or

$$\bar{\mu}_Z \frac{n_0}{\sum_i n_i} N' = \bar{\mu}_Z \frac{N'}{Z_{rot}}$$

$$= \frac{2\mu_0^2 E_0}{3\left(2\dfrac{h^2}{8\pi^2 I}\right)} \frac{N'}{\dfrac{8\pi^2 I k T}{h^2}}$$

$$= \frac{\mu_0^2 E_0}{3kT} N'$$

a result obtained in Sec. 16.1 by a classical method. The present derivation also shows how the dipole moment may be computed, when the classical rotational partition function is not a good approximation.

Problems

16.301   Write an expression for the moment of inertia of the acetylene molecule (linear, symmetrical) in terms of the C—C and C—H distances and atomic masses. Does it have a pure rotational spectrum?

16.302   Indicate the locations of the principal axes for the following molecules: (a) methyl chloride; (b) formaldehyde; (c) water; (d) benzene.

16.303   Which of the molecules in Problem 16.302 can have a pure rotational spectrum?

16.304   Consider the carbon skeleton of cyclopropane (equal C—C distances). Indicate the location of the principal axes; show that, if x and y are chosen in the plane of the molecule, I_{xy} is zero for any orientation with respect to the carbons.

*16.305   Compute the angle, in radians, at which the two lines described in Fig. 16.302 intersect. By what amount would the C—O distance change if the $h/8\pi^2 I$ value for the S^{34} isotopic molecule were to increase by 4 in the last digit? (This is probably close to the precision of the measurement.)

*16.306   The $h/8\pi^2 I$ values, in megacycles per second, for the three isotopic species of nitrous oxide, $N^{14}N^{14}O^{16}$, $N^{15}N^{14}O^{16}$, and $N^{14}N^{14}O^{18}$, are 12,561.66, 12,137.30, and 11,859.11, respectively. The atomic masses of N^{14} and N^{15} are 14.00751 and 15.00489, respectively. It may be advantageous to develop a simple expression for the change in moment of inertia, in terms of the change in $h/8\pi^2 I$. Determine the N—N and N—O distances by the second method.

16.307   Indicate the number of structural parameters for each of the following molecules, and the minimum number of isotopic species which would have to be studied to determine the structure: (a) formaldehyde; (b) NOCl (nonlinear); (c) methylene chloride, CH_2Cl_2; (d) NH_2Cl (nonplanar).

4.   Vibrational Spectra of Polyatomic Molecules

A molecule or ion composed of $\mathcal{N}$ atoms has $3\mathcal{N} - 6$ vibrational degrees of freedom (Sec. 4.3). If it is possible to determine all the corresponding vibrational frequencies, a statistical mechanical calculation may be carried out to predict the vibration contribution to various thermodynamic properties. An important part of the vibrational analysis requires the knowledge of the configuration (symmetry) of the molecule or ion; often this may be obtained from a study of the vibrational spectrum. In addition, a study of vibrational frequencies can lead to important information concerning molecular binding and suggest approximate values of vibrational frequencies for related molecules and for activated complexes.

Configuration Determination. In the earlier discussion of diatomic molecules, we noted that some have no vibrational spectra, whereas others do; the difference lies in the greater symmetry which causes homonuclear molecules to have a zero dipole moment even displaced from the equilibrium distance. We also noted that molecules which have vibrational spectra show transitions $\Delta v = 2, 3$, etc., which are forbidden in a strictly harmonic oscillator. Similar observations apply to poly-atomic molecules, with more variety.

All polyatomic molecules are found to show some vibrational transitions. If there is no symmetry, then all vibrations are allowed by selection rules. If the molecule has symmetry, some of the vibrations may be forbidden (and rigorously so) and/or also some of the vibrations may be doubly or triply degenerate. In a general way the higher the molecular symmetry, the more numerous are cases of forbidden bands and degeneracy. It may be noted that absence of symmetry is not always desirable; the spectrum may be confused by overlapping of closely spaced bands.

The energy levels for $3\mathcal{N} - 6$ vibrational degrees of freedom are characterized by $3\mathcal{N} - 6$ independent vibrational quantum numbers; these might be labeled $v_1, v_2, \ldots$, etc. We shall distinguish spectrum transitions called *fundamentals* which must satisfy two requirements. First, only one of these quantum numbers may change; second, the change is by plus or minus one. For absorption spectra of gases at ordinary temperatures, most molecules are in the ground vibrational state with all quantum numbers zero, and the final state of a fundamental transition has one of these quantum numbers equal to one, and all the others still zero. Spectrum transitions may also appear in which one quantum number changes by more than one (*overtone*) and in which several quantum numbers change (*combination*).

The proper discussion of configuration and much of the whole subject of vibrations in symmetrical molecules require the use of the mathematical theory of groups. We shall describe some applications to molecular spectra, but merely quote the results obtained by group theory.

Consider triatomic molecules of the type AB_2. There are four distinct symmetry types for their bonding. These are, together with the point-group symmetry designation, linear and symmetrical, B—A—B ($D_{\infty h}$); linear and unsymmetrical, A—B—B or B——A—B ($C_{\infty v}$); nonlinear and symmetrical, $B \diagup A \diagdown B$ (C_{2v}); and nonlinear and unsymmetrical, $A \diagup B \diagdown B$ or $A \diagup B \diagdown B$ (C_s). Symmetry, of course, says nothing about the values of bond distances and angles, and also nothing about the type and location of bonds; the nonlinear structures could be cyclic, and the same results would apply. In Table 16.401 are collected the group theory predictions for the vibrational spectrum in each symmetry classification.

There are, for $D_{\infty h}$, four vibrational degrees of freedom; the spectrum shows only two fundamentals for two reasons. First, one of the vibrations has $d\mu/dQ = 0$; second, two other vibrations are degenerate and occur exactly superimposed at the same frequency and thus appear as one band. The $C_{\infty v}$ type shows three fundamentals, even though it has four vibrational degrees of freedom, because of two

Table 16.401   Number of Allowed
Fundamentals in the Infrared
Spectra of AB_2 Molecules, Accord-
ing to Symmetry

Symmetry	Allowed Fundamentals
$D_{\infty h}$	2
$C_{\infty v}$	3
C_{2v}	3
C_s	3

vibrations which are degenerate. For both bent structures, C_{2v} and C_s, all vibrational fundamentals are allowed.

The symmetry designations used here are the kind usually employed by spectroscopists; compare Fig. 15.507, which shows 32 different symmetry characteristics, or point-group symmetries. The symmetries are labeled by both the spectroscopic (Schoenflies) and the crystallographic notations. The symbol C_{2v}, for instance, means that there is a two-fold rotation symmetry axis, and also vertical mirror planes (planes such that the two-fold axis lies in each plane). For C_s, the only symmetry element is the single mirror plane.

The symbols $D_{\infty h}$ and $C_{\infty v}$ do not appear in Fig. 15.507; they are not possible symmetries of a set of crystal lattice points. A single molecule has a greater variety of symmetry elements than a crystal lattice. For instance, $C_{\infty v}$ is symmetrical with respect to rotation by *any* angle about the C_∞ axis (here molecular axis); there are also vertical mirror planes. For $D_{\infty h}$, all symmetry operations of $C_{\infty v}$ are present, plus a *horizontal* mirror plane (perpendicular to the C_∞ axis) as well as two-fold rotation axes perpendicular to the C_∞ axis.

Table 16.402 shows the strong bands which are observed in the gas-phase spectra of carbon dioxide, sulfur dioxide, nitrous oxide, and water. Since CO_2 shows only two strong bands, its configuration is found to be linear and symmetrical; this conclusion is consistent with all other information, such as zero dipole moment. For the last three substances, all of which show three strong bands, we can thus far conclude only that they are not symmetrical linear molecules. More information is needed to prove that one is linear, and the other two are nonlinear. Note that the four molecules in Table 16.402 do not represent all four symmetry types in Table 16.401. Stable AB_2 triatomic molecules of C_s symmetry are surprisingly rare (except for isotopic derivatives).

Table 16.402   Strong Infrared Bands
of Some AB_2-Type Molecules

Molecule	Bands, cm^{-1}
CO_2	2349, 667
N_2O	2224, 1285, 589
SO_2	1361, 1151, 519
H_2O	3756, 3652, 1595

Table 16.403 shows the predictions for carbon tetrachloride, assuming a regular tetrahedral as opposed to a square coplanar symmetry; note that both these configurations have zero dipole moment. The spectrum of CCl_4 shows only two strong bands, at 310 and 797 cm^{-1}, indicating tetrahedral symmetry. This result

Table 16.403   Number of Allowed
Fundamentals for AB_4 Molecules
According to Symmetry

Symmetry	Allowed Fundamentals
Tetrahedral (T_d)	2
Square planar (D_{4h})	3

is, of course, no surprise, since chemists had evidence of it for many years based on the number of isomeric multiply substituted carbon compounds.

A bit of reflection suggests some pitfalls in this method. Suppose that two different vibrations fall very close together and appear as a single one, or that another is quite weak and escapes detection, or perhaps an overtone or combination is mistaken for a fundamental. A complete determination of all fundamental vibrations, coupled with a satisfactory explanation of the overtone and combination bands observed, would greatly strengthen a configuration determination and be useful in other ways. This often involves a complementary method of observation, the Raman spectrum; its discussion requires examination of the symmetry of molecular vibrations.

Symmetry of Fundamental Vibrations. Each of the fundamentals in a symmetrical molecule, according to group theory, must be of a definite symmetry type or symmetry *species*. The various symmetry types are distinguished by the symmetry which remains if the molecule is viewed at an instant when it is displaced from the equilibrium position.

To show the results of such group theory treatment, we have sketched in Fig. 16.401 some idealized vibrational displacements for the configurations assumed in the discussion of AB_2 molecules. The reader is cautioned against a literal interpretation; actual vibrational displacements in real molecules within each symmetry species may be combinations of those sketched. In fact, the group theory results may be applied to analysis of spectra with no reference to any such sketches;

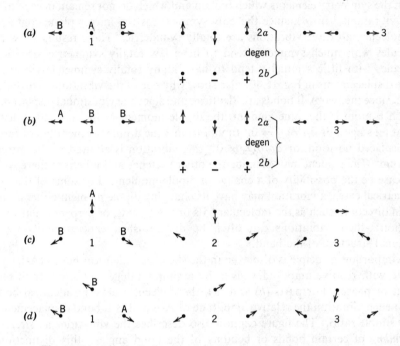

Fig. 16.401   Idealized vibrational displacements in AB_2 molecules.

(a) $D_{\infty h}$ symmetry: 1: in-phase stretching; 3: out-of-phase stretching; 2a and 2b: (degenerate) bending.

(b) $C_{\infty v}$ symmetry: 1: BB stretching; 3: AB stretching; 2a and 2b: (degenerate) bending.

(c) C_{2v} symmetry: 1: in-phase stretching; 3: out-of-phase stretching; 2: bending.

(d) C_s symmetry: 1: AB stretching; 2: BB stretching; 3: bending.

however, they are helpful in clarifying the existence or absence of dipole moment change with vibration (selection rules), and displaying the relations between displacements of identical bonds. All vibrational displacements must in general be of such relative magnitudes that neither translation nor rotation of the molecule is produced. The ratio of the displacement at atom A to that at atom B thus depends on the ratio of atomic masses.

Symmetry species and their vibrations are broadly classified as *totally symmetric* and *nontotally symmetric*; there may be several kinds of nontotally symmetric vibrations. Inspection of the sketches in Fig. 16.401 shows that the following vibrations are totally symmetric: 1 in (a); 1 and 3 in (b); 1 and 2 in (c); and all three in (d). The vibrations in each part have been numbered according to long-established custom in spectroscopy. In (a), vibration 3 destroys the mirror plane perpendicular to the axis of the molecule, though it retains the mirror planes which contain the axis; vibrations 2 (which are degenerate) have the opposite behavior with respect to these mirror planes. In (b), there is no mirror plane perpendicular to the molecular axis, so both 1 and 3 are totally symmetric. The student may obtain the symmetry elements which remain and which do not remain in each of the other vibrations. In (d), since the only symmetry is the mirror plane containing the molecule, all three vibrations are totally symmetric. These results show that molecules with much symmetry tend to have few totally symmetric vibrations; molecules with little symmetry tend to have many totally symmetric vibrations.

The displacements in Fig. 16.401 also show why one of the vibrations is forbidden in (a); since the two A-B bonds are identical, and since the vibrational displacement of each B atom is the same amount, the dipole moment of the molecule must be zero at all stages, or $\partial\mu/\partial Q_1 = 0$. In vibration 3 the dipole is generally not zero in the displaced position, or $\partial\mu/\partial Q_3 \neq 0$; this vibration is allowed in the infrared spectrum. The student may examine the other sketches and note that there will in each case be the possibility of a change in dipole moment. For some of the more symmetrical cases, a vibration may have its changing dipole moment either along a certain direction, such as the molecular axis or the C_2 axis, or perpendicular to this direction; these vibrations can often be distinguished experimentally by the rotational structure of the band.

An important principle is displayed in the sketches; identical bonds (A-B) must vibrate with relative amplitudes given by a simple integer ratio, either in phase or out of phase. For parts (b) and (d), the molecules have no identical bonds, and in each vibration the relative amplitude of A-B and B-B bond displacements is in no simple ratio. The figure caption also describes the vibrations as *stretching* or *bending* of certain bonds or bending of the bond angles; this distinction is rigorously true only where demanded by symmetry. In the linear molecules, the bending vibration is always in a different symmetry species from the stretching, so that there is no possibility of one fundamental vibration having both bending and stretching character. However, for 1 and 2 of (c), and for all three vibrations of (d), stretching and bending vibrations are in the same symmetry species and an actual vibration may then be a mixture of bending and stretching. Even so, the distinction between stretching and bending vibrations is usually approximately valid.

The Raman Spectrum. All the discussion so far in this section was concerned with infrared spectra. There is another way in which a molecule may interact with light, by a type of inelastic scattering. The light quantum may give up part of its energy to raise the molecule from one level to another, and be scattered with a lower frequency,

$$h\nu_0 = h\nu_{\text{molec}} + h\nu_{\text{sc}} \tag{16.401}$$

where ν_0 and ν_{sc} denote the frequencies of incident and scattered light; $h\nu_{\text{molec}}$ is a difference between certain molecular energies. This kind of inelastic scattering was first predicted by A. Smekal in 1923 and first observed experimentally by

C. V. Raman in 1928; the technique is usually referred to as the *Raman effect* or *Raman scattering*, as contrasted to Rayleigh scattering.

Rayleigh scattering itself is quite weak; Raman scattering is found for most conditions to be even substantially weaker. It is necessary to use a very intense light source for ν_0 and usually liquid-phase samples so as to concentrate many molecules into the scattering volume. Figure 16.402 shows the essential arrangement and a typical Raman spectrum obtained.

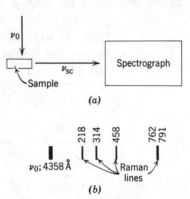

(a)

(b)

Some of the greatest utility of the Raman spectrum lies in the fact that it obeys different selection rules from the infrared spectrum, and for symmetrical molecules one can often find fundamentals in the Raman spectrum which are missing (forbidden) from the infrared. The selection rules for the Raman effect depend upon the molecular polarizability, in contrast to the selection rules for the infrared, which depend upon the dipole moment. A fundamental vibration is allowed in the Raman spectrum if the molecular polarizability changes during vibration. Since the polarizability is a tensor quantity, in contrast to the vector nature of the dipole moment, we shall not attempt a complete discussion of Raman selection rules.

Fig. 16.402 (*a*) Arrangement for observation of Raman spectra. (*b*) Raman spectrum of carbon tetrachloride; the wave-number shifts from the 4358 Å exciting line are also shown (by permission from Herzberg, *Spectra of Diatomic Molecules*, D. van Nostrand, 1950).

The selection rules always allow the totally symmetric fundamentals to appear in the Raman spectrum. For highly symmetrical molecules, the Raman spectrum thus furnishes vibrational frequencies that are absent from the infrared spectrum. For example, carbon dioxide is expected to show the in-phase stretching vibration, ν_1; however, selection rules forbid the appearance of ν_2 and ν_3 which are allowed in the infrared. The Raman spectrum of carbon dioxide actually shows two strong vibrations, at 1285 and 1388 cm^{-1}, which are absent from the infrared. Two, rather than one, Raman vibrations occur because an overtone of the bending vibration happens to fall close to a fundamental: $2\nu_2$ is close to ν_1. The wave functions of ν_1 and $2\nu_2$ then become extensively mixed, so that each of the observed lines is partially ν_1 and partially $2\nu_2$ in character. This explanation was first given by E. Fermi, and is called *Fermi resonance*. It also occurs in the spectra of many other substances; see the pair of lines at 762 and 791 cm^{-1} in CCl_4 (Fig. 16.402).

Vibrations, other than totally symmetric, may be allowed by the selection rules, but no general statements can be made. There is an experimental criterion which can be applied to distinguish between totally symmetric and nontotally symmetric fundamentals in the Raman spectrum, by a study of their polarization. This generally means using polarized light to excite the Raman spectrum, and determining the polarization of the Raman scattered light. The theory shows that all totally symmetric vibrations must give polarized Raman lines; those nontotally symmetric vibrations which occur give depolarized Raman lines.

The group theory predictions for numbers of infrared and Raman fundamentals for the four symmetry types of AB_2 are collected in Table 16.404 along with polarization predictions for Raman vibrations. It would appear that $C_{\infty v}$ and C_{2v}

Table 16.404   Numbers of Predicted Infrared and Raman Fundamentals for Various Configurations of AB_2 Molecules

Symmetry	Number of Infrared Fundamentals	Number and Polarization of Raman Fundamentals
$D_{\infty h}$	2	1 pol.
$C_{\infty v}$	3	2 pol., 1 depol.
C_{2v}	3	2 pol., 1 depol.
C_s	3	3 pol.

should give identical results and thus be indistinguishable; however, examination of Fig. 16.401 reveals that the depolarized Raman vibration is, for $C_{\infty v}$, a bending vibration; for C_{2v} it is a stretching vibration. Since stretching vibrations are usually found at higher frequencies than bending vibrations, a distinction between all four is possible on the basis of infrared and Raman data combined. Table 16.405 shows some infrared and Raman fundamentals for certain molecules, from which

Table 16.405   Strong Infrared and Raman Vibrations for Certain AB_2 Molecules

Molecule	Infrared	Raman
CO_2	667, 2349 cm^{-1}	1285* and 1388* (one vibr.)
N_2O	589, 1285, 2224	1285*, 2224
SO_2	518, 1151, 1362	524*†, 1151*, 1336†

* Polarized.
† Liquid phase.

the configuration may be determined. Examples of C_s symmetry in AB_2 molecules are rather rare; S_2O probably has this configuration, though it is quite unstable and therefore only infrared data seem to be available.

The Principle of Mutual Exclusion. The CO_2 molecule (Table 16.405) seems different from the others listed, since none of the fundamentals appears in both the infrared and the Raman. This is an example of the so-called *principle of mutual exclusion*, another result obtained by group theory: if a molecule has a center of symmetry ($\bar{1}$ or i), then the infrared and the Raman spectra will be mutually exclusive; if a vibration appears in the infrared, it must not appear in the Raman; if a vibration appears in the Raman, it must not appear in the infrared. Returning to the earlier example of carbon tetrachloride, we find (Fig. 16.402) that the Raman spectrum (liquid phase) shows strong vibrations at 218, 314, 458, and 791 cm^{-1}; since one (or more, here) of these is the same as an infrared vibration, the molecule cannot have a center of symmetry. This also rules out the square planar structure, as did the total number of strong infrared bands.

Mutual exclusion does not mean that all vibrations must appear either in the infrared or in the Raman; for some molecules with center of symmetry, there are vibrations forbidden to appear in either infrared or Raman. The twisting vibration of ethylene and one of the bending vibrations of sulfur hexafluoride are examples. Rough frequency values for such vibrations may sometimes be inferred from statistical calculation of thermodynamic properties and comparison with experimental

Table 16.406   Fundamental Vibrations (cm^{-1}) of Various $CX_n Y_{4-n}$ Molecules, with Approximate Descriptions*

CCl_4	218 (bend), 314 (bend), 458 (stretch), 791 (stretch)
$CHCl_3$	260 (CCl bend), 364 (CCl bend), 667 (CCl stretch), 760 (CCl stretch), 1205 (CH bend), 3033 (CH stretch)
CH_2Cl_2	283 (CCl bend), 704 (CCl stretch), 737 (CCl stretch), 899 (CH bend), 1155 (twist), 1266 (CH bend), 1429 (CH bend), 2984 (CH stretch), 3048 (CH stretch)
CH_3Cl	732 (CCl stretch), 1015 (CH bend), 1355 (CH bend), 1455 (CH bend), 2966 (CH stretch), 3042 (CH stretch)
CH_4	2914 (stretch), 1527 (bend), 3020 (stretch), 1306 (bend)

* By permission from G. Herzberg, *Infrared and Raman Spectra of Polyatomic Molecules*, D. van Nostrand Co., New York, 1945.

values, or from combination or overtone bands in which the forbidden band is allowed to participate according to symmetry selection rules; or as in the case of ethylene by an isotopic substitution of deuterium from some of the hydrogen, thus lowering the symmetry and relaxing the selection rules.

As a final example of the effect of symmetry on vibrational spectra, Fig. 16.403 presents the fundamental vibrations of the series of related molecules CCl_4, $CHCl_3$, CH_2Cl_2, CH_3Cl, CH_4. All contain five atoms and hence have nine vibrational degrees of freedom, but differ considerably with respect to symmetry. The numbers on the diagrams show the degeneracies of vibrations, and the letters i and R indicate whether the vibration is allowed in the infrared and/or Raman. The most symmetrical molecules, CCl_4 and CH_4, show only two fundamental infrared bands (representing, though, six degrees of freedom), while the least symmetrical, CH_2Cl_2, shows eight bands (each singly degenerate). Table 16.406 lists the various bands shown in Fig. 16.403, together with approximate descriptions in terms of stretching

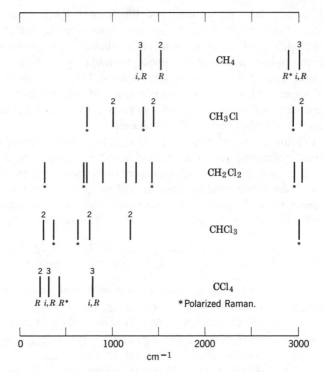

Fig. 16.403   Fundamental vibrations of CH_4 and its chlorine derivatives. Numbers indicate degeneracies; letters indicate which vibrations are allowed in the infrared and the Raman. All vibrations in CH_3Cl, CH_2Cl_2, and $CHCl_3$ are allowed in both infrared and Raman except that 1155 cm^{-1} is not allowed in the infrared for CH_2Cl_2.

and bending of various bonds. The number of stretching vibrations of a given type (e.g., CH stretching) is given by the total number of such bonds in the molecule. The description of other vibrations is often quite arbitrary; angle bending vibrations may involve changes in two or more different bond angles.

Rotational Selection Rules.   As in the vibrational spectra of diatomic molecules, gas-phase vibrational spectra of polyatomic molecules may show rotational structure. This structure is governed by rotational selection rules, which are essentially the same as for rotational spectra described in Sec. 16.3. The selection rules which are applicable depend on the rotational type of the molecule, and also on the direction in which the dipole moment oscillates with vibrational displacement.

For linear molecules, the dipole moment is required by symmetry to oscillate along the axis or perpendicular to it; the selection rules are called parallel and perpendicular, respectively. The parallel vibration selection rules are

$$\Delta J = +1 \quad \text{or} \quad -1$$

while for perpendicular vibrations they are

$$\Delta J = +1, 0, \quad \text{or} \quad -1$$

The parallel band of a linear molecule, since its selection rules are just like those of the diatomic molecule, appears just as the vibrational band of a diatomic molecule. The perpendicular band will have parts on either side of the center which are like those of the diatomic molecule, but in the center there will be a strong absorption due to the transitions $J = 1 \rightarrow 1, 2 \rightarrow 2$, etc., which (very nearly) coincide. Transitions which obey the selection rules $\Delta J = -1, 0$, and $+1$ are called P, Q, and R

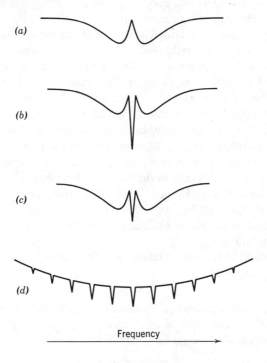

Fig. 16.404   Vibrational band contours in the gas phase: (*a*) linear molecule, parallel band; (*b*) linear molecule, perpendicular band; (*c*) symmetric top, parallel band; (*d*) symmetric top, perpendicular band. Absorption increases in the downward direction.

transitions, respectively; the entire set of P transitions which appear in a spectrum is called the P branch, and similarly the Q branch and R branch. If the P and/or R branch lines in a vibrational band can be resolved and their frequencies measured, an analysis may be carried out as indicated previously to determine the moment of inertia. This is particularly important in molecules which have no dipole moment (such as CO_2 and C_2H_2) since their pure rotational transitions cannot be measured by microwave spectroscopy.

Even if the P and R branches cannot be resolved, there is some useful information in the general shape or contour of a vibrational band as shown in Fig. 16.404. The presence or absence of a Q branch is easily discernible, and hence one can determine whether the vibration of the linear molecule is parallel or perpendicular.

For symmetric top molecules, the dipole moment is required in fundamentals to oscillate either parallel or perpendicular to the unique inertial axis. The parallel and perpendicular selection rules are just as for rotational transitions (Sec. 16.3). The parallel selection rules are the same as the perpendicular selection rules for the linear molecule and give a band of the same general appearance. The perpendicular selection rules are different; each possible K transition, such as $K = 0 \to 1, 1 \to 2$, or $-1 \to -2$, gives rise to a "sub-band" consisting of P, Q, and R branches; if the two distinct principal moments of inertia are quite different, the final result may be extensive overlapping in the P and R branches of the sub-bands, with only the Q branches discernible above a background absorption, as shown in Fig. 16.404.

One might think that the analysis of the perpendicular band should give an accurate value of the difference in reciprocal moments of inertia (Eq. 16.303). Unfortunately, the spacings of Q branches are also greatly affected by angular momentum originating in the vibration. This effect can be studied by analysis of such bands and is occasionally useful in the determination of force constants.

In the condensed phase; i.e., liquid, solution, and solid, most molecules are not free to rotate. As a result, there are no rotational branches as in the gas; vibrational transitions still occur, but usually in the liquid with a single absorption maximum and a small, but finite, width. In the solid phase, one frequently finds narrow bands with several absorption maxima; these have frequently been shown to arise either from coupling between vibrations of adjacent molecules or from reduced symmetry in the crystal environment.

Force Constants in Polyatomic Molecules.   The potential energy of a diatomic molecule was expressed by

$$V = \tfrac{1}{2}kr^2 \tag{2.107}$$

where r is the displacement from equilibrium bond length and k is the force constant. For a polyatomic molecule with several bonds, such as the bent unsymmetrical AB_2, an obvious extension would be

$$V = \tfrac{1}{2}(k_1 r_1^2 + k_2 r_2^2) \tag{16.402}$$

where subscripts 1 and 2 refer to the A-B and the B-B bonds, respectively. There is also a definite bond angle, so that another coordinate is needed to describe completely all possible internal displacements. This coordinate might be the A-B (nonbonded) distance, but the choice of the ABB angle instead turns out to be more convenient and according to the principles of directed valence.

The complete quadratic potential function must also contain cross terms, such as $r_1 r_2$, in addition to the square terms, with the final result, for bent unsymmetrical AB_2,

$$V = \tfrac{1}{2}(k_1 r_1^2 + k_2 r_2^2 + k_3 \alpha^2 + k_{12} r_1 r_2 + k_{13} r_1 \alpha + k_{23} r_2 \alpha) \tag{16.403}$$

where k_1, k_2, and k_3 are principal force constants, and the others are interaction force constants; α denotes the displacement from the equilibrium bond angle.

In the diatomic molecule, the frequency of vibration was related to the force constant by a simple equation in which the reduced mass also appeared. For polyatomic molecules, the vibration frequencies are related to the force constants and to some terms similar to reduced masses. These latter terms originate in the kinetic energy of vibration and can be calculated from the masses of the atoms, bond distances, and bond angles; all kinetic energy terms are uniquely determined once the structure has been deduced. From such kinetic energy terms, combined with the force constants according to a prescribed way, a determinantal equation is obtained; the solutions to this determinantal equation are the calculated vibration frequencies (or, more accurately, their squares). The opposite process, starting with experimental vibration frequencies and computing the force constants, is directly possible only in the smallest, highly symmetrical molecules. In most systems, the problem is to choose a set of force constants which yield calculated vibration frequencies in agreement with experiment. Even for such a small molecule as the nonlinear unsymmetrical AB_2 there is a quandary; the potential energy expression contains six unknown force constants, but there are only three experimental vibration frequencies. Many different combinations of force constants can give the correct numbers for the frequencies; which combination is correct? There is at present no completely satisfactory answer. Among the methods which have been used are the omission of all interaction constants; the inclusion of a limited number of interaction constants; the study of several related molecules and the transfer of force constants for the same or similar bonds and groups; the use of isotopic molecules; and the use of other physical measurements related to force constants.

The setting of all interaction constants equal to zero is rather drastic. In carbon dioxide, for example, this results in stretching force constants of the C-O bond having calculated values of 14.2 and 16.8×10^5 dynes cm^{-1} for different vibrations, a difference of almost 20 per cent. The inclusion of some interaction constants has been more successful; a rather good method utilizes the determination of relative values for interactions, based upon the reasonable idea of repulsion forces between nonbonded atoms. This method, called the Urey-Bradley force field, is often combined with transfer of force constants between similar molecules, though it must be remembered that a different molecular environment might cause changes in the force constant of a bond or group.

The use of isotopic derivatives is excellent, in principle. The mass factors in the equations are changed, but the force constants are not, when one or more atoms is replaced by a heavier or lighter isotope; this means that more experimental information is available. Some limitations are found in the existence of isotope equations which must be obeyed, whatever the actual values of force constants. One example is the *Teller-Redlich product rule*; as applied to the bent ABB molecule, it is of the form

$$\frac{\nu_1 \nu_2 \nu_3}{\nu_1^* \nu_2^* \nu_3^*} = \text{const} \tag{16.404}$$

where ν_1, ν_2, ν_3 and ν_1^*, ν_2^*, ν_3^* are the vibrational fundamental frequencies of two different isotopic species, and the constant has a definite value determined by the masses of the atoms and the moments of inertia (structure) of the molecule.

Another limitation is sometimes found in the rather small shifts in vibration frequency produced by substitution of isotopes of heavier atoms; this leads to rather large uncertainties in some of the force constants.

The force constants of a polyatomic molecule govern not only the vibration frequencies but also such properties as the angular momentum of a perpendicular vibration, the amplitudes of vibration, which in turn determine the widths of certain lines in the calculated results from electron diffraction investigations, and the amount of bending and stretching of the bonds and angles due to rotation (centrifugal distortion effects). These independent experimental observations have

Table 16.407   Some Force Constants for Simple Molecules,
× 10^{-5} dyne cm^{-1}*

Molecule	Force Constant				
	k_1	k_2	k_{12}	k_3/r^2	k_{13}/r
CO_2	15.5	15.5	2.6	0.57	...
CS_2	7.5	7.5	1.2	0.23	...
N_2O†	17.88	11.39	2.72	0.49	...
H_2O	8.43	8.43	−0.20	0.77	0.50

* By permission from E. B. Wilson, J. C. Decius, and P. C. Cross, *Molecular Vibrations*, McGraw-Hill Book Co., New York, 1955.
† NN bond = 1, NO = 2.

proved useful in determination of force constants in some molecules, though in some cases they seem to yield constants with substantial uncertainties.

For molecules with more symmetry, there will be a smaller total number of distinct force constants. If the AB_2 molecule is bent and symmetrical, the constants k_1 and k_2 in Eq. 16.403 must be equal, as must also k_{13} and k_{23}. This reduces the total number to four, and isotopic substitution may furnish enough information to permit the determination of all force constants. In the most symmetrical molecule, linear symmetrical AB_2, symmetry requirements also show that k_{13} must be zero; this leaves only three constants to be determined from three vibrational frequencies. The number of distinct force constants is equal to the number of vibration frequencies only for molecules in which each of the fundamental vibrations is of a different symmetry species.

A few force constants are listed in Table 16.407. These were obtained using interaction as well as principal force constants.

ILLUSTRATION. Determine the change in potential energy produced (a) by stretching both bonds in carbon dioxide by 0.1 Å; (b) by stretching one bond and simultaneously contracting the other by 0.1 Å; (c) by bending the bond angle through 5 degrees (bond length is 1.16 Å).

The appropriate constants from Table 16.407 are substituted into Eq. 16.403:

(a)
$$V = \tfrac{1}{2}[15.5(0.1 \times 10^{-8})^2 + 15.5(0.1 \times 10^{-8})^2$$
$$+ 2.6(0.1 \times 10^{-8})(0.1 \times 10^{-8})] \times 10^5$$
$$= 0.168 \times 10^{-11} \text{ erg}$$

if both bonds are stretched;

(b)
$$V = \tfrac{1}{2}[15.5(0.1 \times 10^{-8})^2 + 15.5(-0.1 \times 10^{-8})^2$$
$$+ 2.6(+0.1 \times 10^{-8})(-0.1 \times 10^{-8})] \times 10^5$$
$$= 0.142 \times 10^{-11} \text{ erg}$$

if one bond is stretched and the other is contracted;

(c)
$$V = \tfrac{1}{2}(0.57 \times 10^5)(1.16 \times 10^{-8})^2(5/57.3)^2$$
$$= 0.292 \times 10^{-13} \text{ erg}$$

if the bond angle is bent.

---

*Table 16.408   Characteristic Group Vibration Frequencies**

Group	Frequency, cm^{-1}
CH_3 (alkane)	2862–2882 and 2952–2972
CH_2 (alkane)	2843–2863 and 2916–2936
$C=CH_2$	3010–3040 and 3075–3095
$C=CH-C$	3010–3040
$C\equiv CH$	2100–2140 and about 3300
$O-H$	3590–3650†
$CH_2\overset{\displaystyle O}{\overset{\|}{C}}CH_2$	1705–1725
$CH=CH-\overset{\displaystyle O}{\overset{\|}{C}}-$	1665–1685
$Ph‡-\overset{\displaystyle O}{\overset{\|}{C}}-$	1680–1700
$CX‡-\overset{\displaystyle O}{\overset{\|}{C}}-$	1725–1745
$CX-\overset{\displaystyle O}{\overset{\|}{C}}-CX$	1745–1765

* According to L. J. Bellamy, *The Infrared Spectra of Complex Molecules*, Second Edition, Methuen and Co., London, 1958.

† Shifts to lower frequencies due to hydrogen bonding.

‡ Ph denotes aromatic group, X a halogen.

The preceding discussion of vibrational spectra has been theoretically oriented, with emphasis on such aspects as molecular symmetry, selection rules, and force constants. A more empirical approach is often very useful in structural work on unknown molecules, and also in qualitative organic analysis. The spectra of a series of known compounds, with a common group of atoms, often display frequencies common to all molecules. Table 16.408 lists a few of the correlations found this way; the vibrations are due to C—H or O—H stretching, and C=O stretching.

Problems

16.401   Deduce, by inspection of Fig. 16.401, the directions of dipole moment changes for the vibrations in (*a*), (*b*), and (*c*).

16.402   Some other observed vibrations in the following molecules are as listed. Assign these as overtones or combinations, and state the number of quanta of each fundamental involved. (Perfect agreement is not possible because of anharmonicity.)

> Nitrous oxide: 1168, 1867, 2462, 2563, 2798, 3481 cm^{-1}
> Carbon tetrachloride: 1006, 1107, 1575
> Sulfur dioxide: 2296, 1665, 3011, 1876, 3431, 1535

16.403   Describe and sketch the fundamental vibrations of acetylene, C_2H_2, linear and symmetrical, in terms of in-phase and out-of-phase stretching and bending. Indicate which vibrations should be polarized Raman, parallel infrared, and perpendicular infrared.

16.404   What is the change in potential energy in the water molecule when one bond stretches by 0.05 Å, the other bond contracts by 0.08 Å, and the angle changes by contracting 2°? The O-H bond distance is 0.96 Å.

5. Electronic States and Spectra of Diatomic Molecules

In this section we return to a consideration of the hydrogen molecule (Chapter 4), both according to the Heitler-London method and according to the molecular orbital method. We shall not pursue further the discussion of methods for obtaining highly accurate energies and other properties, but describe mainly extensions of the Heitler-London and molecular orbital methods to molecules with more electrons. We begin with a review and extension of the variation method discussed in Sec. 4.1.

The Secular Equation.   Consider a system for which the Hamiltonian operator is known, and consider two trial wave functions, ψ_1 and ψ_2, not necessarily solutions of the Schrödinger equation. The energy corresponding to each trial wave function alone can be computed by the expressions (see Eq. 4.105)

$$\epsilon_1 = \frac{\int \psi_1^* H \psi_1 \, d\tau}{\int \psi_1^* \psi_1 \, d\tau} ; \quad \epsilon_2 = \frac{\int \psi_2^* H \psi_2 \, d\tau}{\int \psi_2^* \psi_2 \, d\tau} \qquad (16.501)$$

It is also possible to write a combination of ψ_1 and ψ_2 as a trial wave function, $a\psi_1 + b\psi_2$. The energy for this function is

$$\epsilon = \frac{\int (a\psi_1 + b\psi_2)^* H (a\psi_1 + b\psi_2)\, d\tau}{\int (a\psi_1 + b\psi_2)^* (a\psi_1 + b\psi_2)\, d\tau} \tag{16.502}$$

According to the variation method, the energy of a trial wave function can never be lower than the true energy of the ground state; adjustment of the coefficients a and b is then tried, to find the values which give the lowest energy to Eq. 16.502. The minimum value of energy is found by taking partial derivatives with respect to a and b and setting them equal to zero; of course, this procedure may also locate energy maxima as well as minima. For brevity, we denote integrals by the following symbols

$$\int \psi_1^* H \psi_1\, d\tau = H_{11}, \quad \int \psi_1^* H \psi_2\, d\tau = H_{12}, \text{ etc.}$$

$$\int \psi_1^* \psi_1\, d\tau = S_{11}, \quad \int \psi_1^* \psi_2\, d\tau = S_{12}, \text{ etc.} \tag{16.503}$$

If the wave functions ψ_1, ψ_2, etc., were eigenfunctions of H, the integrals in Eq. 16.503 would reduce to very simple expressions. The integrals containing the Hamiltonian operator would either be zero, as H_{12}, or an allowed energy level, as $H_{11} = \epsilon_1$. The remaining integrals would be unity, as S_{11}, provided the functions were normalized, or else zero, as S_{12}, since eigenfunctions are orthogonal. Usually the ψ_i's are neither eigenfunctions nor orthogonal, so the integrals must be computed. The integral S_{12} is an *overlap integral*; one-electron overlap integrals are discussed further below. From Eqs. 16.502 and 16.503, and using the general relations that $H_{12} = H_{21}$, true for all Hamiltonian operators, and $S_{12} = S_{21}$, we have

$$\epsilon = \frac{a^2 H_{11} + 2ab H_{12} + b^2 H_{22}}{a^2 S_{11} + 2ab S_{12} + b^2 S_{22}} \tag{16.504}$$

$$\frac{\partial \epsilon}{\partial a} = \frac{2a H_{11} + 2b H_{12}}{a^2 S_{11} + 2ab S_{12} + b^2 S_{22}} - \frac{a^2 H_{11} + 2ab H_{12} + b^2 H_{22}}{(a^2 S_{11} + 2ab S_{12} + b^2 S_{22})^2}(2a S_{11} + 2b S_{12})$$

$$= \frac{2a(H_{11} - \epsilon S_{11}) + 2b(H_{12} - \epsilon S_{12})}{a^2 S_{11} + 2ab S_{12} + b^2 S_{22}} \tag{16.505}$$

If we set this equal to zero we have

$$0 = a(H_{11} - \epsilon S_{11}) + b(H_{12} - \epsilon S_{12}) \tag{16.506}$$

In similar fashion, from the derivative with respect to b we obtain

$$0 = a(H_{21} - \epsilon S_{12}) + b(H_{22} - \epsilon S_{22}) \tag{16.507}$$

These may be regarded as two simultaneous equations for the determination of the two quantities a and b. The equations can have nonzero solutions for a and b only if the determinant of the coefficients is zero

$$\begin{vmatrix} H_{11} - \epsilon S_{11} & H_{12} - \epsilon S_{12} \\ H_{21} - \epsilon S_{12} & H_{22} - \epsilon S_{22} \end{vmatrix} = 0 \qquad (16.508)$$

This equation, called the secular equation, is of great importance. Corresponding to the use of three, four, etc., functions ψ_i in the trial function, one obtains secular equations which have three, four, etc., rows. The nature of the functions ψ_i was not specified; for various choices different approximate treatments are obtained. We shall illustrate some of these in the following.

Two Approximation Methods.   The Heitler-London treatment of the hydrogen molecule was described briefly in Sec. 4.1. This is an example of the *valence bond* method applied to the simplest molecule; the method has also been applied to a great many other molecules. The other method which has been widely used is the *molecular orbital* method. Neither one gives very high accuracy, but both are useful in the correlation of experimental information and for the general understanding of chemical bonding which they afford. We are not examining the methods to see which one is "correct," for neither gives results in precise agreement with experiment.

A useful viewpoint, though not historical, is to compare the way in which each method groups the terms in the Hamiltonian operator for the hydrogen molecule, which is (see Eq. 4.103 and Fig. 4.102)

$$H = \mathcal{T}_1 + \mathcal{T}_2 + e^2 \left(-\frac{1}{r_{A1}} - \frac{1}{r_{B2}} - \frac{1}{r_{A2}} - \frac{1}{r_{B1}} + \frac{1}{r_{AB}} + \frac{1}{r_{12}} \right) \quad (16.509)$$

where $\mathcal{T}_1$ denotes the kinetic energy operator for electron 1, etc.

The Valence Bond Method.   The valence bond method, which for H_2 is the same as the Heitler-London method, may be viewed as arising from the grouping of terms in Eq. 16.509 as

$$H = \mathcal{T}_1 - \frac{e^2}{r_{A1}} + \mathcal{T}_2 - \frac{e^2}{r_{B2}} + e^2 \left(-\frac{1}{r_{A2}} - \frac{1}{r_{B1}} + \frac{1}{r_{AB}} + \frac{1}{r_{12}} \right)$$

or

$$H = H_{A1} + H_{B2} + e^2 \left(-\frac{1}{r_{A2}} - \frac{1}{r_{B1}} + \frac{1}{r_{AB}} + \frac{1}{r_{12}} \right)$$

$$= H_{A1} + H_{B2} + H' \qquad (16.510)$$

recognizing that the terms H_{A1} and H_{B2} are simply the Hamiltonian for the hydrogen atom with electron 1 on nucleus A, and that for the hydrogen atom with electron 2 on nucleus B, respectively. If the molecule dissociates into atoms in this way, then the last four terms will become zero. By methods of Sec. 3.1, since the Hamiltonian is just a sum of terms, the appropriate wave function is the product

$$\psi_1 = N e^{-r_{A1}/a_0} N e^{-r_{B2}/a_0} = \psi_A(1)\psi_B(2) \qquad (16.511)$$

where N is a normalizing constant. With a slightly different grouping of terms, the Hamiltonian may be written

$$H = H_{A2} + H_{B1} + e^2\left(-\frac{1}{r_{A1}} - \frac{1}{r_{B2}} + \frac{1}{r_{AB}} + \frac{1}{r_{12}}\right) \qquad (16.512)$$

Appropriate to this Hamiltonian at large interatomic distances is the function

$$\psi_2 = Ne^{-r_{A2}/a_0}Ne^{-r_{B1}/a_0} = \psi_A(2)\psi_B(1) \qquad (16.513)$$

Now the use of Eq. 16.501 makes it possible to compute the energy corresponding to either of these wave functions, which gives a result quite far from experimental molecular energy (see Sec. 4.1). For the wave functions given by Eqs. 16.511 and 16.513

$$H_{11} = H_{22}, \quad S_{11} = S_{22}$$

With these relations, Eqs. 16.506 and 16.507 yield

$$a = b, \quad \text{or} \quad a = -b$$

and the wave functions

$$\psi_{\text{sing}} = \psi_1 + \psi_2, \quad \psi_{\text{trip}} = \psi_1 - \psi_2$$

where ψ_{sing} and ψ_{trip} must be multiplied by singlet and triplet spin functions, respectively (see Sec. 3.4). The energies are found to be

$$\epsilon_{\text{sing}} = \frac{H_{11} + H_{12}}{1 + S_{12}}, \quad \epsilon_{\text{trip}} = \frac{H_{11} - H_{12}}{1 - S_{12}} \qquad (16.514)$$

Using the grouping of terms in Eq. 16.510, the result is

$$\epsilon_{\text{sing}} = 2\epsilon_H + \frac{J + K}{1 + S^2}; \quad \epsilon_{\text{trip}} = 2\epsilon_H + \frac{J - K}{1 - S^2} \qquad (16.515)$$

where ϵ_H is the energy of a hydrogen atom in its lowest state, S_{12} is replaced by S^2, and

$$J = \int \psi_A^*(1)\psi_B^*(2)H'\psi_A(1)\psi_B(2) \, d\tau$$

$$K = \int \psi_B^*(1)\psi_A^*(2)H'\psi_A(1)\psi_B(2) \, d\tau \qquad (16.516)$$

The quantities J and K are known as the *coulomb* and *exchange* integrals, respectively; S is the one-electron overlap integral

$$S = \int \psi_A^*(1)\psi_B(1) \, d\tau = \int \psi_A^*(2)\psi_B(2) \, d\tau$$

Of these three integrals, the overlap integral is the simplest to compute and the easiest to visualize. At any point in space, one forms the product of the value of the wave function (centered at the A nucleus) at the point, and the value of the wave function (centered at the B nucleus) at that point; such products are added through all space. In order to have a nonzero product at any point in space, the wave functions centered at *both* nuclei must have nonzero values there. If the atoms are very far apart, the products will be zero at all points, and the overlap integral will be zero. As the atoms approach each other, the overlap integral becomes nonzero and positive at distances of a few angstroms; its value is still less than 1 even at the bonding distance, using normalized functions ψ_i.

Both the coulomb and the exchange integrals are found to be negative. Therefore, the total (electronic) energy of the molecule with the ψ_S function is somewhat less than that of two isolated hydrogen atoms, $2\epsilon_H$ (the electronic energy remaining after dissociation of the molecule). The expression $(J + K)/(1 + S^2)$ then represents the magnitude of the bond dissociation energy of hydrogen, calculated by the Heitler-London method. In the triplet state, J and K appear with opposite sign, so the relative values must be known in order to determine the relative stability of the molecule. The magnitude of K exceeds that of J (though both are negative near the bond distance); very roughly, J is about 10 to 15 per cent of the magnitude of K. The triplet state then corresponds to an energy higher than that of two isolated hydrogen atoms. This is an unstable state which can have only transient existence.

The coulomb and exchange integrals are, in a general way, proportional to the overlap integral. That is, at distances (or for symmetry combinations) where the overlap integral is zero, the coulomb and exchange integrals are also zero; at distances such that the overlap integral is not zero, the coulomb and exchange integrals are not zero.

For this reason, the familiar statement is made about chemical bonding, "Orbitals must overlap appreciably in order to form chemical bonds." Of course, the overlapping itself does not produce bonding, but rather the favorable values of coulomb and exchange integrals give rise to a stable molecule for the singlet state with the two electrons of opposite spin. In the triplet state, overlapping of orbitals produces an unstable "molecule" which rapidly dissociates.

The basic idea that a pair of atoms may be bonded together by a pair of electrons with opposite spins occupying a pair of overlapping orbitals is also useful in other molecules. The electron pair bond was suggested by G. N. Lewis long before the Heitler-London treatment of hydrogen. Directed valence is also understood; the (approximate) 90° angles in H_2O and H_2S are due to the most favorable overlap and hence largest exchange integrals for such a configuration (coulomb energy is independent of angle). Since the bonds contain pairs of electrons with opposite spins, the total spin of a molecule with an even number of electrons should be zero, giving a singlet state.

One must not forget that all the previous discussion has been based on a certain choice of trial wave functions, in terms of which certain integrals arose. It is perhaps unfortunate that physical reality has been given to this mathematical device; frequent reference is seen to the "exchange phenomenon," "exchange energy," "electrons exchanging locations," etc. With a different set of trial wave functions, the integrals called coulomb and exchange might emerge in much different form, or not at all. As an illustration, we shall consider the molecular orbital method.

The Molecular Orbital Method.   Instead of grouping terms from the Hamiltonian for the hydrogen molecule (Eq. 16.509) as in Eq. 16.510 we choose to group them as follows

$$H = \left(\mathscr{T}_1 - \frac{e^2}{r_{A1}} - \frac{e^2}{r_{B1}} + \frac{e^2}{r_{AB}} \right) + \left(\mathscr{T}_2 - \frac{e^2}{r_{A2}} - \frac{e^2}{r_{B2}} + \frac{e^2}{r_{AB}} \right) - \frac{e^2}{r_{AB}} + \frac{e^2}{r_{12}}$$

$$(16.517)$$

The set of terms in the first set of parentheses represents only electron 1; it is interacting with positive charges on nuclei A and B, and there is also a coulomb repulsion of the two nuclei. This is just the model for a hydrogen molecule ion, H_2^+. We shall turn from the hydrogen molecule and consider solutions of the hydrogen molecule ion equation, also by the secular equation method. Now as trial functions to be used with H_{MO}, the Hamiltonian for H_2^+, the normalized hydrogen functions

$$\psi_A(1) = Ne^{-r_{A1}/a_0}, \quad \text{and} \quad \psi_B(1) = Ne^{-r_{B1}/a_0}$$

are appropriate.   The secular equation again gives us two combinations,

$$\psi_+ = \psi_A(1) + \psi_B(1), \quad \text{and} \quad \psi_- = \psi_A(1) - \psi_B(1) \qquad (16.518)$$

One of these, ψ_+, forms a stable bond (energy lower than that of a hydrogen atom and a proton separated to large distances), and the other leads to an "unstable bond." Of course, even the stable H_2^+ will readily combine with an electron to form H_2, but H_2^+ is found as a stable *ion* in an electric discharge through hydrogen gas.

The energies of H_2^+, according to the wave functions ψ_+ and ψ_-, are

$$\epsilon_+ = \frac{H_{AA} + H_{AB}}{1 + S}$$

$$(16.519)$$

$$\epsilon_- = \frac{H_{AA} - H_{AB}}{1 - S}$$

where $H_{AA} = \int \psi_A H_{MO} \psi_A \, d\tau$, a coulomb integral (though different from 16.516), and $H_{AB} = \int \psi_A H_{MO} \psi_B \, d\tau$, a *resonance* integral. The resonance integral is negative, so the ϵ_+ state corresponds to a stable bond, the ϵ_- state to an unstable "bond."

Numerical values for the bond distance and bond dissociation energy calculated by this method are 1.32 Å and 1.76 ev respectively. Experimental values, obtained from spectroscopic measurements, are 1.06 Å and 2.79 ev. The accuracy of the simple wave function is not very great, but it does at least account for the major part of the bond energy.

In similar fashion, the terms in the second set of parentheses of Eq. 16.517 give the stable wave function $\psi_A(2) + \psi_B(2)$. Returning to the problem of the hydrogen molecule, and recalling the ideas of Sec. 3.1, an appropriate wave function for the molecule might be

$$\psi_{MO} = [\psi_A(1) + \psi_B(1)][\psi_A(2) + \psi_B(2)] \qquad (16.520)$$

Now the molecular energy may be computed without the aid of a secular equation, since the terms in the first parentheses of Eq. 16.517 are independent of coordinates of electron 2, and similarly for the second parentheses. The bond energy, according to this approach, is 2.68 ev, at the distance 0.85 Å. While this does not agree too well with experiment (Table 16.501) it indicates bonding. But notice that there was never any mention in this treatment of an exchange integral, exchange energy, or exchange phenomenon.

Comparison of Valence Bond and Molecular Orbital Methods. The relationship of the molecular orbital wave function to that of the valence bond method may be seen by expanding Eq. 16.520

$$\psi_{\text{MO}} = \psi_A(1)\psi_B(2) + \psi_A(2)\psi_B(1) + \psi_A(1)\psi_A(2) + \psi_B(1)\psi_B(2)$$

We have written the terms in such an order that the first two are just the total Heitler-London valence bond function. The two remaining terms are referred to as

*Table 16.501   Comparison of Some Calculated and Observed Quantities in the Hydrogen Molecule**

Calculation Type	Energy, ev	Distance, Å
Valence bond (Heitler-London)	3.14	0.87
Valence bond with variable exponent coefficient	3.76	0.74
Valence bond with variable exponent coefficient plus ionic	4.00	0.75
Molecular orbital	2.68	0.85
Molecular orbital with variable exponent coefficient	3.47	0.73
Experiment	4.72	0.74

* By permission, according to C. A. Coulson, *Valence*, Oxford University Press, London, 1952.

ionic: the $\psi_A(1)\psi_A(2)$ term, for instance, represents a spherically symmetrical distribution of electrons around nucleus A; the third and fourth terms are said to "represent" the structures $H_A^- H_B^+$ and $H_A^+ H_B^-$, respectively.

The difficulty with the molecular orbital method is, then, that each of the ionic functions $\psi_A(1)\psi_A(2)$ and $\psi_B(1)\psi_B(2)$ is included with weight equal to that of each of the parts of the Heitler-London function. A better procedure is to take the valence bond function, include the ionic functions with an adjustable coefficient q and choose the coefficient so as to minimize the energy.

$$\psi_{\text{VB + ionic}} = \psi_A(1)\psi_B(2) + \psi_A(2)\psi_B(1) + q[\psi_A(1)\psi_A(2) + \psi_B(1)\psi_B(2)]   \quad (16.521)$$

Upon doing this, a better value is obtained. Table 16.501 summarizes some of the values obtained in the various calculations described, along with the experimental value. The entries in Table 16.501 "with variable exponent coefficient" describe calculations in which the wave functions were of the form $e^{-\alpha r/a_0}$, with the parameter α adjusted to give the best energy. For the valence bond type of calculation, the optimum value of α was found to be 1.166. In the hydrogen atom α is of course 1; thus the electron distribution about the atoms is somewhat contracted when they combine to form a molecule, according to this approximation.

The molecular orbital method may also be improved by considering another possible way of assigning the two electrons among the two molecular orbitals. If both electrons are placed in the ψ_- orbital, Eq. 16.518, then the wave function may be expanded to yield:

$$\psi'_{MO} = \psi_A(1)\psi_A(2) + \psi_B(1)\psi_B(2) - \psi_A(1)\psi_B(2) - \psi_A(2)\psi_B(1) \quad (16.522)$$

Now this function and ψ_{MO} (Eq. 16.520) may be mixed, with adjustable coefficients, and the minimum energy calculated.

$$\psi_{MO+CI} = a\psi_{MO} + b\psi'_{MO} \quad (16.523)$$

Comparison of this sum, called *molecular orbital with configuration interaction*, with the valence bond plus ionic function (Eq. 16.521) shows that they are identical.

The extension of such treatments to diatomic molecules with more than two electrons is a formidable task, though some progress is being made. However, the concept of increased stability by inclusion of ionic structures along with covalent has been very fruitful in correlating a large number of thermochemical data. The outlines of such a treatment will now be described.

Electronegativities and Bond Energies. We have noted, in Table 16.501, that a calculation which includes ionic structures along with the valence bond (or covalent) structure yields an energy for the hydrogen molecule in better agreement with experiment than the calculation which omits ionic structures. Such mixing of ionic and covalent structures should also be important in other molecules, especially those in which two unlike atoms are bonded and have different attraction for electrons. L. Pauling has shown how such ionic-covalent resonance may be treated, using bond energies in a simple expression.

Consider the gaseous diatomic molecules A_2, B_2, and AB; denote their experimental single bond dissociation energies D_{A_2}, D_{B_2}, and D_{AB}, respectively. The bonds A-A and B-B are assumed to be essentially covalent. If the A-B bond were also essentially covalent, Pauling assumed its energy would be given by the average (arithmetic mean) of the A-A and B-B bond energies. For some molecules AB this average is quite close to the experimental energy; for others, the magnitude of the average is less than the observed A-B bond energy. The difference was ascribed to ionic-covalent resonance. It was found that the differences could be correlated rather well by the expression

$$D_{AB} - \tfrac{1}{2}(D_{A_2} + D_{B_2}) = (x_A - x_B)^2 \quad (16.524)$$

where x_A and x_B denote the *electronegativities* of the atoms A and B, respectively.

It is not really necessary that all or any of A_2, B_2, and AB actually be diatomic molecules; Eq. 16.524 may also be applied to the energies of single bonds, which may be obtained from a study of polyatomic molecules (Table 9.203).

Equation 16.524 does not establish an absolute electronegativity scale, but only a relative one. The arbitrary choice of an electronegativity value for one element, however, then makes it possible to list unique electronegativities for the various elements. In early work, hydrogen was assigned the value $x_H = 0$; more recently, $x_H = 2.1$ (see Table 16.502).

Table 16.502   Electronegativity Values for Some Elements* ($ev^{1/2}$)

H 2.1	Si 1.8	As 2.0
C 2.5	P 2.1	
N 3.0	S 2.5	Se 2.4
O 3.5	Cl 3.0	Br 2.8
F 4.0	Ge 1.8	I 2.5

* By permission according to L. Pauling, *The Nature of the Chemical Bond*, Third Edition, Cornell University Press, Ithaca, N.Y., 1960.

Other methods of obtaining an estimate of the covalent AB bond energy have been used; the geometric mean, rather than arithmetic mean, is found to be more widely applicable and has better theoretical basis than the arithmetic mean. However, the left-hand side of Eq. 16.524 is simply the thermochemical heat of formation, provided the substances A_2, B_2, and AB are all diatomic gases; such simplification is not possible when using the geometric mean.

The Molecular Orbital Method for Homonuclear Diatomic Molecules.   Although a thorough and quantitative discussion of the molecular orbital method is not appropriate here, it is possible to give a qualitative indication of relative energy levels and electron configurations, reminiscent of the earlier discussion (Chapter 3) of atoms in the periodic table. This method also encompasses the configurations of excited states and is convenient for a discussion of selection rules and electronic transitions.

The molecular orbitals for H_2^+ were formed from combinations of the $1s$ atomic hydrogen orbitals (Eq. 16.518). One can also form molecular orbitals by combinations of $2s$, $2p$, $3s$, etc., atomic hydrogen wave functions; these will, of course, correspond to the various excited electronic states of the ion H_2^+. However, if the nuclei are not hydrogen but have greater charge, more than two electrons are present in a neutral molecule. Molecular orbital states formed by combinations of $2s$, $2p$, $3s$, etc., atomic functions (not limited to hydrogen atom functions) are then necessary, since the Pauli exclusion principle limits any molecular orbital to a maximum of two electrons. Some early calculations on excited states of H_2^+, and also some more recent calculations on first-row diatomic molecules, give relative energies for the various molecular orbitals. These energy levels are confirmed by study of the electronic spectra of such diatomic molecules.

Figure 16.501 shows the molecular orbital energy levels for homonuclear diatomic molecules; use of this figure is very similar to that of Fig. 3.301 for atoms. The ground electronic state of a particular molecule is obtained by successively filling

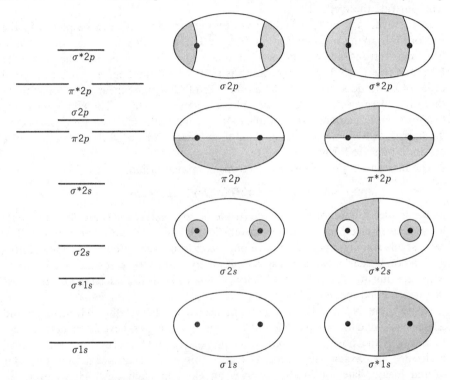

Fig. 16.501   Energy levels for molecular orbitals of homo- nuclear diatomic molecules (schematic).

Fig. 16.502   Diagrams of molecular orbitals for homo- nuclear diatomic molecules, showing symmetry properties (schematic). Shading represents regions in which the orbital is negative; clear regions are those in which the orbital is positive.

the lowest-energy molecular orbitals with pairs of electrons (Pauli exclusion prin- ciple) until all electrons are used. For degenerate orbitals, electrons are inserted one at a time rather than placing two in one degenerate orbital and none in its partner. Since such single electrons do not need to have opposed spins, various multiplicities may result; the state of maximum spin multiplicity, as in atoms, is found to have the lowest energy.

Figure 16.502 shows the symmetry properties of these molecular orbitals. There are several notations for the various orbitals; the one used here suggests the type of atomic orbitals which might be combined to form the molecular orbital. A molecular orbital is said to be *bonding* if it aids in formation of a stable molecule (the orbital energy decreases as the two atoms are brought together from a large distance); it is said to be *antibonding* if otherwise. Antibonding orbitals are indicated by an asterisk; bonding orbitals have none. To estimate bond order, the total number of antibonding electrons is subtracted from the number of bonding electrons; one-half the difference is the predicted *bond order*. Some examples will illustrate the method.

In the hydrogen molecule, there are two electrons; both can be placed in the $\sigma 1s$ orbital, giving a configuration $(\sigma 1s)^2$. There are two bonding and no antibonding electrons, and a bond order of one (single bond). Consider the possibility of a molecule He_2. The configuration is $(\sigma 1s)^2(\sigma^* 1s)^2$ and corresponds to a bond order of zero; no such molecule has ever been found experimentally. But suppose that only three electrons were available, as in the ion He_2^+. The configuration is $(\sigma 1s)^2(\sigma^* 1s)$ with a bond order of one half. Such a stable species is found in electric discharges in helium gas; when He_2^+ combines with an electron two separate helium atoms are formed.

The molecule N_2 has fourteen electrons, a configuration

$$(\sigma 1s)^2(\sigma^* 1s)^2(\sigma 2s)^2(\sigma^* 2s)^2(\pi 2p)^4(\sigma 2p)^2$$

and a predicted bond order of three (triple bond). Oxygen is somewhat different; it has sixteen electrons, a number insufficient to fill both the $\pi^* 2p$ orbitals. The most stable state is expected to have one electron in each of the $\pi^* 2p$ orbitals; this gives a bond order of two and a spin multiplicity of three (triplet state) in agreement with experiment. The spin multiplicity is more difficult to understand on the basis of valence bond methods.

Positive ions N_2^+ and O_2^+ are found in electric discharges through nitrogen and oxygen gas, and their experimental dissociation energies have been determined. In nitrogen the positive ion has a smaller dissociation energy than the neutral molecule; in oxygen the reverse is true. This is in accord with the molecular orbital ideas. The ionization removes an electron from the highest level: in nitrogen it is a bonding electron; in oxygen, an antibonding electron.

As an indication of the variation in scale appropriate to Fig. 16.501 for different molecules, Table 16.503 (taken from J. C. Slater) presents some calculated energies of molecular orbitals. In earlier work, it was assumed that the $\sigma 2p$ orbital was lower in energy than the $\pi 2p$ orbital; these calculated results and more recent experimental spectra suggest that usually the $\pi 2p$ orbital is the lower. One such experimental result is the finding that carbon has a singlet ground state and not a triplet; however, there is a triplet state which lies only 0.076 electron volt (or 1740 cal mole^{-1}) higher in energy. It is interesting to note that the first calculation for nitrogen predicts that $\pi 2p$ is lower; the second says that $\sigma 2p$ is lower. Experiment gives a lower value for $\pi 2p$. This comparison does not necessarily mean the first calculation is the better; the total computed molecular energy by the second calculation is closer to experiment.

Electronic Selection Rules in Homonuclear Molecules.   The selection rules for electronic transitions are based on the transition moment integral of Eq. 16.205

$$\int \psi_0^* \mu \psi_f \, d\tau = \int \psi_{e0}^* \psi_{v0}^* \mu \psi_{ef} \psi_{vf} \, d\tau \qquad (16.525)$$

where the Born-Oppenheimer approximation (Sec. 4.1) has been used to factor the total wave function into an electronic and a vibrational part; the rotational wave

Table 16.503   Calculated Energies (in Rydbergs; see p. 76) of One-Electron Molecular Orbitals for Some Diatomic Molecules *

Molecule	$\sigma 1s$	$\sigma^* 1s$	$\sigma 2s$	$\sigma^* 2s$	$\pi 2p$	$\sigma 2p$	$\pi^* 2p$
Li_2	−4.88	−4.88	−0.36	0.06	. . .	. . .	. . .
B_2	−15.35	−15.35	−1.36	−0.70	−0.68	0.02	. . .
C_2	−22.68	−22.67	−2.06	−0.97	−0.84	−0.04	0.53
N_2	−31.44	−31.44	−2.90	−1.46	−1.16	−1.09	0.55
N_2†	−31.29	−31.29	−2.84	−1.43	−1.09	−1.11	0.60
O_2	−41.19	−41.19	−3.04	−1.96	−1.10	−1.11	−0.79

* By permission, according to J. C. Slater, *Quantum Theory of Molecules and Solids*, Vol. 1, McGraw-Hill Book Co., New York, 1963.

† Different calculation, using slightly different atomic orbitals.

function does not appear, since we are considering only the molecule-fixed coordinate system.   The dipole moment operator is denoted μ and now in contrast to the vibrational selection rules (infrared spectra) contains the instantaneous positions of electrons.   The x-component, for instance, with an arbitrary origin for the coordinate system is given by

$$\mu_x = Zex_j + Zex_k - e \sum_{i=1}^{n} x_i \qquad (16.526)$$

where e denotes the electronic charge, x_i the x coordinate of the ith electron, x_j and x_k the x coordinates of the two nuclei with charges $+Ze$.   Similar expressions hold for the y and z components of the dipole moment operator.   If the midpoint of the bond is chosen as the origin of coordinates, the nuclear terms will cancel each other and leave only the electron terms.   Since the operator then contains no explicit vibrational coordinate, Eq. 16.525 may be written

$$\int \psi_0^* \mu_x \psi_f \, d\tau = \left[-e \int \psi_{e0}^* \left(\sum_i x_i \right) \psi_{ef} \, d\tau_e \right] \left[\int \psi_{v0}^* \psi_{vf} \, d\tau_v \right] \qquad (16.527)$$

If a certain transition is to have nonzero intensity, both integrals on the right-hand side must be nonzero.   Consideration of the second integral will be postponed; all electronic functions and coordinates are contained in the first integral.   If we assume the individual molecular orbitals of excited states are the same as those of the ground state, the simplest possible transition would be that in which all but one of the electrons remains in the same molecular orbital, and only one electron changes. For a homonuclear molecule, the electrons remaining in the same orbitals contribute nothing to Eq. 16.527; only the integration over the electron which changes can contribute anything. This is so since the unchanging electron integrations simply give the average x coordinate of each electron, which is the midpoint of the bond and hence zero.

Consider the hydrogen molecule. According to the molecular orbital approximation, the ground state has both electrons in the $\sigma 1s$ orbital. A possible excited state might be $\sigma 1s\sigma*1s$; if the wave functions are written out

$$\psi_{\text{ground}} = [\psi_A(1) + \psi_B(1)][\psi_A(2) + \psi_B(2)]$$

and

$$\psi_{\text{excited}} = [\psi_A(1) + \psi_B(1)][\psi_A(2) - \psi_B(2)]$$

we see that only electron 2 need be treated. It can be shown that, if we choose the molecular axis as the x axis, the x component gives a nonvanishing integral, since the product $x_2[\psi_A(2) - \psi_B(2)]$ is positive for both positive and negative x_2 values; this is multiplied by $[\psi_A(2) + \psi_B(2)]^*$, which is positive everywhere and hence the integral is positive. The transition is said to be allowed. The transition to $\sigma 1s\sigma 2s$ is found to be forbidden; examination shows that the x, y, and z components each gives zero since the integral contains an equal positive and negative contribution. A transition such as $(\sigma 1s)^2 \rightarrow \sigma 1s\pi 2p$ is allowed, though for a component perpendicular to the axis of the molecule, rather than parallel to it. Just as in vibrational bands of linear molecules, electronic transitions with components parallel and perpendicular to the molecular axis may be distinguished by the absence or the presence of a Q branch, respectively, in the rotational structure.

The second integral of Eq. 16.527 is called the *vibrational overlap* integral; note that it is *not* the orthogonality integral, since ψ_{v0} and ψ_{vf} belong to different electronic states. Within a certain allowed electronic transition, the vibrational overlap integral determines which of the many possible vibrational transitions are strong, and which are weak. This leads to the Franck-Condon principle discussed below.

Electronic Spectra of Diatomic Molecules. For diatomic molecules almost all electronic transitions are found in the visible and ultraviolet regions of the spectrum. If the transition can be observed in both absorption and emission, the analysis is considerably simplified; this is most convenient for transitions in which one of the levels involved is the ground electronic state.

Experimental electronic spectra reveal a profusion of lines, as shown in Fig. 16.503. Both upper and lower electronic states may have vibrational energy levels; and, frequently accompanying the electronic transition, transitions are observed between many different pairs of vibrational levels, with intensities governed by the overlap integral in Eq. 16.527. Furthermore, each such vibrational-electronic transition is accompanied by rotational structure (P, R, and sometimes Q branch). The maximum complexity is rarely reached, even in an emission spectrum, because of limitations imposed by the vibrational overlap integral.

Figure 16.504 shows schematically two different electronic states and several vibrational levels in each electronic state. For sufficiently large values of the vibrational quantum number v, the vibrational wave functions are characterized by short ranges of r for which the magnitudes of $\psi(r)$ are large. If the regions of large magnitude in two vibrational wave functions (belonging to two different electronic states) occur in the same range of r, the overlap integral may be large; otherwise it is small. If v is not too small, the large magnitude of $\psi(r)$ is usually found close to

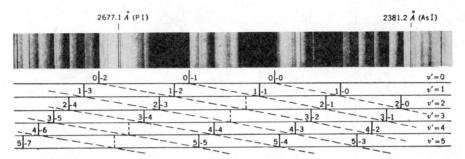

Fig. 16.503   Part of the emission spectrum of the PN molecule. The pairs of numbers below the spectrum indicate the vibrational quantum numbers in the upper and the lower electronic states, respectively. (The prime always indicates the upper of two states.) (By permission from G. Herzberg, *Spectra of Diatomic Molecules*, D. van Nostrand, 1950.)

the classical turning points, or values of r for which the vibrational energy equals the classical potential energy. The probability of a vibrational transition (accompanying the electronic transition) is thus much greater if the final vibrational state has a classical turning point at essentially the same r value as a classical turning point in the initial state; this is a form of the *Franck-Condon principle*. If one or both vibrational quantum numbers is small, the vibrational overlap integrals must be examined.

An example of the Franck-Condon principle is found in the emission spectrum of PN, shown in Fig. 16.503. Transitions such as $v = 2$ in the upper electronic state to $v = 2$ in the lower electronic state, and also $v = 3$ to 3, 4 to 5, and 5 to 6 are exceedingly weak because of the small magnitude of the corresponding overlap integrals.

Continuous and Diffuse Spectra.   Figure 16.504 also suggests another possibility. If the Franck-Condon transition corresponds to a final state above the energy of dissociation in one of the electronic states the molecule dissociates. Since the levels are continuous above the dissociation limit, the spectrum is also continuous. The beginning of such a continuous region, in absorption, often furnishes an excellent means of obtaining the dissociation energy of the molecule.

Figure 16.505 shows the absorption spectrum of iodine at ordinary temperatures; almost all of the molecules are initially in the lowest vibrational level of the ground electronic state. The absorption is discrete down to a wavelength of about 4995 Å; Herzberg gives the onset of continuous absorption as 20,037 cm^{-1}. At this point there is no excess kinetic energy of the fragments; the only possible excess energy is electronic excitation in the atoms. Iodine atoms, according to the atomic spectrum, have energy levels 0 (ground state) and 7603 cm^{-1} (as well as much higher levels which need not be considered). The approximate thermal value of 35 kcal mole^{-1} for the dissociation energy of I_2 suffices to determine that at 20,037 cm^{-1}

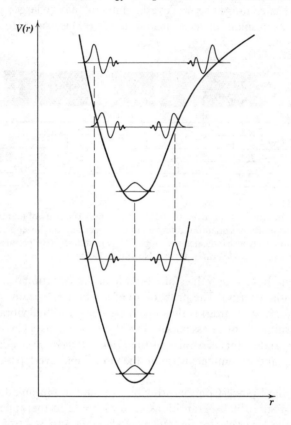

Fig. 16.504   The Franck-Condon principle. Schematic potential energy curves, some vibrational energy levels, and parts of vibrational wave functions in two different electronic states of a diatomic molecule. Vertical dashed lines connect vibrational wave functions which have a large overlap integral. The actual vertical separation of the two curves would be much greater than that shown.

the products of dissociation are one ground state and one excited state atom. The difference, 20,037 − 7603 cm^{-1}, is then the dissociation energy of a ground state iodine molecule into two ground state atoms.

This method is capable of great precision, provided a suitable spectrum transition can be found giving atoms with no kinetic energy at the dissociation limit.

A phenomenon very closely related to dissociation after absorption of light is called *predissociation*; an experimental spectrum is shown in Fig. 16.506. The explanation of this phenomenon requires three different potential energy curves,

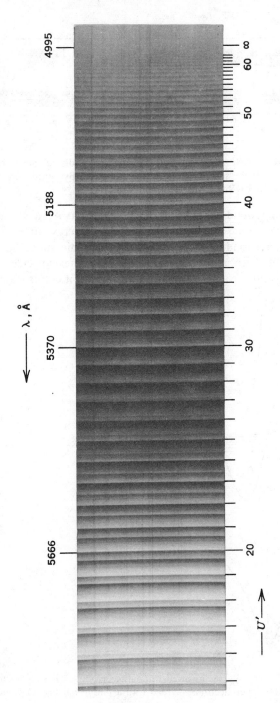

Fig. 16.505 Part of the absorption spectrum of iodine. The numbered lines indicate vibrational quantum numbers in the upper electronic state, for molecules which originate in $v = 0$ of the lower electronic state. (By permission from G. M. Barrow, *Molecular Spectroscopy*, McGraw-Hill Book Co., New York, 1962.)

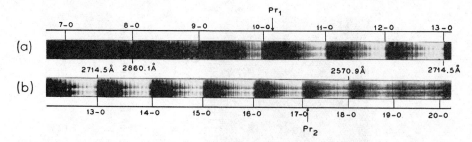

Fig. 16.506   Part of the absorption spectrum of S_2 vapor, showing two predissociations   Note that (*a*) and (*b*) are adjacent parts of the spectrum and overlap slightly. (By permission from G. Herzberg, *Spectra of Diatomic Molecules*, D. van Nostrand, 1950.)

as shown in Fig. 16.507. The ground electronic state is depicted as *A*; absorption of light raises molecules to electronic state *B*, with its potential energy curve. This state "crosses" curve *C*, corresponding to still another electronic state; in the vicinity of the crossing point there is a finite probability that the molecule may undergo a nonradiative transition from state *B* to state *C*. Once it enters state *C*,

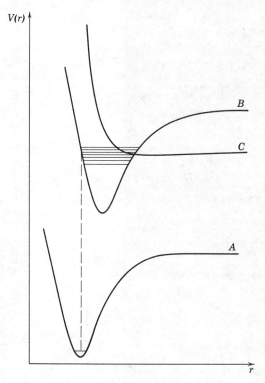

Fig. 16.507   Schematic potential energy curves involved in predissociation. The sketch shows only those vibrational levels in the upper electronic state *B* with a fairly high Franck-Condon probability for absorption from the ground electronic state *A*.

the molecule immediately dissociates. Therefore, the lifetime of a molecule in state B is quite different above and below the crossing point. With a short lifetime, the energy levels become broad (uncertainty principle, Sec. 1.3) and hence so do the spectrum lines.

In an emission experiment, the experimental evidence for predissociation is more dramatic. If the emission is from state B to some lower state, a molecule below the

(a)

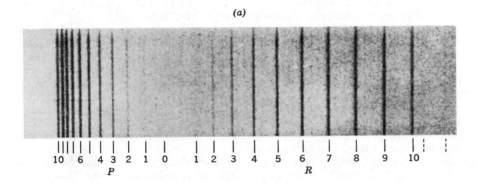

(b)

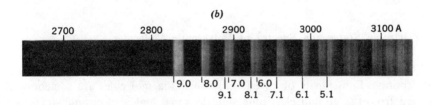

Fig. 16.508 (a) Part of the emission spectrum of CaH at about 3533 Å. Note how the emission suddenly ceases above the rotational level $J = 10$ in this particular vibrational level of the upper electronic state. (By permission from G. Herzberg, *Spectra of Diatomic Molecules*, D. van Nostrand, 1950.) (b) Part of the emission spectrum of S_2. Note absence of transitions originating in vibrational levels greater than $v = 9$ in the upper electronic state; compare Fig. 16.506. (By permission from A. G. Gaydon, *Dissociation Energies and Spectra of Diatomic Molecules*, Second Edition, Chapman and Hall, London, 1953.)

crossing point has only one way to lose its energy, by radiation. Above the crossing point, the molecule may either radiate its energy or lose it by crossing to state C and dissociating. Thus the emission intensity is much weaker above the crossing point; in some cases it is completely absent, though strong emission is found just below; see Fig. 16.508.

Predissociation measurements are used to determine dissociation energies in the same fashion as are convergence limits. These spectroscopic methods are capable of the highest precision; several of the General References list many dissociation energies obtained by such spectroscopic methods.

Problems

16.501   Write molecular-orbital-theory electron configurations for the diatomic molecules Li_2, Be_2, B_2, C_2, and F_2. What are the bond order and spin multiplicity predicted for each? What change in bond order would be expected for the corresponding positive ions and the corresponding negative ions?

16.502   Explain why the total calculated energy of a molecule such as N_2 cannot be obtained simply by adding the appropriate energies from Table 16.503.

16.503   According to Table 16.503, what are the two lowest-energy electronic absorption transitions for C_2 and N_2? Determine whether each should give rise to parallel or perpendicular bands.

16.504   The IBr molecule spectrum shows a good convergence limit at $18,345 \pm 25$ cm^{-1}. Energy levels for the iodine and bromine atoms are 0, 7598; 0, 3685 cm^{-1}, respectively, and other much higher values.

(a) From this information alone, list the possible values of the bond dissociation energy of IBr.

(b) Another convergence limit of IBr is found at $14,660 \ cm^{-1}$. Now what are the possible values of bond dissociation energy?

(c) The heat of formation of IBr gas at $25°C$ from elements in their standard states is $\Delta H = +9.75$ kcal $mole^{-1}$; dissociation energies of I_2 and Br_2 are about 35 and 45.5 kcal $mole^{-1}$, respectively. What is now the spectroscopic value for the IBr bond dissociation energy, in wave number units and in kilocalories per mole?

6. Electronic States and Spectra of Polyatomic Molecules

Electronic spectra of polyatomic molecules may be observed in emission or in absorption. Emission is observed only when the molecules are somehow first excited from the ground electronic state to some higher electronic state. Since chemical decomposition occurs frequently on such excitation, spectra are more frequently observed in absorption. Electronic absorption spectra are generally found in the visible or untraviolet regions although, for a few substances, some electronic transitions may even be found in the infrared. Unlike the rotational and vibrational spectrum regions, in which certain highly symmetrical molecules exhibit no absorption, all molecules show electronic absorption spectra. An electronic spectrum frequently exhibits vibrational structure; the gas-phase spectra of small, symmetrical molecules may even show rotational structure under high resolving power. As suggested in Table 16.503, inner-shell electrons are bound much more tightly than outer-shell or valence electrons; electronic transitions involving inner-shell electrons occur at much shorter wavelengths, approaching or reaching the X-ray region. We shall not deal with such transitions. Even valence-shell transitions may occur over a wide range of wavelengths.

The Vacuum Ultraviolet. As a matter of convenience, the part of the ultraviolet spectral region which lies at wavelengths below about 2000 Å is called the vacuum ultraviolet region. The name stems from the fact that strong absorption by oxygen and other atmospheric gases may require evacuation of the spectrometer. All molecules absorb in the vacuum ultraviolet. Frequently, polyatomic molecules with only single bonds show no electronic transitions at wavelengths longer than 2000 Å; i.e., beyond the vacuum ultraviolet. Molecules with multiple bonds usually show some absorption at wavelengths greater than 2000 Å.

In the vacuum ultraviolet, much of the absorption is continuous or diffuse, which suggests that a dissociation or predissociation may be occurring. A quantum of wavelength 2000 Å corresponds to an energy of about 143 kcal mole^{-1} and this amount of energy is adequate to break most chemical bonds (Sec. 17.1).

Another type of molecular absorption in the vacuum ultraviolet is quite sharp, often not even showing much vibrational structure. These absorptions usually occur in one or more series, ending in a continuum, with frequencies and intensities similar to electronic spectra of one of the atoms in the molecule; such series are called *Rydberg* series. These series are believed due to the excitation of a valence shell electron, often from an unshared pair or multiple bond, to other orbitals having successively larger principal quantum numbers (compare the atomic hydrogen spectrum, Sec. 3.2). The frequencies in a Rydberg series can usually be fitted to an expression of the form

$$v = A - \frac{R}{(n + B)^2} \tag{16.601}$$

where A and B are empirical constants, and R is the Rydberg constant, 109,737 in wave-number units. The quantity A, which is the limit of v as $n \rightarrow \infty$, is an ionization potential of the molecule and may be obtained precisely from good sharp data. Figure 16.601 shows part of the vacuum ultraviolet spectrum of benzene vapor. Four different Rydberg series have been located, and all of them lead to a value for the ionization potential of 9.247 ev.

Before proceeding to a more extensive discussion of ultraviolet spectra at longer wavelengths, we describe some types of atomic orbitals which are important in bonding of polyatomic molecules.

Directional Bonding and Orbital Hybridization.   We noted in the discussion of diatomic molecules (Sec. 16.5) that the overlapping of atomic orbitals from two atoms provides a qualitative criterion for chemical bonding. This criterion is also applicable for polyatomic molecules. The ground state of an oxygen atom has the configuration $1s^2 2s^2 2p^4$ with two of the p orbitals available for bonding; the filled $1s$, $2s$, and $2p$ cannot participate in bonding. The partially filled p orbitals can be combined with the $1s$ orbitals of two hydrogen atoms to form chemical bonds. The s orbitals are spherically symmetrical and have no preferred direction; however, the p orbitals are directed along two lines at right angles (Fig. 3.207). The overlapping criterion thus suggests that the water molecule should have its two O-H bonds at an angle of 90°. This conclusion is also reached by a more detailed analysis; it is found that the coulomb integrals are independent of bond angle, but that the exchange integrals vary with bond angle and yield the minimum molecular energy for an angle of 90°. The actual bond angle is somewhat larger, 105°; this may be due to repulsion between the hydrogens which was neglected in this simple model.

The larger H_2S molecule, i.e., $r_{S-H} > r_{O-H}$, has an angle much closer to 90°, as would be expected for a reduction in hydrogen repulsions.

Similar considerations suggest that nitrogen should form a molecule NH_3, with bond angles of 90°. The experimental value, 106°, is again a little larger, possibly for a similar reason.

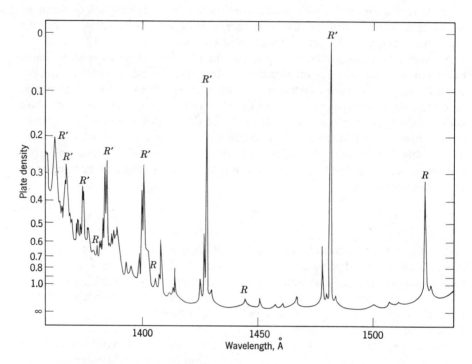

Fig. 16.601   Vacuum ultraviolet absorption spectrum of benzene in the 1350–1500 Å region. Two different Rydberg series are marked R and R', respectively. [By permission from P. G. Wilkinson, *J. Mol. Spect.*, **6**, 1 (1956).]

An understanding of bond angles in hydrocarbons actually requires more than the considerations of the previous paragraph. The compounds ethane, ethylene, and acetylene have HCC bond angles of about 109°, 116°, and 180°, respectively, although bonds using only carbon $2p$ orbitals are expected on the above basis to have 90° angles. In fact, the ground state configuration of the carbon atom, $1s^2 2s^2 2p^2$, would suggest a covalence of two, rather than the observed value of four; however, an excited state of carbon may have one of the $2s$ electrons promoted to the vacant $2p$ orbital giving a covalence of four. A CX_4 molecule formed by the use of three $2p$ and one $2s$ orbitals would be unsymmetrical. The $2s$ orbital has no preferred direction; however, the bonded atom would presumably be most stable at the greatest distance from the three atoms bonded to $2p$ orbitals, resulting in three XCX angles of 125°14′. The other three XCX angles would be 90° ($2p$ orbitals). The structures of actual CX_4 molecules such as methane are, of course, symmetrical with six equal bond angles of 109°28'. Other saturated hydrocarbons such as ethane and propane are found to have angles close to this value.

The carbon atom is believed to use mixed or hybridized orbitals in such bonding, rather than orbitals which are exclusively s or p in their directional character. Pauling considered the mixing of an s and a p angular atomic wave function, with adjustable coefficients a and b.

$$\psi_{hyb}(\theta, \varphi) = a\psi_s(\theta, \varphi) + b\psi_p(\theta, \varphi) \qquad (16.602)$$

The hybridized function, $\psi_{hyb}(\theta, \varphi)$, must of course be normalized in order to give

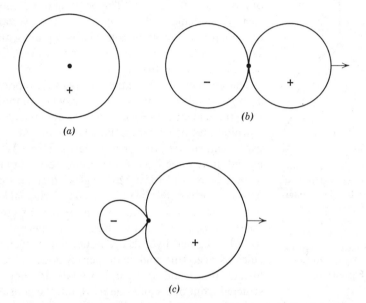

Fig. 16.602   Planar sections of the angular dependence of (a) s orbitals; (b) p orbitals; (c) sp^3 hybrid orbitals. Black dots denote the origin of coordinates, and arrows show directions of maxima in (b) and (c). The same scale was used for all three figures.

valid comparisons for different ratios of a to b. For any b to a ratio, it is always possible to find the direction in which ψ_{hyb} is a maximum. On comparing these maximum values for different b to a ratios, one finds that the ratio $3^{1/2}$ gives the largest maximum, $\psi_{hyb} = 2.00$. This numerical value is relative to the maximum of the s angular function, rather than the actual maximum given by Eqs. 3.220. Note in those equations that all angular functions contain $(4\pi)^{-1/2}$ as a common factor. On this basis the maximum for the s function is 1.00, and for p functions is 1.73. The angular dependence of this hybrid orbital is shown in Fig. 16.602, along with that of an s and of a p orbital. The figure suggests that the hybrid orbital should have a very substantial overlap with an orbital on another atom, and hence be effective in bonding. If the s and p functions in Eq. 16.602 are normalized, the values $a = \frac{1}{2}$ and $b = 3^{1/2}/2$ yield a normalized hybrid function with the largest maximum value. The quantities $a^2 = \frac{1}{4}$ and $b^2 = \frac{3}{4}$ represent the fractional contributions of s and p character to the hybrid, or 25 per cent s and 75 per cent p character. Such orbitals are simply denoted sp^3 orbitals.

We can also start with one s orbital and three p orbitals (p_x, p_y, and p_z) and form four hybrid sp^3 orbitals. All four are identical in shape, but differ in spatial orientation. Their directions of maximum probability form angles of 109°28′ with each other (Fig. 16.603). These orbitals are also called *tetrahedral* hybrids, since these are the same angles as are formed by the four vertices of a regular tetrahedron. The bonding in a compound such as methane is then ascribed to the overlapping of these four sp^3 orbitals from a carbon atom with four $1s$ orbitals from four hydrogen atoms, with each bond containing two electrons.

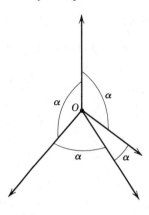

The sp^3 hybrids are not the only ones of importance. Two p orbitals and one s orbital may be combined to form three identical *trigonal* hybrids, denoted sp^2; one p orbital and one s orbital may be combined to form two identical *digonal* hybrids, denoted sp. Trigonal hybrids have directions of maximum probability which lie in a plane and form 120° angles; digonal hybrids form an angle of 180° (see Fig. 16.604). Trigonal hybrid orbitals are important in such molecules as ethylene and benzene for which the HCC bond angles are close to 120°; digonal hybrids are important in such molecules as acetylene and hydrogen cyanide, which are linear. If sp^2 and sp hybrid orbitals are both constructed from one s and one p orbital, the constants a

Fig. 16.603 Relative directions of the maxima in a set of four sp^3 hybrid orbitals. The six angles α are all 109°28′, but for clarity only four are shown. Each direction should have a curve like Fig. 16.602(c), with all origins at O, as in Fig. 16.604.

and b in Eq. 16.602 are $3^{-1/2}$ and $(\frac{2}{3})^{1/2}$, and $2^{-1/2}$ and $2^{-1/2}$, respectively. For carbon atoms with trigonal or digonal hybridization, one or two of the p orbitals, respectively, do not participate in hybridization; these are considered below in a discussion of pi electrons.

In Fig. 16.602 the choice of the orbital which should form the strongest bond is clearly seen; the sp^3 orbital would obviously overlap most efficiently with an orbital of an adjacent atom. The choice between sp^3 sp^2, and sp hybrid orbitals is less clear. The method used to obtain the optimum coefficients in Eq. 16.602 suggests that the bonding strength is in the order $sp^3 > sp^2 > sp$, since the maximum values of the angular functions are 2.00, 1.992, and 1.932, respectively. However, this order is opposite to the order suggested by experimental results on C-H bond energies, bond lengths, and stretching force constants (see Table 16.601). The calculation of overlap integrals agrees with the relative experimental ordering. Slater functions (see p. 70) were employed, with the atoms located at appropriate bonding distances. For C-C bonds the overlap integrals were found to be 0.67, 0.78, and 0.88 for sp^3,

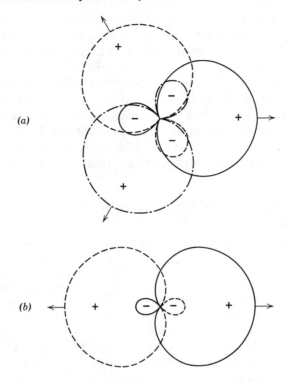

Fig. 16.604   Planar sections of the angular dependence of (a) a set of three sp^2 hybrid orbitals; (b) a set of two sp hybrid orbitals. Arrows show directions of maxima. Scale is the same as in Fig. 16.602.

sp^2, and sp hybrids, respectively. The differences were less marked for C-H bonds, with values of 0.72, 0.74, and 0.76 for sp^3, sp^2, and sp carbon hybrids overlapping with $1s$ hydrogen orbitals. The values vary with the interatomic distance chosen, but in all cases the same relative order is found; see A. Maccoll, *Trans. Faraday Soc.*, **46**, 369 (1950).

   The pi-Electron Approximation.   In the remainder of this section we will confine

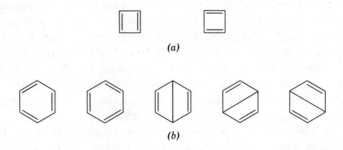

Fig. 16.605   Valence bond structures of (a) cyclobutadiene and (b) benzene.

the discussion to the electronic states of molecules containing multiple bonds, and having all or most of their atoms in a plane. For such molecules, we may distinguish two types of atomic orbitals, depending on their symmetry with respect to reflection in the plane of the molecule. Sigma orbitals are changed into themselves (i.e., unchanged) by this reflection; pi orbitals into minus themselves. In benzene, for instance, the $1s$ orbitals of the hydrogen atoms and the sp^2 hybrid carbon orbitals are sigma orbitals. Each carbon atom also has one p orbital, unhybridized, which is directed perpendicular to the plane of the molecule; these are the pi orbitals. The sigma orbitals form six C-H sigma bonds, and six C-C sigma bonds; a pair of electrons with opposite spins constitutes each of the sigma bonds. These

Table 16.601   Effect of Hybridization on C-H *Bond Properties**

Molecule	Hybridization	Bond Length, Å	Stretching Force Constant, $\times 10^{-5}$ dynes cm^{-1}	Bond Energy, kcal mole^{-1}
CH radical	p	1.120	4.09	83
CH_4	sp^3	1.094	4.88	$\sim$100
C_2H_4	sp^2	1.079	5.05	$\sim$106
C_2H_2	sp	1.057	5.88	$\sim$121

* In part, by permission from A. D. Walsh, *Trans. Faraday Soc.*, **43**, 60 (1947).

sigma electrons are believed to be quite strongly localized to their respective bonds; the pi electrons are strongly delocalized in benzene and similar molecules.

Since many molecular properties seem to be governed largely by the pi electrons, most theoretical calculations for such molecules are carried out for the pi electrons only. In such cases the sigma electrons are assumed to remain essentially unchanged during a spectral transition; this simplification is also used in comparing some of the properties of chemically similar substances such as olefins or ketones. Since such calculations yield useful predictions and correlations of experimental measurements, the pi electron approximation seems to be justified. For any but the smallest molecules, inclusion of sigma electrons would almost hopelessly complicate the calculation: benzene, under the pi electron approximation, has six electrons; inclusion of sigma electrons would change it into a thirty-electron problem (forty-two electrons, if the carbon $1s$ electrons were included).

Within the framework of the pi electron approximation, there are two alternative directions which calculations may take. One of these is a *first-principles* or almost entirely theoretical treatment in which the molecular geometry (bond distances and bond angles) constitutes the only experimental information employed. The various integrals are all calculated using appropriate wave functions determined by the variation method. Such calculations are exceedingly involved, and have thus far only been done for a few simple pi electron molecules such as ethylene, butadiene, and benzene. The agreement between theory and experiment in the ultraviolet spectrum of benzene is less than perfect. We shall not discuss this type of work further.

A second direction which pi electron calculations may assume is *semiempirical*; rather than writing explicit wave functions and computing the necessary integrals, we write a secular equation more or less directly. The elements in the secular equation (fundamentally certain integrals) are regarded as parameters to be chosen so that the solutions of the secular equation are in agreement with experiment. Such a treatment is often applied to a series of similar molecules, with the requirement that similar parameters for different molecules are given identical values for the entire series. Several examples of semiempirical treatments are given below. These are the valence bond and molecular orbital approximation methods. Both of these approximation methods use a set of pi atomic orbitals located on the pertinent nuclei, and a number of electrons (usually equal to the number of pi orbitals).

The Valence Bond Method. The method is based on the Slater determinants which can be written using the pi orbitals and the spin functions α and β. Frequently only the singlet states are of interest for molecules with an even number of electrons; this substantially reduces the number of determinants to be considered. Singlet states are formed from determinants in each of which there are equal numbers of α and of β spin functions; other determinants can contribute only to states with higher multiplicity.

ILLUSTRATION.   Write a Slater determinant for the pi electrons which may contribute to the singlet states of cyclobutadiene. Show that there are six such determinants.

Since the only atomic orbitals considered are p_z (z axis perpendicular to the molecular plane), it is not necessary to repeatedly write the quantum designations as $2p$, which is necessary for the Slater determinants in atoms, Sec. 3.4. The four $2p_z$ orbitals centered on the four carbon atoms can be simply denoted a, b, c, and d; electrons are denoted by numbers in parentheses, and the two spin functions by α and β. For convenience, the orbital functions a, b, c, and d will always be written in the first, second, third, and fourth rows, respectively, of the determinant. This need not cause us to omit determinants, since the rows of any determinant may be interchanged, and change only the sign but not the absolute value of the determinant.

Consider the first column of a Slater determinant. If we choose a certain set of spin functions for these four elements, all the remaining entries are fixed with no possibility of further choice. There are 2^4 possible choices, in all, but sets such as $\alpha\alpha\alpha\alpha$ and $\alpha\beta\alpha\alpha$ cannot contribute to the singlet states. The choice $\alpha\beta\beta\alpha$ is admissible, and yields the Slater determinant

$$\begin{vmatrix} a(1)\alpha(1) & a(2)\alpha(2) & a(3)\alpha(3) & a(4)\alpha(4) \\ b(1)\beta(1) & b(2)\beta(2) & b(3)\beta(3) & b(4)\beta(4) \\ c(1)\beta(1) & c(2)\beta(2) & c(3)\beta(3) & c(4)\beta(4) \\ d(1)\alpha(1) & d(2)\alpha(2) & d(3)\alpha(3) & d(4)\alpha(4) \end{vmatrix}$$

Since there are two α functions, and a choice of four places in the first column where they may be, a total of six Slater determinants results $4!/(2!2!)$. Note that the location of the β functions is fixed, once a choice of α functions has been made.

The number of such Slater determinants increases very rapidly with the size of the molecule. For benzene, with six electrons, there are twenty determinants; for naphthalene, 252 determinants. However, only certain combinations of these determinants can contribute to singlet states. In the formation of spin wave functions for two electrons, we had (Sec. 3.4) the two products $\alpha(1)\beta(2)$ and $\alpha(2)\beta(1)$. The difference of these gives, with a suitable orbital function, a singlet state; however, the sum gives part of a triplet state. Thus two simple spin functions yield only one singlet state. The six Slater determinants for cyclobutadiene may be combined in various ways, but only two of these combinations yield singlet states. Similarly, for benzene there are five singlet combinations, and for naphthalene 42.

In the semi-empirical valence bond method, Slater determinants are not used. It turns out that the singlet combinations of determinants can always be depicted as valence-bond structures, corresponding to the possible ways of arranging the single and double bonds (see Fig. 16.605). The valence-bond secular equation is then written in terms of these structures. Certain "rules" have been deduced for writing the various elements in the secular equation by consideration of the structures and their pairwise relations to one another. These rules are rigorous, except for assumptions in the valence bond method itself. The elements in the secular equation are given in terms of two parameters, Q and K. The Coulomb integral, Q, represents the electrostatic interactions of the pi electrons with each other and with the rest of the molecule; K represents the exchange integral and is a generalization of Eq. 16.516. For example, the secular equation for cyclobutadiene (two structures) is found to be

$$\begin{vmatrix} 4Q + 4K - 4\epsilon & -2Q - 8K + 2\epsilon \\ -2Q - 8K + 2\epsilon & 4Q + 4K - 4\epsilon \end{vmatrix} = 0 \qquad (16.603)$$

The solutions of this equation are found to be $\epsilon = Q + 2K$, and $\epsilon = Q - 2K$. If only one of the valence bond structures were considered, the calculated energy would be $Q + K$. Since exchange integrals are negative quantities, the state with energy $Q + 2K$ is more stable than one of the structures by an amount $|K|$.

The exchange integral may be evaluated "experimentally" from the energy difference between the actual molecule and one valence bond structure. The

energy necessary to separate the actual molecule into gaseous atoms may be
determined by a proper combination of heats of combustion for substances and
enthalpies of formation of gaseous atoms (Sec. 9.2). The valence bond structure
(Fig. 16.605) is not real; we assume that the energy necessary to separate it into
gaseous atoms may be obtained simply by adding the appropriate bond energies such
as are found in Table 9.203. This value is subtracted from the value for the real
molecule; the result is called the experimental *resonance energy*. This procedure
is questionable, but the magnitudes so found are often considerably larger than the
uncertainties in tabulated bond energies.

*Table 16.602   Observed and Calculated Resonance
Energies for Some Aromatic Hydrocarbons**

Substance	Observed, kcal mole^{-1}	Calculated†	$|K|$‡, kcal mole^{-1}
Benzene	35	$-1.11K$	31.5
Naphthalene	61	$-2.04K$	29.9
Anthracene	84	$-2.95K$	28.5
Phenanthrene	92	$-3.02K$	30.5

* By permission according to G. W. Wheland, *Resonance in Organic Chemistry*, John Wiley and Sons, New York, 1955, pp. 132 and 640.

† In terms of the exchange integral, K, as a parameter.

‡ Obtained by equating the entries in column 2 to those in column 3, then solving for K.

Table 16.602 shows a comparison for several aromatic hydrocarbons. The
values of K are quite consistent. Cyclobutadiene, which has not been synthesized,
is not included; the theory thus predicts it should have a resonance energy of
about 30 kcal mole^{-1}.

The complexity of the valence bond method increases very rapidly with the size
of the molecule. In naphthalene, as noted earlier, there are 42 valence bond structures; this means the secular equation would be 42 by 42 (42 rows and 42 columns).
If one is interested only in the ground electronic state, the application of symmetry
results in a secular equation which is only 16 by 16. For anthracene and phenanthrene, each of which has a total of 429 valence bond structures, symmetry considerations reduce the secular equation for the ground state to 126 by 126 and 232 by
232, respectively. It was also found that the anthracene ground state secular equation had only 2096 nonvanishing elements, and the equation for phenanthrene had
only 4262 nonvanishing elements; the values of these elements were found with the
aid of a digital computer. These secular equations were solved (for the lowest
energy level only) to obtain the theoretical resonance energies listed in Table 16.602;
solutions were obtained with a digital computer.

The valence bond method is clearly too unwieldy for general use. Also, one should remember that several approximations are used in it. Overlap integrals of atomic orbitals between adjacent atoms are ignored, exchange integrals are assumed equal throughout the molecule even though distances of different kinds of bonds in a molecule are known to be different, and all ionic structures (two pi electrons on one atom) are omitted. In a semiquantitative way, however, the valence bond aproach is still useful.

The Molecular Orbital Method. In contrast to the complexity of most calculations in the valence bond method, calculations by the molecular orbital method are quite simple. It is possible, then, to treat a wide variety of molecules,

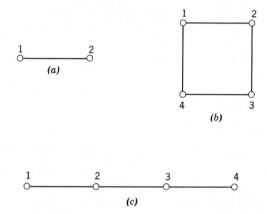

Fig. 16.606   The numbering of carbon atoms and pi orbitals in (*a*) ethylene, (*b*) cyclobutadiene, and (*c*) butadiene, used in Eqs. 16.604–16.606.

including substituted hydrocarbons and heterocyclic compounds. We discussed the molecular orbital method for diatomic molecules in Sec. 16.5; the treatment of polyatomic molecules is quite similar, except that only pi orbitals and pi electrons are considered.

The molecular orbital treatment of H_2^+ in Sec. 16.5 involved the use of coulomb, resonance, and overlap integrals which were calculated from certain explicit atomic functions. In the simple molecular orbital method (for polyatomic molecules), coulomb and resonance integrals are regarded as parameters; furthermore, most overlap integrals are assumed to be zero. The method is often called the Hückel molecular orbital (HMO) method.

We shall consider the molecules ethylene and butadiene to illustrate the treatment. We number the carbon pi orbitals as in Fig. 16.606; these orbitals are then the functions ψ_1, ψ_2, etc., in Eqs. 16.503. All coulomb integrals, which have the form

$$\int \psi_i^* H \psi_i \, d\tau = H_{ii}$$

are assumed equal to each other and commonly denoted α. All resonance integrals, which have the form

$$\int \psi_i^* H \psi_j \, d\tau = H_{ij}$$

are assumed equal to each other and denoted β if i and j represent adjacent (bonded) atoms; all other resonance integrals are set equal to zero. The pi orbitals are assumed to be normalized, so that the overlap integrals $S_{ii} = 1$; all overlap integrals S_{ij} are set equal to zero (Eq. 16.503).

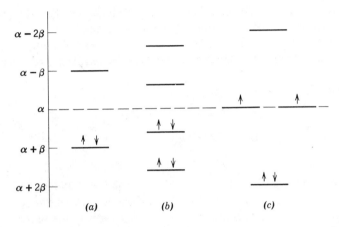

Fig. 16.607 Molecular orbital energy levels of (a) ethylene, (b) butadiene, and (c) cyclobutadiene. The electron distribution in the ground state is also indicated.

With these drastic assumptions the secular equation becomes, for ethylene,

$$\begin{vmatrix} \alpha - \epsilon & \beta \\ \beta & \alpha - \epsilon \end{vmatrix} = 0 \qquad (16.604)$$

and for butadiene,

$$\begin{vmatrix} \alpha - \epsilon & \beta & 0 & 0 \\ \beta & \alpha - \epsilon & \beta & 0 \\ 0 & \beta & \alpha - \epsilon & \beta \\ 0 & 0 & \beta & \alpha - \epsilon \end{vmatrix} = 0 \qquad (16.605)$$

The energy levels obtained by solving the ethylene equation are $\alpha + \beta$ and $\alpha - \beta$; see Fig. 16.607. Since β is a negative quantity, the level $\alpha + \beta$ has the lower energy. As for the diatomic molecule, the levels are successively filled with pi electrons to describe the ground electronic state; the two pi electrons of the ethylene molecule are placed in the $\alpha + \beta$ level with opposite spins. The pi electron energy is in this approximation just the sum, or $2\alpha + 2\beta$; since a pi electron without bonding has an energy α, the quantity -2β is a measure of the pi bond energy.

Consider the butadiene molecule. Equation 16.605 yields energy levels of $\alpha + \frac{1}{2}(5^{1/2} + 1)\beta$, $\alpha + \frac{1}{2}(5^{1/2} - 1)\beta$, $\alpha - \frac{1}{2}(5^{1/2} - 1)\beta$, and $\alpha - \frac{1}{2}(5^{1/2} + 1)\beta$; see Fig. 16.607. Two of the four pi electrons are placed in the lowest level, and the other two in the next level to complete the ground electronic state. The total pi electron energy is now $4\alpha + 2(5^{1/2})\beta$, and the pi bonding energy is -4.472β. Note that this is greater than twice the pi bonding energy of ethylene; butadiene is predicted to be more stable than if it had two isolated, noninteracting ethylene-type double bonds. The energy difference, -0.472β, is called *delocalization energy* and corresponds to the resonance energy in valence bond theory.

ILLUSTRATION.   Determine the effect of cyclization on butadiene by calculating the energy levels and delocalization energy of cyclobutadiene.

The atoms are numbered as in Fig. 16.606, yielding a secular equation like that for butadiene, except now there is a nonzero resonance integral between atoms 1 and 4.

$$\begin{vmatrix} \alpha - \epsilon & \beta & 0 & \beta \\ \beta & \alpha - \epsilon & \beta & 0 \\ 0 & \beta & \alpha - \epsilon & \beta \\ \beta & 0 & \beta & \alpha - \epsilon \end{vmatrix} = 0 \qquad (16.606)$$

The energy levels are found to be $\alpha + 2\beta$, α, α, and $\alpha - 2\beta$ and, in contrast to those for ethylene and butadiene, exhibit degeneracy. A rule found by Hund states that the lowest electronic state will always display the maximum multiplicity (with electrons assigned to the lowest orbitals consistent with the Pauli principle). The ground state of cyclobutadiene is thus predicted to be a triplet, with parallel spins (compare oxygen in Sec. 16.5). The total pi-electron energy is now $4\alpha + 4\beta$, and the delocalization energy is zero; this fact is consistent with the failure of attempts thus far to synthesize the substance. This result should be contrasted with the substantial resonance energy calculated for cyclobutadiene by the valence bond method.

This simple molecular orbital method stands in marked contrast to the careful setting up and solving of Schrödinger equations, such as was done or outlined in Chapters 2 and 3. Many important factors have been approximated or even neglected here. Some of these are clear from the steps in the procedure just given. If the resonance integral is nonzero for adjacent atoms, the overlap integral should also be nonzero. And why should all coulomb integrals be equal? In butadiene, the terminal carbons might well have a coulomb integral different from that of the central carbons. Likewise, the resonance integral should probably have a value varying with location in the molecule. This simple treatment overestimates the importance of ionic structures, just as the molecular orbital treatment of the hydrogen molecule does (Sec. 16.5). In fact, the HMO method is equivalent to the use of wave functions which violate the Pauli principle; i.e., the functions are not completely antisymmetric in exchange of any pair of electrons.

The HMO theory is thus not an accurate description of electronic molecular constitution; its utility lies in its simplicity. The method is applied to resonance energies, electronic spectra, dipole moments, bond distances, electron spin resonance spectra, ionization potentials, rates of reaction, and other properties. However, for different properties such as spectra and resonance energies, different values of β may be obtained semiempirically. Even for a single property, distinct series of compounds may give different values of β.

Electronic Spectra and Molecular Orbital Methods. A variety of excellent measurements of electronic spectra has been made for unsaturated hydrocarbons. There are numerous theoretical approaches to such spectra; we have limited this discussion to two methods: the HMO treatment and the treatment of R. Pariser and R. G. Parr (discovered independently by J. A. Pople). The first method is very easy to apply and correlates some data quite well; the second method is more difficult but makes use of some experimental spectral information to yield calculated results which agree rather well with a variety of spectra and other properties.

HMO Treatment of Electronic Spectra. Electronic spectral transitions involve both orbitals which are filled and those which are empty in the ground electronic state. As in diatomic molecules, we may distinguish between *bonding* orbitals, denoted π, which have energy less than α; and *anti-bonding* orbitals, denoted π^*, which have energy greater than α. Note that we are here discussing only the pi orbitals; in molecules with substituted functional groups, the unshared pairs or *nonbonding* electrons and orbitals, n, may also be important in the spectra. For systems containing a linear chain of conjugated double bonds, we shall consider electronic transitions to involve one electron, as discussed in connection with diatomic molecules. With this assumption, we may directly compare an experimental transition frequency with the difference between two calculated energy levels given by the theory. Only the electronic transition of longest wavelength is considered; it is assumed to correspond to the energy difference between the highest filled level and the lowest unfilled level; i.e., to a $\pi \rightarrow \pi^*$ transition. This is a transition allowed by the selection rules.

Figures 16.608–10 show several plots of spectral frequencies and calculated energy differences. The data in each series can be fitted quite well by straight lines; from their slopes the values of β are obtained. Earlier workers had required that the correlation lines pass through the origin, based on the limiting behavior of the theoretical energy levels as the length of the conjugated carbon chain approaches infinity. A more empirical approach which drops this requirement and also permits different values of β for different series clearly gives a much better correlation.

In aromatic hydrocarbons the situation is different. The electronic spectrum of a typical member is found to contain several distinct electronic transitions at wavelengths in the same region. This suggests that more than two molecular orbitals may be involved. The longest wavelength transition is associated with a transition from the highest filled orbital to the lowest empty orbital. Other transitions might be from an orbital immediately below the highest filled orbital up to the lowest unfilled orbital, or from the highest filled orbital up to the second lowest

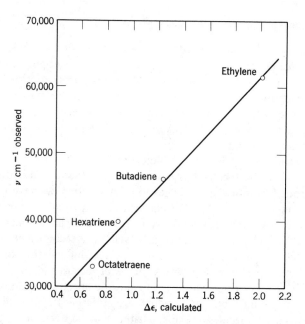

Fig. 16.608 Correlation of electronic transition at longest wavelength with HMO calculated value for some linear polyenes. Calculated value is in units of β. [By permission from A. Streitweiser, Jr., *Molecular Orbital Theory for Organic Chemists*, John Wiley and Sons, New York, 1961.]

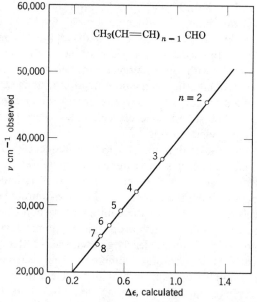

Fig. 16.609 Correlation of electronic transition at longest wavelength with HMO calculated value for some polyene aldehydes. Calculated value is in units of β. [By permission from A. Streitweiser, Jr., *Molecular Orbital Theory for Organic Chemists*, John Wiley and Sons, New York, 1961.]

638

empty orbital. These three transitions are assigned to three series of electronic transitions in aromatic spectra, and three correlations are obtained as in Figs. 16.608–10. Different values of β are needed in each series. In addition, the experimental spectra of aromatic hydrocarbons also show (weak) singlet-triplet transitions at wavelengths different from those for singlet-singlet transitions. The

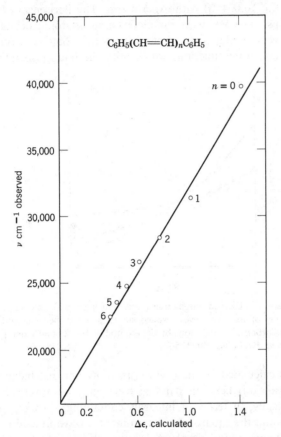

Fig. 16.610 Correlation of electronic transition at longest wavelength with HMO calculated value for some α,ω-diphenylpolyenes. Calculated value is in units of β. [By permission from A. Streitweiser, Jr., *Molecular Orbital Theory for Organic Chemists*, John Wiley and Sons, New York, 1961.]

HMO theory predicts that singlet-singlet and singlet-triplet transitions should coincide. An approach which is less empirical is clearly desirable.

The Method of Pariser and Parr. This method is a useful combination of nonempirical calculation (p. 631) with appeal to experiment in establishing best values for certain integrals. The method employs molecular orbital wave functions as a framework, but with certain refinements. The resonance integral, β, is still an empirical parameter; however, it varies with bond distance in a prescribed way.

The coulomb integral, α, is not a parameter, but may vary from atom to atom within a molecule. The value used for α is obtained uniquely in the course of the calculation, and depends on the electron densities at the various atoms in the molecule. Thus far, this method does not sound greatly different from the HMO method, which proceeds at this stage to compare MO energy levels (obtained from secular equations such as Eq. 16.604, 5) with experiment. The Pariser and Parr method requires further steps. The MO wave functions (sums of atomic orbitals) are combined by methods very similar to those used in writing Slater determinants (Sec. 3.4) to yield molecular wave functions which obey the Pauli principle. The total

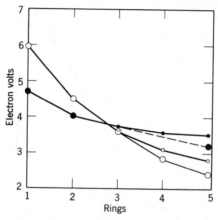

Fig. 16.611   Comparison of observed (large circles and light lines) with calculated (small circles and heavy lines) energies of the two lowest excited singlet states in benzene and several polynuclear aromatic hydrocarbons. Calculations by the method of Pariser and Parr. [By permission from R. Pariser, *J. Chem. Phys.*, **24**, 250 (1956).]

pi electron energy is calculated for these wave functions, and also includes explicitly the interaction (repulsion) between pairs of electrons. Such repulsions are expressed, mathematically, in terms of integrals containing e^2/r_{ab} (r_{ab} is the interelectronic distance) and the square of a determinantal wave function. Since such wave functions are composed of simple molecular orbitals, which are in turn sums of pi atomic orbitals, a rather large number of integrals over atomic orbitals results from the expansion of these electron repulsion terms. Pariser and Parr found that by omitting certain of these terms, and also by omitting the overlap integrals S_{ij} if i and j refer to pi atomic orbitals on different atoms, two important advantages were obtained. First, the calculations were greatly simplified; second, the calculated energies and related properties were found to be essentially the same as those calculated with inclusion of all repulsion and overlap terms. This omission of certain electron repulsion terms *and* of certain overlap integrals is called the assumption of *zero differential overlap*. It should be noted that most of the values used for electron repulsion integrals over atomic orbitals are calculated values, obtained by using either atomic wave functions or certain simple models; in one case the value used is empirical. That one is the repulsion energy corresponding to both electrons occupying a pi atomic orbital (p_z) on the same atom.

Some results obtained by Pariser with the use of this method are shown in Figs. 16.611 and 16.612. The aromatic hydrocarbons treated were benzene through

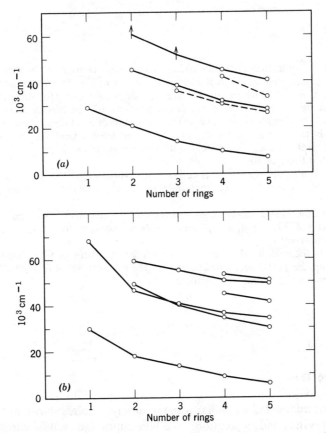

Fig. 16.612   Comparison of observed (*a*) and calculated (*b*) energies of triplet states in benzene and several polynuclear aromatic hydrocarbons. Calculations by the method of Pariser and Parr. [By permission from G. Porter, *Proc. Chem. Soc.*, 291 (1959).]

pentacene ($C_{22}H_{14}$). The method was "calibrated" with the spectrum of benzene; all energies for the other compounds were calculated without use of any further spectral data. The agreement is quite remarkable, and even includes rather good predictions of the intensities. The triplet energies are also given quite well by this method.

While the electronic spectra of aromatic hydrocarbons are fairly well understood, the spectra of heterocyclic aromatic substances are not so well interpreted and calculated. A further complication is caused by the nonbonding electrons; there are

$n \to \pi^*$ transitions in the spectrum, in addition to the $\pi \to \pi^*$ transitions as found in the hydrocarbons. Some Pariser-Parr calculations have been made for simple heterocyclic molecules, including the nonbonding electrons, and fairly good agreement was obtained with experiment.

Problems

16.601   Use the ionization potential and estimated wavelengths for the three Rydberg transitions of longest wavelength in the series R' shown in Fig. 16.601 to determine the value of B ($0.2 < B < 1.1$) in Eq. 16.601, and to assign values of n for these transitions.

16.602   Compute the maximum and minimum values for the angular dependence of sp^3, sp^2, and sp hybrid orbitals, relative to the maximum of s orbitals taken as one.

16.603   Verify that there are twenty and 252 Slater determinants for the pi electrons of benzene and naphthalene, respectively, with equal numbers of α and β spin functions. How many would there be for eight pi electrons?

16.604   Sketch all the possible valence bond structures for the pi electrons of cyclooctatetraene C_8H_8. Note, however, that the substance is found to have essentially no resonance energy.

*16.605   Write the HMO secular equation for the pi electrons of benzene. Verify by substitution that $\alpha + 2\beta$, $\alpha + \beta$, $\alpha - \beta$, and $\alpha - 2\beta$ are some of the roots. (Expand the determinant to simplify.)

16.606   Verify the calculated value of $\Delta\epsilon$ shown for butadiene in Fig. 16.608.

16.607   Set up the HMO secular equation for the pi electrons of fulvene, C_6H_6, with the carbon atoms in the planar arrangement:

7. Ligand Field Theory

The student is undoubtedly familiar with the variety of colors shown by transition metal ions in crystals and in solution: the blue cupric ion, yellow chromate ion, violet and green chromic ion, etc. Ligand field theory and the closely related crystal field theory provide a theoretical explanation for the structure, spectra, and magnetic properties of compounds containing transition metals.

An atom or ion having its $3d$ orbitals filled with ten electrons usually forms colorless (white) compounds with no unusual magnetic properties, as does an ion or atom with the $3d$ orbitals empty. When the $3d$ orbitals are partially filled, however, the ion often forms colored compounds which have unusual magnetic properties as well. The mere existence of a partially filled $3d$ shell does not by itself permit a detailed theoretical explanation of the observed spectrum; this requires a consideration of the *ligands*, the nearest-neighboring ions or molecules which surround and accompany the ion of interest in such compounds. In crystal field theory the ligands are considered simply as point charges in a fixed geometrical relationship to the transition metal ion; the electrons and orbitals of the ligands are not considered. In ligand field theory, however, the electrons and orbitals of the ligands are explicitly included. It is a molecular orbital approach, with the molecular orbitals formed by combining one or more orbitals of each ligand and the five d orbitals of the transition metal ion. The d electrons from the central ion and pertinent electrons from the ligands are considered as occupying some of these molecular orbitals and giving rise to spectra in the usual molecular orbital fashion (Secs. 16.5 and 16.6). We shall consider only the crystal field theory approach; the books of Orgel and of Ballhausen (see References) treat both ligand field and crystal field theory. It should be noted that crystal field theory is applicable to ions in solution as well as to those in the solid phase; the theory is so named because it was first applied to elucidate the properties of certain ions in crystals.

d **Orbitals and Splitting of Degeneracy.**   In the discussion of many-electron atoms in Chapter 3, we saw that the five $3d$ orbitals are degenerate. This arises because Eq. 3.302 for one electron contains a potential energy term independent of angle, that is, spherically symmetric; the angular equations can be separated and solved apart from the radial equation. However, this separation is possible only in the gas phase, when other atoms or ions are far away. When the atom of interest is part of a solid crystal or present in a solution, the ligands may disturb the spherically symmetric potential by introducing angular dependence; Eq. 3.302 is no longer separable into independent radial and angular equations.

Consider a symmetrical arrangement of ligands around the central ion, which is taken as the origin of a coordinate system. The ligands are all at the same distance from the origin, with one on each of the positive and negative parts of the x, y, and z axes. This kind of arrangement is called *octahedral*, since a regular octahedron is formed by connecting the ligands with straight lines.

It can be shown theoretically that this arrangement of ligands causes a partial removal of the degeneracy in the d orbitals. Instead of one five-fold degenerate set as in the gas phase, we have two sets: one has two-fold and the other has three-fold degeneracy. Examination of the shapes and orientations of the d orbitals helps to clarify this matter on a qualitative basis. Figure 3.207 gives the angular dependence of the d orbitals; for simplicity we consider the ligands as negative point charges. The interaction of an electron in a d orbital with the octahedral arrangement of six ligands governs the splitting of the degeneracy.

The d_{xy} orbital, for instance, has regions of high electron probability in the spaces between the ligands; the $d_{x^2-y^2}$ orbital, on the other hand, has regions of high electron probability pointing directly at the four ligands in the xy plane. The latter orbital, then, should have a higher energy than the former because of repulsion between like charges. The shapes of the d_{xz} and d_{yz} orbitals are just like those of the d_{xy} orbital, and they also correspond to high electron probability in between the ligands: they should all have the same energy. The d_{xy}, d_{yz}, and d_{xz} orbitals constitute the triply degenerate set which is found by theory.

The d_{z^2} orbital has a unique shape, unlike that of any of the others; it is therefore not possible to determine its relative energy by inspection. Theory shows that its energy in the octahedral field is the same as the energy of the $d_{x^2-y^2}$ orbital; these two constitute the doubly degenerate set. The triply degenerate set is usually denoted by the group theory symbol t_{2g}, and the doubly degenerate set by e_g as in

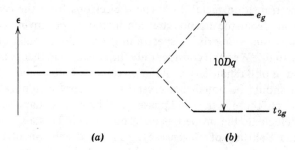

(a)   (b)

Fig. 16.701   Energy levels of one-electron d atomic orbitals (a) in the gas phase, (b) in the presence of an octahedral field of six negative charges.

Fig. 16.701. These symbols should merely represent the names of classes of orbitals to the student.

Application to Spectra. The simplest possible system is an ion with one d electron and the six ligands in an octahedral arrangement. Titanium in the oxidation state $+3$ has one d electron and appears to form a nearly regular octahedral

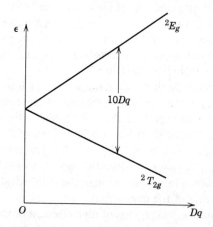

Fig. 16.702   The relationship between energies of atomic states and the crystal field parameter Dq for one d electron in an octahedral field. A Dq value of zero corresponds to the atomic state ^2D, as in the gas phase.

complex in water solution, $Ti(H_2O)_6^{+++}$. The ground electronic state is described by the configuration (t_{2g}), and only one excited state is possible, with the configuration (e_g). Note that we are not considering excited states in which the electron is promoted out of the d orbitals. The electronic spectrum of aqueous solutions containing $Ti(H_2O)_6^{+++}$ is found to consist of essentially one band at approximately 20,300 cm^{-1}; this gives directly the energy difference between the t_{2g} and the e_g orbitals.

In the analysis of spectra by crystal field theory, it is helpful to have a graph which displays the relations between the splitting of t_{2g} and e_g orbitals (represented by 10 Dq) and the resulting energies of atomic states. Such a graph for one d electron, Fig. 16.702, simply consists of two straight lines. Note that energy states of ions are denoted by capital letters, in contrast to the representation of the orbitals by small letters. For Ti(H$_2$O)$_6^{+++}$ the parameter Dq has the value 2030 cm^{-1}, but it might

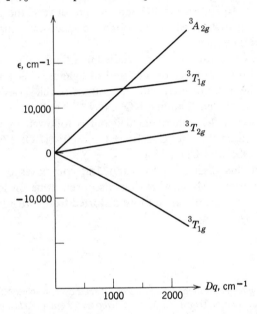

Fig. 16.703   The relationship between energies of atomic states and the crystal field parameter Dq for two d electrons in an octahedral field. A Dq value of zero corresponds to the two atomic states ^3P and ^3F, with the latter the ground state, as in the gas phase. [By permission from L. E. Orgel, *J. Chem. Phys.*, **23**, 1004 (1955).]

have quite a different value for a different central ion with one d electron, or for a different set of ligands.

When an ion has several d electrons, they may be arranged in various ways among the t_{2g} and the e_g orbitals. Consider an ion with two d electrons. The electron spins may be parallel (triplet states) or antiparallel (singlet states). We shall discuss only triplet states which include the ground state. Triplet states can result from three different kinds of arrangements: first, both electrons in t_{2g} orbitals; second, both electrons in e_g orbitals; and third, one electron each in the t_{2g} and in the e_g orbital. Application of group theory then shows the first arrangement gives rise to a $^3T_{1g}$ atomic state, the second arrangement to a $^3A_{2g}$ state, and the third arrangement to the two states $^3T_{1g}$ and $^3T_{2g}$. The relationship of these atomic states (with ligands) to the gas-phase atomic states is shown in Fig. 16.703.

This figure was obtained by calculations in which the known spacing of the ^3F and ^3P levels (from gas-phase atomic emission spectroscopy) and assumed values of the parameter Dq were used. Note the greater complexity of Fig. 16.703 as compared to Fig. 16.702.

Figure 16.703 has been applied to the spectrum of $V(H_2O)_6^{+++}$, which contains absorptions at 17,100 and 25,000 cm^{-1} assigned as $^3T_{1g} \rightarrow {}^3T_{2g}$ and $^3T_{1g} \rightarrow {}^3T_{1g}$, respectively. If the parameter Dq is given the value 1900 cm^{-1}, the separation between T_{1g} and T_{2g} in Fig. 16.703 is just 17,100 cm^{-1}, the observed value. At this same Dq value, Fig. 16.703 shows the separation between the two different T_{1g} levels is 28,500 cm^{-1}; however, the other observed spectrum transition is found at 25,000 cm^{-1}, in fair agreement.

A wide variety of complexes has been studied in a similar fashion, and Dq values have been obtained for a number of ions and of ligands. Certain regularities are apparent, such as the order of increasing magnitude in the series I$^-$, Br$^-$, Cl$^-$, F$^-$, C_2H_5OH, H_2O, NH_3, ethylenediamine, NO_2^-, CN$^-$. An illustration is found in the complexes of chromium $+3$, where each ligand is followed by the experimental Dq value in cm^{-1} (according to Orgel): Cl$^-$, 1360; H_2O, 1740; NH_3, 2160; ethylenediamine, 2190; and CN$^-$, 2630.

We have limited this discussion to octahedral complexes of one and two d electron ions in solution. Much work has also been done on ions with more d electrons, on other configurations, on those distorted from a regular geometry, and on ions in crystal lattices.

References

Ballhausen, C. J., *Introduction to Ligand Field Theory*, McGraw-Hill, New York, 1962.
Orgel, L. E., *An Introduction to Transition Metal Chemistry: Ligand Field Theory*, Methuen and
    Co., London, 1960.

Problem

16.701   Use Fig. 16.703 to estimate the spectrum frequencies for two d electrons in an octahedral field, with the ligand field parameter Dq of (a) 1000 cm^{-1} and (b) 1500 cm^{-1}.

8. Nuclear and Electron Magnetic Resonance; Ortho-Para States

Bulk Magnetic Properties. In the following discussion of magnetic resonance, we shall need to refer to certain magnetic properties of matter. Since these properties can be defined and measured without reference to the ultimate structure of matter in terms of atoms and molecules, they are called bulk properties. It will, however, be useful to discuss these properties also in terms of molecular magnetization. The behavior of matter in a magnetic field is similar to that of matter in an electric field, though there are important differences.

Suppose we have a magnet which produces a uniform, constant magnetic field $\mathcal{H}$ in a vacuum. A sample placed in this field acquires a magnetization, or magnetic moment, denoted $\mathcal{M}$ and measured per unit volume (1 cc). The ratio $\mathcal{M}/\mathcal{H}$ is defined as the *volume magnetic susceptibility*, χ_v; it is dimensionless (a pure number). A similar definition of electric susceptibility could have been given in Sec. 15.3; instead the electric moment due to the applied field was defined for one molecule rather than for 1 cc, so the proportionality constant (α, polarizability) has dimensions of volume.

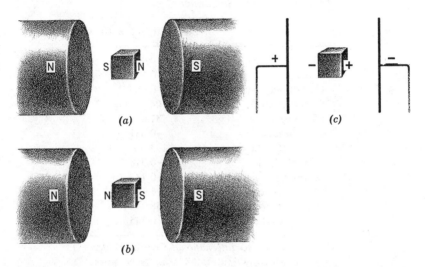

Fig. 16.801 Comparison of the two types of bulk magnetization, and electric polarization: (*a*) paramagnetic, (*b*) diamagnetic, (*c*) electric.

The most familiar kind of magnetic behavior is that of a piece of iron or certain alloys which acquire a large magnetic moment in an applied field. This is called *ferromagnetism*, and is also characterized by the fact that $\mathcal{M}$ is not proportional to $\mathcal{H}$ except for small fields; when $\mathcal{H}$ is large, $\mathcal{M}$ approaches a limiting or saturation value. At small fields the apparent susceptibilities for some materials are as high as several thousand. Ferromagnetism is of technological importance but is a rather rare phenomenon; comparatively few materials display it. It is due to interactions between the magnetic atoms in the field, which makes its theoretical treatment rather complex.

Magnetic phenomena of much wider occurrence are *diamagnetism* and *paramagnetism*. In both of these the induced magnetic moment $\mathcal{M}$ is proportional to the applied field $\mathcal{H}$ at all values; they differ in the sense or direction of the induced moment. In a diamagnetic substance the induced moment is opposite to the applied field; in a paramagnetic substance the induced moment is in the same direction as the applied field; see Fig. 16.801. The behavior of matter in an electric field is also shown for comparison; note that electric polarization is always in the same direction as the applied field. The susceptibilities of diamagnetic samples are extremely small, as shown in Table 16.801; paramagnetic susceptibilities (where found) are substantially larger. Diamagnetism is believed to be universal; in paramagnetic substances the larger positive susceptibility results in a net positive value. Magnetic susceptibilities may be determined by measuring the force on a sample in a magnetic field (see Selwood, References).

*Table 16.801   Volume Magnetic Susceptibilities of Some Substances**

Substance	Susceptibility $\times 10^6$
Acetone	-0.460
Benzene	-0.626
Carbon tetrachloride	-0.684
Cobalt chloride	304
Copper sulfate	31.0
Cyclohexane	-0.631
Manganese dioxide	193
Methyl iodide	-0.918
Methylene chloride	-0.733
Methylene iodide	-1.160
Nickel chloride	158
Potassium dichromate	0.345

* According to *International Critical Tables*, Vol. 6, McGraw-Hill Book Co., New York, 1929. Note that negative susceptibilities correspond to diamagnetism, others to paramagnetism.

The molecular basis of diamagnetism and of paramagnetism may be discussed by comparison with the basis of electric polarization. If the sample molecules have permanent magnetic moments, the field exerts a force tending to orient these moments (see Fig. 16.802) just as in the electric case; this is the basis of paramagnetism. If the sample molecules have no permanent magnetic moment, the field causes only an induced magnetic moment. Placing such a molecule into a magnetic field may be compared to moving a macroscopic closed loop of wire into a magnetic field. In the latter case a voltage is induced, which causes a current to flow in the loop of wire. This current generates a magnetic field opposite to the main magnetic field; the resistance of the loop causes the current to decay to zero when the loop is not moving in the field. In the molecular case the induced current is a circulation of electrons within the molecule; these currents and their associated opposition magnetic field persist as long as the molecule is in the field (no "resistance" on a molecular scale). The contrasting behavior of electric and magnetic fields with respect to polarization effects is shown in Fig. 16.803. The nonpolar molecule acquires an electric moment in the same sense as the applied field, owing to the electrical forces on the positive nuclei and negative electrons.

Magnetic susceptibility measurements have been important in the study of paramagnetic substances, when the paramagnetism arises from electron spin or orbital

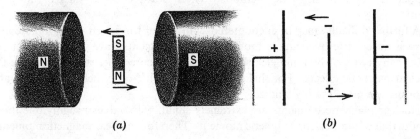

(a)　　　　　　　　　　　　(b)

Fig. 16.802　The forces tending to orient permanent moments in (a) a magnetic field; (b) an electric field.

motion. Paramagnetism also arises from nuclear spins, but this effect is too small to permit detection by bulk susceptibility measurements; resonance methods must be employed. The use of resonance methods is also important in electronic paramagnetism, as they yield much more information than do susceptibility measurements.

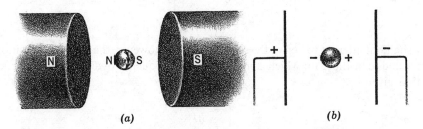

(a)　　　　　　　　　　　　(b)

Fig. 16.803　Contrasting polarization of a molecule with no permanent magnetic or electric moments (a) in a magnetic field, (b) in an electric field. The induced magnetic and electric dipoles are indicated, as is also the induced direction of electron circulation in (a).

Nuclear Spin and Magnetic Moment. We noted in Sec. 3.2 that electrons have intrinsic angular momentum and magnetic moment, and that there is an electron spin quantum number with allowed values $m_s = +\frac{1}{2}$ and $-\frac{1}{2}$. Some nuclei also have intrinsic angular momentum and magnetic moment; the treatment is similar to that used for electrons, though more extensive.

A magnetic nucleus may have only certain values for the component of its intrinsic angular momentum along a given direction. The maximum component, in units of $h/2\pi$, is denoted I and called the *nuclear spin;* each isotope has a characteristic nuclear spin. Examination of all known nuclear spins reveals three general rules. First, a nucleus with an even number of protons and an even number of neutrons has a nuclear spin of zero. Second, a nucleus with an odd mass number has a half-integral nuclear spin. Third, a nucleus with an odd number of protons and an odd number of neutrons has an integral nuclear spin, but not zero. Such common nuclei as carbon-12, oxygen-16, and sulfur-32 thus have no nuclear spin and cannot be studied by nuclear magnetic methods. Their isotopic nuclei may permit such studies.

A further difficulty may be encountered with nuclei for which $I \geq 1$; these also possess an electric quadrupole moment. Such moments have strong interactions with many types of bonding electrons and may obscure or greatly complicate the nuclear magnetic effects. For this reason nuclei with $I = \frac{1}{2}$, such as hydrogen and fluorine, are more readily studied.

Nuclear magnetic moments are extremely small, with values roughly one thousandth that of the electron magnetic moment. Therefore nuclear magnetic moments, denoted μ, are expressed in terms of the nuclear magneton, $\mu_N = eh/4\pi m_p c = 5.0493 \times 10^{-24}$ erg gauss^{-1}, rather than in terms of the Bohr magneton used in Sec. 3.2; m_p is the mass of the proton. Some typical nuclear magnetic moments in nuclear magnetons are $\mu = 2.7927$ for hydrogen, $\mu = 2.6273$ for fluorine, and $\mu = 0.70216$ for carbon-13.

Nuclear Energies and Transitions in a Magnetic Field.   Consider a magnetic nucleus placed in a steady, uniform magnetic field $\mathscr{H}$. The component of nuclear spin angular momentum in the direction of the field is quantized, with allowed values given by $m_I = -I, -I + 1, \ldots, +I$. The energies of such states are

$$\epsilon = -\mu \frac{m_I}{I} \mathscr{H} \tag{16.801}$$

We shall not attempt to derive the selection rules; however, the allowed transitions are found to be those for which $\Delta m_I = \pm 1$. The frequency of an allowed transition is thus given by

$$\nu = \frac{\mu \mathscr{H}}{hI} \tag{16.802}$$

For protons in a field of 10,000 gauss, Eq. 16.802 yields a frequency of about 42.6 megacycles; this is in a convenient range for ordinary radiofrequency techniques.

A schematic diagram of an apparatus for observing transitions allowed by Eq. 16.802 is shown in Fig. 16.804. One may vary either the radiation frequency, ν, or $\mathscr{H}$. The latter is more convenient, since a fixed radiofrequency may then be used. When Eq. 16.802 is satisfied, the sample absorbs energy from the radiation; a plot of the energy absorption vs. magnetic field looks generally similar to an optical absorption spectrum (Chapters 2, 4, and earlier sections of this chapter) and is called a *nuclear magnetic resonance (NMR) spectrum*. Under the most favorable conditions, such absorption lines may be very narrow; a change of the magnetic field as small as 0.001 per cent may cause the nuclear absorption to shift to a different frequency and hence disappear. Such sharpness of the lines imposes stringent requirements on the stability of the oscillator frequency and the magnetic field strength, and also on the homogeneity of the field.

Liquid-phase samples are generally employed, since they give sharp, reasonably strong absorptions.   Gases give sharp absorptions, but usually they are inconveniently weak, since the number of nuclei per unit volume is relatively small.   Solid samples give very much broader absorptions.

The Chemical Shift.   The nuclear magnetic resonance spectra of the liquids water, benzene, cyclohexane, and tetramethylsilane are alike in that they each show just a single, sharp line.   They differ, however, in the value of magnetic field required to yield proton resonance at the same fixed frequency.   Such a dependence on the chemical environment of the nucleus is called the *chemical shift*.   The

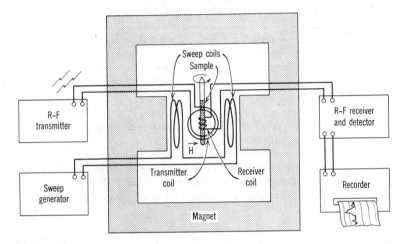

Fig. 16.804   Schematic diagram of an NMR spectrometer [by permission from Staff, Varian Associates, *NMR and EPR Spectroscopy*, Pergamon Press, New York, 1960].

differences in applied magnetic field at resonance are proportional to the applied magnetic field; that is, at 5000 gauss the difference between the water and cyclohexane resonance fields is 0.018 gauss, while at 10,000 gauss the difference is 0.036 gauss.   For this reason, the observed chemical shifts are divided by the field strength at resonance for a reference substance, and reported as a pure number; see Table 16.802.   The sign convention is such that a substance which requires a higher field than the reference is assigned a positive chemical shift, and vice versa. Since the shifts are so small, they are multiplied by 10^6 and reported as parts per million (ppm).

Chemical shifts may arise from three sources: intermolecular effects, either specific or nonspecific, and intramolecular effects. The nonspecific intermolecular effect is due to the magnetic susceptibility of the medium, which slightly alters the field as it enters the sample. The resulting chemical shift contribution may be calculated for standard sample shapes by simple algebraic expressions which involve the difference in volume susceptibilities of sample and reference substances; such shifts are frequently about twice the susceptibility difference.

An example of a specific intermolecular effect is hydrogen bonding, which occurs in water, alcohols, acids, etc. Its determination might involve dilution of the substance in an inert solvent or measurement of the gas-phase spectrum.

The shift which remains after the observed value has been corrected for both kinds of intermolecular effects is the intramolecular chemical shift. For protons the range of such shifts spans about 15 ppm in various chemical substances; the shift is caused by differences in the way that molecular electrons interact with the

Table 16.802   Chemical Shifts from NMR Spectra of Some Pure Liquids*

Substance	Chemical Shift, ppm
Sulfuric acid	−10.0
Benzene	−5.3
Methylene chloride	−4.2
Water	−3.60
Cyclohexane	0.00 (reference)
Tetramethylsilane	1.6

* By permission according to Pople, Schneider, and Bernstein, *High-Resolution Nuclear Magnetic Resonance*, McGraw-Hill Book Co., New York, 1959.

applied magnetic field. In principle, it should be possible to calculate chemical shifts by theory; however, accurate calculations have been carried through for only a very few simple molecules. The shift in this type of calculation is composed of two parts, called *diamagnetic* and *paramagnetic*. The diamagnetic circulation of electrons around a nucleus gives rise to a magnetic field which opposes and partially cancels the external field. A high concentration of electrons around a nucleus thus gives a large positive shift, and vice versa. For example, strong acids have proton resonances at quite low fields; the electron density around such protons is less than that around protons in a hydrocarbon.

The paramagnetic part is similar to the discussion of the Stark effect (Sec. 16.3), where we saw that placing a polar molecule into an electric field results in each rotational state wave function acquiring a slight contribution from a few neighboring rotational state wave functions. However, in the magnetic case the molecule need not even have a permanent magnetic moment; any molecule, except one with a spherically symmetric electron distribution, is affected. Placing such a molecule in a magnetic field causes the ground electronic state to become mixed with slight contributions from *many* different excited electronic states of different multiplicity. For a singlet ground state the excited triplet states are the ones which are mixed; since triplet states have very different magnetic properties, the magnetic field at the nucleus is slightly altered. This additional field is always in such a direction as to reinforce the applied field. The diamagnetic and paramagnetic parts of the calculated chemical shift then produce opposing effects: the former tends to decrease, the latter to increase, the magnetic field at the nucleus. For protons the two parts are found to be the same order of magnitude; for fluorine nuclei the paramagnetic part is an order of magnitude larger than the diamagnetic part.

In spite of the fact that chemical shifts have been predicted theoretically for only a few molecules, the empirical study of such shifts has been found very useful in structure determination; no attempt is made to apply corrections for the diamagnetic shielding by electrons in the molecule. Examples of some chemical shifts are shown in Table 16.803; note that aromatic, aliphatic, and olefinic protons

Table 16.803 Some Characteristic Chemical Shifts of Protons in NMR Spectra*

Group	Chemical Shift, ppm
C—H, aliphatic	2.8 to 4.2
C—H, olefinic	−1.6 to 0.5
C—H, aromatic	−2.8 to −1.2
C—H, aldehyde	−5.0 to −4.3
O—H, organic acids	−7.2 to −5.6

* By permission according to Meyer, Saika, and Gutowsky, *J. Am. Chem. Soc.*, **75**, 4567 (1953).

have rather different chemical shifts and thus usually give absorptions in distinct regions of the NMR spectrum. A further useful feature of NMR spectra is that the area under the absorption peak of any kind of magnetic nucleus is directly proportional to the number of such nuclei in the sample. The relative areas of absorptions caused by different kinds of protons may then be used to determine the relative numbers of such protons.

Spin-Spin Splitting. A further feature of most NMR spectra which is also helpful in structural work is due to a coupling between spins of different kinds of nuclei in the molecule. A simple example is found in the spectrum of acetaldehyde, which contains one aldehyde proton and three identical methyl protons (Fig. 16.805). The absorption region denoted A has three times the area of the region denoted B; thus A corresponds to methyl, and B to aldehyde protons. When the magnetic field has the proper value for methyl resonance, the aldehyde protons give no absorption. However, the aldehyde protons are in the magnetic field; in some molecules this proton has nuclear spin function α, with $m_I = +\frac{1}{2}$, while in other molecules this proton has nuclear spin function β, with $m_I = -\frac{1}{2}$. The magnetic field at the methyl protons is slightly different for these two spin functions; therefore the methyl proton resonance is split into two peaks. The aldehyde

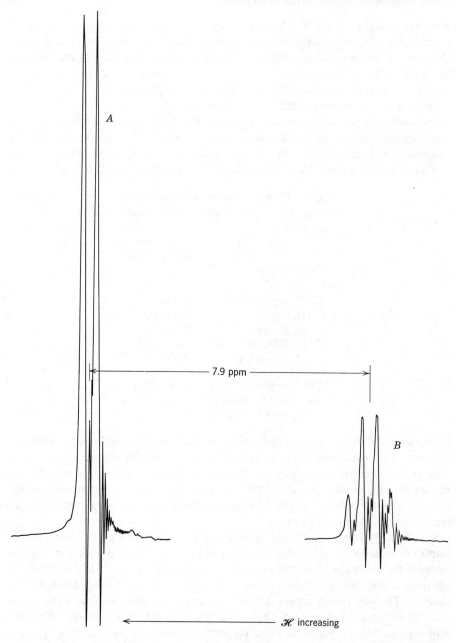

Fig. 16.805   The NMR spectrum of acetaldehyde, CH₃CHO. The spacing of all adjacent peaks is 2.85 cycles sec⁻¹. Regions *A* and *B* consist of two and four peaks, respectively; the additional small peaks are due to transient effects.

proton resonance, however, is split into four distinct peaks. This is due to the various possible spin functions of the methyl protons, each of which may have α or β spin functions. Note that experimentally this does not give rise to eight peaks (2^3) but only four. Table 16.804 lists the eight possible combinations of spin functions, and also shows the Σm_I for each. The magnetic field at the aldehyde proton, due to the methyl protons, depends only on Σm_I, but not on the way in which this sum is obtained. Since each of the eight methyl spin functions is equally probable, there will be three times as many molecules which have $\Sigma m_I = \frac{1}{2}$ as there are which have $\Sigma m_I = \frac{3}{2}$. In Fig. 16.805 the two central peaks of region B correspond to Σm_I of $\frac{1}{2}$ and $-\frac{1}{2}$; the two outer peaks correspond to Σm_I of $\frac{3}{2}$ and $-\frac{3}{2}$. Note that the central peaks are three times as intense as the outer ones.

Table 16.804   Spin Functions for Three Nuclei with $I = \frac{1}{2}$

Function	Σm_I
$\alpha(1)\alpha(2)\alpha(3)$	$+\frac{3}{2}$
$\alpha(1)\alpha(2)\beta(3)$; $\alpha(1)\beta(2)\alpha(3)$; $\beta(1)\alpha(2)\alpha(3)$	$+\frac{1}{2}$
$\alpha(1)\beta(2)\beta(3)$; $\beta(1)\alpha(2)\beta(3)$; $\beta(1)\beta(2)\alpha(3)$	$-\frac{1}{2}$
$\beta(1)\beta(2)\beta(3)$	$-\frac{3}{2}$

Such splitting of resonance peaks due to coupling with other magnetic nuclei is called *spin-spin splitting*. It can be distinguished experimentally from a chemical shift by the fact that the splitting (e.g., between the two methyl peaks in acetaldehyde) is independent of magnetic field strength. In a spectrum such as that in Fig. 16.805, the separation between adjacent peaks is equal to the *spin-spin coupling constant J*. For acetaldehyde J has a value of 2.85 cycles sec^{-1}; other molecules have proton-proton coupling constants ranging from very small values up to about 20 cycles sec^{-1}. A magnetic nucleus is believed to be coupled to another magnetic nucleus in the same molecule through the bonding electrons; the electronic wave function thus governs the values of the spin-spin coupling constants. The agreement between theoretical values calculated from approximate electronic wave functions and experimental values obtained from NMR spectra is reasonably good for a number of systems. The experimental values can also be used directly to provide useful clues to the structure of a new compound.

The spin-spin splitting patterns in NMR spectra can often be used to determine the numbers of equivalent nuclei in several sets in a molecule. Figure 16.806 shows the fluorine NMR spectrum of the substance CSF_8; at the far right there is a symmetrical set of five peaks, each of which is further split into two peaks. The five peaks must arise from coupling to four equivalent fluorine nuclei, and the further doubling from coupling to one different fluorine. The area of this part of the spectrum is three-eighths of the total area, which is consistent with the assignment of this region to the resonance of a CF_3 group. The structure of the molecule, shown

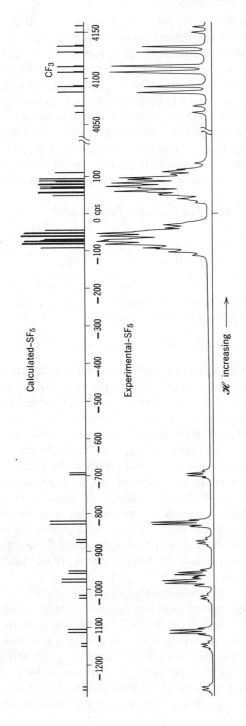

Fig. 16.806 The NMR spectrum of CSF_8, run at 40 megacycles. In the calculation values of 145, 22, and 6 cycles sec^{-1} were assumed for the spin-spin coupling constants J_{ab}, J_{ac}, and J_{bc}, respectively, and values of 102.8 and -23.8 ppm were assumed for the chemical shifts δ_{ac} and δ_{ab}, respectively. [By permission according to Merrill, Williamson, Cady, and Eggers, *Inorg. Chem.*, **1**, 215 (1962).]

in Fig. 16.807, may be considered an SF_6 molecule with one fluorine replaced by the CF_3 group. The sulfur is bonded to four equivalent fluorines and to one which is different, as shown in the figure.

The remaining absorptions in Fig. 16.806 are quite complex; this due to the fact that the spin-spin coupling constant and the chemical shift are of comparable magnitude for the two kinds of SF fluorines. It is still possible to account for the observed spectrum by a calculation which assumes the chemical shifts and spin-spin splitting constants shown in the caption to Fig. 16.806; the resulting calculated line positions and intensities are shown above the experimental spectrum. In fluorine NMR spectra the chemical shifts and spin-spin coupling constants are both substantially larger than in proton NMR spectra.

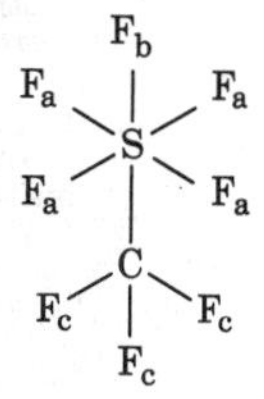

Electron Spin Resonance.   We have seen in the earlier parts of this section that nuclei with nonzero magnetic moments have distinct energy levels in a magnetic field (Eq. 16.801). Molecules or atoms may in addition have nonzero magnetic moments of electronic origin; this leads in similar fashion to distinct energy levels in a magnetic field. In such systems, the magnetic moment may arise from orbital angular momentum, from the intrinsic electron spin angular momentum, or from a combination of them. The last case is important in the study of atoms in the gas phase and in the study of compounds which contain atoms having partially filled d or f orbitals. However, in many compounds the energy levels in a magnetic field are governed almost entirely by the spin, with essentially no contribution from the orbital momentum. In the present discussion we shall treat electronic magnetic moment as arising entirely from the spin. We shall also limit this treatment further to organic free radicals which are in liquid solutions; these species contain one unpaired electron. The discussion of systems with several unpaired electrons, or of solids, or of molecules containing transition metal or rare earth atoms is considerably more complex. For the latter, electronic orbital moments are also important, and the term *electron paramagnetic resonance* (EPR) is more appropriate.

We saw in Sec. 3.2 that the application of a magnetic field $\mathscr{H}$ splits the degeneracy of electron spin; the α and β spin functions are separated by an energy interval $\Delta\epsilon = 2.0023\mu_B\mathscr{H}$, where μ_B is the Bohr magneton, p. 63. Radiation of frequency $\Delta\epsilon/h$ can cause transitions between these energy levels. Figure 16.808 shows the essential parts of an apparatus for observation of such transitions, and it is quite similar to that used in nuclear resonance; the main difference is that the radiation is of much higher frequency since the Bohr magneton is so much larger than the nuclear magneton. The magnetic field could be reduced a thousand-fold to permit working in the range of 50 megacycles, as for nuclear resonance; however, this would greatly reduce the sensitivity and require a much larger concentration of radicals to produce a usable signal. Typical values of the magnetic field and radiation frequency are about 3400 gauss and 9500 megacycles, respectively.

Fig. 16.807 The structure of CSF_8. The two types of SF fluorines are distinguished by F_a and F_b.

An electron spin resonance (ESR) spectrometer is a highly selective and sensitive instrument. It responds only to the unpaired electrons in the sample; solvent molecules and other solutes in which all the electrons are paired yield no signal. The sensitivity to organic free radicals in solution is illustrated by the current working concentration range of 10^{-4} to 10^{-6} mole liter^{-1}.

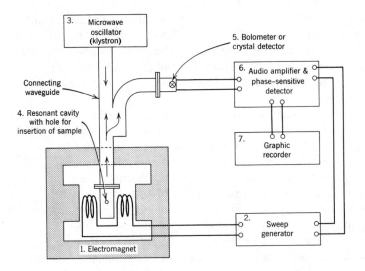

Fig. 16.808   Schematic diagram of an electron spin resonance spectrometer (by permission from Staff, Varian Associates, *NMR and EPR Spectroscopy*, Pergamon Press, New York, 1960).

ESR spectroscopy with its high sensitivity and selectivity, has been used in the study of many kinds of problems. One such application is in the detection and kinetic study of free radicals. Many reactions are assumed on the basis of conventional rate studies to proceed by a free radical mechanism; the presence of radicals in such a reaction mixture can often be verified directly by ESR methods. It is also possible to determine the concentration of free radicals, and study their rate of formation and disappearance as a function of radiation or other system parameters.

A second application, which we shall discuss at greater length, is in the study of structure and electron distribution in organic free radicals. The experimental basis for this application is in the *hyperfine structure*, or multiplicity and spacing of lines, found in the ESR spectrum. Since a free radical has only one unpaired electron, the presence of any fine structure is perhaps unexpected. Theory shows, however, that the spin of the odd electron can interact with magnetic nuclei in the molecule, and the resulting spectrum is reminiscent of NMR spectra with (nuclear) spin-spin coupling. The NMR spectrum can be very complex, if the chemical shift is of the same order of magnitude as the spin-spin splitting; there is, in ESR spectra of free radicals in solution, no comparable complication.

Figure 16.809 shows schematically the energy levels of an unpaired electron spin in a magnetic field. In part a, the electron is not interacting with any magnetic nuclei, so that the $\alpha(e)$ and $\beta(e)$ levels are both single; the ESR spectrum would contain just one line. In part b, the electron spin is interacting with a single magnetic nucleus of spin $\frac{1}{2}$, and this splits the electron spin energy levels. Note that this splitting is not due to the energy of the nucleus in the external field as in Eq. 16.801 (which gives rise to the NMR spectrum) but due to the *interaction* of nuclear and electron spin; the energy difference, $\frac{1}{2}a$, is independent of applied magnetic field.

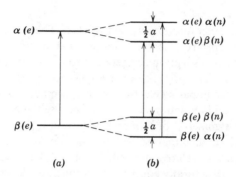

Fig. 16.809   The energy levels of electron spin in a magnetic field, (a) no interaction with nuclear spins; (b) electron spin interacting with one nucleus of spin $\frac{1}{2}$. The nuclear and electron spin functions are distinguished by n and e, respectively. Vertical arrows show allowed transitions. The energy spacing $\frac{1}{2}a$ is usually much smaller, relative to the spacing of $\alpha(e)$ and $\beta(e)$ levels.

Note also that in the two electron spin energy levels, the opposite nuclear functions yield the lower energy, that is, if $\alpha(e)\alpha(n)$ has a lower energy than $\alpha(e)\beta(n)$, then $\beta(e)\beta(n)$ has a lower energy than $\beta(e)\alpha(n)$. Theory shows that the selection rules permit transitions in the electron spin, but not simultaneously in the nuclear spin; the resulting spectrum then would consist of two lines, the hyperfine components, separated by a frequency interval a/h. If the electron is interacting with n equivalent nuclei of spin $\frac{1}{2}$, each electron spin energy level is split into $n + 1$ levels since the interaction energy depends only on Σm_I. The ESR spectrum then consists of $n + 1$ equally spaced hyperfine components, with a symmetrical intensity distribution similar to the nuclear case.

An example of such hyperfine splitting is shown by an intermediate substance formed when p-benzohydroquinone is oxidized to p-benzoquinone (see Fig. 16.810). The oxidation is conveniently accomplished by adding some base to a solution of the hydroquinone in the presence of oxygen gas or air. The hydroquinone and quinone have all their electrons paired and hence show no ESR spectrum; the intermediate, the semiquinone, has one unpaired electron and gives an ESR spectrum which is reproduced in Fig. 16.811. Note that most ESR spectra are recorded

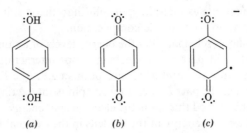

(a)   (b)   (c)

Fig. 16.810   The structures of (a) p-benzohydroquinone, (b) p-benzoquinone, and (c) p-benzo-semiquinone ion.

as derivative spectra rather than absorption spectra. The general shape of the upper half of a derivative spectrum is the same as that of an absorption spectrum; however, the maximum absorption corresponds to the point at which the derivative curve crosses the axis. The presence of five lines in Fig. 16.811 is consistent with the assumption that the unpaired electron interacts equally with the four protons in the radical. This equal interaction could arise because the protons are structurally equivalent owing to symmetry, or to a coincidence in a nonsymmetrical structure. Such a coincidental equal unpaired electron density is very improbable, so the presence of five lines with relative intensities $1:4:6:4:1$ may be taken to show the free radical has four structurally equivalent protons. Radicals with less than four protons, and those with more than four protons, give still different spectra from which structural information can similarly be obtained.

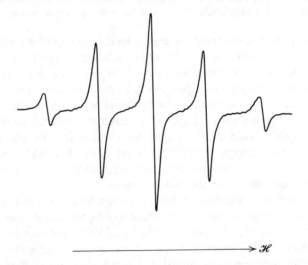

Fig. 16.811   The ESR spectrum of p-benzosemiquinone ion. Separation of adjacent peaks is 2.33 gauss. The ordinate represents the derivative of the absorption curve at each value of the magnetic field. [By permission, according to B. Venkataraman and G. K. Fraenkel, *J. Am. Chem. Soc.*, **77**, 2707 (1955).]

We have thus far done very little with a, the electron spin–nuclear spin coupling parameter, except to mention that it is independent of the applied magnetic field. By theory it can be shown that the coupling and resultant splitting are directly proportional to the unpaired electron density (square of the wave function) at the magnetic nucleus; the proportionality constant contains only known quantities such as electron and nuclear magnetic moments. The splitting for hydrogen atoms ($1s$) in the gas phase was measured by I. I. Rabi in an atomic beam experiment and found to be 506.8 gauss. The semiquinone measurements then show that the unpaired electron density at the protons is 2.33/507 times that at the proton in the hydrogen atom. Thus the experimental splitting of lines in an ESR spectrum yields direct information about the wave function of an electron in a radical, with the magnetic nucleus acting as a "probe." Note, however, that the unpaired electron density is given only at the magnetic nucleus; the value is not given by experiment for any other places in the molecule. In theories of electronic structure of unsaturated organic molecules (Sec. 16.6) we treat the electron distributions at the carbon atoms; in contrast, the measured values of unpaired electron density are given at the hydrogen atoms. It would thus seem that no comparison of theory and experiment is possible.

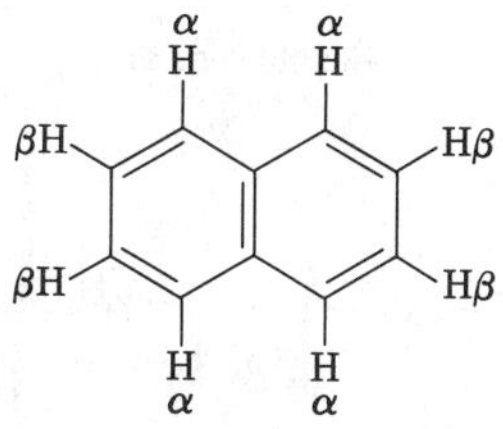

Fig. 16.812   The eight protons in naphthalene, which fall into two different sets, denoted α and β.

A way out of this difficulty has been found by H. M. McConnell and others. They have shown that the unpaired electron density at a hydrogen atom in an organic free radical is *proportional* to the unpaired electron density at the carbon to which it is bonded. In this way the measured spectral splitting for protons, a_H, yields "experimental" unpaired electron densities at the carbons for comparison with theory. An example of this application is found in the ESR spectrum of naphthalene negative ion, which is formed by adding an alkali metal to a dilute naphthalene solution in tetrahydrofuran; this system was first studied by S. I. Weissman and co-workers.

Naphthalene contains two sets of equivalent protons, with four in each set; the sets are distinguished by α and β in Fig. 16.812. If the negative ion has the same symmetry as naphthalene itself, there will be two sets of four equivalent protons interacting with the unpaired electron. One set would produce a symmetrical five-line hyperfine splitting with a spacing determined by a_H for that set. The interaction of the protons in the second set would produce a splitting of each line from the first set into five lines, with spacing determined by a_H for the second set. If the two sets have different a_H values, and if there is no overlapping, the hyperfine structure should display twenty-five lines. Figure 16.813 shows the ESR spectrum of naphthalene negative ion, and indeed there are twenty-five lines. The analysis of the spectrum shows that the two splitting constants are 4.90 and 1.83 gauss; these lead to unpaired electron densities at the α and β carbon atoms which are compared in Table 16.805 with various calculated values. The general agreement is good.

Free radicals are also generated by other methods, such as dissolving aromatic hydrocarbons in concentrated sulfuric acid and by electrolysis of appropriate solutions. In the last method, which is especially convenient, the electrolysis cell functions also as the sample container in the ESR spectrometer, so that the free radicals may be observed by ESR simultaneously with their generation by electrolysis. Literally hundreds of free radicals have been generated by these and other

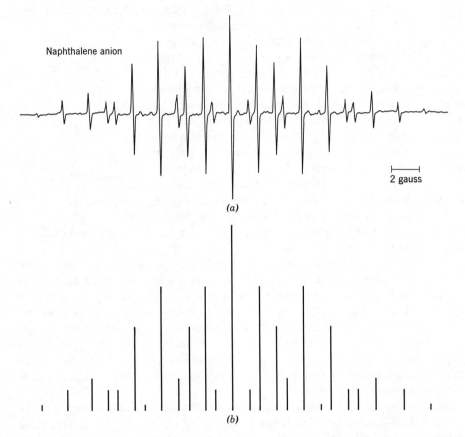

Naphthalene anion

2 gauss

(a)

(b)

Fig. 16.813 The ESR spectrum of naphthalene negative ion. (a) Experimental spectrum; (b) theoretical spacings and intensities of lines with a_H of 4.90 and 1.83 gauss for the α and β protons, respectively. [By permission, according to A. Carrington, *Quart. Rev.* **17**, 67 (1963).]

methods, and the hyperfine splittings in their ESR spectra have been measured. This information has stimulated much theoretical work on electron densities in free radicals.

Ortho-Para States. We have seen in the preceding parts of this section that nuclear spin wave functions are important in the resonance absorption processes which may take place in a magnetic field. Nuclear spin wave functions are also important in the absence of a magnetic field, particularly for the ways in which they may be combined with rotational wave functions for molecules containing several magnetic nuclei.

Effect of Nuclear Wave Functions on Rotation of Gases. The heat capacity of heteronuclear diatomic gases has been dealt with adequately in Chapter 6. However, the explanation of the rotational heat capacity of homonuclear diatomic

Table 16.805   *Comparison of Calculated and Observed Unpaired Electron Densities in Naphthalene Negative Ion,* $C_{10}H_8^-$

Method	Density at α Carbon, ρ_α	Density at β Carbon, ρ_β
Hückel MO	0.181	0.069
Valence bond*	0.187	0.072
Hückel plus config. int.†	0.221	0.054
Approximate Pariser-Parr‡	0.211	0.055
Experiment §	0.21	0.08

* According to Schug, Brown, and Karplus, *J. Chem. Phys.*, **35**, 1873 (1961).

† According to G. J. Hoijtink, *Mol. Phys.*, **1**, 157 (1958).

‡ According to A. D. McLachlan, *Mol. Phys.*, **3**, 233 (1960).

§ Using a proportionality constant with magnitude 23 ± 1 gauss between observed spectrum splitting and unpaired electron density at the carbon atom.

gases, in particular that of hydrogen, involves the consideration of the overall symmetry requirements in the combined nuclear and rotational eigenfunctions. This consideration is necessary, because a rotation through 180° has the effect of interchanging like nuclei. Both the nuclear and rotational wave functions break down into two classes: the symmetrical wave functions, which remain the same, and the antisymmetrical ones, which change sign on nuclear interchange.

Interchanging the two ends of the molecule involves changes in the angles θ and φ. Reference to Fig. 3.201 shows that φ is changed into $\varphi + \pi$, since we must use the other end of the molecule from which to project a point into the xy plane. The angle θ is necessarily changed into $\pi - \theta$. For the case of the rotational functions, the situation is quite simple. Those with even values of J (Eq. 3.220) are symmetrical; thus for $J = 0, 2, 4$, etc., the rotational wave function is identical when the value of $\pi - \theta$ is substituted for θ, and $\pi + \varphi$ for φ. For odd values of J, the functions are antisymmetrical; thus for $J = 1, 3, 5$, etc., this angle substitution gives the same absolute value but with a change in sign.

For the nuclear wave function three cases are to be distinguished.

(1) Heteronuclear diatomic molecule. If atom A has ρ_A nuclear spin wave functions possible, and atom B has ρ_B wave functions possible, there are a total of $\rho_A \rho_B$ combinations possible. There are thus a large number of nuclear spin isomers possible in a heteronuclear diatomic molecule. However, they all have the same moment of inertia, and rotation through 180° produces a distinguishable configuration of the molecule. Thus there are no restrictions on the value of the rotational quantum number.

(2) Homonuclear diatomic molecule composed of odd mass-number nuclei. If a homonuclear diatomic molecule is composed of odd particles (Fermions), the overall wave function is required to be antisymmetrical. If there are ρ wave functions available to the individual nuclei, it can be shown that there are $(\frac{1}{2})\rho(\rho - 1)$ antisymmetrical wave functions for the combined nuclei. These must be used with symmetrical rotational wave functions to get wave functions that are in an overall sense antisymmetrical. There are also $(\frac{1}{2})\rho(\rho + 1)$ symmetrical wave functions. These must be combined with antisymmetrical rotational wave functions to produce overall wave functions that are antisymmetrical. Note that there is a total of ρ^2 wave functions for the nuclear functions of both types.

(3) Homonuclear diatomic molecules composed of even mass number nuclei. In this case, the overall wave functions must be symmetrical. This result can be obtained by multiplying the $(\frac{1}{2})\rho(\rho - 1)$ antisymmetrical wave functions with the antisymmetrical rotational functions since $-1 \times (-1) = 1$. The $(\frac{1}{2})\rho(\rho + 1)$ symmetrical wave functions for the nuclei must be used with the symmetrical rotational wave functions.

The Case of the Hydrogen and Deuterium Molecules. For the case of hydrogen we have an odd particle with possible nuclear spins of $+\frac{1}{2}$ and $-\frac{1}{2}$. Therefore $\rho = 2$. If the two individual nuclear wave functions are α and β, and the nuclei numbered 1 and 2, the symmetrical nuclear functions are $\frac{1}{2}2(3) = 3$ in number

$$\alpha(1)\alpha(2)$$
$$\beta(1)\beta(2)$$

and

$$\alpha(1)\beta(2) + \alpha(2)\beta(1)$$

The single antisymmetrical wave function is

$$\alpha(1)\beta(2) - \alpha(2)\beta(1)$$

The first three wave functions remain unchanged if 1 and 2 are interchanged; the last one changes sign.

Possible wave functions for the molecule are thus

$$[\alpha(1)\alpha(2)]R(J) \qquad J \text{ odd}$$

or

$$[\alpha(1)\beta(2) - \alpha(2)\beta(1)]R(J) \quad J \text{ even}$$

which are both antisymmetrical overall; $R(J)$ denotes a rotational wave function.

For deuterium, where the particle is of even mass, with possible spins of $+1$, 0, and -1, $\rho = 3$. We thus have an additional individual nuclear wave function γ which yields additional symmetrical wave functions

$$\gamma(1)\gamma(2)$$

$$\alpha(1)\gamma(2) + \alpha(2)\gamma(1)$$

and

$$\beta(1)\gamma(2) + \beta(2)\gamma(1)$$

for a total of six, and additional antisymmetrical wave functions

$$\alpha(1)\gamma(2) - \alpha(2)\gamma(1)$$

and

$$\beta(1)\gamma(2) - \beta(2)\gamma(1)$$

for a total of three.

Possible wave functions for the molecule are symmetrical ones of the type

$$[\gamma(1)\gamma(2)]R(J = 2)$$

or

$$[\alpha(1)\beta(2) - \alpha(2)\beta(1)]R(J = 3), \text{ etc.}$$

which are both symmetrical overall.

Even and Odd Partition Functions for Rotation. Two different summations must be written for the partition functions for rotation of the various nuclear-spin species of diatomic homonuclear molecules. Instead of Eq. 6.403 summed over all J values we have

$$Z_{\text{odd}} = \sum_{J=1,3,\text{etc.}}^{\infty} (2J + 1) \exp\left[\frac{-J(J + 1)h^2}{8\pi^2 IkT}\right] \tag{16.803}$$

and

$$Z_{\text{even}} = \sum_{J=0,2,4,\text{etc.}}^{\infty} (2J + 1) \exp\left[\frac{-J(J + 1)h^2}{8\pi^2 IkT}\right] \tag{16.804}$$

At high temperatures, these expressions approach the same limit, which is one-half the value of Z_{rot} for a heteronuclear diatomic molecule, but at low temperatures they are quite different in value, Z_{even} being much larger.

Now in the absence of a magnetic field, the energy of the various spin isomers is the same, except for the rotational part. The energy difference due to the orientation of the nuclear spins is negligible. Thus one might expect that the total partition function for homonuclear gases might be a weighted sum according to the abundance of the symmetrical and antisymmetrical nuclear species. Thus for H_2 we might expect

$$Z_{\text{rot}} = 3Z_{\text{odd}} + Z_{\text{even}} \tag{16.805}$$

and for D_2

$$Z_{\text{rot}} = 3Z_{\text{odd}} + 6Z_{\text{even}} \tag{16.806}$$

Note that these expressions are sums and not averages; this is due to the fact that inclusion of nuclear spin functions results in increased degeneracy. However, these partition functions, when differentiated, do not reproduce the experimental data.

Correct Account of the Heat Capacity of Hydrogen and Deuterium. When we write a total partition function such as Eq. 16.805 we imply that all of the spin isomers are in equilibrium with each other. This means that the single term with $J = 0$ will eventually dominate the partition function at low enough temperature.

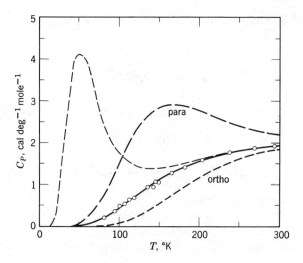

Fig. 16.814 Rotational heat capacity of hydrogen as a function of temperature. The broken lines represent the theoretical rotational heat capacities of ortho-, para-, and equilibrium-hydrogen; the full line, that of the 3:1 room-temperature mixture (normal). The circles represent the observed heat capacities after subtraction of the translational contribution $5R/2$. (From G. Herzberg, *Spectra of Diatomic Molecules*, D. van Nostrand, Princeton, N.J., 1950.)

This term will be unity, while all the other J values which have higher energies will give rise to terms that approach zero. This means that all the hydrogen molecules would be able to reach the lowest rotational state, and that all then have become antisymmetric in the spin function. Similarly, for deuterium at low enough temperatures all the molecules would be in symmetric spin states.

However, when not subject to a magnetic field or other outside influence, the experimental fact is that on cooling the spin isomers remain in the previously established proportion. For hydrogen or deuterium formed at high temperature, this proportion is in the ratio of the number of nuclear spin eigenfunctions.

Therefore, hydrogen or deuterium gas behaves as a mixture of two independent species. The species with symmetrical spin wave function are called *ortho*; those with antisymmetrical spin wave functions are called *para*. Thus ordinary hydrogen gas behaves as a mixture of 3/4 ortho hydrogen with a specific heat calculated from Z_{odd} and 1/4 para hydrogen, with specific heat calculated from Z_{even}. In contrast deuterium behaves as a mixture of 2/3 ortho deuterium with a specific heat calculated from Z_{even} and 1/3 para deuterium with a specific heat calculated from Z_{odd}. The results are shown in Fig. 16.814.

If ordinary hydrogen is stored as a liquid it changes over a period of a few hours or days into para-hydrogen; this transformation can be accelerated by means of a paramagnetic salt, which acts as a catalyst. We can describe this transformation as a chemical reaction with a slow but measurable velocity. For this reason ordinary hydrogen cannot be stored as a liquid, even in a perfect Dewar vessel, because the heat of transformation to para-hydrogen is enough to vaporize it. Thus for the successful storage and shipment of liquid hydrogen, it must be transformed to the equilibrium mixture of almost pure para-hydrogen as it is liquefied. For this reason a catalyst is placed in the liquefaction chamber.

References

Carrington, A., *Quart. Rev.*, **17**, 67–99 (1963).

Fowler, R. H., and E. A. Guggenheim, *Statistical Thermodynamics*, Cambridge University Press, Cambridge, England, 1939.

Ingram, D. J. E., *Free Radicals as Studied by Electron Spin Resonance*, Butterworths, London, 1958.

Pople, J. A., W. G. Schneider, and H. J. Bernstein, *High Resolution Nuclear Magnetic Resonance*, McGraw-Hill Book Co., New York, 1959.

Selwood, P. W., *Magnetochemistry*, Second Edition, Interscience Publishers, New York, 1956.

Problems

16.801 Natural phosphorus is composed entirely of phosphorus-31, with nuclear spin of $\frac{1}{2}$ and magnetic moment 1.1305 nuclear magnetons. (*a*) If the magnetic field is such as to yield proton resonance at 60 megacycles, what frequency would be required for phosphorus resonance? (*b*) Sketch the predicted NMR spectrum for the PH_4^+ ion, in both the proton and phosphorus regions.

16.802 How many sets of equivalent protons are found in the *o*-benzosemiquinone ion? Sketch the shape of the predicted ESR spectrum, assuming that all the lines are resolved.

*16.803 Verify the correctness of the calculated spectrum line positions and intensities shown in Fig. 16.813.

16.804 Write out the nuclear spin wave functions for four identical nuclei of spin $\frac{1}{2}$. Determine the number of functions for each of the values of Σm_I.

16.805 A substance has the formula $C_{10}H_{12}$. Explain how you could use NMR spectroscopy to decide between the several alternate structures:

$$(a) \qquad\qquad (b) \qquad\qquad (c)$$

16.806   Write symmetrical and antisymmetrical nuclear spin wave functions for a homonuclear diatomic molecule in which the nuclear spins are $\frac{3}{2}$. What are the high-temperature proportions of ortho and para states?

9. Review Problems

16.901   The dipole moment of a real heteronuclear molecule is more complex than that given by Eq. 16.201. The right-hand side also contains terms such as $\mu_2 Q^2$ and $\mu_3 Q^3$. Determine the vibrational selection rules for such a real molecule, by successive applications of Eq. 16.209.

*16.902   Cyanogen bromide, BrCN, has been extensively studied in the microwave spectrum. The $h/8\pi^2 I$ values have been obtained for a number of isotopic species; the following list gives the mass numbers of the isotopic molecular species, followed by the $h/8\pi^2 I$ value in megacycles per second. Obtain C–N and C–Br bond distances by the substitution method for several different isotopic combinations, and compare the values obtained.

79–12–14	4120.198	79–13–14	4073.373
81–12–14	4096.788	81–13–14	4049.608
79–12–15	3944.846	81–12–15	3921.787

Atomic masses (O^{16} scale) are $C^{13} = 13.00747$; $Br^{79} = 78.94365$; $Br^{81} = 80.94232$.

16.903   The nitronium ion, NO_2^+, exists in certain solutions and solids. It is found to have only one Raman active vibration, at 1400 cm^{-1} (polarized); the strong infrared bands are found at 2360 and 540 cm^{-1} (no infrared found at 1400). What is the configuration of the nitronium ion? A weak infrared band is found at 3735 cm^{-1}; to what is it due?

16.904   Show how valence bond functions, including the spin, may be written for the hydrogen molecule by appropriate combinations of Slater-type determinants; see Chapter 3. Do this for both the singlet and the triplet states.

16.905   Show that, for a planar molecule, only two of the three principal moments of inertia are independent.

*16.906   Derive an expression for the shifts of the $J = 1$ levels of a polar linear molecule in an electric field. Use this result to obtain an expression for the shift of the $J = 0 \rightarrow 1$ line of the pure rotational spectrum caused by the presence of an electric field.

*16.907   Verify the relative intensities shown in Fig. 16.304 for the components of the $J = 1 \rightarrow 2$ transition of the pure rotational spectrum in the presence of an electric field.

16.908   What are the zero-point energies for CCl_4, CH_4, and CH_2Cl_2?

16.909   Estimate the wavelengths for the transitions from the ground electronic states to the two lowest excited singlet states and to the lowest triplet state in benzene and in pentacene.

General References

Allen, H. C., Jr., and P. C. Cross, *Molecular Vib-Rotors*, John Wiley and Sons, New York, 1963.

Barrow, G. M., *Introduction to Molecular Spectroscopy*, McGraw-Hill Book Co., New York, 1962.

Bauman, R. P., *Absorption Spectroscopy*, John Wiley and Sons, New York, 1962.

Coulson, C. A., *Valence*, Oxford University Press, Oxford, 1952.

Daudel, R., R. Lefebvre, and C. Moser, *Quantum Chemistry; Methods and Applications*, Interscience Publishers, New York, 1960.

Gaydon, A. G., *Dissociation Energies and Spectra of Diatomic Molecules*, Chapman and Hall, London, 1953.

Gordy, W., W. V. Smith, and R. F. Trambarulo, *Microwave Spectroscopy*, John Wiley and Sons, New York, 1953.

Herzberg, G., *Infrared and Raman Spectra of Polyatomic Molecules*, D. van Nostrand, Princeton, N.J., 1945.

Herzberg, G., *Spectra of Diatomic Molecules*, Second Edition, D. van Nostrand, Princeton, N.J., 1950.

Pauling, L., *The Nature of the Chemical Bond*, Third Edition, Cornell University Press, Ithaca, N.Y. 1960.

Simpson, W. T., *Theories of Electrons in Molecules*, Prentice-Hall, Englewood Cliffs, N.J., 1962.

Slater, J. C., *Quantum Theory of Molecules and Solids*, Vol. I, McGraw-Hill Book Co., New York, 1963.

Streitwieser, A., Jr., *Molecular Orbital Theory for Organic Chemists*, John Wiley and Sons, New York, 1961.

Townes, C. H., and A. L. Schawlow, *Microwave Spectroscopy*, McGraw-Hill Book Co., New York, 1955.

Wilson, E. B., Jr., J. C. Decius, and P. C. Cross, *Molecular Vibrations*, McGraw-Hill Book Co., New York, 1955.

Chapter Seventeen

Reaction Rates under

Nonequilibrium Conditions

The earlier discussion of reaction rates was concerned with systems in which the relative populations of excited states of a given species were governed by statistical thermodynamic considerations for the particular ambient temperature concerned. Previously, we had one example of a reaction system, namely, unimolecular reactions in the fall-off region, in which the steady state populations of excited states were not described by the Boltzmann distribution law (Sec. 14.4). We consider now the production of excited states by activation techniques other than the random walk collisional excitation process described in Chapter 13, which applies most frequently to systems in thermal equilibrium.

A great variety of excitation methods has been used, including slapping a molecule with a paddle, literally. A few techniques have been described in Sec. 14.3 in connection with fast reactions. Some of the methods upon which much effort has been expended include the excitation of molecules by bombardment with visible or ultraviolet light photons as in photochemistry, with electrons as in mass spectral studies, and with β, γ, and α particles as in radiation chemistry. These three areas will now be described briefly, along with some related phenomena.

1. Photochemistry

The initial event in a photochemical process is the absorption of radiation. It was pointed out by Grotthuss as early as 1818 that only the absorbed radiation can bring about photolysis, i.e., chemical change. As described by Einstein and Stark, a quantum of energy can directly bring about the destruction of only the molecule by which it is absorbed—the *law of photochemical equivalence*. Avogadro's number of photons, an amount of energy called the *einstein* (comparable to the faraday in electrochemistry), may at most directly cause the reaction of a mole of absorber. Of course, if chain processes ensue, secondary reaction can cause destruction of more molecules of reactant. The *quantum yield* ϕ is defined as

$$\phi = \frac{\text{number of molecules reacted}}{\text{number of photons absorbed}} \qquad (17.101)$$

The measurement of the amount of light absorbed or transmitted by the reaction mixture is the subject of *actinometry*.

Unless the exciting transition is an allowed process, involving no change in spin multiplicity, the intensity of absorption has usually been too small to encourage chemical investigation, since the selection rules prohibit a spin multiplicity change. Hence the initial excited state has almost invariably been a singlet state, like the usual ground state.

Types of Transitions.   Three of the processes described by M. Kasha are the most important ones in photochemistry (see Sec. 16.6):

(*a*) An $n \rightarrow \pi^*$ transition indicated by the upper state $^1(n, \pi^*)$, where the super-prefix refers to a singlet state; this corresponds to promotion of an electron from a nonbonding n orbital into the lowest unoccupied orbital which is an antibonding π orbital. The asterisk indicates electronic excitation, *not* an activated complex. This transition is important for aldehydes and ketones.

(*b*) A $\pi \rightarrow \pi^*$ transition indicated by the upper state $^1(\pi, \pi^*)$; this transition corresponds to promotion of an electron from a bonding π orbital. Prominent examples are the absorption of polyenes and aromatic compounds in the visible and ultraviolet.

(*c*) A $\sigma \rightarrow \pi^*$ transition, indicated by the upper state $^1(\sigma, \pi^*)$; this corresponds to promotion of an electron from a bonding σ orbital. These transitions are not as significant in ordinary photochemistry in the visible and near ultraviolet but are of importance in photochemical studies in the far and vacuum ultraviolet.

The Primary Process.   By a primary process in a photochemical system is usually meant one which leads to chemical products. However, a number of other possible events can occur (Fig. 17.101). The relative importance of the processes that actually follow the initial excitation is somewhat dependent on the lifetime τ of the initial excited state, i.e., on the nature of the original transition. By the principle of detailed balance, the latter is proportional to the square of the transition moment integral (Eq. 16.205). As a rough rule,

$$\tau = \frac{10^{-4}}{\epsilon} \qquad (17.102)$$

Here ϵ is the extinction coefficient in *Beer's law* for the intensity of incident light I after passage through a path of l cm in the absorbing medium,

$$I = I_0 e^{-\epsilon c l} \tag{17.103}$$

I_0 is the initial radiation intensity, and c is the molar concentration of the medium. Following excitation there may occur

(a) Radiative transition to the ground state or *fluorescence*; the characteristic rate is frequently of the order 10^8 to 10^9 sec^{-1} for (π, π^*) states and 10^4 to 10^7 sec^{-1} for (n, π^*) states.

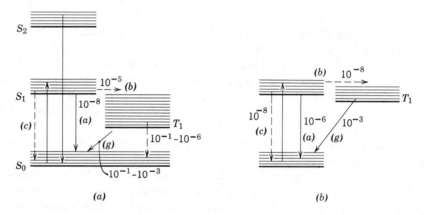

Fig. 17.101 Electronic energy state diagram for molecules with (*a*) (π,π^*) states and (*b*) (n,π^*) states. The numbers quoted are unimolecular lifetimes (seconds). The full lines represent radiative processes and the broken lines nonradiative processes. Initial excitation takes place from the ground state S_0 to various vibrational levels of the first (or higher) excited singlet state. This is followed by (*a*) fluorescence, (*b*) intersystem crossing to triplet T states, (*c*) internal conversion, (*g*) phosphorescence. [Adapted with permission from R. M. Hochstrasser and G. B. Porter, *Quart. Revs.*, **13**, 146 (1959).]

(b) *Intersystem crossing* from the singlet to a triplet state which is favored for (n, π^*) states, relative to (π, π^*) states.

(c) *Internal conversion* by nonradiative transition to the ground state.

(d) Collision *quenching* or nonradiative energy transfer to another molecule; this process, photosensitization, will be treated in more detail later.

(e) Unimolecular or bimolecular reaction.

(f) Predissociation, discussed in Chapter 16, p. 620.

It is evident that process (*d*) and, in part, process (*e*) depend upon pressure. Reaction by (*e*) may be supplemented by another reaction process following (*b*),

(g) The triplet state may, if stable, undergo a radiative transition to the ground state—*phosphorescence*; the nature of this process was clarified by the work of G. N. Lewis in the early forties. Spin angular momentum conservation, which restricts a multiplicity change, causes the characteristic relaxation time for this process to be of the order of as much as one million times longer than for fluorescence. This property of the triplet states makes possible the existence of the laser. Phosphorescence of biacetyl has been studied intensively by photochemists. Alternate processes of the triplet state include unimolecular or bimolecular reaction.

Internal conversion by (c) produces highly vibrationally excited ground state molecules which decompose or isomerize. This is apparently what happens, in preference to intersystem crossing, on illumination of cycloheptatriene, 1,3-hexadiene, and other di- and tri-enes with ultraviolet light, e.g.,

$$H_2C{=}CH{-}CH{=}CH{-}CH_2{-}CH_3 \rightarrow \text{(cyclic structure with } {-}CH_3)$$

The characteristic rate of reaction (b) is slower for $^1(\pi, \pi^*)$ than $^1(n, \pi^*)$ states, in general,

$$^1(\pi, \pi^*) \rightarrow {}^3(\pi, \pi^*), \quad k \sim 10^5 \text{ sec}^{-1}$$

and

$$^1(n, \pi^*) \rightarrow {}^3(n, \pi^*), \quad k \sim 10^8 \text{ sec}^{-1}$$

This arises in part because the energy separation of the $^1(n, \pi^*)$ and $^3(n, \pi^*)$ states is smaller than for the $^1(\pi, \pi^*)$ and $^3(\pi, \pi^*)$ (Fig. 17.101); the triplet states lie lower.

Process (g) is slower for the $^3(\pi, \pi^*)$ state than for the $^3(n, \pi^*)$ state.

Variation of the photolysis excitation energy can give rise to different excited states, with corresponding alteration of observed behavior. For example, lowering the excitation wavelength below 3100 Å in the photolysis of various ketones enhances the rate of singlet state decomposition while decreasing the rate of intersystem crossing.

Stern-Volmer Equation.   It is evident that, following the initial absorption of a light quantum, there is a whole array of simultaneous and consecutive processes which may ensue. We consider one simple composite scheme as follows:

$$A + h\nu \xrightarrow{I} A^* \qquad \text{(excitation)}$$

$$A^* \xrightarrow{k_d} Pr \qquad \text{(decomposition)}$$

$$A^* + M \xrightarrow{k_q} A + M \quad \text{(quenching)}$$

$$A^* \xrightarrow{k_f} A + h\nu \quad \text{(fluorescence)}$$

The rate of excitation is assumed to be constant and characterized by the light intensity, I, in suitable units. Then the steady state approximation for the non-equilibrium concentration of C_{A^*} gives

$$\frac{dC_{A^*}}{dt} \approx 0 = I - k_d C_{A^*} - k_q C_{A^*} C_M - k_f C_{A^*} \qquad (17.104)$$

and

$$C_{A^*} = \frac{I}{k_d + k_q C_M + k_f}$$

so

$$\frac{dC_{\text{Pr}}}{dt} = k_d C_{\text{A}*} = \frac{I}{1 + \dfrac{k_q C_{\text{M}} + k_f}{k_d}} \tag{17.105}$$

The quantum yield ϕ_d for reaction is given by dividing Eq. 17.105 by I,

$$\phi_d = \frac{1}{1 + \dfrac{k_q C_{\text{M}} + k_f}{k_d}} \tag{17.106}$$

Similarly the rate of fluorescence is given by $I_f = k_f C_{\text{A}*}$, where I_f is the steady state fluorescence rate or intensity. Then the ratio of I/I_f, on rearranging Eq. 17.104, is

$$\frac{I}{I_f} = 1 + \frac{k_d + k_q C_{\text{M}}}{k_f} \tag{17.107}$$

Equation 17.107 is a form of the equation of 0. Stern and M. Volmer (1919). For an experimental system which follows this reaction scheme, a plot of $[(I/I_f) - 1]$ against the total pressure, or C_{M}, gives the intercept k_d/k_f and the slope k_q/k_f.

ILLUSTRATION.   To show the behavior of a system according to the Stern-Volmer equation.

The following rates of hydrogen production were reported by R. Srinivasan [*J. Chem. Phys.*, **38**, 1039 (1963)] for the photolysis of cyclohexadiene at 2537 Å:

P, mm:	0.30	0.85	1.50	2.35	4.75	10.25	23.10
H_2, μmoles min^{-1}:	0.295	0.256	0.214	0.202	0.119	0.072	0.032

No fluorescence was observed; instead, internal conversion to vibrationally excited ground electronic state molecules was rapid, and the reaction scheme is as follows:

$$\text{CH} + h\nu \xrightarrow{\;I\;} \text{CH*} \qquad \text{(electronic excitation)}$$

$$\text{CH*} \xrightarrow{\;k_i\;} \text{CH'} \qquad \text{(internal conversion)}$$

$$\text{CH'} \xrightarrow{\;k_d\;} \text{H}_2 + \text{benzene} \qquad \text{(decomposition)}$$

$$\text{CH'} + \text{M} \xrightarrow{\;k_q\;} \text{CH} + \text{M} \qquad \text{(quenching)}$$

Collisional de-excitation or quenching of vibrationally hot cyclohexadiene molecules leads to their stabilization. The particular Stern-Volmer relation which holds here is found by means of the steady state approximation as follows:

$$C_{\text{CH'}} = \frac{I}{k_d + k_q C_{\text{M}}}$$

$$\frac{dC_{\text{H}_2}}{dt} = k_d C_{\text{CH'}} = \frac{k_d I}{k_d + k_q C_{\text{M}}}$$

or

$$\frac{1}{dC_{\text{H}_2}/dt} = \frac{1}{I} + \frac{k_q}{k_d I} C_{\text{M}}, \quad \text{and} \quad \phi_{\text{H}_2} = \frac{k_d}{k_d + k_q C_{\text{M}}}$$

Thus a plot of the reciprocal of the rate of hydrogen production vs. pressure gives a straight line with a positive slope and intercept (Fig. 17.102). The light intensity is in microeinsteins min⁻¹.

Secondary Processes. Production of radicals or atoms as a consequence of photoinduced decomposition or reaction may be followed by a variety of processes analogous to those described in Sec. 14.7. For example, as mentioned in connection with the hydrogen-bromine and hydrogen-chlorine reactions, these chain processes may be initiated by light absorption instead of by thermal atom production. The sequence of reactions described for the thermal system will then occur.

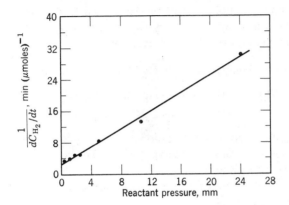

Fig. 17.102 Variation of inverse yield for H_2 production as a function of pressure in photolysis of cyclohexadiene (data of Srinivasan).

The acetone photolysis is probably the most-studied photochemical reaction. It has been investigated at wavelengths from 1800 to 3600 Å, and temperatures from 0 to 500°C. The situation in this case, however, is more complicated than for the hydrogen-bromine reaction, where light absorption produced simple bromine atoms of known characteristics. Since the energetics and relative shapes and positions of the excited electronic states of complex molecules are not well known, the subsequent processes are frequently difficult to predict or even to discern experimentally.

ILLUSTRATION. The form of the rate expression for the hydrogen-bromine reaction initiated by light.

If yellow light is absorbed by the system at a constant rate, the initiation rate expression, $2k_1 C_{Br_2} C_M$, of Chapter 14, is replaced by twice the light intensity $2I$. Then Eq. 14.708 becomes for $t = 0$, where $C_{HBr} = 0$,

$$\frac{dC_{HBr}}{dt} = \left(2\frac{I}{k_5}\right)^{1/2} k_2 C_{H_2}$$

The initial rate is proportional to the square root of the light intensity. This was verified experimentally by M. Bodenstein and H. Lutkemeyer (1924). The student may derive the full rate expression.

Photosensitization. Excitation may occur indirectly, by a *collision of the second kind* upon illumination of an absorbing system. In this process, electronic excitation of one species is converted into translational, rotational, or vibrational energy of another species. Internal conversion may be regarded as an internal collision of the second kind.

Consider a mercury atom in its ground electronic state, $(^1S_0)$. (The new *subscript* quantum number represents a particular combination of the spin and orbital angular momenta, and is simply part of the label used to designate a particular energy state.) When a mixture of mercury vapor and ethylene is irradiated with light of wavelength 2537 Å, the following reactions occur:

$$Hg(^1S_0) \xrightarrow[\text{2537 Å}]{h\nu} Hg(^3P_1) \qquad (a)$$

$$Hg(^3P_1) + C_2H_4 \longrightarrow Hg(^1S_0) + C_2H_4^{*\prime} \quad (b)$$

$$C_2H_4^{*\prime} \longrightarrow C_2H_2^* + H_2 \qquad (c)$$

where the prime signifies vibrational excitation and electronic excitation of ethylene to the lowest triplet state occurs to conserve spin angular momentum. The excited ethylene molecule may decompose by (c).

The reverse type of energy-transfer process is termed a *collision of the first kind*; an example is given in Sec. 17.4.

The collisional process (b) that causes deactivation of the sensitizer is also called quenching. Table 17.101 gives examples of *quenching* cross sections σ_q^2 of some substances for $Hg(^3P_1)$. These cross sections are simply the effective collisional cross sections of the partners for the process in question. Small values of σ_q^2 correspond to effectively elastic collisions.

Table 17.101   Quenching Cross Sections of Various Substances with $Hg(^3P_1)$*

Substance:	C_2H_4	C_4H_8	CH_4	C_2H_6	C_3H_7	H_2	O_2	He
σ_q^2, Å:	22	30	0.2	0.5	1.7	6	13	<0.1

* See R. J. Cvetanović, second reference of this section, for more values.

Atomic sensitizers have been the most widely used. Different atoms, excited to different states (Table 17.102), have been used to bring the molecule to varying energy levels. Some of the most extensively investigated reactions have been the photosensitized reactions of alkanes and alkenes. In addition to mercury, $Zn(^3P_1)$ and $Cd(^3P_1)$ may also be used to produce excited triplet state ethylene. Quantum yields may be defined in terms of the efficiency of conversion of light absorbed by sensitizers into reaction events. Only mercury photosensitization provides enough energy (112 kcal mole^{-1}) to bring about reaction (c); $\phi_{Hg} \sim 0.5$, $\phi_{Zn} \geq \phi_{Cd} \simeq 0$.

Reaction (d) does not occur. If the singlet ($^1P_1$) states of mercury, cadmium, and zinc are used, reaction (d) of photosensitized singlet ethylene can proceed.

$$C_2H_4^{*\prime} \rightarrow C_2H_3 + H \quad (d)$$

Table 17.102   Energy of Excitation for Various Electronic Transitions of Atomic Sensitizers

Sensitizer	Excitation Energy Available		Atomic Transition
	Å	kcal mole^{-1}	
Hg	2537	112.2	$^3P_1 \rightarrow {}^1S_0$
	1849	153.9	$^1P_1 \rightarrow {}^1S_0$
Zn	3076	92.5	$^3P_1 \rightarrow {}^1S_0$
	2139	133.4	$^1P_1 \rightarrow {}^1S_0$
Cd	3261	87.3	$^3P_1 \rightarrow {}^1S_0$
	2288	124.4	$^1P_1 \rightarrow {}^1S_0$
Na	5890	{48.3}	$^2P_{3/2} \rightarrow {}^2S_{1/2}$
	5896		$^2P_{1/2} \rightarrow {}^2S_{1/2}$
Xe	1470	194	$^1P_1 \rightarrow {}^1S_0$

Molecular sensitizers have also been employed. Examples include the use of benzophenone and SO_2 molecules, which bring about the decomposition of diazomethane and isomerization of butene-2, respectively,

$$Bz \xrightarrow[3200\ \text{Å}]{h\nu} Bz^*$$

$$Bz^* + CH_2N_2 \longrightarrow Bz + CH_2N_2^*$$

$$CH_2N_2^* \longrightarrow CH_2 + N_2$$

and

$$SO_2 \xrightarrow[2537\ \text{Å}]{h\nu} SO_2^*$$

$$SO_2^* + cis\text{-butene} \longrightarrow SO_2 + cis\text{-butene-}2^{*\prime}$$

$$cis\text{-butene-}2^{*\prime} \longrightarrow trans\text{-butene-}2^{*\prime} \xrightarrow{M} trans\text{-butene-}2$$

References

Hochstrasser, R., and G. B. Porter, *Quart. Revs.*, **13**, 146 (1959).

Noyes, W. A. Jr., G. S. Hammond, and J. N. Pitts, Editors, *Advances in Photochemistry*, Vol. 1, Interscience Publishers, a division of John Wiley and Sons, New York, 1963, and volumes following.

Steacie, E. W. R., *Atomic and Free Radical Reactions*, Second Edition, Reinhold Publishing Co., New York, 1954.

Problems

17.101   Find the energy in ergs corresponding to an einstein of radiation of wavelength 2537 Å; 3180 Å; 1180 Å.

17.102   Using the bond dissociation energy of bromine molecules given in Sec. 14.7, find the longest wavelength of light that can bring about dissociation.

*17.103   The yield of I_2 from HI was obtained by Warburg (1918) as 0.72×10^{-2} and 1.04×10^{-2} mole kcal^{-1} of light energy at 2070 and 2820 Å, respectively. Why is the value less at lower energy? What is the quantum yield in both cases? Devise a secondary mechanism that leads to destruction of more HI.

*17.104   Uranyl oxalate was studied as an actinometric solution by W. Leighton and G. S. Forbes [*J. Am. Chem. Soc.*, **52**, 3139 (1930)]. The quantum yield for decomposition into CO, CO_2, etc., was 0.58 at 4350 Å. If 10^{-5} einstein of light is first passed through a Cl_2-H_2 mixture, other workers found that the apparent yield in the actinometric solution dropped to 0.145, as based on the initial light intensity, and 0.5 mole of HCl was produced. Find the quantum yield for Cl_2 reaction. Can you explain it?

17.105   Using Fig. 17.102, find the approximate ratio of k_q/k_d for the photolysis of cyclohexadiene.

2. Excitation by Electron Impact

One method of exciting atoms and molecules which has been widely applied in recent years is electron impact. The collision may take place in the ionization chamber of a mass spectrometer, so that the various ions produced are conveniently detected and analyzed. Ion currents as low as 10^{-15} amp are detected. The ionization chamber contains the gas under study at a pressure of 10^{-5} to 10^{-6} mm. The electron beam (Fig. 17.201) which enters the ionization chamber usually has a spread of energies, i.e., is inhomogeneous; however, "monoenergetic" electron sources, having a spread of energies of only 0.01 to 0.1 ev, are also used. Upon collision with the electron, which usually has an energy of 5 to 100 volts, the molecule may undergo a number of processes. Not all of these processes are amenable to direct kinetic study; but most are of importance for the understanding of the relevant rate processes and provide important information about the structure and energetics of molecules and ions. We shall consider these latter aspects first.

Ionization Potentials and Molecular Energy Levels.   The first ionization potential I of an atom or molecule is the amount of energy required to remove the most weakly bound electron from the species in question (Chapter 3). It provides information about the valence binding of the electrons, as do measurements of second, third, etc., ionization potentials. Some characteristic ionization curves are shown in Fig. 17.202. Deduction of the correct value of I from such curves is frequently difficult, and a calibration gas of known ionization potential has sometimes been used in admixture with the substance in question as a guide.

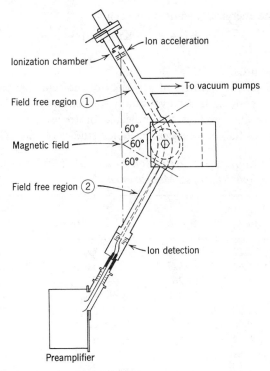

Fig. 17.201   Schematic drawing showing a Nier 60° sector-type mass spectrometer [adapted with permission from *Rev. Sci. Instr.*, **18**, 398 (1947)].

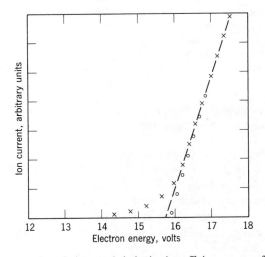

Fig. 17.202   Representation of characteristic ionization efficiency curves for $Ar + e^- \rightarrow Ar^+ + 2e^-$ ($I = 15.76$ ev): × × ×, inhomogeneous electron beam; – – –, extrapolation; ○ ○ ○, results of the kind obtained by Fox with an electron beam effectively homogeneous to 0.1 ev, showing elimination of foot of curve.

In this way, the energies of transitions such as

$$Kr + e^- \rightarrow Kr^+(^2P_{3/2}) + 2e^-$$
$$\rightarrow Kr^+(^2P_{1/2}) + 2e^-$$

have been measured.

Information on the spacings of a variety of molecule-ion states has also been obtained, corresponding to removal of a first electron from other than the highest (least stable) orbital level of the molecule or to excitation above the ground electronic state of the ion product. Detailed studies of this kind have been made

Table 17.201   Some First Ionization Potentials (ev) Determined by Electron Impact and by Spectroscopic Measurement

Species	Electron Impact	Spect.	Species	Electron Impact	Spect.
H	13.62	13.595	O_2	12.1	12.2
H_2	15.44	15.427	H_2O	12.67	12.61
C	11.1	11.264	F_2	16.5	. . .
CH	. . .	11.1	Cl_2	11.80	11.32
CH_2	11.9	. . .	Br_2	10.92	. . .
CH_3	9.96	. . .	I_2	9.41	. . .
C_2H_5	8.72	. . .	F	. . .	17.42
C_6H_5	9.89	. . .	Cl	13.0	13.01
CH_4	13.12	. . .	N_2	15.60	15.58
C_2H_6	11.65	. . .	HCl	12.78	12.90
C_2H_4	10.56	. . .	HBr	11.69	12.09
C_2H_2	11.42	11.41	NH_3	10.52	. . .
C_6H_6	9.21	9.24	He	24.46	24.580
Na	5.15	5.38	Ne	21.53	21.559
K	4.34	4.339	Ar	15.77	15.755
Rb	4.18	4.176	Kr	14.00	13.996
Cs	3.19	3.893	Xe	12.15	12.127

* Selected values by permission from F. H. Field and J. L. Franklin, *Electron Impact Phenomena*, Academic Press, New York, 1957.

of the excited levels of O_2^+. Such measurements provide some of the best, and are sometimes the sole, source of information on molecular orbital levels. The comparison of I values in Table 12.201 with those determined spectroscopically shows the complementary nature of these two methods, as well as the greater intrinsic accuracy of the spectroscopic measurements.

Appearance Potentials. In addition to the parent ion, smaller ions may arise as a result of bond rupture, e.g.,

$$BC + e \rightarrow BC^+ + 2e^- - I(BC)$$

or

$$BC + e \rightarrow B + C^+ + 2e^- - A(C^+)$$

In general, the energy required to bring about dissociation will cause the appearance potential $A(C^+)$ of C^+ to be greater than $I(BC)$.

By the first law of thermodynamics we have

$$A(C^+) = I(BC) + D(B\!-\!C^+) \tag{17.201}$$

where $D(B\!-\!C^+)$ is the bond dissociation energy for the process

$$BC^+ \rightarrow B + C^+$$

It is evident that another cycle,

$$BC \rightarrow B + C - D(B\!-\!C)$$
$$C + e^- \rightarrow C^+ + 2e^- - I(C)$$

provides the relation

$$A(C^+) = I(C) + D(B\!-\!C) \tag{17.202}$$

From Eqs. 17.201 and 17.202 the value of $D(B\!-\!C^+)$ and of $D(B\!-\!C)$ can be found in terms of the other quantities. As a practical matter, illustrated for transitions to the excited state E'' in Fig. 17.203, the measured value of $A(C^+)$ is frequently greater than the true value; the species B and C^+ are produced with excess relative kinetic energy because the transition from the ground state surface G to the BC^+ surface is to a point above the dissociation limit of the ion.

Franck-Condon Restrictions.   It appears that the transitions which occur under electron impact are vertical in the same sense as radiation-induced transitions, and the transition probabilities, χ, are subject to the Franck-Condon conditions (Sec. 16.5)

$$\chi(\psi_g, \psi_e) \propto \left\{ \int \psi_g \psi_e \, dr \right\}^2 \tag{17.203}$$

where χ depends on the square of the overlap integral of the vibrational wave functions of the ground state and excited state involved in the transition. Two of the many possible cases are shown in Fig. 17.203. It is evident that the overlap is large for $G \rightarrow E'$ when $v = 0$, $v' = 0$, and small for $v = 0$, $v' \gg 0$.

Electron Affinity.   Negative ions may also be formed in the ionization chamber by electron attachment, e.g., by the two mechanisms

$$BC + e^- \rightarrow B^- + C$$
$$BC + e^- \rightarrow B^- + C^+ + e^-$$

Then, in the first case, we have the thermochemical equation

$$A(B^-) = D(B\!-\!C) - E(B^-) \tag{17.204}$$

where $E(B^-)$ is the electron affinity of B, and the equation assumes no excess energy of the products. The second mechanism leads to a different thermochemical expression in which $I(C^+)$ also appears on the right side.

Mass Spectra.   Under usual conditions of operation of a mass spectrometer, the collision of electrons having energies of 40 to 80 ev with a molecule produces a

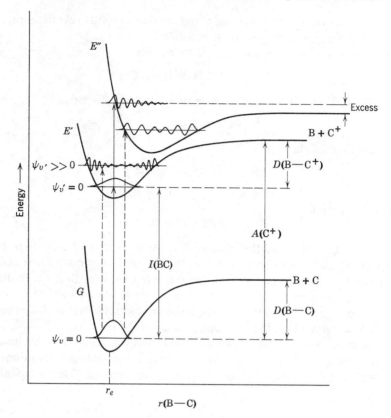

Fig. 17.203 Franck-Condon transitions, $G \rightarrow E$, for two possible excited potential surface relationships. The surfaces are simplified for the diatomic molecule case, BC. The transition $G \rightarrow E'$ is mainly from $v = 0$ to $v' = 0$. The principal transitions, $G \rightarrow E''$, are to the vibrational continuum and give the species B and C^+ having excess kinetic energy. The solid arrows (single head) at the left of diagram indicate transitions of highest probability, while dotted arrows illustrate possible transitions of lesser probability and importance.

highly excited molecule-ion. A number of reaction paths for the ion are usually possible at the energy concerned. For example, four simultaneous primary rupture processes can occur for propane:

$$C_3H_8^+ \rightarrow n\text{-}C_3H_7^+ + H$$
$$\rightarrow C_3H_6^+ + H_2$$
$$\rightarrow C_2H_5^+ + CH_3$$
$$\rightarrow C_2H_4^+ + CH_4$$

The primary products still have sufficient energy to decompose further in a variety of ways. The observed spectrum in Fig. 17.204 is summarized in Table 17.202 in terms of the relative intensity of various mass peaks. The peak at mass 45 is due to

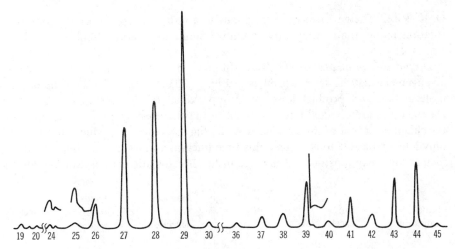

Fig. 17.204 Portion of mass spectrum of propane obtained with 70-ev electrons. The peak heights are proportional to ion intensities. The peaks at $m/e = 19, 19.5, 20$, and 20.5 correspond to doubly charged ions of twice the mass. The three metastable peak details are also shown on an enlarged scale.

1.1 per cent of C^{13} in ordinary carbon so that, for three carbon atoms, m_{45} should equal $(3 \times 0.011)m_{44}$; similarly m_{30} should be $(2 \times 0.011)m_{29}$. The energy distributions of the originally formed excited molecule-ions are not well known but are evidently nonequilibrium in nature and may be approximated. H. Rosenstock, H. Eyring, *et al.* have postulated that the excess internal energy of the molecule-ion is efficiently randomized and that the unimolecular Rice-Ramsperger-Kassel theory (Chapter 14) may be applied to the rate of unimolecular decomposition. This they have done, in the language of absolute rate theory, with use of classical statistical mechanics. A fairly good representation of some aspects of the observed mass spectrum has been obtained in this way. The treatment can be improved by use of a quantum statistical formulation given by R. A. Marcus and

Table 17.202   Mass Spectrum of Propane*

m/e:	45	44[†]	43	42	41	40	39.2[‡]	39	38	37	36	30	29[§]
Relative abundance:	0.91	29.2	23.1	5.86	12.9	2.63	0.15	17.5	4.66	2.63	0.26	2.19	100

m/e:	28	27	26	25.1[‡]	25	24.1[‡]	24	16	15	14	13	12
Relative abundance:	59.5	40.3	8.22	0.22	0.55	0.03	0.04	0.16	5.90	1.78	0.49	0.20

* By permission from the American Petroleum Institute, *Tables of Mass Spectral Data,* Project 44, Serial No. 2, Consolidated mass spectrometer model 21-102, 50-ev beam of electrons.
[†] Parent ion.
[‡] Metastable peak which arises from decomposition of parent by split-off of H_2.
[§] Most abundant ion, arbitrarily given weight 100.

O. K. Rice. Their treatment corresponds to a more realistic molecular vibration-rotation model than the greatly simplified single degenerate oscillator model of Eq. 14.414.

Decomposition of Metastable Ions.   In many mass spectrometers the sequential arrangement may be schematized as in Fig. 17.205 (cf. Fig. 17.201). The original molecule-ion and product ions spend approximately 10^{-6} sec in the ionization chamber and are directed out of exit slit of the chamber by a repeller electrode in the chamber. Most of the ions collected by the detector are produced in this time; only a few molecule-ions survive this time interval and issue from the slit. If any further ion decomposition takes place in the electrostatic acceleration region, the

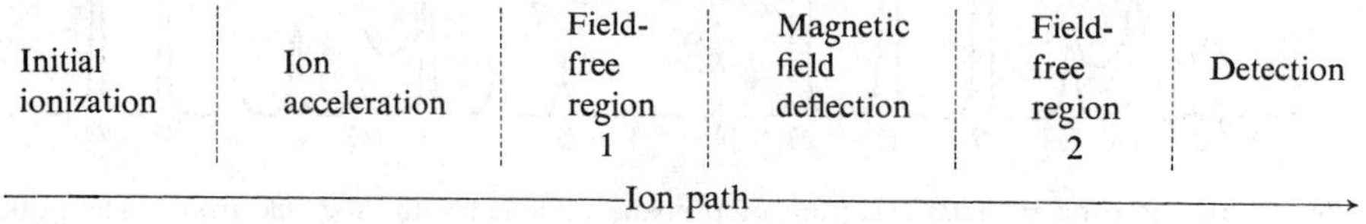

Initial ionization	Ion acceleration	Field-free region 1	Magnetic field deflection	Field-free region 2	Detection

———————————————————————————Ion path—————————————————————————→

Fig. 17.205   Schematic ion path in mass spectrometer.

product ions are not brought into focus and are lost. Ions which dissociate in the field-free region 1 appear as so-called *metastable* ions; these peaks are characteristically broadened and are detected as apparent nonintegral (usually) masses m_m, given by the relation

$$m_m = \frac{m_p^2}{m_d} \tag{17.205}$$

where m_d is the mass of the dissociating ion and m_p is the mass of the product ion. Figure 17.204 contains a few such peaks. This process can be measured directly for quantitative rate investigation.

ILLUSTRATION.   W. A. Chupka [*J. Chem. Phys.*, **30**, 191 (1959)] has given a sample calculation of the relative amounts of various ion products detected in a given experimental arrangement. We consider a parent ion which can decompose into a product ion.

Let 2×10^{-6} sec be the average time spent by the parent molecule-ion in the ionization region; 1×10^{-6} sec the average time it spends in the acceleration region; 5×10^{-6} sec the time spent in the field-free region 1; 3×10^{-6} sec the time in the magnetic field; and 5×10^{-6} sec the time in the field-free region 2; ions dissociating in this latter region are still detected as the original ion mass, but ions dissociating in the magnetic field are lost. Let the total number of original parent ions be N. Then by Eq. 13.708:

(1) No. of parent ions detected $= N \exp\left[-k(2 + 1 + 5 + 3)10^{-6}\right]$
$$= N \exp\left(-11 \times 10^{-6}\,k\right)$$

where k is the specific decomposition rate constant.

(2) No. of metastable ions detected $= [N \exp [-k(2+1)10^{-6}]\}$
$$- \{N \exp [-k(2+1+5)10^{-6}]\}$$

where the first term gives the number of parent ions that enter region 1, and the second gives the number that leave.

(3) No. of product ions detected $= N - N \exp (-k \times 2 \times 10^{-6})$

The student may calculate the fractions represented by (1), (2), and (3) for $k = 10^4$, 3×10^5, and 10^7 sec^{-1}, and make a smooth plot of *fractions* vs. rate constant.

Photoionization Studies. Some of the features of photochemical studies may be combined with the mass spectrographic technique. The initial ionization may be brought about by the use of a vacuum ultraviolet photon beam ($\lambda > 1500$ Å) with a narrow spread, instead of by an electron beam. The resulting spectrum is simplified, and the accuracy of thermodynamic determinations enhanced.

Ion-Molecule Reactions. At the conventional operating pressure of the ionization chamber of $\sim 10^{-5}$ mm, the ions produced experience no further collisions before issuing from the exit slit into the acceleration region. At a pressure higher by a factor of 10^2 to 10^3, secondary collision processes with neutral molecules occur. Simple charge transfer can take place

$$P^+ + R \rightarrow P + R^+$$

e.g.,

$$Xe^+ + C_2H_4 \rightarrow Xe + C_2H_4^+$$

Or charge transfer may be accompanied by dissociation

$$Ar^+ + C_2H_4 \rightarrow Ar + C_2H_2^+ + H_2$$

Displacement reactions have been particularly prominent

$$P^+ + R \rightarrow S^+ + Q$$

e.g.,

$$Kr^+ + H_2 \rightarrow KrH^+ + H$$

and

$$O_2^+ + H_2 \rightarrow HO_2^+ + H$$

At still higher pressures, further reactions of the secondary S^+ ions can be studied. Such processes have led to the discovery of many interesting species, such as CH_5^+ and H_3^+. Frequently, association processes of the kind

$$P^+ + R \rightarrow PR^+$$

are not directly observed because the intermediate PR^+ is very unstable. Such intermediate formation is believed to occur, and the theory for molecule-ion decomposition may also be applied to the competing reaction of PR^+ to explain the various possible secondary ions S^+ formed, e.g.,

$$C_2H_4^+ + C_2H_4 \rightarrow C_4H_8^+ \rightarrow C_3H_5^+ + CH_3$$
$$\rightarrow C_4H_7^+ + H$$

The interesting species H_5^+ has been detected, formed from $H_3^+ + H_2$.

Although ion-molecule reactions have been known for many years in radiation chemistry and electric discharges, such studies have only advanced rapidly through exploitation of the mass spectrometer. These reactions provide novel tests of reaction rate theory. Eyring, Hirschfelder, and Taylor in 1936 gave a treatment, in terms of absolute rate theory, of the reaction

$$H_2 + H_2^+ \rightarrow H_3^+ + H$$

for a thermal equilibrium system.

An analysis of the mass-spectrometer nonequilibrium system may be given as follows. Consider the relative motion of an ion and a molecule. Then the *impact*

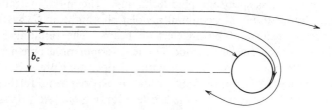

Fig. 17.206   Ion-molecule trajectories.

parameter b is defined as the closest distance at which the particles would pass in the absence of any force between them. The actual interaction potential for an ion and a spherical molecule is

$$V(r) = \frac{-(ze)^2 \alpha}{2r^4} \tag{17.206}$$

where ze is the charge on the ion, and α is the polarizability of the molecule. For each given initial relative velocity, v_r, there is a critical impact parameter b_c such that for $b < b_c$ the attractive force will always draw the particles into collision (Fig. 17.206). Then it may be shown that

$$b_c = \left[\frac{2ze}{v_r} \left(\frac{\alpha}{\mu} \right)^{1/2} \right]^{1/2} \tag{17.207}$$

where μ is the reduced mass. If every collision results in reaction (that is, the activation energy is very small, as seems to be the case) the reaction cross section σ^2, which is a function of v_r, is

$$\sigma^2 v = \pi b_c^2 = \frac{2\pi ze}{v_r} \left(\frac{\alpha}{\mu} \right)^{1/2} \tag{17.208}$$

From Eq. 6.502 and Eq. 13.104, the collision rate is proportional to the product of three factors: (concentrations of collision partners) (collision cross section) (relative speed). Hence the rate of production of secondary ions is

$$\frac{dN_s'^+}{dt} = N_{P^+}' N_R' \sigma^2 v_r = k N_{P^+}' N_R' \tag{17.209}$$

and

$$k = \sigma^2 v_r = 2\pi z e \left(\frac{\alpha}{\mu}\right)^{\frac{1}{2}} \tag{27.210}$$

This is the same as an expression obtained earlier by ART. Equation 17.211 may be related to ion intensities actually observed in the mass spectrometer under the assumptions that the molecule velocities are given by the equilibrium Maxwellian function $f(u,v,w)$ (Eq. 6.117), and that the primary ion velocities v and w, in directions y and z parallel to the exit slit, are also Maxwellian. The ion velocity u in the x direction perpendicular to the exit slit, i.e., in the direction out of the ionization chamber, has superimposed a nonequilibrium contribution dependent on the ion-repeller potential field which drives the ions out of the ionization chamber. If l is the length of path of primary ions in the x direction and E the field intensity, then

$$k = Q \cdot \frac{z e E l^{\frac{1}{2}}}{2 m_{p^+}} \tag{17.211}$$

The first factor of Eq. 17.211 is Q, an observed instrumental reaction cross section; and the second factor, which is the square root of energy divided by mass, is obviously related to relative velocity of the ions, under the condition that the ion energy due to the repeller field of intensity E operating over the distance l, which is

Table 17.203 *Comparison of Calculated Values for Ion-Molecule Reactions with Experimental Rate Constants**

Reaction	$\alpha \times 10^{24}$ cm³	μ, amu	$\dfrac{\alpha_{max}}{\alpha_{min}}$	$k \times 10^9$, cm³ molecule⁻¹ sec⁻¹ Exp.	$k \times 10^9$, cm³ molecule⁻¹ sec⁻¹ Theoret.
$Ar^+ + H_2 \rightarrow ArH^+ + H$	0.7894	1.919	1.40	1.68	1.50
$Ar^+ + HD \rightarrow \begin{cases} ArH^+ + D \\ ArD^+ + H \end{cases}$	0.7829	2.810	1.40	1.43	1.23
$Ar^+ + D_2 \rightarrow ArD^+ + D$	0.7749	3.661	1.40	1.35	1.09
$Kr^+ + H_2 \rightarrow KrH^+ + H$	0.7894	1.969	1.40	0.49	1.47
$Kr^+ + D_2 \rightarrow KrD^+ + D$	0.7749	3.845	1.40	0.30	1.05
$Ne^+ + H_2 \rightarrow NeH^+ + H$	0.7894	1.832	1.40	0.27	1.53
$N_2^+ + D_2 \rightarrow N_2D^+ + D$	0.7749	5.523	1.40	1.72	1.10
$CO^+ + D_2 \rightarrow COD^+ + D$	0.7749	3.523	1.40	1.63	1.11
$O_2 + H_2^+ \rightarrow O_2H^+ + H$	1.60	1.897	1.94	7.56	2.16
$O_2 + D_2^+ \rightarrow O_2D^+ + D$	1.60	3.579	1.94	3.56	1.52
$D_2 + D_2^+ \rightarrow D_3^+ + D$	0.7749	2.015	1.40	1.43	1.45
$HCl^+ + HCl \rightarrow H_2Cl^+ + Cl$	2.63	17.994	1.31	0.44	0.89
$HBr^+ + HBr \rightarrow H_2Br^+ + Br$	3.61	41.001	1.27	0.22	0.67

* By permission from G. Gioumousis and D. P. Stevenson, *J. Chem. Phys.*, **29**, 294 (1958).

$zeEl$, is much greater than the average thermal energy $\frac{1}{2}m_{P+}w^2$, which can be neglected. Q may be related to the measured ion intensities i according to the definition

$$Q = \frac{i_{S+}}{i_{P+}n_R l} \tag{17.212}$$

where the terms in the denominator bring Q to the dimensions of secondary ion intensity per unit primary ion intensity per unit concentration of R per unit length.

Table 17.203 shows the correspondence found between theory and experiment. The agreement is very satisfactory in general. In units of cm^3 molecule^{-1} sec^{-1}, k has the magnitude $\sim 10^{-9}$ or $k = 6 \times 10^{14}$ cm^3 mole^{-1} sec^{-1}, reflecting σ^2 values somewhat greater (ten-fold) than conventional cross-sections. As pointed out by D. P. Stevenson and D. O. Schissler, these large values mean that ion-molecule reactions should be of importance in radiation chemistry systems.

Problems

17.201   Molecule-ions, which decompose by two paths with $k_1 = 10^6$ and $k_2 = 10^5$ sec^{-1}, respectively, spend 10^{-5} sec in the ionization chamber.
(a) What fraction of the ions issue from the chamber?
(b) What fraction decompose in the chamber by the second path?
17.202 $A(CH_3^+)$ from CH_4 is 14.4 ev [Lossing, Ingold, and Henderson, *J. Chem. Phys.*, **22**, 1489 (1954)], and $I(CH_3)$ is given in Table 17.101. Calculate $D(CH_3—H)$. How does this agree with the value of Sec. 9.2?
17.203   Find roughly the ionization chamber pressure at which on the average D_2^+ would make a collision with a D_2 molecule in traversing a distance of 0.25 cm to the exit slit.
17.204   Calculate the percentage of C^{13} in carbon from the mass peaks for $m/e = 30$ and 45 in the spectrum of propane.
17.205   Write the thermochemical equation for $A(B^-)$ according to the second mechanism preceding Eq. 17.204.
17.206   Find what values of apparent masses that the four primary rupture processes for propane described in the text could give rise to as metastable ion peaks.

References

Fox, R. E., *Advances in Mass Spectrometry*, edited by J. Waldron, Pergamon Press, New York, 1959.
McDowell, C. A., *Methods of Experimental Physics*, Vol. 3, edited by D. Williams, Academic Press, New York, 1962, Chap. V.

3. Radiation Chemistry

General Characteristics. Radiation chemistry deals with the chemical consequences of the interaction of matter with very-high-energy particles, such as α and β particles, protons, X- and γ-rays. Figure 17.301 illustrates the variety of

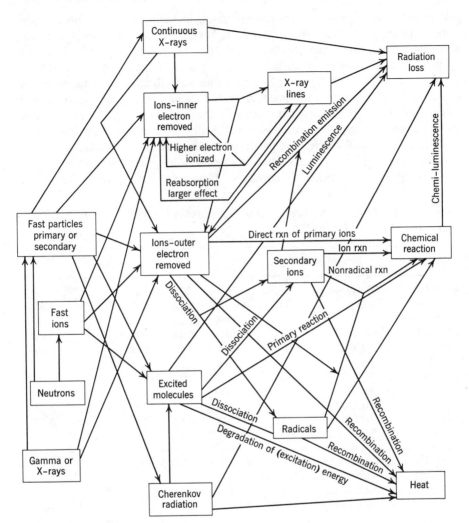

Fig. 17.301   Possible primary and secondary processes in radiation chemistry systems; "the very confusion of the figure illustrates the complexity of the phenomena involved" [by permission from M. Burton, *J. Phys. & Colloid Chem.*, **51**, 611 (1947)].

initial activation processes and subsequent steps. All the processes characteristic of photochemistry and of electron impact can occur in radiation chemistry. Progress in this important area has been difficult but steady.

Studies may arbitrarily be classified as being of two kinds: (1) mechanisms; (2) elementary processes. The work on ion-molecule reactions has re-emphasized their importance in these systems.

Energy Transfer. In their passage through matter, α and β particles undergo cascade energy-wise by transferring energy to electrons or to molecules. An α particle produces an ion pair in various gases, including air, after an average amount of energy, W, of approximately 35 ev has been dissipated. For β particles, W is slightly less. Since the ionization potentials of molecules usually lie in the region of 10 to 15 ev, more than half of the original particle energy is transferred into other forms (Fig. 17.301), i.e., into electronic and vibrational excitation of the original molecules and into the production and excitation of neutral atomic and radical fragments. If the original energy of the bombarding particles is 1 mev (million electron volts), then roughly 3×10^4 ion pairs, and several times more highly reactive neutral species, are produced during its energy cascade.

An important difference exists between excitation by β particles and excitation by α or other heavy particles. In condensed phases, the latter give rise to almost

Table 17.301   Molecular Product and Free Radical Yields of Ionizing Radiations in Aqueous Solutions[*]

Radiation	System	$G_{H_2O_2}$	G_{H_2}	G^a	G^b	G^c	G_{tot}
Co^{60} γ rays	$C_6H_6 + O_2$	. . .	. . .	2.73	. . .	. . .	. . .
Co^{60} γ rays	Fe^{++}	0.87	0.48	2.86	0.69	0.78	4.33
Co^{60} γ rays	Br^-	. . .	0.49	. . .	. . .	. . .	. . .
Co^{60} γ rays	Br^-, O_2	. . .	0.46	2.74	0.92	. . .	3.66
Co^{60} γ rays	HCOOH	0.44	0.44	3.00	0.88	. . .	3.88
2-mev X-rays	Fe^{++}, Ce^{4+}	. . .	0.48	. . .	. . .	. . .	. . .
0.22-mev X-rays	$Fe^{++} + O_2$	0.82	. . .	. . .	. . .	. . .	. . .
0.22-mev X-rays	Fe^{++}	0.62	. . .	. . .	. . .	. . .	. . .
H^3 β rays	HCOOH	. . .	0.51	2.35	1.02	. . .	3.37
Po^{210} α rays	HCOOH	. . .	1.57	0.43	3.14	. . .	3.57
Po^{210} α rays	$Fe^{++} + O_2$	. . .	1.62	. . .	. . .	. . .	. . .

  [*] By permission from E. J. Hart, *Ann. Rev. Phys. Chem.*, **5**, 139 (1954).
  [a] Yield due to reaction $H_2O \rightarrow H + OH$.
  [b] Yield due to reaction $H_2O \rightarrow \frac{1}{2}H_2 + \frac{1}{2}H_2O_2$.
  [c] Yield due to reaction $H_2O \rightarrow H + \frac{1}{2}H_2O_2$.

continuous activation—ionization and excitation—along the path. High-speed electrons produce ionization events approximately 1000 times less frequently and give rise only to local pockets, or *spurs*, of high concentration in radicals and other excited species; diffusion and scavenging can modify the events that occur in these pockets, as well as the probability of intermediates from different spurs coming together. The difference in densities of the reactive species produced by irradiation of the same medium by α and β particles gives different chemical consequences. A γ particle causes effects similar to a β particle, since most of its energy goes into production of high-energy (Compton) electrons which bring about further excitation analogous to β particles. The relative amounts of products formed by various mechanisms upon irradiation of an aqueous solution of formic acid, HCOOH, by

γ, β, and α rays are shown in Table 17.301. The similarity of the relative pro-portions of products (called G values in the table) formed by the first two energy sources, and the difference of these from the proportions arising on α-ray bombard-ment, are clearly evident.

ILLUSTRATION.   Compare the ion-pair-production efficiency of α and β particles and the characteristics of their tracks.

Now a 1-mev α particle may produce an average track density of about 4×10^3 ionizations per micron of path in an organic solvent; a β particle of similar energy may cause only about 4 such events.   Then the average path length per ionization event is:

α particle: path length per initial ionization event $=$
$$10^{-4}/4 \times 10^3 = 2.5 \times 10^{-8}\ cm = 2.5\ Å$$

β particle: path length per initial ionization event $=$
$$10^{-4}/4 = 2500\ Å$$

The α particle causes a linear density of ionization events which corresponds to almost continuous ionization, with correspondingly very high density of various excited species along the track.

Comparison with Photochemistry.   The above multiple excitation sequence is unlike photochemical systems where each photon excites only one molecule. Moreover, the energy distribution of photochemically excited molecules is quite narrow, while that produced by radiation activation in its various manifestations is very broad.   The efficiency of energy absorption in bringing about photolysis was characterized in photochemical systems by the quantum yield ϕ.   The measure of efficiency in radiolysis is G, the total number of substrate molecules converted per 100 ev of energy degraded; values of G may be described for individual products. Table 17.301 illustrates some G values for radiolysis of water on irradiation of various aqueous solutions with different particles.   The data demonstrate the fact that G_{tot} is substantially independent of the type of radiation and added solute, although G^a and G^b depend strongly on particle mass and energy.   Heavy particles are seen to be more efficient for production of H_2.

Problems

17.301   From $G_{H_2O_2}$ (Table 17.301) deduce the fractional contributions of reactions b and c to H_2O_2 production on γ-ray radiolysis of aqueous ferrous ion solutions.

17.302   Estimate the number of ions pairs produced by the degradation of 2-mev X-rays.

17.303   If five hydrogen atoms are produced for each ion pair in Problem 17.302, would this suffice to account for the maximum value of $G_{H_2} = 0.48$ (Table 17.301), assuming that all atoms were to react by $2H \rightarrow H_2$?

4. Hot Atom and Hot Molecule Chemistry

Production of Hot Species. In many radiation and other systems, *hot atoms* and *molecules* or radicals may be of importance. These are (intermediate) product species which have considerable energy in excess of the average at the ambient temperature. The hot reactions have some general identifying characteristics. Inert moderators, such as rare gas atoms, cause the hot species to lose energy and thus affect the yields of various products. Minor amounts of inhibitor or conventional chemical chain breakers have little effect, as does alteration of the ambient temperature, since activation is independent of collision.

Photochemical Production. A good example of the production of hot atoms is afforded by the continuous absorption of ultraviolet light by HI. $D(H\!-\!I)$ is 71 kcal mole^{-1}, and for the process

$$HI \xrightarrow[2537\text{Å}]{h\nu} H^* + I$$

the excess energy, which goes into relative translational energy, is $(112 - 71) = 41$ kcal. Conservation of momentum requires that the hydrogen atom carry most of the excess energy, indicated by an asterisk in the equation. This energy is subject to variation, as by alteration of the frequency of the incident radiation. At 3100 Å, the translation energy of the hydrogen atoms produced is roughly halved. This method could also be applied to HBr.

Production by Chemical Reaction. Exothermic chemical reactions can also give rise to hot species, a process which may be termed *chemical activation.* For example, on addition of hydrogen atoms to propylene at room temperature

$$H + C_3H_6 \rightarrow n\text{-}C_3H_7^* + 37 \text{ kcal}$$

the hot propyl radical, which contains the heat of reaction, may decompose

$$n\text{-}C_3H_7^* \rightarrow CH_3 + H_2C = CH_2$$

The formation of a hot intermediate may be evidenced by other behavior besides decomposition. On reaction of sodium atoms with chlorine molecules

$$Na + Cl_2 \rightarrow NaCl^* + Cl$$

the formation of vibrationally hot sodium chloride results in electronic excitation of sodium atoms by a collision of the first kind

$$NaCl^* + Na(^2S) \rightarrow NaCl + Na(^2P)$$

Production of the intense yellow sodium fluorescence follows, arising by the transition

$$Na(^2P) \rightarrow Na(^2S) + h\nu$$

The most familiar examples of exothermic reactions are undoubtedly flames. The species produced in the reaction zone of a flame display very large deviations from thermal equilibrium. For an acetylene flame in oxygen, spectroscopic measurements reveal that the rotational energy of hydroxyl radicals present in the flame is anomalously high; the average energy corresponds to an "equivalent rotational temperature" of as much as 5400°K, although the flame temperature is less than 3000°K. Thus hot OH radicals are produced. The concentration of ions in the reaction zone may also be anomalously high. Flames produced by oxidation of various hydrocarbons in air or oxygen have been the most studied; flames of other materials, such as the nitrogen compounds NH_3 and N_2H_4, with atmospheres of other gases, such as fluorine F_2, have also been used. The studies of emission spectra and of nonequilibrium in flames have led to a better understanding of these high-temperature exothermic systems.

Reference

International Symposium on Combustion (Annual Proceedings), Academic Press, New York.

Production by the Szilard-Chalmers Reaction. When a radioactive atom in a molecule undergoes nuclear decomposition, the recoil will frequently disrupt the molecule. The unstable atom may be formed *in situ* by capture of a slow neutron, followed by emission of a γ particle, as in the nuclear reaction

$$I^{127} + n \rightarrow I^{\dagger 128} \rightarrow I^{*128} + \gamma$$

which is written in short form as $I^{127}(n,\gamma)I^{128}$; the dagger superscript signifies an excited nucleus, and the asterisk indicates excess translational energy. Bromine and chlorine atoms have been studied similarly.

After neutron irradiation of ethyl iodide, the formation of the recoil-I^{128} atom disrupts the molecule. This sequence was first studied in 1934 by Szilard and Chalmers. The hot I* atom, whether formed from ethyl iodide or from I_2 molecules, may attack other molecules of ethyl iodide

$$I^* + C_2H_5I \rightarrow C_2H_4I_2 + H$$
$$\rightarrow C_2H_4I + HI, \text{ etc.}$$

Other atoms beside halogens may also be used. For many nuclei, the neutron capture process is exothermic by around 8 mev. Upon emission of a 4-mev γ particle by the excited nucleus, its recoil energy will be sufficient to cause bond rupture. Even after bond rupture the recoiling atom still possesses high energy and may cause further excitation or reaction, as just described.

ILLUSTRATION. Find the energy ϵ_r of a recoiling I^{128} atom.

The momentum of a 4-mev γ particle may be found from the well-known (relativistic) Einstein equation $\epsilon = mc^2$. Then

$$m_\gamma c = \frac{\epsilon_\gamma}{c} \tag{17.401}$$

But conservation of linear momentum requires that the momentum acquired by the iodine atom be equal (and opposite in sign), so

$$m_\gamma c = m_I v_I = \frac{\epsilon_\gamma}{c} \tag{17.402}$$

and

$$\epsilon_r = \tfrac{1}{2} m_I v_I^2 = \frac{\epsilon_\gamma^2}{2 m_I c^2}$$

Then 1 ev $= 1.59 \times 10^{-12}$ erg (Chapter 1), and

$$\epsilon_r = \frac{(4 \times 10^6)^2 \times (1.59 \times 10^{-12})^2 \times 6 \times 10^{23}}{2 \times 128 \times 9 \times 10^{20}} \text{ ergs}$$

$$= \frac{(4 \times 10^6)^2 (1.59 \times 10^{-12}) \times 6 \times 10^{23}}{2 \times 128 \times 9 \times 10^{20}} \text{ ev}$$

$$= 67 \text{ ev}$$

Since $D(\text{C—I}) \sim 2$ ev, the translational energy of the iodine atom is 65 ev. The student may show that this corresponds to a velocity of $\sim 10^7$ cm sec^{-1} or an average energy appropriate to a temperature of many thousands of degrees Kelvin.

Production by β Decay. If a molecule contains a radioactive atom, nuclear decay, for example by β emission, will produce a new element of different atomic number. The expulsion of a β particle is *nonadiabatic*, that is, it occurs so suddenly that the atomic electronic distribution cannot adjust sufficiently fast; this profound perturbation creates a highly excited state. Part of this excitation energy of the resulting positive ion may find its way into vibrational excitation, and part into electronic excitation.

Simple examples studied with the aid of a mass spectrometer include

$$CH_3CH_2T \rightarrow CH_3CH_2He^{3+} + \beta \tag{1}$$

and

$$CH_2Br\ CH_2Br^{82} \rightarrow CH_2BrCH_2Kr^{82+} + \beta \tag{2}$$

Reactions (1) and (2) are followed by subsequent processes of the hot "ethyl helium" and "bromoethyl krypton." These new bonds have significant stability, i.e., $D \sim 2$ to 3 ev, since a rare gas *ion is* involved in the bond.

The β-decay energy for tritium is 18 kev (thousand electron volts) and for Br^{82} is 0.47 mev, and the recoil energy provides another source of energy in addition to the excitation due to the nonadiabatic nature of the β emission previously mentioned.

Hot Tritium Atoms. Probably the best-studied example of hot atom chemistry is that of tritium atoms. The hot atoms are produced in the presence of some substrate, usually a hydrocarbon, e.g., by neutron irradiation of He^3 followed by subsequent ejection of a proton, i.e., by the nuclear reaction $He^3(n,p)H^3$. The initial tritium energy is 0.2 mev. Reactions of T^+ ions are not of importance. To enter into chemical combination, the atom must cascade in energy to a value below some critical upper threshold, E_u, above which its energy is too high for collisions of tritium with a substrate hydrocarbon to yield a stabilized tritiated species. Below a lower critical threshold, E_c, the degraded atom no longer has sufficient energy to react. Most of the reaction products of hydrocarbons RCH_3 correspond to formation of the displacement products HT, RCH_2T, RT, etc. From studies of deuterium atom reactions with methane, E_c is found to be $\sim$2 ev, i.e., 45 kcal mole^{-1}; E_u is around 10 to 20 ev as the effective, although indefinite, limit. At these energies, the tritium atom collision with RH is to be considered as an inter-action of tritium with a coupled system of C—H bonds (*epithermal* model), rather than as a collision of tritium with an isolated hydrogen atom (*billiard-ball* model). The latter is appropriate at higher energies of relative translation, where the collision of tritium with a hydrogen atom is over before the latter can interact with its carbon atom partner.

Approach of a tritium atom colinearly with a C—H bond is possibly more effective for production of HT; noncolinear approach at a larger angle to the C—H bond direction may lead instead to C—T bond formation, with displacement of hydrogen but without inversion at the carbon center.

Problems

17.401 What fraction of the excess energy, $h\nu - D$, is carried by hydrogen atoms upon photolytic dissociation of HI? Of HBr?

17.402 Construct a figure for the recoil energy of a nucleus of 100 amu by calculation of the recoil energy for $\epsilon_\gamma = 1, 2, 3$ mev and verify by extrapolation that the ϵ recoil is $\sim$85 ev for $\epsilon_\gamma = 4$ mev.

17.403 If the transition $Na(^2P) \rightarrow Na(^2S)$ corresponds to yellow lines centered at 5893 Å, calculate the energy of the transition in kilocalories per mole; in electron volts.

References

Cross, R. J., and R. Wolfgang, *J. Chem. Phys.*, **35**, 2002 (1961) on hot tritium atoms.
Wexler, S., G. R. Anderson, and L. A. Singer, *J. Chem. Phys.*, **32**, 417 (1960) on β decay.

5. Review Problems

17.501 Express 1 ev, 10 ev, and 1 mev in terms of kilocalories per mole.

*17.502 The photolysis of acetone at room temperature may be described by the mechanism

$$CH_3COCH_3 \xrightarrow{h\nu} CH_3 + CH_3CO$$

$$CH_3CO \xrightarrow{k_b} CH_3 + CO$$

$$2CH_3CO \xrightarrow{k_c} (CH_3CO)_2$$

or

$$2CH_3 \xrightarrow{k_d} C_2H_6$$

or

$$CH_3 + CH_3CO \xrightarrow{k_e} CH_3COCH_3$$

The work of W. A. Noyes, Jr., and coworkers [*J. Am. Chem. Soc.*, **62**, 2052 (1940)] established that the fraction of acetyl radicals which decompose at a given pressure increases from 0.07 at 3130 Å to 0.22 at 2537 Å and to 0.50 at 1850 Å. If $D(CH_3—COCH_3) \simeq$ 80 kcal,

(a) Estimate the value of $D(CH_3—CO)$.

(b) Describe the probable termination step(s) at 3130 Å; at 1850 Å.

(c) How does this mechanism differ from the thermal one? Write a plausible mechanism for photolysis at 3130 Å and 400°C.

*17.503   Estimate the transition energy for excitation of an n electron in acetone (cf. Problem 17.502).

17.504   Estimate the *total relative* collisional quenching *efficiency* of butene and hydrogen with $Hg(^3P_1)$ from the data of Table 17.101.

*17.505   The photolysis of ketene at 3340 Å to yield carbon monoxide and ethylene may be represented by the following processes [G. B. Porter and B. T. Connelly, *Can. J. Chem.*, **36**, 1640 (1958)]:

$$K + h\nu \xrightarrow{k_1} K^+ \text{ (excitation)}$$

$$K^+ \xrightarrow{k_2} Pr \text{ (decomposition)}$$

$$K^+ \xrightarrow{k_3} K \text{ (internal conversion)}$$

$$K^+ + K \xrightarrow{k_4} 2K \text{ (collisional deactivation)}$$

Obtain a Stern-Volmer relation for this reaction scheme, and show that the relation holds for the following two sets of data:

Temperature 37°C

Pressure, mm:	26.0	39.7	47.0	105.3	177.8	384.6
Φ:	0.72	0.72	0.51	0.41	0.37	0.21

Temperature 100°C

Pressure, mm:	26.1	56.7	121.8	299.5
Φ:	0.80	0.74	0.58	0.37

*17.506   Plot the pressure as moles per liter in Problem 17.505 and obtain values for k_4/k_2 in liters per mole at the two temperatures. By use of an Arrhenius plot obtain an approximate activation energy for the reaction process (assume E_a for collisional deactivation = 0).

17.507   For an ion of unit charge and a path length $l = 0.2$ cm, what repeller field intensity is required to give the ion issuing from the exit slit a velocity 100-fold greater than the mean thermal velocity $\bar{u}$ at 225°C? See Eq. 14.318.

17.508   The appearance potentials of various fragments and H atoms from CH_4 are $A(CH_2^+) = 20.2$ volts, $A(CH^+) = 23$ volts, and $A(C^+) = 26.8$ volts. With use of Table 17.201 calculate values of $D(CH_x—H)$, where $x = 0, 1,$ and 2. Compare with Sec. 9.2.

17.509   If the heat of vaporization (atomization) of graphite is 172 kcal mole^{-1}, what is the heat of reaction

$$C(c) + 2H_2(g) \rightarrow CH_4(g)$$

Use the data of Sec. 9.2 and $D(H—H)$ from Table 4.101(A).

17.510 Correct part of the spectrum of Table 17.202 by subtracting the C^{13} contributions to masses 25 to 45 from the tabulated peak intensities, and recalculating on the basis of the revised value of $m_{29} = 100$.

17.511 Using a nonrelativistic linear momentum conservation condition upon the decay of Po^{210} by emission of 5.3-mev α particles, calculate the recoil energy of the resulting lead atom after first deriving the relation

$$\epsilon_{\text{recoil}} = m_\alpha \cdot \frac{\epsilon_\alpha}{m_{\text{recoil}}}$$

General References

Field, F. H., and J. L. Franklin, *Electron Impact Phenomena*, Academic Press, New York, 1957.

Friedlander, G., and J. W. Kennedy, *Introduction to Radiochemistry*, John Wiley and Sons, New York, 1949.

Lind, S. C., C. J. Hochandel, and J. A. Ghormley, *Radiation Chemistry of Gases*, Reinhold Publishing Corp., New York, 1961.

Noyes, W. A., Jr., and P. A. Leighton, *The Photochemistry of Gases*, Reinhold Publishing Corp., New York, 1941.

Steacie, E. W. R., *Atomic and Free Radical Reactions*, Second Edition, Reinhold Publishing Corp., New York, 1954.

Wahl, A. C., and N. A. Bonner, Editors, *Radioactivity Applied to Chemistry*, John Wiley and Sons, New York, 1951.

Chapter Eighteen

Phenomena at Interfaces

Introduction. In the majority of chemical systems more than one phase is present, and consequently there are interfaces between these phases. In many applications, the quantity of material near enough to the interface to be influenced by it is negligible. This is particularly true in the phase equilibrium of large masses. In other cases, however, the material at the interface cannot be neglected and, indeed, may be of paramount importance. In rate processes, such as biological reactions at cell walls or heterogeneous catalysis, the limiting rate process may be at the interface, even though the quantity of material present at any one time is relatively small. Although it is possible to give a rigorous treatment of the thermodynamics of the surface phases, the theory is much more complicated than that for bulk phases. We will give only a partial account of some of the more simple situations, and indicate some difficulties that exist in further treatment.

1. Surface of a Single Component

Surface Energy of a Liquid. Certain surfaces, such as cellulose, are wetted by water; that is, it will spread out and cover the surface. Other surfaces, such as wax, are not wetted by water, which forms droplets on the surface. Any liquid, including water, forms droplets when it is in contact with air or its own vapor in a vacuum. These phenomena are explained in terms of surface energies that tend to a minimum.

We will first take up the surface energy of a liquid in contact with only its own vapor or an inert gas. Figure 18.101 gives a schematic representation of two vessels. They have an equal surface of contact between the liquid and the vessel and an equal capacity for liquid. The only difference is the amount of exposed surface. The free energy of the two arrangements is nevertheless different. We write, for the liquid and its surface, including surface work

$$dF = -S\,dT + V\,dp + \mu\,dn + \gamma\,d\mathcal{A} \qquad (18.101)$$

where γ is the surface free energy per unit area, and $\mathcal{A}$ is the surface area. If we

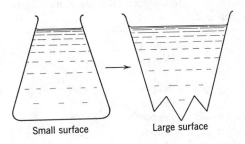

Small surface   Large surface

Fig. 18.101   Schematic representation of a change in the area of a vapor–liquid interface with the number of moles of liquid and container–liquid interface area held constant.

assume that the area is plane and large, γ does not depend on the area $\mathcal{A}$. Then, on integrating Eq. 18.101 at constant T and P,

$$F = n\mu + \gamma\mathcal{A} \qquad (18.102)$$

At constant number of moles, temperature, and pressure, only the surface contributes to dF

$$dF = \gamma\,d\mathcal{A} \qquad (18.103)$$

ILLUSTRATION.   The units of γ.

Note that $\gamma\mathcal{A}$ has the units of energy, just as PV does. Thus γ has the units of energy per square centimeter, which is equivalent to force per centimeter. It is often called the *surface tension*. This arises from a "thought experiment." A surface piston of length unity is arranged so that it can move to create or destroy surface area of the liquid. We correct for any other work done by the piston in exposing its own surface to the liquid. The force associated with moving the piston a distance dx can be found from the total surface energy change associated with the movement dx, if the piston has unit width.

$$dF = \gamma\,d\mathcal{A} = \gamma\,dx$$

and

$$\text{Force} = -\partial F/\partial x = -\gamma$$

Therefore $-\gamma$ is the force, or tension, associated with moving a piston of unit width.

Ordinarily, the surface tension of a liquid is measured in air, or in an inert gas atmosphere, because of the experimental problems associated with the evaporation of the liquid in a vacuum. The quantity measured is logically distinct from, but practically equivalent to, the true surface energy of the surface in a vacuum, in most cases. Some values of the surface tension so measured are given in Table 18.101. Note that the surface tension is always positive and decreases with increasing temperature.

Table 18.101   Surface Tension of Liquids

Substance	In Contact with	Temperature, °C	Surface Tension, dynes cm^{-1}
Acetic acid	Vapor	10	28.8
Acetic acid	Vapor	20	27.8
Acetic acid	Vapor	50	24.8
Argon	Vapor	−188	13.2
Bromine	Vapor	20	41.5
Carbon tetrachloride	Vapor	20	26.95
Carbon tetrachloride	Vapor	200	6.53
Ethyl alcohol	Air	0	24.05
Ethyl alcohol	Vapor	10	23.61
Ethyl alcohol	Vapor	20	22.75
Ethyl alcohol	Vapor	30	21.89
Mercury	Vapor	0	370
Neon	Vapor	−248	5.50
Water	Air	18	73.05

Surface Tension near the Critical State. The distinction between the surface energy of a pure phase and the surface tension of a liquid as it can be measured becomes clear and important as the critical state is approached. The density of the liquid and that of the gas phase approach one another. There is no feasible way of preparing a bare surface of the liquid in this region. There is never any way of preparing a bare and unsupported surface for a gas. Any surface prepared would dissipate immediately into the vacuum. The energy of the interface between the liquid and the saturated vapor is still measurable, up to the critical temperature. Above the critical temperature there is no interface and thus no interfacial energy. We reserve the term surface tension for this interfacial energy below and up to the critical temperature. It follows an approximate law as a function of temperature, near the critical temperature

$$\gamma = \text{const} \, (\rho_l - \rho_g)^4 \qquad (18.104)$$

where ρ_l and ρ_g are the densities of the liquid and gas phases, respectively. These densities become equal and the surface tension goes to zero at the critical temperature.

Vapor Pressure of Spherical Drops.   The chemical potential of a large quantity of liquid bounded by a plane surface is not affected by evaporation, because the area does not change as evaporation proceeds. Thus, from Eq. 18.102, the only effect on the total free energy of the liquid phase F is caused by a change in the number of moles. On the other hand, evaporation from a free-floating spherical drop of radius r causes a change in area. We assume that the free energy is made up of two contributions, one from the bulk liquid and one from the surface area of the drop

$$F_{total} = n\mu_0 + 4\pi r^2 \gamma \tag{18.105}$$

Here, μ_0 is the bulk chemical potential that corresponds to a vapor pressure P_0, that of the saturated vapor at equilibrium for a large sample or drop. We will assume that this is constant for any size drop, and that the bulk density and other properties are constant right up to the surface of the drop. The radius can then be eliminated in favor of the number of moles n

$$\tfrac{4}{3}\pi r^3 = \frac{nM}{\rho_l} \tag{18.106}$$

We have here expressed the volume of the drop in terms of the number of moles, the molecular weight, M, and the density of the liquid. From these relationships, we find, by expressing F_{total} in terms of n, differentiating, and then reintroducing the variable r,

$$\mu = \frac{\partial F}{\partial n} = \mu_0 + \frac{2M\gamma}{\rho_l r} \tag{18.107}$$

or

$$RT \ln \frac{P}{P_0} = \frac{2M\gamma}{\rho_l r} \tag{18.108}$$

This result indicates that the vapor pressure of a drop increases exponentially with the reciprocal of the radius of the drop. It must be pointed out, however, that the effect is large only when the drop is so small that the assumptions are beginning to be quite unreliable. For a raindrop of radius 100 Å, the vapor pressure of water is increased by a factor of only 1 per cent. Only when the drop reaches the size of the order of 10 Å does the effect become large. By this time, there are so few molecules on the "inside" of the drop that it is doubtful what values should be taken for μ_0 and γ.

Nevertheless, this result is of qualitative importance. First, it indicates that small drops will have a higher vapor pressure than large ones, so that large drops will grow at the expense of smaller ones. It also indicates that finely divided substances have a higher chemical potential than the bulk material. Finally, it poses a dilemma about the mechanism of condensation.

Supersaturation and Nucleation.   It is well known that ordinary vapors, such as water vapor, can exist at higher concentrations than the equilibrium vapor pressure. The most familiar laboratory example is the Wilson cloud chamber, where a supersaturated atmosphere has been formed by rapid adiabatic expansion of a mixture of air and saturated water vapor. The function of the air is simply to slow down the diffusion of the water vapor to the walls of the cloud chamber where it can immediately condense. The reason that the water vapor does not condense out in the middle of the chamber is that, as predicted by Eq. 18.108, the vapor pressure of every small droplet, which must be formed before it can grow to a larger droplet, is very much higher than the saturation vapor pressure. How, then, can a liquid *begin* to condense out? There are essentially two mechanisms. First, a foreign nucleus, either purposely or accidentally included

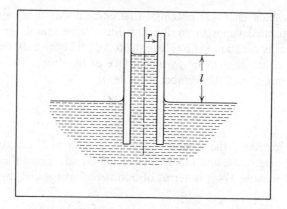

Fig. 18.102   Capillary rise in a cylindrical tube.

in the air, may form a wettable plane surface that starts the growth of a drop. This is the ordinary mechanism of the formation of raindrops in the atmosphere.

However, if the air is dust free, a second mechanism is required. Fluctuations in the density of the water molecules allows spontaneous and temporary self-nucleation to occur. Calculations show that the rate of successful formation of these nuclei is very low unless a rather large degree of supersaturation is present; otherwise they evaporate so rapidly that they have little chance of growing into stable raindrops. Thus, an ordinary vapor, free of dust, can sustain a degree of supersaturation of 10 or 20 per cent almost indefinitely.

Capillary Rise; Measurement of Surface Tension. If a glass tube is placed in water (Fig. 18.102), the water in the tube rises above the level of the water in the beaker. This effect is a general phenomenon with liquids that wet glass. It arises because the glass is presumed to be covered with a film of water that has nearly the normal surface tension, and that this rise annihilates some of the surface area exposed inside the glass tube and thus lowers the free energy. This rise is, of course, opposed by the gravitational work of lifting the water in the capillary to form the column of water. If the capillary rise is a distance l in a tube of radius r, the gravitational work of increasing the height of the water, dl, is

$$dW = -\pi r^2 g \rho_l l \, dl$$

where g is the acceleration of gravity. The change in surface free energy is

$$dF^s = \gamma \, d\mathcal{A} = 2\pi\gamma r \, dl$$

At equilibrium

$$dF_{total} = dF^s + dW = 0$$

from which we find

$$\gamma = \tfrac{1}{2} r g \rho_l l \tag{18.109}$$

From the capillary rise l and the radius of the tube we can calculate the surface tension.

There are a number of assumptions and qualifications. First, the meniscus is curved, and we must take an average of its position to define l. Second, the radius of the tube depends on the thickness of the wet layer. These difficulties are minimized by going to a large tube, but then, of course, the capillary rise becomes so small that it is difficult to measure it over the wide expanse of liquid in the beaker.

In any case, the assumption that the glass is completely wet before the rise takes place is difficult to justify. Perhaps the most convincing argument is found when a variety of glass tubes of different size, composition, and history gives the same value of γ.

Problems

18.101   Calculate the capillary rise effect for water in tubes 1 micron in diameter contained in a living plant. How does this compare with the osmotic pressure effect for transport of water up a plant stem, if the solutions involved are approximately 1 molar, and the surface tension is that of pure water?

18.102   Derive an expression for capillary rise between two parallel plates.

18.103   Advance an explanation of why mercury is depressed in a capillary. How can this depression be used to calculate the surface tension of mercury?

18.104   Evaluate the constant in Eq. 18.104 from the data for water at room temperature. At 220°C the density of liquid water is approximately 0.89 g cm^{-3}, and the vapor pressure 20 atm. Calculate an approximate value for the surface tension at this temperature.

18.105   Calculate the size of rain droplet required to raise the surface vapor pressure by 10 per cent. Calculate the number of molecules present.

2. Surface Films and Adsorption on Liquid Surfaces

We have already encountered the problem of a surface film in the consideration of the capillary rise in a tube with a wet surface. There is a more general and difficult problem that considers the distribution of a solution component between the bulk phases and the surfaces between them. For example, surface active agents, such as detergents, although soluble in water, may tend to accumulate in the air–water interface. However, we will consider here only those surface films that are effectively insoluble in the bulk liquid or solid phase upon which they are formed.

Location of the Surface. The idea of a surface between two phases, occupying two adjacent volumes, is at first sight quite simple. However, its exact location presents some problems. A simple, plane interface between two phases of a one-component system might, for example, be placed where the concentration is undergoing its most rapid change. This definition involves some microscopic or molecular measurements that are foreign to thermodynamics. A better definition locates the surface at that position where the concentration in the bulk of one phase, times its volume, plus a similar product for the other phase, gives the total amount of material present in the interface and both bulk phases (Fig. 18.201).

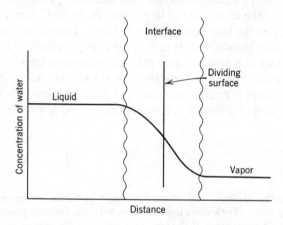

Fig. 18.201 The average concentration of a material upon passing from the liquid to the gaseous phase. The dividing surface is located so as to make the net deviations from the bulk concentrations cancel on the two sides of the interface.

A similar treatment is possible for a two-component system, if we select a particular or principal component (component 1). Then the total amount of component 1 can be made equal to the sum of the products of concentration of component 1 and the volume in the bulk phases. However, this locates the surface, and therefore the total amount of component 2 is not necessarily equal to the sum of the concentration times the volume of the two phases. There is in general an excess quantity n_2^s of component 2 that can be either positive or negative. The *surface concentration* of this component per unit area of the surface is given the symbol Γ_2. Note that, by definition of the dividing surface, $\Gamma_1 = 0$. In most cases Γ_2 will be positive, but the student should not forget that it can be negative in the general thermodynamic formulation.

Then the total bulk free energy, aside from that due to the surface area, is

$$F_b = n_1\mu_1 + n_2^b\mu_2$$

where n_1 is the total amount of component 1, and n_2^b is the total amount of component 2, aside from the quantity n_2^s in the surface. The surface free energy is defined as the difference between the total free energy and the bulk free energy, and the symbols F^s and A^s can be used interchangeably. Since the dividing surface is two dimensional, $V^s = 0$ and thus $F^s = A^s + PV^s = A^s$.

Thermodynamic Treatment of Surface Layers. Consider a film of insoluble material on a surface, for example, of water. If the amount of material on the surface is held constant, and if there is no change in temperature, pressure, or composition, the change in surface free energy with area is

$$dF^s = \gamma \, d\mathscr{A} \tag{18.201}$$

which is just the work of creating a surface of area $d\mathscr{A}$. However, since there is now a material contaminating the surface, we can no longer treat the surface tension γ as a constant because an increase in the surface area will change the surface concentrations. If we allow material (labeled "2") to leave or enter the surface, we must include the material so transferred.

$$dF^s = \gamma \, d\mathscr{A} + \mu_2 \, dn_2^s \tag{18.202}$$

If we integrate this expression at constant surface composition (γ and μ_2 stay constant as $\mathscr{A}$ and n_2 increase), then

$$F^s = \gamma \mathscr{A} + \mu_2 n_2^s \tag{18.203}$$

Upon differentiation this expression becomes

$$dF^s = \gamma \, d\mathscr{A} + \mathscr{A} \, d\gamma + \mu_2 \, dn_2^s + n_2^s \, d\mu_2 \tag{18.204}$$

By comparison with Eq. 18.202, we obtain the surface analog of the Gibbs-Duhem equation (Eq. 8.327)

$$\mathscr{A} \, d\gamma + n_2^s \, d\mu_2 = 0 \tag{18.205}$$

We can make this equation more useful if we introduce the concept of surface concentration, i.e., concentration per unit surface area

$$\Gamma_2 = \frac{n_2^s}{\mathscr{A}} \tag{18.206}$$

to obtain the result

$$d\gamma + \Gamma_2 \, d\mu_2 = 0 \tag{18.207}$$

called the *Gibb's adsorption equation.*

We shall consider specific applications of this equation later, but there is a general result if a positive concentration of material 2 is present at the surface. Consider the process of introducing component 2 into a surface of component 1, starting at a surface tension γ_0 for the pure reference component with $\Gamma_2 = 0$ up to the given values of Γ_2, μ_2, and γ. If Γ_2 is positive, then, as the chemical potential of component 2 is increased, the second term in Eq. 18.207 is positive and so $d\gamma$ must be negative. This result means that a component which concentrates in the surface reduces the surface tension of a pure liquid. There is an important practical consequence of this result. It is easy to find materials, such as soaps, that are sparingly soluble and yet reduce the surface tension of water greatly; but it is difficult to find materials that will raise the surface tension of a liquid very greatly, unless a relatively large quantity is introduced.

Spreading Pressure of a Film.   The surface tension γ changes, of course, as we go from a pure liquid surface to a surface containing a second component. In certain cases this difference can be directly produced and measured. For example, if an oil is placed on the surface of water, where it is insoluble, it may simply draw up into droplets. This occurs if its own surface tension is not affected by water; that is, if it is not wet by water. On the other hand, if a material, such as acetic acid, that is soluble in water is placed on the top of a water surface, it will, of course, dissolve and not form a film. There are, however, materials that are intermediate in behavior, for example, the higher fatty acids. These, such as the C_{14} carboxylic acid, which is almost insoluble in water, spread out as a film on

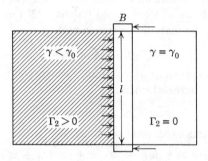

Fig. 18.202   A schematic representation of a surface trough, with a barrier B of length l for measuring surface spreading pressure (by permission from K. L. Wolf, *Physik und Chemie der Grenzflächen*, Vol. II, Springer-Verlag, Berlin, 1959).

water. The common explanation of this behavior is that one end of the molecule, the COOH group, is wet by water (*hydrophilic*) but that the long hydrocarbon chain (*hydrophobic*) will not be dragged into solution by relatively small end groups. A so-called surface active molecule of this type is viewed as having a hydrophilic "head" and a hydrophobic "tail".

A concept of this kind is very useful for visualizing what happens on a liquid surface, but is really a distinction in degree rather than kind. Actually, both the nonpolar oil, with no hydrophilic head, and the long-chain fatty acid have a small solubility in bulk water. Also the molecules of the oil have a small but definite tendency to spread out in a dilute film. On the other hand, if too much fatty acid is placed on a surface, it will form a floating island of excess material itself. However, with the choice of a suitable material it is possible to float a nonvolatile surface film on water or other liquid, and experimentally measure its pressure. The setup is schematically illustrated in Fig. 18.202. A flat tray is filled to the brim and intersected by a movable barrier. When a measured quantity of nonvolatile, insoluble material, such as a fatty acid, is placed on one side of the barrier and not on the other, the area of the surface available to the surface film of acid can be varied by moving the barrier from one side to the other. Suppose that the barrier is displaced an amount $d\mathscr{A}$, to increase the area on the acid side. The free energy change is

$$dF_{acid} = +\gamma \, d\mathscr{A}$$

However, in so increasing the area on the acid side, the area has been decreased on the bare side, so there is a corresponding free energy change

$$dF_{bare} = -\gamma_0 \, d\mathscr{A}$$

where γ_0 is the surface tension of the pure liquid. The net free energy change is

$$dF^s = (\gamma - \gamma_0) \, d\mathscr{A} \tag{18.208}$$

The spreading pressure is defined as the negative derivative of the free energy with respect to area, just as ordinary pressure is defined in Eq. 7.415. So we have for the spreading pressure

$$\phi = \frac{-dF^s}{d\mathscr{A}} = \gamma_0 - \gamma \tag{18.209}$$

It is possible to actually arrange a balance to measure this spreading pressure as a

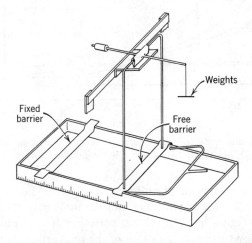

Fig. 18.203   A typical balance and trough for measuring surface spreading pressure (by permission from K. L. Wolf, *Physik und Chemie der Grenzflächen*, Vol. II, Springer-Verlag, Berlin, 1959).

force on the barrier. It is, of course, per unit length of barrier rather than for the whole barrier, so that in the set up illustrated in Fig. 18.203 the required weights that will hold the barrier in place must be converted to a force in dynes, and divided by the length of the barrier.

Pressure-Area Measurements. When suitable substances are spread in a film on water, it is possible to measure the pressure as a function of the area occupied. Some measurements of this type are shown in Fig. 18.204 for a homologous series of fatty acids. Qualitatively the results are the same as for the isotherms of an imperfect gas condensing to a liquid. However, instead of changing temperature, which is difficult on a water surface, as the number of carbon atoms increases, the hydrophobic forces gain over the hydrophilic part of the molecule, and so the film has a greater tendency to condense.

The dashed curve in the figure is the ideal gas law in two dimensions

$$\phi \mathscr{A} = kT \tag{18.210}$$

if $\mathscr{A}$ is the area per molecule. If the film is dilute enough, that is, if the area per molecule is large enough, this ideal behavior (two dimensions) is approached.

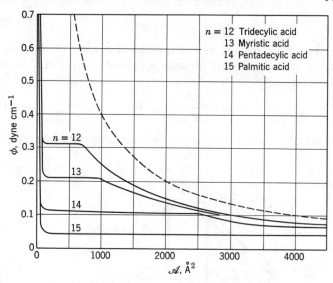

Fig. 18.204   Room-temperature spreading pressure-area curves for some homologous fatty acids (by permission from K. L. Wolf, *Physik und Chemie der Grenzflächen*, Vol. II, Springer-Verlag, Berlin, 1959).

At higher densities, a variety of phenomena may occur. For example, as we have seen in Fig. 18.204, two-dimensional condensation may take place. That this constant-pressure region in the isotherm corresponds to a phase separation in two dimensions follows from an extension of the phase rule. A rigorous treatment would deny this interpretation, in that a pure phase is indefinite in extent and constant in composition, whereas a surface phase has one limited dimension. However, observation of the film as it condenses shows two distinct regions of the surface, and makes it legitimate to extend the notion of phases to two dimensions. As the phase on the surface is further compressed, it is bound to break out of the two-dimensional film that is only one molecule thick. Some qualitative pictures of the stages of compression of a film are shown in Fig. 18.205. Ultimately, of course, the surface film becomes thick enough so that it is properly treated as an ordinary three-dimensional phase.

Any attempt to consider the intermediate region of thick films and film instability, the formation of lenses of flattened droplets on the surface, and other topics is beyond the scope of this treatment. Nonequilibrium states intrude, and there are a number of areas of controversy. The interested student would do well to look at more than one of the General References on the subject.

Mobile Monolayers: Derivation of the Ideal Gas Law in Two Dimensions. If the surface layer of molecules is free to move in the two dimensions parallel to the surface, then it is appropriate to apply the partition function for a particle in

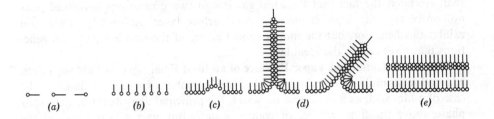

Fig. 18.205   Pictorial representation of stages in the compression of a film of molecules, comprising a hydrophilic head and hydrophobic tail, supported on water (by permission from K. L. Wolf, *Physik und Chemie der Grenzflächen*, Vol. II, Springer-Verlag, Berlin, 1959). (*a*) A very dilute film. The tails lie upon the water. (*b*) The tails begin to interact, with two-dimensional condensation. (*c*) The film begins to be pushed up as the capacity of a monolayer is exceeded. (*d*) A duplex film is being pushed out of the surface. (*e*) The duplex film, hydrophobic side out, forms a triple film with the monolayer on the water.

a two-dimensional box of size $a \times b = \mathscr{A}$. Thus, the translational partition function (Eqs. 16.106, 16.115)

$$Z_{\text{trans (2)}} = \frac{(2\pi mkT)^{\frac{1}{2}}a}{h} \frac{(2\pi mkT)^{\frac{1}{2}}b}{h}$$
$$= \frac{2\pi mkT\mathscr{A}}{h^2} \tag{18.211}$$

This partition function is for one molecule in an area $\mathscr{A}$. The free energy contribution per molecule in the two-dimensional surface film is then

$$F^s = A^s = -kT \ln Z_{\text{trans (2)}} \tag{18.212}$$

from which we calculate, by means of Eq. 18.209,

$$\phi = \frac{kT}{\mathscr{A}}$$

which is the two-dimensional analog of the perfect gas law (Eq. 18.210). In making this derivation we have neglected the motion of the adsorbed molecule normal to the surface. By the fact that it remains on the surface, the molecule must be bound by some attraction, such as van der Waals forces, to the surface. Most simply, we may regard it as being at the bottom of a harmonic potential well as far as motion away from the surface is concerned. The total partition function for all degrees of freedom for motion of the molecule as a whole and internally is thus

$$Z_{total} = Z_{trans}Z_{vib}Z_{int} \tag{18.213}$$

where Z_{trans} is for two degrees of freedom, Z_{vib} for one degree of freedom, and Z_{int} for the rest of the degrees of freedom of the molecule.

This type of partition function is said to describe a mobile monolayer. As we shall see later, the fact that the ideal gas law in two dimensions is obeyed does not prove that the layer is mobile. Any surface layer, sufficiently dilute, will exhibit this behavior, but the mobile model is one of the simplest partition functions that gives rise to the ideal law.

Chemical Potential and Vapor Pressure of an Ideal Film. We can use the Gibbs adsorption formula to calculate the chemical potential of a surface film. In the case of a film such as a fatty acid on water, the principal constituent of the vapor phase above the film will be, of course, water. But even a nearly nonvolatile material, such as a higher fatty acid, will have a definite vapor pressure P_2. This pressure, since it is small enough to be reckoned ideal, will be related to the chemical potential of the adsorbed film as

$$\mu_2 = \mu_2^\circ + kT \ln P_2$$

For a number of molecules N_2 in the surface, we may write the two-dimensional ideal gas law as

$$\phi \mathscr{A} = N_2 kT \tag{18.214}$$

or, by means of Eqs. 18.206 and 18.209,

$$\phi = \gamma_0 - \gamma = \Gamma_2 kT$$

We find then that

$$d\mu_2 = kT \, d \ln P_2$$

and

$$d\gamma = -kT \, d\Gamma_2$$

If we insert these values in Eq. 18.207,

$$-d \ln \Gamma_2 + d \ln P_2 = 0$$

which integrates to give

$$-\ln \Gamma_2 + \ln P_2 = \text{const}$$

or

$$\Gamma_2 = kP_2 \tag{18.215}$$

The amount adsorbed is thus proportional to the pressure; that is, the system obeys Henry's law.

Adsorption Isotherms. Equation 18.215 is the simplest case of an adsorption isotherm, that is, an equation that relates the amount adsorbed to the pressure in the gas phase of a given component. Sometimes, as for films on liquids, attention is concentrated on the spreading pressure-area curves; at other times the isotherm equation is emphasized. The Gibbs adsorption formula allows these formulations to be interchanged or expressed in terms of each other. For the case of adsorbed films on solids, it is theoretically possible to speak of spreading pressure, but practically impossible to measure these functions directly. Therefore, for this kind of surface film, we shall emphasize the isotherm.

Dispersions and Colloids. We made some attempt to treat small particles in Sec. 18.1, where an approximation to the vapor pressure of small droplets was developed. In a multicomponent system, the situation is more complicated. For example, in addition to forming enriched surface films in the air–water interface, soaps and other surface active agents may aggregate to form association polymers in solution called *micelles*. These are in equilibrium with monomer molecules. Such a system is properly treated as a one-phase system. On the other hand, dispersions of droplets of oil in water, in the form of an emulsion, show microscopic evidence of two phases, although the dispersed phase may not be large enough to be treated as a simple bulk phase.

In general, systems of this type may be divided into two classes. First, we have the lyophilic colloids, which are equilibrium solutions of giant molecules that can be treated by the theory of solutions (Chapter 12). These systems are different from ordinary solutions only in the scale of the effects; thus, osmotic effects are much smaller for a given weight concentration, and molecular interaction is a more important factor for these solutions than for those of ordinary molecular weight.

Second, we have the lyophobic colloids or "unstable" solutions, which consist of small regions of another phase, such as metallic gold, dispersed and stabilized in water or other medium in such a way that they will not precipitate a bulk phase. Complex electrical forces that result from the adsorption of electrolytes on the large surfaces present are important in the theory of these systems. We will not consider these multicomponent systems further, but it should be pointed out that the methods of light scattering discussed in Chapter 15 are very important in the study of both types of colloids.

Surface Films on Solids. As far as surface properties are concerned, a solid differs from a liquid in that it holds its shape by virtue of its mechanical rigidity, so that the surface exposed is not necessarily in an equilibrium state. At first sight this fact would appear to make it difficult to apply thermodynamics to systems involving a solid surface, but this is not so if the surface undergoes no irreversible change during a thermodynamic process. This requirement rules out the fruitful application of simple thermodynamics to the destruction or creation of surface in a one-component system. However, a second component can be introduced in a reversible manner, and thermodynamics applied to the metastable state consisting of a "frozen" solid surface and a liquid or vapor in equilibrium with it.

Problems

18.201 Draw a schematic diagram of a water (liquid)–water (vapor) interface, with a line that shows the concentration of water as the interface is passed, and indicate the dividing surface that makes the surface concentration zero. Add another concentration line for a nonvolatile substance that is sparingly soluble and accumulates in the interface. Indicate where the surface would have to be placed to make the concentration of this component zero in the interface.

18.202   (a) Add to the expression for dF^s (Eq. 18.201) terms to account for the free energy change of the two bulk phases in contact. (b) Integrate to obtain the expression for the total free energy of the three regions.

18.203   Repeat the first part of Problem 18.202 for dA, the Helmholtz free energy. Obtain an expression for the total Helmholtz free energy of the surface.

18.204   Calculate the concentration, in moles per square centimeter, of a C_{14} fatty acid required to reduce the room-temperature surface tension of water by 0.1 dyne. How many pounds of this material would be needed to achieve the same effect on a square mile of water surface? (Hint: Use perfect gas law in two dimensions.)

18.205   What does Eq. 18.209 indicate as to the maximum spreading pressure possible? How does this prediction compare with that of Eq. 18.210? What might be expected to happen as the temperature was raised, at constant composition of the liquid phase?

3. Physical Adsorption of Gases on Solid Surfaces

We shall treat adsorption of a gas on a solid in two sections. Although we will not discuss adsorption on a solid from the liquid phase, it can be treated by similar techniques and equations. We shall first consider physical adsorption, which is of use in determining the surface area of solids. In the next section, we will consider chemisorption and reactions at surfaces.

Gas Adsorption: Chemical and Physical. When a material, such as metallic nickel, is exposed to a gas (e.g., hydrogen), it is possible that there will be a thorough and irreversible uptake of the gas on the surface. The heat released by such a process has been measured calorimetrically and is of the order of magnitude associated with the formation of chemical bonds in a compound, i.e., 20 to 100 kcal mole^{-1} of gas. Such reactions, for that is what they are, are specific in nature, and take place only under the right conditions of adsorbent gas and temperature.

On the other hand, almost all solid surfaces will condense a large quantity of a vapor if the temperature is low enough. In the temperature region near the boiling point of typical liquids, this phenomenon is usually quite pronounced and easily measurable. The reason is that the same forces that are responsible for liquid condensation also act between the solid surface and the vapor molecules. These are the so-called physical or van der Waals forces that act between all molecules, including the rare gases.

It is difficult to decide clearly whether the adsorption of certain gases, such as water vapor on silica, is physical or chemical. However, if we confine our attention to the rare gases and certain other nonpolar gases, we can be quite sure that the forces involved are not chemical in nature. This is shown when the heats of adsorption per mole of vapor are measured; instead of corresponding in magnitude to the formation of chemical bonds, heats are comparable to the heats of condensation of the vapors involved, i.e., of the order of 1 to 10 kcal mole.$^{-1}$

We shall first consider the simplest type of adsorption on a solid surface, where the surface is viewed as the source of a potential energy field that slightly concentrates the gas near it. This case has the advantage that it can be treated quite simply. We shall then proceed to develop an approximate treatment of actual condensation at a surface.

Materials Used in Adsorption Studies on Solids. Any solid surface as an *adsorbent*, with any volatile substance as an *adsorbate*, is a conceivable system. However, certain substances are particularly suitable for study. Carbon, in the form of carbon black or charcoal, is often used. Charcoals have been prepared with very large surface areas, up to 1000 m² g⁻¹. Carbon blacks have surface areas ranging from 10 to 500 m² g⁻¹.

One particular carbon black, designated P-33 (2700°), has been studied more thoroughly than any other surface. It is prepared by heating ordinary carbon black to a temperature of 2700°C in an electric furnace. This treatment has the effect of removing volatile impurities, as well as causing the crystallites to assume a nearly graphitic structure. The resulting material has an area of about 10 m² g⁻¹. The advantage of this surface is that it is simple in composition with a relatively large amount of one (basal) plane exposed, and thus with enough surface to make measurements possible.

Another thoroughly investigated surface is that of a particular sample of anatase (TiO_2) with a similar surface area. This material, however, is not elemental in composition, and it is possible that the surface does not have a constant composition. Different crystal planes may be exposed in unknown proportions. Also it adsorbs water strongly and may be "dirty" (contaminated on the surface). Many studies have also been made on alumina (Al_2O_3) and silica (SiO_2), which can be prepared with high surface areas.

There has also been work on single crystals and evaporated films of materials, such as metals and salts. Very often, the cleaner and better-defined the surface, the smaller is the area available for measurement. Since we will be largely concerned with the quantitative interpretation of thermodynamic measurements, this poses a problem of significance of results versus accuracy.

As far as adsorbates are concerned, we shall restrict our treatment here to the rare gases and other simple non-polar gases.

High-Temperature, Low-Pressure Measurements. If measurements are made in the temperature range far above the critical temperature of the adsorbate (room temperature and above for argon) the amount of adsorption is very small. However, if we use large surface areas (several thousand square meters in a 20 ml bulb) or very accurate measuring techniques, the interaction of gas molecules with the surface is measurable. Consider a glass sample bulb filled with a large quantity of high surface area powder. If we introduce a certain number of moles of gas into the bulb, the perfect gas law will define an apparent volume, which is, of course, not necessarily the geometrical volume of the bulb. The ideal gas law defines an apparent volume, however,

$$V_{ap} = \frac{nRT}{P} \tag{18.301}$$

At a given temperature this volume will be a function of pressure, unless the temperature is quite high. We therefore make several measurements, if necessary, with different values of n and P, and extrapolate the value of V_{ap} to zero pressure. When this is done, we find that the extrapolated or zero pressure V_{ap} is still a strongly dependent function of the temperature if the bulb contains enough surface area. Of course, for an empty bulb, even if the gas were imperfect, such an extrapolation would yield the true volume of the bulb, which would vary only slightly and linearly as the coefficient of expansion of the glass indicated. With a powder such as carbon black in the bulb, we get, instead, a strong dependence

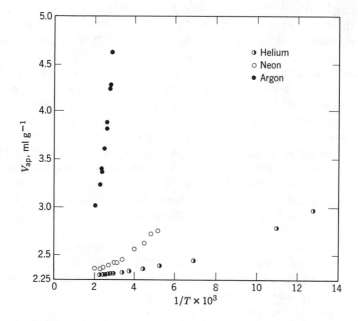

Fig. 18.301   Values of apparent volume for a sample of carbon black plotted against reciprocal temperature.

on temperature. Some measurements of the apparent volume of a bulb containing carbon black are shown in Fig. 18.301. Even the helium values have a strong dependence on temperature. At first sight, it might appear that the infinite temperature ($1/T = 0$) extrapolation value might be the same for the three gases. However, the heavier and larger gases extrapolate to a slightly smaller volume than the helium data.

Apparatus.   In order to make high-temperature measurements on a relatively low surface area powder, an accurate apparatus is required. This is shown schematically in Fig. 18.302. The sample is contained in the copper bulb A, which is maintained at a constant temperature by the shields C. The temperature is measured by means of the platinum resistance thermometer B. The whole is enclosed in the Dewar vessel D. Once the system is charged with gas, there is no need to manipulate any stopcock. Various pressures are reached by parallel combinations of the ice-jacketed pipets E. The pressure is measured with the extremely accurate manometer system HJK, which is thermostated and designed to minimize the error from external volume corrections.

Theoretical Treatment.   As long as we operate in the region where the apparent volume is independent of pressure, or, alternatively, extrapolate to zero pressure,

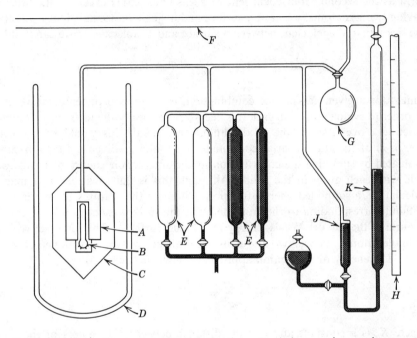

Fig. 18.302   Diagram of apparatus. A, Cell chamber; B, platinum resistance thermometer; C, shield; D, Dewar vessel; E, burets; F, vacuum manifold; G, gas storage; H, meter bar; J, constant-volume leg; K, vacuum leg of manometer.

we can assume that the adsorbed molecules (the molecules interacting with the surface) are not interacting with each other in any way. This condition simplifies the theory. Each molecule can be treated as interacting independently with the energy field from the solid surface. The effect of this field at very short distances is, of course, to repel the molecules of the gas and prevent them from entering the solid. At somewhat larger distances but still close to the surface, the effect of the field is to concentrate the gas. The effect on concentration of the field can be calculated by integrating the Boltzmann factor for this energy over the entire volume available to the gas

$$V_{\mathrm{ap}} = \int_{V_{\mathrm{geo}}} e^{-\epsilon/kT}\, dV \qquad (18.302)$$

Since an integration over V_{geo} of $(-1)\, dV$ equals $-V_{geo}$, this expression can be rearranged to read

$$V_{ap} - V_{geo} = \int (e^{-\epsilon/kT} - 1)\, dV$$

Now, because the integral goes to zero at large distances from the surface, the range of integration can be made effectively infinite. This formula is in the same form as the second virial coefficient of a gas (Eq. 6.511) except that, instead of having two gas atoms, we have a surface and a single molecule. This is, in effect, the second virial coefficient between a surface and a molecule, so we can write

$$B_{AS} = V_{ap} - V_{geo} = \int (e^{-\epsilon/kT} - 1)\, dV = f(T) \qquad (18.303)$$

which, for a given gas-surface combination, is a function of temperature alone. In order to evaluate this integral, it is necessary to specify the form of the potential function ϵ over the volume of the bulb. In general, this would be a function $\epsilon(x, y, z)$ of the three spatial coordinates x, y, and z. Such a function can be evaluated by summing the contribution to the interaction energy of a gas molecule with each atom in the solid. Although this is quite feasible as a machine calculation, a simplified energy function will show the features of the argument without corresponding to the true energy at the surface exactly.

Form of the van der Waals Energy at a Plane Surface. The force between two nonpolar atoms, such as two argon atoms, is attractive at large distance of separation. The energy of interaction approaches the form (Sec. 6.5)

$$\epsilon_a = \frac{-K_a}{r^6} \qquad (6.506)$$

where K_a is a constant and r is the distance between the centers of the atoms. This expression is true, of course, only at relatively large distances. Higher-power terms enter as the atoms come nearer each other. However, if we are concerned only with the attractive term, which is the one that is responsible for condensation, we may now assert that a similar interaction is taking place between the atoms in the solid and the atoms that are undergoing adsorption. At first sight it would appear that we would have the same form of attraction, multiplied many times by all the atoms present in the solid. This would give rise to an adsorption energy of the same form as Eq. 6.506 but with a different and larger constant. This argument, however, fails to take account of the fact that as the adsorbed atom reaches a perpendicular distance r from the nearest atom in the surface all the other surface atoms are at a greater distance away. We must sum over terms like Eq. 6.506, but with the appropriate values of r for each solid atom-gas atom distance entered.

A limiting form of the result of this summation can be obtained in a simple way. If an adsorbed atom is right on the surface, it is interacting effectively with only the few atoms in its immediate vicinity. Those atoms of the solid that are a few molecular diameters away contribute only a few percent to the total interaction, because they are two or three times as far away, and their contribution is therefore reduced by factors of 2^6 or 3^6. If, however, the atom to be adsorbed is quite a few molecular diameters away from the surface, although each interaction it has with the individual atoms of the solid is greatly diminished, the relative distance between the closest atoms perpendicularly below it, and those some few molecular diameters away in the solid, is much closer to unity. Thus the *relative* contribution of these somewhat more distant atoms is increased, or, in other words, the number of solid atoms that are effectively interacting with the adsorbed atom increases as the distance of the adsorbed atom increases.

This effect is shown pictorially in Fig. 18.303. A cone spreading out from the adsorbed atom includes a large constant fraction of the atoms of the solid that

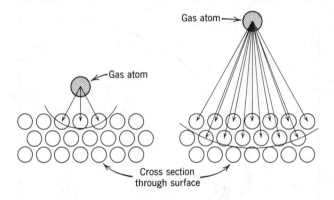

Fig. 18.303   Interaction of a gas atom with a surface, at shorter and longer distances from the surface.

contribute most to the interaction energy. As the distance r increases and the cone gets larger, it intercepts a larger area of the surface. The total number of atoms in the *surface* intersected by this cone rises as r^2. We might thus expect that the interaction energy of the adsorbed atom with the surface would fall off with the expression

$$\frac{r^2}{r^6} = \frac{1}{r^4}$$

and this would indeed be true if the solid were only one atom thick. However, the atoms in the layers below the surface layer also contribute to the van der Waals energy, and to a first approximation this contribution is independent of the atoms in between. Thus, the effective volume of interacting solid atoms is within a hemispherical volume defined by the intersection of the cone with the solid surface (Fig. 18.303). This effective volume (and thus the number of solid atoms in it) is proportional to the cube of the distance from the surface, and so the form of the interaction energy is

$$\epsilon_{ads} \sim \frac{r^3}{r^6} \qquad\qquad (18.304)$$

$$= \frac{-K_s}{r^3}$$

This is the so-called *cube law* of surface attraction. It is fundamental to the interpretation of physical adsorption. Even though the London law (Eq. 6.506)

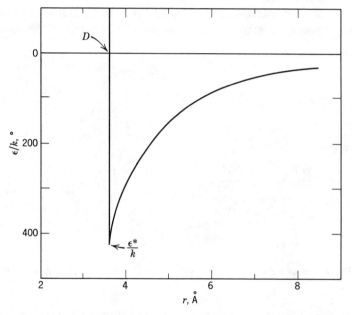

Fig. 18.304 Potential functions for gas-surface interaction (scale appropriate for neon and carbon).

is approximate, and the integration over the atoms of the solid is a further approximation, the cube law gives the order of magnitude and general shape to be expected for the energy of interaction as a function of the distance from the surface. It must be used in conjunction with a suitable repulsive term. The simplest possible potential is shown in Fig. 18.304. The cube law is used right up to the surface until, at a distance of closest approach D, a hard sphere cut-off is used as the repulsive term. Such a potential, although very crude, serves to show the general features of the interaction of atoms with a surface.

Comparison of Theory and Experiment.   Given a particular potential function, such as the hard sphere cut-off-cube law attraction function, the integration indicated in Eq. 18.303 can be performed. This simple potential is characterized by two parameters: D, the distance of closest approach, and ϵ^*, the magnitude of the (negative) energy at this distance. The only other parameters are the area of the solid, $\mathcal{A}$ and V_{geo}, the volume of the bulb. The problem can be put in dimensionless form by using the parameter containing reduced variables, ϵ^*/kT for temperature, and $(V_{ap} - V_{geo})/\mathcal{A}D$ for the apparent volume. In terms of these variables, we get a single dimensionless curve that relates apparent volume to temperature. A $\log V$ versus $1/T$ plot is nearly linear, and the master plot is shown as a solid line in Fig. 18.305.

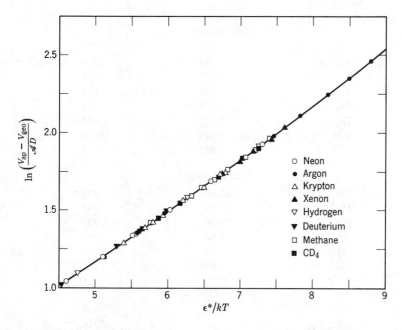

Fig. 18.305   A reduced-variable plot for the interaction data of several gases with graphitized carbon black, P-33(2700°). Data are all fitted to this one curve by choice of the parameters ϵ^* and AD.

All experimental points can be made to fall on this line by choice of the constants ϵ^*, $\mathcal{A}D$, and V_{geo}. The first has the units of energy per molecule or mole, and the second and third are volumes.

Values of the Constants.   The value of V_{geo} depends on the particular bulb used and the density of packing, and, although some conclusions can be drawn if it is not the same for every gas in a particular bulb over a given sample, its value is not of interest here. Some values of the other two constants are tabulated in Table 18.301. The value of ϵ^*/k, when multiplied by the gas constant $R \approx 2$, gives the energy in calories per mole. This is the value of the interaction energy of the gas molecules when in contact with the surface. The values increase in the expected manner as the molecular weight increases. We shall consider the values of $\mathscr{A}D$, the excluded volume of the surface, later in this section.

Formula for the Energy of Adsorption. It is desirable to have a theoretical estimate of the adsorption energy to compare with the experimental values (Table 18.301). The treatment is again based on London's explanation of dispersion

Table 18.301   Values of $\mathscr{A}D$ and ϵ^*/k

Adsorbate	$\mathscr{A}D \times 10^3$, ml g^{-1}	ϵ^*/k, °K
P-33 (2700°) carbon black		
Ne	4.240	435
Ar	5.149	1229
Kr	4.782	1651
Xe	5.942	2117
H_2	5.159	653
D_2	5.110	657
CH_4	4.448	1659
CD_4	4.851	1624
Porous glass		
He	22.10	342
H_2	22.90	992
Ne	20.50	775
Ar	15.60	1900
O_2	12.10	2060
N_2	9.80	2150
Saran charcoal		
H_2	378	935
CH_4	324	2320
He	283	315
Ne	289	640
Ar	300	1830

energy. The Kirkwood-Müller formulation of the interaction energy of an atom with a surface gives the energy at distance D from the center surface atoms as

$$\epsilon = -\frac{N_0 mc^2}{\pi D^3} \frac{\alpha_1 \alpha_2}{\dfrac{\alpha_1}{\chi_1} + \dfrac{\alpha_2}{\chi_2}} \tag{18.305}$$

All these constants are readily available. N_0 is the number of adsorbent atoms per cubic centimeter; mc^2 is the mass of the electron times the velocity of light squared; α and χ are polarizability and diamagnetic susceptibility per atom; the subscripts 1 and 2 refer to the adsorbent and adsorbate atoms, respectively.

Analysis of ϵ^*; the Value of D.   The chief difficulty in evaluating van der Waals energy is the choice of the distance D in Eq. 18.305. The reason is that it enters to the third power, whereas the other constants occur to the first power or even enter in ratios so that errors tend to cancel. Equation 18.305 can best be thought of as an expression that gives ϵ as a function of D^{-3} with a known coefficient. With this in mind, it is appropriate to use the measured values of ϵ^* in Table 18.301 to calculate the corresponding values of D. The effect of errors in ϵ^* is minimized, because a cube root is taken. The reverse calculation of ϵ^* from an estimate of D is much more uncertain because D must be cubed. For example, values of ϵ^*, calculated on the basis of tables of estimated van der Waals radii, can be hopelessly out of accord with the experiment. However, the values of D calculated by the reverse process are quite reasonable, particularly on the well-characterized and nearly uniform P-33 (2700°) carbon black. The results are shown in Table 18.302.

Table 18.302   Distances of Closest Approach (in Å) from Kirkwood-Müller Equation

Adsorbate	P-33 (2700°) Carbon Black	Porous Glass	Saran Charcoal
H_2	2.62	1.86	2.30
D_2	2.62		
CH_4	3.71		3.30
CD_4	3.74		
O_2		1.89	
N_2		1.99	
He		1.87	2.47
Ne	3.62	1.93	2.55
Ar	3.67	2.20	2.90
Kr	3.76		
Xe	3.99		

Adsorption Isotherms.   When the temperature is lowered to the vicinity of the boiling point of the adsorbing gas, the quantity adsorbed can become quite large and easily measurable. This is the conventional range of temperature in which adsorption measurements are made.

If a bulb is filled with a powder having a large surface area the volume is reduced by the volume of the powder, but adsorption on the surface of the powder can also take place. If we select a gas, such as helium, and work at a temperature high enough so that the adsorption is negligible, the so-called dead space of the bulb plus powder can be defined in terms of the helium pressure

$$V_{\text{dead}} = \frac{n_{\text{He}} R T}{P_{\text{He}}}$$
(18.306)

This volume closely corresponds to the geometrical volume of the bulb minus the volume of the powder.

If now we introduce a quantity of a vapor that is adsorbed, the pressure will be less than that predicted for an equivalent amount of helium. There is an apparent volume

$$V_{ap} = \frac{nRT}{P} > V_{dead} \qquad (18.307)$$

Thus, a certain number of moles of the gas is abstracted as an adsorbed quantity, n_{ads}. The rest of the gas, still in the gas phase, equal in moles to $n - n_{ads}$, is acting as a gas in the dead space volume. The number of moles adsorbed can be calculated from the equation

$$V_{dead} = \frac{(n - n_{ads})RT}{P} \qquad (18.308)$$

This equation at constant temperature serves to define the adsorption isotherm, that is, the number of moles adsorbed as a function of pressure, in terms of measurements with the gas or vapor in question, plus measurements with the volume-defining gas such as helium. The necessity of employing a reference gas such as helium is a disadvantage. The method of apparent volumes discussed previously is to be preferred when the quantity adsorbed is very small, because it avoids the use of a reference gas.

It is customary to plot the number of moles adsorbed, or some proportional quantity, such as the volume adsorbed, expressed as vapor at STP, against the pressure at constant temperature. In general, if we are dealing with a vapor below the critical temperature, it is convenient to render the pressure dimensionless by dividing by the saturation pressure of the bulk phase P_0. This reduced pressure P/P_0 then covers the range zero to one, and makes the reference state for pressure the bulk phase of the condensed gas.

A typical isotherm for a nonpolar gas on a nonporous solid is shown in Fig. 18.306. There is initially a strong uptake of gas at almost zero pressure. Then the pressure rises rapidly with a gradual increase in the amount of gas adsorbed. This is followed by an upturn of the isotherm near the saturation pressure of the gas which anticipates the onset of bulk condensation. There are other types of isotherms. For example, the upturn near saturation may be terminated by a horizontal portion, for the case of a porous adsorbent. The pores are filled with adsorbed material, and no further adsorption is possible. The type of isotherm shown is typical of physical adsorption on a plane surface, where adsorption is not limited by pore size.

An Explanation of the Typical Isotherm. The process of adsorption from a condensed reference state such as a liquid consists of the transfer of a number of molecules from the liquid state to the adsorbed state on the surface of the solid. This process is accompanied by a change in free energy. The change in free energy depends, of course, on the number of molecules already adsorbed on the surface

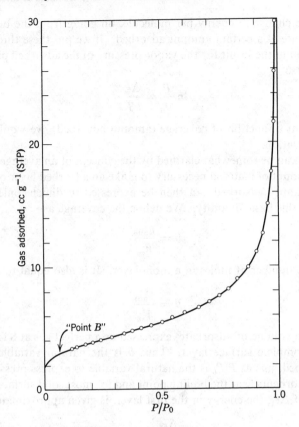

Fig. 18.306   Adsorption isotherm for nitrogen on anatase at 77°K (by permission from W. D. Harkins, *The Physical Chemistry of Surface Films*, Reinhold Publishing Co., New York, 1952).

and is thus a function of surface coverage. If we assume that the structure of the adsorbed phase is the same as that of the bulk phase, then the only difference in the molecular environment is the surface energy; there is no entropy change. The chemical potential of the bulk phase is equal to the chemical potential of the gas phase in equilibrium with it

$$\mu_{\text{bulk}} = \mu^0 + RT \ln P_0 \tag{18.309}$$

and similarly the chemical potential of the adsorbed phase is

$$\mu_{\text{ads}} = \mu^0 + RT \ln P \tag{18.310}$$

Since we assume that only an energy change is associated with the process of transfer from the bulk phase to the adsorbed phase, we have, per mole of material transferred,

$$\Delta F = \mu_{\text{ads}} - \mu_{\text{bulk}} = \mathbf{N} \, \Delta\epsilon \tag{18.311}$$

where $\Delta\epsilon$ is the change in energy per molecule, on going from the bulk phase to the adsorbed state at a certain amount adsorbed. If we put these three equations together, we obtain the result for the vapor pressure of the adsorbed phase relative to the bulk phase

$$\ln \frac{P}{P_0} = \frac{\Delta\epsilon}{kT} \tag{18.312}$$

If we knew $\Delta\epsilon$ as a function of coverage (amount adsorbed), we would then have an isotherm equation.

The problem can be somewhat clarified by the concept of an average monolayer, which is the amount of material necessary to make an adsorbed layer one molecule thick. The quantity adsorbed can then be expressed in dimensionless fractions or multiples of this basic quantity. We define the coverage as

$$\theta = \frac{n_{\text{ads}}}{n_m} \tag{18.313}$$

where n_m is the number of moles in a monolayer. It is also equal to the ratio

$$\theta = \frac{V_{\text{ads}}}{V_m} \tag{18.314}$$

where V_m is the volume of adsorbate, expressed as a perfect gas at STP, necessary to form one complete surface layer. Thus θ is the natural variable to express quantity adsorbed, just as P/P_0 is the natural variable to express pressure.

For most adsorbents near the boiling point and for most solid surfaces, the order of magnitude of $\Delta\epsilon_1$, the energy in the first layer, is given approximately by

$$\frac{-\Delta\epsilon_1}{kT} \approx 10$$

Therefore, according to Eq. 18.312, this first layer condenses as a pressure given by

$$\ln \left(\frac{P}{P_0}\right)_1 \approx -10$$

or about $P/P_0 = 10^{-3}$. This is reflected in the isotherm shown in Fig. 18.306. The abrupt rise of the isotherm from zero adsorption and pressure is due to this strong adsorption. Now, the second layer is approximately twice as far away from the surface as the first, and so the second layer should be forming at an energy that is less by a factor 2^3. This follows from the cube law, Eq. 18.304. Therefore, for the second layer,

$$\ln \left(\frac{P}{P_0}\right)_2 = \frac{-10}{8} = -1.2$$

or the pressure of the second layer should be about $P/P_0 = 0.3$. This is why the isotherm bends over, and the pressure rises much more rapidly with the coverage, as the second layer is completed. Now the energy in the third layer will be reduced by a factor 3^3, and in the fourth layer 4^3, etc.; and similar calculations show that the position of the isotherm as it becomes asymptotic to the $P/P_0 = 1$ axis is predicted in a qualitative fashion, at least.

Thus, if we assume a value of $\Delta\epsilon$ in the first layer, and apply the cube law in succeeding layers, we can produce a curve that coincides very well with the typical isotherm.

Development of Steps in an Isotherm. Further evidence to support the idea that a monolayer of material is adsorbed when the knee of the isotherm is reached came from studies on very uniform surfaces. Ordinary surfaces are likely to be energetically quite heterogeneous as far as the energy of adsorption in the first layer is concerned. This heterogeneity can be caused by lattice defects and impurities, for example. However, it is possible to work with the carbon black P-33 (2700°), which has a graphite-like surface that is quite homogenous. Argon and krypton isotherms on this surface are shown in Fig. 18.307. Note that the argon

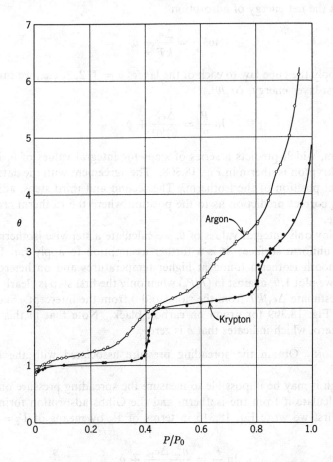

Fig. 18.307   The adsorption of argon and krypton on graphitized carbon black at 77°K.

isotherm shows a series of waves corresponding to the formation of layers. The evidence is much clearer for krypton. Here the value of $\Delta\epsilon$ in the first layer is enough larger to show the formation of real steps. It is logical to presume that these steps correspond to the formation of successive monolayers. The height of each step corresponds to the quantity of gas necessary to form a monolayer.

A Working Isotherm. In order to find the value of $\Delta\epsilon_1$ for various combinations of substances, it is desirable to have an isotherm equation that can be fitted to the data. Equation 18.312 will provide the basis for such an equation if it is modified slightly. Note that in the krypton isotherm, Fig. 18.307, the amount adsorbed does not reach infinity as the pressure reaches P_0. This reflects the fact that the surface layers of adsorbed material are slightly perturbed by the underlying solid lattice of the graphite. This effect can be expressed in terms of a slight degree of misfit or incompatibility between the lattices of the krypton and of the carbon. The energy associated with this defect, called δ, must be added to Eq. 18.312 to get the net energy of adsorption

$$\ln\frac{P}{P_0} = \frac{\Delta\epsilon}{kT} + \delta$$

If we then apply the cube law to each of the layers $\theta = 1, 2, 3$, etc., we can replace $\Delta\epsilon$ by the first-layer energy, $\Delta\epsilon_1/\theta^3$.

$$\ln\frac{P}{P_0} = \frac{\Delta\epsilon_1}{kT\theta^3} + \delta \tag{18.315}$$

This isotherm, which predicts a series of steps for integral values of θ, is shown fitted to the krypton isotherm in Fig. 18.308. The agreement with the data is good in the general position of the isotherm. The second and third steps, adjusted to fit, lead to a correct prediction as to the position where the isotherm crosses the $P/P_0 = 1$ line.

If we employ only integral values of θ, we calculate a stepwise isotherm appropriate for a uniform surface; it is a further assumption to apply Eq. 18.315 to the usual smooth isotherm found at higher temperatures and on heterogeneous surfaces. If we plot $1/\theta^3$ against $\ln(P/P_0)$ when only the first step is clearly defined, we can still estimate $\Delta\epsilon_1/kT$ from the slope and δ from the intercept. Such a plot is shown in Fig. 18.309 for argon on carbon black. Note that in this case the intercept is zero, which indicates that δ is zero.

ILLUSTRATION. Obtain the spreading pressure associated with the isotherm Eq. 18.315.

Although it may be impossible to measure the spreading pressure on a solid, we can calculate it from the isotherm and the Gibbs adsorption formula, Eq. 18.207. First we write Eq. 18.315 in terms of Γ_2 by means of $\Gamma_2 = n_m\theta/\mathscr{A}$. Thus

$$\ln\frac{P}{P_0} = \frac{n_m^3\,\Delta\epsilon_1}{kT\mathscr{A}^3\Gamma_2^3} + \delta$$

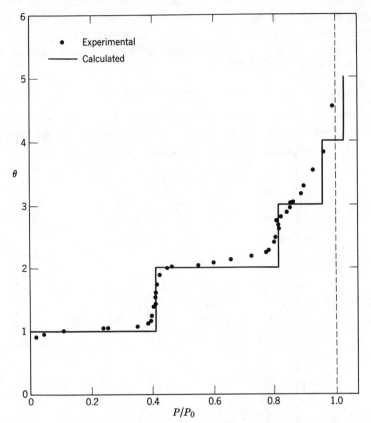

Fig. 18.308   The isotherm, Eq. 18.315, fitted at integral values of θ to the steps in the krypton isotherm, Fig. 18.307. Note the intersection of the predicted isotherm with the $P/P_0 = 1$ axis.

and

$$d\mu_2 = RT\,d\ln P = \mathrm{N}kT\,d\ln P = -\frac{\mathrm{N}3n_m^3\,\Delta\epsilon_1}{\mathscr{A}^3\Gamma_2^4}\,d\Gamma_2$$

If we insert this result in the Gibbs equation

$$-\,d\gamma = d\phi = \Gamma_2\,d\mu_2$$

we find

$$d\phi = -\frac{\mathrm{N}3n_m^3\,\Delta\epsilon_1}{\mathscr{A}^3\Gamma_2^3}\,d\Gamma_2$$

Upon integration

$$\phi = \frac{3}{2}\,\frac{\mathrm{N}n_m^3\,\Delta\epsilon_1}{\mathscr{A}^3}\,\frac{1}{\Gamma_2^2} + \text{const}$$

This is of the form

$$\phi = \frac{\text{const}}{\theta^2} + \text{const}$$

which does not reduce to the ideal gas law in two dimensions at zero coverage. This reflects the fact that the isotherm does not approach Henry's law at low coverages. Since, at low enough coverages, all films become ideal, this is a defect of the isotherm Eq. 18.315.

Calculation of $\Delta \epsilon_1$ *Values.*   Various isotherms can be plotted to obtain estimates for $\Delta \epsilon_1$ from experiment, by the use of Eq. 18.315. Although this is an

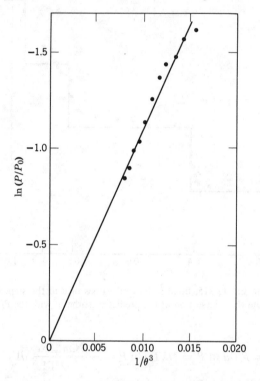

Fig. 18.309   The argon data, Fig. 18.307, plotted for integral and non-integral values of θ, according to the linear plot suggested by Eq. 18.315. Note the predicted intercept of zero.

approximation, it is possible to compare these energies with values calculated by means of the Kirkwood-Müller expression, Eq. 18.305.

In order to calculate $\Delta \epsilon_1$, it is necessary to employ this formula twice, because not only must the adsorption energy in the first layer be calculated, but also the reference energy of the bulk phase must be subtracted. Therefore, it is possible to have negative values of $-\Delta \epsilon_1$ which correspond to the (rare) case of no adsorption.

Some comparisons between experimental and calculated values of $-\Delta \epsilon_1$ are shown in Table 18.303. In general, there is quite satisfactory agreement. The values of D used to obtain this agreement were those for the lattice distance between planes in the solid rare gases.

Table 18.303 *Rare Gas-Solid Interaction Energies*

System	$-(\Delta\epsilon_1/kT)$	
	Kirkwood-Müller	Experimental
Na_2O-Kr	−0.4	0.05
NaOH-Kr	0.9	1.0
NaBr-Kr	4.7	2.8
AgI-Ar	9.7	11.0
Xe-Ar	2.6	1.2
KCl-Ar	2.5	2.5
CaF_2-Ar	2.5	2.2
CaF_2-Xe	−0.2	0.1

The "Point B" Method of Surface Area Measurement. In the preceding treatment we have shown that the greatest change in pressure with coverage comes between the first and second layers. This would imply that the coverage of one monolayer comes somewhere near the "knee" of the isotherm, labeled "point B in Fig. 18.306. This point was first emphasized by Emmett and forms the physical basis of the celebrated BET (Brunauer, Emmett, and Teller) method of measuring surface area. For, if we take the number of moles adsorbed at point B, and multiply by Avogadro's number and the area per molecule of adsorbate, we can estimate the number of molecules in one layer. The surface area can be calculated from the number of molecules in this layer. If we use nitrogen as the adsorbent and assign the area of 16.2 Å² per molecule to it, the so-called standard BET area is obtained. This procedure is by far the most important method of measuring surface area.

ILLUSTRATION. An estimate of surface area.

If we examine Fig. 18.306, we observe that "point B" occurs at about 3 ccg⁻¹ adsorption, the gas being measured at STP. We convert this to molecules

$$\frac{3 \times 6 \times 10^{23}}{22,400} = 8 \times 10^{19}$$

and then to area

$$8 \times 10^{19} \times 16.2 \times 10^{-20} = 13 \text{ m}^2/\text{g}$$

The molecular area of 16.2 implies a higher precision, but the actual reliability of surface areas probably does not extend beyond ±10 per cent.

Independent Estimate of Surface Area. From the estimate of D (Table 18.302) the values of the volume $\mathscr{A}D$ in Table 18.301 can be used to calculate the area of the powders (Table 18.304). This method of estimating area has a number of advantages. First, it is independent of any estimate of molecular area or diameter on the surface. Also, it treats each gas independently. If a gas such as helium reaches a greater area than one composed of larger molecules, this fact becomes evident. Furthermore, the temperature of measurement is so high that equilibrium is quickly attained, and such problems as capillary condensation and hysteresis of adsorption do not arise.

Table 18.304   Areas Computed from Values of $\mathscr{A} D$ and D
Surface areas in square meters per gram

Adsorbate	P-33 (2700°) Carbon Black	Porous Glass	Saran Charcoal
H_2	19.69	123	1575
D_2	19.45		
CH_4	11.99		980
CD_4	12.97		
O_2		64	
N_2		49	
He		118	1145
Ne	11.71	106	1135
Ar	14.03	71	1030
Kr	12.72		
Xe	14.89		
BET	12.5	117	2070

On the other hand, the absolute value of the area calculated turns out to be sensitive to the choice of potential. The largest areas come from the sharpest potential function. A more rounded-bottom potential may reduce the apparent area by 50 per cent. Clearly, it is desirable to know the potential at the surface, but this independent method requires that at least the functional form of the potential be known before the area can be calculated. Another and obvious disadvantage is that the experiments, at least for low surface area powders, are very difficult.

Problems

18.301   Calculate the approximate maximum surface area possible if 1 gram of graphite is peeled, atomic layer by layer, to expose both faces of each layer to the gas phase. (Density of graphite = 2.3 g cm^{-3}; interplanar spacing = 3.3 Å.)

18.302   What approximations are involved in using the inverse cube law for the energy of attraction at the surface?

18.303   What law of attraction would be appropriate for the approach of a molecule such as argon to a very long rod-like molecule such as tobacco mosaic virus?

18.304   Use the cube law and the position of the steps in Fig. 18.307 to estimate $\Delta\epsilon_1$ for argon.

18.305   Some typical isotherm data for nitrogen on a silica catalyst are presented below. Plot and estimate the BET area. Mass of sample $= 0.15$ g; $T = 77°$K.

$$V_{ads}(STP): \quad 3.5 \quad 3.8 \quad 4.0 \quad 5.5 \quad 6.1 \quad 7.8 \quad 12.0 \quad 25.0$$
$$P/P_0: \qquad\quad 0.01 \quad 0.05 \quad 0.11 \quad 0.30 \quad 0.40 \quad 0.60 \quad 0.83 \quad 0.95$$

18.306   Plot the data from Problem 18.305 to obtain an estimate of $\Delta\epsilon_1$.

4. Chemical Adsorption and Heterogeneous Catalysis

When a gas such as oxygen collides with a surface like that of solid sodium, it is possible that a chemical reaction will take place. In some cases, such as this particular one, the reaction will normally proceed until the sodium is oxidized completely to produce a bulk phase of oxide. In other cases, no reaction will take place. But very often only a superficial reaction occurs, which leaves the underlying solid phase unchanged. Thus, hydrogen will react with a clean surface of nickel, under such condition that bulk conversion to nickel hydride is not taking place. Only a surface layer of hydride is formed; this phenomenon is called chemical adsorption, or *chemisorption*.

Heat of Chemisorption. Although the isotherms for chemisorption are important, often the reaction of the gas with the surface is so avid that the equilibrium pressure of gas is too small to be measured accurately. For this reason attention is focused on the heat of adsorption, that is, the heat released per mole when a quantity of gas is reacted with the surface. For the case of chemisorption, these heats are quite large and relatively easy to measure.

Some calorimetric measurements of the heat of adsorption of hydrogen on evaporated nickel films are shown in Fig. 18.401. Note that the heats are a function of the amount adsorbed. The quantity plotted is called the *differential heat of adsorption*. If a small amount of hydrogen, Δn moles, is introduced, an amount of heat, ΔQ, is released. The differential heat is defined as a limit

$$Q_{diff} = \underset{(\lim \Delta n \to 0)}{\frac{\Delta Q}{\Delta n}} \qquad\qquad (18.401)$$

$$= \frac{dQ}{dn}$$

Units of Heat and Coverage. Some care about the units and the mode of representation is necessary. The heat is almost always given in calories per mole of gas (H_2, etc.) adsorbed, but it is often plotted against a relative coverage rather than the coverage in moles. This coverage is given the symbol θ as in Sec. 18.3, but it has a slightly different interpretation. It is best thought of as a number nominally less than 1

$$\theta = \frac{n_{ads}}{n_{max}} \qquad\qquad (18.402)$$

where n_{max} is the amount of gas adsorbed when the pressure is raised to some relatively large value, beyond which little, if any, further adsorption can be measured. Ideally, in a case such as hydrogen on nickel, this maximum would be a definite quantity dictated by the number of lattice sites on the surface capable of reacting with hydrogen. Actually, this apparent maximum is often a function of temperature, and so the best practice is to use the actual number of moles adsorbed with an auxiliary indication on the graph as to the apparent maximum.

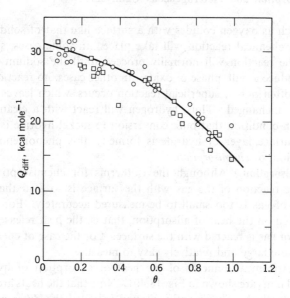

Fig. 18.401   Differential heat of adsorption of hydrogen on nickel (by permission from O. Beeck, *Advances in Catalysis*, Vol. II, Academic Press, New York, 1950).

Integral Heat of Adsorption. The differential heat of adsorption represents the amount of heat (per mole) associated with a very small change in coverage from θ to $\theta + d\theta$. It is possible to consider the heat per mole associated with covering the surface, starting with a bare surface ($\theta = 0$). This quantity is called the integral heat of adsorption. It can be found from the differential heat by calculating the total heat (not per mole) up to the given coverage, and then dividing by the coverage. Thus the total heat is

$$Q_{total} = \int_0^{n_{ads}} Q_{diff}\, dn_{ads} = n_{max} \int Q_{diff}\, d\theta \qquad (18.403)$$

whence is obtained the integral heat per mole

$$Q_{int} = \frac{Q_{total}}{n_{ads}} \qquad (18.404)$$

If the differential heat is a constant with respect to coverage, then the total heat is proportional to the amount adsorbed, and so the integral heat is also constant and equal to the differential heat. This very simple situation is seldom, if ever, met in practice for a surface reaction. For a reaction in the gas phase, where the gases are dilute or ideal, the heat of reaction per mole is constant, so it is not necessary to make any distinction; we speak simply of the heat.

ILLUSTRATION.   Relationship between differential and integral heats of adsorption.

The plot of the heat of adsorption as a function of coverage is actually a curve, but it can often be approximated by a straight line.

Suppose that the differential heat started at zero coverage at some value Q_0 and declined linearly to zero as the coverage reached $\theta = 1$. What is the value of the integral heat? The differential heat can be written

$$Q_{\text{diff}} = Q_0(1 - \theta)$$

From this expression we find

$$Q_{\text{total}} = n_{\max} \int Q_0(1 - \theta) \, d\theta$$

$$= n_{\max} Q_0(\theta - \tfrac{1}{2}\theta^2)$$

and

$$Q_{\text{int}} = \frac{Q_{\text{total}}}{n_{\max}\theta}$$

$$= Q_0(1 - \tfrac{1}{2}\theta)$$

which is also a linear function. For a completed monolayer, the integral heat ($\theta = 1$) is equal to one-half Q_0, the initial heat of adsorption. We see that, even though the differential heat sinks to zero, the average heat, as reflected by the integral heat, may still be large when the surface is covered.

We have considered the heat of adsorption before the adsorption isotherm, because it is possible to make heat measurements even when the pressure is so low that an isotherm is not verifiable. We shall now proceed to discuss the simplest isotherm for chemisorption, which applies only when the heat of adsorption is constant.

The Langmuir Isotherm Equation.   Suppose that there are n_s sites per square centimeter of surface that can react with (adsorb) a gas molecule A, according to a reaction $s + A = sA$. The pressure of gas molecules is P_A, and the fraction of sites occupied is θ. An equilibrium constant can be set up, in terms of the partition functions of the species. If we choose to set up the equilibrium constant in terms of pressure, we can apply Eq. 11.303 to the reaction between atom A and bare site s,

$$A + s = As$$

With a total number of sites n_s, and a fraction θ occupied

$$K_P = \frac{\theta n_s}{(1 - \theta)n_s P_A} = \frac{N}{RT}\frac{Z_{sA}}{Z_s \phi_A}e^{-\epsilon_0/kT} \tag{18.405}$$

$$= k_A$$

We have developed this expression from the general relationship Eq. 11.303 by the substitution of $\Delta n = -1$ for this particular reaction, and by the substitution of the volume-independent partition functions for the surface species. The partition function for the gas (ϕ_A) is written without the volume term and has units of vol^{-1}. We have also indicated that K_P is usually written as k_A for the adsorption reaction.

This equation can now be solved to give the Langmuir equation,

$$\frac{\theta}{1 - \theta} = P_A\left(\frac{Z_{sA}N}{Z_s\phi_A RT}\right)e^{-\epsilon_0/kT} = k_A P_A \tag{18.406}$$

or

$$\theta = \frac{k_A P_A}{1 + k_A P_A} \tag{18.407}$$

where k_A is a constant with the dimensions pressure^{-1}. The constant k_A is often replaced by a constant $1/P_0$, as an alternative form

$$\frac{\theta}{1 - \theta} = \frac{P}{P_0} \tag{18.408}$$

ILLUSTRATION.   Meaning of the constant P_0.

When the Langmuir equation is written in the form of Eq. 18.408, the constant P_0 reflects the strength of adsorption or the difficulty of desorption. From an examination of the equation it appears that an infinite pressure is required to make $\theta = 1$ and a zero pressure to make $\theta = 0$ for total desorption. However, the surface is just half-covered at $P = P_0$. This is the characteristic or median pressure for the isotherm, and represents a pressure at which desorption and adsorption are balanced to make covered or uncovered sites equally probable.

The Langmuir equation is linear in its early portion, when θ is small. Thus, concentration is proportional to pressure, as in a perfect gas or an ideal solution at low concentration. However, a new phenomenon is encountered at higher coverage, that of saturation, where further increase of the gas pressure or activity fails to raise concentration above a certain maximum. A plot of the Langmuir equation, which shows the characteristic saturation at higher pressure, is shown in Fig. 18.402. Since many reaction velocities depend on the surface concentration, rather than activity (pressure), the reaction rate stops increasing linearly with pressure or concentration in the bulk. This is a characteristic feature of surface reactions as contrasted with homogeneous ones.

Adsorption with Dissociation.   If, say, hydrogen is adsorbed from the gas as atoms on the sites, then the reaction is $H_2 + 2s = 2(H - s)$, and the equilibrium constant of Eq. 18.405 is changed accordingly.   The net result, for a diatomic gas adsorbed atomically, is

$$\frac{\theta}{1 - \theta} = k_{A_2} P_{A_2}^{\frac{1}{2}}$$

or

$$\theta = \frac{k_{A_2} P_{A_2}^{\frac{1}{2}}}{1 + k_{A_2} P_{A_2}^{\frac{1}{2}}} \qquad (18.409)$$

Since many of the simple gases that take part in a chemical reaction are diatomic in the gas phase and are adsorbed as atoms, the form of the Langmuir equation with square root pressure is more often applicable than the simple form.   For

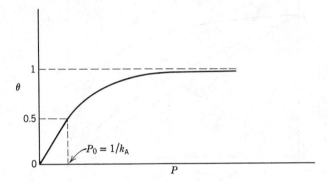

Fig. 18.402   Plot of the Langmuir adsorption isotherm.   The pressure at which $P = P_1$ and $\theta = 0.5$ is indicated.

polyatomic gases that dissociate to form fragments the expression on the left-hand side stays the same, but the pressure of a gas that dissociates is raised to the reciprocal power of the number of particles that it gives.

   This complication often renders the expressions for rates involving diatomic molecules rather complicated, although they may reduce to quite similar curves when numerical values are determined.   Therefore, without much other justification, simple mechanisms often ignore the dissociation of gases and treat them as being adsorbed molecularly on double sites.   Actually, the only direct evidence for atomic adsorption of hydrogen is the fact, observed by Langmuir, that a heated tungsten filament emits hydrogen atoms rather than molecules.

   Kinetic Derivation of the Langmuir Isotherm.   The original method of deriving the Langmuir isotherm equated two rates.   One was the rate of adsorption, which is supposed proportional to the fraction of the surface bare, and to the pressure. The other was the rate of desorption, which was viewed as a spontaneous uni-molecular decomposition of constant rate proportional in total rate to the fraction of surface covered.

$$k'P_A(1 - \theta) = k''\theta \qquad (18.410)$$

This expression can easily be arranged to yield the Langmuir equation. However, the derivation assumes a particular mechanism, and it is by no means true that this is the correct mechanism for adsorption. The advantage of the more complicated derivation involving partition functions is that no mechanism need be assumed. In the next paragraph, we shall give evidence which indicates that a more complicated mechanism operates in the process of chemisorption.

van der Waals Preadsorption. It has become increasingly clear that molecules undergoing chemisorption do not pass directly, upon collision with the surface, from the state of freely translating gas molecules to the final chemisorbed species. J. A. Becker showed that the rate of adsorption of gases such as nitrogen on a clean tungsten ribbon does not fall off with the expected factor $1 - \theta$ (Fig. 18.403).

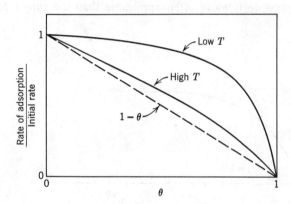

Fig. 18.403 Schematic representation of the relative rate of adsorption of gas on a tungsten ribbon as coverage increases. Dashed line represents results to be expected if adsorption took place directly from the gas phase.

Instead, at low temperatures, the rate tends to stay nearly constant until the film of nitrogen is complete. This behavior is due to capture of the nitrogen molecule in the van der Waals field of the solid, which may then wander over the surface until vacant chemisorption sites are found. At sufficiently high temperature, the rate begins to fall off with coverage, according to the $1 - \theta$ law. In the changeover region, the van der Waals energy is presumably somewhere in the range near RT, which, for the temperatures involved, is 1 or 2 kcal. The study of rare gas atoms over a wide variety of surfaces maintained at elevated temperatures described in Sec. 18.3 has confirmed the existence of such energies, which are quite general and might go as high as 10 kcal for complex molecules like butane and benzene.

It is important to consider that reaction between this physically adsorbed layer and the contents of the chemisorbed layer is always possible. This possibility largely takes the place of direct reaction with a gas molecule impinging on the surface (the Rideal mechanism) in describing mechanisms. Reactions are approximately $\exp(-\epsilon/kT)$ more likely than by direct striking, where ϵ is the (negative) energy of "sticking" in the van der Waals layer. The pressure dependence of the kinetics is unchanged, however, because in general the value of ϵ is too small to cause Langmuir saturation at the temperature of the reaction, and the van der Waals concentration and the rate of striking are both simply proportional to pressure.

Diffusion through Porous Solids. Another evidence of the van der Waals layer comes from the study of the movement of gases through tiny pores or capillaries in solids. The traditional analysis of this process was to consider that the gas moved in straight lines between the geometric walls, which had no other interaction than to reflect the particle. This analysis yielded a rate of transport that was a function of P, T, and the diameter of the tube only. If this is modified to allow for the gas molecule to spend a fraction of the time stuck to the wall and thus immobilized, this idealized rate is reduced by a factor equal to the fraction of the time, on the average, that the molecule is free. In some cases, however, the rate of transport is faster rather than slower than the ideal rate. This can be explained if the gas molecules are concentrated in the neighborhood of the walls by a van der Waals field, but otherwise still able to move parallel to the wall. This means that the pore appears larger, but only because it can hold more traveling gas than the perfect gas law allows in the geometrical volume.

Discussion of the Langmuir Equation; Microscopic Reversibility. An alternative and seemingly reasonable derivation of the Langmuir equation does not give the same result. Suppose that the molecules always stuck to the surface by van der Waals attraction, and wandered until they found a bare site; however, retain the assumption that on desorption they are emitted directly into the gas. Then the $1 - \theta$ vanishes from the left-hand side of Eq. 18.410 and the Langmuir equation is not obtained. Instead we find

$$k'P_A = k''\theta$$

or that the coverage increases linearly and indefinitely with pressure. This difference is a direct consequence of the fact that in this second set of mechanisms, although all states are accessible, a cyclic process is involved, and the law of microscopic reversibility is violated (Sec. 14.2). If we consider a van der Waals preadsorption, but include the reverse processes in every case, then the Langmuir equation is found as it should be.

ILLUSTRATION. Show that a proper formulation of an intermediate adsorbed state leads to the Langmuir equation.

We now have to distinguish between the loosely held material of concentration θ_1 and the chemisorbed material of concentration θ. A dynamic equilibrium between these two quantities is assumed

$$k'\theta_1(1 - \theta) = k''\theta(1 - \theta_1) \tag{a}$$

That is, the rate of adsorption into the chemisorbed layer depends on the concentration in the intermediate layer that is loosely held, *and* the amount of vacant space in the strongly held layer. Similarly, desorption depends both on

the amount in the chemisorbed layer and the probability of space in the intermediate layer.

Likewise, the various modes of leaving and reaching the loosely bound layer
balance

$$\frac{d\theta_1}{dt} = k_1'(1 - \theta_1)P + k''\theta(1 - \theta_1) - k_1''\theta_1 - k'\theta_1(1 - \theta) \tag{b}$$

If we subtract Eq. a from Eq. b, we find

$$\frac{\theta_1}{1 - \theta_1} = (\text{const}) \, P$$

Substitution of this result back into Eq. a gives the Langmuir equation.

Mixed Langmuir Isotherm.   If two gases A and B are adsorbed at once to an
extent θ_A and θ_B, then the isotherms are

$$\frac{\theta_A}{1 - \theta_A - \theta_B} = k_A P_A$$

$$\frac{\theta_B}{1 - \theta_A - \theta_B} = k_B P_B \tag{18.411}$$

The student should prove this result from a kinetic argument.

Assumptions of the Langmuir Equation.   It is important to understand that the
Langmuir treatment assumes (1) identical sites (as to energy of adsorption and any
other property); (2) no interaction between adsorbed atoms; and (3) vibrational
modes of the adatom (adsorbed atom) parallel to the surface, rather than translation. Also (4), in the case of mixed adsorption, A and B compete for the same
sites, with, however, different energies for the two species on identical sites.

Limitations of the Langmuir Equation.   We have enumerated carefully the
assumptions that go into the Langmuir equation, but we have not considered how
they affect its application. In the past these limitations have often been ignored,
with the result that many errors have been perpetrated. An example from the
dissociation of hydrocarbon gases makes clear the very restrictive nature of the
assumptions. First, the assumption of no interaction, applied to methane, would
imply that all the bonds were of equal strength, as they are subjected to successive
rupture. This is known not to be so. But all the "sites" in methane are "identical."
Thus for the "adsorption" of hydrogen on isolated carbon atoms, we have a
uniform "surface" with interaction, if we speak in the language of adsorption.
Second, if we go on to propane and consider the same process, we introduce
heterogeneity in the "adsorption" sites, as between a methylene and methyl
hydrogen. It is difficult here to conceive of a case where there is site difference without interaction. But where there is site difference, it is likely to be much more
important than interaction, as in, for example, the tertiary hydrogen in isobutane.
This is also considered to be likely for adsorption sites. Thus, if we were able to
take a complex hydrocarbon skeleton and cover it with hydrogen atoms by degrees,

the return in terms of heat per mole of hydrogen would be a function of the degree of hydrogenation; however, it would be quite arbitrary in most cases to say that this difference in heat was caused solely by interaction of the hydrogen atoms or, on the other hand, by the differences in the skeletal positions alone. We do know, however, that the "Langmuir" treatment of such a situation would be justified only if both effects could be ignored.

ILLUSTRATION. Calculate the spreading pressure of a film that obeys the Langmuir equation at low values of θ.

At low values of θ, the Langmuir equation states that θ is proportional to the pressure. Since Γ_2 is proportional to θ, this means that

$$P = \text{const } \Gamma_2$$

From the Gibbs adsorption equation we have

$$d\phi = \Gamma_2 \, d\mu_2 = \Gamma_2 \, RT \, d \ln P$$

If we substitute the relationship for P from the Langmuir equation

$$d\phi = \Gamma_2 \, RT \, d \ln (\text{const } \Gamma_2)$$
$$= RT \, d\Gamma_2$$

If we integrate this expression, with the condition that $\phi = 0$ when $\Gamma_2 = 0$, we obtain

$$\phi = RT\Gamma_2$$

which is equivalent to the perfect gas law in two dimensions. We thus see that the Langmuir equation, which does not assume a gas-like, mobile monolayer, nevertheless leads to the two-dimensional ideal gas law when the isotherm is equivalent to Henry's law. This is a general result.

Adsorption on a Heterogeneous Surface; the Freundlich Isotherm. If a surface contains a number of sites of different adsorption energy, one value of the constant P_0 is not enough to characterize it. Each different site or group of sites will have a different value of P_0 distinguished by the label $P_0(i)$. Then the total coverage will be the sum of the coverages on each type of site

$$\theta_{\text{total}} = \sum_i f_i \theta_i \qquad (18.412)$$

where f_i is the fraction of sites that are characterized by a given value of $P_0(i)$. The total coverage is then given as a sum of individual Langmuir terms

$$\theta_{\text{total}} = \sum_i \frac{f_i [P/P_0(i)]}{1 + [P/P_0(i)]} \qquad (18.413)$$

Thus, for any distribution of sites given by the values of f_i and the corresponding values of $P_0(i)$, it is possible to express θ_{total} as a function of the gas pressure P.

One particular isotherm is found for an exponential distribution of sites as a function of the energy of adsorption in Eq. 18.405. This takes the simple form

$$\theta_{\text{total}} = \frac{kT}{\epsilon_m}\left(\frac{P}{P_m}\right)^{kT/\epsilon_m} \tag{18.414}$$

where P_m and ϵ_m are constant. This equation implies that, if the logarithm of the amount adsorbed is plotted against the logarithm of the pressure, a straight line

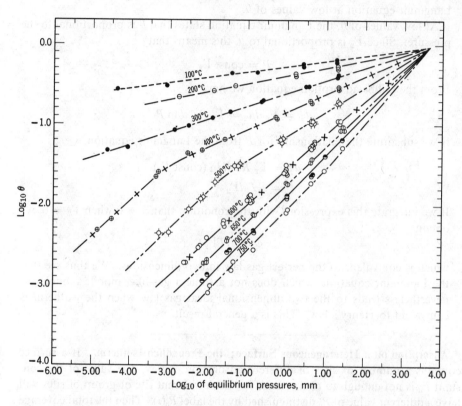

Fig. 18.404 Adsorption of hydrogen on tungsten powder, plotted according to the Freundlich isotherm [by permission from W. Frankenburg, *J. Am. Chem. Soc.*, **66**, 1827 (1944)].

will result with slope kT/ϵ_m. Some data for the adsorption of hydrogen on tungsten powder, so plotted, are shown in Fig. 18.404. Note that rather good straight lines result.

The early part of the Langmuir isotherm, at low value of θ, also gives a straight line on a log-log plot, but the slope, for the adsorption of a monotonic atomic gas, is unity or one half for adsorption with dissociation. Note that these data, at the lowest coverage and the highest temperature, do show the slope characteristic of Langmuir adsorption with dissociation.

However, the rest of the plots show a smaller slope, which is approximately proportional to temperature, as suggested by Eq. 18.414. It is clear then that one explanation of these data is that adsorption is taking place on a heterogeneous surface.

Meaning of the Constants in the Freundlich Equation.   If we examine the Freundlich equation, Eq. 18.414, it is apparent that P_m is the pressure at which $\theta_{\text{total}} = 1$. It is obtained by extrapolating the isotherms at different temperatures and observing where they intersect. Because the data are usually presented on a log-log plot (as in Fig. 18.404), any measure of the quantity adsorbed will give the same slope, so the reduction of actual data to this particular measure of coverage is seldom required. Although in principle, as the pressure is increased indefinitely, θ_{total} can exceed unity, P_m is usually of the order of several atmospheres, and so in practice the coverage is fractional.

The constant ϵ_m gives a measure of the distribution of site energies. For the Langmuir equation the constant ϵ_0 (Eq. 18.405) is fixed, but a distribution of these energies is postulated to explain the Freundlich equation. The distribution is of the form

$$f_\epsilon \sim e^{\epsilon/\epsilon_m} \tag{18.415}$$

which, since ϵ is negative for strong adsorption, predicts that the abundance of sites of a particular energy ϵ falls off exponentially with the value of the energy. The larger the constant modulus ϵ_m is, the more rapidly the distribution falls off.

Isotherms and Heats of Adsorption.   If we have an equilibrium isotherm

$$P = f(\theta) \tag{18.416}$$

whether for chemisorption or physical adsorption, that gives the pressure over the surface (assumed ideal) versus the amount adsorbed, it is possible to make some thermodynamic calculations. For the chemical potential of the gas we can write

$$\mu_{\text{gas}} = \mu_g^\circ + RT \ln P \tag{18.417}$$

For the chemical potential of the adsorbed material

$$\mu_{\text{ads}} = \mu_{\text{gas}} \tag{18.418}$$

if equilibrium is maintained. We then have, from the combination of Eqs. 18.416–18.418,

$$\mu_{\text{ads}} = \mu_g^\circ + RT \ln [f(\theta)] \tag{18.419}$$

If we differentiate with respect to T, holding the quantity adsorbed constant, we find, by Eq. 7.626,

$$\frac{\partial(\mu_{\text{ads}}/T)}{\partial(1/T)} = \bar{H}_{\text{ads}} = \bar{H}_g^\circ + \left[\frac{\partial\{R \ln [f(\theta)]\}}{d(1/T)} \right]_\theta \tag{18.420}$$

The differential heat of adsorption is related to the enthalpies of the adsorbed and the gas phase by the expression

$$Q_{\text{diff}} = \bar{H}_g - \bar{H}_{\text{ads}} \tag{18.421}$$

ILLUSTRATION. Heat of adsorption from the Langmuir and Freundlich isotherms.

If we take the Langmuir equation in the form of Eq. 18.408,

$$\ln P = \ln [f(\theta)] = \ln P_0 + \ln \frac{\theta}{1 - \theta}$$

If we differentiate this at constant θ,

$$\bar{H}_{\text{ads}} = \bar{H}_g + \frac{d(\ln P_0)}{d(1/T)}$$

(Because P_0 is a function of T alone, we do not use partial derivative symbols.)
Therefore

$$Q_{\text{diff}} = \frac{-d(\ln P_0)}{d(1/T)} = f(T)$$

which is a positive quantity, since P_0 usually increases with rising temperature,
and is independent of θ. It is also independent of coverage, which substan-
tiates this assertion about the Langmuir equation.

From the Freundlich equation, Eq. 18.414,

$$\ln P = \ln P_m + \frac{\epsilon_m}{kT} \ln \theta$$

From this we find

$$Q_{\text{diff}} = \frac{-d(\ln P_m)}{d(1/T)} - \epsilon_m \ln \theta$$

Now, as we have observed (Fig. 18.403) that P_m is substantially independent of
temperature, the first term is unimportant. The latter term predicts a heat of
adsorption that falls off with the logarithm of coverage to become zero at $\theta = 1$.

Collision Number. In a similar fashion as in homogeneous reactions, the
collision number puts an *upper bound* on how fast a gas can react with a surface.
The collision number of N' molecules per cubic centimeter with a wall of 1 cm²
area has been given in Eq. 6.218

$$\mathscr{L}_w = N' \left(\frac{kT}{2\pi m} \right)^{1/2} \tag{6.218}$$

If it is necessary for the colliding molecule to surmount some activation energy
barrier to react with the surface, as suggested by H. S. Taylor, then reasoning
entirely analogous to that used in developing the collision theory for reactions in
the gas phase will give an expression of the form

$$\text{Rate} = \mathscr{L}_w \mathscr{P}_w e^{-\epsilon^*/kT} \tag{18.422}$$

where ϵ^* is an activation energy and $\mathscr{P}_w$ a probability factor. However, reaction
with the surface is not necessarily the rate-determining factor in a surface reaction;
we shall proceed to develop some of the possible mechanisms and rate expressions
for surface reactions.

The Michaelis-Menten Mechanism.   The simplest mechanism for reaction at a surface can be thought of as based on Langmuir adsorption of a single reactant, but actually the same mechanism was proposed before the Langmuir equation was derived. It was developed to explain the saturation effect observed when the rate at which an enzyme reacts with its substrate is studied as a function of concentrations. If the substrate is bound reversibly in an unreacted state to active sites on the enzyme E, the situation is the same as in Langmuir adsorption. If we use θ to mean the fraction of enzyme sites that are covered, θ will depend on the substrate concentration as in Eq. 18.407

$$\theta = \frac{kc_s}{1 + kc_s} \qquad (18.423)$$

This expression is derived from the equilibrium

$$S + E \rightleftharpoons S\text{-}E$$

If the bound substrate reacts as a rate-determining step to produce products and the bare enzyme again

$$S\text{-}E \rightarrow E + products$$

the rate is clearly proportional to the concentration of the enzyme-substrate complex S-E, or

$$Rate = const\ c_e\theta$$

where c_e is the total concentration of the enzyme, and θ is the fraction complexed with the substrate. We thus see that the rate is

$$Rate = \frac{const\ c_s c_e}{1 + kc_s} \qquad (18.424)$$

This expression fits the qualitative features of enzyme reactions; the rate is proportional to the enzyme concentration over the whole concentration range, but proportional to the substrate concentration only at the lower concentrations. At higher concentrations, the effect of saturation of the enzyme with substrate is felt.

Langmuir Rate Expressions.   The Langmuir equation can be used to develop expressions for the pressure dependence of reactions at surfaces. For example, suppose two chemisorbed species A and B are reacting in the surface layer in the fashion $A + B \rightarrow$ products which disappear readily into the gas phase. The reaction is clearly proportional to the product $\theta_A\theta_B$, and these coverages are given by Eq. 18.411. Suppose furthermore that θ_A is close to unity and thus there is only a small amount of bare surface and B on the surface. The rate of this particular reaction type can then be shown to be proportional to P_B/P_A. On the other hand, if the surface is largely bare, the rate becomes proportional to $P_A P_B$.

Another possibility is that the reaction is between one species, say A, in the chemisorbed layer, and species B coming from above, in the gas. Then, if A is strongly adsorbed, the rate is proportional to P_B alone or, if weakly adsorbed, to $P_A P_B$ again. (Notice that the latter expression may come from two mechanisms; there is nothing unique about these explanations.)

Non-Langmuir Rate Expressions.   It is quite possible to have rates determined by mechanisms where no Langmuir equilibrium is involved. Suppose, for example, that A is adsorbed at a rate $k_A P_A(1 - \theta)$ and never desorbed. It is removed by reaction with B from the gas phase at a rate $k_B P_B \theta$. In the steady state, these two rates are equal, which leads to a rate of reaction

$$\text{Rate} = \frac{k_A k_B P_A P_B}{(k_A P_A + k_B P_B)} \tag{18.425}$$

This expression reduces to $k_A P_A$ if θ is small, and to $k_B P_B$ if θ is large.

An example of a typical catalytic reaction will now be considered.

Ethylene Hydrogenation.   Beeck and Wheeler investigated the hydrogenation of ethylene over a wide variety of evaporated metal films. Some of their results on nickel, which are typical of a catalytic investigation, are as follows:

1. The reaction is first order in H_2 and zero order in C_2H_4.

2. Hydrogen is rapidly ("instantaneously") adsorbed up to a certain quantity, and then no more goes on. This quantity measures the number of sites on the nickel, and is proportional to the weight of the film. This fact shows that the film has a porous structure and a large area.

3. It is impossible to pump this hydrogen off.

4. Ethylene is similarly adsorbed, up to a certain quantity. A further quantity of ethylene will react slowly to produce ethane. The residue on the surface is thus "acetylenic" in composition.

5. Neither the ethylene nor the actylenic residues can be pumped off.

6. Ethylene reacts instantaneously with the surface covered with hydrogen to produce ethane.

7. Hydrogen reacts only slowly to partially remove the adsorbed (preadsorbed) ethylene.

8. Ethylene is adsorbed with much greater energy than hydrogen.

9. Wheeler has stated that the rate of reaction is approximately equal to the rate of adsorption of hydrogen, calculated on the basis of the same activation energy, and a probability factor $\mathscr{P}_w \approx 1$ (Eq. 18.423).

Beeck interpreted the kinetics of this reaction on the basis of a Langmuir equilibrium. If (a) the surface is largely covered, (b) mostly with ethylene, (c) dissociation is ignored, and (d) ethylene and hydrogen compete for the same (double) sites, then

$$\theta_{H_2} = (\text{const}) \times \frac{P_{H_2}}{P_{Et}} \tag{18.426}$$

If "gas-phase" or van der Waals ethylene reacts with this adsorbed hydrogen, that rate is proportional to the ethylene pressure. The net kinetics then come out right.

Non-Langmuir Mechanism.   The fact that it is much easier to react the adsorbed species off the surface than to evaporate them off (by pumping) suggests that a steady-state coverage of the surface is maintained by adsorption followed by reaction, rather than desorption. The steady-state equations are

$$\frac{d\theta_{H_2}}{dt} = (1 - \theta_{H_2} - \theta_{Et})k_1 P_{H_2} - \theta_{H_2} k_2 P_{Et}$$

$$\frac{d\theta_{Et}}{dt} = (1 - \theta_{H_2} - \theta_{Et})k_3 P_{Et} - \theta_{Et} k_4 P_{H_2}$$

If the ethylene coverage is assumed to be unity, the main term contributing to the reaction rate is of the form $P_{H_2}^2/P_{Et}$, which does not reproduce the kinetics.

If, however, the ethylene residues on the surface have reached a condition so that none can be removed and none added, the problem reduces to that of a single component, H_2, adsorbing on the residual surface, and then being removed from above, the case that led to Eq. 18.425. This equation reduces to the correct kinetics in the limit $k_A P_A$ small, that is, θ_{H_2} small, as suggested by Wheeler. It should be pointed out that we have considered only three out of many possible interpretations of this reaction.

It would be possible to extend the variety of mechanisms considered, but these few will suffice to show the principles involved; also, there are no examples of reactions that adhere quantitatively and unequivocally to some definite mechanism. Heterogeneity of the surface and interaction of reactants on the surface, as well as progressive poisoning and loss of activity, combine to make treatments based on simple models only of qualitative significance.

Problems

18.401   Suppose that the differential heat of adsorption is linear in θ but does not go to zero with $\theta = 1$, but rather to a value Q_1. Calculate an expression for the integral heat of adsorption.

18.402   If the nickel film used to obtain the heats shown in Fig. 18.401 has a surface area of 100 cm², with the $hkl = 100$ face exposed, calculate the number of nickel atoms in the surface. (See Table 15.601(A) for structure.) If each could react with one hydrogen atom, how many cubic centimeters (STP) of H_2 would be required? What is the BET V_m for this surface? (Use standard area for N_2.)

18.403   Set up partition functions and derive the Langmuir isotherm for adsorption of a diatomic gas with dissociation.

18.404   Suppose that A reacts to form B (a rearrangement) on the surface and that B is adsorbed also (mixed Langmuir equation). Work out expressions for the rate in terms of P_A and P_B. Get the limiting behavior as the pressure of B goes to zero or very high, etc.

18.405   If every molecule that struck a surface became chemisorbed, calculate how long it would take to cover a surface such as nickel with a monolayer of O_2 at various pressures, ranging from 10^{-4} to 10^{-12} mm Hg. The answers need be only approximate. Take $T = 77°K$.

5. Review Problems

18.501   Some of the data in Table 18.101 are for several temperatures. Since surface tension is a free energy, the data can be used to find heats and entropies of surface formation. Treat these as independent of temperature, and find values for two of the substances listed.

18.502   In view of Problem 18.501 and the effect of temperature on surface tension, what generalization can be made about the sign of the free energy, heat, and entropies of surface formation?

18.503   Plot schematic concentration curves at an oxygen–water interface. Add a third component to the sketch that has a negative surface concentration.

18.504   Harkins proposed the following equation of state for a condensed surface layer

$$\phi = a - b/\Gamma_2$$

where a and b are constants. Use the Gibbs adsorption equation to calculate the vapor pressure of such a film, if composed of slightly volatile material.

18.505   Write an analog for the virial equation of state for a two-dimensional film. How would the second virial coefficient be defined in a two-dimensional film (cf. Eq. 6.511)?

18.506   Calculate the inert gas pressure required to force the liquid in a capillary down to the level of the outside liquid surface, in terms of the surface tension and diameter of the tube.

18.507   Propose a two-dimensional version of the van der Waals equation of state.

18.508   Use the values tabulated in Table 18.303 to calculate a stepwise isotherm for krypton on sodium hydroxide, and for argon on potassium chloride. Take the value of δ to be zero.

18.509   Some nitrogen isotherm data are presented below. Calculate the surface area per gram. Weight of sample = 0.1 g; $T = 77°K$.

$$P, \text{mm Hg}: \quad 2 \quad 7 \quad 35 \quad 60 \quad 210$$

$$V_{ads}(\text{STP}): \quad 2.0 \ 2.4 \ 2.7 \ 2.8 \ 4.0$$

18.510   Solve the mixed Langmuir equations (Eq. 18.411) for θ_A in terms of P_A and P_B.

18.511   Suppose that the integral heat of adsorption had the form

$$Q_{int} = Q_0 - Q_a\theta$$

where Q_0 and Q_a are constants. What is the differential heat?

18.512   The rate of hydrogenation of ethylene over copper has been found in certain cases to be proportional to hydrogen pressure and inversely proportional to ethylene pressure. Propose a Langmuir mechanism that will give these results.

General References

Alexander, A. E., and P. Johnson, *Colloid Science* (2 vols.), Oxford University Press, Oxford, England, 1949.

Advances in Catalysis, Vol. I *et seq.*, Academic Press, New York, 1949 to date.

Emmett, P. H., Editor, *Catalysis*, Vol. I *et seq.*, Reinhold Publishing Co., New York, 1954–.

Flory, P. J., *Principles of Polymer Chemistry*, Cornell University Press, Ithaca, New York, 1953.

Fowler, R. H., and E. A. Guggenheim, *Statistical Thermodynamics*, Cambridge University Press, Cambridge, England, 1939.

Harkins, W. D., *Physical Chemistry of Surface Films*, Reinhold Publishing Co., New York, 1952.

Wolf, K. L., *Physik und Chemie der Grenzflächen*, Springer-Verlag, Berlin, 1959.

Young, D. M., and A. D. Crowell, *Physical Adsorption of Gases*, Butterworths, Washington, D.C., 1962.

Appendix

Table 1.401 Some Special Integrals

---

1. $\int x^n e^{ax}\,dx = \dfrac{x^n e^{ax}}{a} - \dfrac{n}{a}\int x^{n-1} e^{ax}\,dx$

2. $\int_0^\infty x^n e^{-ax}\,dx = \dfrac{n!}{a^{n+1}}$, n is a positive integer, $a > 0$

3. $\int_0^\infty e^{-ax^2}\,dx = \dfrac{1}{2}\sqrt{\dfrac{\pi}{a}} = \dfrac{1}{2}\int_{-\infty}^{+\infty} e^{-ax^2}\,dx$; $\int_0^{0.48a^{-1/2}} e^{-ax^2}\,dx = \dfrac{1}{4}\sqrt{\dfrac{\pi}{a}}$

4. $\int_0^\infty x^{2n} e^{-ax^2}\,dx = \dfrac{1 \cdot 3 \cdots (2n-1)}{2^{n+1}}\sqrt{\dfrac{\pi}{a^{2n+1}}} = \dfrac{1}{2}\int_{-\infty}^{+\infty} x^{2n} e^{-ax^2}\,dx$

5. $\int_0^\infty x e^{-ax^2}\,dx = \dfrac{1}{2a}$

6. $\int_0^\infty x^{2n+1} e^{-ax^2}\,dx = \dfrac{n!}{2a^{n+1}}$

7. $\int x \sin x\,dx = \sin x - x \cos x$

8. $\int \sin^2 x\,dx = \tfrac{1}{2}x - \tfrac{1}{4}\sin 2x$

9. $\int x \sin^2 x\,dx = \dfrac{x^2}{4} - \dfrac{x \sin 2x}{4} - \dfrac{\cos 2x}{8}$

10. $\int x^2 \sin^2 x\,dx = \dfrac{x^3}{6} - \left(\dfrac{x^2}{4} - \dfrac{1}{8}\right)\sin 2x - \dfrac{x \cos 2x}{4}$

11. $\int \sin^3 x\,dx = -\tfrac{1}{3}\cos x\,(\sin^2 x + 2)$

12. $\int \sin^n x\,dx = -\dfrac{\sin^{n-1} x \cos x}{n} + \dfrac{n-1}{n}\int \sin^{n-2} x\,dx$

13. $\int \sin ax \sin bx\,dx = \dfrac{\sin(a-b)x}{2(a-b)} - \dfrac{\sin(a+b)x}{2(a+b)}$

14. $\int \cos^m x \sin^n x\,dx = \dfrac{\cos^{m-1} x \sin^{n+1} x}{m+n} + \dfrac{m-1}{m+n}\int \cos^{m-2} x \sin^n x\,dx$

$= \dfrac{\sin^{n-1} x \cos^{m+1} x}{m+n} + \dfrac{n-1}{m+n}\int \cos^m x \sin^{n-2} x\,dx$

15. $\int_0^\infty \dfrac{x^3}{e^x - 1}\,dx = \dfrac{\pi^4}{15}$

---

*Table 4.101 Some Related Properties of Ground
State Diatomic Molecules**

Molecule	r_e,† Å	μ	ω_e, cm^{-1}	$x_e\omega_e$	D, ev
H_2	0.741	0.5040	4395.2	118.0	4.476
HD	0.741	0.6719	3817.1	94.96	4.511
HT	. . .	0.7556	3608.3	87.6	4.524
D_2	0.741	1.007	3118.5	64.1	4.554
T_2	. . .	1.5085	2553.8	43.87	4.588
HI^{127}	1.604	1.000	2309.5	39.7	3.06
HBr^{79}	1.414	0.996	2649.7	45.2	3.75
HCl^{35}	1.275	0.980	2989.7	52.0	4.43
F_2^{19}	1.435	9.502	892.1	. . .	. . .
Cl_2^{35}	1.988	17.49	564.9	4.0	2.475
$Br^{79}Br^{81}$	2.283	39.96	323.2	1.07	1.97
I_2^{127}	2.667	63.47	214.6	0.61	1.54
Na_2^{23}	3.079	11.50	159.2	0.73	0.73
$Na^{23}Cl$	2.51	13.95	380	1	3.58
N_2^{14}	1.094	7.00	2359.6	14.46	9.76
$N^{14}O^{16}$	1.151	7.47	1904.0	14.0	. . .
O_2^{16}	1.207	8.00	1580.4	12.07	5.08

* Selected values by permission from a much larger compilation
by G. Herzberg, *Spectra of Diatomic Molecules*, D. Van Nostrand
Co., Princeton, N.J., 1950.
† Note that these distances refer to the minima in the potential
energy curves, rather than to an energy level of the molecule. The
values of r_0, the average distance in the ground vibrational state,
differ slightly from those given here.

Table 5.301 Harmonic Oscillator Functions*

	1	2	3	4
	$u = \dfrac{hv}{kT}$	$= \dfrac{u}{e^u - 1}$	$= \dfrac{u^2 e^u}{(e^u - 1)^2}$	$= [-\ln(1 - e^{-u})]$
	0.001	0.9995	1.0000	6.9083
	0.005	0.9975	1.0000	5.3008
	0.010	0.9950	1.0000	4.6102
	0.050	0.9752	0.9998	3.0206
	0.10	0.9508	0.9992	2.3522
	0.15	0.9269	0.9981	1.9711
	0.20	0.9033	0.9967	1.7077
	0.25	0.8802	0.9948	1.5087
	0.30	0.8575	0.9925	1.3502
	0.35	0.8352	0.9898	1.2197
	0.40	0.8133	0.9868	1.1096
	0.45	0.7919	0.9832	1.0150
	0.50	0.7707	0.9794	0.9327
	0.55	0.7501	0.9752	0.8602
	0.60	0.7295	0.9705	0.7958
	0.65	0.7100	0.9655	0.7383
	0.70	0.6905	0.9602	0.6864
	0.75	0.6715	0.9544	0.6393
	0.80	0.6528	0.9484	0.5965
	0.85	0.6345	0.9420	0.5576
	0.90	0.6166	0.9353	0.5218
	0.95	0.5991	0.9282	0.4890
	1.00	0.5820	0.9207	0.4587
	1.05	0.5652	0.9130	0.4307
	1.10	0.5489	0.9050	0.4047
	1.15	0.5329	0.8967	0.3807
	1.20	0.5172	0.8882	0.3584
	1.25	0.5019	0.8795	0.3376
	1.30	0.4870	0.8706	0.3182
	1.35	0.4725	0.8613	0.3001
	1.40	0.4582	0.8516	0.2831
	1.45	0.4444	0.8417	0.2673
	1.50	0.4308	0.8318	0.2525
	1.55	0.4176	0.8218	0.2386
	1.60	0.4048	0.8115	0.2255
	1.65	0.3922	0.8010	0.2133
	1.70	0.3800	0.7903	0.2017
	1.75	0.3681	0.7796	0.1909
	1.80	0.3564	0.7688	0.1807
	1.85	0.3451	0.7578	0.1711
	1.90	0.3342	0.7467	0.1620
	1.95	0.3235	0.7354	0.1535
	2.00	0.3130	0.7241	0.1454
	2.10	0.2931	0.7013	0.1303
	2.20	0.2743	0.6783	0.1172
	2.30	0.2565	0.6553	0.1054
	2.40	0.2397	0.6320	0.0948
	2.50	0.2236	0.6089	0.0854
	2.60	0.2085	0.5859	0.0769
	2.70	0.1944	0.5630	0.0692
	2.80	0.1813	0.5404	0.0624
	2.90	0.1689	0.5182	0.0562
	3.00	0.1572	0.4963	0.0507
	3.10	0.1462	0.4747	0.0458
	3.20	0.1360	0.4536	0.0413
	3.30	0.1264	0.4329	0.0373
	3.40	0.1173	0.4128	0.0336
	3.50	0.1090	0.3933	0.0304
	3.60	0.1011	0.3743	0.0275
	3.70	0.0938	0.3559	0.0248
	3.80	0.0870	0.3318	0.0223
	3.90	0.0806	0.3208	0.0200
	4.00	0.0746	0.3041	0.0180
	4.20	0.0640	0.2726	0.0148
	4.40	0.0547	0.2437	0.0119
	4.60	0.0467	0.2169	0.0097
	4.80	0.0398	0.1927	0.0079
	5.00	0.0339	0.1707	0.0063
	5.20	0.0289	0.1507	0.0052
	5.40	0.0245	0.1328	0.0042
	5.60	0.0208	0.1168	0.0034
	5.80	0.0178	0.1024	0.0027
	6.00	0.0149	0.0898	0.0022
	6.50	0.0098	0.0636	0.0010
	7.00	0.0064	0.0446	
	7.50	0.0042	0.0310	0.0003

* Excerpted from J. E. and M. G. Mayer, *Statistical Mechanics*, John Wiley and Sons, New York, 1940.

*Table 7.201   Molar Heat Capacities, $\bar{C}_P^\circ$, cal mole^{-1} deg^{-1}, at
1 Atm Pressure and at 298°K and Above*

$$\bar{C}_P^\circ = a + bT + cT^{-2} *$$

Substance	a	$b \times 10^3$	$c \times 10^{-5}$	Upper Temp. Limit, °K
Al(c)	4.94	2.96	. . .	932
Al$_2$O$_3$(c)	27.49	2.82	−8.38	1800
AlN(c)	5.47	7.80	. . .	900
Br$_2$(g)	8.92	0.12	−0.30	3000
Cd(c)	5.31	2.94	. . .	594
CdCl$_2$(c)	14.64	9.60	. . .	841
Ca(c)(α)	5.25	3.44	. . .	713
Ca(OH)(c)	19.07	10.80	. . .	700
CaO(c)	11.67	1.08	−1.56	2000
CaCl$_2$(c)	17.18	3.04	−0.60	1055
CaCO$_3$ (calcite)	24.98	5.24	−6.20	1200
C (graphite)	4.03	1.14	−2.04	2500
C (diamond)	2.27	3.06	−1.54	1200
CO(g)	6.79	0.98	−0.11	2500
CO$_2$(g)	10.57	2.10	−2.06	2500
CH$_4$(g)	5.65	11.44	−0.46	1500
C$_2$H$_2$(g)	12.13	3.84	−2.46	2000
Cl$_2$(g)	8.85	0.16	−0.68	3000
Cu(c)	5.41	1.50	. . .	1357
CuO(c)	9.27	4.80	. . .	1250
F$_2$(g)	8.26	0.60	−0.84	2500
Au(c)	5.66	1.24	. . .	1336
H$_2$(g)	6.52	0.78	0.12	3000
H$_2$O(g)	7.30	2.46	. . .	2750
H$_2$S(g)	7.81	2.96	−0.46	2300
HBr(g)	6.41	1.24	0.15	2000
HCl(g)	6.27	1.24	0.30	2000
HF (g)	6.55	0.72	0.17	4000
HI(g)	6.39	1.42	0.14	2000
HCN(g)	9.41	2.70	−1.44	2500
I$_2$(c)	9.59	11.90	. . .	368
I$_2$(g)	8.94	0.14	−0.17	3000
Fe(c)(α)	3.04	7.58	0.60	1033
Pb(c)	5.29	2.80	0.23	600
PbO(c) (red)	10.60	4.00	. . .	900
Mg(c)	4.97	3.04	0.04	923
MgO(c)	10.18	1.74	−1.48	2100
Mg(OH)$_2$(c)	13.04	15.80	. . .	600
Hg(l)	6.44	. . .	−0.19	630
N$_2$	6.83	0.90	−0.12	3000
N$_2$O	10.92	2.06	−2.04	2000

Table 7.201 (Continued)

Substance	a	$b \times 10^3$	$c \times 10^{-5}$	Upper Temp. Limit, °K
NO	7.03	0.92	−0.14	2500
$NH_3(g)$	7.11	6.00	−0.37	1800
$NH_4Cl(c, \alpha)$	11.80	32.00	. . .	458
O_2	7.16	1.00	−0.40	3000
O_3	11.23	1.92	−2.16	1500
$Ag(c)$	5.09	2.04	0.36	1234
$AgCl(c)$	14.88	0.50	−2.70	728
$Na(c)$	4.02	9.04	. . .	371
$NaCl(c)$	10.98	3.90	. . .	1073
$Na_2CO_3(c)$	27.13	15.62	−4.78	1124
$S(rh)$	3.58	6.24	. . .	369
$SO_2(g)$	11.04	1.88	−1.84	2000
$SO_3(g)$	13.90	6.10	−3.22	1500
$Zn(c)$	5.35	2.40	. . .	693
$ZnO(c)$	11.71	1.22	−2.18	2000
$ZnS(c)$	12.16	1.24	−1.36	1200

* K. K. Kelley, "High-Temperature Heat Content, Heat Capacity, and Entropy Data for the Elements and Inorganic Compounds," *U.S. Bur. Mines Bull.* 584, 1960.

$$\bar{C}_P^\circ = a + bT + cT^2†$$

	a	$b \times 10^3$	$c \times 10^7$	
$C_2H_6(g)$	2.195	38.282	−110.01	1500
$C_3H_8(g)$	2.258	57.636	−175.94	1500
$n\text{-}C_4H_{10}$	4.357	72.552	−221.45	1500
n-Hexane	7.313	104.906	−323.97	1500
$C_6H_6(g)$	−0.283	77.936	−262.96	1500
$C_2H_4(g)$	2.706	29.160	−90.59	1500
$CH_3OH(g)$	4.398	24.274	−68.55	1000
$C_2H_5OH(g)$	3.578	49.847	−169.91	1000
CH_3COCH_3	5.371	49.227	−151.82	1000

† H. M. Spencer, "Hydrocarbons and Related Compounds," *J. Am. Chem. Soc.*, **67**, 1859 (1945) and references cited therein.

*Table 7.302 Secondary Reference Temperature Points** (see Table 7.301)
Under a pressure of 1 standard atmosphere, except for the triple points.

	Temperature, °C (Int. 1948)
Temperature of equilibrium between solid carbon dioxide and its vapor $t_p = [-78.5 \text{ to } +12.12(P/P_0 - 1) - 6.4(P/P_0 - 1)^2]°C$	−78.5
Temperature of equilibrium between solid mercury and liquid mercury	−38.87
Temperature of equilibrium between ice and air-saturated water	0.000
Temperature of triple point of phenoxybenzene (diphenyl ether)	26.88
Temperature of transition of sodium sulphate decahydrate	32.38
Temperature of triple point of benzoic acid	122.36
Temperature of equilibrium between solid indium and liquid indium	156.61
Temperature of equilibrium between liquid naphthalene and its vapor $t_p[=218.0 + 44.4(P/P_0 - 1) - 19(P/P_0 - 1)^2]°C$	218.0
Temperature of equilibrium between solid tin and liquid tin	231.91
Temperature of equilibrium between liquid benzophenone and its vapor $t_p + [305.9 + 48.8(P/P_0 - 1) - 21(P/P_0 - 1)^2]°C$	305.9
Temperature of equilibrium between solid cadmium and liquid cadmium	321.03
Temperature of equilibrium between solid lead and liquid lead	327.3
Temperature of equilibrium between liquid mercury and its vapor	356.58
$t_p = [356.58 + 55.552(P/P_0 - 1) - 23.03(P/P_0 - 1)^2 + 14.0(P/P_0 - 1)^3]°C$	
Temperature of equilibrium between solid aluminum and liquid aluminum	660.1
Temperature of equilibrium between solid copper and liquid copper (in a reducing atmosphere)	1083
Temperature of equilibrium between solid nickel and liquid nickel	1453
Temperature of equilibrium between solid cobalt and liquid cobalt	1492
Temperature of equilibrium between solid palladium and liquid palladium	1552
Temperature of equilibrium between solid platinum and liquid platinum	1769
Temperature of equilibrium between solid rhodium and liquid rhodium	1960
Temperature of equilibrium between solid iridium and liquid iridium	2443
Temperature of melting tungsten	3380

* H. F. Stimson, *NBS J. Research,* **65A,** 139 (1961).

*Table 8.201 Vaporization and Fusion Data for Some Elements and Compounds**

Substance	t_{bp}, °C	ΔH_{vap}, kcal mole^{-1}	ΔS_{vap}, cal mole^{-1} deg^{-1}	t_{mp}, °C	ΔH_{fus}, kcal mole^{-1}	ΔS_{fus}, cal mole^{-1} deg^{-1}
O_2	−182.97	1.630	18.07	−218.76	0.106	1.95
H_2O	100.00	9.717	26.04	0.00	1.4363	5.258
Cl_2	− 34.06	4.878	20.40	−101.0	1.531	8.89
HCl	− 85.05	3.86	20.5	−114.2	0.476	2.99
I_2	...	...	...	113.6	3.74	9.67
S	444.6	2.5	3.5	119	0.293	0.75
SO_2	− 10.02	5.955	22.63	− 75.48	1.769	8.95
H_2SO_4	...	...	...	10.35	2.36	8.32
N_2	−195.82	1.33	17.24	−210.01	0.172	2.72
NO	−151.77	3.293	27.13	−163.65	0.550	5.02
NH_3	− 33.43	5.581	23.28	− 77.76	1.351	6.914
CH_4	−161.49	1.955	17.51	− 82.48	0.225	2.48
CCl_4	76.7	7.17	20.5	− 22.9	0.6	2.4
$CHCl_3$	61.2	7.02	20.99	− 63.5	2.2	10.5
CS_2	46.25	6.40	20.0	−112.1	1.05	6.52
C_2H_6	− 88.63	3.517	19.06	−183.27	0.683	7.60
C_2H_4	−103.7	3.237	19.10	−169.19	0.801	7.702
$SnCl_4$	113	8.3	21.5	− 33.3	2.19	9.13
Pb	1750	43.0	21.3	327.4	1.22	2.03
$PbCl_2$	954	29.6	24.1	498	5.7	7.4
Zn	907	27.43	23.24	419.5	1.595	2.303
$ZnCl_2$	756	30.9	30.0	275	5.5	10
Cd	767	23.86	22.94	320.9	1.46	2.46
$CdCl_2$	980	29.4	23.5	568	5.3	6.3
Ag	2193	60.72	24.62	960.8	2.70	2.19
AgCl	1557	43.7	23.9	455	3.16	4.34
Fe	2800	...	...	1535	3.6	2.0
Mn	2087	53.7	22.8	1244	3.50	2.31

* From *NBS Circ.* 500, 1952.

Table 9.201 Standard Enthalpies of Formation, ΔH°_{for}*, kcal mole^{-1} at 25°C** (Ions are in aqueous solution.)

Substance	ΔH°_{for}	Substance	ΔH°_{for}	Substance	ΔH°_{for}
Al^{3+}	−125.4	$CS_2(l)$	21.0	NO_3^-	− 49.37
$Al_2O_3(\alpha)$	−399.09	$HCN(g)$	31.2		
$SbCl_3$	− 91.34	CN^-	36.1	NH_3	− 11.04
$As_4O_6(s)$	−313.94	$CO_3^=$	−161.6	NH_4^+	− 31.74
Ba^{++}	−128.67	HCO_3^-	−165.2	$HNO_3(l)$	− 41.40
BaO	−133.4	HCl	− 22.02	NH_4Cl	− 75.38
$BaCO_3$	−291.3	Cl^-	− 40.02	$H_2O(l)$	− 68.32
$BaSO_4$	−350.2	ClO_3^-	− 23.5	$H_2O(g)$	− 57.78
Be^{++}	− 93	Cu^{++}	15.39	OH^-	− 54.96
Bi_2O_3	−137.9	CuO	− 37.1	PO_4^{3-}	−306.9
$BiCl_3$	− 90.61	F^-	− 78.66	K^+	− 60.04
$BF_3(g)$	−265.4	$HF(g)$	− 64.2	KCl	−104.17
		I^-	− 13.37	KOH	−101.78
$Br_2(g)$	7.34	$I_2(g)$	14.88	Ag^+	25.31
Br^-	− 28.90	HI	6.20	Ag_2O	− 7.3
$HBr(g)$	− 8.66	$Fe(OH)_2$	−135.8	AgO	− 3.0
Cd^{++}	− 17.3	Fe_2O_3	−196.5	$AgCl$	− 30.36
Ca^{++}	−129.77	FeS	− 22.72	$AgBr$	− 23.78
CaO	−151.9	Fe^{++}	− 21.0	$AgNO_3$	− 29.43
$CaCO_3$	−288.45	Fe^{3+}	− 11.4	Na^+	− 57.28
(calcite)		Pb^{++}	− 0.39	$NaOH$	−102.0
Diamond	0.45	PbO	− 52.4	$NaCl$	− 98.23
CO	− 26.42	PbO_2	− 66.12	$NaBr$	− 86.03
CO_2	− 94.05	$PbSO_4$	−219.50	Na_2CO_3	−270.3
CH_4	− 17.89	Li^+	− 66.55	$S^=$	10.0
C_2H_6	− 20.24	Mg^{++}	−110.4	H_2S	− 4.815
C_3H_8	− 24.82	MgO	−143.84	SO_2	− 70.96
C_2H_4	12.50	Mn^{++}	− 52.3	$SO_3(g)$	− 94.45
C_2H_2	54.19	Hg_2Cl_2	− 63.32	$SO_4^=$	−216.9
$CH_3OH(l)$	− 57.02	MnO_2	−124.5	H_2SO_4	−193.91
$C_2H_5OH(l)$	− 66.4	$Ni(OH)_2$	−128.6	Zn^{++}	− 36.43
$C_2H_5OH(g)$	− 56.24	N_2O	19.49	ZnO	− 83.17
$C_6H_6(l)$	11.718	NO	21.60	$ZnCO_3$	−194.2
$C_6H_6(g)$	19.820	NO_2	8.09	$ZnSO_4$	−233.9
$CCl_4(l)$	− 33.3				

* From *NBS Circ.* 500.

Table 9.204   Integral Heats of Solution, kcal mole⁻¹, at 25°C*

Moles of Water per Mole of Solute	Integral Heats of Solution				
	H_2SO_4	HCl	NaOH	NH_4Cl	NaCl
∞	−22.99	−18.003	−10.246	3.62	0.930
20,000	−21.42	−17.978			
5,000	−20.18	−17.952	−10.196	3.652	0.972
3,000	−19.72	−17.940		3.66	
1,000	−18.78	−17.893	−10.149	3.69	1.004
800	−18.63				
400	−18.21	−17.839		3.72	1.020
200	−17.91	−17.778	−10.110	3.73	1.016
100	−17.68	−17.693	−10.11	3.75	0.982
50	−17.53	−17.557	−10.16	3.76	0.892
25	−17.28	−17.315	−10.23	3.78	0.726
15	−16.77	−17.01	−10.24		0.570
10	−16.02	−16.651	−10.158	3.81	0.464
8	−15.44	−16.35	−10.021		0.452
6	−14.52	−15.79	− 9.53		
4	−12.92	−14.67	− 8.229		
3	−11.71	−13.63	− 6.904		
2	−10.02	−11.71			
1	− 6.71	− 6.31			

* *NBS Circ.* 500, "Selected Values of Chemical Thermodynamic Properties."

Table 9.301   Some Standard Entropies $\bar{S}°$, cal mole^{-1} deg^{-1}, at 25°C
(Ions are in aqueous solutions.)

Ar	36.98	CH_4	44.50	HI	49.31	NH_4Cl	22.6
Al	6.77	C_2H_6	54.85	Fe	6.49	O_2	49.00
Al^{3+}	−74.9	C_3H_8	64.51	Fe^{++}	−27.1	$H_2O(l)$	16.72
$Al_2O_3(\alpha)$	12.19	C_2H_4	52.45	Fe^{3+}	−70.1	$H_2O(g)$	45.11
Sb	10.5	C_2H_2	48.00	Fe_2O_3	21.5	OH^-	− 2.52
$SbCl_3$	44.5	$CH_3OH(l)$	30.3	$Fe(OH)_2$	19	P(w)	10.6
As	8.4	$CH_3OH(g)$	56.8	FeS	16.1	$PO_4{}^{3-}$	−52
$As_4O_6(s)$	51.2	$C_2H_5OH(l)$	38.4	Kr	39.91	K	15.2
Ba	16	$C_2H_5OH(g)$	67.4	Pb	15.51	K^+	24.5
Ba^{++}	3	$C_6H_6(l)$	41.30	Pb^{++}	5.1	KCl	19.76
BaO	16.8	$C_6H_6(g)$	64.34	$PbSO_4$	35.2	Ag	10.2
$BaCO_3$	26.8	$CCl_4(l)$	51.25	PbO (red)	16.2	Ag^+	17.67
$BaSO_4$	31.6	$CS_2(l)$	36.10	PbO_2	18.3	Ag_2O	29.09
Be	2.28	$HCN(g)$	48.23	Li	6.70	AgCl	22.97
Bi	13.6	CN^-	28.2	Li^+	3.4	AgBr	25.60
Bi_2O_3	36.2	$CO_3{}^=$	−12.7	Mg	7.77	$AgNO_3$	33.68
$BiCl_3(s)$	45.3	$HCO_3{}^-$	22.7	Mg^{++}	−28.2	Na	12.2
B	36.65	HCl	44.62	MgO	6.4	Na^+	14.4
$BF_3(g)$	60.70	Cl_2	53.29	Mn	7.59	NaCl	17.3
$Br_2(l)$	36.4	Cl^-	13.17	Mn^{++}	−20	Na_2CO_3	32.5
$Br_2(g)$	58.64	ClO^{3-}	39.0	MnO_2	127	S(Rh)	7.62
Br^-	19.29	Cu	7.96	$Hg(l)$	18.5	$S^=$	5.3
$HBr(g)$	47.44	Cu^{++}	−23.6	Hg_2Cl_2	46.8	H_2S	49.15
Cd	12.3	CuO	10.4	Ne	34.95	SO_2	59.40
Cd^{++}	−14.6	e^-	15.6	Ni	7.2	$SO_3(g)$	61.24
Ca	9.95	F_2	48.6	$Ni(OH)_2$	19.0	$SO_4{}^=$	4.1
Ca^{++}	−13.2	F^-	− 2.3	$N_2O(g)$	52.58	Sn	12.3
CaO	9.5	$HF(g)$	41.47	$NO(g)$	50.34	Xe	40.53
$CaCO_3$ (calcite)	22.2	He	30.13	$NO_2(g)$	57.47	Zn	9.95
Graphite	1.36	H_2	31.21	$NO_3{}^-$	35.0	Zn^{++}	−25.45
Diamond	0.58	I^-	26.14	$NH_3(g)$	46.01	ZnO	10.5
CO	47.30	$I_2(s)$	27.9	N_2	45.77	$ZnCO_3$	19.7
CO_2	51.06	$I_2(g)$	62.28	$NH_4{}^+$	26.97	$ZnSO_4$	29.8
				$HNO_3(l)$	37.19		

Table 11.202 Force Constants for the Lennard-Jones (6-12) Potential*

Force constants are given here for a number of substances which are polar and/or nonspherical and hence are not described by the Lennard-Jones potential. These constants along with the tabulated functions based on the Lennard-Jones potential may, however, be useful for purposes of calculations until the theory needed for describing complex molecules has been developed.

Gas	ε^*/k °K	σ, Å	$b_0 = \frac{2}{3}\pi N\sigma^3$, cc mole^{-1}
Noble gases			
Ne	35.60	2.749	26.21
	34.9	2.78	27.10
Ar	119.8	3.405	49.80
	122	3.40	49.58
Kr	171	3.60	58.86
	158	3.597	58.7
Xe	221	4.100	86.94
	217	3.963	78.5
Simple polyatomic gases			
Air	99.2	3.522	55.11
	102	3.62	60.34
N_2	95.05	3.698	63.78
	95.9	3.71	64.42
O_2	117.5	3.58	57.75
	118	3.46	52.26
CO	100.2	3.763	67.22
CO_2	189	4.486	113.9
	205	4.07	85.05
NO	131	3.17	40
N_2O	189	4.59	122
CH_4	148.2	3.817	70.16
CF_4	152.5	4.70	131.0
SF_6	200.9	5.51	211.1

* Adapted by permission from Hirschfelder, Curtiss, and Bird, *Molecular Theory of Gases and Liquids*, John Wiley and Sons, New York, 1954.

Table 11.203 The Virial Coefficient for the Lennard-Jones 6-12 Potential*

$$B(T) = b_0 B^*(T^*)$$
$$T^* = kT/\epsilon^*$$
$$b_0 = \tfrac{2}{3}\pi N\sigma^3$$

T^*	B^*	T^*	B^*
0.30	−27.88	2.00	−0.63
0.35	−18.75	2.10	−0.55
0.40	−13.80	2.20	−0.48
0.45	−10.75	2.30	−0.42
		2.40	−0.36
0.50	− 8.72		
0.55	− 7.27	2.50	−0.31
0.60	− 6.20	2.60	−0.27
0.65	− 5.37	2.70	−0.22
0.70	− 4.71	2.80	−0.18
		2.90	−0.15
0.75	− 4.18		
0.80	− 3.73	3.00	−0.12
0.85	− 3.36	3.10	−0.08
0.90	− 3.05	3.20	−0.06
0.95	− 2.77	3.30	−0.03
		3.40	0.00
1.00	− 2.54		
1.05	− 2.33	3.50	0.01
1.10	− 2.15	3.60	0.04
1.15	− 1.98	3.70	0.06
1.20	− 1.84	3.80	0.08
		3.90	0.10
1.25	− 1.70		
1.30	− 1.58	4.00	0.12
1.35	− 1.48	4.10	0.13
1.40	− 1.38	4.20	0.15
1.45	− 1.28	4.30	0.16
		4.40	0.17
1.50	− 1.20		
1.55	− 1.12	4.50	0.19
1.60	− 1.05	4.60	0.20
1.65	− 0.99	4.70	0.21
1.70	− 0.92	4.80	0.22
		4.90	0.23
1.75	−0.87	5.0	0.24
1.80	−0.81	6.0	0.32
1.85	−0.76	7.0	0.36
1.90	−0.71	8.0	0.41
1.95	−0.67	9.0	0.44

Table 11.203 (Continued)

T*	B*	T*	B*
10.0	0.46	80.0	0.48
20.0	0.53	90.0	0.47
30.0	0.53	100.0	0.46
40.0	0.52		
50.0	0.51	200.0	0.41
		300.0	0.38
60.0	0.50	400.0	0.36
70.0	0.49		

* Adapted by permission from Hirschfelder, Curtiss, and Bird, *Molecular Theory of Gases and Liquids,* John Wiley and Sons, New York, 1954.

Table 11.301 Selected Values of Relative Free-Energy and Enthalpy Functions*

Substance	$T°K$				
	298.16°	400°	600°	800°	1000°

Relative Free Energy Functions, $-\left(\dfrac{\bar{F}° - \bar{H}_0°}{T}\right)$, cal mole^{-1} deg^{-1}

Substance	298.16°	400°	600°	800°	1000°
H_2	24.423	26.422	29.203	31.186	32.738
O_2	42.061	44.112	46.968	49.044	50.697
N_2	38.817	40.861	43.688	45.711	47.306
$H_2O(g)$	37.165	39.505	42.766	45.128	47.010
C (graphite)	0.5172	0.824	1.477	2.138	2.771
CO	40.350	42.393	45.222	47.254	48.860
CO_2	43.555	45.828	49.238	51.895	54.109
CH_4	36.46	38.86	42.39	45.21	47.65
C_2H_4	43.98	46.61	50.70	54.19	57.29
C_2H_2	39.976	42.451	46.313	49.400	52.005
C_2H_6	45.27	48.24	53.08	57.29	61.11
C_3H_8	52.73	56.48	62.93	68.74	74.10
NO	42.980	45.134	48.090	50.202	51.864

Relative Enthalpy Functions, $\dfrac{\bar{H}° - \bar{H}_0°}{T}$, cal mole^{-1} deg^{-1}

Substance	298.16°	400°	600°	800°	1000°
H_2	6.7877	6.8275	6.8825	6.9218	6.9658
O_2	6.942	6.981	7.132	7.320	7.497
N_2	6.9502	6.9559	6.9967	7.0857	7.2025
$H_2O(g)$	7.941	7.985	8.137	8.362	8.608
C (graphite)	0.8437	1.275	1.997	2.602	3.075
CO	6.951	6.959	7.016	7.125	7.257
CO_2	7.506	7.987	8.871	9.612	10.222
CH_4	8.039	8.307	9.249	10.401	11.56
C_2H_4	8.47	9.28	11.22	13.10	14.76
C_2H_2	8.021	8.853	10.212	11.249	12.090
C_2H_6	9.578	10.74	13.36	15.95	18.28
C_5H_8	11.78	13.89	18.22	22.20	25.67
NO	7.359	7.302	7.302	7.387	7.506

* By permission from *Selected Values of Physical and Thermodynamic Properties of Hydrocarbons and Related Compounds,* American Petroleum Institute, 1953.

*Table 15.601   Common Crystal Structures of Selected Elements**

Element	Structure	Density at 20°C, g cm^{-3}	Lattice Constants at Room Temperature, Å		Atomic Volume, cm^3 mole^{-1}	Nearest Neighbor Distance, Å
			a	c or Axial Angle		
Aluminum	*fcc*	2.70	4.04		9.99	2.86
Argon	*fcc*		5.43(20°K)			3.83
Barium	*bcc*	3.5	5.01		39	4.34
Beryllium	hep	1.82	2.27	3.59	4.96	2.22
Bismuth	Rhombo-hedral	9.80	4.74	$\alpha = 57°41'$	21.3	3.10
Boron	Complex	2.3			4.7	
Cadmium	*hcp*	8.65	2.97	5.61	13.0	2.97
Calcium	*fcc*	1.55	5.56		25.9	3.93
Carbon	Diamond	3.51	3.56			1.54
Cerium	*fcc*	6.9	5.14		20	3.64
Cesium	*bcc*	1.9	6.05(92°K)		70	5.24
Chromium	*bcc*	7.19	2.88		7.23	2.49
Cobalt	*hcp*	8.9	2.51	4.07	6.6	2.50
Copper	*fcc*	8.96	3.61		7.09	2.55
Gadolinium	*hcp*	7.95	3.62	5.75	19.7	3.55
Germanium	Diamond	5.36	5.65		13.5	2.44
Gold	*fcc*	19.32	4.07		10.2	2.88
Helium	*hcp*		3.57(2°K)	5.83		3.57
Iron (α)	*bcc*	7.87	2.86		7.1	2.48
Lanthanum	*fcc*	6.15	5.29			3.73
Lead	*fcc*	11.34	4.94		18.27	3.49
Lithium	*bcc*	0.53	3.50		13	3.03
Magnesium	*hcp*	1.74	3.20	5.20	14.0	3.19
Manganese	Complex	7.43			7.39	2.24
Molybdenum	*bcc*	10.2	3.14		9.41	2.72
Neon	*fcc*		4.52(20°K)			3.20
Nickel	*fcc*	8.90	3.52		6.59	2.49
Niobium	*bcc*	8.57	3.29		10.8	2.85
Palladium	*fcc*	12.0	3.88		8.89	2.74
Platinum	*fcc*	21.45	3.92		9.10	2.77
Potassium	*bcc*	0.86	5.33		45	4.62
Rubidium	*bcc*	1.53	5.62(92°K)		55.9	4.87
Silicon	Diamond	2.33	5.43		12.0	2.35
Silver	*fcc*	10.49	4.08		10.28	2.88
Sodium	*bcc*	0.97	4.28		24	3.71
Strontium	*fcc*	2.6	6.05		34	4.30
Tantalum	*bcc*	16.6	3.30		10.9	2.85
Thalium	*hcp*	11.85	3.45	5.51	17.24	3.40
Tin (gray)	Diamond	5.75	6.46			
Titanium	*hcp*	4.54	2.95	4.73	10.6	2.91
Tungsten	*bcc*	19.3	3.16		9.53	2.73
Uranium	Complex	18.7			12.7	2.76
Vanadium	*bcc*	6.0	3.03		8.5	2.63
Xenon	*fcc*		6.24(92°K)			4.41
Zinc	*hcp*	7.13	2.66	4.94	9.17	2.66
Zirconium	*bcc*	6.5	3.61(850°C)		14	3.16

* By permission from C. Kittel, *Elementary Solid State Physics*, John Wiley and Sons, 1962.

Table 15.602   Crystal Radii and Univalent Radii of Ions (Angstroms)*

				H^-	He	Li^+	Be^{++}	B^{3+}	C^{4+}	N^{5+}	O^{6+}	F^{7+}
				2.08		0.60	0.31	0.20	0.15	0.11	0.09	0.07
				(2.08)	(0.93)	(0.60)	(0.44)	(0.35)	(0.29)	(0.25)	(0.22)	(0.19)
C^{4-}	N^{3-}	$O^=$	F^-	Ne		Na^+	Mg^{++}	Al^3	Si^{4+}	P^{4+}	S^{6+}	Cl^{7+}
2.60	1.71	1.40	1.36			0.95	0.65	0.50	0.41	0.34	0.29	0.26
(4.14)	(2.47)	(1.76)	(1.36)	(1.12)		(0.95)	(0.82)	(0.72)	(0.65)	(0.59)	(0.53)	(0.49)
Si^{4-}	P^{3-}	$S^=$	Cl^-	Ar		K^+	Ca^{++}	Sc^{3+}	Ti^{4+}	V^{5+}	Cr^{6+}	Mn^{7+}
2.71	2.12	1.84	1.81			1.33	0.99	0.81	0.68	0.59	0.52	0.46
(3.84)	(2.79)	(2.19)	(1.81)	(1.54)		(1.33)	(1.18)	(1.06)	(0.96)	(0.88)	(0.81)	(0.75)
						Cu^+	Zn^{++}	Ga^{3+}	Ge^{4+}	As^{5+}	Se^{6+}	Br^{7+}
						0.96	0.74	0.62	0.53	0.47	0.42	0.39
						(0.96)	(0.88)	(0.81)	(0.76)	(0.71)	(0.66)	(0.62)
Ge^{4-}	As^{3-}	$Se^=$	Br^-	Kr		Rb^+	Sr^{++}	Y^{3+}	Zr^{4+}	Cb^{5+}	Mo^{6+}	
2.72	2.22	1.98	1.95			1.48	1.13	0.93	0.80	0.70	0.62	
(3.71)	(2.85)	(2.32)	(1.95)	(1.69)		(1.48)	(1.32)	(1.20)	(1.09)	(1.00)	(0.93)	
						Ag^+	Cd^{++}	In^{3+}	Sn^{4+}	Sb^{5+}	Te^{6+}	I^{7+}
						1.26	0.97	0.81	0.71	0.62	0.56	0.50
						(1.26)	(1.14)	(1.04)	(0.96)	(0.89)	(0.82)	(0.77)
Sn^{4-}	Sb^{3-}	$Te^=$	I^-	Xe		Cs^+	Ba^{++}	La^{3+}	Ce^{4+}			
2.94	2.45	2.21	2.16			1.69	1.35	1.15	1.01			
(2.70)	(2.95)	(2.50)	(2.16)	(1.90)		(1.69)	(1.53)	(1,39)	(1.27)			
						Au^+	Hg^{++}	Tl^{3+}	Pb^{4+}	Bi^{5+}		
						1.37	1.10	0.95	0.84	0.74		
						(1.37)	(1.25)	(1.15)	(1.06)	(0.98)		

* By permission from L. Pauling, *The Nature of the Chemical Bond*, Cornell University Press, 1960. Univalent radii are in parentheses. See Pauling for an explanation.

ANSWERS TO SELECTED PROBLEMS

The following answers to some of the problems in the text are given to indicate, for the benefit of the student, the magnitudes of the correct numerical solutions. The quantities have been rounded in many cases and hence do not necessarily represent the total number of significant figures possible from the information given in the problems.

Chapter One
Sec. 4: *2*, 6100°K; *4*, (*a*) 3.6×10^{-5} cm³; *6*, (*a*) 1.25×10^{-3} cm (Wien), 1.53×10^{-2} cm (R-J); *9*, 4.8×10^{33} ergs sec⁻¹, 2.2×10^{24} ergs sec⁻¹; *11*, (*a*) 3.3×10^{-15} g cm sec⁻¹, 3.75×10^3 mev; *12*, 6.2×10^{-12} erg particle⁻¹; *14*, 1.32×10^{-12} cm; 2.6×10^{-11} cm.

Chapter Two
Sec. 1: *1*, 1.15×10^{-8} cm, 2.3×10^{-11} erg.
Sec. 2: *1*, 2.6×10^{11} ergs; *2*, 2938 cm⁻¹, −52 cm⁻¹; *4*, 2.07×10^3 cm⁻¹; *6*, 7.9×10^{-14} erg.
Sec. 3: *1*, 7.9×10^{-10} cm; *2*, 5.6×10^{-10} cm.
Sec. 4: *1*, 49; *3*, 0.04, 5.3×10^{-5}.
Sec. 8: *1*, 4.3×10^3 dynes cm⁻¹, 9.9×10^{-27} erg, 5.3×10^2 ergs, 2.7×10^{28}; *3*, 4.8×10^5 dynes cm⁻¹, 3.2×10^5 dynes cm⁻¹; *4*. 4.8×10^{34}; *8*, $0.5m_e$, $0.999m_e$.

Chapter Three
Sec. 2: *2*, 1.22×10^{-5} cm; *3*, 2.6×10^{10}; *10*, 0.32; *11*, 1.1×10^{-2}, 8.9×10^{-3}.
Sec. 3: *3*, 3.5×10^{-21} erg.
Sec. 5: *3*, 0.22; *6*, $\tfrac{1}{2}m_e$, a_0, $4a_0$, 8.2×10^{-12} erg, 1.09×10^{-11} erg; *8*, 6, 4, and 2.

Chapter Four
Sec. 1: *1*, 2.7×10^{-8} cm, 6.4×10^{12} sec⁻¹, 3.1×10^2 cal mole⁻¹, 1.1×10^{-9} cm; *3*, 1.68×10^{17} to 4.7×10^{15} to 1.
Sec. 2: *1*, 6.8×10^9 sec⁻¹, 1.37×10^{10} sec⁻¹, 2.1×10^{10} sec⁻¹; *3*, 2.884×10^3 cm⁻¹, 2.07×10^3 cm⁻¹; *4*, 10.43 cm⁻¹.
Sec. 4: *1*, 2.56×10^3 cm⁻¹, 3.8×10^5 dynes cm⁻¹, 1.43×10^{-8} cm; *2*, 1795, 1804, 1813, 1829, 1837, 1845 cm⁻¹; *6*, 6, 13, 66.

Chapter Five
Sec. 1: *1*, 0, 0; *2*, 0.70, 0.89; *3*, 0.25, 0.21, 0.98×10^{-3}, 0.98×10^{-3}; *4*, 6.2, 25, 37, 25, 6.2; *5*, 0.32, 0.42, 0.07, 0.07, 0.07, 0.05, 4×10^{-3}; *6*, 0.03, 0.06, 0.08, 0.11, 0.14, 0.17, 0.14, 0.11, 0.08, 0.06, 0.03; *7*, 0.98×10^{-3}, 0.34, 0.50.
Sec. 2: *2*, 4.1×10^{12}; *3*, 15, 7.1, 4.6; *6*, 0, 5.6 × 10⁻⁷, 1.3×10^{-2}.
Sec. 3: *1*, 0, 0.56, 2.1; *2*, 3.3×10^{-14} erg, 5.0×10^{-14} erg, 1.4×10^{-13} erg; *3*, 0 erg², 0 erg, 1.4×10^{-27} erg², 3.7×10^{-14} erg, 1.9×10^{-26} erg², 1.4×10^{-13} erg; *6*, 0, $10^{10^{22.4}}$, $10^{10^{22.9}}$.

Sec. 4: *2*, 7.6×10^6 ergs, 9.4×10^{-7} erg^2; *4*, $2.3 \times 10^{2\circ}$K.
Sec. 5: *1*, 48, 24, 12, 12, 4; *3*, 3.2×10^{-11}, 0.19, 6.2×10^{-26}, 7.1×10^{-4}, 0.60, 2.7×10^{-8}.

Chapter Six

Sec. 1: *2*, 1.2×10^{18}; *7*, 2.1×10^{-16} g cm sec^{-1}, 3.1×10^7 cm sec^{-1}; *8*, 6.3×10^{12}.
Sec. 2: *1*, (*a*) 0.04; *3*, 1.0×10^{-3} cm^2; *5*, 0.039 ev, 890 cal mole^{-1}; *6*, $1.5 \times 10^{7\circ}$K; *7*, 8×10^7 sec.
Sec. 3: *1*, 4.58×10^6 dynes cm^{-2}.
Sec. 4: *4*, 1000°K: H$_2$ 5.7, Br$_2$ 4,290; *5*, H$_2$ 178°, Br$_2$ 0.23°K.
Sec. 5: *2*, 6.0×10^9 collisions sec^{-1}.
Sec. 6: *5*, $3.6 \times 10^{-14\circ}$K, 88°K; *7*, 4.5×10^{18} molecules sec^{-1}; *10*, 0.873r*, 0.915r*, 1.23r*, 0.890r*.

Chapter Seven

Sec. 2: *1*, 4.9×10^{10} ergs, 1.17 kcal; *2*, 4 joules, 2.04×10^4 g; *3*, -1.7×10^{10} ergs; *5*, Q, $-W = 3.2$ kcal, ΔE, $\Delta H = 0$; *7*, -140 cal; *9*, 7.4 liters, 1.43 atm; *10*, -1.37 kcal, -1.44 kcal; *11*, 306.4°K; *13*, 307.2°K, 1.09 atm; *16*, 386°K, 3.4×10^2 cal; *19*, -0.14 deg atm^{-1}; *20*, 983 cal; *21*, 7.23 cal deg^{-1} mole^{-1}.
Sec. 3: *1*, 404°K, 8×10^4 cal, 467.4°K, 282.8°K; *3*, 784 cal deg^{-1}, 416°K, 195 cal deg^{-1}; *4*, -2.4 cal deg^{-1}; *6*, 1.14 cal deg^{-1}, 0; *7*, 0, 6.5 cal deg^{-1}; *8*, 4 cal deg^{-1}.
Sec. 4: *1*, -1.06 kcal; *3*, p.g. -1.9 kcal; *4*, $27 - 38.2S_1$, $17 - 38.2S_1$ cal.
Sec. 5: *1*, 49.2, 97.0, 194, 424, 1192, 1830 atm; *2*, $-39.6 - 8B$ l-atm; *4*, 0.042; *5*, 242 cal mole^{-1}, 0, -0.81 cal deg^{-1} mole^{-1}.
Sec. 6: *2*, 3.1 kcal mole^{-1}; *3*, 2.7 kcal mole^{-1}; *5*, 34.9 liters mole^{-1}; *6*, 1.58 kcal mole^{-1}, *8*, 17.7 cm^3 mole^{-1}
Sec. 7: *1*, (*a*) ΔE, $\Delta H = 0$, Q, $-W = 240$ cal, $\Delta S = 0.64$ cal deg^{-1}, ΔA, $\Delta F = -240$ cal, (*b*) Q, $W = 0$, all others same as (*a*); *3*, 0, *b*, *R*; *4*, 310.8°K, 8.3 kcal; *5*, 36 cal deg^{-1} (total); *6*, 1.6, 4.5 cal deg^{-1} mole^{-1}; *8*, $\ln f = 2B\bar{V}^{-1} + \ln (RT\bar{V}^{-1})$; *9*, -14 kcal mole^{-1}; *11*, $\bar{V}_1 = 18$, $\bar{V}_2 = 38.8$ cm^3 mole^{-1}, $d = 1.11$ g cm^{-3}.

Chapter Eight

Sec. 1: *1*, (*a*) 2, (*b*) 2, (*c*) 1, (*d*) 2, (*e*) 2.
Sec. 2: *1*, 7.36 kcal mole^{-1}, 21 cal mole^{-1} deg^{-1}; *3*, 269.7°C; *4*, 0.23 atm; *6*, 21.4 cal mole^{-1} deg^{-1}; *7*, $\ln P_{mm} = -5857T^{-1} - 2.43 \ln T - 0.634 \times 10^{-2}T + 38.8$; *9*, 21.8 cal mole^{-1} deg^{-1}; *10*, 13.5, 1.8 mm Hg.
Sec. 3: *1*, $X_{hx} = 0.5$, 0.75 (gas); *2*, -868 cal mole^{-1}; *4*, $X = 0.26$; *6*, 0.99; *8*, 440°K; *9*, 229 atm, 20.1 mm Hg; *11*, 23.7 mm Hg, 0.49 atm; *12*, 446 atm; *14*, 5.5; *18*, *ca*. 1:1; *19*, 78.8 g.
Sec. 4: *1*, 10; *2*, 0.94 g H$_2$O per g mix.; *3*, 371.8°K, $X = 0.04$.
Sec. 5: *2*, 1125 mm Hg; *3*, 10^{-38} mm Hg; *5*, 26.8 mm Hg; *7*, $X_b = 0.56$ (liq), 0.52 (vapor); *10*, $X = 0.96$; *11*, 8.3×10^2 ft.

Chapter Nine

Sec. 1: *1*, 2.3×10^5 cal; *2*, 78 cal deg^{-1}; *4*, 0, -742 cal.
Sec. 2: *2*, 11 kcal mole^{-1}; *3*, (*a*) -135.3, -134.7, (*b*) -27.5, -26.9, (*c*) -305.2, -305.8, (*d*) -1498.7, -1500.5 kcal; *5*, -94 kcal mole^{-1}; *7*, 6.24 kcal mole^{-1}, -1.4 kcal mole^{-1}; *8*, -10.7 kcal; *11*, -66.7, -54.3, -52.8 kcal mole^{-1}; *12*, 79.2, 141.3 kcal mole^{-1}; *13*, 119.2 kcal mole^{-1}; *14*, -14 kcal; *16*, *ca*. 1900°K.
Sec. 3: *1*, 28.7 cal mole^{-1} deg^{-1}; *2*, 25 cal mole^{-1} deg^{-1}; *3*, 2.74, 0 cal deg^{-1}; *5*, 7.8×10^{-2} atm; *6*, -34, -0.77 kcal, 9.05, 80.5 cal deg^{-1}.

Sec. 4: *1*, 83 kcal; *2*, -4.47 kcal mole^{-1}; *4*, -56.7 kcal mole^{-1}, -54 kcal mole^{-1};
   6, 0.92, -48 cal mole^{-1};
   7, $-1.9 \times 10^4 + 12.17T \ln T - 4.38 \times 10^{-3}T^2 + 0.49 \times 10^5 T^{-1} - 31T$ cal;
   9, -250.4 kcal.
Sec. 5: *1*, -83.5, -125 cal, 1.7 cal deg^{-1}; *2*, 0, -485 cal, 17 cal deg^{-1};
   4, $2.16 \times 10^4 - 0.03T \ln T + 0.015 \times 10^{-3}T^2 - 0.06 \times 10^5 T^{-1} + 3.1T$ cal;
   6, -36.1 kcal mole^{-1}; *8*, 1.34 cal mole^{-1}; *9*, 26.3 cal deg^{-1}.

Chapter Ten
Sec. 1: *1*, (*a*) 6.34, 0.103, (*b*) 0.27, 0.307; *2*, -783, -862 cal mole^{-1}, -55 cal;
   4, 0.54, 6.4.
Sec. 2: *1*, 0.0698, 4.163, 3.417; *3*, 1.3×10^2; *4*, 20%; *6*, 21.6 kcal, 41.9 cal deg^{-1},
   0.049 atm, 0.4; *7*, 51 kcal, 33.4 cal deg^{-1}, P_2 0.54, P_4 0.46 atm; *9*, 35.1,
   57.9 kcal, 19 cal deg^{-1}, 20%, *ca.* 0%.
Sec. 3: *1*, $P_t = 1.7 \times 10^{-8}$ atm; *2*, (*a*) 1, 1.2×10^{-5}, (*b*) 1, 6.2×10^{-7} atm;
   3, 1130°K; *4*, 2.8×10^{-12} atm; *5*, -7.83 kcal; *6*, 3×10^{-18} atm;
   8, 0.1978 mole in A, 0.0022 mole in B.
Sec. 4: *1*, $\Delta F°$ 25.3, 40.9, 24.3, 133.2 kcal, $\Delta H°$ 43.3, -12, 122, 229 kcal,
   $\Delta S°$ 6.0, -17.6, 32.6, 32.0 cal deg^{-1}; *3*, 13.8 kcal, 34.3 cal deg^{-1}, 3.5 kcal;
   6, $m = 0.0266$, $c = 0.00532$, $d = 0.0354$.

Chapter Eleven
Sec. 2: *2*, 17.8, 20.8, 17.5, 26.0, 5.3, 23.3, 10.6 cal mole^{-1} deg^{-1}; *5*, -44 cc mole^{-1};
   6, 119, 408, 578, 748°K; *8*, 9.3×10^{-4}, 9.1×10^{-4} l mole^{-1}.
Sec. 3: *1*, 20%; *2*, 3.5×10^{11}; *3*, 2×10^{-12}.
Sec. 4: *1*, -3.66 (*P* in atm); *3*, 35.96 (45.77) cal mole^{-1} deg^{-1}.
Sec. 6: *1*, 8.8×10^{-12} erg molecule^{-1}; *3*, 10^7 (0.65×10^7) erg deg^{-1} mole^{-1};
   4, 5.2×10^{28}, 6.9×10^{20}; *5*, 28, 16 kcal mole^{-1}; *6*, 28 kcal mole^{-1}.
Sec. 7: *1*, -145 cc mole^{-1}; *3*, 1.1×10^{-22} (at 200°C); *4*, 1.86×10^3;
   5, 10 cal mole^{-1} deg^{-1}, 1.4×10^{-39} g cm^2; *6*, 13.05, 37.28,
   0.73 cal mole^{-1} deg^{-1}.

Chapter Twelve
Sec. 3: *1*, 1.1 volts; *2*, 0.0706 volt; *3*, 0.223 volt; *4*, 1.8×10^{-10}, 0.8 volt.
Sec. 4: *1*, 135 Å; *2*, 4.5×10^{-13} atm; *3*, 1.6 kcal mole^{-1}; *4*, 7×10^{-7} mole l^{-1};
   6, 0.355 volt; *8*, 3.6×10^{-9} mole l^{-1}; *9*, -0.0363 volt.

Chapter Thirteen
Sec. 1: *1*, 1.2×10^{-2} mm Hg; *3*, (*a*) 1.3×10^{-9}, (*b*) $\frac{1}{2}$.
Sec. 2: *2*, (*a*) 1:0.4:0.2:0.1:0.013, (*b*) 0.65 cm^2 sec^{-1} at 10^3 mm.
Sec. 3: *1*, (*a*) 1:1.9:1.9:2.2:0.36, (*b*) 2.1×10^{-4} poise.
Sec. 4: *2*, (*a*) 2.0×10^3 g cm sec^{-3} deg^{-1}.
Sec. 5: *1*, 1.31 ohms, 1.31×10^6 ohms; *2*, 138 cm^2 ohm^{-2} equiv^{-1}, 0.92;
   3, 6.2×10^{-4} cm sec^{-1}; *4*, $t_+ = 0.49$, 0.40, 0.44, 0.39.
Sec. 6: *2*, 2×10^7 atoms sec^{-1}.
Sec. 7: *1*, 8.9×10^{-2} lb; *2*, A 3.8×10^{-4} sec^{-1}, B 2.2×10^{-3} sec^{-1};
   $t_{1/2} = 1820$ sec; *3*, $\frac{1}{2}$ order is best overall; *4*, 1.7; *5*, 5.3×10^{-5} sec^{-1},
   1.3×10^4 sec; *7*, $1/10^3$, $1/(10^3 \times 6 \times 10^{23})$, $1/(kT)^2$; *9*, NO$_2$ 2, H$_2$ $\frac{1}{2}$.
Sec. 8: *1*, (*a*) 1.0×10^{10}, 1.0×10^4, 1.0×10^{-2} cm; *3*, 1.1×10^{23} collisions sec^{-1},
   1.4×10^{-4} poise, 1.25×10^5 cm sec^{-1}, 5.4×10^2 cm^2 sec^{-1}; *5*, 153.6, 135.9,
   130.1, 146.1, 139.5, all in units of cm^2 ohm^{-1} equiv^{-1}; *11*, 9.4×10^4 sec;
   12, 0.34 cc cm^{-2} sec^{-1}.

Chapter Fourteen

Sec. 2: *1*, Molecularity, (*a*) uni, (*b*) bi, (*c*) uni, (*d*) bi; *2*, No.

Sec. 3: *4*, 0.24:0.51:0.25; *6*, 27.5 kcal mole^{-1}; *7*, $<$ 125 cal mole^{-1}; *8* (*a*), 3.6 × 10^{-7}, (*b*) 1.4 × 10^{-6}; *9*, 0.89; *11*, $n = 2$, 1.4 × 10^{-73}, $n = 10$, 5.2 × 10^{-66}.

Sec. 4: *1*, 300°, 3.4 × 10^{-70}, 3.4 × 10^{-70}, 3000°, 1.2 × 10^{-7}, 1.2 × 10^{-7}; *4*, 6.2 × 10^8 atoms sec^{-1}; *5*, 8.1 × 10^4:1; *9*, 57 sec^{-1}.

Sec. 5: *1*, k (l^2 mole^{-2} sec^{-1}) = 3.6 × 10^{41}k (cm^6 moles^{-2} sec^{-1}); *2*, (*a*) larger, (*b*) smaller.

Sec. 6: *2*, 1.6 × 10^{-4} sec^{-1}.

Sec. 7: *3*, $\frac{1}{2}$; *7*, 40 kcal mole^{-1}.

Sec. 8: *2*, 10^8 sec^{-1}; *4*, 2.5 Å, 7.26 × 10^{10} ergs mole^{-1}.

Sec. 9: *1*, 1.3 × 10^{-15} erg molecule^{-1}, 5.3 × 10^{-15} erg molecule^{-1}; *3*, 9.2 kcal mole^{-1}; *4*, range is a factor of 100; *7*, 5500 times longer than the ordinary duration of a collision; *10*, No.

Chapter Fifteen

Sec. 2: *1*, ca. 0.

Sec. 3: *3*, 1.02, 1.008.

Sec. 4: *1*, 1.03 × 10^6; *2*, 1.7; *3*, sph, $d = 1370$ Å; rod, $l = 2240$ Å.

Sec. 5: *1*, 0.7a, c; *2*, tetragonal *I*; *5*, 0.7a, 0.866a; *6*, 6, 8, 12; *7*, 54°44′; *8*, 2.7 Å.

Sec. 6: *2*, 5, 11; *4*, 2.82 Å; *5*, 2.16, 2.63 g cm^{-3}; *6*, 4.27 Å; *9*, 3.44 Å; *10*, 1.63; *11*, 1.54 Å.

Sec. 8: *4*, 6.7 × 10^8.

Chapter Sixteen

Sec. 1: *1*, 1.0, 1.7, 2.0 debyes; *5*, 3.7 debyes, 15 cc mole^{-1}.

Sec. 3: *5*, 4.1 × 10^{-3}, 1.1 × 10^{-4} Å; *6*, 1.13, 1.19 Å.

Sec. 4: *4*, 3.8 × 10^{-13} erg.

Sec. 5: *4*, 1.47 × 10^4 cm^{-1}.

Sec. 6: *1*, 1.0.

Sec. 8: *1*, 2.43 × 10^7 cycles sec^{-1}.

Sec. 9: *2*, 1.16, 1.79 Å.

Chapter Seventeen

Sec. 1: *1*, 2537 Å, 4.7 × 10^{12} ergs einstein^{-1}; *2*, 6200 Å; *5*, 3.4 (for k_q in units of mm^{-1} min^{-1} and $I = 2.7$ einsteins min^{-1}).

Sec. 2: *1*, (*a*) 1.7 × 10^{-5}, (*b*) 0.091; *2*, 4.4 ev; *6*, 42.0, 40.1, 19.1, 17.8.

Sec. 3: *1*, 0.40, 0.45; *2*, 5.7 × 10^4.

Sec. 4: *1*, HI, 0.992.

Sec. 5: *1*, 23.06 kcal mole^{-1}; *4*, 1:1.02; *7*, 685 volts cm^{-1}; *8*, For $X = 0, 1, 2$, $D = 3.8, 3.6, 3.9$ ev; *9*, 0.8 ev endothermic.

Chapter Eighteen

Sec. 1: *1*, 3 × 10^3 cm, 2.5 × 10^4 cm; *4*, 73.1, 44; *5*, 1.1 × 10^{-6} cm, 2 × 10^5.

Sec. 2: *4*, 4.2 × 10^{-12} mole cm^{-2}, 5.5 × 10^{-2} lb.

Sec. 3: *1*, 2.6 × 10^3 m^2; *4*, 10^{-13} erg; *5*, 15 m^2/g; *6*, 4 × 10^{-13} erg.

Sec. 4: *2*, 16.2 × 10^{16}, 3 × 10^{-3} cc, 2.3 × 10^{-3}; *5*, 10^{-2} sec, 10^6 sec.

Sec. 5: *9*, 100 m^2.

INDEX